HIGHER MATHEMATICS

FOR

STUDENTS OF CHEMISTRY AND PHYSICS

HIGHER MATHEMATICS

FOR

STUDENTS OF CHEMISTRY AND PHYSICS

WITH SPECIAL REFERENCE TO PRACTICAL WORK

BY

J. W. MELLOR, D.Sc., F.R.S.

WITH A PREFATORY NOTE

BY DONALD G. MILLER, ASSISTANT PROFESSOR OF CHEMISTRY
UNIVERSITY OF LOUISVILLE

DOVER PUBLICATIONS, INC.

" The first thing to be attended to in reading any algebraic treatise is the gaining a perfect understanding of the different processes there exhibited, and of their connection with one another. This cannot be attained by a mere reading of the book, however great the attention which may be given. It is impossible in a mathematical work to fill up every process in the manner in which it must be filled up in the mind of the student before he can be said to have completely mastered it. Many results must be given of which the details are suppressed, such are the additions, multiplications, extractions of square root, etc., with which the investigations abound. These must not be taken in trust by the student, but must be worked by his own pen, which must never be out of his hand, while engaged in any algebraical process."—DE MORGAN, *On the Study and Difficulties of Mathe matics*, 1831.

Library of Congress Catalog Card Number: 55-3376

Manufactured in the United States of America

Dover Publications, Inc.
180 Varick Street
New York 14, N.Y.

Dedicated

to

My Wife

PREFATORY NOTE

THE PURPOSE of Mellor's *Higher Mathematics* is primarily to present in convenient form those mathematical techniques which are useful to chemists and physicists. Since 1912, the date of the fourth edition, the requisite mathematical needs of most physicists and physical chemists have risen somewhat above the level of *Higher Mathematics*. However, there still remains the very large body of other chemists to whom a knowledge of mathematics beyond ordinary calculus would be quite profitable. Many among this group have come to feel that mathematics is unnecessarily difficult because that subject is often taught without any slant towards those who will use it. It is this group that Mellor has intended to reach. In order to make the material easier to assimilate, Mellor has emphasized throughout the application of the pure mathematics to practical problems and the translation of mathematical concepts into the more familiar ones of chemistry and physics, and to this end almost all the illustrative examples are taken from these fields. The general plan is to exhibit the mathematical techniques and their immediate applications to experimental phenomena with only a skeleton of theory, since in this way the acquisition of practical methods is not obstructed by an undue emphasis on rigor. Moreover, from the large collection of different techniques, mostly on an intermediate level, a conception of the types of problems which can be handled by these methods is obtained.

In a book written in all essential parts at the beginning of this century, there is bound to be some material, other than numerical examples and quoted data, which is out-of-date. None of it, however, is serious. Two examples may be cited. The discussions of heat in the sections on thermodynamics do not emphasize the fact that δq is really an inexact differential. Adequate treatments are now given, however, in almost all thermodynamics texts. The discussion of "infinitesimals" in §§13 and 14 is not too satisfactory in view of the changes in emphasis and standards of rigor since 1900. Because the newer approach is now contained in all elementary calculus books, the intuitive "infinitesimals" need not be considered although it may be noted that some of these less rigorous concepts still exist in much of the literature of the physical sciences.

Because of its intermediate level and because it is so strongly slanted towards physical science, *Higher Mathematics* is especially suitable as a textbook for a terminal undergraduate course in mathematics for chemistry students. Such a subject should have calculus prerequisites and might best be given as part of the chemistry curriculum concurrently with physical chemistry. In view of the movement towards increasing the mathematical attainments of all scientists, it is suggested that a course of this type be required for all chemistry majors other than those planning more elaborate programs of advanced mathematics. This plan is perhaps most suitable for small colleges that do not have sufficient enrollments to provide separate mathematics sections for science students. Of course, many of the problems and data are somewhat outdated for textbook use, but the instructor can readily find suitable replacements, variations, and more modern applications in a supplementary problem book such as that of Sillen, Lange, and Gabrielson: *Problems in Physical Chemistry*, Prentice-Hall.

Since there are several intermediate texts on higher mathematics available, the question of how *Higher Mathematics* compares with them naturally arises. Most of these texts are intended primarily for engineers or physicists, with few or no applications to chemical problems. There are perhaps two volumes with considerable emphasis on the needs of chemists; these are the well-known Margenau and Murphy: *The Mathematics of Physics and Chemistry*, Van Nostrand, and Daniels: *Mathematical Preparation for Physical Chemistry*, McGraw-Hill. The material in Daniels is not on a sufficiently high level since most of it is now covered in the required elementary calculus courses. On the other hand, the excellent Margenau and Murphy is considerably more advanced than *Higher Mathematics*, and its appeal is to the theoretician whose background in general is more comprehensive. *Higher Mathematics*, then, stands in the intermediate position, and no competing text is yet at hand. It is a work that can stimulate the interest of chemists in useful advanced mathematics; it is also handy as a reference book for those who wish to review forgotten material; and it is an appropriate textbook for a course in the mathematics of chemistry. It is indeed fortunate, then, that Dover has responded to demand and decided to reprint it once more.

DONALD G. MILLER
University of Louisville

1954

PREFACE TO THE FOURTH EDITION.

THE fourth edition is materially the same as the third. I have, however, corrected the misprints which have been brought to my notice by a number of students of the book, and made a few verbal alterations and extensions of the text. I am glad to say that a German edition has been published ; and to observe that a large number of examples, etc., peculiar to this work and to my *Chemical Statics and Dynamics* have been "absorbed" into current literature.

J. W. M.

THE VILLAS, STOKE-ON-TRENT,
13*th December*, 1912.

PREFACE TO THE SECOND EDITION.

I AM pleased to find that my attempt to furnish an Introduction to the Mathematical Treatment of the Hypotheses and Measurements employed in scientific work has been so much appreciated by students of Chemistry and Physics. In this edition, the subject-matter has been rewritten, and many parts have been extended in order to meet the growing tendency on the part of physical chemists to describe their ideas in the unequivocal language of mathematics.

J. W. M.

4th July, 1905.

PREFACE TO THE FIRST EDITION.

It is almost impossible to follow the later developments of physical or general chemistry without a working knowledge of higher mathematics. I have found that the regular text-books of mathematics rather perplex than assist the chemical student who seeks a short road to this knowledge, for it is not easy to discover the relation which the pure abstractions of formal mathematics bear to the problems which every day confront the student of Nature's laws, and realize the complementary character of mathematical and physical processes.

During the last five years I have taken note of the chief difficulties met with in the application of the mathematician's x and y to physical chemistry, and, as these notes have grown, I have sought to make clear how experimental results lend themselves to mathematical treatment. I have found by trial that it is possible to interest chemical students and to give them a working knowledge of mathematics by manipulating the results of physical or chemical observations.

I should have hesitated to proceed beyond this experimental stage if I had not found at The Owens College a set of students eagerly pursuing work in different branches of physical chemistry, and most of them looking for help in the discussion of their results. When I told my plan to the Professor of Chemistry he encouraged me to write this book. It has been my aim to carry out his suggestion, so I quote his letter as giving the spirit of the book, which I only wish I could have carried out to the letter.

"The Owens College,
"Manchester.

"My Dear Mellor,
        "If you will convert your ideas into words and write a book explaining the inwardness of mathematical operations as applied to chemical results, I believe you will confer a benefit on many students of chemistry. We chemists, as a tribe, fight shy of any symbols but our own. I know very well you have the power of winning new results in chemistry and discussing them mathematically. Can you lead us up the high hill by gentle slopes? Talk to us chemically to beguile the way? Dose us, if need be, 'with learning put lightly, like powder in jam'? If you feel you have it in you to lead the way we will try to follow, and perhaps some of the youngest of us may succeed Wouldn't this be a triumph worth working for? Try.
                "Yours very truly,
                        "H. B. Dixon."

May, 1902.

CONTENTS.

(The bracketed numbers refer to pages.)

CHAPTER I.—THE DIFFERENTIAL CALCULUS.

CHAPTER II.—COORDINATE OR ANALYTICAL GEOMETRY.

CHAPTER VI.—HOW TO SOLVE NUMERICAL EQUATIONS.

CHAPTER VII.—HOW TO SOLVE DIFFERENTIAL EQUATIONS.

CHAPTER VIII.—FOURIER'S THEOREM.

APPENDIX II.—REFERENCE TABLES.

INTRODUCTION.

" Bientôt le calcul mathématique sera tout aussi utile au chimiste que la balance." [1]—P. SCHÜTZENBERGER.

WHEN Isaac Newton communicated the manuscript of his " Methodus fluxionum " to his friends in 1669 he furnished science with its most powerful and subtle instrument of research. The states and conditions of matter, as they occur in Nature, are in a state of perpetual flux, and these qualities may be effectively studied by the Newtonian method whenever they can be referred to number or subjected to measurement (real or imaginary). By the aid of Newton's calculus the mode of action of natural changes from moment to moment can be portrayed as faithfully as these words represent the thoughts at present in my mind. From this, the law which controls the whole process can be determined with unmistakable certainty by pure calculation—the so-called Higher Mathematics.

This work starts from the thesis [2] that so far as the investigator is concerned,

Higher Mathematics is the art of reasoning about the numerical relations between natural phenomena ; and the several sections of Higher Mathematics are different modes of viewing these relations.

---

[1] Translated : "Ere long mathematics will be as useful to the chemist as the balance ". (1880.)

[2] In the *Annalen der Naturphilosophie*, 1, 50, 1902, W. Ostwald maintains that mathematics is only a language in which the results of experiments may be conveniently expressed ; and from this standpoint criticises I. Kant's *Metaphysical Foundations of Natural Science*.

For instance, I have assumed that the purpose of the Differential Calculus is to inquire how natural phenomena change from moment to moment. This change may be uniform and simple (Chapter I.); or it may be associated with certain so-called "singularities" (Chapter III.). The Integral Calculus (Chapters IV. and VII.) attempts to deduce the fundamental principle governing the whole course of any natural process from the law regulating the momentary states. Coordinate Geometry (Chapter II.) is concerned with the study of natural processes by means of "pictures" or geometrical figures. Infinite Series (Chapters V. and VIII.) furnish approximate ideas about natural processes when other attempts fail. From this, then, we proceed to study the various methods — tools — to be employed in Higher Mathematics.

This limitation of the scope of Higher Mathematics enables us to dispense with many of the formal proofs of rules and principles. Much of Sidgwick's [1] trenchant indictment of the educational value of formal logic might be urged against the subtle formalities which prevail in "school" mathematics. While none but logical reasoning could be for a moment tolerated, yet too often "its most frequent work is to build a *pons asinorum* over chasms that shrewd people can bestride without such a structure".[2]

So far as the tyro is concerned theoretical demonstrations are by no means so convincing as is sometimes supposed. It is as necessary to learn to "think in letters" and to handle numbers and quantities by their symbols as it is to learn to swim or to ride a bicycle. The inutility of "general proofs" is an everyday experience to the teacher. The beginner only acquires confidence by reasoning about something which allows him to test whether his results are true or false; he is really convinced only after the principle has been verified by actual measurement or by arithmetical illustration. "The best of all proofs," said Oliver Heaviside

[1] A. Sidgwick, *The Use of Words in Reasoning.* (A. & C. Black, London.)
[2] O. W. Holmes, *The Autocrat of the Breakfast Table.* (W. Scott, London.)

in a recent number of the *Electrician*, "is to set out the fact descriptively so that it can be seen to be a fact". Remembering also that the majority of students are only interested in mathematics so far as it is brought to bear directly on problems connected with their own work, I have, especially in the earlier parts, explained any troublesome principle or rule in terms of some well-known natural process. For example, the meaning of the differential coefficient and of a limiting ratio is first explained in terms of the velocity of a chemical reaction ; the differentiation of exponential functions leads us to compound interest and hence to the " Compound Interest Law " in Nature ; the general equations of the straight line are deduced from solubility curves ; discontinuous functions lead us to discuss Mendeléeff's work on the existence of hydrates in solutions ; Wilhelmy's law of mass action prepares us for a detailed study of processes of integration ; Harcourt and Esson's work introduces the study of simultaneous differential equations ; the equations of motion serve as a basis for the treatment of differential equations of the second order ; Fourier's series is applied to diffusion phenomena, etc., etc. Unfortunately, this plan has caused the work to assume more formidable dimensions than if the precise and rigorous language of the mathematicians had been retained throughout.

I have sometimes found it convenient to evade a tedious demonstration by reference to the " regular text-books ". In such cases, if the student wants to " dig deeper," one of the following works, according to subject, will be found sufficient : B. Williamson's *Differential Calculus*, also the same author's *Integral Calculus*, London, 1899 ; A. R. Forsyth's *Differential Equations*, London, 1902 ; W. W. Johnson's *Differential Equations*, New York, 1899.

Of course, it is not always advisable to evade proofs in this summary way. The fundamental assumptions—the so-called premises—employed in deducing some formulæ must be carefully checked and clearly understood. However correct the reasoning may have been, any limitations introduced as premises must, of necessity, reappear in the conclusions. The resulting formulæ can, in consequence, only be applied to data which satisfy the limiting conditions. The results deduced in Chapter IX. exemplify, in a forcible manner, the perils which attend the indiscriminate application of mathematical formulæ to experimental data. Some formulæ are particularly liable to mislead. The "probable error" is one of the greatest sinners in this respect.

The teaching of mathematics by means of abstract problems is a good old practice easily abused. The abuse has given rise to a widespread conviction that "mathematics is the art of problem solving," or, perhaps, the prejudice dates from certain painful reminiscences associated with the arithmetic of our school-days.

Under the heading "Examples" I have collected laboratory measurements, well-known formulæ, practical problems and exercises to illustrate the text immediately preceding. A few of the problems are abstract exercises in pure mathematics, old friends, which have run through dozens of text-books. The greater number, however, are based upon measurements, etc., recorded in papers in the current science journals (Continental, American or British) and are used in this connection for the first time.

It can serve no useful purpose to disguise the fact that a certain amount of drilling, nay, even of drudgery, is necessary in some stages, if mathematics is to be of *real* use as a working tool, and not employed simply for quoting the results of others. The proper thing, obviously, is to make the beginner feel that he is gaining strength and power during the drilling. In order to guide the student along the right path, hints and explanations have been appended to those exercises which have been found to present any difficulty. The subject-matter contains no difficulty which has not been mastered by beginners of average ability without the help of a teacher.

The student of this work is supposed to possess a working knowledge of elementary algebra so far as to be able to solve a set of simple simultaneous equations, and to know the meaning of a few trigonometrical formulæ. If any difficulty should arise on this head, it is very possible that the appendix will contain what is required on the subject. I have, indeed, every reason to suppose that beginners in the study of Higher Mathematics most frequently find their ideas on the questions discussed in §§ 10, 11, and the appendix, have grown so rusty with neglect as to require refurbishing.

I have also assumed that the reader is acquainted with the elementary principles of chemistry and physics. Should any illustration involve some phenomenon with which he is not acquainted, there are two remedies—to skip it, or to look up some text-book. There is no special reason why the student should waste time with illustrations in which he has no interest.

It will be found necessary to procure a set of mathematical tables containing the common logarithms of numbers and numerical values of the natural trigonometrical ratios. Such sets can be purchased from a penny upwards. The other numerical tables required for reference in Higher Mathematics are reproduced in Appendix II.

HIGHER MATHEMATICS

FOR

STUDENTS OF CHEMISTRY AND PHYSICS

CHAPTER I.

THE DIFFERENTIAL CALCULUS.

"The philosopher may be delighted with the extent of his views, the artificer with the readiness of his hands, but let the one remember that without mechanical performance, refined speculation is an empty dream, and the other that without theoretical reasoning, dexterity is little more than brute instinct."—S. JOHNSON.

§ 1. On the Nature of Mathematical Reasoning.

HERBERT SPENCER has defined a law of Nature as a proposition stating that a certain uniformity has been observed in the relations between certain phenomena. In this sense a law of Nature expresses a mathematical relation between the phenomena under consideration. Every physical law, therefore, can be represented in the form of a mathematical equation. One of the chief objects of scientific investigation is to find out how one thing depends on another, and to express this relationship in the form of a mathematical equation—symbolic or otherwise—is the experimenter's ideal goal.[1]

There is in some minds an erroneous notion that the methods of higher mathematics are prohibitively difficult. Any difficulty that might arise is rather due to the complicated nature of the

---

[1] Thus M. Berthelot, in the preface to his celebrated *Essai de Mécanique Chimique fondée sur la thermochemie* of 1879, described his work as an attempt to base chemistry wholly on those mechanical principles which prevail in various branches of physical science. E. Kant, in the preface to his *Metaphysischen Anfangsgründen der Naturwissenschaft*, has said that in every department of physical science there is only so much science, properly so called, as there is mathematics. As a consequence, he denied to chemistry the name "science". But there was no "Journal of Physical Chemistry" in his time (1786).

phenomena alone.   A. Comte has said in his *Philosophie Positive*, " our feeble minds can no longer trace the logical consequences of the laws of natural phenomena whenever we attempt to simultaneously include more than two or three essential factors ".[1]   In consequence it is generally found expedient to introduce " simplifying assumptions " into the mathematical analysis.   For example, in the theory of solutions we pretend that the dissolved substance behaves as if it were an indifferent gas.   The kinetic theory of gases, thermodynamics, and other branches of applied mathematics are full of such assumptions.

By no process of sound reasoning can a conclusion drawn from limited data have more than a limited application.   Even when the comparison between the observed and calculated results is considered satisfactory, the errors of observation may quite obscure the imperfections of formulæ based on incomplete or simplified premises.   Given a sufficient number of " if's," there is no end to the weaving of " cobwebs of learning admirable for the fineness of thread and work, but of no substance or profit ".[2]   The only safeguard is to compare the deductions of mathematics with observation and experiment " for the very simple reason that they are only deductions, and the premises from which they are made may be inaccurate or incomplete.   We must remember that we cannot get more out of the mathematical mill than we put into it, though we may get it in a form infinitely more useful for our purpose." [3]

The first clause of this last sentence is often quoted in a parrot-like way as an objection to mathematics.   Nothing but real ignorance as to the nature of mathematical reasoning could give rise to such a thought.   No process of sound reasoning can establish a result not contained in the premises.   It is admitted on all sides that any demonstration is vicious if it contains in the conclusion anything *more* than was assumed

---

[1] I believe that this is the key to the interpretation of Comte's strange remarks : " Every attempt to employ mathematical methods in the study of chemical questions must be considered profoundly irrational and contrary to the spirit of chemistry. . . . If mathematical analysis should ever hold a prominent place in chemistry—an aberration which is happily almost impossible—it would occasion a rapid and widespread degeneration of that science."—*Philosophie Positive*, 1830.

[2] F. Bacon's *The Advancement of Learning*, Oxford edit., 32, **1869.**

[3] J. Hopkinson's *James Forrest Lecture*, 1894.

in the premises.[1] Why then is mathematics singled out and condemned for possessing the essential attribute of all sound reasoning ?

Logic and mathematics are both mere tools by which " the decisions of the mind are worked out with accuracy," but both must be *directed* by the mind. I do not know if it is any easier to see a fallacy in the assertion that " when the sun shines it is day ; the sun always shines, therefore it is always day," than in the statement that since $(\frac{5}{2} - 3)^2 = (\frac{5}{2} - 2)^2$, we get, on extracting roots, $\frac{5}{2} - 3 = \frac{5}{2} - 2$; or $3 = 2$. We must possess a clear conception of any physical process before we can attempt to apply mathematical methods ; mathematics has no symbols for confused ideas.

It has been said that no science is established on a firm basis unless its generalizations can be expressed in terms of number, and it is the special province of mathematics to *assist* the investigator in finding numerical relations between phenomena. After experiment, then mathematics. While a science is in the experimental or observational stage, there is little scope for discerning numerical relations. It is only *after* the different workers have " collected data " that the mathematician is able to deduce the required generalization. Thus a Maxwell followed Faraday, and a Newton completed Kepler.

It must not be supposed, however, that these remarks are intended to imply that a law of Nature has ever been represented by a mathematical expression with perfect exactness. In the best of generalizations, hypothetical conditions invariably replace the complex state of things which actually obtains in Nature.

Most, if not all, the formulæ of physics and chemistry are in the earlier stages of a process of evolution. For example, some exact experiments by Forbes, and by Tait, indicate that Fourier's formula for the conduction of heat gives somewhat discordant results on account of the inexact simplifying assumption : " the quantity of heat passing along a given line is proportional to the rate of change of temperature "; Weber has pointed out that

---

[1] Inductive reasoning is, of course, good guessing, not *sound* reasoning, but the finest results in science have been obtained in this way. Calling the guess a " working hypothesis," its consequences are tested by experiment in every conceivable way. For example, the brilliant work of Fresnel was the sequel of Young's undulatory theo. of light, and Hertz's finest work was suggested by Maxwell's electro-magnetic theories.

Fick's equation for the diffusion of salts in solution must be modified to allow for the decreasing diffusivity of the salt with increasing concentration ; and finally, van der Waals, Clausius, Rankine, Sarrau, etc., have attempted to correct the simple gas equation : $pv = RT$, by making certain assumptions as to the internal structure of the gas.

There is a prevailing impression that once a mathematical formula has been theoretically deduced, the law, embodied in the formula, has been sufficiently demonstrated, provided the differences between the "calculated" and the "observed" results fall within the limits of experimental error. The important point, already emphasized, is quite overlooked, namely, that any discrepancy between theory and fact is masked by errors of observation. With improved instruments, and better methods of measurement, more accurate data are from time to time available. The errors of observation being thus reduced, the approximate nature of the formulæ becomes more and more apparent. Ultimately, the discrepancy between theory and fact becomes too great to be ignored. It is then necessary to "go over the fundamentals". New formulæ must be obtained embodying less of hypothesis, more of fact. Thus, from the first bold guess of an original mind, succeeding generations progress step by step towards a comprehensive and a complete formulation of the several laws of Nature.

§ 2. The Differential Coefficient.

Heracleitos has said that "everything is in motion," and daily experience teaches us that changes are continually taking place in the properties of bodies around us. Change of position, change of motion, of temperature, volume, and chemical composition are but a few of the myriad changes associated with bodies in general.

Higher mathematics, in general, deals with magnitudes which change in a continuous manner. In order to render such a process susceptible to mathematical treatment, the magnitude is supposed to change during a series of very short intervals of time. The shorter the interval the more uniform the process. This conception is of fundamental importance. To illustrate, let us consider the chemical reaction denoted by the equation :

Cane sugar → Invert sugar.

The velocity of the reaction, or the amount [1] of cane sugar transformed in unit time, will be

$$\text{Velocity of chemical action} = \frac{\text{Amount of substance produced}}{\text{Time of observation}} \quad . \quad (1)$$

This expression only determines the average velocity, V, of the reaction during the time of observation. If we let x_1 denote the amount of substance present at the time, t_1, when the observation commences, and x_2 the amount present at the time t_2, the average velocity of the reaction will be

$$V = \frac{x_1 - x_2}{t_2 - t_1}; \quad \therefore \quad V = \frac{\delta x}{\delta t}, \quad . \quad . \quad . \quad . \quad (2)$$

where δx and δt respectively denote differences $x_1 - x_2$, and $t_2 - t_1$. As a matter of fact the reaction progresses more and more slowly as time goes on. Of course, if sixty grams of invert sugar were produced at the end of one minute, and the velocity of the reaction was quite uniform during the time of observation, it follows that one gram of invert sugar would be produced every second. We understand the **mean or average velocity** of a reaction in any given interval of time, to be the amount of substance which would be formed in unit time if the velocity remained uniform and constant throughout the interval in question. But the velocity is *not* uniform—it seldom is in natural changes. In consequence, the average velocity, sixty grams per *minute*, does not represent the rate of formation of invert sugar during any particular *second*, but simply the fact observed, namely, the mean rate of formation of invert sugar during the time of observation.

Again, if we measured the velocity of the reaction during one second, and found that half a gram of invert sugar was formed in that interval of time, we could only say that invert sugar was produced at the rate of half a gram per second during the time of observation. But in that case, the average velocity would more accurately represent the actual velocity during the time of observation, because there is less time for the velocity of the reaction to vary during one than during sixty seconds.

---

[1] By "amount of substance" we understand "number of gram-molecules" per litre of solution. "One gram-molecule" is the molecular weight of the substance expressed in grams. *E.g.*, 18 grms. of water is 1 gram-molecule ; 27 grms. is 1·5 gram-molecules ; 36 grms. is 2 gram-molecules, etc. We use the terms "amount," "quantity," "concentration," and "active mass" synonymously.

By shortening the time of observation the average velocity approaches more and more nearly to the actual velocity of the reaction during the whole time of observation. In order to measure the velocity of the reaction at any instant of time, it would be necessary to measure the amount of substance formed during an infinitely short instant of time. But any measurement we can possibly make must occupy *some* time, and consequently the velocity of the particle has time to alter while the measurement is in progress. It is thus a physical impossibility to measure the velocity at any instant; but, in spite of this fact, it is frequently necessary to reason about this ideal condition.

We therefore understand by **velocity at any instant**, the mean or average velocity during a very small interval of time, with the proviso that we can get as near as we please to the actual velocity at any instant by taking the time of observation sufficiently small. An instantaneous velocity is represented by the symbol

$$\frac{dx}{dt} = V, \quad . \quad . \quad . \quad . \quad . \quad (3)$$

where dx is the symbol used by mathematicians to represent an infinitely small amount of something (in the above illustration, invert sugar), and dt a correspondingly short interval of time. Hence it follows that neither of these symbols *per se* is of any practical value, but their quotient stands for a perfectly definite conception, namely, *the rate of chemical transformation measured during an interval of time so small that all possibility of error due to variation of speed is eliminated.*

NUMERICAL ILLUSTRATION.—The rate of conversion of acetochloranilide into p-chloracetanilide, just *exactly* four minutes after the reaction had started, was found to be 4·42 gram-molecules per minute. The "time of observation" was infinitely small. When the measurement occupied the whole four minutes, the average velocity was found to be 8·87 gram-molecules per minute; when the measurement occupied two minutes, the average velocity was 5·90 units per minute; and finally, when the time of observation occupied one minute, the reaction apparently progressed at the rate of 4·70 units per minute. Obviously then we approximate more closely to the actual velocity, 4·42 gram-molecules per minute, the smaller the time of observation.

The idea of an instantaneous velocity, measured during an interval of time so small that no perceptible error can affect the result, is constantly recurring in physical problems, and we shall soon see that the so-called "methods of differentiation" will actually enable us to find the velocity or rate of change under these conditions. The quotient dx/dt is known as the **differential coefficient** of x with respect to t. The value of x obviously depends upon what value is assigned to t, the time of observation; for this reason, x is called the **dependent variable,** t the **independent variable.** *The differential coefficient is the only true measure of a velocity at any instant of time.* Our "independent variable" is sometimes called the **principal variable ;** our " dependent variable " the **subsidiary variable.**

Just as the idea of the velocity of a chemical reaction represents the amount of substance formed in a given time, so the velocity of any motion can be expressed in terms of the differential coefficient of a distance with respect to time, be the motion that of a train, tramcar, bullet, sound-wave, water in a pipe, or of an electric current.

The term " velocity " not only includes the *rate* of motion, but also the *direction* of the motion. If we agree to represent the velocity of a train travelling southwards to London, positive, a train going northwards to Aberdeen would be travelling with a negative velocity. Again, we may conventionally agree to consider the rate of formation of invert sugar from cane sugar as a positive velocity, the rate of decomposition of cane sugar into invert sugar as a negative velocity.

It is not necessary, for our present purpose, to enter into refined distinctions between rate, speed, and velocity. Velocity is of course directed speed. I shall use the three terms synonymously.

The concept velocity need not be associated with bodies. Every one is familiar with such terms as " the velocity of light," "the velocity of sound," and "the velocity of an explosion-wave ". The chemical student will soon adapt the idea to such phrases as, "the velocity of chemical action," "the speed of catalysis," "the rate of dissociation," "the velocity of diffusion," "the rate of evaporation," etc. It requires no great mental effort to extend the notion still further. If a quantity of heat is added to a substance at a uniform rate, the quantity of heat, Q, added per degree rise of temperature, θ, corresponds exactly with the idea of a distance traversed per second of time. Specific heat, therefore, may be represented by the differential coefficient $dQ/d\theta$. Similarly, the increase in volume per degree rise of temperature is represented by the differential coefficient $dv/d\theta$; the decrease in volume per unit of pressure, p, is represented by the ratio $-dv/dp$, where the negative sign signifies that the volume decreases with increase of pressure. In these examples, it has been assumed that unit mass or unit volume of substance is operated upon, and therefore the differential coefficients respectively represent specific heat, coefficient of expansion, and coefficient of compressibility.

From these and similar illustrations which will occur to the reader, it will be evident that the conception called by mathematicians "the differential coefficient" is not new. Every one consciously or unconsciously uses it whenever a "rate," "speed," or a "velocity" is in question.

§ 3. Differentials.

It is sometimes convenient to regard dx and dt, or more generally dx and dy, as very small quantities which determine the course of any particular process under investigation. These small magnitudes are called *differentials* or *infinitesimals*. Some one has defined differentials as small quantities "verging on nothing". Differentials may be treated like ordinary algebraic magnitudes. The quantity of invert sugar formed in the time dt is represented by the differential dx. Hence from (3), if $dx/dt = V$, we may write in the language of differentials

$$dx = V.dt.$$

I suppose that the beginner has only built up a vague idea of the magnitude of differentials or infinitesimals. They seem at once to exist and not to exist. I will now try to make the concept more clearly defined.

§ 4. Orders of Magnitude.

If a small number n be divided into a million parts, each part,[1] $n \times 10^{-6}$ is so very small that it may for all practical purposes be neglected in comparison with n. If we agree to call n a *magnitude of the first order*, the quantity $n \times 10^{-6}$ is a *magnitude of the second order*. If one of these parts be again subdivided into a

---

[1] Note $10^4 =$ unity followed by four cyphers, or 10,000. 10^{-4} is a decimal point followed by three cyphers and unity, or $10^{-4} = \frac{1}{10\,000} = 0.0001$. This notation is in general use.

million parts, each part, $n \times 10^{-12}$, is extremely small when compared with n, and the quantity $n \times 10^{-12}$ is *a magnitude of the third order*. We thus obtain a series of magnitudes of the first, second, and higher orders,

$$n, \quad \frac{n}{1,000000}, \quad \frac{n}{1000000,000000}, \ldots,$$

each one of which is negligibly small in comparison with those which precede it, and very large relative to those which follow.

This idea is of great practical use in the reduction of intricate expressions to a simpler form more easily manipulated. It is usual to reject magnitudes of a higher order than those under investigation when the resulting error is so small that it is outside the limits of the "errors of observation" peculiar to that method of investigation.

Having selected our unit of smallness, we decide what part of this is going to be regarded as a small quantity of the first order. Small quantities of the second order then bear the same ratio to magnitudes of the first order, as the latter bear to the unit of measurement. In the "theory of the moon," for example, we are told that $\frac{1}{12}$ is reckoned small in comparison with unity ; $(\frac{1}{12})^2$ is a small magnitude of the second order ; $(\frac{1}{12})^3$ of the third order, etc. Calculations have been made up to the sixth or seventh orders of small quantities.

In order to prevent any misconception it might be pointed out that "great" and "small" in mathematics, like "hot" and "cold" in physics, are purely relative terms. The astronomer in calculating interstellar distances comprising millions of miles takes no notice of a few thousand miles ; while the physicist dare not neglect distances of the order of the ten thousandth of an inch in his measurements of the wave length of light.

A term, therefore, is not to be rejected simply because it *seems* small in an absolute sense, but only when it appears small in comparison with a much larger magnitude, and when an exact determination of this small quantity has no appreciable effect on the magnitude of the larger. In making up a litre of normal oxalic acid solution, the weighing of the 63 grams of acid required need not be more accurate than to the tenth of a gram. In many forms of analytical work, however, the thousandth of a gram is of fundamental importance ; an error of a tenth of a gram would stultify the result.

§ 5. Zero and Infinity.

The words "infinitely small" were used in the second paragraph. It is, of course, impossible to conceive of an infinitely small
or of an infinitely great magnitude, for if it were possible to retain
either of these quantities before the mind for a moment, it would
be just as easy to think of a smaller or a greater as the case might
be. In mathematical thought the word " **infinity** " (written : ∞)
signifies the *properties* possessed by a magnitude greater than any
finite magnitude that can be named. For instance, the greater
we make the radius of a circle, the more approximately does the
circumference approach a straight line, until, when the radius is
made infinitely great, the circumference may, without committing
any sensible error, be taken to represent a straight line. The consequences of the above definition of infinity have led to some of
the most important results of higher mathematics. To summarize, infinity represents neither the magnitude nor the value
of any particular quantity. *The term "infinity" is simply an
abbreviation for the property of growing large without limit. E.g.,*
"tan 90° = ∞ " means that as an angle approaches 90°, its tangent grows indefinitely large. Now for the opposite of greatness—
smallness.

In mathematics two meanings are given to the word " zero ".
The ordinary meaning of the word implies the total absence of
magnitude ; we shall call this **absolute zero.** Nothing remains
when the thing spoken of or thought about is taken away. If four
units be taken from four units absolutely nothing remains. There
is, however, another meaning to be attached to the word different
from the destruction of the thing itself. If a small number be
divided by a billion we get a small fraction. If this fraction be
raised to the billionth power we get a number still more nearly
equal to absolute zero. By continuing this process as long as we
please we continually approach, but never actually reach, the
absolute zero. In this relative sense, zero—**relative zero**—is
defined as "an infinitely small" or "a vanishingly small number,"
or "a number smaller than any assignable fraction of unity".
For example, we might consider a point as an infinitely small
circle or an infinitely short line. To put these ideas tersely, *absolute zero implies that the thing and all the properties are absent ;
relative zero implies that however small the thing may be its*

property of growing small without limit is alone retained in the mind.

EXAMPLES.—(1) After the reader has verified the following results he will understand the special meaning to be attached to the zero and infinity of mathematical reasoning. n denotes any finite number; and "?" an indeterminate magnitude, that is, one whose exact value cannot be determined.

$\infty + \infty = \infty$; $\infty - \infty = ?$; $n \times 0 = 0$; $0 \times 0 = 0$; $n \times \infty = \infty$; $0/0 = ?$; $n/0 = \infty$; $0/n = 0$; $\infty/0 = \infty$; $0/\infty = 0$; $n/\infty = 0$; $\infty/n = \infty$.

(2) Let $y = 1/(1 - x)$ and put $x = 1$, then $y = \infty$; if $x < 1$, y is positive; and when $x > 1$, y is negative.[1] Thus a variable magnitude may change its sign when it becomes infinite.

If the reader has access to the *Transactions of the Cambridge Philosophical Society* (**11**. 145, 1871), A. de Morgan's paper "On Infinity," is worth reading in connection with this subject.

§ 6. Limiting Values.

I. The sum of an infinite number of terms may have a finite value. Converting $\frac{1}{9}$ into a decimal fraction we obtain

$$\tfrac{1}{9} = 0 \cdot 11111 \ldots \text{ continued to infinity,}$$
$$\tfrac{1}{9} = \tfrac{1}{10} + \tfrac{1}{100} + \tfrac{1}{1000} + \ldots \text{ to infinity,}$$

that is to say, the sum of an infinite number of terms is equal to $\frac{1}{9}$ —a finite term ! If we were to attempt to perform this summation we should find that as long as the number of terms is finite we could never actually obtain the result $\frac{1}{9}$. We should be ever getting nearer but never get actually there.

If we omit all terms after the first, the result is $\frac{1}{90}$ less than $\frac{1}{9}$; if we omit all terms after the third, the result is $\frac{1}{9,000}$ too little; and if we omit all terms after the sixth, the result is $\frac{1}{9,000,000}$ less than $\frac{1}{9}$, that is to say, the sum of these terms continually approaches but is never actually equal to $\frac{1}{9}$ as long as the number of terms is finite. $\frac{1}{9}$ is then said to be the **limiting value** of the sum of this series of terms.

Again, the perimeter of a polygon inscribed in a circle is less than the sum of the arcs of the circle, *i.e.*, less than the circum-

---

[1] The *signs of inequality* are as follows: " $\neq$ " denotes "is not equal to"; " $>$," "is greater than"; " $\not>$," "is not greater than"; " $<$," "is less than"; and " $\not<$," "is not less than". For " $\equiv$ " read "is equivalent to" or "is identical with". The symbol $>\!\!-$ has been used in place of the phrase "is greater than or equal to," and $-\!\!<$, in place of "is equal to or less than".

ference of the circle.   In Fig. 1, let the arcs AaB, BbC...be

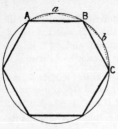

FIG. 1.

bisected at a, b...Join Aa, aB, Bb, ...
Although the perimeter of the second polygon is greater than the first, it is still less
than the circumference of the circle.   In
a similar way, if the arcs of this second
polygon are bisected, we get a third polygon whose perimeter approaches yet nearer
to the circumference of the circle.   By
continuing this process, a polygon may be
obtained as nearly equal to the circum-
ference of a circle as we please.   The circumference of the circle is
thus the limiting value of the perimeter of an inscribed polygon.
when the number of its sides is increased indefinitely.

In general, *when a variable magnitude x continually approaches
nearer and nearer to a constant value n so that x can be made to
differ from n by a quantity less than any assignable magnitude, n
is said to be the limiting value of x.*

From page 8, it follows that dx/dt is the limiting value [1] of
$\delta x/\delta t$, when t is made less than any finite quantity, however small.
This is written, for brevity,

$$\frac{dx}{dt} = \mathrm{Lt}_{t\,=\,0}\,\frac{\delta x}{\delta t}\,;$$

in words "dx/dt is the limiting value of $\delta x/\delta t$ when t becomes
zero" or rather relative zero, *i.e.*, small without limit.   This notation is frequently employed.

The sign " = " when used in connection with differential coefficients does not mean "is equal to," but rather "can be made
as nearly equal to as we please".   We could replace the usual
"=" by some other symbol, say "⇒," if it were worth while.[2]

*II. The value of a limiting ratio depends on the relation be-
tween the two variables.*   Strictly speaking, the limiting value of

---

[1] Although differential quotients are, in this work, written in the form "dx/dt,"
d^2x/dt^2..., the student in working through the examples and demonstrations, should
write $\dfrac{dx}{dt}$, $\dfrac{d^2x}{dt^2}$ ... The former method is used to economize space.

[2] The symbol "$x \doteq 0$" is sometimes used for the phrase "as x approaches zero".
"$\underset{x\,=\,0}{\lim}$" "$\underset{x\,\doteq\,0}{\lim}$"; or "$\pounds$" are also used instead of our "$\mathrm{Lt}_{x\,=\,0}$," meaning "the
limit of ... as x approaches zero".

the ratio $\delta x/\delta t$ has the form $\frac{0}{0}$, and as such is indeterminate—indeterminate, because $\frac{0}{0}$ may have any numerical value we please. It is not difficult to see this, for example, $\frac{0}{0}=0$, because $0 \times 0 = 0$; $\frac{0}{0} = 1$, because $0 \times 1 = 0$; $\frac{0}{0} = 2$, because $0 \times 2 = 0$; $\frac{0}{0} = 15$, because $0 \times 15 = 0$; $\frac{0}{0} = 999,999$, because $0 \times 999,999 = 0$, etc.

EXAMPLE.—There is a "hoary-headed" puzzle which goes like this: Given $x = a$; $\therefore x^2 = xa$; $\therefore x^2 - a^2 = xa - a^2$; $\therefore (x - a)(x + a) = a(x - a)$; $\therefore x + a = a$; $\therefore 2a = a$; $\therefore 2 = 1$. Where is the fallacy? Ansr. The step $(x - a)(x + a) = a(x - a)$ means $(x + a) \times 0 = a \times 0$, *i.e.*, no times $x + a =$ no times a, and it does not necessarily follow that $x + a$ is therefore equal to a.

For all practical purposes the differential coefficient dx/dt is to be regarded as a fraction or quotient. The quotient dx/dt may also be called a "rate-measurer," because it determines the velocity or rate with which one quantity varies when an extremely small variation is given to the other. The actual value of the ratio dx/dt depends on the relation subsisting between x and t.

Consider the following three illustrations : If the point P move on the circumference of the circle towards a fixed point Q (Fig. 2), the arc x will diminish at the same time as the chord y. By bringing the point P sufficiently near to Q, we obtain an arc and its chord each less than any given line, that is, the arc and the chord continually approach a ratio of equality. Or, the limiting value of the ratio $\delta x/\delta y$ is unity.

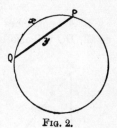

FIG. 2.

$$\therefore \text{Lt}_{y=0} \frac{\delta x}{\delta y} = \frac{dx}{dy} = 1.$$

It is easy to show this numerically. Let us start with an angle of 60° and compare the length, dx, of the arc with the length, dy, of the corresponding chord.

Angle at Centre.	dx.	dy.	$\frac{dx}{dy}$.
60°	1·0472	1·0000	1·0472
30°	0·5236	0·5176	1·0115
10°	0·1745	0·1743	1·0013
5°	0·0873	0·0872	1·0003
1°	0·0175	0·0175	1·0000

A chord of 1° does not differ from the corresponding arc in the first four decimal places ; if the angle is 1′, the agreement extends through the first seven decimal places ; and if the angle be 1″, the agreement extends through the first fifteen decimals. The arc and its chord thus approach a ratio of equality.

If ABC (Fig. 3) be any right-angled triangle such that $AB = BC$; by Pythagoras' theorem or Euclid, i., 47, and vi., 4,

$$AB : AC = x : y = 1 : \sqrt{2}.$$

If a line DE, moving towards A, remain parallel to BC, this proportion will remain constant even though each side of the triangle ADE is made less than any assignable magnitude, however small. That is

$$\mathrm{Lt}_{y\,=\,0}\, \frac{\delta x}{\delta y} = \frac{dx}{dy} = \frac{1}{\sqrt{2}}.$$

Let ABC be a triangle inscribed in a circle (Fig. 4), when BC is a diameter and BAC is a right angle. Draw AD perpendicular to BC. Then by Euclid, vi., 8

$$BC : AC = AC : DC = x : y.$$

If A approaches C until the chord AC becomes indefinitely small, DC will also become indefinitely small. The above propor-

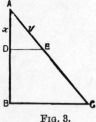

Fig. 3.

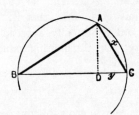

Fig. 4.

tion, however, remains. When the ratio $BC : AC$ becomes in- finitely great, the ratio of AC to DC will also become infinitely great, or

$$\mathrm{Lt}_{y\,=\,0}\, \frac{\delta x}{\delta y} = \frac{dx}{dy} = \infty.$$

It therefore follows at once that *although two quantities may become infinitely small their limiting ratio may have any finite or infinite value whatever.*

EXAMPLE.—Point out the error in the following deduction : " If AB (Fig. 3) is a perpendicular erected upon the straight line BC, and C is any point upon BC, then AC is greater than AB, however near C may be to B, and, therefore, the same is true at the limit, when C coincides with B". Hint.— The proper way to put it is to say that AC becomes more and more nearly equal to AB, as C approaches B, etc.

Two quantities are generally said to be equal when their difference is zero. This does not hold when dealing with differentials. The difference between two infinitely small quantities may be zero and yet the quantities are not equal. Infinitesimals can only be regarded as equal when their ratio is unity.

§ 7. The Differential Coefficient of a Differential Coefficient.

Velocity itself is generally changing. The velocity of a falling stone gradually increases during its descent, while, if a stone is projected upwards, its velocity gradually decreases during its ascent. Instead of using the awkward term "the velocity of a velocity," the word **acceleration** is employed. If the velocity is increasing at a uniform rate, the acceleration, F, or rate of change of velocity, or rate of change of motion, is evidently

$$\text{Acceleration} = \frac{\text{Increase of velocity}}{\text{Time}}; \quad F = \frac{V_2 - V_1}{t_2 - t_1} = \frac{\delta V}{\delta t}, \quad (1)$$

where V_1 and V_2 respectively denote the velocities at the beginning, t_1, and end, t_2, of the interval of time under consideration ; and δV denotes the small change of velocity during the interval of time δt.

In order to fix these ideas we shall consider a familiar experiment, namely, that of a stone falling from a vertical height. Observation shows that if the stone falls from a position of rest, its velocity, at the end of 1, 2, 3, 4, and 5 seconds is

$$32, 64, 96, 128, 160,$$

feet per second respectively. In other words, the velocity of the descending stone is *increasing* from moment to moment. The above reasoning still holds good. Let ds denote the distance traversed during the infinitely short interval of time dt. The velocity of descent, at any instant, is evidently

$$\frac{ds}{dt} = V. . \quad . \quad . \quad . \quad . \quad (2)$$

Next consider the rate at which the velocity changes from one moment to another. This change is obviously the limit of the ratio $\delta V / \delta t$, when δt is zero. In other words

$$\frac{dV}{dt} = F. \quad . \quad . \quad . \quad . \quad (3)$$

Substituting for V, we obtain the second differential coefficient

$$F = \frac{d\left(\dfrac{ds}{dt}\right)}{dt}$$

which is more conveniently written

$$\frac{d^2s}{dt^2} = F, \left(\text{NOT } F = \frac{ds^2}{dt^2}\right). \quad . \quad . \quad . \quad (4)$$

This expression represents the rate at which the velocity is increasing at any instant of time. In this particular example the acceleration is due to the earth's gravitational force, and g is usually written instead of F.

The ratio d^2x/dt^2 is called the **second differential coefficient** of x with respect to t. Just as the first differential coefficient of x with respect to t signifies a velocity, so does *the second differential coefficient of x with respect to t denote an acceleration.*

The velocity of most chemical reactions gradually *diminishes* as time goes on. Thus, the rate of transformation of cane sugar into invert sugar, after the elapse of 0, 30, 60, 90, and 130 minutes was found to be represented by the numbers [1]

$$15\cdot4, \ 13\cdot7, \ 12\cdot4, \ 11\cdot4, \ 9\cdot7,$$

respectively.

If the velocity of a body increases, the velocity gained per second is called its acceleration ; while if its velocity decreases, its acceleration is really a **retardation.** Mathematicians often prefix a negative sign to show that the velocity is diminishing. Thus, the rate at which the velocity of the chemical reaction changes is, with the above notation,

$$F = -\frac{d^2x}{dt^2}. \quad . \quad . \quad . \quad (5)$$

In our two illustrations, the stone had an acceleration of 32 units (feet per second) per second ; the chemical reaction had an acceleration of $-0\cdot00073$ units per second, or of $-0\cdot044$ units per minute. See also page 155.

In a similar way it can be shown that the *third differential coefficient* represents the rate of change of acceleration from moment to moment ; and so on for the higher differential coefficients $d^n x/dt^n$, which are seldom, if ever, used in practical work. A few words on notation.

---

[1] Multiplied by 10^3.

§ 8. Notation.

It is perhaps needless to remark that the letters δ, $\triangle$, d, d^2, ...[1] do not represent algebraic magnitudes. They cannot be dissociated from the appended x and t. These letters mean nothing more than that x and t have been taken small enough to satisfy the preceding definitions.

Some mathematicians reserve the symbols δx, δt, $\triangle x$, $\triangle t$, ... for small *finite* quantities ; dx, dt ... have no meaning *per se*. As a matter of fact the symbols dx, dt ... are constantly used in place of δx, δt, ..., or $\triangle x$, $\triangle t$. ... In the ratio $\dfrac{dx}{dt}$, $\dfrac{d}{dt}$ is the **symbol of an operation** performed on x, as much as the symbols "$\div$" or "$/$" denote the operation of division. In the present case *the operation has been to find the limiting value of the ratio* $\dfrac{\delta x}{\delta t}$ *when δt is made smaller and smaller without limit ;* but we constantly find that dx/dt is used when $\delta x/\delta t$ is intended. For convenience, D is sometimes used as a symbol for the operation in place of d/dx. The notation we are using is due to Leibnitz ;[2] Newton, the discoverer of this calculus, superscribed a small dot over the dependent variable for the first differential coefficient, two dots for the second, thus $\dot{x}$, $\ddot{x}$ ...

In special cases, besides $\dfrac{dy}{dx}$ and $\dot{y}$, we may have $\dfrac{d}{dx}(y)$, dy_x, x_y, x_1, x' ... for the first differential coefficient ; $\dfrac{d^2y}{dx^2}$, $\ddot{y}$, $\left(\dfrac{d}{dx}\right)^2 y$, x_2, x'' ... for the second differential coefficient ; and so on for the higher coefficients, or derivatives as they are sometimes called.

The operation of finding the value of the differential coefficients of any expression is called **differentiation**. The **differential calculus** is that branch of mathematics which deals with these operations.

§ 9. Functions.

If the pressure to which a gas is subject be altered, it is known that the volume of the gas changes in a proportional way. The

---

[1] For " ... " read "etc." or "and so on ".

[2] The history of the subject is somewhat sensational. See B. Williamson's article in the *Encyclopædia Britannica*, Art. " Infinitesimal Calculus ".

two magnitudes, pressure p and volume v, are interdependent. Any variation of the one is followed by a corresponding variation of the other. In mathematical language this idea is included in the word "*function*"; v is said to be a function of p. The two related magnitudes are called **variables**. Any magnitude which remains invariable during a given operation is called a **constant**.

In expressing Boyle's law for perfect gases we write this idea thus :

$$\text{Dependent variable} = f \text{ (independent variable)},$$

or $$v = f(p),$$

meaning that "v is some function of p". There is, however, no particular reason why p was chosen as the independent variable. The choice of the dependent variable depends on the conditions of the experiment alone. We could here have written

$$p = f(v)$$

just as correctly as $v = f(p)$. In actions involving time it is customary, though not essential, to regard the latter as the independent variable, since time changes in a most uniform and independent way. Time is the natural independent variable.

In the same way the area of a circle is a function of the radius, so is the volume of a sphere; the pressure of a gas is a function of the density; the volume of a gas is a function of the temperature; the amount of substance formed in a chemical reaction is a function of the time; the velocity of an explosion wave is a function of the density of the medium; the boiling point of a liquid is a function of the atmospheric pressure; the resistance of a wire to the passage of an electric current is a function of the thickness of the wire; the solubility of a salt is a function of the temperature, etc.

The independent variable may be denoted by x, when writing in general terms, and the dependent variable by y. The relation between these variables is variously denoted by the symbols :

$$y = f(x); \; y = \phi(x); \; y = F(x); \; y = \psi(x); \; y = f_1(x) \ldots$$

Any one of these expressions means nothing more than that "y *is some function of* x". If x_1, y_1; x_2, y_2; $x_3, y_3, \ldots$ are corresponding values of x and y, we may have

$$y = f(x); \; y_1 = f(x_1); \; y_2 = f(x_2) \ldots$$

"Let $y = f(x)$" means "take any equation which will enable you to calculate y when the value of x is known".

The word "function" in mathematical language thus implies

that for every value of x there is a determinate value of y. If v_0 and p_0 are the corresponding values of the pressure and volume of a gas in any given state, v and p their respective values in some other state, Boyle's law states that $pv = p_0v_0$. Hence,

$$p = \frac{p_0v_0}{v} \; ; \; \text{or,} \; v = \frac{p_0v_0}{p}.$$

The value of p or of v can therefore be determined for any assigned value of v or p as the case might be.

A similar rule applies for all physical changes in which two magnitudes simultaneously change their values according to some fixed law. It is quite immaterial, from our present point of view, whether or not any mathematical expression for the function $f(x)$ is known. For instance, although the pressure of the aqueous vapour in any vessel containing water and steam is a function of the temperature, the actual *form* of the expression or function showing this relation *is not known ;* but the laws connecting the volume of a gas with its temperature and pressure are *known* functions — Boyle's, and Charles' laws. The concept thus remains even though it is impossible to assign any rule for calculating the value of a function. In such cases the corresponding value of each variable can only be determined by actual observation and measurement. In other words, $f(x)$ *is a convenient symbol to denote any mathematical expression containing* **x**.

From pages 8 and 17, since

$$y = f(x),$$

the differential coefficient dy/dx is another function of x, say $f'(x)$,

$$\frac{dy}{dx} = f'(x), \; \text{or,} \; \frac{df(x)}{dx} = f'(x).$$

Similarly the second derivative, d^2y/dx^2, is another function of x, say $f''(x)$,

$$\frac{df'(x)}{dx} = f''(x) \; ; \; \frac{d^2y}{dx^2} = f''(x) \; ; \; \frac{d^2f(x)}{dx^2} = f''(x) \; ;$$

and so on for the higher differential functions.

The above investigation may be extended to functions of three or more variables. Thus, the volume of a gas is a function of the pressure and temperature ; the amount of light absorbed by a solution is a function of the thickness and concentration of the solution ; and the growth of a tree depends upon the fertility of the soil, the rain, solar heat, etc. We have tacitly assumed, in our preceding illustration, that the temperature was constant. If the pressure and temperature vary simultaneously, we write

$$v = f(p, T).$$

I must now make sure that the reader has clear ideas upon the subjects discussed in the two following articles; we will then pass directly to the "calculus" itself.

§ 10. Proportionality and the Variation Constant.

When two quantities are so related that any variation (increase or decrease) in the value of the one produces a proportional variation (increase or decrease) in the value of the other, the one quantity is said to be directly proportional to the other, or to vary as, or to vary directly as, the other. For example, the pressure of a gas is proportional to its density; the velocity of a chemical reaction is proportional to the amount of substance taking part in the reaction; and the area of a circle is proportional to the square of the radius.

On the other hand, when two quantities are so related that any increase in the value of the one leads to a proportional decrease in the value of the other, the one quantity is said to be inversely proportional to, or to vary inversely as the other. Thus, the pressure of a gas is inversely proportional to its volume, or the volume inversely proportional to the pressure; and the number of vibrations emitted per second by a sounding string varies inversely as the length of the string.

The symbol " $\propto$ " denotes variation. For $x \propto y$, read "x varies as y"; and for $x \propto y^{-1}$, read "x varies inversely as y". The variation notation is nothing but abbreviated proportion. Let $x_1, y_1; x_2, y_2; \ldots$ be corresponding values of x and y. Then, if x varies as y,

$$x_1 : y_1 = x_2 : y_2 = x_3 : y_3 = \ldots ;$$

or, what is the same thing,

$$\frac{x_1}{y_1} = \frac{x_2}{y_2} = \frac{x_3}{y_3} = \ldots \qquad \cdot \qquad \cdot \qquad \cdot \qquad (1)$$

Since the ratio of any[1] value of x to the corresponding value of y

---

[1] It is perhaps needless to remark that what is true of any value is true for all. If any apple in a barrel is bad, all are bad.

is always the same, it follows at once that x/y is a constant; and xy is a constant when x varies inversely as y, as p and v in "Boyle's law". In symbols, if

$$x \propto y, \ x = ky; \ \text{and if } x \propto \frac{1}{y}, \ x = \frac{k}{y}. \quad . \quad . \quad (2)$$

This result is of the greatest importance. It is utilized in nearly every formula representing a physical process. k is called the **constant of proportionality, or constant of variation.**

We can generally assign a specific meaning to the constant of proportion. For example, if we know that the mass, m, of a substance is proportional to its volume, v,

$$\therefore m = kv.$$

If we take unit volume, $v = 1$, $k = m$, k will then represent the density, *i.e.*, the mass of unit volume, usually symbolized by ρ. Again, the quantity of heat, Q, which is required to warm up the temperature of a mass, m, of a substance $\theta°$ is proportional to $m \times \theta$. Hence,

$$Q = km\theta.$$

If we take $m = 1$, and $\theta = 1°$, k denotes the amount of heat required to raise up the temperature of unit mass of substance $1°$. This constant, therefore, is nothing but the specific heat of the substance, usually represented by C or by σ in this work. Finally, the amount of heat, Q, transmitted by conduction across a plate is directly proportional to the difference of temperature, θ, on both sides of the plate, to the area, s, of the plate, and to the time, t; Q is also inversely proportional to the thickness, n, of the plate. Consequently,

$$Q = k\frac{s\theta t}{n}.$$

By taking a plate of unit area, and unit thickness; by keeping the difference of temperature on both sides of the plate at $1°$; and by considering only the amount of heat which would pass across the plate in unit time, $Q = k$; k therefore denotes the amount of heat transmitted in unit time across unit area of a plate, of unit thickness when its opposite faces are kept at a temperature differing by $1°$. That is to say, k denotes the coefficient of thermal conductivity.

The constants of variation or proportion thus furnish certain specific coefficients or numbers whose numerical values usually depend upon the nature of the substance, and the conditions under which the experiment is performed. The well-known constants: specific gravity, electrical resistance, the gravitation constant, π, and the gas constant, R, are constants of proportion.

Let a gas be in a state denoted by p_1, ρ_1, and T_1, and suppose that the gas is transformed into another state denoted by p_2, ρ_2, and T_2. Let the change take place in two stages :—

First, let the pressure change from p_1 to p_2 while the temperature remains at T_1. Let ρ_1, in consequence, become x. Then, according to Boyle's law,

$$\frac{p_1}{\rho_1} = \frac{p_2}{x} \; ; \; \therefore x = \frac{p_2\rho_1}{p_1}. \qquad \qquad (3)$$

Second, let the pressure remain constant at p_2 while the temperature changes from T_1 to T_2. Let x, in consequence, become ρ_2. Then, by Charles' law,

$$\rho_2 T_2 = x T_1. \qquad \qquad (4)$$

Substituting the above value of x in this equation, we get

$$\frac{p_1}{\rho_1 T_1} = \frac{p_2}{\rho_2 T_2} = \text{constant, say, } R. \quad \therefore \frac{p}{\rho} = RT.$$

We therefore infer that *if x, y, z, are variable magnitudes such that x ∝ y, when z is constant, and x ∝ z, when y is constant, then, x ∝ yz, when y and z vary together;* and conversely, it can also be shown that *if x varies as y, when z is constant, and x varies inversely as z, when y is constant, then, x ∝ y/z when y and z both vary.*

EXAMPLES.—(1) If the volume of a gas varies inversely as the pressure and directly as the temperature, show that

$$\frac{p_1 v_1}{T_1} = \frac{p_2 v_2}{T_2} \; ; \text{ and that } pv = RT. \qquad (5)$$

(2) If the quantity of heat required to warm a substance varies directly as the mass, m, and also as the range of temperature, θ, show that $Q = \sigma m \theta$.

(3) If the velocity, V, of a chemical reaction is proportional to the amount of each reacting substance present at the time t, show that

$$V = kC_1 C_2 C_3 \ldots C_n,$$

where C_1, C_2, C_3, ..., C_n, respectively denote the amount of each of the n reacting substances at the time t, k is constant.

§ 11. The Laws of Indices and Logarithms.

We all know that

$4 \times 4 = 16$, is the *second power* of 4, written 4^2 ;
$4 \times 4 \times 4 = 64$, is the *third power* of 4, written 4^3 ;
$4 \times 4 \times 4 \times 4 = 256$, is the *fourth power* of 4, written 4^4 ;

and in general, the nth power of any number a, is defined as the continued product

$$a \times a \times a \times \ldots n \text{ times} = a^n, \qquad . \quad . \quad (1)$$

where n is called the **exponent, or index** of the number.

By actual multiplication, therefore, it follows at once that $10^2 \times 10^3 = 10 \times 10 \times 10 \times 10 \times 10 = 10^{2+3} = 10^5 = 100,000$; or, in general symbols,

$$a^m \times a^n = a^{m+n}; \text{ or, } a^x \times a^y \times a^z \times \ldots = a^{x+y+z+\ldots}, \qquad (2)$$

a result known as the **index law.**

All numbers may be represented as different powers of one fundamental number. $E.g.$,

$$1 = 10^0; \ 2 = 10^{\cdot 301}; \ 3 = 10^{\cdot 477}; \ 4 = 10^{\cdot 602}; \ 5 = 10^{\cdot 699}; \ \ldots$$

The power, index or exponent is called a **logarithm,** the fundamental number is called the **base** of the system of logarithms. Thus if

$$a^n = b,$$

n is the logarithm of the number b to the base a, and is written

$$n = \log_a b.$$

For convenience in numerical calculations tables are generally used in which all numbers are represented as different powers of 10. The logarithm of any number taken from the table thus indicates what power of 10 the selected number represents. Thus if

$$10^3 = 1000; \text{ and } 10^{1 \cdot 0413927} = 11;$$

then $3 = \log_{10} 1000$; and $1 \cdot 0413927 = \log_{10} 11$.

We need not use 10. Logarithms could be calculated to any other number employed as base. If we replace 10 by some other number, say, $2 \cdot 71828$, which we represent by e, then

$$1 = e^0; \ 2 = e^{0 \cdot 693}; \ 3 = e^{1 \cdot 099}; \ 4 = e^{1 \cdot 386}; \ 5 = e^{1 \cdot 609}; \ \ldots$$

Logarithms to the base $e = 2 \cdot 71828$ are called **natural, hyperbolic, or Napierian logarithms.** Logarithms to the base 10 are called **Briggsian, or common logarithms.**

Again,

$$3 \times 5 = (10^{0 \cdot 4771}) \times (10^{0 \cdot 6990}) = 10^{1 \cdot 1761} = 15,$$

because, from a table of common logarithms,

$$\log_{10} 3 = 0 \cdot 4771; \ \log_{10} 5 = 0 \cdot 6990; \ \log_{10} 15 = 1 \cdot 1761.$$

Thus we have performed arithmetical multiplication by the simple addition of two logarithms. Generalizing, to multiply two or more numbers, add the logarithms of the numbers and find the number whose logarithm is the sum of the logarithms just obtained.

EXAMPLE.—Evaluate 4×80,

$$\log_{10} 4 = 0\text{·}6021$$
$$\log_{10} 80 = 1\text{·}9031$$
$$\text{Sum} = 2\text{·}5052 = \log_{10} 320.$$

This method of calculation holds good whatever numbers we employ in place of 3 and 5 or 4 and 80. Hence the use of logarithms for facilitating numerical calculations. We shall shortly show how the operations of division, involution, and evolution are as easily performed as the above multiplication.

From what has just been said it follows that

$$\frac{10^3}{10^2} = 10^{3-2} = 10^1 = 10\;;\text{ or generally, } \frac{a^m}{a^n} = a^{m-n}. \quad . \quad (3)$$

Hence the rule : To divide two numbers, subtract the logarithm of the divisor (denominator of a fraction) from the logarithm of the dividend (numerator of a fraction) and find the number corresponding to the resulting logarithm.

EXAMPLES.—(1) Evaluate $60 \div 3$.

$$\log_{10} 60 = 1\text{·}7782$$
$$\log_{10} 3 = 0\text{·}4771$$
$$\text{Difference} = 1\text{·}3011 = \log_{10} 20.$$

(2) Show that $2^{-2} = \frac{1}{4}$; $10^{-2} = \frac{1}{100}$; $3^3 \times 3^{-3} = 1$.

(3) Show that $a^x \times a^{1-x} = a$; $p \div p^{\frac{1}{x}} = p^{1-\frac{1}{x}}$; $a^x \div a = a^{-(1-x)}$.

The general symbols $a, b, \ldots m, n, \ldots x, y, \ldots$ in any general expression may be compared with the blank spaces in a bank cheque waiting to have particular values assigned to date, amount (£ s. d.), and sponsor, before the cheque can fulfil the specific purpose for which it was designed. So must the symbols, $a, b, \ldots$ of a general equation be replaced by special numerical values before the equation can be applied to any specific process or operation.

It is very easy to miss the meaning of the so-called " properties of indices," unless the general symbols of the text-books are thoroughly tested by translation into numerical examples. The majority of students require a good bit of practice before a general expression appeals to them with full force. Here, as elsewhere, it is not merely necessary for the student to think that he "understands the principle of the thing," he must actually work out examples for himself. " In scientiis ediscendis prosunt exempla magis quàm præcepta "[1] is as true to-day as it was in Newton's time. For example, how many realise why mathematicians write $e^0 = 1$, until some such illustration as the following has been worked out?

$$2^2 \times 2^0 = 2^{2+0} = 2^2 = 4 = 2^2 \times 1.$$

The same result, therefore, is obtained whether we multiply 2^2 by 2^0 or by 1, *i.e.*,

$$2^2 \times 2^0 = 2^2 \times 1 = 2^2 = 4.$$

Hence it is inferred that [2]

$$2^0 = 1, \text{ and generally that } a^0 = 1. \qquad . \qquad . \qquad (4)$$

EXAMPLE.—From the Table on page 628, show that

$$\log_e 3 = 1 \cdot 0986 ; \; \log_e 2 = 0 \cdot 6932 ; \; \log_e 1 = 0. \qquad . \qquad . \qquad (5)$$

And, since

$$e \times e \times e \times \dots n \text{ times} = e^n ; \; \dots ; \; e \times e \times e = e^3 ; \; e \times e = e^2 ; \; e = e^1 ;$$
$$\therefore \log_e e^n = n ; \; \dots \log_e e^3 = 3 ; \; \log_e e^2 = 2 ; \; \log_e e^1 = 1 = \log_e e. \quad . \qquad (6)$$

I am purposely using the simplest of illustrations, leaving the reader to set himself more complicated numbers. No pretence is made to rigorous demonstration. We assume that what is true in one case, is true in another. It is only by so collecting our facts one by one that we are able to build up a general idea. The beginner should always satisfy himself of the truth of any abstract principle or general formula by applying it to particular and simple cases.

To find the relation between the logarithms of a number to different bases. Let n be a number such that $a^a = n$; or, $a = \log_a n$; and $\beta^b = n$, or, $b = \log_\beta n$. Hence $a^a = \beta^b$. "Taking logs" to the base a, we obtain

$$a = b \log_a \beta,$$

since $\log_a a$ is unity. Substitute for a and b, and we get

$$\log_a n = \log_\beta n \cdot \log_a \beta. \qquad . \qquad . \qquad . \qquad (7)$$

In words, the logarithm of a number to the base β may be obtained from the logarithm of that number to the base a by multiplying it by $1/\log_a \beta$. For example, suppose $a = 10$ and $\beta = e$,

$$\log n = \frac{\log_{10} n}{\log_{10} e}, \qquad . \qquad . \qquad . \qquad . \qquad (8)$$

---

[1] Which may be rendered : "In learning we profit more by example than by precept".

[2] Some mathematicians define a^n as $1 \times a \times a \times a \dots n$ times ; $a^3 = 1 \times a \times a \times a$; $a^2 = 1 \times a \times a$; $a^1 = 1 \times a$; and a^0 as $1 \times a$ no times, that is unity itself. If so, then I suppose that 0^0 must mean 1×0 no times, *i.e.*, 1 ; and $1/0^0$ must mean $1/(1 \times 0$ no times), *i.e.*, unity.

where the subscript in $\log_e n$ is omitted. It is a common practice to omit the subscript of the "log" when there is no danger of ambiguity. Hence, since $\log_{10} 2\cdot71828 = 0\cdot4343$, and $\log_e 10 = 2\cdot3026$, where $2\cdot71828$ is the nominal value of e (page 25) :—

To pass from natural to common logarithms

$$\left.\begin{array}{l} \text{Common log} = \text{natural log} \times 0\cdot4343 \\ \log_{10} a = \log_e a \times 0\cdot4343 \end{array}\right\} \quad . \qquad \textbf{(9)}$$

To pass from common to natural logarithms

$$\left.\begin{array}{l} \text{Natural log} = \text{common log} \times 2\cdot3026 \\ \log_e a = \log_{10} a \times 2\cdot3026 \end{array}\right\} \quad . \qquad \textbf{(10)}$$

The number $0\cdot4343$ is called the **modulus** of the Briggsian or common system of logarithms. When required it is written M or μ. It is sufficient to remember that the natural logarithm of a number is $2\cdot3026$ times as great as the common logarithm.

By actual multiplication show that

$$(100)^3 = (10^2)^3 = 10^{2 \times 3} = 10^6,$$

and hence, to raise a number to any power, multiply the logarithm of the number by the index of the power and find the number corresponding to the resulting logarithm.

$$(a^m)^n = a^{mn}. \qquad . \qquad . \qquad . \qquad \textbf{(11)}$$

EXAMPLE.—Evaluate 5^2.

$$5^2 = (5)^2 = (10^{0\cdot6990})^2 = 10^{1\cdot3980} = 25,$$

since reference to a table of common logarithms shows that

$$\log_{10} 5 = 0\cdot6990; \quad \log_{10} 25 = 1\cdot3980.$$

From the index law, above

$$10^{\frac{1}{2}} \times 10^{\frac{1}{2}} = 10^{\frac{1}{2} + \frac{1}{2}} = 10^1 = 10.$$

That is to say, $10^{\frac{1}{2}}$ multiplied by itself gives 10. But this is the definition of the square root of 10.

$$\therefore (\sqrt{10})^2 = \sqrt{10} \times \sqrt{10} = 10^{\frac{1}{2}} \times 10^{\frac{1}{2}} = 10.$$

A fractional index, therefore, represents a root of the particular number affected with that exponent. Similarly,

$$\sqrt[3]{8} = 8^{\frac{1}{3}}, \text{ because } \sqrt[3]{8} \times \sqrt[3]{8} \times \sqrt[3]{8} = 8^{\frac{1}{3}} \times 8^{\frac{1}{3}} \times 8^{\frac{1}{3}} = 8.$$

Generalizing this idea, the nth root of any number a, is

$$\sqrt[n]{a} = a^{\frac{1}{n}}. \qquad . \qquad . \qquad . \qquad \textbf{(12)}$$

To extract the root of any number, divide the logarithm of

the number by the index of the required root and find the number corresponding to the resulting logarithm.

EXAMPLES.—(1) Evaluate $\sqrt[3]{8}$ and $\sqrt[7]{93}$.

$\sqrt[3]{8} = (8)^{\frac{1}{3}} = (10^{0 \cdot 9031})^{\frac{1}{3}} = 10^{0 \cdot 3010} = 2$; $\sqrt[7]{93} = (93)^{\frac{1}{7}} = (10^{1 \cdot 9685})^{\frac{1}{7}} = 10^{0 \cdot 2812} = 1 \cdot 91$, since, from a table of common logarithms,

$\log_{10} 2 = 0 \cdot 3010$; $\log_{10} 8 = 0 \cdot 9031$; $\log_{10} 1 \cdot 91 = 0 \cdot 2812$; $\log_{10} 93 = 1 \cdot 9685$.

(2) Perhaps this will amuse the reader some idle moment. Given the obvious facts $\log \frac{1}{2} = \log \frac{1}{2}$, and $3 > 2$; combining the two statements we get $3 \log \frac{1}{2} > 2 \log \frac{1}{2}$; $\therefore \log(\frac{1}{2})^3 > \log(\frac{1}{2})^2$; $\therefore (\frac{1}{2})^3 > (\frac{1}{2})^2$; $\therefore \frac{1}{8} > \frac{1}{4}$; $\therefore 1$ is greater than 2. Where is the fallacy?

The results of logarithmic calculations are seldom absolutely correct because we employ approximate values of the logarithms of the particular numbers concerned. Instead of using logarithms to four decimal places we could, if stupid enough, use logarithms accurate to sixty-four decimal places. But the discussion of this question is reserved for another chapter. If the student has any difficulty with logarithms, after this, he had better buy F. G. Taylor's *An Introduction to the Practical Use of Logarithms*, London, 1901.

§ 12. Differentiation, and its Uses.

The differential calculus is not directly concerned with the establishment of any relation between the quantities themselves, but rather with the momentary state of the phenomenon. This momentary state is symbolised by the differential coefficient, which thus conveys to the mind a perfectly clear and definite conception altogether apart from any numerical or practical application. I suppose the proper place to recapitulate the uses of the differential calculus would be somewhere near the end of this book, for only there can the reader hope to have his faith displaced by the certainty of demonstrated facts. Nevertheless, I shall here illustrate the subject by stating three problems which the differential calculus helps us to solve.

In order to describe the whole history of any phenomenon it is necessary to find the law which describes the relation between the various agents taking part in the change as well as the law describing the momentary states of the phenomenon. There is a close connection between the two. The one is conditioned by the other. Starting with the complete law it is possible to calculate the momentary states and conversely.

I. The calculation of the momentary states from the complete law. Before the instantaneous rate of change, dy/dx, can be determined it is necessary to know the law, or form of the function connecting the varying quantities one with another. For instance, Galileo found by actual measurement that a stone falling vertically downwards from a position of rest travels a distance of $s = \frac{1}{2}gt^2$ feet in t seconds. Differentiation of this, as we shall see very shortly, furnishes the actual velocity of the stone at any instant of time, $V = gt$. In the same manner, Newton's law of inverse squares follows from Kepler's third law; and Ampère's law, from the observed effect of one part of an electric circuit upon another.

II. The calculation of the complete law from the momentary states. It is sometimes possible to get an idea of the relations between the forces at work in any given phenomenon from the actual measurements themselves, but more frequently, a less direct path must be followed. The investigator makes the most plausible guess about the momentary state of the phenomenon at his command, and dresses it up in mathematical symbols. Subsequent progress is purely an affair of mathematical computation based upon the differential calculus. Successful guessing depends upon the astuteness of the investigator. This mode of attack is finally justified by a comparison of the experimental data with the hypothesis dressed up in mathematical symbols, and thus

> The golden guess
> Is morning star to the full round of truth.

Fresnel's law of double refraction, Wilhelmy's law of mass action, and Newton's law of heat radiation may have been established in this way. The subtility and beauty of this branch of the calculus will not appear until the methods of integration have been discussed.

III. The eduction of a generalization from particular cases. A natural law, deduced directly from observation or measurement, can only be applied to particular cases because it is necessarily affected by the accidental circumstances associated with the conditions under which the measurements were made. Differentiation will eliminate the accidental features so that the essential circumstances, common to all the members of a certain class of phenomena, alone remain. Let us take one of the simplest of illustrations, a train travelling with the constant velocity of thirty miles an hour. Hence, $V = 30$. From what we have already said, it will be clear that the rate of change of velocity, at any moment, is zero. Otherwise expressed, $dV/dt = 0$. The former equation, $V = 30$, is only true of the motion of one particular object, whereas $dV/dt = 0$, is true of the motion of all bodies travelling with a constant velocity. In this sense one reliable observation might give rise to a general law.

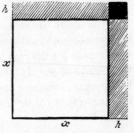

The mechanical operations of finding the differential coefficient of one variable with respect to another in any expression are no more difficult than ordinary algebraic processes. Before describing the practical methods of differentiation it will be instructive to study a geometrical illustration of the process.

Fig. 5.

Let x (Fig. 5) be the side of a square, and let there be an increment [1] in the area of the square due to an increase of h in the variable x.

The original area of the square $= x^2$.
The new area $= (x + h)^2 = x^2 + 2xh + h^2$.
The increment in the area $= (x + h)^2 - x^2 = 2xh + h^2$ . . (3)

This equation is true, whatever value be given to h. The smaller the increment h the less does the value of h^2 become. If this increment h ultimately become indefinitely small, then h^2, being of a very small order of magnitude, may be neglected. For example, if when $x = 1$,

$h = 1$, increment in area $= 2 + 1$;
$h = \frac{1}{10}$,   „   „ $= 0\cdot2 + \frac{1}{100}$;
$h = \frac{1}{1000}$, „   „ $= 0\cdot002 + \frac{1}{1,000,000}$, etc.

If, therefore, dy denotes the infinitely small increment in the area, y, of the square corresponding to an infinitely small increment dx in two adjoining sides, x, then, in the language of differentials,

Increment $y = 2xh$, becomes, $dy = 2x \cdot dx$.   . (4)

The same result can be deduced by means of limiting ratios. For instance, consider the ratio of any increment in the area, y, to any increment in the length of a side of the square, x.

---

[1] When any quantity is increased, the quantity by which it is increased is called its *increment*, abbreviated "incr."; a decrement is a negative increment.

$$\frac{\text{Increment } y}{h} = \frac{\text{Incr. } y}{\text{Incr. } x} = \frac{\delta y}{\delta x} = \frac{2xh + h^2}{h} = 2x + h,$$

and when the value of h is zero

$$\frac{dy}{dx} = \text{Lt}_{h=0} \frac{\delta y}{\delta x} = 2x. \qquad . \qquad . \qquad . \qquad (5)$$

To measure the rate of change of any two variables, we fix upon one variable as the standard of reference. When x is the standard of reference for the rate of change of the variable y, we call dy/dx the **x-rate of y**. In practical work, the rate of change of time, t, is the most common standard of reference. If desired we can interpret (4) or (5) to mean

$$\frac{dy}{dt} = 2x \frac{dx}{dt},$$

In words, the rate at which y changes is $2x$ times the rate at which x changes.

EXAMPLES.—(1) Show, by similar reasoning to the above, that if the three adjoining sides, x, of a cube receive an increment h, then $\text{Lt}_{h=0} \frac{\delta y}{\delta x} = 3x^2$.

(2) Prove that if the radius, r, of a circle be increased by an amount h, the increment in the area of the circle will be $(2rh + h^2)\pi$. Show that the limiting ratio, dy/dx, in this case is $2\pi r$. Given, area of circle $= \pi r^2$.

The former method of differentiation is known as "Leibnitz's method of differentials," the latter, "Newton's method of limits". It cannot be denied that while Newton's method is rigorous, exact, and satisfying, Leibnitz's at once raises the question:

§ 13. Is Differentiation a Method of Approximation only ?

The method of differentiation might at first sight be regarded as a method of approximation, for these small quantities appear to be rejected only because this *may* be done without committing any sensible error. For this reason, in its early days, the calculus was subject to much opposition on metaphysical grounds. Bishop Berkeley[1] called these limiting ratios "the ghosts of departed quantities". A little consideration, however, will show that these small quantities *must* be rejected in order that no error may be committed in the calculation. The process of elimination is essential to the operation.

---

[1] G. Berkeley, *Collected Works*, Oxford, **3**, 44, 1901.

There has been a good bit of tinkering, lately, at the foundations of the calculus as well as other branches of mathematics, but we cannot get much deeper than this : assuming that the quantities under investigation are continuous, and noting that the smaller the differentials the closer the approximation to absolute accuracy, our reason is satisfied to reject the differentials, when they become so small as to be no longer perceptible to our senses. The psychological process that gives rise to this train of thought leads to the inevitable conclusion that this mode of representing the process is the true one. Moreover, if this be any argument, the validity of the reasoning is justified by its results.

The following remarks on this question are freely translated from Carnot's *Réflexions sur la Métaphysique du Calcul Infinitésimal*.[1] " The essential merit, the sublimity, one may say, of the infinitesimal method lies in the fact that it is as easily performed as a simple method of approximation, and as accurate as the results of an ordinary calculation. This immense advantage would be lost, or at any rate greatly diminished, if, under the pretence of obtaining a greater degree of accuracy throughout the whole process, we were to substitute for the simple method given by Leibnitz one less convenient and less in accord with the probable course of the natural event. If this method is accurate in its results, as no one doubts at this day ; if we always have recourse to it in difficult questions, what need is there to supplant it by complicated and indirect means ? Why content ourselves with founding it on inductions and analogies with the results furnished by other means when it can be demonstrated directly and generally, more easily, perhaps, than any of these very methods ? The objections which have been raised against it are based on the false supposition that the errors made by neglecting infinitesimally small quantities during the actual calculation are still to be found in the result of the calculation, however small they may be. Now this is not the case. The error is of necessity removed from the result by elimination. It is indeed a strange thing that every one did not from the very first realise the true character of infinitesimal quantities, and see that a conclusive answer to all objections lies in this indispensable process of elimination."

The beginner will have noticed that, unlike algebra and arith-

---

[1] Paris, 215, 1813.

metic, higher mathematics postulates that number is capable of gradual growth. The differential calculus is concerned with the rate at which quantities increase or diminish. There are three modes of viewing this growth :—

I. Leibnitz's "method of infinitesimals or differentials". According to this, a quantity is supposed to pass from one degree of magnitude to another by the continual addition of infinitely small parts, called *infinitesimals* or *differentials*. Infinitesimals may have different orders of magnitude. Thus, the product $dx.dy$ is an infinitesimal of the second order, infinitely small in comparison with the product $y.dx$, or $x.dy$.

In a preceding section it was shown that when each of two sides of a square receives a small increment h, the corresponding increment in the area is $2xh + h^2$. When h is made indefinitely small and equal to say dx, then $(dx)^2$ is vanishingly small in comparison with $x.dx$. Hence,

$$dy = 2x . dx.$$

In calculations involving quantities which are ultimately made to approach the limit zero, the higher orders of infinitesimals may be rejected at any stage of the process. Only the lowest orders of infinitesimals are, as a rule, retained.

II. Newton's "method of rates or fluxions". Here, the velocity or rate with which the quantity is generated is employed. The measure of this velocity is called a *fluxion*. A fluxion, written $\dot{x}, \dot{y}$, ..., is equivalent to our $dx/dt, dy/dt, \ldots$

These two methods are modifications of one idea. It is all a question of notation or definition. While Leibnitz referred the rate of change of a dependent variable y, to an independent variable x, Newton referred each variable to "uniformly flowing" time. Leibnitz assumed that when x receives an increment dx, y is increased by an amount dy. Newton conceived these changes to occupy a certain time dt, so that y increases with a velocity $\dot{y}$, as x increases with a velocity $\dot{x}$. This relation may be written symbolically,

$$dx = \dot{x}dt, \; dy = \dot{y}dt \; ; \; \therefore \frac{\dot{y}}{\dot{x}} = \frac{\frac{dy}{dt}}{\frac{dx}{dt}} = \frac{dy}{dx}.$$

The method of fluxions is not in general use, perhaps because of its more abstruse character. It is occasionally employed in mechanics.

III. Newton's "method of limits". This has been set forth in § 2. The ultimate limiting ratio is considered as a fixed quantity to which the ratio of the two variables can be made to approximate as closely as we please. "The limiting ratio," says Carnot, "is neither more nor less difficult to define than an infinitely small quantity.... To proceed rigorously by the method of limits it is necessary to lay down the definition of a limiting ratio. But this is the definition, or rather, this ought to be the definition, of an infinitely small quantity." "The difference between the method of infinitesimals and that of limits (when exclusively adopted) is, that in the latter it is usual to retain evanescent quantities of higher orders until the end of the calculation and then neglect them. On the other hand, such quantities are neglected from the commence-ment in the infinitesimal method from the conviction that they cannot affect the final result, as they must disappear when we proceed to the limit" (*Encyc. Brit.*). It follows, therefore, that the psychological process of reducing quantities down to their limiting ratios is equivalent to the rejection of terms involving the higher orders of infinitesimals. These operations have been indicated side by side on pages 31 and 32.

The methods of limits and of infinitesimals are employed in-discriminately in this work, according as the one or the other appeared the more instructive or convenient. As a rule, it is easier to represent a process mathematically by the method of infinit-esimals. The determination of the limiting ratio frequently involves more complicated operations than is required by Leibnitz's method.

§ 14. The Differentiation of Algebraic Functions.

We may now take up the routine processes of differentiation. It is convenient to study the different types of functions—alge-braic, logarithmic, exponential, and trigonometrical—separately. An **algebraic function** of x is an expression containing terms which involve only the operations of addition, subtraction, multi-plication, division, evolution (root extraction), and involution. For instance, $x^2y + \sqrt[3]{x} + y^{\frac{1}{2}} - ax = 1$ is an algebraic function. Func-tions that cannot be so expressed are termed **transcendental**

functions. Thus, $\sin x = y$, $\log x = y$, $e^x = y$ are transcendental functions.

On pages 31 and 32 a method was described for finding the differential coefficient of $y = x^2$, by the following series of operations:—(1) Give an arbitrary increment h to x in the original function; (2) Subtract the original function x^2 from the new value of $(x + h)^2$ found in (1); (3) Divide the result of (2) by h the increment of x; and (4) Find the limiting value of this ratio when $h = 0$.

This procedure must be carefully noted; it lies at the basis of all processes of differentiation. In this way it can be shown that

if $y = x^2$, $\dfrac{dy}{dx} = 2x$; if $y = x^3$, $\dfrac{dy}{dx} = 3x^2$; if $y = x^4$, $\dfrac{dy}{dx} = 4x^3$, etc.

By actual multiplication we find that

$$(x + h)^2 = (x + h)(x + h) = x^2 + 2hx + h^2;$$
$$(x + h)^3 = (x + h)^2(x + h) = x^3 + 3hx^2 + 3h^2x + h^3;$$

. . . .　　　　. . . .　　　　　　. . . .

Continuing this process as far as we please, we shall find that

$$(x+h)^n = x^n + \frac{n}{1}x^{n-1}h + \frac{n(n-1)}{1.2}x^{n-2}h^2 + \ldots + \frac{n}{1}xh^{n-1} + h^n. \quad (1)$$

This result, known as the **binomial theorem**, enables us to raise any expression of the type $x + h$ to any power of n (where n is positive integer, *i.e.*, a positive whole number, not a fraction) without going through the actual process of successive multiplication. A similar rule holds for $(x - h)^n$. Now try if this is so by substituting $n = 1$, 2, 3, 4, and 5 successively in (1), and comparing with the results obtained by actual multiplication.

It is convenient to notice that the several sets of binomial coefficients obey the law indicated in the following scheme, as n increases from 0, 1, 2, 3. . . .

$$(a + b)^0 = 1$$
$$(a + b)^1 = 1 \quad 1$$
$$(a + b)^2 = 1 \quad 2 \quad 1$$
$$(a + b)^3 = 1 \quad 3 \quad 3 \quad 1$$
$$(a + b)^4 = 1 \quad 4 \quad 6 \quad 4 \quad 1$$
$$(a + b)^5 = 1 \quad 5 \quad 10 \quad 10 \quad 5 \quad 1$$
$$(a + b)^6 = 1 \quad 6 \quad 15 \quad 20 \quad 15 \quad 6 \quad 1$$

I. The differential coefficient of any power of a variable. To find the differential coefficient of

$$y = x^n.$$

Let each side of this expression receive a small increment so that y becomes $y + h'$ when x becomes $x + h$;

$$\therefore (y + h') - y = \text{Incr. } y = (x + h)^n - x^n.$$

From the binomial theorem, (1) above,

$$\text{Incr. } y = nx^{n-1}h + \tfrac{1}{2}n(n-1)x^{n-2}h^2 + \ldots$$

Divide by increment x, namely h.

$$\frac{\text{Incr. } y}{h} = \frac{\text{Incr. } y}{\text{Incr. } x} = nx^{n-1} + \tfrac{1}{2}n(n-1)x^{n-2}h + \ldots$$

Hence when h is made zero

$$\text{Lt}_{h=0} \frac{\text{Incr. } y}{\text{Incr. } x} = \text{Limit}_{h=0} \frac{(x+h)^n - x^n}{h} = nx^{n-1}.$$

That is to say

$$\frac{dy}{dx} = \frac{d(x^n)}{dx} = nx^{n-1}. \qquad . \qquad . \qquad . \qquad (2)$$

Hence the rule :—The differential coefficient of any power of x is obtained by diminishing the index by unity and multiplying the power of x so obtained by the original exponent (or index).

EXAMPLES.—(1) If $y = x^6$; show that $dy/dx = 6x^5$. This means that y changes $6x^5$ times as fast as x. If $x = 1$, y increases 6 times as fast as x ; if $x = -2$, y decreases $-6 \times 32 = -192$ times as fast as x.

(2) If $y = x^{20}$; show that $dy/dx = 20x^{19}$.

(3) If $y = x^5$; show that $dy/dx = 5x^4$.

(4) If $y = x^3$; show that $dy/dx = 300$, when $x = 10$.

Later on we deduce the binomial theorem by differentiation. The student may think we have worked in a vicious circle. This need not be. The differential coefficient of x^n may be established without assuming the binomial theorem. For instance, let

$$y = x^n,$$

and suppose that when x becomes $x_1 = x + h$, y becomes y_1 ; then we have

$$\frac{y_1 - y}{x_1 - x} = \frac{x_1^n - x^n}{x_1 - x} = x_1^{n-1} + xx_1^{n-2} + \ldots + x^{n-1},$$

by division. But $\text{Lt}_{h=0} x_1 = x$;

$$\therefore \frac{dy}{dx} = x^{n-1} + x^{n-1} + \ldots \text{ to } n \text{ terms} = nx^{n-1}.$$

II. *The differential coefficient of the sum or difference of any number of functions.* Let u, v, $w \ldots$ be functions of x ; y their

sum.   Let u_1, v_1, w_1, ..., y_1, be the respective values of these
functions when x is changed to $x + h$, then

$$y = u + v + w + \ldots ; y_1 = u_1 + v_1 + w_1 + \ldots$$
$$\therefore y_1 - y = (u_1 - u) + (v_1 - v) + (w_1 - w) + \ldots,$$

by subtraction ; dividing by h,

$$\frac{\text{Incr. } y}{h} = \frac{\text{Incr. } u}{h} + \frac{\text{Incr. } v}{h} + \frac{\text{Incr. } w}{h} + \ldots,$$

or, $$\text{Lt}_{h=0} \frac{\text{Incr. } y}{\text{Incr. } x} = \frac{dy}{dx} = \frac{du}{dx} + \frac{dv}{dx} + \frac{dw}{dx} + \ldots \quad . \quad (3)$$

If some of the symbols have a minus, instead of a plus, sign a
corresponding result is obtained.   For instance, if

$$y = u - v - w - \ldots,$$

then $$\frac{dy}{dx} = \frac{du}{dx} - \frac{dv}{dx} - \frac{dw}{dx} - \ldots \quad . \quad . \quad . \quad (4)$$

Hence the rule :—The differential coefficient of the sum or
difference of any number of functions is equal to the sum or difference of the differential coefficients of the several functions.

*III. The differential coefficient of the product of a variable and
a constant quantity.*   Let

$$y = ax^n ;$$

Incr. $y = a(x + h)^n - ax^n = anx^{n-1}h + \dfrac{an(n-1)}{2!}x^{n-2}h^2 + \ldots$

Therefore

$$\text{Lt}_{h=0} \frac{\text{Incr. } y}{h} = \frac{dy}{dx} = anx^{n-1} . \quad . \quad . \quad (5)$$

Hence the rule :—The differential coefficient of the product of
a variable quantity and a constant is equal to the constant multiplied by the differential coefficient of the variable.

IV. The differential coefficient of any constant term is zero.
Since a constant term is essentially a quantity that does not vary,
if y be a constant, say, equal to a; then da/dt must be absolute
zero.   Let

$$y = (x^n + a) ;$$

then, following the old track,

Incr. $y = (x + h)^n + a - (x^n + a) ;$

$$\therefore \text{Incr. } y = \frac{n}{1} x^{n-1}h + \frac{n(n-1)}{2!} x^{n-2}h^2 + \ldots$$

$$\therefore \text{Lt}_{h=0} \frac{\text{Incr. } y}{\text{Incr. } x} = \frac{dy}{dx} = nx^{n-1}, \quad . \quad . \quad (6)$$

where the constant term has disappeared.

For the sake of brevity we have written $1! = 1 ; 2! = 1 \times 2$; $3! = 1 \times 2 \times 3 ; n! = 1 \times 2 \times 3 \times \ldots \times (n-2) \times (n-1) \times n.$ ' Strictly speaking, 0! has no meaning ; mathematicians, however, find it convenient to make $0! = 1$. This notation is due to Kramp. "$n!$" is read "factorial n".

V. *The differential coefficient of a polynomial* [1] *raised to any power.* Let

$$y = (ax + x^2)^n.$$

If we regard the expression in brackets as one variable raised to the power of n, we get

$$dy. = n(ax + x^2)^{n-1} d(ax + x^2).$$

Differentiating the last term, we get

$$\frac{dy}{dx} = n(ax + x^2)^{n-1}(a + 2x). \qquad . \quad . \quad (7)$$

Hence the rule : — The differential coefficient of a polynomial raised to any power is obtained by diminishing the exponent of the power by unity and multiplying the expression so obtained by the differential coefficient of the polynomial and the original exponent.

EXAMPLES.—(1) If $y = x - 2x^2$, show that $dy/dx = 1 - 4x$.

(2) If $y = (1 - x^2)^3$, show that $dy/dx = -6x(1 - x^2)^2$. This means that y changes at the rate of $-6x(1 - x^2)^2$ for unit change of x ; in other words, y changes $-6x(1 - x^2)^2$ times as fast as x.

(3) If the distance, s, traversed by a falling body at the time t, is given by the expression $s = \frac{1}{2}gt^2$, show that the body will be falling with a velocity $ds/dt = gt$, at the time t.

(4) Young's formula for the relation between the vapour pressure p and the temperature θ of isopentane at constant volume is, $p = b\theta - a$, where a and b are empirical constants. Hence show that the ratio of the change of pressure with temperature is constant and equal to b.

(5) Mendeléeff's formula for the superficial tension s of a perfect liquid at any temperature θ is, $s = a - b\theta$, where a and b are constants. Hence show that rate of change of s with θ is constant. Ansr. $- b$.

(6) One of Callendar's formulæ for the variation of the electrical resistance R of a platinum wire with temperature θ is, $R = R_0(1 + a\theta + \beta\theta^2)$, where a and β and R_0 are constants. Find the increase in the resistance of the wire for a small rise of temperature. Ansr. $dR = R_0(a + 2\beta\theta)d\theta$.

(7) The volume of a gram of water is nearly $1 + a\,(\theta - 4)^2$ ccs. where θ denotes the temperature, and a is a constant very nearly equal to $8\cdot 38 \times 10^{-6}$. Show that the coefficient of cubical expansion of water at any temperature θ is equal to $2a(\theta - 4)$. Hence show that the coefficients of cubical expansion of water at $0°$ and $10°$ are respectively $- 67\cdot 04 \times 10^{-6}$, and $+ 100\cdot 56 \times 10^{-6}$.

---

[1] A *polynomial* is an expression containing two or more terms connected by plus or minus signs. Thus, $a + bx$; $ax + by + z$, etc. A *binomial* contains two such terms.

(8) A piston slides freely in a circular cylinder (diameter 6 in.). At what rate is the piston moving when steam is admitted into the cylinder at the rate of 11 cubic feet per second? Given, volume of a cylinder $= \pi r^2 h$. Hint. Let v denote the volume, x the height of the piston at any moment. Hence, $v = \pi(\tfrac{1}{4})^2 x$; $\therefore dv = \pi(\tfrac{1}{4})^2 dx$. But we require the value of dx/dt. Divide the last expression through with dt, let $\pi = \tfrac{22}{7}$,

$$\therefore \frac{dx}{dt} = \frac{dv}{dt} \times 16 \times \frac{7}{22} = 56 \text{ ft. per sec.}$$

(9) If the quantity of heat, Q, necessary to raise the temperature of a gram of solid from $0°$ to $\theta°$ is represented by $Q = a\theta + b\theta^2 + c\theta^3$ (where a, b, c, are constants), what is the specific heat of the substance at $\theta°$. Hint. Compare the meaning of $dQ/d\theta$ with your definition of specific heat. Ansr. $a + 2b\theta + 3c\theta^2$.

(10) If the diameter of a spherical soap bubble increases uniformly at the rate of $0\cdot1$ centimetre per second, show that the capacity is increasing at the rate of $0\cdot2\pi$ centimetre per second when the diameter becomes 2 centimetres. Given, volume of a sphere, $v = \tfrac{1}{6}\pi D^3$,

$$\therefore dv = \tfrac{1}{2}\pi D^2 dD, \therefore dv/dt = \tfrac{1}{2} \times \pi \times 2^2 \times 0\cdot1 = 0\cdot2\pi.$$

(11) The water reservoir of a town has the form of an inverted conical frustum with sides inclined at an angle of $45°$ and the radius of the smaller base 100 ft. If when the water is 20 ft. deep the depth of the water is decreasing at the rate of 5 ft. a day, show that the town is being supplied with

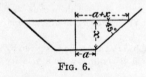

FIG. 6.

water at the rate of $72,000\,\pi$ cubic ft. *per diem*. Given, frustum, y, of cone $= \tfrac{1}{3}\pi \times$ height $\times (a^2 + ab + b^2)$, where a, and b are the radii of the circular ends. Hint. Let a (Fig. 6) denote the radius of the smaller end, x the depth of the water. First show that $a + x$ is the radius of the reservoir at the surface of the water. Hence, $y = \tfrac{1}{3}\pi\{(a + x)^2 + a(a + x) + a^2\}x$; $\therefore dy = \pi(a^2 + 2ax + x^2)dx$, etc.

(12) If a, b, c are constants, show that $dy/dx = b$, when $x = 0$, given that $y = a + bx + cx^2$. Hint. Substitute $x = 0$ *after* the differentiation.

(13) The area of a circular plate of metal is expanding by heat. When the radius passes through the value 2 cm. it is increasing at the rate of $0\cdot01$ cm. per second. How fast is the area changing? Ansr. $0\cdot04\pi$ sq. cm. per second. Hint. Radius $= x$ cm.; area $= y$ sq. cm.; $\therefore$ area of circle $= y = \pi x^2$. Hence, $dy/dt = 2\pi x \cdot dx/dt$; when $x = 2$, $dx/dt = 0\cdot01$, etc.

VI. The differential coefficient of the product of any number of functions. Let

$$y = uv$$

where u and v are functions of x. When x becomes $x + h$, let u, v, and y become u_1, v_1, and y_1. Then $y_1 = u_1 v_1$; $y_1 - y = u_1 v_1 - uv$, add and subtract uv_1 from the second member of this last equation, and transpose the terms so that

$$y_1 - y = u(v_1 - v) + v_1(u_1 - u).$$

In the language of differentials we may write this relation

$$dy = d(uv) = udv + vdu. \quad . \quad . \quad . \quad (8)$$

Or, divide by δx, and find the limit when $\delta x = 0$, thus,

$$\text{Lt}_{\varepsilon_x=0} \frac{\delta y}{\delta x} = u\frac{dv}{dx} + v\frac{du}{dx},$$

$$\therefore \frac{dy}{dx} = \frac{d(uv)}{dx} = u\frac{dv}{dx} + v\frac{du}{dx} \quad . \quad . \quad . \quad (9)$$

Similarly, by taking the product of three functions, say,

$$y = uvw.$$

Let $vw = z$; then $y = uz$. From (8), therefore

$$dy = z.du + u.dz = vw.du + u.d(vw);$$

$$\therefore dy = vw.du + u(w.dv + v.dw);$$

$$\therefore dy = vw.du + uw.dv + uv.dw, \quad . \quad . \quad (10)$$

in differential notation. To pass into differential coefficients, divide by dx. This reasoning may obviously be extended to the product of a greater number of functions.

Hence the rule :—The differential coefficient of any number of functions is obtained by multiplying the differential coefficient of each separate function by the product of all the remaining functions and then adding up the results.

EXAMPLES.—(1) If the volume, v, of gas enclosed in à vessel at a pressure p, be compressed or expanded without loss of heat, it is known that the relation between the pressure and volume is $pv^\gamma = \text{constant}$; γ is also a constant. Hence, prove that for small changes of pressure, $dv/dp = -v/\gamma p$.

(2) If $y = (x - 1)(x - 2)(x - 3)$, $dy/dx = 3x^2 - 12x + 11$.

(3) If $y = x^2(1 + ax^2)(1 - ax^2)$, $dy/dx = 2x - 6a^2x^5$.

(4) Show geometrically that the differential of a small increment in the capacity of a rectangular solid figure whose unequal sides are x, y, z is denoted by the expression $xydz + yzdx + zxdy$. Hence, show that if an ingot of gold expands uniformly in its linear dimensions at the rate of $0\cdot001$ units per second, its volume, v, is increasing at the rate of $dv/dt = 0\cdot110$ units per second, when the dimensions of the ingot are 4 by 5 by 10 units.

The process may be illustrated by a geometrical figure similar to that of page 31. In the rectangle (Fig. 7) let the unequal sides be represented by x and y. Let x and y be increased by their differentials dx and dy. Then the increment of the area will be represented by the shaded parts, which are in turn represented by

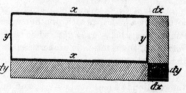

FIG. 7.

the areas of the parallelograms $xdy + ydx + dxdy$, but at the limit $dx.dy$ vanishes, as previously shown.

VII. The differential coefficient of a fraction, or quotient. Let

$$y = \frac{u}{v},$$

where u and v are functions of x. Hence, $u = vy$, and from (9)

$$du = vdy + ydv ; \therefore du = vd\left(\frac{u}{v}\right) + \frac{u}{v}dv,$$

on replacing y by its value u/v. Hence, on solving,

$$d\left(\frac{u}{v}\right) = \frac{du - \frac{u}{v}dv}{v} ; \therefore d\left(\frac{u}{v}\right) = \frac{vdu - udv}{v^2}, \quad . \quad (11)$$

in the language of differentials ; or, dividing through with dx we obtain, in the language of differential coefficients,

$$\frac{dy}{dx} = \frac{v\frac{du}{dx} - u\frac{dv}{dx}}{v^2}. \quad . \quad . \quad . \quad (12)$$

In words, to find the differential coefficient of a fraction or of a quotient, subtract the product of the numerator into the differential coefficient of the denominator, from the product of the denominator into the differential coefficient of the numerator, and divide by the square of the denominator.

A special case occurs when the numerator of the fraction a/x is a constant, a, then

$$y = \frac{a}{x} ; dy = \frac{x.da - a.dx}{x^2} = \frac{-a.dx}{x^2} ; \therefore \frac{dy}{dx} = -\frac{a}{x^2}. \quad (13)$$

In words, the differential coefficient of a fraction a/x whose numerator is constant is minus the constant divided by the square of the denominator.

EXAMPLES.—(1) If $y = x/(1 - x)$; show that $dy/dx = 1/(1 - x)^2$.

(2) If x denotes the number of gram molecules of a substance A transformed by a reaction with another substance B, at the time t, experiment shows that $x/(a - x) = akt$, when k is constant. Hence, show that the velocity of the reaction is proportional to the amounts of A and B present at the time t. Let a denote the number of gram molecules of A, and of B present at the beginning of the reaction. Hint. Show that the velocity of the reaction is equal to $k(a - x)^2$, and interpret the result.

(3) If $y = (1 + x^2)/(1 - x^2)$, show that $dy/dx = 4x/(1 - x^2)^2$.

(4) If $y = a/x^n$, show that $dy/dx = - na/x^{n+1}$.

(5) The refractive index, μ, of a ray of light of wave-length λ is, according to Christoffel's dispersion formula

$$\mu = \mu_0 \sqrt{2} / \{ \sqrt{1 + \lambda_0/\lambda} + \sqrt{1 - \lambda_0/\lambda} \},$$

where μ_0 and λ_0 are constants. Find the change in the refractive index corresponding to a small change in the wave-length of the light. Ansr. $d\mu/d\lambda = - \mu^3 \lambda_0^2 / \{ 2\lambda^3 \mu_0^2 \sqrt{(1 - \lambda_0^2/\lambda^2)} \}$. It is not often so difficult a differentiation occurs in practice. The most troublesome part of the work is to reduce

$$\frac{d\mu}{d\lambda} = - \frac{\sqrt{\tfrac{1}{2}} \mu_0 \lambda_0 \{ \sqrt{(1 + \lambda_0/\lambda)} - \sqrt{(1 - \lambda_0/\lambda)} \}/\lambda^2}{\sqrt{(1 - \lambda_0^2/\lambda^2)} \{ \sqrt{(1 + \lambda_0/\lambda)} + \sqrt{(1 - \lambda_0/\lambda)} \}^2},$$

to the answer given. Hint. Multiply the numerator and denominator of the right member with the factor $4\mu_0^2 (\sqrt{1 + \lambda_0/\lambda} + \sqrt{1 - \lambda_0/\lambda})$, and take out the terms which are equal to μ of the original equation to get μ^3. Of course the student is *not* using this abbreviated symbol of division. See footnote, page 14. I recommend the beginner to return to this, and try to do it without the hints. It is a capital exercise for revision.

VIII. The differential coefficient of a function affected with a fractional or negative exponent. Since the binomial theorem is true for any exponent positive or negative, fractional or integral, formula (2) may be regarded as quite general. The following proof for fractional and negative exponents is given simply as an exercise. Let

$$y = x^n.$$

First. When n is a positive fraction. Let $n = p/q$, where p and q are any integers, then

$$y = x^{\frac{p}{q}}. \qquad . \qquad . \qquad . \qquad . \qquad (14)$$

Raise each term to the qth power, we obtain the expression $y^q = x^p$. By differentiation, using the notation of differentials, we have

$$qy^{q-1}dy = px^{p-1}dx.$$

Now raise both sides of the original expression, (14), to the $(q - 1)$th power, and we get

$$y^{q-1} = x^{\frac{pq-p}{q}}.$$

Substitute this value of y^{q-1} in the preceding result, and we get

$$\frac{dy}{dx} = \frac{p}{q} \cdot \frac{x^{p-1}x^{p/q}}{x^p}; \text{ or, } \frac{dy}{dx} = \frac{p}{q}x^{\frac{p}{q}-1}, \qquad . \qquad . \qquad (15)$$

which has exactly the same form as if n were a positive integer.

Second. When n is a negative integer or a negative fraction. Let

$$y = x^{-n};$$

then $y = 1/x^n$. Differentiating this as if it were a fraction, (13) above, we get $dy/dx = - nx^{n-1}/x^{2n}$, which on reduction to its simplest terms, assumes the form

$$\frac{dy}{dx} = \frac{d(x^{-n})}{dx} = - nx^{-n-1}.$$

Thus the method of differentiation first given is quite general.

A special case occurs when $y = \sqrt{x}$, in that case $y = x^{\frac{1}{2}}$;

$$\frac{dy}{dx} = \frac{d(x^{\frac{1}{2}})}{dx} = \frac{1}{2\sqrt{x}} = \frac{1}{2}x^{-\frac{1}{2}}. \qquad . \qquad . \qquad (16)$$

In words, the differential coefficient of the square root of a variable is half the reciprocal of the square root of the variable.

EXAMPLES.—(1) Matthiessen's formula for the variation of the electrical resistance R of a platinum wire with temperature θ, between 0° and 100° is $R = R_0(1 - a\theta + b\theta^2)^{-1}$. Find the increase in the resistance of the wire for a small change of temperature. Ansr. $dR/d\theta = R^2(a - 2b\theta)/R_0$. Note a and b are constants ; $dR = - R_0(1 - a\theta + b\theta^2)^{-2}d(1 - a\theta + b\theta^2)$; multiply and divide by R_0 ; substitute for R from the original equation, etc

(2) Siemens' formula for the relation between the electrical resistance of a metallic wire and temperature is, $R = R_0(1 + a\theta + b\sqrt{\theta})$ Hence, find the rate of change of resistance with temperature. Ansr. $R_0(a + \frac{1}{2}b\theta^{-\frac{1}{2}})$.

(3) Batschinski (*Bull. Soc. Imp. Nat. Moscow*, 1902) finds that the product $\eta(\theta + 273)^3$ is constant for many liquids of viscosity η, at the temperature θ. Hence, show that if A is the constant, $d\eta/d\theta = - 3\eta/(\theta + 273)$.

(4) Batschinski (*l. c.*) expresses the relation between the "viscosity parameter," η, of a liquid and the critical temperature, θ, by the expression $M^{\frac{1}{2}}\theta^{\frac{7}{6}}\eta m^{\frac{2}{3}} = B$, where B, M, and m are constants. Hence show that $d\eta/d\theta = - \frac{7}{6}\eta/\theta$.

IX. The differential coefficient of a function of a function. Let

$$u = \phi(y) ; \text{ and } y = f(x).$$

It is required to find the differential coefficient of u with respect to x. Let u and y receive small increments so that when u becomes u_1, y becomes y_1 and x becomes x_1. Then

$$\frac{u_1 - u}{x_1 - x} = \frac{u_1 - u}{y_1 - y} \cdot \frac{y_1 - y}{x_1 - x},$$

which is true, however small the increment may be. At the limit, therefore, when the increments are infinitesimal

$$\frac{du}{dx} = \frac{du}{dy} \cdot \frac{dy}{dx} \qquad . \qquad . \qquad . \qquad (17)$$

I may add that we do not get the first member by cancelling out the dy's of the second. The operations are

$$\frac{d}{dx}(u) = \frac{d}{dy}(u) \; \frac{d}{dx}(y).$$

In words, (17) may be expressed: the differential coefficient of a function with respect to a given variable is equal to the product of the differential coefficient of the function with respect to a second function and the differential coefficient of the second function with respect to the given variable. We can get a physical meaning of this formula by taking x as time. In that case, the rate of change of a function of a variable is equal to the product of the rate of change of that function with respect to the variable, and the rate of change of the variable.

The extension to three or more variables will be obvious. If $u = \phi(w)$, $w = \psi(y)$, $y = f(x)$, it follows that

$$\frac{du}{dx} = \frac{du}{dw} \cdot \frac{dw}{dy} \cdot \frac{dy}{dx} \qquad \cdots \qquad (18)$$

With the preceding notation, it is evident that the relation

$$\frac{x_1 - x}{y_1 - y} \cdot \frac{y_1 - y}{x_1 - x} = 1$$

is true for all finite increments, we assume that it also holds when the increments are infinitely small; hence, at the limit,

$$\frac{dx}{dy} \cdot \frac{dy}{dx} = 1 \; ; \; \text{or,} \; \frac{dx}{dy} = \frac{1}{\dfrac{dy}{dx}} \qquad (19)$$

We have seen that if y is a function of x then x is a function of y; the latter, however, is frequently said to be an *inverse function* of the former, or the former an inverse function of the latter. This is expressed as follows: If $y = f(x)$, then $x = f^{-1}(y)$, or, if $x = f(y)$, then $y = f^{-1}(x)$.

EXAMPLES.—(1) If $y = x^n/(1 + x)^n$, show that $dy/dx = nx^{n-1}/(1 + x)^{n+1}$.

(2) If $y = 1/\sqrt{(1 - x^2)}$, show that $dy/dx = x/\sqrt{(1 - x^2)^3}$.

(3) The use of formula (17) often simplifies the actual process of differentiation; for instance, it is required to differentiate the expression $u = \sqrt{(a^2 - x^2)}$. Assume $y = a^2 - x^2$. Then, $u = \sqrt{y}$, $y = a^2 - x^2$; and $dy/dx = -2x$; $du/dy = \frac{1}{2}y^{-\frac{1}{2}}$, from (16); hence, from (17), $du/dx = -x(a^2 - x^2)^{-\frac{1}{2}}$. This is an easy example which could be done at sight; it is given here to illustrate the method.

By the application of these principles any algebraic function which the student will encounter in physical science,[1] may be

---

[1] K. Weierstrass has shown that there are some continuous functions which have not yet been differentiated, but, as yet, they have no physical application except perhaps to vibrations of very great velocity and small amplitude. See J. Harkness and F. Morley's *Theory of Functions*, London, 65, 1893.

differentiated. Before proceeding to transcendental functions, that is to say, functions which contain trigonometrical, logarithmic or other terms not algebraic, we may apply our knowledge to the well-known equations of Boyle and van der Waals.

§ 15. The Gas Equations of Boyle and van der Waals.

In van der Waals' equation, at a constant temperature,

$$\left(p + \frac{a}{v^2}\right)(v - b) = \text{constant}, \quad . \quad . \quad . \quad (1)$$

where b is a constant depending on the volume of the molecule, a is a constant depending on intermolecular attraction. Differentiating with respect to p and v, we obtain, as on pages 40 and 41,

$$(v - b)d\left(p + \frac{a}{v^2}\right) + \left(p + \frac{a}{v^2}\right)d(v - b) = 0,$$

and therefore

$$\frac{dv}{dp} = - \frac{v - b}{p - \frac{a}{v^2} + \frac{2ab}{v^3}} \quad . \quad . \quad . \quad (2)$$

The differential coefficient dv/dp measures the compressibility of the gas. If the gas strictly obeyed Boyle's law, $a = b = 0$, and we should have

$$\frac{dv}{dp} = - \frac{v}{p}. \quad . \quad . \quad . \quad (3)$$

The negative sign in these equations means that the volume of the gas decreases with increase of pressure. Any gas, therefore, will be more or less sensitive to changes of pressure than Boyle's law indicates, according as the differential coefficient of (2) is greater or less than that of (3), that is according as

$$\frac{v - b}{p - \frac{a}{v^2} + \frac{2ab}{v^3}} \gtreqless \frac{v}{p}; \quad \therefore pv - pb \gtreqless pv - \frac{a}{v} + \frac{2ab}{v^2}; \quad \therefore pb \gtreqless \frac{a}{v} - \frac{2ab}{v^2};$$

$$\therefore pv \gtreqless \frac{a}{b} - \frac{2a}{v} . . \quad . \quad . \quad . \quad (4)$$

If Boyle's law were strictly obeyed

$$pv = \text{constant}, \quad . \quad . \quad . \quad . \quad (5)$$

but if the gas be less sensitive to pressure than Boyle's law indicates, so that, in order to produce a small contraction, the pressure has to be increased a little more than Boyle's law demands, pv increases with increase of pressure; while if the gas be more sensitive to pressure than Boyle's law provides for, pv decreases with increase of pressure.

Some valuable deductions as to intermolecular action have been drawn by comparing the behaviour of gases under compression in the light of equations similar to (4) and (5). But this is not all. From (5), if c = constant, $v = c/p$, which gives on differentiation

$$\frac{dv}{dp} = -\frac{c}{p^2}.$$

or the ratio of the decrease in volume to the increase of pressure, is inversely as the square of the pressure. By substituting $p = 2, 3, 4, \ldots$ in the last equation we obtain

$$-\frac{dv}{dp} = \frac{1}{4}; \frac{1}{9}; \frac{1}{16}; \ldots$$

where c = unity. In other words, the greater the pressure to which a gas is subjected the less the corresponding diminution in volume for any subsequent increase of pressure. The negative sign means that as the pressure increases the volume decreases.

§ 16. The Differentiation of Trigonometrical Functions.

Any expression containing trigonometrical ratios, sines, cosines, tangents, secants, cosecants, or cotangents is called a **trigonometrical function**. The elements of trigonometry are discussed in Appendix I., on page 606 *et seq.*, and the beginner had better glance through that section. We may then pass at once *in medias res*. There is no new principle to be learned.

I. The differential coefficient of sin x is cos x. Let y become y_1, when x changes to $x + h$, consequently,

$y = \sin x$; and $y_1 = \sin(x + h)$; $\therefore y_1 - y = \sin(x + h) - \sin x$.
By (39), page 612,

$$y_1 - y = 2\sin\frac{h}{2}\cos\left(x + \frac{h}{2}\right).$$

Divide by h and

$$\frac{y_1 - y}{h} = \frac{\sin\frac{1}{2}h}{\frac{1}{2}h}\cos\left(x + \frac{h}{2}\right).$$

But the value of $\dfrac{\sin x}{x}$ approaches unity, page 611, as x approaches zero, therefore,

$$\text{Lt}_{h=0}\frac{y_1 - y}{h} = \cos x; \therefore \frac{dy}{dx} = \frac{d(\sin x)}{dx} = \cos x \quad . \quad \textbf{(1)}$$

The rate of change of the sine of an angle with respect to the angle is equal to the cosine of the angle. When x increases from 0 to $\frac{1}{2}\pi$, the rate of increase of sine x is positive because cos x is then positive, as indicated on page 610; and similarly, since cos x is negative from $\frac{1}{2}\pi$ to π, as the angle increases from $\frac{1}{2}\pi$ to π, sine x decreases, and the rate of increase of sin x is negative.

If x is measured in degrees, we must write

$$\frac{d(\sin x^{\circ})}{dx} = \frac{d(\sin \frac{\pi}{180}x^{c})}{dx} = \frac{\pi}{180}\cos\frac{\pi x^{c}}{180} = \frac{\pi}{180}\cos x^{\circ},$$

since the radian measure of an angle = angle in degrees $\times \frac{1}{180}\pi$, where $\pi = 3\cdot 1416$, as indicated on page 606.

NUMERICAL ILLUSTRATION.—You can get a very fair approximation to the fact stated in (1), by taking h small and finite. Thus, if $x = 42^{\circ}\ 6'$; and $h = 1'$; $x + h = 42^{\circ}\ 7'$;

$$\therefore \frac{\text{Incr. } y}{\text{Incr. } x} = \frac{\sin(x + h) - \sin x}{h \text{ in radians}} = \frac{0\cdot 0002158}{0\cdot 0002909} = 0\cdot 74183.$$

But $\cos x = 0\cdot 74198$; $\cos(x + h) = 0\cdot 74178$; so that when h is $\frac{1}{60}^{\circ}$, dy/dx lies somewhere between $\cos x$ and $\cos(x + h)$. By taking smaller and smaller values of h, dy/dx approaches nearer and nearer in value to $\cos x$.

II. The differential coefficient of cos x is $- \sin x$. Let us put $y = \cos x$; and $y_1 = \cos(x + h)$; $y_1 - y = \cos(x + h) - \cos x$. From the formula (41) on page 612, it follows that

$$y_1 - y = -2\sin\frac{h}{2}\sin\left(x + \frac{h}{2}\right); \text{ or } \frac{y_1 - y}{h} = -\frac{\sin\frac{1}{2}h}{\frac{1}{2}h}\sin\left(x + \frac{h}{2}\right);$$

and at the limit when $h = 0$,

$$\text{Lt}_{h=0}\ \frac{y_1 - y}{h} = -\sin x; \therefore \frac{dy}{dx} = \frac{d(\cos x)}{dx} = -\sin x \qquad (2)$$

The meaning of the negative sign can readily be deduced from the definition of the differential coefficient. The differential coefficient of cos x with respect to x represents the rate at which cos x increases when x is slightly increased. The negative sign shows that this rate of increase is negative, in other words, cos x diminishes as x increases from 0 to $\frac{1}{2}\pi$. When x passes from $\frac{1}{2}\pi$ to π cos x increases as x increases, the differential coefficient is then positive.

III. The differential coefficient of tan x is sec$^2 x$. Using the results already deduced for sin x and cos x, and remembering that sin x/cos x is, by definition, equal to tan x, let $y = \tan x$, then

$$\frac{d(\tan x)}{dx} = \frac{d\left(\frac{\sin x}{\cos x}\right)}{dx} = \frac{\cos x \dfrac{d(\sin x)}{dx} - \sin x \dfrac{d(\cos x)}{dx}}{\cos^2 x} = \frac{\cos^2 x + \sin^2 x}{\cos^2 x}$$

But the numerator is equal to unity (19), page 611.   Hence

$$\frac{d(\tan x)}{dx} = \frac{1}{\cos^2 x} = \sec^2 x. \quad . \quad . \quad . \quad (3)$$

In the same way it can be shown that

$$\frac{d(\cot x)}{dx} = -\operatorname{cosec}^2 x. \quad . \quad . \quad . \quad (4)$$

The remaining trigonometrical functions may be left for the reader to work out himself. The results are given on page 193.

EXAMPLES.—(1) If $y = \cos^n x$; $dy/dx = -n\cos^{n-1}x . \sin x$.

(2) If $y = \sin^n x$; $dy/dx = n\sin^{n-1}x . \cos x$.

(3) If a particle vibrates according to the equation $y = a\sin(qt - \epsilon)$, what is the velocity at any instant when a, q and ϵ are constant? The answer is $aq\cos(qt - \epsilon)$.

(4) If $y = \sin^2(nx - a)$; $dy/dx = 2n\sin(nx - a)\cos(nx - a)$.

(5) Differentiate $\tan\theta = y/x$. Ansr. $d\theta = (xdy - ydx) \div (x^2 + y^2)$. Hint. $\sec^2\theta . d\theta = (1 + \tan^2\theta)d\theta$; $\therefore \dfrac{x^2 + y^2}{x^2}d\theta = \dfrac{xdy - ydx}{x^2}$, etc.

(6) If the point P moves upon a circle, with a centre O and radius 18 cm., AB is a diameter; MP is a perpendicular upon AB, show that the speed of M on the line AB is 226 cm. per second when the angle $BOP = a = 30°$; and P travels round the perimeter four times a second. Sketch a diagram. Here $OM = y = r\cos a = 18\cos a$; $\therefore dy/dt = -(18\sin a)da/dt$. But $da/dt = 4 \times 2\pi$ since $\pi = $ half the circumference; $\sin 30° = \frac{1}{2}$;

$\therefore dy/dt = -18 \times \frac{1}{2} \times 8\pi = -9 \times 8 \times 3 \cdot 1416 = -226$ cm. per sec. (nearly).

§ 17. The Differentiation of Inverse Trigonometrical Functions. The Differentiation of Angles.

The equation, $\sin y = x$, means that y is an angle whose sine is x. It is sometimes convenient to write this another way, viz.,

$$\sin^{-1}x = y,$$

meaning that $\sin^{-1}x$ is an *angle* whose sine is x. Thus if $\sin 30° = \frac{1}{2}$, we say that 30° or $\sin^{-1}\frac{1}{2}$ is an angle whose sine is $\frac{1}{2}$. Trigonometrical ratios written in this reverse way are called **inverse trigonometrical functions**. The superscript " -1 " has no other signification when attached to the trigonometrical ratios. Note, if $\tan 45° = 1$, then $\tan^{-1}1 = 45°$; $\therefore \tan(\tan^{-1}1) = \tan 45°$. Some writers employ the symbols arc sin x; arc tan x; ... for our $\sin^{-1}x$; $\tan^{-1}x$; ...

The differentiation of the inverse trigonometrical functions may be illustrated by proving that the differential coefficient of $\sin^{-1}x$ is $1/\sqrt{(1 - x^2)}$. If $y = \sin^{-1}x$, then $\sin y = x$, and

$$\frac{dx}{dy} = \cos y \; ; \; \text{or } \frac{dy}{dx} = \frac{1}{\cos y},$$

But we know from (19), page 611, that

$$\cos^2 y + \sin^2 y = 1 \; ; \; \text{or } \cos y = \pm \sqrt{(1 - \sin^2 y)} = \pm \sqrt{(1 - x^2)},$$

for by hypothesis $\sin y = x$. Hence

$$\frac{d(\sin^{-1}x)}{dx} = \frac{dy}{dx} = \frac{1}{\cos y} = \pm \frac{1}{\sqrt{1 - x^2}}.$$

The fallacy mentioned on page 5 illustrates the errors which might enter our work unsuspectingly by leaving the algebraic sign of a root extraction undetermined. Here the ambiguity of sign means that there are a series of values of y for any assigned value of x between the limits ± 1. Thus, if n is a positive integer, we know that $\sin x = \sin (n\pi \pm x)$; the $+$ sign obtains if n is even; the negative sign if n is odd. This means that if x satisfies $\sin^{-1}y$, so will $\pi \pm x$; $2\pi \pm x$; ... If we agree to take $\sin^{-1}y$ as the angle between $-\frac{1}{2}\pi$ and $+\frac{1}{2}\pi$, then there will be no ambiguity because $\cos y$ is then necessarily positive. The differential coefficient is then positive, that is to say,

$$\frac{d(\sin^{-1}x)}{dx} = \frac{1}{\sqrt{(1 - x^2)}}. \quad \cdot \quad \cdot \quad \cdot \quad (1)$$

Similarly,

$$\frac{d(\cos^{-1}x)}{dx} = - \frac{1}{\sin y} = - \left(\frac{1}{\pm \sqrt{1 - x^2}} \right) = - \frac{1}{\sqrt{1 - x^2}}. \quad (2)$$

The ambiguity of sign is easily decided by remembering that $\sin y$ is positive when y lies between π and 0. Again, if $y = \tan^{-1}x$, $x = \tan y$, $dx/dy = 1/\cos^2 y$. But $\cos^2 y = 1/(1 + \tan^2 y) = 1/(1 + x^2)$ (page 612). Hence

$$\frac{d(\tan^{-1}x)}{dx} = \cos^2 y = \frac{1}{1 + x^2} \quad \cdot \quad \cdot \quad \cdot \quad (3)$$

The differential coefficient of $\tan^{-1}x$ is an important function, since it appears very frequently in practical formulæ. It follows in a similar manner that

$$\frac{d(\cot^{-1}x)}{dx} = - \frac{1}{1 + x^2}. \quad \cdot \quad \cdot \quad \cdot \quad (4)$$

The remaining inverse trigonometrical functions may be left as an exercise for the student.   Their values will be found on page 193.

EXAMPLES.—(1) Differentiate $y = \sin^{-}\ [x/\surd(1 + x^2)]$. $\mathrm{Sin}\ y = x/\sqrt{1+x^2}$ hence $\cos y\, dy = dx/(1 + x^2)^{\frac{3}{2}}$.   But $\cos y = \surd(1 - \sin^2 y) = \surd[1 - x^2/(1 + x^2)]$. Substituting this value of $\cos y$ in the former result we get, on reduction, $dy/dx = (1 + x^2)^{-1}$, the answer required.   Note the steps:

$(1 + x^2)^{-\frac{1}{2}}dx - x^2(1 + x^2)^{-\frac{3}{2}}dx = (1 + x^2)^{-\frac{3}{2}}(1 + x^2 - x^2)dx$, etc.   Also $\cos y \times (1 + x^2)^{\frac{3}{2}} = (1 + x^2)^{-\frac{1}{2}}(1 + x^2)^{\frac{3}{2}} = (1 + x^2)$.

(2) If $y = \sin^{-1}x^2 ; dy/dx = 2x(1 - x^4)^{-\frac{1}{2}}$.

(3) If $y = \tan^{-1}\dfrac{x}{\sqrt{1 - x^2}} ;\ \dfrac{dy}{dx} = \dfrac{1}{\sqrt{1 - x^2}}$.   See formula (22), page 612.

§ 18. The Differentiation of Logarithms.

Any expression containing logarithmic terms is called a **logarithmic function.** $E.g.,\ y = \log x + x^3$.   To find the differential coefficient of $\log x$.   Let

$$y = \log x ;\ \text{and}\ y_1 = \log(x + h).$$

Where y_1 denotes the value of y when x is augmented to $x + h$. By substitution,

$$\frac{y_1 - y}{h} = \frac{\log(x + h) - \log x}{h} ;$$

but we know, page 26, that $\log a - \log b = \log\dfrac{a}{b}$, therefore

$$\frac{\text{Incr. } y}{\text{Incr. } x} = \frac{1}{h}\log\left(\frac{x + h}{x}\right) = \frac{1}{h}\log\left(1 + \frac{h}{x}\right),$$

and
$$\frac{dy}{dx} = \mathrm{Lt}_{h\,=\,0}\frac{1}{h}\log\left(1 + \frac{h}{x}\right).\quad\quad\cdot\quad\quad\cdot\quad\quad\cdot\quad\quad(1)$$

The limiting value of this expression cannot be determined in its present form by the processes hitherto used, owing to the nature of the terms $1/h$ and h/x.   The calculation must therefore be made by an indirect process.   Let us substitute

$$\frac{h}{x} = \frac{1}{u} ;\ \therefore \frac{1}{h} = \frac{u}{x}.$$

$$\therefore \frac{1}{h}\log\left(1 + \frac{h}{x}\right) = \frac{1}{x}\cdot u\log\left(1 + \frac{1}{u}\right) = \frac{1}{x}\cdot\log\left(1 + \frac{1}{u}\right)^u.$$

As h decreases u increases, and the limiting value of u when h becomes vanishingly small, is infinity.   The problem now is to find what is the limiting value of $\log(1 + u^{-1})^u$ when u is infinitely great.   In other words, to find the limiting value of the above expression when u increases without limit.

$$\therefore \frac{dy}{dx} = \text{Lt}_{u = \infty} \frac{1}{x} \cdot \log\left(1 + \frac{1}{u}\right)^{u} \quad . \quad . \quad (2)$$

According to the binomial theorem, page 36,

$$\left(1 + \frac{1}{u}\right)^{u} = 1 + \frac{u}{1} \cdot \frac{1}{u} + \frac{u(u-1)}{2!} \cdot \frac{1}{u^2} + \ldots;$$

dividing out the u's in each term, and we get

$$\left(1 + \frac{1}{u}\right)^{u} = 2 + \frac{\left(1 - \frac{1}{u}\right)}{2!} + \frac{\left(1 - \frac{1}{u}\right)\left(1 - \frac{2}{u}\right)}{3!} + \ldots$$

The limiting value of this expression when u is infinitely great is evidently equal to the sum of the infinite series of terms

$$1 + \frac{1}{1} + \frac{1}{2!} + \frac{1}{3!} + \frac{1}{4!} + \ldots \text{ to infinity.} \quad . \quad (3)$$

Let the sum of this series of terms be denoted by the symbol e. By taking a sufficient number of these terms we can approximate as close as ever we please to the absolute value of e. If we add together the first seven terms of the series we get 2·71826

$$
\begin{aligned}
1 + \tfrac{1}{1} \quad\quad &= 2\cdot00000 \\
\tfrac{1}{2!} \quad\quad &= 0\cdot50000 \\
\tfrac{1}{3!} = \tfrac{1}{3} \cdot \tfrac{1}{2!} &= 0\cdot16667 \\
\tfrac{1}{4!} = \tfrac{1}{4} \cdot \tfrac{1}{3!} &= 0\cdot04167 \\
\tfrac{1}{5!} = \tfrac{1}{5} \cdot \tfrac{1}{4!} &= 0\cdot00833 \\
\tfrac{1}{6!} = \tfrac{1}{6} \cdot \tfrac{1}{5!} &= 0\cdot00139 \\
\tfrac{1}{7!} = \tfrac{1}{7} \cdot \tfrac{1}{6!} &= \overline{0\cdot00020} \\
\end{aligned}
$$

Sum of first seven terms $= \overline{2\cdot71826}$

The value of e correct to the ninth decimal place

$$e = 2\cdot718281828\ldots$$

This number, like $\pi = 3\cdot14159265\ldots$, plays an important *rôle* in mathematics. Both magnitudes are incommensurable and can only be evaluated in an approximate way.

Returning now to (2), it is obvious that

$$\frac{dy}{dx} = \frac{d(\log x)}{dx} = \frac{1}{x} \log e \quad . \quad . \quad . \quad (4)$$

This formula is true whatever base we adopt for our system of logarithms. If we use 10, $\log_{10} e = 0\cdot43429\ldots = $ (say) M,

and
$$\frac{dy}{dx} = \frac{d(\log_{10} x)}{dx} = \frac{M}{x}. \quad . \quad . \quad (5)$$

Since $\log_e a = 1$, from (6), page 27, we can put expression (4) in a much simpler form by using a system of logarithms to the base e, then

$$\frac{dy}{dx} = \frac{d(\log_e x)}{dx} = \frac{1}{x} \qquad . \qquad . \qquad . \qquad \textbf{(6)}$$

Continental writers variously use the symbols L, l, ln, lg, for "log" and "log nep"; "nat log," or "hyp log," for "$\log_e$." "Nep" is an abbreviation for "Neperian," a Latinized adjectival form of Napier's name.—J. Napier was the inventor of logarithmic computation. You will see later on where "hyp log" comes from.

EXAMPLES.—(1) If $y = \log ax^4$, show that $dy/dx = 4/x$.

(2) If $y = x^n \log x$, show that $dy/dx = x^{n-1}(1 + n \log x)$.

(3) What is meant by the expression, $2 \cdot 71828^{n \times 2 \cdot 3026} = 10^n$? Ansr. If n is a common logarithm, then $n \times 2 \cdot 3026$ is a natural logarithm. Note, $e = 2 \cdot 71828$.

(4) A. Dupre (1869) represented the relation between the vapour pressures, p, of a substance and the absolute temperature T by the equation

$$\log p = \frac{a}{T} + b \log T + c. \quad \therefore \frac{d(\log p)}{dT} = \frac{A + BT}{T^2};$$

a result resembling van't Hoff's well-known equation. Hence show that if a, b, c, A, B are all constants, $dp/dT = p(A + BT)/T^2$.

In seeking the differential coefficient of a complex function containing products and powers of polynomials, the work is often facilitated by taking the logarithm of each member separately before differentiation. The compound process is called **logarithmic differentiation.**

EXAMPLES.—(1) Differentiate $y = x^n/(1 + x)^n$. Here $\log y = n \log x - n \log (1 + x)$, or $dy/y = ndx/x(1 + x)$. Hence $dy/dx = yn/x(1 + x) = nx^{n-1}/(1 + x)^{n+1}$.

(2) Differentiate $x^4(1 + x)^n/(x^3 - 1)$.

Ansr. $\{(n + 1)x^4 + x^3 - (n + 4)x - 4\}x^3(1 + x)^{n-1}(x^3 - 1)^{-2}$.

(3) Establish (10), page 41, by log differentiation. In the same way, show that $d(xyz) = yzdx + zxdy + xydz$.

(4) If $y = x(a^2 + x^2)\sqrt{a^2 - x^2}$; $dy/dx = (a^4 + a^2x^2 - 4x^4)(a^2 - x^2)^{-\frac{1}{2}}$.

(5) If $y = \log \sin x$; $dy/dx = d(\sin x)/\sin x = \cot x$.

(6) How much more rapidly does the number x increase than its logarithm? Here $d(\log x)/dx = 1/x$. The number, therefore, increases more rapidly or more slowly than its logarithm according as $x > $ or < 1. If $x = 1$, the rates are the same. If common logarithms are employed, M will have to be substituted in place of unity. E.g., $d(\log_{10} x)dx = M/x$.

(7) If the relation between the number of molecules x of substances A and B transformed in the chemical reaction : $A + B = C + D$, and the time t be

represented by the equation

$$\log \frac{b(a-x)}{a(b-x)} = (a-b)kt$$

where k is constant, and a and b respectively denote the amounts of **A** and **B** present when $t = 0$, show that the velocity of the reaction is proportional to the amounts of **A** and **B** actually present at the time t. Hint. Show that the velocity of the reaction is proportional to $(a-x)(b-x)$ and interpret.

§ 19. The Differential Coefficient of Exponential Functions.

Functions in which the variable quantity occurs in the index are called **exponential functions**. Thus, a^x, e^x and $(a+x)^x$ are exponential functions. A few words on the transformation of logarithmic into exponential functions may be needed. It is required to transform $\log y = ax$ into an exponential function. Remembering that $\log a$ to the base a is unity, it makes no difference to any magnitude if we multiply it by such expressions as $\log_a a$, ; $\log_{10} 10$; and $\log_e e$. Thus, since $\log_e(e^{ax}) = ax \log_e e$; if $\log_e y = ax$, we can write

$$\log_e y = ax \log_e e = \log_e e^{ax} ; \therefore y = e^{ax},$$

when the logarithms are removed. In future "log" will generally be written in place of "$\log_e$". "Exp x" is sometimes written for "e^x"; "Exp$(-x)$" for "e^{-x}".

EXAMPLES.—(1) If $y = e^{\log x}$; show $y = x$.
(2) If $\log I = -an$; $I = e^{-an}$.
(3) If $\theta = be^{-at}$; $\log b - \log \theta = at$.
(4) If $\log_e z = a\theta$; $\log_{10} z = 0.4343a\theta$.
(5) Show that if $\log y_0 - \log y = kct$; $y = y_0 e^{-kct}$.

The differentiation of exponential functions may be conveniently studied in three sections :
(i) Let

$$y = e^x.$$

Take logarithms, and then, differentiating, we get

$$\log y = x \log e ; \frac{dy}{y} = dx, \text{ or } \frac{dy}{dx} = e^x ;$$

in other words, the differential coefficient of e^x is e^x itself, or,

$$\frac{d(e^x)}{dx} = e^x \quad . \quad . \quad . \quad . \quad . \quad (1)$$

The simplicity of this equation, and of (6) in the preceding section, explains the reason for the almost exclusive use of natural logarithms in higher mathematics.

(ii) Let

$$y = a^x.$$

As before, taking logarithms, and differentiating, we get

$$\log y = x \log a \; ; \; \frac{dy}{dx} = y \log a \; ; \; \therefore \frac{d(a^x)}{dx} = a^x \log_e a \; . \qquad (2)$$

In words, the differential coefficient of a constant affected with a variable exponent is equal to the product of the constant affected with the same exponent into the logarithm of the constant.

(iii) Let

$$y = x^z,$$

where x and z are both variable. Taking logarithms, and differentiating

$$\log y = z \log x \; ; \; \frac{dy}{y} = \log x dz + \frac{z dx}{x} \; ;$$

$$\therefore dy = x^z \log x dz + z x^{z-1} dx \qquad . \qquad . \qquad (3)$$

If x and z are functions of t, we have

$$\frac{d(x^z)}{dt} = \frac{dy}{dt} = x^z \log x \frac{dz}{dt} + z x^{z-1} \frac{dx}{dt} \qquad . \qquad . \qquad (4)$$

EXAMPLES.—(1) The amount, x, of substance transformed in a chemical reaction at the time t is given by the expression $x = ae^{-kt}$, where a denotes the amount of substance present at the beginning of the reaction, hence show that the velocity of the chemical reaction is proportional to the amount of substance undergoing transformation. Hint. Show that $dx/dt = -kx$, and interpret.

(2) If $y = (a^x + x)^2$, $dy/dx = 2(a^x + x)(a^x \log a + 1)$.

(3) If $y = a^{nx}$, $dy/dx = na^{nx} \log a$.

(4) From Magnus' empirical formula for the relation between the pressure of aqueous vapour and temperature

$$p = ab^{\frac{\theta}{\gamma + \theta}} \; ; \; \therefore \frac{dp}{d\theta} = \frac{a\gamma \log b}{(\gamma + \theta)^2} \cdot b^{\frac{\theta}{\gamma + \theta}},$$

where a, b, γ are constants. This differential coefficient represents the increase of pressure corresponding with a small rise of temperature, say, roughly from θ° to $(\theta + 1)^\circ$.

(5) Biot's empirical formula for the relation between the pressure of aqueous vapour, p, and the temperature, θ, is

$$\log p = a + ba^\theta - c\beta^\theta \; ; \; \text{show } \frac{dp}{d\theta} = pba^\theta \log a - pc\beta^\theta \log \beta.$$

(6) Required the velocity of a point which moves according to the equation $y = ae^{-\lambda t} \cos 2\pi(qt + \epsilon)$. Since velocity $= dy/dt$, the answer is $-ae^{-\lambda t}\{\lambda \cos 2\pi(qt + \epsilon) + 2\pi q \sin 2\pi(qt + \epsilon)\}$.

(7) The relation between the amount, x, of substance formed by two consecutive unimolecular reactions and the time t or the intensity of the "excited" radioactivity of thorium or radium emanations at the time t, is given by the expression

$$x = 1 + \frac{k_2}{k_1 - k_2} e^{-k_1 t} - \frac{k_1}{k_1 - k_2} e^{-k_2 t}; \therefore \frac{dx}{dt} = \frac{k_1 k_2}{k_1 - k_2}\left(e^{-k_2 t} - e^{-k_1 t}\right),$$

where k_1 and k_2 are constants. Show that the last expression represents the velocity of the change.

(8) The viscosity, η, of a mixture of non-electrolytes (when the concentrations of the substances with viscosity coefficients A, B, C, ... are x, y, z, ... respectively) is $\eta = A^x B^y C^z$ ... Show that for a small change in x, y, z ... $d\eta$ becomes $\eta(adx + bdy + cdz)$, where $\log A = a$, $\log B = b$, $\log C = c$. Hint. Take logs before differentiation.

§ 20. The "Compound Interest Law" in Nature.

I cannot pass by the function e^x without indicating its great significance in physical processes. From the above equations it follows that if

$$y = Ce^{ax}; \text{ then } \frac{dy}{dx} = be^{ax} \quad . \quad . \quad . \quad (1)$$

where a, b and C are constants, b, by the way, being equal to $aC \log_e e$. C is the value of y when $x = 0$. Why? It will be proved later on that this operation may be reversed under certain conditions, and if

$$\frac{dy}{dx} = be^{ax}, \text{ then } y = Ce^{ax}, \quad . \quad . \quad . \quad (2)$$

where a, b and C are again constant. All these results indicate that the rate of increase of the exponential function e^x is e^x itself. *If, therefore, in any physical investigation we find some function, say y, varying at a rate proportional to itself (with or without some constant term) we guess at once that we are dealing with an exponential function.* Thus if

$$\frac{dy}{dx} = \pm \, ay; \text{ we may write } y = Ce^{ax}, \text{ or } Ce^{-ax}, \quad (2a)$$

according as the function is increasing or decreasing in magnitude.

Money lent at compound interest increases in this way, and hence the above property has been happily styled by Lord Kelvin "the compound interest law" (*Encyc. Brit.*, art. "Elasticity," 1877). A great many natural phenomena possess this property. The following will repay study:—

ILLUSTRATION 1.—*Compound interest.* If £100 is lent out at 5 % per annum, at the end of the first year £105 remains. If this be the principal for a second year, the interest during that time will be charged not only on the original £100, but also on the additional £5.   To put this in more general terms, let £p_0 be lent at $r \, °/_o$ per annum, at the end of the first year the interest amounts to $\frac{r}{100}p_0$, and if p_1 be the principal for the second year, we have at the end of the first year

$$p_1 = p_0(1 + \tfrac{r}{100});$$

and at the end of the second year,

$$p_2 = p_1(1 + \tfrac{r}{100}) = p_0(1 + \tfrac{r}{100})^2.$$

If this be continued year after year, the interest charged on the increasing capital becomes greater and greater until at the end of t years, assuming that the interest is added to the capital every year,

$$p = p_0(1 + \tfrac{r}{100})^t \quad . \quad . \quad . \quad . \quad (3)$$

EXAMPLE.—Find the amount (interest + principal) of £500 for 10 years at 5 $°/_o$ compound interest.   The interest is added to the principal annually. From (3), $\log p = \log 500 + 10 \log 1·05$; $\therefore p = $ £814 8s. (nearly).

Instead of adding the interest to the capital every twelve months, we could do this monthly, weekly, daily, hourly, and so on.   If Nature were our banker she would not add the interest to the principal every year, rather would the interest be added to the capital continuously from moment to moment.   *Natura non facit saltus.*   Let us imagine that this has been done in order that we may compare this process with natural phenomena, and approximate as closely as we can to what actually occurs in Nature.   As a first approximation, suppose the interest to be added to the principal every month.   It can be shown in the same way that the principal at the end of twelve months, is

$$p = p_0(1 + \tfrac{r}{12.100})^{12} \quad . \quad . \quad . \quad (4)$$

If we next assume that during the whole year the interest is added to the principal every moment, say n per year, we may replace 12 by n, in (4), and

$$p = p_0\left(1 + \frac{r}{100n}\right)^n . \quad . \quad . \quad . \quad (5)$$

For convenience in subsequent calculation, let us put

$$\frac{r}{100n} = \frac{1}{u}, \text{ so that } n = \frac{ur}{100}.$$

From (5) and formula (11), page 28,

$$p = p_0\left\{\left(1 + \frac{1}{u}\right)^u\right\}^{\frac{r}{100}}.$$

But $(1 + 1/u)^u$ has been shown in (3), page 52, to be equivalent to e when u is infinitely great; hence, writing $\frac{r}{100} = a$,

$$p = p_0 e^a \; ;$$

which represents the amount of active principal bearing interest at the end of one year on the assumption that the interest is added to the principal from moment to moment. At the end of t years therefore, from (3),

$$p = p_0 e^{at} \; ; \; \text{or,} \; p = p_0 e^{\frac{r}{100}t}. \quad . \quad . \quad . \quad (6)$$

EXAMPLE.—Compare the amount of £500 for 10 years at 5°/₀ compound interest when the interest is added annually by the banker, with the amount which would accrue if the interest were added each instant it became due. In the first case, use (3), and in the latter (6). For the first case $p =$£814 8s.; for the second $p =$£824 7s.

ILLUSTRATION 2.—*Newton's law of cooling.* Let a body have a uniform temperature θ_1, higher than its surroundings, it is required to find the rate at which the body cools. Let θ_0 denote the temperature of the medium surrounding the body. In consequence of the exchange of heat, the temperature of the body gradually falls from θ_1 to θ_0. Let t denote the time required by the body to fall from θ_1 to θ. The temperature of the body is then $\theta - \theta_0$ above that of its surroundings. The most probable supposition that we can now make is that the rate at which the body loses heat $(- dQ)$ is proportional to the difference between its temperature and that of its surroundings. Hence

$$- \frac{dQ}{dt} = k(\theta - \theta_0),$$

where k is a coefficient depending on the nature of the substance.

From the definition of specific heat, if s denotes the specific heat of unit mass of substance.

$$Q = s(\theta - \theta_0), ; \; \text{or} \; dQ = s d\theta.$$

Substitute this in the former expression. Since $k/s = $ constant $=$ a (say) and $\theta_0 = 0°$ C., we obtain

$$- \frac{d\theta}{dt} = a\theta, \quad . \quad . \quad . \quad . \quad (7)$$

or, in words, the velocity of cooling of a body is proportional to the difference between its temperature and that of its surroundings. This is generally styled Newton's law of cooling, but it does not quite express Newton's idea (*Phil. Trans.*, **22**, 827, 1701).

Since the rate of diminution of θ is proportional to θ itself, we

guess at once that we are dealing with the compound interest law,
and from a comparison with (1) and (2a) above, we get

$$\theta = be^{-at}, \quad \cdots \quad (8)$$

or $$\log b - \log \theta = at. \quad \cdots \quad (9)$$

If θ_1 represents the temperature at the time t_1, and θ_2 the
temperature at the time t_2, we have

$$\log b - \log \theta_1 = at_1, \text{ and } \log b - \log \theta_2 = at_2.$$

By subtraction, since a is constant, we get

$$a = \frac{1}{t_1 - t_2} \cdot \log \frac{\theta_2}{\theta_1}, \quad \cdots \quad (10)$$

The validity of the original "simplifying assumption" as to the
rate at which heat is lost by the body must be tested by comparing
the result expressed in equation (10) with the results of experiment.
If the logical consequence of the assumption agrees with facts,
there is every reason to suppose that the working hypothesis is
true.   For the purpose of comparison we may use A. Winkelmann's
data, published in *Wied. Ann.*, **44**, 177, 429, 1891, for the rate of
cooling of a body from a temperature of 19·9° C. to 0° C.

If θ denote the temperature of the body after the interval of
time $t_1 - t_2$ and $\theta_2 = 19·9$, $\theta_1 = \theta$, remembering that in practical
work Briggsian logarithms are used, we obtain, from (10), the
expression

$$\frac{1}{t_1 - t_2} \cdot \log_{10}\frac{\theta_2}{\theta} = \text{constant, say } k.$$

Winkelmann's data for θ and $t_1 - t_2$ are to be arranged as
shown in the following table :—

θ.	$t_2 - t_1$.	k (calculated).
18·9	3·45	0·006490
16·9	10·85	0·006540
14·9	19·30	0·006511
12·9	28·80	0·006537
10·9	40·10	0·006519
8·9	53·75	0·006502
6·9	70·95	0·006483

Hence, k is constant within the limits of certain small irregular
variations due to experimental error.   Thus the truth of the supposition is established within the limits of the errors incidental to
Winkelmann's method of measurement.

This is a typical example of the way in which the logical deductions of an hypothesis are tested. There are other methods. For instance, Dulong and Petit (*Ann. Chim. Phys.*, [2], **7**, 225, 337, 1817) have made the series of exact measurements shown in the first and second columns of the following table:—

θ, excess of temp. of body above that of medium.	V, velocity of cooling $= d\theta/dt$.			
	Observed.	Calculated by the formula of:		
		Newton.	Dulong and Petit.	Stefan.
220°	8·81	6·82	8·97	8·95
200°	7·40	6·20	7·41	7·44
180°	6·10	5·58	6·06	6·11
160°	4·89	4·96	4·91	4·95
140°	3·88	4·34	3·92	3·94
120°	3·02	3·72	3·08	3·05
100°	2·30	3·10	2·35	2·30

If we knew the numerical value of the constant a in formula (7), this expression could be employed to calculate the value of $d\theta/dt$ for any given value of θ. To evaluate a, substitute the observed values of V and θ in (7) and take the mean of the different results so obtained. Thus, $a = 0\cdot031$. The third column shows the velocities of cooling calculated on the assumption that Newton's law is true. The agreement between the experimental and theoretical results is very poor. Hence it is necessary to seek a second approximation to the true law. With this object, Dulong and Petit have proposed

$$V = b(c^\theta - 1), \quad . \quad . \quad . \quad . \quad (11)$$

as a second approximation. Here $b = 2\cdot037$, $c = 1\cdot0077$. Column 4 shows the velocity of cooling calculated from Dulong and Petit's law. The agreement between theory and fact is now very close. This formula, however, has no theoretical basis. It is the result of a guess. Stefan's guess is that

$$V = a\{(273 + \theta)^4 - (273)^4\}, \quad . \quad . \quad (12)$$

where $a = 10^{-11} \times 16\cdot72$. The calculated results in the fifth column are quite as good as those attending the use of Dulong and Petit's formula. Galitzine has pointed out that Stefan's formula can be established on theoretical grounds.

It is a very common thing to find different formulæ agree, so far as we can test them, equally well with facts. *The reader must, therefore, guard against implicit faith in this criterion—the agreement between observed and calculated results—as an infallible experimentum crucis.*

Lord Kelvin once assumed that there was a complete transformation of thermal into electrical energy in the chemical action of a galvanic element. Measurements made by Joule and himself with a Daniell element gave results in harmony with theory. The agreement was afterwards shown to be illusory. Success in explaining facts is not necessarily proof of the validity of an hypothesis, for, as Leibnitz puts it, " le vrai peut être tiré du faux," in other words, it is possible to infer the truth from false premises.

A little consideration will show that it is quite legitimate to deduce the numerical values of the above constants from the experiments themselves. For example, we might have taken the mean of the values of k in Winkelmann's table above, and applied the test by comparing the calculated with the observed values of either $t_2 - t_1$, or of θ.

EXAMPLES.—(1) To again quote from Winkelmann's paper, if, when the temperature of the surrounding medium is 99·74°, the body cools so that when

$$\theta = 119\text{·}97°, \quad 117\text{·}97°, \quad 115\text{·}97°, \quad 113\text{·}97°, \quad 111\text{·}97°, \quad 109\text{·}97°;$$
$$t = \quad 0, \quad\quad 12\text{·}6 \quad\quad 26\text{·}7 \quad\quad 42\text{·}9 \quad\quad 61\text{·}2 \quad\quad 83\text{·}1.$$

Do you think that Newton's law is confirmed by these measurements? Hint. Instead of assuming that $\theta_0 = 0$, it will be found necessary to retain θ_0 in the above discussion. Do this and show that the above results must be tested by means of the formula

$$\frac{1}{t_2 - t_1} \cdot \log_{10} \frac{\theta_2 - \theta_0}{\theta_1 - \theta_0} = \text{constant.}$$

(2) What will be the temperature of a bowl of coffee in an hour's time if the temperature ten minutes ago was 80°, and is now 70° above the temperature of the room? Assume Newton's law of cooling. Ansr. 31·2° above the surrounding temperature. Hint. From (8), $70 = 80 \cdot e^{-10a}$; $\therefore a = 0\text{·}0134$; and again, $x = 80 \cdot e^{-0\text{·}0134 \times 70}$. We cannot apply the amended laws—Dulong and Petit's, and Stefan's—until we have taken up more advanced work. See (14) and (15), page 372.

ILLUSTRATION 3.—*The variation of atmospheric pressure with altitude* above sea-level can be shown to follow the compound interest law. Let p_0 be the pressure in centimetres of mercury at the so-called datum line, or sea-level, p the pressure at a height h above this level. Let ρ_0 be the density of air at sea-level (Hg = 1). Now the pressure at the sea-level is produced by the weight of the superincumbent air, that is, by the weight of a column of air of a height h and constant density ρ_0. This weight is equal to $h\rho_0$. If the downward pressure of the air were constant, the barometric pressure would be lowered ρ_0 centimetres for every centimetre rise above sea-level. But by Boyle's law the decrease in the density of air is proportional to the pressure, and if ρ denote the density of air at a height dh above sea-level, the pressure dp is given by the expression

$$dp = - \rho dh.$$

If we consider the air arranged in very thin strata, we may regard the density of the air in each stratum as constant. By Boyle's law

$$\rho p_0 = \rho_0 p \; ; \; \text{or}, \; \rho = \rho_0 p / p_0.$$

Substituting this value of ρ in the above formula, we get

$$\frac{dp}{dh} = - \frac{\rho_0 p}{p_0} \quad . \quad . \quad . \quad . \quad (13)$$

The negative sign indicates that the pressure decreases vertically upwards. This equation is the compound interest law in another guise. The variation in the pressure, as we ascend or descend, is proportional to the pressure itself. Since p_0/ρ_0 is constant, we have on applying the compound interest law to (13),

$$p = \text{constant} \times e^{-\frac{\rho_0}{p_0} h}.$$

We can readily find the value of the constant by noting that at sea-level $h = 0$; $e^0 = 1$; $p = \text{constant} \times e^0 = p_0$. Substituting these values in the last equation, we obtain

$$p = p_0 e^{-\frac{\rho_0}{p_0} h}, \quad . \quad . \quad . \quad (14)$$

a relation known as Halley's law. Continued p. 260, Ex. (2).

ILLUSTRATION 4.—*The absorption of actinic energy from light passing through an absorbing medium.* The intensity, I, of a beam of light is changed by an amount dI after it has passed through a layer of absorbing medium dl thick in such a way that

$$dI = - aIdl,$$

where a is a constant depending on the nature of the absorbing medium and on the wave length of light. The rate of variation in the intensity of the light is therefore proportional to the intensity of the light itself, in other words, the compound interest law again appears. Hence

$$\frac{dI}{dl} = - aI \; ; \; \text{or} \; I = \text{constant} \times e^{-m}.$$

If I_0 denote the intensity of the incident light, then when

$$l = 0, \ I = I_0 = \text{constant.}$$

Hence the intensity of the light after it has passed through a medium of thickness l, is

$$I = I_0 e^{-al} \quad . \quad . \quad . \quad . \quad (15)$$

EXAMPLES.—(1) A 1·006 cm. layer of an aqueous solution of copper chloride (2·113 gram molecules per litre) absorbed 18·13 °/$_o$ of light in the region $\lambda = 551$ to 554 of the spectrum. What °/$_o$ would be absorbed by a layer of the same solution 7·64 cm. thick? Ansr. 78·13 °/$_o$. Hint. Find a in (15) from the first set of observations; $I_0 = 100$, $I = 81·87$; ∴ $a = 0·1989$. See T. Ewan's paper "On the Absorption Spectra of some Copper Salts in Aqueous Solution" (Phil. Mag., [5], 33, 317, 1892). Use Table IV., page 616.

(2) A pane of glass absorbs 2 °/$_o$ of the light incident upon it. How much light will get through a dozen panes of the same glass? Ansr. 78·66 °/$_o$. Hint. $I_0 = 100$; $I = 98$; $a = 0·02$. Use Table IV., page 616.

ILLUSTRATION 5.—*Wilhelmy's law for the velocity of chemical reactions.* Wilhelmy as early as 1850 published the law of mass action in a form which will be recognised as still another example of the ubiquitous law of compound interest. "The amount of chemical change in a given time is directly proportional to the quantity of reacting substance present in the system."

If x denote the quantity of changing substance, and dx the amount of substance which disappears in the time dt, the law of mass action assumes the dress

$$\frac{dx}{dt} = -kx,$$

where k is a constant depending on the nature of the reacting substance. It has been called the *coefficient of the velocity of the reaction*, its meaning can be easily obtained by applying the methods of § 10. This equation is probably the simplest we have yet studied. It follows directly, since the rate of increase of x is proportional to x, that

$$x = be^{-kt},$$

where b is a constant whose numerical value can be determined if we know the value of x when $t = 0$. The negative sign indicates that the velocity of the action diminishes as time goes on.

EXAMPLES.—(1) If a volume v of mercury be heated to any temperature θ, the change of volume dv corresponding to a small increment of temperature $d\theta$, is found to be proportional to v, hence $dv = av d\theta$. Prove Bosscha's formula, $v = e^{a\theta}$, for the volume of mercury at any temperature θ. Ansr. $v = be^{a\theta}$, where a, b are constants. If we start with unit volume of mercury at $0°$, $b=1$ and we have the required result.

(2) According to Nordenskjöld's solubility law, in the absence of supersaturation, for a small change in the temperature, $d\theta$, there is a change in the solubility of a salt, ds, proportional to the amount of salt s contained in the solution at the temperature θ, or $ds = asd\theta$ where a is a constant. Show that the equation connecting the amount of salt dissolved by the solution with the temperature is $s = s_0 e^{a\theta}$, where s_0 is the solubility of the salt at $0°$.

(3) If any dielectric (condenser) be subject to a difference of potential, the density ρ of the charge constantly diminishes according to the relation $\rho = be^{-at}$, where b is an empirical constant; and a is a constant equal to the product 4π into the coefficient of conductivity, c, of the dielectric, and the time, t, divided by the specific inductive capacity, μ, i.e., $a = 4\pi ct/\mu$. Hence show that the gradual discharge of a condenser follows the compound interest law. Ansr. Show $d\rho/dt = -a\rho$.

(4) One form of Dalton's empirical law for the pressure of saturated vapour, p, between certain limits of temperature, θ, is, $p = ae^\theta$. Show that this is an example of the compound interest law.

(5) The relation between the velocity V of a certain chemical reaction and temperature, $\theta°$, is $\log V = a + b\theta$, where a and b are constants. Show that we are dealing with the compound interest law. What is the logical consequence of this law with reference to reactions which (like hydrogen and oxygen) take place at high temperatures (say $500°$), but, so far as we can tell, not at ordinary temperatures?

(6) The rate of change of a radioactive element is represented by $dN/dt = -rN$ where N denotes the number of atoms present at the time t, and r is a constant. Show that the law of radioactive change follows the "compound interest law".

§ 21. Successive Differentiation.

The differential coefficient derived from any function of a variable may be either another function of the variable, or a constant. The new function may be differentiated again in order to obtain the second differential coefficient. We can obtain the third and higher derivatives in the same way. Thus, if $y = x^3$,

The first derivative is, $\dfrac{dy}{dx} = 3x^2$;

The second derivative is, $\dfrac{d^2y}{dx^2} = 6x$;

The third derivative is, $\dfrac{d^3y}{dx^3} = 6$;

The fourth derivative is, $\dfrac{d^4y}{dx^4} = 0$.

It will be observed that each differentiation reduces the index of the power by unity. If the index n is a positive integer the number of derivatives is finite.

In the symbols $\frac{d^2}{dx^2}(y)$, $\frac{d^3}{dx^3}(y)$ ..., the superscripts simply denote that the differentiation has been repeated 2, 3... times. In differential notation we may write these results

$$d^2y = 6x \cdot dx^2 \; ; \; d^3y = 6dx^3 \; ; \ldots$$

The symbol dx^2, dx^3 ..., meaning $dx \cdot dx$, $dx \cdot dx \cdot dx$ ..., must not be confused with $dx^2 = d(x^2) = 2x \cdot dx$; $dx^3 = d(x)^3 = 3x^2 \cdot dx \ldots$

The successive differential coefficients sometimes repeat themselves; for instance, on differentiating

$$y = \sin x$$

we obtain successively

$$\frac{dy}{dx} = \cos x \; ; \; \frac{d^2y}{dx^2} = -\sin x \; ; \; \frac{d^3y}{dx^3} = -\cos x \; ; \; \frac{d^4y}{dx^4} = \sin x \; ; \ldots$$

The fourth derivative is thus a repetition of the original function, the process of differentiation may thus be continued without end, every fourth derivative resembling the original function. The simplest case of such a repetition is

$$y = e^x,$$

which furnishes

$$\frac{dy}{dx} = e^x \; ; \; \frac{d^2y}{dx^2} = e^x \; ; \; \frac{d^3y}{dx^3} = e^x \; ; \ldots$$

The differential coefficients are all equal to the original function and to each other.

EXAMPLES.—(1) If $y = \log x$; show that $d^4y/dx^4 = -6/x^4$.

(2) If $y = x^n$; show that $d^4y/dx^4 = n(n-1)(n-2)(n-3)x^{n-4}$.

(3) If $y = x^{-2}$; show that $d^3y/dx^3 = -24x^{-5}$.

(4) If $y = \log(x+1)$; show that $d^2y/dx^2 = -(x+1)^{-2}$.

(5) Show that every fourth derivative in the successive differentiation of $y = \cos x$ repeats itself.

Just as the first derivative of x with respect to t measures a velocity, *the second differential coefficient of x with respect to t measures an acceleration* (page 17). For instance, if a material[1]

---

[1] A *material point* is a fiction much used in applied mathematics for purposes of calculation, just as the atom is in chemistry. An atom may contain an infinite number of "material points" or particles.

point, P, move in a straight line AB (Fig. 8) so that its distance, s, from a fixed point O is given by the equation $s = a \sin t$, where a represents the distance OA or OB, show that the acceleration

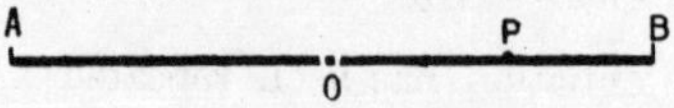

FIG. 8.

due to the force acting on the particle is proportional to its distance from the fixed point.   The velocity, V, is evidently

$$V = \frac{ds}{dt} = a \cos t ; \qquad . \quad . \quad . \quad (1)$$

and the acceleration, F, is

$$F = \frac{dV}{dt} = \frac{d^2s}{dt^2} = - a \sin t = - s, \quad . \quad . \quad (2)$$

the negative sign showing that the force is attractive, tending to lessen the distance of the moving point from O.   To obtain some idea of this motion find a set of corresponding values of F, s and V from Table XIV., page 609, and (1) and (2) above.   The result is

If t =	0	$\frac{1}{2}\pi$	π	$\frac{3}{2}\pi$	$2\pi \ldots$
V =	a	0	$-a$	0	$a \ldots$
s =	0	a	0	a	$0 \ldots$
F =	0	$-a$	0	$-a$	$0 \ldots$
P is at	O	B	O	A	$O \ldots$

A careful study of these facts will convince the reader that the point is oscillating regularly in a straight line, alternately right and left of the point O.   In this sense, the equation $d^2s/dt^2 = - s$ describes the motion of the particle.   It is called an **equation of motion**.   An equation like $ds/dt = a \cos t$, or $d^2s/dt^2 = - s$, containing differentials or differential coefficients is called a **differential equation**.

EXAMPLES.—(1) If a body falls from a vertical height according to the law $s = \frac{1}{2}gt^2$, where g represents the acceleration due to the earth's gravity, show that g is equal to the second differential coefficient of s with respect to t.

(2) If the distance traversed by a moving point in the time t be denoted by the equation $s = at^2 + bt + c$ (where a, b and c are arbitrary constants), show that the acceleration is constant.

(3) Experiments show that the velocity acquired by a body in falling from a height s is given by the expression $V^2 = 2g(s^{-1} - s_0^{-1})r^2$, where g denotes the acceleration of gravitation at the earth's surface, and r the radius of the

earth. Show that the acceleration of a body at different distances from the earth's centre is inversely as the square of its distance (Newton's law). Hint. Differentiate the equation as it stands ; divide by dt and cancel out the v on one side of the equation with ds/dt on the other. Hence, $d^2s/dt^2 = -gr^2/s^2$ remains. Now show that if a body falls freely from an infinite distance the maximum velocity with which it can reach the earth is less than seven miles per second, neglecting the resistance of the air. In the original equation, s_0 is ∞, and $s = r = 3,962$ miles; $g = 32\frac{1}{6}$ feet $= 0.00609$ miles. $\therefore$ Ansr. $= 6.95$ miles per sec.

(4) Show that the motion of a point at a distance $s = a \cos qt$ from a certain fixed point is given by the equation $d^2s/dt^2 = -q^2s$.

(5) Show that the first and second derivatives of De la Roche's vapour pressure formula, $p = ab^{\theta/(m+n\theta)}$, where a, b, m, and n are constants, are

$$\frac{dp}{d\theta} = \frac{m \log b}{(m + n\theta)^2} ab^{\frac{\theta}{m+n\theta}}; \quad \frac{d^2p}{d\theta^2} = \frac{m \log b\{m \log b - 2n(m + n\theta)\}}{(m + n\theta)^4} ab^{\frac{\theta}{m+n\theta}}.$$

Fortunately, in applying the calculus to practical work, only the first and second derivatives are often wanted, the third and fourth but seldom. The calculation of the higher differential coefficients may be a laborious process. **Leibnitz's theorem,** named after its discoverer, helps to shorten the operation. It also furnishes us with the general or nth derivative of the function which is useful in discussions upon the theory of the subject. We shall here regard it as an exercise upon successive differentiation. The direct object of Leibnitz's theorem is *to find the nth differential coefficient of the product of two functions of x in terms of the differential coefficients of each function.*

On page 40, the differential coefficient of the product of two variables was shown to be

$$\frac{dy}{dx} = \frac{d(uv)}{dx} = v\frac{du}{dx} + u\frac{dv}{dx},$$

where u and v are functions of x. By successive differentiation and analogy with the binomial theorem (1), page 36, it may be shown that

$$\frac{d^n(uv)}{dx^n} = v\frac{d^nu}{dx^n} + n\frac{dv}{dx} \cdot \frac{d^{n-1}u}{dx^{n-1}} + \ldots + u\frac{d^nv}{dx^n} \tag{1}$$

The reader must himself prove the formula, as an exercise, by comparing the values of $d^2(uv)/dx^2$; $d^3(uv)/dx^3$; ..., with the developments of $(x + h)^2$; $(x + h)^3$; ..., of page 36.

EXAMPLES.—(1) If $y = x^4 \cdot e^{ax}$, find the value of d^3y/dx^3. Substitute x^4 and e^{ax} respectively for v and u in (1). Thus,

$v = x^4$; $\therefore dv/dx = 4x^3$; $d^2v/dx^2 = 12x^2$; $d^3v/dx^3 = 24x$;

$u = e^{ax}$; $\therefore du/dx = ae^{ax}$; $d^2u/dx^2 = a^2e^{ax}$; $d^3u/dx^3 = a^3e^{ax}$.

From (1)

$$\frac{d^3y}{dx^3} = v\frac{d^3u}{dx^3} + n\frac{dv}{dx}\cdot\frac{d^2u}{dx^2} + \frac{n(n-1)}{2!}\cdot\frac{d^2v}{dx^2}\cdot\frac{du}{dx} + u\frac{n(n-1)(n-2)}{3!}\cdot\frac{d^3v}{dx^3};$$

$$= e^{ax}\Big(a^3v + 3a^2\frac{dv}{dx} + 3a\frac{d^2v}{dv^2} + \frac{d^3v}{dx^3}\Big); \quad \cdot \quad \cdot \quad \cdot \quad \cdot \quad \cdot \quad (2)$$

$$= e^{ax}(a^3x^4 + 12a^2x^3 + 36ax^2 + 24x).$$

(2) If $y = \log x$, show that $d^6y/dx^6 = -5!/x^6$.

If we pretend, for the time being, that the symbols of operation $\frac{d}{dx}$, $\Big(\frac{d}{dx}\Big)^2$, $\Big(\frac{d}{dx}\Big)^3$, in (2), represent the magnitudes of an operation, in an algebraic sense, we can write

$$\frac{d^3(e^{ax}v)}{dx^3} = e^{ax}\Big(a + \frac{d}{dx}\Big)^3 v = e^{ax}(a + D)^3v, \quad \cdot \quad (3)$$

instead of (2), and substituting D for $\frac{d}{dx}$. The expression $(a + D)^3$ is supposed to be developed by the binomial theorem, page 36, and dv/dx, d^2v/dx^2, ..., substituted in place of Dv, D^2v, ..., in the result. Equation (3) would also hold good if the index 3 were replaced by any integer, say n. This result is known as the *symbolic form of Leibnitz's theorem*.

§ 22. Partial Differentiation.

Up to the present time we have been principally occupied with functions of one independent variable x, such that

$$u = f(x) ;$$

but functions of two, three or more variables may occur, say

$$u = f(x, y, z, \ldots),$$

where the variables x, y, z, ... are independent of each other. Such

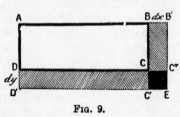

functions are common. As illustrations, it might be pointed out that the area of a triangle depends on its base and altitude; the volume of a rectangular box depends on its three dimensions; and the volume of a gas depends on the temperature and pressure.

Fig. 9.

I. Differentials.

To find the differential of a function of two independent variables. This can be best done in the following manner, partly graphic and partly analytical. In Fig. 9, the area u of the rectangle $ABCD$, with the sides x, y, is given by the function

$$u = xy.$$

Since x and y are independent of each other, the one may be supposed to vary, while the other remains unchanged. The function, therefore, ought to furnish two differential coefficients, the one resulting from a variation in x, and the other from a variation in y.

First, let the side x vary while y remains unchanged. The area is then a function of x alone. y remains constant.

$$\therefore (du)_y = ydx, \quad \cdot \quad \cdot \quad \cdot \quad \cdot \quad (1)$$

where $(du)_y$ represents the area of the rectangle $BB'C''C$. The subscript denoting that y is constant.

Second, in the same way, suppose the length of the side y changes, while x remains constant, then

$$(du)_x = xdy, \quad \cdot \quad \cdot \quad \cdot \quad \cdot \quad (2)$$

where $(du)_x$ represents the area of the rectangle $DD'C'C$. Instead of using the differential form of these variables, we may write the differential coefficients

$$\left(\frac{du}{dx}\right)_y = y; \text{ and } \left(\frac{du}{dy}\right)_x = x; \text{ or } \frac{\partial u}{\partial x} = y; \text{ and } \frac{\partial u}{\partial y} = x,$$

in C. G. J. Jacobi's notation, where $\dfrac{``\partial\,"}{\partial x}$ is the symbol of differentiation when all the variables, other than x, are constant. Substituting these values of x and y in (1) and (2), we obtain

$$(du)_y = \frac{\partial u}{\partial x}dx; \quad (du)_x = \frac{\partial u}{\partial y}dy.$$

Lastly, let us allow x and y to vary simultaneously, the total increment in the area of the rectangle is evidently represented by the figure $D'EB'BCD$.

$$\text{Incr. } u = BB'CC'' + DD'CC' + CC'C''E$$
$$= ydx + xdy + dx \cdot dy.$$

Neglecting infinitely small magnitudes of the second order, we get

$$du = ydx + xdy; \quad \cdot \quad \cdot \quad \cdot \quad (3)$$

or

$$du = \frac{\partial u}{\partial x}dx + \frac{\partial u}{\partial y}dy, \quad \cdot \quad \cdot \quad (4)$$

which is also written in the form

$$du = \left(\frac{du}{dx}\right)_y dx + \left(\frac{du}{dy}\right)_x dy. \quad \cdot \quad \cdot \quad (5)$$

In equations (3) and (4), du is called the **total differential** of the function ; $\frac{\partial u}{\partial x}dx$ the **partial differential** of u with respect to x when y is constant; and $\frac{\partial u}{\partial y}dy$ the partial differential of u with respect to y when x is constant. Hence the rule : The total differential of two (or more) independent variables is equal to the sum of their partial differentials.

The physical meaning of this rule is that the total force acting on a body at any instant is the sum of every separate action. When several forces act upon a material particle, each force produces its own motion independently of all the others. The actual velocity of the particle is called the *resultant* velocity, and the several effects produced by the different forces are called the *component* velocities. There is here involved an important principle— the principle of **the mutual independence of different reactions ;** or the principle of the coexistence of different reactions—which lies at the base of physical and chemical dynamics. The principle might be enunciated in the following manner :—

When a number of changes are simultaneously taking place in any system, each one proceeds as if it were independent of the others ; the total change is the sum of all the independent changes. Otherwise expressed, the total differential is equal to the sum of the partial differentials representing each change. The mathematical process thus corresponds with the actual physical change.

To take a simple illustration, a man can swim at the rate of two miles an hour, and a river is flowing at the rate of one mile an hour. If the man swims down-stream, the river will carry him one mile in one hour, and his swimming will carry him two miles in the same time. Hence the man's actual rate of progress down-stream will be three miles an hour. If the man had started to swim up-stream against the current, his actual rate of progress would be the difference between the velocity of the stream and his rate of swimming. In short, the man would travel at the rate of one mile an hour against the current.

This means that the total change in u, when x and y vary, is made up of two parts : (i) the change which would occur in u if x alone varied, and (ii) the change which would occur in u if y alone varied.

Total variation = variation due to x alone + variation due to y alone.

If the meaning of the different terms in

$$du = \frac{\partial u}{\partial x}dx + \frac{\partial u}{\partial y}dy$$

is carefully noted, it will be found that *the equation is really expressed in differential notation*, not differential coefficients.   The partial derivative $\partial u/\partial x$ represents the *rate* of change in the magnitude of u when x is increased by an amount ∂x, y being constant ; similarly $\partial u/\partial y$ stands for the *rate* of change in the magnitude of u when y is increased by an amount ∂y, x being constant.   The rate of change $\partial u/\partial x$ multiplied by dx, furnishes the *amount* of change in the magnitude of u when x increases by an amount dx, y being constant ; and similarly $(\partial u/\partial y)\, dy$ is the magnitude of the change u when y increases an amount dy, x being maintained constant.

EXAMPLES.—(1) If $u = x^3 + x^2y + y^3$

$\dfrac{\partial u}{\partial x} = 3x^2 + 2xy$; $\dfrac{\partial u}{\partial y} = x^2 + 3y^2$; $\therefore du = (3x^2 + 2xy)dx + (x^2 + 3y^2)dy$.

(2) If $u = x \log y$; $du = \log y.\, dx + x.\, dy/y$.

(3) If $u = \cos x.\sin y + \sin x.\cos y$;

$\quad du = (dx + dy)(\cos x \cos y - \sin x \sin y) = (dx + dy)\{\cos(x + y)\}$.

(4) If $u = x^y$; $du = yx^{y-1}dx + x^y \log x\, dy$.

(5) The differentiation of a function of three independent variables may be left as an exercise to the reader.   Neglecting quantities of a higher order, if u be the volume of a rectangular parallelopiped [1] having the three dimensions x, y, z, independently variable, then $u = xyz$, and

$$du = \frac{\partial u}{\partial x}dx + \frac{\partial u}{\partial y}dy + \frac{\partial u}{\partial z}dz ; \quad . \quad . \quad . \quad . \quad (6)$$

or an infinitely small increment in the volume of the solid is the sum of the infinitely small increments resulting when each variable changes independently of the others.   Show that

$$du = yz\,dx + xz\,dy + xy\,dz. \quad . \quad . \quad . \quad . \quad (7)$$

(6) If the relation between the pressure p, and volume v, and temperature θ of a gas is given by the gas law $pv = RT$, show that the total change in pressure for a simultaneous change of volume and temperature is

$$\left(\frac{\partial p}{\partial v}\right)_\theta = -\frac{RT}{v^2} = -\frac{p}{v} ; \; \left(\frac{\partial p}{\partial T}\right)_v = \frac{R}{v} = \frac{p}{T} ; \; \therefore dp = -\frac{p}{v}dv + \frac{p}{T}dT.$$

This expression is only true when the changes dT and dv are made infinitesimal.   The observed and calculated values of dp, arranged side by side

---

[1] Mis-spelt " parallelopiped " by false analogy with " parallelogram ".   I follow the will of custom—*quem penes arbitrium est et jus et norma loquendi.*   Etymologically the word should be spelt " parallelepiped ".   It only adds new interest to learn that the word is derived from " παραλληλεπιπεδον used by Plutarch and others " ; and makes one lament the decline of classics.

in the following table (from J. Perry's *The Steam Engine*, London, 564, 1904), show that even when dv and dT are relatively large, the observed values agree pretty well with the calculated results, but the error becomes less and less as dT and dv are made smaller and smaller :—

T	dT by difference.	v	dv by difference.	p Obs.	dp	
					Calc.	Obs.
500	—	14·4	—	2000	—	—
501	1·0	14·5	0·1	1990·2	−9·8	−9·9
500·1	0·1	14·41	0·01	1999·2	−1·0	−0·90
500·01	0·01	14·40	0·001	1999·9	−0·1	−0·10

(7) Clairaut's formula for the attraction of gravitation, g, at different latitudes, L, on the earth's surface, and at different altitudes, H, above mean tide level, is

$$g = 980 \cdot 6056 - 2 \cdot 5028 \cos 2L - 0 \cdot 000003H, \text{ dynes.}$$

Discuss the changes in the force of gravitation and in the weight of a substance with change of locality. Note, "weight" is nothing more than a measure of the force of gravitation.

II. *Differential Coefficients.*

To find the differential coefficient of a function of two independent variables. If the variables x and y are both functions of t (say), we may pass directly from differentials to differential coefficients by dividing through with dt, thus

$$\frac{du}{dt} = \frac{\partial u}{\partial x} \cdot \frac{dx}{dt} + \frac{\partial u}{\partial y} \cdot \frac{dy}{dt},$$

which may also be written

$$\frac{du}{dt} = \left(\frac{du}{dx}\right)_y \frac{dx}{dt} + \left(\frac{du}{dy}\right)_x \frac{dy}{dt}. \quad \cdot \quad \cdot \quad \cdot \quad \textbf{(8)}$$

In words, the total variation of a function of x and y is equal to the partial derivative of the function when y is constant multiplied by the rate of variation of x, added to the partial derivative of the function when x is constant multiplied by the rate of variation of y. If the function remains constant while its variables change, the total rate of change of the function is zero,

$$\frac{\partial u}{\partial x} \cdot \frac{dx}{dt} + \frac{\partial u}{\partial y} \cdot \frac{dy}{dt} = 0 \quad \cdot \quad \cdot \quad \cdot \quad \textbf{(9)}$$

Examples of this will be given very shortly.

When there is likely to be any doubt as to what variables have been assumed constant, a subscript is appended to the lower corner on the right of the bracket. The subscripts can only be omitted when there is no possibility of confusing the variables which have been assumed constant. For example, the expression $\partial C_v / \partial T$ may have one of three meanings.

$$\left(\frac{dC_v}{dT}\right)_v ; \quad \left(\frac{dC_v}{dT}\right)_p ; \quad \left(\frac{dC_v}{dT}\right)_\phi.$$

Perry suggests [1] the use of the alternative symbols

$$\frac{\partial C_v}{\partial_v T} ; \quad \frac{\partial C_v}{\partial_p T} ; \quad \frac{\partial C_v}{\partial_\phi T}$$

I have just explained the meanings of the partial derivatives of u with respect to x and y. Let me again emphasize the distinction between the partial differential coefficient $\partial u / \partial x$, and the differential coefficient du/dx. In $\partial u / \partial x$, y is treated as a constant; in du/dx, y is treated as a function of x. The partial derivative denotes the rate of change of u per unit change in the value of x when the other variable or variables remain constant; du/dx represents the *total* rate of change of u when all the variables change simultaneously.

EXAMPLE.—If y and u are functions of x such that

$$y = \sin x; \quad u = x \sin x, \quad . \quad . \quad . \quad . \quad (10)$$

we can write the last expression in several ways. The rate of change of u with respect to x (y constant) and to y (x constant) will depend upon the way y is compounded with x. The total rate of change of u with respect to x will be the same in all cases. For example, we get, from equations (10),

$u = xy; \; \therefore \; du = y \, . \, dx + x \, . \, dy; \; u = x \sin x; \; \therefore \; du = (x \cos x + \sin x)dx;$

$u = \sin^{-1} y \, . \, \sin x; \; \therefore \; du = \sin^{-1} y \, . \, \cos x \, . \, dx + \sin x \, . \, (1 - y^2)^{-\frac{1}{2}} \, dy.$

The partial derivatives are all different, but du/dx, in every case, reduces to $\sin x + x \cos x$.

Many illustrations of functions with properties similar to those required in order to satisfy the conditions of equation (8) may occur to the reader. The following is typical:—When rhombic crystals are heated they may have different coefficients of expansion in different directions. A cubical portion of one of these crystals at one temperature is not necessarily cubical at another. Suppose a rectangular parallelopiped is cut from such a crystal, with faces parallel to the three axes of dilation. The volume of the crystal is

$$v = xyz,$$

[1] J. Perry, *Nature*, **66**, 53, 271, 520, 1902 ; T. Muir, same references.

where x, y, z are the lengths of the different sides. Hence

$$\frac{\partial v}{\partial x} = yz \,;\; \frac{\partial v}{\partial y} = xz \,;\; \frac{\partial v}{\partial z} = xy.$$

Substitute in (6) and divide by $d\theta$, where $d\theta$ represents a slight rise of temperature, then

$$\frac{dv}{d\theta} = yz\frac{dx}{d\theta} + xz\frac{dy}{d\theta} + xy\frac{dz}{d\theta}\,;\; \text{or,}\; \frac{1}{v}\cdot\frac{dv}{d\theta} = \frac{1}{x}\cdot\frac{dx}{d\theta} + \frac{1}{y}\cdot\frac{dy}{d\theta} + \frac{1}{z}\cdot\frac{dz}{d\theta},$$

where the three terms on the right side respectively denote the coefficients of linear expansion, λ, of the substance along the three directions, x, y, or z. The term on the left is the *coefficient of cubical expansion*, a. For isotropic bodies, $a = 3\lambda$, since

$$\frac{1}{x}\cdot\frac{dx}{d\theta} = \frac{1}{y}\cdot\frac{dy}{d\theta} = \frac{1}{z}\cdot\frac{dz}{d\theta}.$$

EXAMPLES.—(1) Loschmidt and Obermeyer's formula for the coefficient of diffusion of a gas at $T°$ (absolute), assuming k_0 and T_0 are constant, is

$$k = k_0\left(\frac{T}{T_0}\right)^n \frac{p}{760},$$

where k_0 is the coefficient of diffusion at 0° C. and p is the pressure of the gas. Required the variation in the coefficient of diffusion of the gas corresponding with small changes of temperature and pressure. Put

$$a = \frac{k_0}{760T_0^n}\,;\; \frac{\partial k}{\partial T}dT = apnT^{n-1}dT\,;\; \frac{\partial k}{\partial p}dp = aT^n dp.$$

$$\therefore dk = \frac{\partial k}{\partial T}dT + \frac{\partial k}{\partial p}dp.\; \therefore dk = \frac{(npdT + Tdp)k_0 T^{n-1}}{760T_0^n}.$$

(2) Biot and Arago's formula for the index of refraction, μ, of a gas or vapour at $\theta°$ and pressure p is

$$\mu - 1 = \frac{\mu_0 - 1}{1 + a\theta}\cdot\frac{p}{760},$$

where μ_0 is the index of refraction at 0°, a the coefficient of expansion of the gas with temperature. What is the effect of small variations of temperature and pressure on the index of refraction? Ansr. To cause it to vary by an amount $d\mu = \dfrac{\mu_0 - 1}{760}\left(\dfrac{dp}{1 + a\theta} - \dfrac{pad\theta}{(1 + a\theta)^2}\right).$

(3) If $y = f(x + at)$, show that $dx/dt = a$. Hint. Find $\partial y/\partial x$, and $\partial y/\partial t$; divide the one by the other.

(4) If $u = xy$, where x and y are functions of t, show that (8) reduces to our old formula (9), page 41,

$$\frac{du}{dt} = x\frac{dy}{dt} + y\frac{dx}{dt}. \quad . \quad . \quad . \quad . \quad (11)$$

(5) If x is a function of t such that $x = t$, show that on differentiation with respect to t, $u = xy$ becomes

$$\frac{du}{dt} = \frac{\partial u}{\partial x} + \frac{\partial u}{\partial y}\cdot\frac{dy}{dt}. \quad . \quad . \quad . \quad (12)$$

since dt/dt is self-evidently unity.

(6) If x and y are functions of t, show that on differentiation of $u = xy$ with respect to t,

$$\frac{du}{dt} = \frac{\partial u}{\partial y} \cdot \frac{dy}{dt} ; \ \frac{du}{dy} = \frac{\partial u}{\partial t} \cdot \frac{dt}{dy} . \quad \bullet \quad \bullet \quad \bullet \quad (13)$$

A result obtained in a different way on page 44.

§ 23. Euler's Theorem on Homogeneous Functions.

One object of Euler's theorem is to eliminate certain arbitrary conditions from a given relation between the variables and to build up a new relation free from the restrictions due to the presence of arbitrary functions. I shall however revert to this subject later on. Euler's theorem also helps us to shorten the labour involved in making certain computations. According to Euler's theorem: *In any homogeneous function, the sum of the products of each variable with the partial differential coefficients of the original function with respect to that variable is equal to the product of the original function with its degree.* In other words, if u is a homogeneous function [1] of the nth degree, Euler's theorem states that if

$$u = \Sigma a x^\alpha y^\beta \quad \bullet \quad \bullet \quad \bullet \quad \bullet \quad (1)$$

when $a + \beta = n$, then [2]

$$x \frac{\partial u}{\partial x} + y \frac{\partial u}{\partial y} = nu . \quad \bullet \quad \bullet \quad \bullet \quad (2)$$

The proof is instructive. By differentiation of the homogeneous function,

$$u = a x^\alpha y^\beta + b x^{\alpha_1} y^{\beta_1} + \ldots = \Sigma a x^\alpha y^\beta,$$

when $a + \beta = \alpha_1 + \beta_1 = \ldots = n$, we obtain

$$\frac{\partial u}{\partial x} = \Sigma a \alpha x^{\alpha - 1} y^\beta ; \ \text{and} \ \frac{\partial u}{\partial y} = \Sigma a \beta x^\alpha y^{\beta - 1}.$$

Hence, finally, by multiplying the first with x, and the second with y, and adding the two results, we obtain

$$x \frac{\partial u}{\partial x} + y \frac{\partial u}{\partial y} = \Sigma a (\alpha + \beta) x^\alpha y^\beta = n \Sigma a x^\alpha y^\beta = nu.$$

The theorem may be extended to include any number of variables

---

[1] An **homogeneous function** is one in which all the terms containing the variables have the same degree. Examples : $x^2 + bxy + z^2$; $x^4 + xyz^2 + x^3 y + x^2 z^2$ are homogeneous functions of the second and fourth degrees respectively.

[2] The sign "Σ" is to be read "the sum of all terms of the same type as ...," or here "the sum of all terms containing x, y and constants". The symbol "Π" is sometimes used in the same way for "the product of all terms of the type".

so that if

$$u = \Sigma x^n f\left(\frac{y}{x}, \frac{z}{x}, \ldots\right) \quad . \quad . \quad . \quad (3)$$

we may write down at once,

$$x\frac{\partial u}{\partial x} + y\frac{\partial u}{\partial y} + \ldots = nu \quad . \quad . \quad . \quad (4)$$

and we have got rid of the conditions imposed upon u in virtue of the arbitrary function $f(\ldots)$.

EXAMPLES.—(1) If $u = x^2y + xy^2 + 3xyz$, then $x\frac{\partial u}{\partial x} + y\frac{\partial u}{\partial y} + z\frac{\partial u}{\partial z} = 3u$. Prove this result by actual differentiation. It of course follows directly from Euler's theorem, since the equation is homogeneous and of the third degree.

(2) If $u = \dfrac{x^3 + x^2y + y^3}{x^2 + xy + y^2}$; $x\dfrac{\partial u}{\partial x} + y\dfrac{\partial u}{\partial y} = u$, since the equation is of the first degree and homogeneous.

(3) If $u = f\left(\dfrac{x}{y}\right)$, show that $x\dfrac{\partial u}{\partial x} + y\dfrac{\partial u}{\partial y} = 0$. Here n in (3) is zero. Prove the result by actual differentiation.

§ 24. Successive Partial Differentiation.

We can get the higher partial derivatives by combining the operations of successive and partial differentiation. Thus when

$$u = x^2 + y^2 + x^2y^3,$$

the first derivatives of u with respect to x, when y is constant, and to y, when x is constant are respectively

$$\frac{\partial u}{\partial x} = 2x + 2y^3x; \quad \frac{\partial u}{\partial y} = 2y + 3x^2y^2; \quad . \quad . \quad (1)$$

repeating the differentiation,

$$\frac{\partial^2 u}{\partial x^2} = 2(1 + y^3); \quad \frac{\partial^2 u}{\partial y^2} = 2(1 + 3x^2y), \quad . \quad . \quad (2)$$

If we had differentiated $\partial u/\partial x$ with respect to y, and $\partial u/\partial y$ with respect to x, we should have obtained two identical results, viz. :—

$$\frac{\partial^2 u}{\partial y \partial x} = 6y^2x, \text{ and } \frac{\partial^2 u}{\partial x \partial y} = 6y^2x. \quad . \quad . \quad (3)$$

The higher partial derivatives are independent of the order of differentiation. By differentiation of $\partial u/\partial x$ with respect to y, assuming x to be constant, we get $\dfrac{\partial\left(\dfrac{\partial u}{\partial x}\right)}{\partial y}$, which is written $\dfrac{\partial^2 u}{\partial y \partial x}$; on the other hand, by the differentiation of $\dfrac{\partial u}{\partial y}$ with respect to x, assuming y to be constant, we obtain $\dfrac{\partial^2 u}{\partial x \partial y}$.   That is to say

$$\frac{\partial^2 u}{\partial y \partial x} = \frac{\partial^2 u}{\partial x \partial y}. \quad \cdot \quad \cdot \quad \cdot \quad (4)$$

This was only proved in (3) for a special case.   As soon as the reader has got familiar with the idea of differentiation, he will no doubt be able to deduce the general proof for himself, although it is given in the regular text-books.   The result stated in (4) is of great importance.

EXAMPLE.—If $y = e^{ax + \beta t + \gamma}$ is to satisfy the equation

$$\frac{\partial^2 y}{\partial x^2} = A \frac{\partial^2 y}{\partial t^2} + B \frac{\partial y}{\partial t},$$

show that $a^2 = A\beta^2 + B\beta$, where α, β, γ, are constants.   Hint. First find the three derivatives and substitute in the second equation ; reduce.

§ 25. Complete or Exact Differentials.

To find the condition that u may be a function of x and y in the equation

$$du = Mdx + Ndy, \quad \cdot \quad \cdot \quad \cdot \quad (5)$$

where M and N are functions of x and y.   We have just seen that if u is a function of x and y

$$du = \frac{\partial u}{\partial x}dx + \frac{\partial u}{\partial y}dy, \quad \cdot \quad \cdot \quad \cdot \quad (6)$$

that is to say, by comparing (5) and (6)

$$M = \frac{\partial u}{\partial x}; \; N = \frac{\partial u}{\partial y}.$$

Differentiating the first with respect to y, and the second with respect to x, we have, from (4)

$$\frac{\partial M}{\partial y} = \frac{\partial N}{\partial x}. \quad \cdot \quad \cdot \quad \cdot \quad (7)$$

In text-books on differential equations this condition is shown to be necessary and sufficient in order that certain equations may be solved, or "integrated" as it is called.   Equation (7) is called **Euler's criterion of integrability.**   An equation that satisfies this condition is said to be a **complete or an exact differential.**

EXAMPLE.—Show that $ydx - xdy = 0$, is not exact, and that $ydx + xdy = 0$ is a complete differential.   Hint. $\partial M/\partial y = \partial y/\partial y$; and $\partial N/\partial x = -\partial x/\partial x$; hence, in the first case, $\partial M/\partial y$ is not equal to $\partial N/\partial x$, and therefore the equation is not exact ; etc.

§ 26. Integrating Factors.

The equation

$$Mdx + Ndy = 0 \quad . \quad . \quad . \quad . \quad (8)$$

can always be made exact by multiplying through with some function of x and y, called an integrating factor. (M and N are supposed to be functions of x and y.)

Since M and N are functions of x and y, (8) may be written

$$\frac{dy}{dx} = - \frac{M}{N}, \quad . \quad . \quad . \quad . \quad (9)$$

or the variation of y with respect to x is as $- M$ is to N; that is to say, x is some function of y, say

$$f(x, y) = a,$$

then from (5), page 69,

$$\frac{\partial f(x,y)}{\partial x}dx + \frac{\partial f(x,y)}{\partial y}dy = 0. \quad . \quad . \quad (10)$$

By a transformation of (10), and a comparison of the result with (9), we find that

$$\frac{dy}{dx} = - \frac{\dfrac{\partial f(x,y)}{\partial x}}{\dfrac{\partial f(x,y)}{\partial y}} = - \frac{M}{N} \quad . \quad . \quad . \quad (11)$$

Hence

$$\frac{\partial f(x,y)}{\partial x} = \mu M; \text{ and } \frac{\partial f(x,y)}{\partial y} = \mu N, \quad . \quad . \quad (12)$$

where μ is either a function of x and y, or else a constant. Multiplying the original equation by the integrating factor μ, and substituting the values of μM, μN obtained in (12), we obtain

$$\frac{\partial f(x,y)}{\partial x}dx + \frac{\partial f(x,y)}{\partial y}dy = 0,$$

which fulfils the condition of exactness. The function $f(x, y)$ is to be derived in any particular case from the given relation between x and y.

EXAMPLE.—Show that the equation $ydx - xdy = 0$ becomes exact when multiplied by the integrating factor $1/y^2$.

$$\frac{\partial M}{\partial y} = - \frac{1}{y^2}; \frac{\partial N}{\partial x} = - \frac{1}{y^2}.$$

Hence $\partial M/\partial y = \partial N/\partial x$, the condition required by (7). In the same way show that $1/xy$ and $1/x^2$ are also integrating factors.

Integrating factors are very much used in solving certain forms of differential equations (q.v.), and in certain important equations which arise in thermodynamics.

§ 27. Illustrations from Thermodynamics.

As a first approximation we may assume that the change of state of every homogeneous liquid, or gaseous substance, is completely defined by some law connecting the pressure, p, volume, v, and temperature, T. This law, called the *characteristic equation*, or the *equation of state* of the substance, has the form

$$f(p, v, T) = 0. \qquad . \qquad . \qquad . \qquad (1)$$

Any change, therefore, is completely determined when any two of these three variables are known.   Thus, we may have

$$p = f_1(v, T) \; ; \; v = f_2(p, T) \; ; \; \text{or,} \; T = f_3(p, v). \qquad . \qquad (2)$$

Confining our attention to the first, we obtain, by partial differentiation,

$$dp = \left(\frac{\partial p}{\partial v}\right)_T dv + \left(\frac{\partial p}{\partial T}\right)_v dT, \qquad . \qquad . \qquad (3)$$

The first partial derivative on the right represents the coefficient of elasticity of the gas, the second is nothing but the so-called coefficient of increase of pressure with temperature at constant volume.   If the change takes place at constant pressure, $dp = 0$, and (3) may be written in the forms

$$\left(\frac{dv}{dT}\right)_p = - \frac{\left(\dfrac{dp}{dT}\right)_v}{\left(\dfrac{dp}{dv}\right)_T} \; ; \; \text{or,} \; \left(\frac{dp}{dT}\right)_v = - \frac{\dfrac{1}{v}\left(\dfrac{dv}{dT}\right)_p}{\dfrac{1}{v}\left(\dfrac{dv}{dp}\right)_T}. \qquad . \qquad (4)$$

The subscript is added to show which factor has been supposed constant during the differentiation.   Note the change of $\partial v / \partial T$ to dv/dT at constant pressure.   The first of equations (4) states that the change in the volume of a gas when heated is equal to the ratio of the increase of pressure with temperature at constant volume, and the change in the elasticity of the gas ; the second tells us that the ratio of the coefficients of thermal expansion and of compressibility is equal to the change in the pressure of the gas per unit rise of temperature at constant volume.

EXAMPLES.—(1) Show that a pressure of 60 atmospheres is required to keep unit volume of mercury at constant volume when heated 1° C. Coefficient of expansion of Hg = 0·00018 = $\frac{1}{v}\left(\dfrac{dv}{dT}\right)_p$; of compressibility = 0·000003 = $-\frac{1}{v}\left(\dfrac{dv}{dp}\right)_T$.   M. Planck, *Vorlesungen über Thermodynamik.* Leipzig, 8, 1897.

(2) J. Thomsen's formula for the amount of heat Q disengaged when one

molecule of sulphuric acid, H_2SO_4, is mixed with n molecules of water, H_2O, is $Q = 17860\, n/(1\cdot798 + n)$ cals. Put $a = 17860$ and $b = 1\cdot798$, for the sake of brevity. If x of H_2SO_4 be mixed with y of H_2O, the quantity of heat disengaged by the mixture is x times as great as when one molecule of H_2SO_4 unites with y/x molecules of water. Since $y/x = n$ in Thomsen's formula $Q = x \times ay/(bx + y)$ cals. If dx of acid is now mixed with x of H_2SO_4 and y of H_2O, show that the amount of heat liberated is

$$\frac{\partial Q}{\partial x}dx = \frac{ay^2}{(bx + y)^2}dx \; ; \; \text{or,} \; \frac{an^2}{(b + n)^2}dx \text{ cals.}$$

In the same way the amount of heat liberated when dy of water is added to a similar mixture is

$$\frac{\partial Q}{\partial y}dy = \frac{ab}{(b + n)^2}dy \text{ cals.}$$

Let Q, T, p, v, represent any four variable magnitudes whatever. By partial differentiation

$$dQ=\left(\frac{\partial Q}{\partial T}\right)_v dT+\left(\frac{\partial Q}{\partial v}\right)_T dv=\left(\frac{\partial Q}{\partial T}\right)_p dT+\left(\frac{\partial Q}{\partial p}\right)_T dp=\left(\frac{\partial Q}{\partial p}\right)_v dp+\left(\frac{\partial Q}{\partial v}\right)_p dv. \quad (5)$$

Equate together the second and last members of (5), and substitute the value of dp from (3), in the result. Thus,

$$\left(\frac{\partial Q}{\partial T}\right)_v dT+\left(\frac{\partial Q}{\partial v}\right)_T dv=\left(\frac{\partial Q}{\partial p}\right)_v\left(\frac{\partial p}{\partial T}\right)_v dT+\left(\frac{\partial Q}{\partial p}\right)_v\left(\frac{\partial p}{\partial v}\right)_T dv+\left(\frac{\partial Q}{\partial v}\right)_p dv. \quad (6)$$

Put $dv = 0$, and divide by dT,

$$\left(\frac{dQ}{dT}\right)_v = \left(\frac{\partial Q}{\partial p}\right)_v\left(\frac{\partial p}{\partial T}\right)_v. \quad \cdot \quad \cdot \quad \cdot \quad \cdot \quad (7)$$

Again, by partial differentiation

$$dT = \left(\frac{\partial T}{\partial p}\right)_v dp + \left(\frac{\partial T}{\partial v}\right)_p dv. \quad \cdot \quad \cdot \quad \cdot \quad \cdot \quad (8)$$

Substitute this value of dT in the last two members of (5),

$$\left(\frac{\partial Q}{\partial T}\right)_p\left(\frac{\partial T}{\partial p}\right)_v dp+\left(\frac{\partial Q}{\partial T}\right)_p\left(\frac{\partial T}{\partial v}\right)_p dv+\left(\frac{\partial Q}{\partial p}\right)_T dp=\left(\frac{\partial Q}{\partial p}\right)_v dp+\left(\frac{\partial Q}{\partial v}\right)_p dv. \quad (9)$$

Put $dp = 0$, and write the result

$$\left(\frac{\partial Q}{\partial T}\right)_p\left(\frac{\partial T}{\partial v}\right)_p = \left(\frac{\partial Q}{\partial v}\right)_p. \quad \cdot \quad \cdot \quad \cdot \quad \cdot \quad (10)$$

By proceeding in this way, the reader can deduce a great number of relations between Q, T, p, v, quite apart from any physical meaning the letters might possess. If Q denotes the quantity of heat added to a substance during any small changes of state, and p, v, T, the pressure, volume and absolute temperature of the substance, the above formulæ are then identical with corresponding formulæ in thermodynamics. Here, however, the relations have been deduced without any reference to the theory of heat. Under these circumstances, $(dQ/\partial T)_v dT$ represents the quantity of heat required for a small rise of temperature at constant volume: $(\partial Q/\partial T)_v$ is nothing but the specific heat of the substance at constant volume, usually written C_v; similarly, $(\partial Q/\partial T)_p$ is the specific heat of constant pressure, written C_p; and $(\partial Q/\partial v)_T$ and $(\partial Q/\partial p)_T$ refer to the two latent heats.

These results may be applied to any substance for which the relation $pv = RT$ holds good. In this case,

$$\left(\frac{\partial p}{\partial T}\right)_v = \frac{R}{v}, \ldots; \quad \therefore \quad v\left(\frac{\partial Q}{\partial T}\right)_v = R\left(\frac{\partial Q}{\partial p}\right)_v, \ldots \qquad \text{by (7)}$$

EXAMPLES.—(1) A little ingenuity, and the reader should be able to deduce the so-called Reech's Theorem:

$$\gamma = \frac{C_p}{C_v} = \frac{\left(\dfrac{\partial p}{\partial v}\right)_Q}{\left(\dfrac{\partial p}{\partial v}\right)_T}, \qquad \cdots \qquad (11)$$

employed by Clément and Desormes for evaluating γ. See any text-book on physics for experimental details. Hint. Find dp for v and Q; and for v and T as in (3); use (7) and (10).

(2) By the definition of adiabatic and isothermal elasticities (page 113),
$$E_\phi = - v(\partial p/\partial v)_\phi \; ; \quad \text{and } E_T = - v(\partial p/\partial v)_T, \text{ respectively.}$$
The subscripts ϕ and T indicating, in the former case, that there has been neither gain nor loss of heat, in other words that Q has remained constant, and in the latter case, that the temperature remained constant during the process $\partial p/\partial v$. Hence show from the first and last members of (5), when Q is constant,

$$v\left(\frac{\partial p}{\partial v}\right)_\phi = - \frac{v\left(\dfrac{\partial Q}{\partial v}\right)_p}{\left(\dfrac{\partial Q}{\partial p}\right)_v}.$$

From (7), (10) and (4), we get the important result

$$\frac{E_\phi}{E_T} = - \frac{\left(\dfrac{\partial Q}{\partial v}\right)_p}{\left(\dfrac{\partial Q}{\partial p}\right)_v\left(\dfrac{\partial p}{\partial v}\right)_T} = \frac{\left(\dfrac{\partial Q}{\partial T}\right)_p\left(\dfrac{\partial T}{\partial v}\right)_p\left(\dfrac{\partial p}{\partial T}\right)_v}{\left(\dfrac{\partial Q}{\partial T}\right)_v\left(\dfrac{\partial p}{\partial v}\right)_T} = \frac{\left(\dfrac{\partial Q}{\partial T}\right)_p}{\left(\dfrac{\partial Q}{\partial T}\right)_v} = \frac{C_p}{C_v} = \gamma. \quad (12)$$

According to the second law of thermodynamics, for reversible changes "the expression dQ/T is a perfect differential". It is usually written $d\phi$, where ϕ is called the entropy of the substance. From the first two members of (5), therefore,

$$\frac{dQ}{T} = d\phi = \frac{1}{T}\left(\frac{\partial Q}{\partial T}\right)_v dT + \frac{1}{T}\left(\frac{\partial Q}{\partial v}\right)_T dv, \quad \cdots \quad (13)$$

is a perfect differential. From (7), page 77, therefore,

$$\frac{d}{dv}\left(\frac{1}{T} \cdot \frac{\partial Q}{\partial T}\right)_v = \frac{d}{dT}\left(\frac{1}{T} \cdot \frac{\partial Q}{\partial v}\right)_T; \text{ or } \left(\frac{\partial C_v}{\partial v}\right)_T = \left(\frac{\partial L}{\partial T}\right)_v - \frac{L}{T}, \quad (14)$$

where C_v has been written for $(\partial Q/\partial T)_v$, L for $(\partial Q/\partial v)_T$.

According to the first law of thermodynamics, when a quantity of heat dQ is added to a substance, part of the heat energy dU is spent in the doing of internal work among the molecules of the substance and part is expended in the mechanical work of expansion, $p . dv$ against atmospheric pressure. To put this symbolically,

$$dQ = dU + pdv \; ; \; \text{or} \; dU = dQ - pdv. \quad . \quad . \quad . \quad (15)$$

Now dU is a perfect differential. This means that however much energy U, the substance absorbs, all will be given back again when the substance returns to its original state. In other words, U is a function of the state of the substance (see page 385). This state is determined, (2) above, when any two of the three variables p, v, T, are known.

For the first two members of (5), and the last of equations (15), therefore,

$$dU = C_v . dT + L . dv - pdv = C_v . dT + (L - p)dv, \quad . \quad (16)$$

is a complete differential. In consequence, as before,

$$\left(\frac{\partial C_v}{\partial v}\right)_T = \left(\frac{\partial L}{\partial T}\right)_v - \left(\frac{\partial p}{\partial T}\right)_v. \quad . \quad . \quad . \quad (17)$$

From (14) and (17),

$$\left(\frac{\partial p}{\partial T}\right)_v = \frac{1}{T}\left(\frac{\partial Q}{\partial v}\right)_T. \quad . \quad . \quad . \quad . \quad (18)$$

a "law" which has formed the starting point of some of the finest deductions in physical chemistry.

EXAMPLES.—(1) Establish Mayer's formula, for a perfect gas.

$$C_p - C_v = R, \quad . \quad . \quad . \quad . \quad (19)$$

Hints: (i.) Since $pv = RT$, $(\partial p/\partial T)_v = R/v$; $\therefore (\partial Q/\partial v)_T = RT/v = p$, by (18). (ii.) Evaluate dv as in (3), and substitute the result in the second and third members of (5). (iii.) Equate dp to zero. Find $\partial v/\partial T$ from the gas equation, use (18), etc. Thus,

$$\left(\frac{\partial Q}{\partial T}\right)_v + \left(\frac{\partial Q}{\partial v}\right)_T\left(\frac{\partial v}{\partial T}\right)_p = \left(\frac{\partial Q}{\partial T}\right)_p ; \; \left(\frac{\partial Q}{\partial T}\right)_v + \left(\frac{\partial Q}{\partial v}\right)_T . \frac{R}{p} = \left(\frac{\partial Q}{\partial T}\right)_p ; \; \text{etc.}$$

(2) Establish the so-called "Four thermodynamic relations" between p, v, T, ϕ, when any two are taken as independent variables.

$$\left(\frac{\partial T}{\partial v}\right)_\phi = -\left(\frac{\partial p}{\partial \phi}\right)_v ; \; \left(\frac{\partial \phi}{\partial v}\right)_T = \left(\frac{\partial p}{\partial T}\right)_v ; \; \left(\frac{\partial T}{\partial p}\right)_\phi = \left(\frac{\partial v}{\partial \phi}\right)_p ; \; \left(\frac{\partial \phi}{\partial p}\right)_T = -\left(\frac{\partial v}{\partial T}\right)_p.$$

It is possible that in some future edition of this work a great deal of the matter in the next chapter will be deleted, since "graphs and their properties" appears in the curriculum of most schools. However, it is at present so convenient for reference that I have decided to let it remain.

CHAPTER II.

COORDINATE OR ANALYTICAL GEOMETRY.

"Order and regularity are more readily and clearly recognised when exhibited to the eye in a picture than they are when presented to the mind in any other manner."—DR. WHEWELL.

§ 28. Cartesian Coordinates.

THE physical properties of a substance may, in general, be concisely represented by a geometrical figure. Such a figure furnishes an elegant method for studying certain natural changes, because the whole history of the process is thus brought vividly before the mind. At the same time the numerical relations between a series of tabulated numbers can be exhibited in the form of a picture and their true meaning seen at a glance.

Let xOx' and yOy' (Fig. 10) be two straight lines at right angles to each other, and intersecting at the point O, so as to divide the plane of this paper into four quadrants I, II, III and IV. Let P_1 be any point in the first quadrant yOx; draw P_1M_1 parallel to Oy and P_1N parallel to Ox. Then, if the lengths OM_1 and P_1M_1 are known, the position of the point P with respect to these lines follows directly from the properties of the rectangle NP_1M_1O (Euclid, i., 34). For example, if OM_1 denotes three units, P_1M_1 four units, the position of the point P_1 is found by marking off three units along Ox to the right and four units along Oy vertically upwards. Then by drawing NP_1 parallel to Ox, and P_1M_1 parallel to Oy, the position of the given point is at P_1, since,

$$P_1M_1 = ON = 4 \text{ units}; \ NP_1 = OM_1 = 3 \text{ units}.$$

$x'Ox$, yOy' are called **coordinate axes** or "frames of reference" (Love). If the angle yOx is a right angle the axes are said to be **rectangular**. Conditions may arise when it is more convenient

to make yOx an oblique angle, the axes are then said to be **oblique.**
xOx' is called the **abscissa or x-axis,** yOy' the **ordinate or y-axis.**
The point O is called the **origin;** OM_1 the **abscissa** of the point
P, and P_1M_1 the **ordinate** of the same point. In referring the position of a point to a pair of coordinate axes, the abscissa is always
mentioned first, P_1 is spoken of as the point whose coordinates are
3 and 4; it is written "the point $P_1(3, 4)$". In memory of its
inventor, René Descartes, this system of notation is sometimes
styled the system of **Cartesian coordinates.**

The usual conventions of trigonometry are made with respect
to the algebraic sign of a point in any of the four quadrants. Any
abscissa measured from the origin to the right is positive, to the

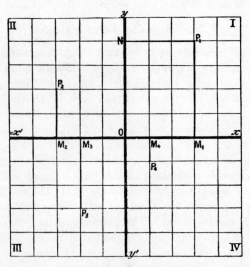

FIG. 10.—Cartesian Coordinates—Two Dimensions.

left, negative; ordinates measured vertically upward are positive,
and in the opposite direction, negative. For example, if a and
b be any assigned number of units corresponding respectively to
the abscissa and ordinate of some given point, then the Cartesian coordinates of the point P_1 are represented as P_1 $(a,\ b)$, of
P_2 as $P_2(-a,\ b)$, of P_3 as $P_3(-a,\ -b)$ and of P_4 as $P_4(a,\ -b)$.
Points falling in quadrants other than the first are not often met
with in practical work.

Thus, any point in a plane represents two things, (1) its horizontal distance along some standard line of reference—the x-axis, and (2) its vertical distance along some other standard line of reference—the y-axis.

When the position of a point is determined by two variable magnitudes (the coordinates), the point is said to be *two dimensional*.

We are always making use of coordinate geometry in a rough way. Thus, a book in a library is located by its shelf and number; and the position of a town in a map is fixed by its latitude and longitude. See H. S. H. Shaw's "Report on the Development of Graphic Methods in Mechanical Science," *B. A. Reports*, 373, 1892, for a large number of examples.

§ 29. Graphical Representation.

Consider any straight or curved line OP situate, with reference to a pair of rectangular co-ordinate axes, as shown in Fig. 11. Take any abscissæ OM_1, OM_2, OM_3, ... OM, and through M_1,

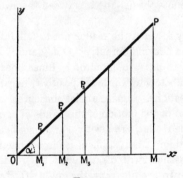

Fig. 11.

M_2 ... M draw the ordinates M_1P_1, M_2P_2 ... MP parallel to the y-axis. The ordinates all have a definite value dependent on the slope of the line [1] and on the value of the abscissæ. If x be any abscissa and y any ordinate, x and y are connected by some definite law called **the equation of the curve.**

It is required to find the equation of the curve OP. In the triangle OPM

$$MP = OM \tan MOP,$$

---

[1] Any straight or curved line when referred to its coordinate axes, is called a "*curve*".

or $$y = x \tan a, \qquad \cdot \qquad \cdot \qquad \cdot \qquad (1)$$

where a denotes the positive angle MOP. But if $OM = MP$,

$$\tan MOP = \frac{MP}{OM} = 1 = \tan 45°.$$

The equation of the line OP is, therefore,

$$y = x; \qquad \cdot \qquad \cdot \qquad \cdot \qquad (2)$$

and the line is inclined at an angle of 45° to the x-axis.

It follows directly that both the abscissa and ordinate of a point situate at the origin are zero. A point on the x-axis has a zero ordinate; a point on the y-axis has a zero abscissa. Any line parallel to the x-axis has an equation

$$y = b; \qquad \cdot \qquad \cdot \qquad \cdot \qquad (3)$$

any line parallel to the y-axis has an equation

$$x = a, \qquad \cdot \qquad \cdot \qquad \cdot \qquad (4)$$

where a and b denote the distances between the two lines and their respective axes.

It is necessary to warn the reader not to fall into the bad habit of writing the line OM indifferently "OM" and "MO" so that he will have nothing to unlearn later on. Lines measured from left to right, and from below upwards are positive; negative, if measured in the reverse directions. Again, angles measured in the normal or clockwise direction of the motion of the hands of a watch, when the watch is facing the reader, are positive, and negative if measured in the opposite direction. Many difficulties in connection with optical problems, for instance, will disappear if the reader pays careful attention to this. In the diagram, the angle MOP will be positive, POM negative. The line MP is positive, PM negative. Hence, since

$$\tan MOP = \frac{+\ MP}{+\ OM} = +\ ; \ \tan POM = \frac{-\ PM}{+\ OM} = -\ .$$

§ 30. Practical Illustrations of Graphical Representation.

Suppose, in an investigation on the relation between the pressure, p, and the weight, w, of a gas dissolved by unit volume of a solution, we obtained the following successive pairs of observations,

$$p = \tfrac{1}{4}, \quad 2, \quad 4, \quad 8 \ldots = x.$$
$$w = \tfrac{1}{8}, \quad 1, \quad 2, \quad 4 \ldots = y.$$

By setting off on millimetre, coordinate or squared paper (Fig. 12) points $P_1(\tfrac{1}{4}, \tfrac{1}{8})$, $P_2(2, 1)$ ..., and drawing a line to pass through all these points, we are said to **plot the curve**. This has been done in Fig. 12. The only difference between the lines OP of Figs. 11 and 12 is in their slope towards the two axes.

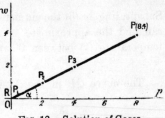

FIG. 12.—Solution of Gases in liquids.

From equation (1) we can put

$$w = p \tan a, \text{ or } \tan a = \tfrac{1}{2},$$

that is to say, an angle whose tangent is $\tfrac{1}{2}$. This can be found by reference to a table of natural tangents. It is 26° 33′ (approx.). Putting $\tan a = m$, we may write

$$w = mp, \quad \cdots \quad \cdots \quad (5)$$

where m is a constant depending on the nature of the gas and liquid used in the experiment. Equation (5) is the mathematical expression for the solubility of a gas obeying *Henry's law*, viz.: " At constant temperature, the weight of a gas dissolved by unit volume of a liquid is proportional to the pressure ". The curve OP is a graphical representation of Henry's law.

To take one more illustration. The solubility of potassium chloride, λ, in 100 parts of water at temperatures, θ, between 0° and 100° is approximately as follows:

$$\theta = 0°, \quad 20°, \quad 40°, \quad 60°, \quad 80°, \quad 100° = x,$$
$$\lambda = 28\cdot5, \quad 39\cdot7, \quad 49\cdot8, \quad 59\cdot2, \quad 69\cdot5, \quad 79\cdot5 = y.$$

By plotting these numbers, as in the preceding example, we obtain a curve QP (Fig. 13) which, instead of passing through the origin at O, cuts the y-axis at the point Q such that

$$OQ = 28\cdot5 \text{ units } = b \text{ (say)}.$$

If OP' be drawn from the point O parallel to QP, then the equation for this line is obviously, from (5),

$$\lambda = m\theta ;$$

but since the line under consideration cuts the y-axis at Q,

$$\lambda = m\theta + b, \quad \cdots \quad \cdots \quad (6)$$

where $b = OQ$. In these equations, b, λ and θ are known, the value of m is therefore obtained by a simple transposition of (6),

$$m = \frac{\lambda - b}{\theta} = \tan 27° 43' = 0·5254.$$

Substituting in (6) the numerical values of m and $b(= 28·5)$,[1] we can find the approximate solubility of potassium chloride at any temperature (θ) between 0° and 100° from the relation

$$\lambda = 0·5128\theta + 28·5.$$

The curve QP in Fig. 13 is a graphical representation of the

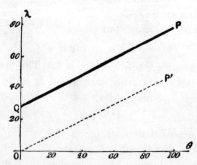

Fig. 13.—Solubility Curve for KCl in water.

variation in the solubility of KCl in water at different temperatures.

Knowing the equation of the curve, or even the form of the curve alone, the probable solubility of KCl for any unobserved temperature can be deduced, for if the solubility had been determined every 10° (say) instead of every 20°, the corresponding ordinates could still be connected in an unbroken line. The same relation holds however short the temperature interval. From this point of view the solubility curve may be regarded as the path of a point moving according to some fixed law. This law is defined by the equation of the curve, since the coordinates of every point on the curve satisfy the equation. The path described by such a point is called the **picture, locus or graph of the equation.**

EXAMPLES.—(1) Let the reader procure some " squared " paper and plot : $y = \frac{1}{2}x - 2$; $2y + 3x = 12$.

(2) The following experimental results have been obtained :—

When $x =$ 0,   1,   10,   20,   30,...
$y = -3$, $-1·56$, $11·40$, $25·80$, $40·20$,...

[1] Determined by a method to be described later.

(a) Plot the curve.   (b) Show (i) that the slope of the curve to the x-axis is nearly $1\cdot44 = \tan \alpha = \tan 55°$, (ii) that the equation to the curve is $y = 1\cdot44x - 3$.   (c) Measure off 5 and 15 units along the x-axis, and show that the distance of these points from the curve, measured vertically above the x-axis, represents the corresponding ordinates.   (d) Compare the values of y so obtained with those deduced by substituting $x = 5$ and $x = 15$ in the above equation.   Note the laborious and roundabout nature of process (c) when contrasted with (d).   The graphic process, called *graphic interpolation* (*q.v.*), is seldom resorted to when the equation connecting the two variables is available, but of this anon.

(3) Get some solubility determinations from any chemical text-book and plot the values of the composition of the solution (C, ordinate) at different temperatures ($\theta°$, abscissa), *e.g.*, Loewel's numbers for sodium sulphate are

$$C = 5\cdot0, \qquad 19\cdot4, \qquad 55\cdot0, \qquad 46\cdot7, \qquad 44\cdot4, \qquad 43\cdot1, \qquad 42\cdot2 ;$$
$$\theta° = 0°, \qquad 20°, \qquad 34°, \qquad 50°, \qquad 70°, \qquad 90°, \qquad 103\cdot5°.$$

What does the peculiar bend at 34° mean ?

In this and analogous cases, a question of this nature has to be decided : *What is the best way to represent the composition of a solution ?*   Several methods are available.   The right choice depends entirely on the judgment, or rather on the *finesse*, of the investigator.   Most chemists (like Loewel above) follow Gay Lussac, and represent the composition of the solution as "parts of substance which would dissolve in 100 parts of the solvent".   Etard found it more convenient to express his results as " parts of substance dissolved in 100 parts of saturated solution ".   The right choice, at this day, seems to be to express the results in molecular proportions.   This allows the solubility constant to be easily compared with the other physical constants.   In this way, Gay Lussac's method becomes " the ratio of the number of molecules of dissolved substance to the number, say 100, molecules of solvent " ; Etard's " the ratio of the number of molecules of dissolved substance to any number, say 100, molecules of solution ".

(4) Plot $\log_e x = y$, and show that logarithms of negative numbers are impossible.   Hint.   Put $x = 0, e^{-2}, e^{-1}, 1, e, e^2, \infty$, etc., and find corresponding values of y.

So many good booklets have recently been published upon " Graphical Algebra " as to render it unnecessary to speak at greater length upon the subject here.

§ 31. Properties of Straight Lines.

If equations (1) and (6) be expressed in general terms, using x and y for the variables, m and b for the constants, we can deduce the following properties for straight lines referred to a pair of coordinate axes.

I. A straight line passing through the origin of a pair of rectangular coordinate axes, is represented by the equation

$$y = mx, \qquad . \quad . \quad . \quad . \quad (7)$$

where $m = \tan \alpha = y/x$, a constant representing the slope of the curve. The equation is obtained from (5) above.

II. *A straight line which cuts one of the rectangular coordinate axes at a distance b from the origin, is represented by the equation*

$$y = mx + b \quad . \quad . \quad . \quad . \quad (8)$$

where m and b are any constants whatever. For every value of m there is an angle such that $\tan \alpha = m$. The position of the line is therefore determined by a point and a direction. Equation (8) follows immediately from (6).

III. *A straight line is always represented by an equation of the first degree,*

$$Ax + By + C = 0; \quad . \quad . \quad . \quad (9)$$

and conversely, any equation of the first degree between two variables represents a straight line.[1]

This conclusion is drawn from the fact that any equation containing only the first powers of x and y, represents a straight line. By substituting $m = -A/B$ and $b = -C/B$ in (8), and reducing the equation to its simplest form, we get the general equation of the first degree between two variables : $Ax + By + C = 0$. This represents a straight line inclined to the positive direction of the x-axis at an angle whose tangent is $-A/B$, and cutting the y-axis at a point $-C/B$ below the origin.

IV. *A straight line which cuts each coordinate axis at the respective distances a and b from the origin, is represented by the equation*

$$\frac{x}{a} + \frac{y}{b} = 1 \quad . \quad . \quad . \quad . \quad (10)$$

Consider the straight line AB (Fig. 14) which intercepts the x- and y-axes at the points A and B respectively. Let $OA = a$ $OB = b$. From the equation (9) if

$$y = 0, x = a ; \quad Aa + C = 0, a = -C/A.$$

Similarly if $x = 0, y = b ; \quad Bb + C = 0, b = -C/B.$

Substituting these values of a and b in (9), *i.e.*, in

$$-\frac{A}{C}x - \frac{B}{C}y = 1 ; \text{ and we get } \frac{x}{a} + \frac{y}{b} = 1.$$

---

[1] The reader met with the idea conveyed by a "general equation," on page 26. By assigning suitable values to the constants A, B, C, he will be able to deduce every possible equation of the first degree between the two variables x and y.

There are several proofs of this useful equation.   Formula (10) is
called the **intercept form** of the equa-
tion of the straight line, equation (8)
the **tangent form**.

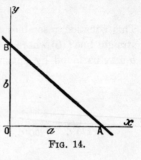

Fig. 14.

V. The so-called **normal or perpendicular form** of the equation of a
straight line is

$$p = x \cos a + y \sin a, \quad \textbf{(11)}$$

where p denotes the perpendicular distance of the line BA (Fig. 14) from the
origin O, and a represents the angle
which this line makes with the x-axis.

Draw OQ perpendicular to AB (Fig. 14).   Take any point $P(x, y)$ and
drop a perpendicular PR on to the x-axis, draw RD parallel to AB cutting OQ
in D.   Drop PC perpendicular on to RD, then $PRC = a = QOA$.   Then,
$OQ = OD + PC \ OD = x \cos a$; $PC = y \sin a$.   Hence follows (11).

Many equations can be readily transformed into the intercept
form and their geometrical interpretation seen at a glance.   For
instance, the equation

$$x + y = 2 \text{ becomes } \tfrac{1}{2}x + \tfrac{1}{2}y = 1,$$

which represents a straight line cutting each axis at the same
distance from the origin.

One way of stating Charles' law is that "the volume of a
given mass of gas, kept at a constant pressure, varies directly as
the temperature".   If, under these conditions, the temperature be
raised $\theta°$, the volume increases the $\tfrac{1}{273}\theta$rd part of what it was at
the original temperature.[1]   Let the original volume, v_0, at 0° C.,

---

[1] Many students, and even some of the text-books, appear to have hazy notions on
this question.   According to "Guy Lussac's law" the increase in the volume of a gas
at any temperature for a rise of temperature of 1°, is a constant fraction of its initial
volume at 0° C. ; "J. Dalton's law" (*Manchester Memoirs*, **5**, 595, 1802), on the other
hand, supposes the increase in the volume of a gas at any temperature for a rise of 1°,
is a constant fraction of its volume at that temperature (the "Compound Interest
Law," in fact).   The former appears to approximate closer to the truth than the latter.
(See page 285.)   J. B. Gay Lussac (*Annales de Chimie*, **43**, 137, 1802) says that Charles
had noticed this same property of gases fifteen years earlier and hence it is sometimes
called Charles' law, or the law of Charles and Gay Lussac.   After inspecting Charles'
apparatus, Gay Lussac expressed the opinion that it was not delicate enough to establish the truth of the law in question.   But then J. Priestley in his *Experiments and
Observations on Different Kinds of Air* (**2**, 448, 1790) says that "from a very coarse
experiment which I made very early I concluded that fixed and common air expanded

be unity ; the final volume v, then at θ°

$$v = 1 + \tfrac{1}{273}\theta.$$

This equation resembles the intercept form of the equation of a straight line (10) where $a = -273$ and $b = 1$. The intercepts a and b may be found by putting x and y, or rather their equivalents,

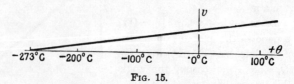

Fig. 15.

θ and v, successively equal to zero. If $\theta = 0$, $v = 1$; if $v = 0$, $\theta = -273$, the well-known absolute zero (Fig. 15).

It is impossible to imagine a substance occupying no space. But this absurdity is the logical consequence of Charles' law when $\theta = -273^{\circ}$. Where is the fallacy? The answer is that Charles' law includes a "simplifying assumption". The total volume occupied by the gas really consists of two parts: (i) the volume actually occupied by the molecules of the substance; and (ii) the space in which the molecules are moving. Although we generally make v represent the total volume, in reality, v only refers to the space in which the molecules are moving, and in that case the conclusion that $v = 0$, when $\theta = -273^{\circ}$ involves no absurdity.

No gas has been investigated at temperatures within four degrees of -273°. However trustworthy the results of an interpolation

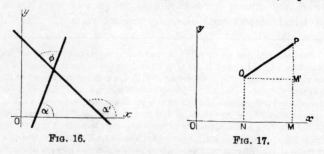

Fig. 16.   Fig. 17.

may be, when we attempt to pass *beyond* the region of measure-

---

alike with the same degree of heat". The cognomen "Priestley's law" would settle all confusion between the three designations "Dalton's," "Gay Lussac's" and "Charles'" of one law.

ment, the extrapolation, as it is called, becomes more or less hazardous. Extrapolation can only be trusted when in close proximity to the point last measured. Attempts to find the probable temperature of the sun by extrapolation have given numbers varying between the 1,398° of Vicaire and the 9,000,000° of Waterston! We cannot always tell whether or not new forces come into action when we get outside the range of observation. In the case of Charles' law, we do know that the gases change their physical state at low temperatures, and the law does not apply under the new conditions.

VI. To find the angle at the point of intersection of two curves whose equations are given. Let the equations be

$$y = mx + b \; ; \; y' = m'x' + b'.$$

Let ϕ be the angle required (see Fig. 16), $m = \tan a$, $m' = \tan a'$. From Euclid, i., 32, $a' - a = \phi$, $\therefore \tan(a' - a) = \tan \phi$. By formula, page 612,

$$\tan \phi = \frac{\tan a' - \tan a}{1 + \tan a \cdot \tan a'} = \frac{m' - m}{1 + mm'} \qquad . \qquad (12)$$

EXAMPLES.—(1) Find the angle at the point of intersection of the two lines $x + y = 1$, and $y = x + 2$. $m = 1$, $m' = -1$; $\tan \phi = -\infty = -90°$.

(2) Find the angle between the lines $3y - x = 0$, and $2x + y = 1$. Ansr. Tan $(81° \; 52') = 7$.

VII. To find the distance between two points in terms of their coordinates. In Fig. 17, let $P(x_1 y_1)$ and $Q(x_2 y_2)$ be the given points. Draw QM' parallel to NM. $OM = x_1$, $MP = y_1$; $ON = x_2$, $NQ = y_2$;

$$M'P = MP - MM' = MP - NQ = y_1 - y_2 ;$$
$$QM' = NM = OM - ON = x_1 - x_2.$$

Since $QM'P$ is a right-angled triangle

$$(QP)^2 = (QM')^2 + (PM')^2.$$
$$\therefore QP = \sqrt{(x_1 - x_2)^2 + (y_1 - y_2)^2}. \qquad . \qquad (13)$$

EXAMPLES.—(1) Show that the distance between the points $(-2, 1)$ and $(-6, -2)$ is 5 units.

(2) Show that the distance from $(10, -18)$ to the point $(3, 6)$ is the same as to the point $(-5, 2)$. Ansr. 25 units in each case.

§ 32. Curves Satisfying Conditions.

The reader should work through the following examples so as to familiarize himself with the conceptions of coordinate geometry. Many of the properties here developed for the straight line can easily be extended to curved lines.

I. The condition that a curve may pass through a given point. This evidently requires that the coordinates of the point should satisfy the equation of the line. Let the equation be in the tangent form

$$y = mx + b.$$

If the line is to pass through the point (x_1, y_1),

$$y_1 = mx_1 + b,$$

and, by subtraction,

$$(y - y_1) = m(x - x_1) \quad . \quad . \quad . \quad \textbf{(14)}$$

which is an equation of a straight line satisfying the required conditions.

EXAMPLES.—(1) The equation of a line passing through a point whose abscissa is 5 and ordinate 3 is $y - mx = 3 - 5m$.

(2) Find the equation of a line which will pass through the point $(4, -4)$ and whose tangent is 2. Ansr. $y - 2x + 12 = 0$.

II. The condition that a curve may pass through two given points. Continuing the preceding discussion, if the line is to pass through (x_2, y_2), substitute x_2, y_2, in (14)

$$(y_2 - y_1) = m(x_2 - x_1); \ \therefore \ m = \frac{y_2 - y_1}{x_2 - x_1}.$$

Substituting this value of m in (14), we get the equation,

$$\frac{y - y_1}{y_2 - y_1} = \frac{x - x_1}{x_2 - x_1}, \quad . \quad . \quad . \quad \textbf{(15)}$$

for a straight line passing through two given points (x_1, y_1) and (x_2, y_2).

EXAMPLES.—(1) Show that the equation of the straight line passing through the points $P_1(2, 3)$ and $P_2(4, 5)$ is $x - y + 1 = 0$. Hint. Substitute $x_1 = 2, x_2 = 4, y_1 = 3, y_2 = 5$, in (15).

(2) Find the equation of the line which passes through the points $P_1(4, -2)$, and $P_2(0, -7)$. Ansr. $5x - 4y = 28$.

III. The coordinates of the point of intersection of two given lines. Let the given equations be

$$y = mx + b \ ; \ \text{and} \ y = m'x + b'.$$

Now each equation is satisfied by an infinite number of pairs of values of x and y. These pairs of values are generally different in the two equations, but there can be one, and only one pair of values of x and y that satisfy the two equations, that is, the coordinates of the point of intersection. The coordinates at this point must satisfy the two equations, and this is true of no other point. The roots of these two equations, obtained by a simple

algebraic operation, are the coordinates of the point required.   The
point whose coordinates are

$$x = \frac{b' - b}{m - m'}\; ;\; y = \frac{b'm - bm'}{m - m'} \qquad . \quad . \qquad (16)$$

satisfies the two equations.

EXAMPLES.—(1) Find the coordinates of the point of intersection of the
two lines $x + y = 1$, and $y = x + 2$.   Ansr. $x = -\frac{1}{2}$, $y = \frac{3}{2}$.   Hint. $m = -1$,
$m' = 1$, $b = 1$, $b' = 2$, etc.

(2) The coordinates of the point of intersection of the curves $3y - x = 1$,
and $2x + y = 3$ are $x = \frac{4}{7}$, $y = \frac{5}{7}$.

(3) Show that the two curves $y^2 = 4x$, and $x^2 = 4y$ meet at the point
$x = 4$, $y = 4$.

IV. The condition that three given lines may meet at a point.
The roots of the equations of two of the lines are the coordinates of
their point of intersection, and in order that this point may be on a
third line the roots of the equations of two of the lines must satisfy
the equation of the third.

EXAMPLES.—(1) If three lines are represented by the equations $5x + 3y = 7$,
$3x - 4y = 10$, and $x + 2y = 0$, show that they will all intersect at a point
whose coordinates are $x = 2$ and $y = -1$.   Solving the last two equations,
we get $x = 2$ and $y = -1$, but these values of x and y satisfy the first equation,
hence these three lines meet at the point $(2, -1)$.

(2) Show that the lines $3x + 5y + 7 = 0$; $x + 2y + 2 = 0$; and $4x - 3y - 10 = 0$,
do not pass through one point.   Hint. From the first and second, $y = 1$,
$x = -4$.   These values do not satisfy the last equation.

*V. The condition that two straight lines may be parallel to one
another.*   Since the lines are to be parallel they must make equal
angles with the x-axis, *i.e.*, angle $a' =$ angle a, or $\tan a' = \tan a$,

$$\therefore m = m', \qquad . \qquad . \qquad . \qquad . \qquad (17)$$

that is to say, the coefficient of x in the two equations must be
equal.

EXAMPLES.—(1) Show that the lines $y = 3x + 9$, and $2y = 6x + 7$ are
parallel.   Hint. Show that on dividing the last equation by 2, the coefficient
of x in each equation is the same.

(2) Find the equation of the straight line passing through $(2, -1)$ parallel
to $3x + y = 2$.   Ansr. $y + 3x = 5$.   Hint. Use (17) and (14). $y + 1 = -3(x - 2)$.

*VI. The condition that two lines may be perpendicular to one
another.*   If the angle between the lines is $\phi = 90°$, see (12),

$$a' - a = 90°,$$

$$\therefore \tan a' = \tan(90 + a) = -\cot a = -\frac{1}{\tan a},$$

$$\therefore m = -\frac{1}{m}, \quad . \quad . \quad . \quad (18)$$

or, the slope of the one line to the x-axis must be equal and opposite in sign to the reciprocal of the slope of the other.

EXAMPLES.—(1) Find the equation of the line which passes through the point (3, 2), and is perpendicular to the line $y = 2x + 5$. Ansr. $x + 2y = 7$. Hint. Use (18) and (14).

(2) Find the equation of the line which passes through the point (2, - 4) and is perpendicular to the line $3y + 2x - 1 = 0$. Ansr. $2y - 3x + 14 = 0$.

§ 33. Changing the Coordinate Axes.

In plotting the graph of any function, the axes of reference should be so chosen that the resulting curve is represented in the most convenient position. In many problems it is necessary to

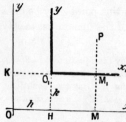

FIG. 18.—Transformation of Axes.

pass from one system of coordinate axes to another. In order to do this the equation of the given line referred to the new axes must be deduced from the corresponding equation referred to the old set of axes.

I. To pass from any system of coordinate axes to another set parallel to the former but having a different origin. Let Ox, Oy (Fig. 18) be the original axes, and KO_1x_1, HO_1y_1 the new axes parallel to Ox and Oy. Let MM_1P be the ordinate of any point P parallel to the axes Oy and O_1y_1. Let h, k be the coordinates of the new origin O_1 referred to the old axes. Let (x, y) be the coordinates of P referred to the old axes Ox, Oy, and (x_1y_1) its coordinates referred to the new axes. Then $OH = h$, $HO_1 = k$,

$$x = OM = OH + HM = OH + O_1M_1 = h + x_1;$$
$$y = MP = MM_1 + M_1P = HO_1 + M_1P = k + y_1.$$

That is to say, we must substitute

$$x = h + x_1; \text{ and } y = k + y_1, \quad . \quad . \quad (19)$$

in order to refer a curve to a new set of rectangular axes. The new coordinates of the point P being

$$x_1 = x - h; \text{ and } y_1 = y - k. \quad . \quad . \quad (20)$$

EXAMPLE.—Given the point (2, 3) and the equation $2x + 3y = 6$, find the coordinates of the former, and the equation of the latter when referred to a set of new axes parallel to the original axes and passing through the point

3, 2). Ansr. $x_1 = x - 3 = 2 - 3 = -1$; $y_1 = y - 2 = 1$. The position of the point on the new axes is $(-1, 1)$. The new equation will be $2(3 + x_1) +$ $3(3 + y_1) = 0$; $\therefore 2x_1 + 3y_1 + 12 = 0$.

II. To pass from one set of axes to another having the same origin but different directions.
Let the two straight lines x_1O and y_1O, passing through O (Fig. 19), be taken as the new system of coordinates.   Let the coordinates of the point P (x, y) when referred to the new axes be x_1, y_1.   Draw MP perpendicular to the old x-axes, and M_1P perpendicular to the new axes, so that the angle $MPM_1 = ROM_1 = a$,

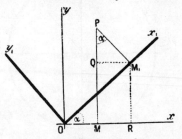

FIG. 19.—Transformation of Axes.

$$OM = x,\ OM_1 = x_1,\ MP = y,\ M_1P = y_1.$$

Draw RM_1 perpendicular and QM_1 parallel to the x-axis.   Then

$$x = OM = OR - MR = OR - QM_1,$$
$$\therefore x = OM_1 \cos a - M_1P \sin a\,;$$
$$\therefore x = x_1 \cos a - y_1 \sin a. \qquad \qquad (21)$$

Similarly
$$y = MP = MQ + QP = RM_1 + QP\,;$$
$$\therefore y = OM_1 \sin a + M_1P \cos a,$$
$$\therefore y = x_1 \sin a + y_1 \cos a. \qquad \qquad (22)$$

Equations (21) and (22) enable us to refer the coordinates of a point P from one set of axes to another.   Solving equations (21) and (22) simultaneously,

$$x_1 = x \cos a + y \sin a\,;\ y_1 = y \cos a - x \sin a. \qquad (23)$$

EXAMPLE.—Find what the equation $x_1^2 - y_1^2 = a^2$ becomes when the axes are turned through $-45°$, the origin remaining the same. Here $\sin(-45°) = -\sqrt{\tfrac{1}{2}}$; $\cos(-45°) = \sqrt{\tfrac{1}{2}}$. From (23), $x_1 = \sqrt{\tfrac{1}{2}}x - \sqrt{\tfrac{1}{2}}y$; $y_1 = \sqrt{\tfrac{1}{2}}x + \sqrt{\tfrac{1}{2}}y$. Hence, $x_1 - y_1 = -\sqrt{2}\cdot y$; $x_1 + y_1 = \sqrt{2}x$; $\therefore x_1^2 - y_1^2 = -2xy$; $\therefore$ from the original equation, $2xy = -a^2$; or, $xy = $ constant.

In order to pass from one set of axes to another set having a different origin and different directions, the two preceding transformations must be made one after another.

§ 34. The Circle and its Equation.

There is a set of important curves whose shape can be obtained by cutting a cone at different angles.   Hence the name *conic sec-*

tions. They include the parabola, hyperbola and ellipse, of which the circle is a special case. I shall describe their chief properties very briefly.

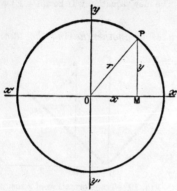

A circle is a curve such that all points on the curve are equi-distant from a given point. This point is called the *centre*, the distance from the centre to the curve is called the *radius*. Let r (Fig. 20) be the radius of the circle whose centre is the origin of the rectangular coordinate axes xOx' and yOy'. Take any point $P(x, y)$ on the circle. Let PM be the ordinate of P. From the definition of a circle OP is constant and equal to r. Then by Euclid, i., 47,

$$(OM)^2 + (MP)^2 = (OP)^2, \text{ or } x^2 + y^2 = r^2, \qquad (1)$$

FIG. 20.—The Circle.

which is said to be the equation of the circle.

In connection with this equation it must be remembered that the abscissæ and ordinates of some points have negative values, but, since the square of a negative quantity is always positive, the rule still holds good. Equation (1) therefore expresses the geometrical fact that all points on the circumference are at an equal distance from the centre.

EXAMPLES.—(1) Required the locus of a point moving in a path according to the equations $y = a \cos t$, $x = a \sin t$, where t denotes any given interval of time. Square each equation and add,

$$y^2 + x^2 = a^2(\cos^2 t + \sin^2 t).$$

The expression in brackets is unity (19), page 611, and hence for all values of t

$$y^2 + x^2 = a^2,$$

i.e., the point moves on the perimeter of a circle of radius a.

(2) To find the equation of a circle whose centre, referred to a pair of rectangular axes, has the coordinates h and k. From (19), previous paragraph,

$$(x - h)^2 + (y - k)^2 = r^2, \qquad (2)$$

where $P(x, y)$ is any point on the circumference. Note the product xy is absent. The coefficients of x^2 and y^2 are equal in magnitude and sign. These conditions are fulfilled by every equation to a circle. Such is

$$3x^2 + 3y^2 + 7x - 12 = 0.$$

(3) The general equation of a circle is

$$x^2 + y^2 + ax + by + c = 0. \qquad (3)$$

Plot (3) on squared paper. Try the effect of omitting ax and of by separately and together. This is a sure way of getting at the meaning of the general equation.

(4) A point moves on a circle $x^2 + y^2 = 25$. Compare the rates of change of x and y when $x = 3$. If $x = 3$, obviously $y = \pm 4$. By differentiation $dy/dt : dx/dt = -x/y = \pm \frac{3}{4}$. The function decreases when x and y have the same sign, *i.e.*, in the first and third quadrants, and increases in the second and fourth quadrants ; y therefore decreases or increases three-quarters as fast as x according to the quadrant.

§ 35. The Parabola and its Equation.

A parabola is a curve such that any point on the curve is equidistant from a given point and a given straight line. The given point is called the *focus*, the straight line the *directrix*, the distance of any point on the curve from the focus is called the *focal radius*. O (Fig. 21) is called *vertex* of the parabola. AK is the directrix; OF, FP, $FP_1 \ldots$ are focal radii ; $OF = AO$; $FP = KP$; $FP_1 = K_1P_1 \ldots$ It can now be proved that the equation of the parabola is given by the expression

$$y^2 = 4ax, \qquad . \qquad . \qquad (1)$$

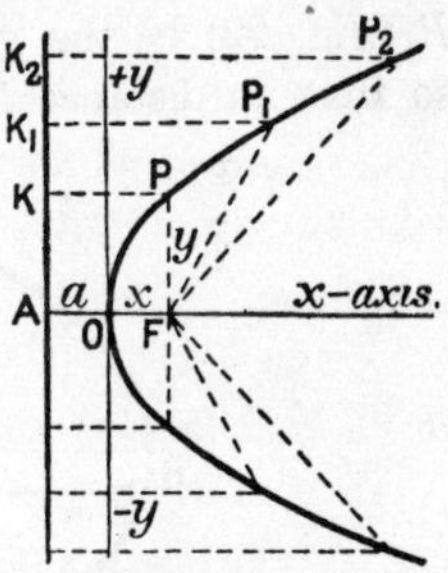

Fig. 21.

where a is a constant equal to AO in the above diagram. In words, this equation tells us that the abscissæ of the parabola are proportional to the square of the ordinates.

Examples.—(1) By a transformation of coordinates show that the parabola represented by equation (1), may be written in the form

$$x = a + by + cy^2, \qquad . \qquad . \qquad . \qquad (2)$$

where a, b, c, are constants. Let x become $x + h$; $y = y + k$; $a = j$ where h, k, and j are constants. Substitute the new values of x and y in (1) ; multiply out. Collect the constants together and equate to a, b and c as the case might be.

(2) Investigate the shape of the parabola. By solving the equation of the parabola, it follows that

$$y = \pm 2 \sqrt{ax}.$$

First. Every positive value of x gives two equal and opposite values of y, that is to say, there are two points at equal distances perpendicular to the x-axis. This being true for all values of x, the part of the curve lying on one side of the x-axis is the mirror image of that on the opposite side [1] ; in this

---

[1] The student of stereo-chemistry would say the two sides were "enantiomorphic".

case the x-axis is said to be *symmetrical* with respect to the parabola. Hence any line perpendicular to the x-axis cuts the curve at two points equidistant from the x-axis.

Second. When $x = 0$, the y-axis just touches [1] the curve.

Third. Since a is positive, when x is negative there is no real value of y, for no real number is known whose square is negative; in consequence, the parabola lies wholly on the right side of the y-axis.

Fourth. As x increases without limit, y approaches infinity, that is to say, the parabola recedes indefinitely from the x or symmetrical-axes on both sides.

§ 36. The Ellipse and its Equation.

An ellipse is a curve such that the sum of the distances of any point on the curve from two given points is always the same. Let P (Fig. 22) be the given point which moves on the curve PP_1 so that its distance from the two fixed points F_1, F_2, called the

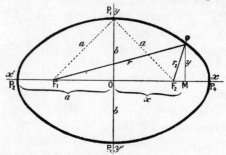

FIG. 22.—The Ellipse.

foci, has a constant value say $2a$. The distance of P from either focus is called the *focal radius*, or *radius vector*. O is the so-called *centre* of the ellipse. The equation of the ellipse

$$\frac{x^2}{a^2} + \frac{y^2}{b^2} = 1 \quad . \quad . \quad . \quad . \quad (1)$$

can now be deduced from the above described properties of the curve. The line P_2P_4 (Fig. 22) is called the *major axis*; P_1P_3 the *minor axis*, their respective lengths being $2a$ and $2b$; the magnitudes a and b are the *semi-axes*; each of the points P_1, P_2, P_3, P_4, is a *vertex*.

EXAMPLES.—(1) Let the point $P(x, y)$ move on a curve so that the position

---

[1] Some mathematicians define a "tangent" to be a straight line which cuts the curve in two coincident points. See *The School World*, **6**, 323, 1904.

of the point, at any moment, is given by the equations, $x = a \cos t$ and $y = b \sin t$; required the path described by the moving point. Square and add; since $\cos^2 t + \sin^2 t$ is unity (page 611), $x^2/a^2 + y^2/b^2 = 1$. The point therefore moves on an ellipse.

(2) Investigate the shape of the ellipse. By solving the equation of the ellipse we get

$$y = \pm\, b\sqrt{1 - \frac{x^2}{a^2}}; \text{ and } x = \pm a\sqrt{1 - \frac{y^2}{b^2}}. \quad \cdot \quad \cdot \quad \cdot \quad (2)$$

First. Since y^2 must be positive, $x^2/a^2 \not> 1$, that is to say, x cannot be numerically greater than a. Similarly it can be shown that y cannot be numerically greater than b.

Second. Every positive value of x gives two equal and opposite values of y, that is to say, there are two points at equal distances perpendicularly above and below the x-axis. The ellipse is therefore symmetrical with respect to the x-axis. In the same way, it can be shown that the ellipse is symmetrical with respect to the y-axis.

Third. If the value of x increases from the zero until $x = \pm a$, then $y = 0$, and these two values of x furnish two points on the x-axis. If x now increases until $x > a$, there is no real corresponding value of y^2. Hence the ellipse lies in a strip bounded by the limits $x = \pm a$; similarly it can be shown that the ellipse is bounded by the limits $y = \pm b$.

Obviously, if $a = b$, the equation of the ellipse passes into that of a circle. The circle is thus a special case of the ellipse.

The absence of first powers of x and y in the equation of the ellipse shows that the origin of the coordinates is at the " centre " of the ellipse. A term in xy shows that the principal axes—major and minor—are not generally the x- and y-axes.

§ 37. The Hyperbola and its Equation.

The hyperbola is a curve such that the difference of the distance of any point on the curve from two fixed points is always the same. Let the point P (Fig. 23) move so that the difference of its distances from two fixed points F, F', called the *foci*, is equal to $2a$. O is the so-called *centre* of the hyperbola; $OM = x$; $MP = y$; $OA = a$; $OB = b$.

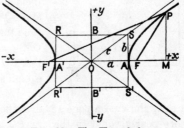

FIG. 23.—The Hyperbola.

Starting from these definitions it can be shown that the equation of the hyperbola has the form

$$\frac{x^2}{a^2} - \frac{y^2}{b^2} = 1. \quad \cdot \quad \cdot \quad \cdot \quad \cdot \quad (1)$$

The x-axis is called the *transverse* or *real axes* of the hyperbola; the y-axis the *conjugate* or *imaginary axes ;* the points A, A' are the *vertices* of the hyperbolas, a is the *real semi-axis*, b the *imaginary semi-axis.*

EXAMPLES.—(1) Show that the equation of the hyperbola whose origin is at its vertex is $a^2y^2 = 2ab^2x + b^2x^2$. Substitute $x + a$ for x in the regular equation. Note that y does not change.

(2) Investigate the shape of the hyperbola. By solving equation (1) for x, and y, we get

$$y = \pm \frac{b}{a}\sqrt{x^2 - a^2}, \text{ and } x = \pm \frac{a}{b}\sqrt{y^2 + b^2}. \qquad . \qquad . \qquad . \qquad (2)$$

First. Since y^2 must be positive, $x^2 \not< a^2$, or x cannot be numerically less than a. No limit with respect to y can be inferred from equation (8).

Second. For every positive value of x, there are two values of y differing only in sign. Hence these two points are perpendicular above and below the x-axis, that is to say, the hyperbola is symmetrical with respect to the x-axis. There are two equal and opposite values of x for all values of y. The hyperbola is thus symmetrical with respect to the y-axis.

Third. If the value of x changes from zero until $x = \pm a$, then $y = 0$, and these two values of x furnish two points on the x-axis. If $x > a$, there are two equal and opposite values of y. Similarly for every value of y there are two equal and opposite values of x. The curve is thus symmetrical with respect to both axes, and lies beyond the limits $x = \pm a$.

Before describing the properties of this interesting curve I shall discuss some fundamental properties of curves in general.

§ 38. The Tangent to a Curve.

We sometimes define a tangent to a curve as a straight line

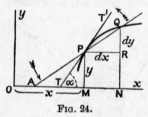

FIG. 24.

which touches the curve at two co-incident points.[1] If, in Fig. 24, P and Q are two points on a curve such that $MP = NR = y$; $RQ = dy$; $OM = x$; $MN = PR = dx$; the straight line $PQ = ds$. Otherwise, the diagram explains itself. Now let the line APQ revolve about the point P. We have already shown, on page 15, that the chord PQ becomes more and more nearly equal to the arc PQ as Q approaches P; when Q

---

[1] Note the equivocal use of the word "tangent" in geometry and in trigonometry. In geometry, a "tangent is a line between which and the curve no other straight line can be drawn," or "a line which just touches but does not cut the curve". The slope of a curve at any point can be represented by a tangent to the curve at that point, and this tangent makes an angle of tan a with the x-axis.

coincides with P, the angle MTP = angle $RPQ = \alpha$; dx, dy and ds are the sides of an infinitesimally small triangle with an angle at P equal to α; consequently

$$\frac{dy}{dx} = \tan \alpha. \qquad . \qquad . \qquad . \qquad . \qquad (1)$$

This is a most important result.   The differential coefficient represents the slope of gradient of the curve.   In other words, the tangent of the angle made by the slope of any part of a curve with the x-axis is the first differential coefficient of the ordinate of the curve with respect to the abscissa.

We can also see very readily that in the infinitely small triangle,

$$dx = ds \cdot \cos \alpha; \, dy = ds \cdot \sin \alpha; \qquad . \qquad . \qquad (2)$$

and, since R is a right angle,

$$(ds)^2 = (dy)^2 + (dx)^2. \qquad . \qquad . \qquad . \qquad (3)$$

If we plot the distances, x, traversed by a particle at different intervals of time (abscissæ); or the amounts of substance, x, transformed in a chemical reaction at different intervals of time, t, we get a curve whose slope at any point represents the velocity of the process at the corresponding interval of time.   This we call a **velocity curve.**   If the curve slopes downwards from left to right, dx/dt will be negative and the velocity of the process will be diminishing; if the curve slopes upwards from left to right, dx/dt will be positive, and the velocity will be increasing.

If we plot the velocity, V, of any process at different intervals of time, t, we get a curve whose slope indicates the rate at which the velocity is changing.   This we call an **acceleration curve.**   The area bounded by an acceleration curve and the coordinate axes represents the distance traversed or the amount of substance transformed in a chemical reaction as the case might be.

Examples.—(1) At what point in the curve $y_1{}^2 = 4x_1$ does the tangent make an angle of 60° with the x-axis?   Here $dy_1/dx_1 = 2/y_1 = \tan 60° = \sqrt{3}$. Ansr. $y_1 = 2\sqrt{\frac{1}{3}}$; $x_1 = \frac{1}{3}$.

(2) Find the tangent of the angle, α, made by any point $P(x, y)$ on the parabolic curve.   In other words, it is required to find a straight line which has the same slope as the curve has which passes through the point $P(x, y)$. Since $y^2 = 4ax$; $dy/dx = 2a/y = \tan \alpha$.   If the tangent of the angle were to have any particular value, this value would have to be substituted in place of dy/dx.   For instance, let the tangent at the point $P(x, y)$ make an angle of 45°.   Since $\tan 45 = $ unity, $2a/y = \tan \alpha = 1$, ∴ $y = 2a$.   Substituting in the original equation $y^2 = 4ax$, we get $x = a$, that is to say, the required tangent

passes through the extremity of the ordinate perpendicular on the focus. If the tangent had to be parallel to the x-axis, tan 0 being zero, dy/dx is equated to zero; while if the tangent had to be perpendicular to the x-axis, since tan $90° = \infty$, $dy/dx = \infty$.

(3) Required the direction of motion at any moment of a point moving according to the equation, $y = a \cos 2\pi(x + \epsilon)$. The tangent, at any time t, has the slope, $- 2\pi a \sin 2\pi(x + \epsilon)$.

(4) E. Mallard and H. le Chatelier represent the relation between the molecular specific heat, s, of carbon dioxide and temperature, θ, by the expression $s = 6\cdot3 + 0\cdot00564\theta - 0\cdot000001,08\theta^2$. Plot the $(\theta, ds/d\theta)$-curve from $\theta = 0°$ to $\theta = 2,000$ (abscissæ). Possibly a few trials will have to be made before the "scale" of each coordinate will be properly proportioned to give the most satisfactory graph. The student must learn to do this sort of thing for himself. What is the difference in meaning between this curve and the (s, θ)-curve?

(5) Show that dx/dy is the cotangent of the angle whose tangent is dy/dx.

Let TP (Fig. 25) be a tangent to the curve at the point $P(x_1, y_1)$. Let $OM = x_1$, $MP = y_1$. Let $y = mx + b$, be the equation of the tangent line TPT'', and $y_1 = f(x_1)$ the equation of the curve, ROP. From (14), page 94, we know that a straight line can only pass through the point $P(x_1. y_1)$, when

$$y - y_1 = m(x - x_1) \qquad . \qquad . \qquad . \qquad (4)$$

where m is the tangent of the angle which the line $y = mx$ makes with the x-axis; and x and y are the coordinates of any point taken at random on the tangent line. But we have just seen that this angle is equal to the first differential coefficient of the ordinate of the curve : hence by substitution

$$y - y_1 = \frac{dy_1}{dx_1}(x - x_1), \qquad . \qquad . \qquad . \qquad (5)$$

which is the required **equation of the tangent** to a curve at a point whose coordinates are x_1, y_1.

EXAMPLES.—(1) Find the equation of the tangent at the point (4, 2) in the curve $y_1^2 = 4x_1$. Here, $dy_1/dx_1 = 1$; $x_1 = 4$, $y_1 = 2$. Hence, from (4), $y = x - 2$ is the required equation.

(2) Required the equation of the tangent to a parabola. Since

$$y_1^2 = 4ax_1, \; dy_1/dx_1 = 2a/y_1.$$

Substituting in (5) and rearranging terms,

$$(y - y_1)y_1 = yy_1 - y_1^2 = 2a(x - x_1).$$

Substituting for y_1^2, we get

$$yy_1 = 2a(x + x_1), \qquad . \qquad . \qquad . \qquad . \qquad (6)$$

as the equation for the tangent line of a parabola. If $x = 0$, tan $\alpha = \infty$, and the tangent is perpendicular to the x-axis and touches the y-axis. To get the point of intersection of the tangent with the x-axis put $y = 0$, then $x = -x_1$. The vertex of the parabola thérefore bisects the x-axis between the point of intersection of the tangent and of the ordinate of the point of tangency.

(3) Find the equation of the tangent to the ellipse,

$$\frac{x_1^2}{a^2} + \frac{y_1^2}{b^2} = 1. \quad \therefore \frac{dy_1}{dx_1} = -\frac{b^2}{a^2}\frac{x_1}{y_1};$$

substituting this value of dy_1/dx_1 in (5), multiply the result by y_1; divide through by b^2; rearrange terms and combine the result with the equation of the ellipse, (1), page 100. The result is the tangent to any point on the ellipse,

$$\frac{xx_1}{a^2} + \frac{yy_1}{b^2} = 1, \quad . \quad . \quad . \quad . \quad (7)$$

where x_1, y_1 are coordinates of any point on the curve and x, y the coordinates of the tangent.

(4) Find the equation of the tangent at any point $P(x_1, y_1)$ on the hyperbolic curve. Differentiate the equation of the hyperbola

$$\frac{x_1^2}{a^2} - \frac{y_1^2}{b^2} = 1. \quad \therefore \frac{dy_1}{dx_1} = \frac{b^2}{a^2}\frac{x_1}{y_1}; \quad \therefore y - y_1 = \frac{b^2}{a^2}\frac{x_1}{y_1}(x - x_1).$$

Multiply this equation by y_1; divide by b^2; rearrange the terms and combine the result with the second of the above equations. We thus find that the tangent to any point on the hyperbola has the equation

$$\frac{xx_1}{a^2} - \frac{yy_1}{b^2} = 1. \quad . \quad . \quad . \quad . \quad (8)$$

At the point of intersection of the tangent to the hyperbola with the x-axis, $y = 0$ and the corresponding value of x is

$$xx_1 = a^2; \text{ or, } x = a^2/x_1, \quad . \quad . \quad . \quad (9)$$

the same as for the ellipse.

From (9) if x_1 is infinitely great, $x = 0$, and the tangent then passes through the origin. The limiting position of the tangent to the point on the hyperbola at an infinite distance away is interesting. Such a tangent is called an **asymptote**. To find the angle which the asymptote makes with the x-axis we must determine the limiting value of

$$\frac{y_1^2}{b^2} = \frac{x_1^2}{a^2} - 1,$$

when x_1 is made infinitely great. Multiply both sides by b^2/x_1^2, and

$$\therefore \frac{y_1^2}{x_1^2} = \frac{b^2}{a^2} - \frac{b^2}{x_1^2}.$$

If x_1 be made infinitely great the desired ratio is

$$\text{Lt}_{x1 = \infty}\frac{y_1^2}{x_1^2} = \frac{b^2}{a^2}, \quad \therefore \text{Lt}_{x1 = \infty}\frac{y_1}{x_1} = \frac{b}{a}.$$

Differentiate the equation of the hyperbola, and introduce this value for x_1/y_1, and we get

$$\frac{dy}{dx} = \tan \alpha \text{ (say)} = \frac{a}{b} \cdot \frac{b^2}{a^2} = \frac{b}{a} \quad . \quad . \quad . \quad (10)$$

If we now construct the rectangle $RSS'R'$ (Fig. 23, page 101) with sides parallel to the axes and cut off $OA = OA' = a$, $OB = OB' = b$, the diagonal in the first quadrant and the asymptote, having the same relation to the two axes, are identical. Since the x- and y-axes are symmetrical, it follows that these conditions hold for every quadrant. Hence, $R'OS$, and ROS' are the asymptotes of the hyperbola.

§ 39. A Study of Curves.

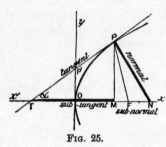

FIG. 25.

A normal line is a perpendicular to the tangent at a given point on the curve, drawn to the x-axis. Let NP be normal to the curve (Fig. 25) at the point P (x_1, y_1). Let $y = mx + b$, be the equation of the normal line; $y_1 = f(x_1)$, the equation of the curve. The condition that any line may be perpendicular to the tangent line TP, is that $m' = -1/m$, (17), page 96.   From (5)

$$y - y_1 = -\frac{1}{m}(x - x_1),$$

or, the **equation of the normal** line is

$$y - y_1 = -\frac{dx_1}{dy_1}(x - x_1) \; ; \quad \text{or,} \quad -\frac{dx_1}{dy_1} = \frac{y - y_1}{x - x_1}. \quad . \quad (1)$$

EXAMPLES.—(1) Find the equation of the normal at the point (4, 3) in the curve $x_1^2 y_1^3 = a$. Here $dx_1/dy_1 = -3x_1/2y_1$. Hence, by substitution in (1), $y = 2x - 5$.

(2) Show that $y = 2(x - 6)$ is the equation of the normal to the curve $4y_1 + x_1^2 = 0$, at the point $(4, -4)$.

(3) The tangent to the ellipse cuts the x-axis at a point where $y = 0$; from (7), page 105,

$$\therefore xx_1 = a^2 \; ; \quad \text{or,} \quad x = a^2/x_1. \quad . \quad . \quad . \quad (2)$$

In Fig. 26 let PT be a tangent to the ellipse, NP the normal.   From (2),

$$F_1T = x + c = a^2/x_1 + c \; ; \quad FT = x - c = a^2/x_1 - c,$$

since $F_1O = OF = c$; $OT = x$; $OM = x_1$,

$$\therefore \frac{F_1T}{FT} = \frac{a^2 + cx_1}{a^2 - cx_1} \quad \cdot \quad \cdot \quad \cdot \quad \cdot \quad \cdot \quad (3)$$

Since $FP = r$, $F_1P = r_1$; $OF = F_1O = c$; $OM = x_1$; $MP = y_1$,

$$r^2 = y_1{}^2 + (c - x_1)^2 ; \; r_1{}^2 = y_1{}^2 + (c + x_1)^2.$$
$$\therefore r^2 - r_1{}^2 = (r + r_1)(r - r_1) = -4cx_1 ;$$

But by the definition of an ellipse, pages 100 and 101,

$$r + r_1 = 2a ; \; \therefore r - r_1 = -2cx_1/a ; \; \therefore r = a - cx_1/a ; \; r_1 = a + cx_1/a.$$

$$\frac{F_1P}{FP} = \frac{r_1}{r} = \frac{a^2 + cx_1}{a^2 - cx_1} . \quad \cdot \quad \cdot \quad \cdot \quad \cdot \quad (4)$$

From (3) and (4), therefore,

$$F_1T : FT = F_1P : FP.$$

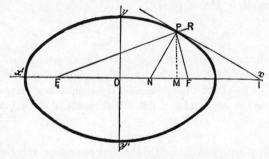

FIG. 26.—The Foci of the Ellipse.

By Euclid, vi., A : "If, in any triangle, the segments of the base produced have to one another the same ratio as the remaining sides of the triangle, the straight line drawn from the vertex to the point of section bisects the external angle". Hence in the triangle FPF_1, the tangent bisects the external angle FPR, and the normal bisects the angle FPF_1.

The preceding example shows that *the normal at any point on the ellipse bisects the angle enclosed by the focal radii ; and the tangent at any point on the ellipse bisects the exterior angle formed by the focal radii.* This property accounts for the fact that if F_1P be a ray of light emitted by some source F_1, the tangent at P represents the reflecting surface at that point, and the normal to the tangent is therefore normal to the surface of incidence. From a well-known optical law, "the angles of incidence and reflection are equal," and since F_1PN is equal to NPF when PF is the reflected ray, all rays emitted from one focus of the ellipse are reflected and concentrated at the other focus. This phenomenon occurs with light, heat, sound and electro-magnetic waves.

To find the length of the tangent and of the normal. The length of the tangent can be readily found by substituting the values MP and TM in the equation for the hypotenuse of a right-angled triangle TPM (Euclid, i., 47); and in the same way the length of the normal is obtained from the known values of MN and PM already deduced.

The **subnormal** of any curve is that part of the x-axis lying between the point of intersection of the normal and the ordinate drawn from the same point on the curve. Let MN be the sub-normal of the curve shown in Fig. 25, then

$$MN = x - x_1,$$

and the length of MN is, from (1),

$$x - x_1 = y_1\frac{dy_1}{dx_1}; \text{ or, } \frac{dy_1}{dx_1} = \frac{x - x_1}{y_1} \quad . \quad . \quad (5)$$

when the normal is drawn from the point $P(x_1, y_1)$.

The **subtangent** of any curve is that part of the x-axis lying between the points of intersection of the tangent and the ordinate drawn from the given point. Let TM (Fig. 25) be the subtangent, then

$$x_1 - x = TM.$$

Putting $y = 0$ in equation (1), the corresponding value for the length, TM, of the subtangent is

$$x_1 - x = y_1\frac{dx_1}{dy_1}; \text{ or, } \frac{dx_1}{dy_1} = \frac{x_1 - x}{y_1}. \quad . \quad . \quad (6)$$

Examples.—(1) Find the length of the subtangent and subnormal lines in the parabola, $y_1{}^2 = 4ax_1$. Since $y_1dy_1/dx_1 = 2a$, the subtangent is $2x_1$; the subnormal, $2a$. Hence the vertex of the parabola bisects the subtangent.

(2) Show that the subtangent of the curve $pv = $ constant, is equal to $- v$.

(3) Let $P(x, y)$ be a point on the parabolic curve (Fig. 27) referred to the coordinate axes Ox, Oy; PT a tangent at the point P, and let KA be the directrix. Let F be the focus of the parabola $y_2 = 4ax$. Join PF. Draw KP parallel to Ox. Join KT. Then $KPFT$ is a rhombus (Euclid, i., 34), for it has been shown that the vertex of the parabola O bisects the subtangent, Ex. (1) above. Hence, $TO = OM$; and, by definition, $AO = OF$;

$$\therefore TA = FM; \text{ and } KP = TF;$$

consequently, the sides KT and PF are parallel, and by definition of the parabola, $KP = PF$, $\therefore$ the two triangles KPT and PTF are equal in all respects, and (Euclid, i., 5) the angle $KPT = $ angle TPF, that is to say, *the tangent to the parabola at any given point bisects the angle made by the focal radius and the perpendicular dropped on to the directrix from the given point.*

In Fig. 27, the angle $TPF = $ angle $TPK = $ opposite angle RPT' (Euclid,

.i., 15). But, by construction, the angles *TPN* and *NPT'* are right angles; take away the equal angles *TPF* and *RPT'* and the angle *FPN* is equal to the angle *NPR*.

The normal at any point on the parabola bisects the angle enclosed by the focal radius and a line drawn through the given point, parallel to the x-axis. This property is of great importance in physics. All light rays falling parallel to the principal (or *x*-) axis on to a parabolic mirror are reflected at the focus *F*, and conversely all light rays proceeding from the focus

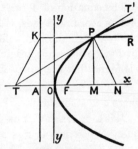

FIG. 27.—TheFocus of the Parabola.

are reflected parallel to the *x*-axis. Hence the employment of parabolic mirrors for illumination and other purposes. In some of Marconi's recent experiments on wireless telegraphy, electrical radiations were directed by means of parabolic reflectors. Hertz, in his classical researches on the identity of light and electromagnetic waves, employed large parabolic mirrors, in the focus of which a "generator," or "receiver" of the electrical oscillations was placed. See D. E. Jones' translation of H. Hertz's *Electric Waves*, London, 172, 1893.

§ 40. The Rectangular or Equilateral Hyperbola.

If we put $a = b$ in the standard equation to the hyperbola, the result is an hyperbola (Fig. 28) for which

$$x^2 - y^2 = a^2, \qquad (1)$$

and since $\tan a = 1 = \tan 45°$, each asymptote makes an angle of 45° with the *x*- or *y*-axes. In other words, the asymptotes bisect the coordinate axes. This special form of the hyperbola is called an *equilateral or rectangular hyperbola.* It follows directly that the asymptotes are at right angles to each other.

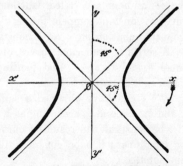

FIG. 28.—The Rectangular Hyperbola.

The asymptotes may, therefore, serve as a pair of rectangular coordinate axes.   This is a valuable property of the rectangular hyperbola.

The equation of a rectangular hyperbola referred to its asymptotes as coordinate axes, is best obtained by passing from one set of coordinates to another inclined at an angle of − 45° to the old set, but having the same origin, as indicated on page 96.   In this way it is found that the equation of the rectangular hyperbola is

$$xy = a, \qquad . \quad . \quad . \quad . \qquad (2)$$

where a is a constant.

It is easy to see that as y becomes smaller, x increases in magnitude.   When $y = 0$, $x = \infty$, the x-axis touches the hyperbola an infinite distance away.   A similar thing might be said of the y-axis.

§ 41. Illustrations of Hyperbolic Curves.

I. The graphical representation of the gas equation, $pv = R\theta$, furnishes a rectangular hyperbola when θ is fixed or constant. The law as set forth in the above equation shows that the volume of a gas, v, varies inversely as the pressure, p, and directly as the temperature, θ.   For any assigned value of θ, we can obtain a series of values of p and v.   For the sake of simplicity, let the constant $R = 1$.   Then if

$$\theta = 1 \begin{cases} p = & 0\cdot1, & 0\cdot5, & 1\cdot0, & 5\cdot0, & 10\cdot0, & \ldots; \\ v = & 10\cdot0, & 2\cdot0, & 1\cdot0, & 0\cdot2, & 0\cdot1, & \ldots; \end{cases}$$

$$\theta = \cdot5 \begin{cases} p = & 0\cdot1, & 0\cdot5, & 1\cdot0, & 5\cdot0, & 10\cdot0, & \ldots; \\ v = & 5\cdot0, & 1\cdot0, & 0\cdot5, & 0\cdot1, & 0\cdot05, & \ldots \text{ etc.} \end{cases}$$

The "curves" of constant temperature obtained by plotting these numbers are called **isothermals**.   Each isothermal (*i.e.,* curve at constant temperature) is a rectangular hyperbola obtained from the equation $pv = R\theta =$ constant, similar to (2), above.

A series of isothermal curves, obtained by putting θ successively equal to θ_1, θ_2, θ_3 ... and plotting the corresponding values of p and v, is shown in Fig. 29.

We could have obtained a series of curves from the variables p and θ, or v and θ, according as we assume v or p to be constant. If v be constant, the resulting curves are called **isometric lines, or isochores**; if p be constant the curves are **isopiestic lines, or isobars**.

II. Exposure formula for a thermometer stem.   When a thermometer stem is not exposed to the same temperature as the bulb, the mercury in the exposed stem is cooled, and a small correction must be made for the consequent contraction of the mercury exposed in the stem.   If x denotes the difference between the temperature registered by the thermometer and the tempera-

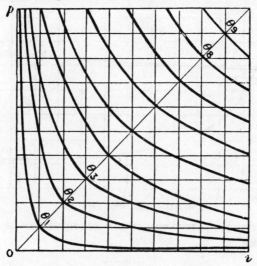

FIG. 29.—Isothermal pv-curves.

ture of the exposed stem, y the number of thermometer divisions exposed to the cooler atmosphere, then the correction can be obtained by the so-called *exposure formula of a thermometer*, namely,

$$\theta = 0\cdot00016xy,$$

which has the same form as equation (2), page 110.   By assuming a series of suitable values for θ (say $0\cdot1\dots$) and plotting the results for pairs of values of x and y, curves are obtained for use in the laboratory.   These curves allow the required correction to be seen at a glance.

III. Dissociation curves.   Gaseous molecules under certain conditions dissociate into similar parts.   Nitrogen peroxide, for instance, dissociates into simpler molecules, thus :

$$N_2O_4 \rightleftharpoons 2NO_2.$$

Iodine at a high temperature does the same thing, I_2 becoming $2I$. In solution a similar series of phenomena occur, KCl becoming K + Cl, and so on.   Let x denote the number of molecules of an acid or salt which dissociate into two parts called *ions*; $(1 - x)$ the number of molecules of the acid, or salt resisting ionization; c the quantity of substance contained in unit volume, that is the

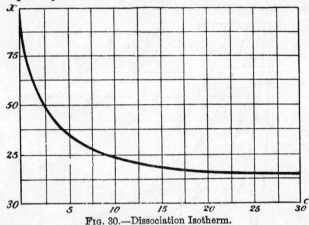

FIG. 30.—Dissociation Isotherm.

concentration of the solution. Nernst has shown that at constant temperature

$$K = \frac{cx^2}{1 - x}$$

where K is the so-called dissociation constant whose meaning is obtained by putting $x = 0.5$. In this case $K = \frac{1}{2}c$, that is to say, K is equal to half the quantity of acid or salt in solution when half of the acid or salt is dissociated.

Putting $K = 1$ we can obtain a series of corresponding values of c and x. For example, if

$$x = .16, \quad 0.25, \quad 0.5, \quad 0.75, \quad 0.94 \ldots;$$
$$\text{then} \quad c = 32, \quad 12, \quad 2, \quad 0.44, \quad 0.07 \ldots$$

It thus appears that when the concentration is very great, the amount of dissociation is very small, and *vice versâ*, when the concentration is small the amount of dissociation is very great. Complete dissociation can perhaps never be obtained. The graphic curve (Fig. 30), called, by Nernst, the **dissociation isotherm**, is asymptotic towards the two axes, but when drawn on a small scale the curve appears to cut the ordinate axis.

IV. The *volume elasticity* of a substance is defined as the ratio of any small increase of pressure to the diminution of volume per unit volume of substance. If the temperature is kept constant during the change, we have **isothermal elasticity,** while if the change takes place without gain or loss of heat, **adiabatic elasticity.** If unit volume of gas, v, changes by an amount dv for an increase of pressure dp, the elasticity, E, is

$$E = -\frac{dp}{\dfrac{dv}{v}} = -v\frac{dp}{dv} \quad (1)$$

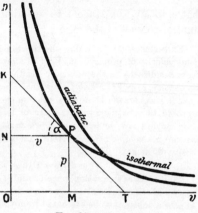

FIG. 31.—pv-curves.

A similar equation can be obtained by differentiating Boyle's law, $pv = $ constant, for an isothermal change of state. The result is that

$$p = -v\frac{dp}{dv} . \quad (2)$$

an equation identical with that deduced for the definition of volume elasticity. The equation $pv = $ constant is that of a rectangular hyperbola referred to its asymptotes as axes.

Let $P(p, v)$ (Fig. 31) be a point on the curve $pv = $ constant. In constructing the diagram the triangles KNP and PMT were made equal and similar (Euclid, i., 26). See Ex. (2) page 108, and note that KN is the vertical subtangent equivalent to $-p$.

$$KN = -NP \tan a = -v \tan KPN = -v\frac{dp}{dv},$$

that is to say, *the isothermal elasticity of a gas in any assigned condition, is numerically equal to the vertical subtangent of the curve* corresponding to the substance in the given state.

But since in the rectangular hyperbola $KN = PM$, *the isothermal elasticity of a gas* is equal to the pressure (2). The adiabatic elasticity of a gas may be obtained by a similar method to that used for equation (1). If the gas be subject to an adiabatic change of pressure and volume it is known that

$$pv^{\gamma} = \text{constant} = C. \quad . \quad . \quad . \quad (3)$$

Taking logarithms, (3) furnishes $\log p + \gamma \log v = \log C$. By differentiation and rearrangement of terms, we get

$$E_{Q} = -v\frac{dp}{dv} = \gamma p, \quad . \quad . \quad . \quad (4)$$

in other words the adiabatic elasticity [1] of a gas is γ times the pressure. A similar construction for the adiabatic curve furnishes

$$KN : PM = KP : PT = \gamma : 1,$$

that is to say, the tangent to an adiabatic curve is divided at the point of contact in the ratio $\gamma : 1$.

EXAMPLES.—(1) Assuming the Newton-Laplace formula that the square of the velocity of propagation, V, of a compression wave (*e.g.*, of sound) in a gas varies directly as the adiabatic elasticity of the gas, E_ϕ, and inversely as the density, ρ, or $V^2 \propto E_\phi/\rho$; show that $V^2 \propto \gamma RT$. Hints: Since the compression wave travels so rapidly, the changes of pressure and volume may be supposed to take place without gain or loss of heat. Therefore, instead of using Boyle's law, $pv =$ constant, we must employ $pv^\gamma =$ constant. Hence deduce $\gamma p = v \cdot dp/dv = E_\phi$. Note that the volume varies inversely as the density of the gas. Hence, if

$$V^2 \propto E_\phi/\rho \propto E_\phi v \propto \gamma pv \propto \gamma RT. \qquad . \qquad . \qquad . \qquad (5)$$

(2) R. Mayer's equation, page 82 and (5) can be employed to determine the two specific heats of any gas in which the velocity of sound is known. Let a be a constant to be evaluated from the known values of R, T, V^2,

$$\therefore C_v = R/(1 - a), \text{ and } C_p = aC_v. \qquad . \qquad . \qquad . \qquad (6)$$

Boynton has employed van der Waals' equation in place of Boyle's. Perhaps the reader can do this for himself. It will simplify matters to neglect terms containing magnitudes of a high order (see W. P. Boynton, *Physical Review*, **12**, 353, 1901).

§ 42. Polar Coordinates.

Instead of representing the position of a point in a plane in terms of its horizontal and vertical distances along two standard lines of reference, it is sometimes more convenient to define the position of the point by a length and a direction. For example, in Fig. 32 let the point O be fixed, and Ox a straight line through O.

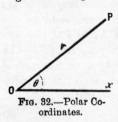

FIG. 32.—Polar Coordinates.

Then, the position of any other point P will be completely defined *if* (1) the length OP and (2) the angle OP makes with Ox, are known. These are called the polar coordinates of P, the first is called the **radius vector**, the latter the **vectorial angle**. The radius vector is generally represented by the symbol r, the vectorial angle by θ, and P is called the point $P(r, \theta)$, O is called the *pole* and Ox the *initial line*. As in trigonometry, the vectorial angle is measured by supposing

---

[1] From other considerations, E_θ is usually written E_ϕ.

the angle θ has been swept out by a revolving line moving from a position coincident with Ox to OP. It is positive if the direction of revolution is contrawise to the motion of the hands of a clock.

To change from polar to rectangular coordinates and *vice versâ*. In Fig. 33, let (r, θ) be the polar coordinates of the point $P(x, y)$. Let the angle $x'OP = \theta$.

I. To pass from Cartesian to polar coordinates.

$$\sin \theta = \frac{MP}{OP} = \frac{y}{r}; \ \cos \theta = \frac{OM}{OP} = \frac{x}{r};$$

$$\therefore y = r \sin \theta \ \text{and} \ x = r \cos \theta, \quad \bullet \quad \bullet \quad (1)$$

which expresses x, and y, in terms of r and θ.

EXAMPLES.—(1) Transform the equation $x^2 - y^2 = 3$ from rectangular to polar coordinates, pole at origin. Ansr. $r^2 \cos 2\theta = 3$. Hint. $\cos^2\theta - \sin^2\theta = \cos 2\theta$.

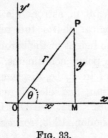

FIG. 33.

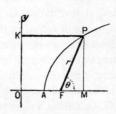

FIG. 34.

(2) Show that $x^2 + y^2 = 9$ represents the same line as $r = 3$. Hint. $r^2(\sin^2\theta + \cos^2\theta) = 9$; and $\sin^2\theta + \cos^2\theta = 1$.

(3) A point P moves along a curve in such a way that the ratio of its distance from a given point F, and from a given straight line OK (Fig. 34) is a constant quantity, say e. Find the path of the point. Hint. In Fig. 34 $FP = eKP$. Let $KP = OM = x$; $MP = y$. Required the equation connecting x and y. $(FP)^2 = (MP)^2 + (FM)^2 = y^2 + (x - a)^2$, where OF is put $= a$. If e is unity, the curve is a parabola; if $e < 1$ the curve is an ellipse; if $e > 1$ the curve is an hyperbola. e is called the eccentricity of the curve. In polar coordinates $KP = OF + FM = a + r \cos \theta$,

$$\therefore e = \frac{r}{a + r \cos \theta}; \ \text{or} \ r = \frac{ae}{1 - e \cos \theta}. \quad \bullet \quad \bullet \quad (2)$$

whether curve be an hyperbola, ellipse or parabola.

II. To pass from polar to Cartesian coordinates. In the same figure

$$\tan \theta = \frac{MP}{OM} = \frac{y}{x} \,;$$

$$r^2 = (OP)^2 = (OM)^2 + (MP)^2 = x^2 + y^2 \,;$$

$$\therefore \theta = \tan^{-1}\frac{y}{x} \,; \quad r = \pm \sqrt{x^2 + y^2} \quad . \quad . \quad (3)$$

which expresses θ, and r, in terms of x and y. The sign of r is ambiguous, but, by taking any particular solution for θ, the preceding remarks will show which sign is to be taken.

Just as in Cartesian coordinates, the graph of a polar equation may be obtained by assigning convenient values to θ (say 0°, 30°, 45°, 60°, 90° . . .) and calculating the corresponding value of r from the equation.

EXAMPLES.—(1) What are the rectangular coordinates of the points (2, 60°), and (2, 45°) respectively? Ansr. (1, $\sqrt{3}$), and ($\sqrt{2}$, $\sqrt{2}$).

(2) Express the equation $r = m \cos \theta$ in rectangular coordinates. Ansr. $x^2 + y^2 = mx$. Hint. $\cos \theta = x/r$; $\therefore r^2 = mx$, etc.

Polar coordinates are particularly useful in astronomical and geodetical investigations. In meteorological charts the relation between the direction of the wind, and the height of the barometer, or the temperature, is often plotted in polar coordinates. The treatment of problems involving direction in space, displacement, velocity, acceleration, momentum, rotation, and electric current are often simplified by the use of vectors. But see O. Henrici and G. C. Turner's *Vectors and Rotors*, London, 1903, for a simple exposition of this subject.

§ 43. Spiral Curves.

The equations of the spiral curves are considerably simplified

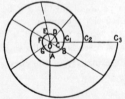

by the use of polar coordinates. For instance, the curve for the logarithmic spiral (Fig. 35), though somewhat complex in Cartesian coordinates, is represented in polar coordinates by the simple equation

$$r = a^\theta, \quad . \quad . \quad (1)$$

where a has a constant value. Hence

FIG. 35.—Logarithmic Spiral.

$$\log r = \theta \log a.$$

Let $C, C_1, C_2, \ldots$ (Fig. 35) be a series of points on the spiral corresponding with the angles $\theta_1, \theta_2, \ldots$; and the radii vectores $r_1, r_2, \ldots$ Hence,

$$\log r_1 = \theta_1 \log a \; ; \; \log r_2 = \theta_2 \log a \ldots$$

Since $\log a$ is constant, say equal to k,

$$\log \frac{r_1}{r_2} = (\theta_1 - \theta_2)k,$$

that is, the logarithm of the ratio of the distance of any two points on the curve from the pole is proportional to the angle between their radii vectores. If r_1 and r_2 lie on the same straight line, then

$$\theta_1 - \theta_2 = 2\pi = 360^\circ \; ; \text{ and } \log \frac{r_1}{r_2} = 2k\pi,$$

π being the symbol used, as in trigonometry, to denote 180°.

Similarly, it can be shown that if r_3, $r_4 \ldots$ lie on the same straight line, the logarithm of the ratio of r_1 to r_3, $r_4 \ldots$ is given by $4k\pi$, $6k\pi \ldots$. This is true for any straight line passing through O; and therefore the spiral is made up of an infinite number of turns which extend inwards and outwards without limit.

If the radii vectores OC, OD, $OE \ldots OC_1$, $OD_1 \ldots$ be taken to represent the number of vibrations of a sounding body in a given time, the angles COD, $DOE \ldots$ measure the logarithms of the intervals between the tones produced by these vibrations. A point travelling along the curve will then represent a tone continuously rising in pitch, and the curve, passing successively through the same line produced, represents the passage of the tone through successive octaves The geometrical periodicity of the curve is a graphical representation of the periodicity perceived by the ear when a tone continuously rises in pitch.

This diagram may also be used to illustrate the Newlands-Mendeléeff law of octaves, by arranging the elements along the curve in the order of their atomic weights. E. Loew (*Zeit. phys. Chem.*, **23**, 1, 1897) represents the atomic weight, W, as a function of the radius vector, r, and the vectorial angle, $\theta : W = f(r, \theta)$, so that $r = \theta = \sqrt{W}$. He thus obtains $W = r\theta$. This curve is the well-known Archimedes' spiral. If r is any radius vector, the distances of the points P_1, P_2, P_3, $\ldots$ from O are

$$r_2 = r + \pi \; ; \; r_4 = r + 3\pi \; ; \; r_6 = r + 5\pi \; ; \; \ldots$$
$$r_3 = r + 2\pi \; ; \; r_5 = r + 4\pi \; ; \; r_7 = r + 6\pi \; ; \; \ldots$$

EXAMPLES.—(1) Plot Archimedes' spiral, $r = a\theta$; and show that the revolutions of the spiral are at a distance of $2a\pi$ from one another.

(2) Plot the hyperbolic spiral, $r\theta = a$; and show that the ratio of the distance of any two points from the pole is inversely proportional to the angles between their radii vectores.

§ 44. Trilinear Coordinates and Triangular Diagrams.

Another method of representing the position of a point in a plane is to refer it to its perpendicular distance from the sides of a

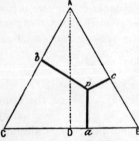

triangle called the *triangle of reference.* The perpendicular distances of the point from the sides are called **trilinear coordinates.** In the equilateral triangle ABC (Fig. 36), let the perpendicular distance of the vertex A from the base BC be denoted by 100 units, and let p be any point within the triangle whose trilinear coordinates are

FIG. 36.—Trilinear Coordinates. pa, pb, pc, then

$$pa + pb + pc = 100.$$

This property[1] has been extensively used in the graphic representation of the composition of certain ternary alloys, and mixtures of salts. Each vertex is supposed to represent one constituent of

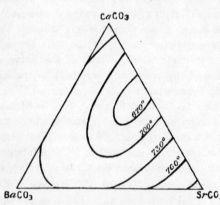

FIG. 37.—Surface of Fusibility.

the mixture. Any point within the triangle corresponds to that mixture whose percentage composition is represented by the trilinear coordinates of that point. Any point on a side of the triangle represents a binary mixture. Fig. 37 shows the melting points of ternary mixtures of isomorphous carbonates

of barium, strontium and calcium. Such a diagram is sometimes called a **surface of fusibility.** A mixture melting at 670° may

---

[1] It is not difficult to see this. Through p draw pG parallel to AC cutting AB at G; through G draw GK parallel to BC cutting AD at F, and AC at K; produce the line ap until it meets GK at E; draw GH perpendicular to AC. Now show that $AF = HG = pb$; that $pE = pc$; that $DF = pc + pa$; and that $DA = pa + pb + pc$.

have the composition represented by any point on the isothermal curve marked 670°, and so on for the other isothermal curves.

In a similar way the composition of quaternary mixtures has been graphically represented by the perpendicular distance of a point from the four sides of a square.

Roozeboom, Bancroft and others have used triangular diagrams with lines ruled parallel to each other as shown in Fig. 38. Sup-

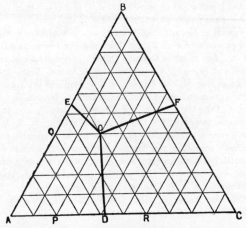

FIG. 38.—Concentration-Temperature diagram.

pose we have a mixture of three salts, A, B, C, such that the three vertices of the triangle ABC represent phases[1] containing 100 °/₀ of each component. The composition of any binary mixture is given by a point on the boundary lines of the triangle, while the composition of any ternary mixture is represented by some point inside the triangle.

The position of any point inside the triangle is read directly from the coordinates *parallel* to the sides of the triangle. For instance, the composition of a mixture represented by the point O is obtained by drawing lines from O *parallel* to the three sides of the triangle OP, OR, OQ. Then start from one corner as origin and measure along the two sides, AP fixes the amount of C, AQ

---

[1] A *phase* is a mass of uniform concentration. The number of phases in a system is the number of masses of different concentration present. For example, at the temperature of melting ice three phases may be present in the H_2O-system, *viz.*, solid ice, liquid water and steam; if a salt is dissolved in water there is a solution and a vapour phase, if solid salt separates out, another phase appears in the system.

the amount of B, and, by difference, CR determines the amount A. For the point chosen, therefore $A = 40$, $B = 40$, $C = 20$.

(i) Suppose the substance A melts at 320°, B at 300°, and C at 305°, and that the point D represents an eutectic alloy [1] of A and C melting at 215°; E, of an eutectic alloy of A and B melting at 207°; F, of an eutectic alloy of B and C melting at 268°.

(ii) Along the line DO, the system A and C has a solid phase; along EO, A and B have a solid phase; and along FO, B and C have a solid phase.

(iii) At the triple point O, the system A, B and C exists in the three-solid, solution and vapour-phases at a temperature at 186° (say).

(iv) Any point in the area $ADOE$ represents a system comprising solid, solution and vapour of A,—in the solution, the two components B and C are dissolved in A. Any point in the area $CDOF$ represents a system comprising solid, solution and vapour of C,—in the solution, A and B are dissolved in C. Any point in the area $BEOF$ represents a system comprising solid, solution and vapour of B,—in the solution, A and C are dissolved in B.

Each apex of the triangle not only represents 100 °/₀ of a substance, but also the temperature at which the respective substances A, B, or C melt; D, E, F also represent temperatures at which the respective eutectic alloys melt. It follows, therefore, that the temperature at D is lower than at either A or C. Similarly the temperature at E is lower than at A or B, and at F lower than at either B or C. The melting points, therefore, rise as we pass from one of the points D, E, F to an apex on either side.

For details the reader is referred to W. D. Bancroft's *The Phase Rule*, Ithaca, 1897.

§ 45. Orders of Curves.

The order of a curve corresponds with the degree of its equation. The degree of any term may be regarded as the sum of the exponents of the variables it contains; the degree of an equation is that of the highest term in it. For example, the equation $xy + x + b^3y = 0$, is of the second degree if b is constant; the equation $x^3 + xy = 0$, is of the third degree; $x^2yz^3 + ax = 0$, is of the sixth degree, and so on. A **line of the first order** is represented by the general equation of the first degree

$$ax + by + c = 0. \qquad . \qquad . \qquad . \qquad \textbf{(1)}$$

This equation is that of a *straight line* only. A **line of the second order** is represented by the general equation of the second degree between two variables, namely,

$$ax^2 + bxy + cy^2 + fx + gy + h = 0. \qquad . \qquad \textbf{(2)}$$

---

[1] An *eutectic alloy* is a mixture of two substances in such proportions that the alloy melts at a lower temperature than a mixture of the same two substances in any other proportions.

This equation includes, as particular cases, every possible form of equation in which no term contains x and y as factors more than twice. The term bxy can be made to disappear by changing the direction of the rectangular axes, and the terms containing fx and gy can be made to disappear by changing the origin of the co-ordinate axes. Every equation of the second degree can be made to assume one of the forms

$$ax^2 + cy^2 = h, \text{ or, } y^2 = fx. \quad . \quad . \quad . \quad (3)$$

The first can be made to represent a *circle*,[1] *ellipse*, or *hyperbola ;* the second a *parabola.* Hence every equation of the second degree between two variables includes four species of curves—circle, ellipse, parabola and hyperbola.

It must be here pointed out that if two equations of the first degree with all their terms collected on one side be multiplied together we obtain an equation of the second degree which is satisfied by any quantity which satisfies either of the two original equations. *An equation of the second degree may thus represent two straight lines,* as well as one of the above species of curves.

The condition that the general equation of the second degree may represent two straight lines is that

$$(bg - 2cf)^2 = (b^2 - 4ac)(g^2 - 4ch). \quad . \quad . \quad (4)$$

The general equation of the second degree will represent a parabola, ellipse, or hyperbola, according as $b^2 - 4ac$, is zero, negative, or positive.

EXAMPLES.—(1) Show that the graph of the equation

$$2x^2 - 10xy + 12y^2 + 5x - 16y - 3 = 0,$$

represents two straight lines.   Hint. $a = 2$; $b = -10$; $c = 12$; $f = 5$; $g = -16$; $h = -3$; $(bg - 2cf)^2 = 1600$; $(b^2 - 4ac)(g^2 - 4ch) = 1600$.

(2) Show that the graph of $x^2 - 2xy + y^2 - 8x + 16 = 0$ represents a parabola.   Hint. From (2), $b^2 - 4ac = -2 \times -2 - 4 \times 1 \times 1 = 0$.

(3) Show that the graph of $x^2 - 6xy + y^2 + 2x + 2y + 2 = 0$ represents a hyperbola.   Here $b^2 - 4ac = -6 \times -6 - 4 \times 1 \times 1 = 32$.

§ 46. Coordinate Geometry in Three Dimensions.—Geometry in Space.

Methods have been described for representing changes in the state of a system involving two variable magnitudes by the locus of a point moving in a plane according to a fixed law defined by

---

[1] The circle may be regarded as an ellipse with major and minor axes equal.

the equation of the curve.   Such was the *pv*-diagram described on page 111.   There, a series of isothermal curves were obtained, when θ was made constant during a set of corresponding changes of *p* and *v* in the well-known equation $pv = R\theta$.

When any three magnitudes, *x, y, z,* are made to vary together we can, by assigning arbitrary values to two of the variables, find corresponding values for the third, and refer the results so obtained to three fixed and intersecting planes called the **coordinate planes.** Of the resulting eight quadrants, four of which are shown in Fig. 39, only the first is utilized to any great extent in mathematical physics.   This mode of graphic representation is called *geometry in space,* or geometry in three dimensions.   The lines formed by the intersection of these planes are the **coordinate axes.**   It is necessary that the student have a clear idea of a few properties of lines and surfaces in working many physical problems.

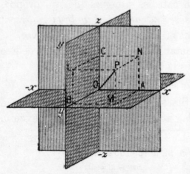

FIG. 39.—Cartesian Coordinates—Three Dimensions.

If we get a series of sets of corresponding values of *x, y, z* from the equation

$$x + y = z,$$

and refer them to coordinate axes in three dimensions, as described below, the result is a *plane* or *surface.*   If one of the variables remains constant, the resulting figure is a *line.* A surface may, therefore, be considered to be the locus of a line moving in space.

I. To find the point whose coordinates OA, OB, OC are given.   The position of the point *P* with reference to the three coordinate planes *xOy, xOz, yOz* (Fig. 39) is obtained by dropping perpendiculars *PL, PM, PN* from the given point on to the three planes.   Complete the parallelopiped, as shown in Fig. 39.   Let *OP* be a diagonal.   Then *LP* = *OA, PN = BO, MP = OC*.   Draw three planes through *A, B, C* parallel respectively to the coordinate planes ; the point of intersection of the three planes, namely *P,* will be the required point.

If the coordinates of *P,* parallel to *Ox, Oy, Oz,* are respectively *x, y* and *z,* then *P* is said to be the point *x, y, z*.   A similar convention with regard to the sign is used as in analytical geometry of two dimensions. It is conventionally agreed that lines measured from below upwards shall be positive, and lines measured from above downwards negative ; lines measured from left to right positive, and from right to left negative ; lines measured inwards from the plane of the paper are negative, lines measured towards the reader are positive.

If a watch be placed in the plane xy with its face pointing upwards, towards $+ z$, the hands of the watch move in a negative direction ; if the watch be in the xz plane with its face pointing towards the reader, the hands also move in a negative direction.

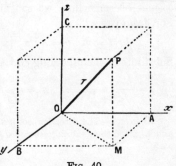

II. To find the distance of a point from the origin in terms of the rectangular coordinates of that point. In Fig. 40, let Ox, Oy, Oz be three rectangular axes, $P(x, y, z)$ the given point such

FIG. 40.

that $MP = z$, $AM = y$, $OA = x$. It is required to find the distance $OP = r$, say.

$$OP^2 = OM^2 + MP^2 ;\ \text{or,}\ r^2 = OM^2 + z^2,$$
but
$$OM^2 = AM^2 + OA^2 = x^2 + y^2.$$
$$\therefore r^2 = x^2 + y^2 + z^2 \qquad . \qquad . \qquad . \qquad (1)$$

In words, the sum of the squares of the three coordinates of a point are equal to the square of the distance of that point from the origin.

EXAMPLE.—Find the distance of the point $(2a, - 3a, 6a)$ from the origin. Hint. $r = \sqrt{4a^2 + 9a^2 + 36a^2} = 7a$.

Let the angle $AOP = a$; $BOP = \beta$; $POC = \gamma$, then

$$x = r \cos a ;\ y = r \cos \beta ;\ z = r \cos \gamma . \qquad . \qquad (2)$$

These equations are true wherever the point P may lie, and therefore the signs of x, y, z are always the same as those of $\cos a$, $\cos \beta$, $\cos \gamma$ respectively. Substituting these values in (1), and dividing through by r^2, we get the following relation between the three angles which any straight line makes with the coordinate axes

$$\cos^2 a + \cos^2 \beta + \cos^2 \gamma = 1. \quad . \quad . \quad . \quad (3)$$

The cosines of the angles a, β, γ which the given line makes with the axes x, y, z respectively are called the **direction cosines,** and are often symbolized by the letters **l, m, n.** Thus (3) becomes

$$l^2 + m^2 + n^2 = 1.$$

If we know r, $\cos a$, $\cos \beta$, and $\cos \gamma$ we are able to fix the position of the point. If a, b, c are proportional to the direction cosines of some line, we can at once find the direction cosines. For, from page 23, if

$$l : a = m : b = n : c \; ; \; \therefore \; l = ra \; ; \; m = rb \; ; \; n = rc.$$

Substitute in the preceding equation, and we get at once

$$l = \frac{a}{\sqrt{a^2 + b^2 + c^2}} \; ; \; m = \frac{b}{\sqrt{a^2 + b^2 + c^2}} \; ; \; n = \frac{c}{\sqrt{a^2 + b^2 + c^2}}.$$

EXAMPLE.—The direction cosines of a line are proportional to 3, – 4, and 2. Find their values. Ansr. $3\sqrt{\frac{1}{29}}$, $-4\sqrt{\frac{1}{29}}$, $2\sqrt{\frac{1}{29}}$. Hint. $a = 3, b = -4$, $c = 2$.

III. *To find the distance between two points in terms of their rectangular coordinates.* Let $P_1(x_1, y_1, z_1)$, $P_2(x_2, y_2, z_2)$ be the given points,

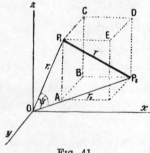

FIG. 41.

it is required to find the distance $P_1 P_2$ in terms of the coordinates of the points P_1 and P_2. Draw planes through P_1 and P_2 parallel to the coordinate planes so as to form the parallelopiped $ABCDE$. Join $P_2 E$. By the construction (Fig. 41), the angle $P_1 E P_2$ is a right angle. Hence

$$(P_1 P_2)^2 = (P_1 E)^2 + (P_2 E)^2 = (P_1 E)^2 + (ED)^2 + (P_2 D)^2.$$

But $P_1 E$ is evidently the difference of the distance of the foot of the perpendiculars from P_1 and P_2 on the x-axis, or $P_1 E = x_2 - x_1$. Similarly, $ED = y_2 - y_1$; $P_2 D = z_2 - z_1$. Hence

$$r^2 = (x_2 - x_1)^2 + (y_2 - y_1)^2 + (z^2 - z_1)^2. \quad . \quad (4)$$

EXAMPLE.—Find the distance between the points $(3, 4, -2)$ and $(4, -3, 1)$. Here $x_1 = 4$; $y_1 = -3$; $z_1 = 1$; $x_2 = 3$; $y_2 = 4$; $z_2 = -2$. Ansr. $r = \sqrt{59}$.

IV. Polar coordinates. Instead of referring the point to its Cartesian coordinates in three dimensions, we may use polar coordinates. Let P (Fig. 42) be the given point whose rectangular coordinates are x, y, z; and whose polar coordinates are r, θ, ϕ, as shown in the figure.

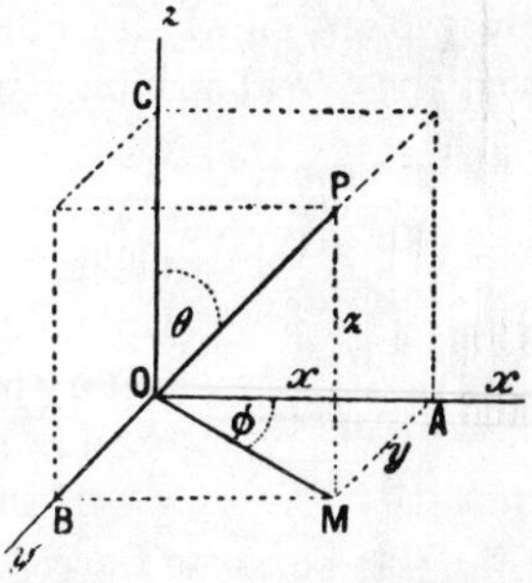

I. To pass from rectangular to polar coordinates. (See page 96.)

$$\left.\begin{aligned}x &= OA = OM\cos\phi = r\sin\theta \cdot \cos\phi\\ y &= AM = OM\sin\phi = r\sin\theta \cdot \sin\phi\\ z &= MP = r\cos\theta.\end{aligned}\right\} \quad \textbf{(5)}$$

II. To pass from polar to rectangular coordinates.

FIG. 42.—Polar Coordinates in Three Dimensions.

$$r = \sqrt{(x^2 + y^2 + z^2)}; \quad \theta = \tan^{-1}\frac{\sqrt{(x^2 + y^2)}}{z}; \quad \phi = \tan^{-1}\frac{y}{x}. \quad \textbf{(6)}$$

EXAMPLES.—(1) Find the rectangular coordinates of the point $(3, 60°, 30°)$ Ansr. $(\frac{3}{4}, \frac{3}{4}\sqrt{3}, \frac{3}{2})$.

(2) Find the polar coordinates of the point $(3, 12, 4)$. Ansr. The point $(13, \tan^{-1}\frac{1}{4}\sqrt{153}, \tan^{-1}4)$.

According to the **parallelogram of velocities**, " if two component velocities OA, OB (Fig. 43) are represented in direction and magnitude by two sides of a parallelogram drawn from a point, O, the resultant velocity can be represented in direction and magnitude by the diagonal, OP, of the parallelogram drawn from that point ". The **parallelopiped of velocities** is an extension of the preceding result into three dimensions. " If three component velocities are represented in direction and magnitude by the adjacent sides of a parallelopiped, OA, OC, OB (Fig. 42), drawn from a point, O, their resultant velocity can be represented by the diagonal of a parallelopiped drawn from that point." Conversely, if the velocity of the moving system is represented in magnitude and direction by the diagonal OP (Fig. 42) of a parallelopiped, this can be resolved into three component velocities represented in direction and magnitude by three sides x, y, z of the parellelopiped drawn from a point.

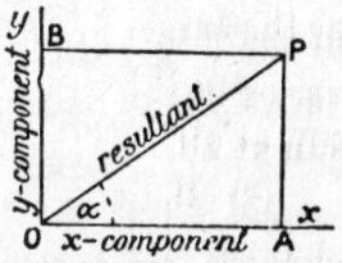

FIG. 43.—Parallelogram of Velocities.

We assume that if any contradictory facts really existed we

should have known them long ago. A continental text-book has forty-five theoretical demonstrations of this important principle. But we are slowly learning the lesson taught by John Stuart Mill that the "real and only proof of any law of Nature...is experi-

ence". The daily comparison of a new rule with experience, and the testing of its consequences under the most diverse conditions is, after the lapse of a reasonable period of time, a more satis- factory proof than clumsy deductions drawn from obscure premises.[1]

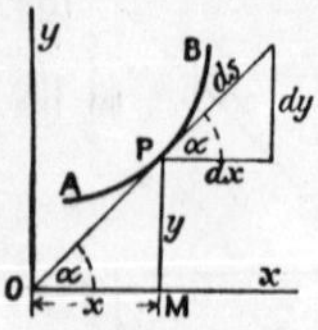

FIG. 44.

If the point P travels along the path APB (Fig. 44) so as to trace a path s units long, then, when $x = OM$, and $y = MP$, let dx, dy, and ds be infinitesimals such that

$$\frac{dx}{ds} = \cos \alpha ; \frac{dy}{ds} = \sin \alpha ; \text{ or, } \frac{dx}{dt} = \frac{ds}{dt} \cos \alpha ; \frac{dy}{dt} = \frac{ds}{dt} \sin \alpha \qquad (7)$$

and

$$(ds)^2 = (dx)^2 + (dy)^2 ; \text{ or, } \left(\frac{ds}{dt}\right)^2 = \left(\frac{dx}{dt}\right)^2 + \left(\frac{dy}{dt}\right)^2. \qquad (8)$$

The corresponding formulæ in three dimensions are very obvious.

EXAMPLES.—(1) A comet moves upon the parabolic path $y^2 = 4ax$; find its rate of approach to the sun which is placed at the focus of its orbit. Let r denote the distance from the focus to any point $P(x, y)$ on the parabola. Hence, from the definition of a parabola $r = x + a$; $\therefore dr/dt = dx/dt$. Or its rate of approach to the sun is the same as its horizontal velocity. Let s de- note the length of the path, then $ds/dt = $ velocity of motion $= V$, say. But by differentiation of the given equation,

$$\frac{dy}{dt} = \frac{2a}{y} \cdot \frac{dx}{dt} ; \therefore V^2 = \left(\frac{ds}{dt}\right)^2 = \left(\frac{dx}{dt}\right)^2 + \frac{4a^2}{y^2}\left(\frac{dx}{dt}\right)^2 \therefore \frac{dx}{dt} = \frac{yV}{\sqrt{y^2 + 4a^2}},$$

or the comet approaches the sun with $y(y^2 + 4a^2)^{-\frac{1}{2}}$ times its velocity. At the vertex of the parabola, $y = 0$, $dx/dt = 0$, or the comet is not approaching the sun at all.

(2) Show that the ordinate of a point moving on the parabola $y^2 = 4x$ changes $2/y$ times as fast as the abscissa ; and if, at the point $x = 4$, the abscissa is changing at the rate of 20 ft. per second, at what rate is the ordinate changing ? Hint. If $x = 4$, $y = \pm 4$; hence

$$\frac{dy}{dt} = \frac{2}{y} \cdot \frac{dx}{dt} ; \therefore \frac{dy}{dt} = \pm \frac{1}{2} \cdot \frac{dx}{dt}.$$

---

[1] E. Mach. Of course we only deal with one velocity. The resolving of one velocity into three component velocities is a mathematical fiction to assist reasoning. This is not necessary in "Vector analysis," page 116, which has replaced "coordinate geometry" in the mathematical treatment of many physical problems.

Hence $dy/dt = \pm \frac{1}{2} \times 20 = \pm 10$. Or the ordinate increases or decreases at the rate of 10 ft. per sec.

(3) Let a particle move with a velocity V in space. From the parallelopiped of velocities, V can be resolved into three component velocities V_1, V_2, V_3, along the x-, y- and z-axes respectively. Hence show that

$$\frac{dx}{dt} = V_1 ;\; \frac{dy}{dt} = V_2 ;\; \frac{dz}{dt} = V_3, \quad \cdot \quad \cdot \quad \cdot \quad \cdot \quad (9)$$

which may be written

$$dx = d(V_1 t + x_0) ;\; dy = d(V_2 t + y_0) ;\; dz = d(V_3 t + z_0), \quad \cdot \quad (10)$$

where x_0, y_0, z_0 are constants. Hence we may write the relation between the space described by the particles in each dimension and the time as

$$x = V_1 t + x_0 ;\; y = V_2 t + y_0 ;\; z = V_3 t + z_0. \quad \cdot \quad \cdot \quad (11)$$

Obviously x_0, y_0, z_0 are the coordinates of the initial position of the particle when $t = 0$. Hence x_0, y_0, z_0 are to be regarded as constants.

If the reader cannot follow the steps taken in passing from (9) to (11), he can take Lagrange's advice to the student of a mathematical text-book : " Allez en avant, et la foi vous viendra," in other words, " go on but return to strengthen your powers. Work backwards and forwards ".

Obviously, x_0, y_0, z_0 represent the positions of the particle at the beginning of the observation, when $t = 0$. Let s denote the length of the path traversed by the particle at the time t, when the coordinates of the point are x, y and z. Obviously, by the aid of Fig. 41,

$$s = \sqrt{(x - x_0)^2 + (y - y_0)^2 + (z - z_0)^2} ;\; \text{or,}\; s = \sqrt{V_1^2 + V_2^2 + V_3^2} \cdot t,$$

from (11). s can therefore be determined from the initial and final positions of the particle.

§ 47. Lines in Three Dimensions.

I. To find the angle between two straight lines whose direction cosines are given. Join OP_1 (Fig. 41) and OP_2. Let ψ be the angle between these two lines. In the triangle $P_2 O P_1$ if $OP_1 = r_1$, $OP_2 = r_2$, $P_1 P_2 = r$, we get from the properties of triangles given on page 603,

$$r^2 = r_1^2 + r_2^2 - 2 r_1 r_2 \cos \psi.$$

Rearranging terms and substituting for r_1 and r_2 in (1), we obtain

$$r_1^2 = x_1^2 + y_1^2 + z_1^2 ;\; r_2^2 = x_2^2 + y_2^2 + z_2^2,$$

$$\therefore \cos \psi = \frac{x_1 x_2 + y_1 y_2 + z_1 z_2}{r_1 r_2}.$$

We can express this another way by substituting,

$$x_1 = r_1 \cos a_1 ;\; x_2 = r_2 \cos a_2 ;\; y_2 = r_2 \cos \beta_2 \dots,$$

as in (2), and we obtain

$$\cos \psi = \cos a_1 \cdot \cos a_2 + \cos \beta_1 \cdot \cos \beta_2 + \cos \gamma_1 \cdot \cos \gamma_2 \quad (12)$$

or, $\cos \psi = l_1 l_2 + m_1 m_2 + n_1 n_2,$.   .   (13)

where ψ represents the angle between two straight lines whose direction cosines are known.

(i) When the lines are perpendicular to one another, $\psi = 90°$, $\therefore \cos \psi = \cos 90° = 0$, and therefore

$$\cos a_1 . \cos a_2 + \cos \beta_1 . \cos \beta_2 + \cos \gamma_1 . \cos \gamma_2 = 0, \qquad (14)$$

or, $x_1 x_2 + y_1 y_2 + z_1 z_2 = 0.$

(ii) If the two lines are parallel,

$$a_1 = a_2 ; \quad \beta_1 = \beta_2 ; \quad \gamma_1 = \gamma_2 \qquad .   .   (15)$$

EXAMPLES.—(1) Find the acute angle between the lines whose direction cosines are $\frac{1}{4}\sqrt{3}, \frac{1}{4}, \frac{1}{2}\sqrt{3}$, and $\frac{1}{4}\sqrt{3}, \frac{1}{4}, -\frac{1}{2}\sqrt{3}$. Hint. $l_1 = l_2 = \frac{1}{4}\sqrt{3}$; $m_1 = m_2 = \frac{1}{4}$; $n_1 = \frac{1}{2}\sqrt{3}$; $n_2 = -\frac{1}{2}\sqrt{3}$. Use (13).

(2) Let V_1, V_2, V_3 be the velocity components (page 125) of a particle moving with the velocity V; let a, β, γ be the angles which the path described by the moving particle makes with the x-, y- and z-axes respectively, then show

$$ds . \cos a = dx ; \therefore \frac{dx/dt}{ds/dt} = \frac{1}{V} . \frac{dx}{dt} = \cos a. \quad .   .   (16)$$

Hence,

$$V_1 = \frac{dx}{dt} = V \cos a ; \ V_2 = \frac{dy}{dt} = V \cos \beta ; \ V_3 = \frac{dz}{dt} = V \cos \gamma ; \quad .   (17)$$

and consequently, from (3),

$$V = ds/dt = \sqrt{V_1^2 + V_2^2 + V_3^2}. \quad .   .   .   (18)$$

The resolved part of V along a given line inclined at angles a_1, β_1, γ_1 to the axes will be

$$V \cos \psi = V_1 \cos a_1 + V_2 \cos \beta_1 + V_3 \cos \gamma_1, \quad .   .   (19)$$

where ψ denotes the angle which the path described by the particle makes with the given line. Hint. Multiply (12) by V, etc.

(3) To find the direction of motion of the particle moving on the line s (i.e., r of Fig. 40). Let a, β, γ denote the angles made by the direction of s with the respective axes x, y, z. With the same notation,

$$\cos a = \frac{x - x_0}{s} ; \ \cos \beta = \frac{y - y_0}{s} ; \ \cos \gamma = \frac{z - z_0}{s}. \quad .   .   (20)$$

Now introduce the values of $x - x_0, y - y_0,$ and of $z - z_0$ from (20), and show that

$$\cos a : \cos \beta : \cos \gamma = V_1 : V_2 : V_3. \quad .   .   (21)$$

II. *Projection.* If a perpendicular be dropped from a given point upon a given plane the point where the perpendicular touches the plane is the **projection of the point** P upon that plane. For instance, in Fig. 39, the projection of the point P on the plane xOy is M, on the plane xOz is N, and on the plane yOz is L.

Similarly, the projection of the point P upon the lines Ox, Oy, Oz is at A, B and C respectively.

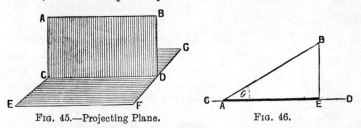

FIG. 45.—Projecting Plane.   FIG. 46.

In the same way the **projection of a curve** on a given plane is obtained by projecting every point in the curve on to the plane. The plane, which contains all the perpendiculars drawn from the different points of the given curve, is called the **projecting plane.** In Fig. 45, CD is the projection of AB on the plane EFG; $ABCD$ is the projecting plane.

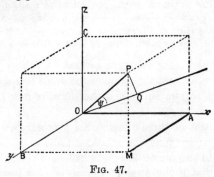

FIG. 47.

EXAMPLES.—(1) The projection of any given line on an intersecting line is equal to the product of the length of the given line into the cosine of the angle of intersection. In Fig. 46, the projection of AB on CD is AE, but $AE = AB \cos \theta$.

(2) In Fig. 47, show that the projection of OP on OQ is the algebraic sum of the projections of OA, AM, MP, taken in this order, on OQ. Hence, if $OA = x$, $OB = AM = y$, $OC = PM = z$ and $OP = r$, from (12)

$$r \cos \psi = x \cos \alpha + y \cos \beta + z \cos \gamma. \quad . \quad . \quad . \quad (22)$$

III. The equation of a straight line in rectangular coordinates. Suppose a straight line in space to be formed by the intersection of two projecting planes. The coordinates of any point on the line of intersection of these planes will obviously satisfy the equation of each plane. Let ab, $a'b'$ be the projection of the given line AB on

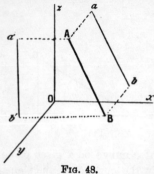

FIG. 48.

the xOz (where $y = 0$) and the yOz (where $x = 0$) planes, then (Fig. 48),
$$x = mz + c \; ; \; y = m'z + c' \qquad (23)$$
Of the four independent constants, m represents the tangent of the angle which the projection of the given line on the xOz plane makes with the x-axis; m' the tangent of the angle made by the line projected on the yOz plane with the y-axis; c is the distance intercepted by the projection of the given line along the x-axis; c' a similar intersection along the y-axis. Hence we infer that two simultaneous equations of the first degree represent a straight line.

EXAMPLE.—The equations of the projections of a straight line on the coordinate planes xz and zy are $x = 2z + 3$, and $y = 3z - 5$. Show that the equation of the projection on the xy plane is $2y = 3x - 19$. $c' = -5$; $c = 3$; $m = 2$; $m' = 3$; eliminate z; etc. Ansr. $2y - 3x + 19 = 0$.

If, now, a particular value be assigned to either variable in either of these equations, the value of the other two can be readily calculated. These two equations, therefore, represent a straight line in space.

The difficulties of three-dimensional geometry are greatly lessened if we bear in mind the relations previously developed for simple curves in two dimensions. It will be obvious, for instance, from page 94, that if the straight line is to pass through a given point (x_1, y_1, z_1), the coordinates of the given point must satisfy the equations of the curve. Hence, from (23), we must also have
$$x_1 = mz_1 + c \; ; \; y_1 = m'z_1 + c'. \qquad (24)$$
Subtracting (24) from (23), we get
$$x - x_1 = m(z - z_1) \; ; \; y - y_1 = m'(z - z_1) \qquad (25)$$
which are the equations of a straight line passing through the point x_1, y_1, z_1.

If the line is to pass through two points x_1, y_1, z_1, and x_2, y_2, z_2, we get, by the method of page 94,
$$\frac{x - x_1}{z - z_1} = \frac{x_2 - x_1}{z_2 - z_1} \; ; \; \frac{y - y_1}{z - z_1} = \frac{y_2 - y_1}{z_2 - z_1}. \qquad (26)$$

which are the equations of the straight line passing through the two given points.

EXAMPLE.—Show that the equations $x + 8z = 19$; $y = 10z - 24$ pass through the points $(3, -4, 2)$ and $(-5, 6, 3)$.

If x, y, z denote the coordinates of any point A on a given straight line; and x_1, y_1, z_1, the known coordinates of another point P on the straight line such that the distance between A and P is r, then it can be shown that the equation of the line assumes the symmetrical form : $r =$

$$\frac{x - x_1}{l} = \frac{y - y_1}{m} = \frac{z - z_1}{n} . \quad . \quad . \quad (27)$$

where l, m and n are the direction cosines of the line. This equation gives us the equation of a straight line in terms of its direction cosines and any known point upon it. (27) is called the **symmetrical equation of a straight line.**

EXAMPLE.—If a line makes angles of 60°, 45°, and 60° respectively with the three axes x, y and z, and passes through the point $(1, -3, 2)$, show that the equation of the line is $x - 1 = \sqrt{\frac{1}{2}}(y + 3) = z - 2$. Hint. $\cos 60° = \frac{1}{2}$; $\cos 45° = \sqrt{\frac{1}{2}}$.

If the two lines

$$x = m_1 z + c_1; \quad y = m_1' z + c_1'; \quad . \quad . \quad (28)$$
$$x = m_2 z + c_2; \quad y = m_2' z + c_2', \quad . \quad . \quad (29)$$

intersect, they must have a point in common, and the coordinates of this point must satisfy both equations. In other words, x, y and z will be the same in both equations—x of the one line is equal to x of the other.

$$\therefore (m_1 - m_2)z + c_1 - c_2 = 0, \quad . \quad . \quad (30)$$
$$(m_1' - m_2')z + c_1' - c_2' = 0. \quad . \quad . \quad (31)$$

But the z of one line is also equal to z of the other, hence, if the relation

$$(c_1' - c_2')(m_1 - m_2) = (c_1 - c_2)(m_1' - m_2'), \quad . \quad (32)$$

subsists the two lines will intersect.

EXAMPLE.—Show that the two lines $x = 3z + 7$, $y = 5z + 8$; and $x = 2z + 3$. $y = 4z + 4$ intersect. Hint. $(8 - 4)(3 - 2) = (7 - 3)(4 - 3)$.

The coordinates of the point of intersection are obtained by substituting (30) or (31) in (28), or (29). Note that if $m_1 = m_1'$ or $m_2 = m_2'$, the values of x, y and z then become infinite, and the two lines will be in parallel planes; if both $m_1 = m_1'$ and $m_2 = m_2'$, they will be parallel.

§ 48. Surfaces and Planes.

I. To find the equation of a plane surface in rectangular co-ordinates. Let *ABC* (Fig. 49) be the given plane whose equation is to be determined. Let the given plane cut the co-ordinate axes at points *A*, *B*, *C* such that $OA = a$, $OB = b$, $OC = c$. From any point $P(x, y, z)$ drop the perpendicular *PM* on to the *yOx* plane. Then $OA' = x$, $MA' = y$ and

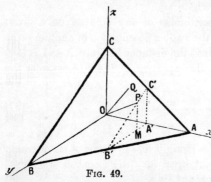

Fig. 49.

$MP = z$. It is required to find an equation connecting the co-ordinates *x*, *y* and *z* respectively with the intercepts *a*, *b*, *c*. From the similar triangles *AOB*, *AA'B'*,

$$OA : BO = A'A : B'A' \text{; or, } a : b = a - x : B'A',$$

$$\therefore B'A' = b - \frac{bx}{a}; \text{ also } B'M = B'A' - MA' = b - y - \frac{bx}{a}.$$

Again, from the similar triangles *COB*, *C'A'B'*, *PMB'*, page 603,

$$OC : BO = MP : B'M;$$

or, $c : b = z : b - y - \dfrac{bx}{a}; \therefore bz = bc - cy - \dfrac{bcx}{a}.$

Divide through by *bc*; rearrange terms and we get the **intercept equation of the plane**, *i.e.*, the equation of a plane expressed in terms of its intercepts upon the three axes:

$$\frac{x}{a} + \frac{y}{b} + \frac{z}{c} = 1, \qquad . \qquad . \qquad . \qquad (33)$$

an equation similar to that developed on page 90. In other words, equation (33) represents a plane passing through the points $(a, 0, 0)$, $(0, b, 0)$, $(0, 0, c)$.

If *ABC* (Fig. 49) represents the face, or plane of a crystal, the intercepts *a*, *b*, *c* on the *x*-, *y*- and *z*-axes are called the *parameters* of that plane. The parameters in crystallography are usually expressed in terms of certain axial lengths assumed unity.   If $OA = a$, $OB = b$, $OC = c$, any other plane, whose intercepts on the x-, y- and z-axes are respectively p, q and r, is defined by the ratios

$$\frac{a}{p} : \frac{b}{q} : \frac{c}{r}.$$

These quotients are called the parameters of the new plane. The reciprocals of the parameters are the *indices* of a crystal face. The several systems of crystallographic notation, which determine the position of the faces of a crystal with reference to the axes of the crystal, are based on the use of parameters and indices.

We may write equation (33) in the form,

$$Ax + By + Cz + D = 0, \qquad . \quad . \quad \textbf{(34)}$$

which is the most general equation of the first degree between three variables. Equation (33) is the **general equation of a plane surface**. It is easily converted into (34) by substituting $Aa + D = 0$, $Bb + D = 0$, $Cc + D = 0$.

EXAMPLES.—(1) Find the equation of the plane passing through the three points $(3, 2, 4)$, $(0, 4, 1)$, and $(-2, 1, 0)$. Ansr. $11x - 3y - 13z + 25 = 0$. Hint. From (33),

$$\frac{3}{a} + \frac{2}{b} + \frac{4}{c} = 1; \ \frac{4}{b} + \frac{1}{c} = 1; \ -\frac{2}{a} + \frac{1}{b} = 1; \ \therefore a = -\frac{25}{11}; \ b = \frac{25}{3}; \ c = \frac{25}{13}.$$

(2) Find the equation of the plane through the three points $(1, 0, 0)$, $(0, 2, 0)$, $(0, 0, 3)$. Ansr. $x + \frac{1}{2}y + \frac{1}{3}z = 1$. Use (33) or (34).

If $OQ = r$ (Fig. 49) be normal, that is, perpendicular to the plane ABC, the projection of OP on OQ is equal to the sum of the projections of OA', PM, MA' on OQ, Ex. (2), page 129. Hence, the perpendicular distance of the plane from the origin is

$$x \cos \alpha + y \cos \beta + z \cos \gamma = r. \qquad . \quad . \quad (35)$$

This is called the **normal equation of the plane**, that is, the equation of the plane in terms of the length and direction cosines of the normal from the origin. From (34), we get

$$\cos^2\alpha : \cos^2\beta : \cos^2\gamma = A^2 : B^2 : C^2;$$

and by componendo,[1]

$$(\cos^2\alpha + \cos^2\beta + \cos^2\gamma) : \cos^2\alpha = A^2 + B^2 + C^2 : A^2.$$

But by (3), the term in brackets on the left is unity, consequently

---

[1] If a, b, c and d are proportional, the text-books on algebra tell us that $a : b = c : d$; and it therefore follows by "invertendo": $b : a = d : c$; and by "alternando": $a : c = b : d$; and by "componendo": $a + b : b = c + d : d$; and by "dividendo": $a - b : b = c - d : d$; and by "convertendo": $a : a - b = c : c - d$ and by "componendo et dividendo": $a \pm b : a \mp b = c \pm d : c \mp d$.

the direction cosines of the normal to the plane are

$$\cos a = \frac{A}{\sqrt{A^2 + B^2 + C^2}};$$

$$\cos \beta = \frac{B}{\sqrt{A^2 + B^2 + C^2}};$$

$$\cos \gamma = \frac{C}{\sqrt{A^2 + B^2 + C^2}}.$$

The ambiguity of sign is removed by comparing the sign of the absolute term in (34) and (35). Dividing equation (34) through with $+ \sqrt{A^2 + B^2 + C^2}$, we can write

$$r = - \frac{D}{\sqrt{A^2_1 + B^2 + C^2}}. \qquad . \qquad . \qquad . \qquad (36)$$

Example.—Find the length of the perpendicular from the origin to the plane whose equation is $2x - 4y + z - 8 = 0$. Ansr. $8\sqrt{\frac{1}{21}}$. Hint. $A = 2$, $B = - 4$, $C = 1$, $D = 8$. Use the right member of the equation (36).

II. Surfaces of revolution. Just as it is sometimes convenient to suppose a line to have been generated by the motion of a point, so surfaces may be produced by a straight or curved line moving according to a fixed law represented by the equation of the curve. The moving line is called the *generator*. Surfaces produced by the motion of straight lines are called **ruled surfaces.** When the straight line is continually changing the plane of its motion, twisted or **skew surfaces**—*surfaces gauches*—are produced. Such is the helix, the thread of a screw, or a spiral staircase. On the other hand, if the plane of the motion of a generator remains constant, a **developable surface** is produced. Thus, if the line rotates round a fixed axis, the surface cut out is called a *surface of revolution.* A *sphere* may be formed by the rotation of a circle about a diameter; a *cylinder* may be formed by the rotation of a rectangle about one of its sides as axis; a *cone* may be generated by the revolution of a triangle about its axis; an *ellipsoid* of revolution, by the rotation of an ellipse about its major or minor axes; a *paraboloid,* by the rotation of a parabola about its axis. If a hyperbola rotates about its transverse axis, two *hyperboloids* will be formed by the revolution of both branches of the hyperbola. On the other hand, only one hyperboloid is formed by rotating the hyperbolas about their conjugate axes. In the former case, the *hyperboloid* is said to be *of two sheets*, in the latter, *of one sheet.*

III. To find the equation of the surface of a right cylinder.

Let one side of a rectangle rotate about Oz as axis. Any point on the outer edge will describe the circumference of a circle. If $P(x, y, z)$ (Fig. 50) be any point on the surface, r the radius of the cylinder, then the required equation is

$$r^2 = x^2 + y^2 . \qquad . \qquad (37)$$

The equation of a right cylinder is thus independent of z. This means that z may have any value whatever assigned to it.

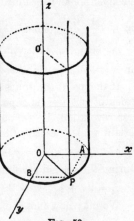

EXAMPLES.—(1) Show that the equation of a right cone is $x^2 + y^2 - z^2\tan^2\phi = 0$, where ϕ represents half the angle at the apex of the cone. Hint. Origin of axes is at apex of cone; let the z-axis coincide with the axis of the cone. Find $O'P'A'$ on the base of the cone resembling OPA (Fig. 50). Hence show $O'P' = z \tan \phi$. But $O'P' = \sqrt{x^2 + y^2}$.

FIG. 50.

(2) The equation of a sphere is $x^2 + y^2 + z^2 = r^2$. Prove this. Centre of sphere at origin of axes. Take a section across z-axis. Find $O'P'A'$; $OP = r$; $(OP)^2 = (OO')^2 + (O'P')^2$, $(O'P')^2 = x^2 + y^2$; $(OO')^2 = z^2$; etc.

The subject will be taken up again at different stages of our work.

§ 49. Periodic or Harmonic Motion.

Let P (Fig. 51) be a point which starts to move from a position of rest with a uniform velocity on the perimeter of a circle. Let xOx', yOy' be coordinate axes about the centre O. Let $P_1, P_2 \ldots$ be positions occupied by the point after the elapse of intervals of $t_1, t_2 \ldots$ From P_1 drop the perpendicular M_1P_1 on to the x-axis. Remembering that if the direction of $M_1P_1, M_2P_2 \ldots$ be positive, that of M_3P_3, M_4P_4 is negative, and the motion of OP as P revolves

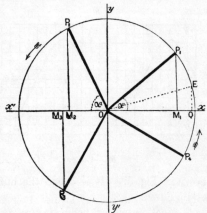

FIG. 51.—Periodic or Harmonic Motion.

about the centre O in the opposite direction to the hands of a clock is conventionally reckoned positive, then

$$\sin a_1 = \frac{+ M_1 P_1}{+ OP_1} \; ; \; \sin a_2 = \frac{+ M_2 P_2}{+ OP_2} \; ; \; \sin a_3 = \frac{- M_3 P_3}{+ OP_3} \; ; \; \sin a_4 = \frac{- M_4 P_4}{+ OP_4}.$$

Or, if the circle have unit radius $r = 1$,

$$\sin a_1 = + M_1 P_1 \; ; \; \sin a_2 = + M_2 P_2 \; ; \; \sin a_3 = - M_3 P_3 \; ; \; \sin a_4 = - M_4 P_4.$$

If the point continues in motion after the first revolution, this series of changes is repeated over and over again. During the first revolution, if we put $\pi = 180°$, and let θ_1, θ_2, ... represent certain angles described in the respective quadrants,

$$\theta_1 = a_1 \; ; \; \theta_2 = \pi - a_2 \; ; \; \theta_3 = \pi + a_3 \; ; \; \theta_4 = 2\pi - a_4.$$

During the second revolution,

$$\theta_1 = 2\pi + a_1 \; ; \; \theta_2 = 2\pi + (\pi - a_2) \; ; \; \theta_3 = 2\pi + (\pi + a_3), \text{ etc.}$$

We may now plot the curve

$$y = \sin a \qquad . \qquad . \qquad . \qquad . \qquad (1)$$

by giving a series of values 0, $\frac{1}{2}\pi$, $\frac{3}{4}\pi$ ... to a and finding the corresponding values of y.   Thus if

$$x = a = 0, \qquad \tfrac{1}{2}\pi, \qquad \pi, \qquad \tfrac{3}{2}\pi, \qquad 2\pi, \qquad \tfrac{5}{2}\pi, \ldots;$$
$$y = \sin 0, \quad \sin \tfrac{1}{2}\pi, \quad \sin \pi, \quad \sin \tfrac{3}{2}\pi, \quad \sin 2\pi, \quad \sin \tfrac{5}{2}\pi, \ldots;$$
$$y = \sin 0°, \; \sin 90°, \; \sin 180°, \; \sin 270°, \; \sin 360°, \; \sin 90°, \ldots;$$
$$y = 0, \qquad 1, \qquad 0, \qquad -1, \qquad 0, \qquad 1, \ldots$$

Intermediate values are $\sin \frac{1}{4}\pi = \sin 45° = \cdot 707$, $\sin \frac{3}{4}\pi = \cdot 707 \ldots$

The curve so obtained has the wavy or undulatory appearance

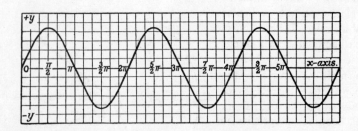

FIG. 52.—Curve of Sines, or Harmonic Curve.

shown in Fig. 52.   It is called the **curve of sines or the harmonic curve.**

A function whose value recurs at fixed intervals when the variable uniformly increases in magnitude is said to be a **periodic**

function. Its mathematical expression is

$$f(t) = f(t + qt) \quad . \quad . \quad . \qquad (2)$$

where q may be any positive or negative integer. In the present case $q = 2\pi$. The motion of the point P is said to be a *simple harmonic motion.* Equation (1) thus represents a simple harmonic motion.

If we are given a particular value of a periodic function of, say, t, we can find an unlimited number of different values of t which satisfy the original function. Thus $2t$, $3t$, $4t, \ldots$, all satisfy equation (2).

EXAMPLES.—(1) Show that the graph of $y = \cos a$ has the same form as the sine curve and would be identical with it if the y-axis of the sine curve were shifted a distance of $\frac{1}{2}\pi$ to the right. [Proof: $\sin(\frac{1}{2}\pi + x) = \cos x$, etc.] The physical meaning of this is that a point moving round the perimeter of the circle according to the equation $y = \cos a$ is just $\frac{1}{2}\pi$, or 90° in advance of one moving according to $y = \sin a$.

(2) Illustrate graphically the periodicity of the function $y = \tan a$. (Note the passage through $\pm \infty$.) Keep your graph for reference later on.

Instead of taking a circle of unit radius, let r denote the magnitude of the radius, then

$$y = r \sin a. \quad . \quad . \quad . \qquad (3)$$

Since $\sin a$ can never exceed the limits ± 1, the greatest and least values y can assume are $- r$ and $+ r$; r is called the **amplitude** of the curve. The velocity of the motion of P determines the rate at which the angle a is described by OP, the so-called **angular velocity.** Let t denote the time, q the angular velocity,

$$\frac{da}{dt} = q \; ; \; \text{or} \; a = qt, \quad . \quad . \quad . \qquad (4)$$

and the time required for a complete revolution is

$$t = 2\pi/q, \quad . \quad . \quad . \qquad (5)$$

which is called the **period of oscillation,** the *periodic value,* or the *periodic time ;* 2π is the **wave length.** If E (Fig. 51) denotes some arbitrary fixed point such that the periodic time is counted from the instant P passes through E, the angle $xOE = \epsilon$, is called the **epoch or phase constant,** and the angle described by OP in the time $t = qt + \epsilon = a$, or

$$y = r \sin(qt + \epsilon). \quad . \quad . \quad . \qquad (6)$$

Electrical engineers call ϵ the "lead" or, if negative, the "lag" of the electric current.

EXAMPLES.—(1) Plot (6), note that the angles are to be measured in radians (page 606), and that one radian is 57·3°. Now let $r = 10$, $\epsilon = 30° = 0·52$ radians. Let q denote 0·5°, or $\frac{1}{114\cdot6}$ radians.

$$\therefore\ y = 10 \sin (0·0087t + 0·52).$$

If $t = 10$, $y = 10 \sin 0·61 = 10 \sin 35°$, from a Table of Radians (Table XIII.). From a Table of Trigonometrical Sines, $10 \sin 35° = 10 \times 0·576 = 5·76$ we get the same result more directly by working in degrees. In this case,

$$y = 10 \sin (\tfrac{1}{2}t° + 30°).$$

If $t = 10$, we have $y = 10 \sin 35°$ as before. Then we find if $r = 10$, $t = 30 = 0·52$ radians, and if

$t =$	0,	120,	300,	480,	720;
$y =$	5,	10,	0,	− 10,	− 5.

Intermediate values are obtained in the same way. The curve is shown in

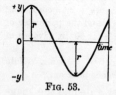

FIG. 53.

Fig. 53. Now try the effect of altering the value of ϵ upon the value of y, say, you put $\epsilon = 0, 45°, 60°, 90°$, and note the effect on Oy (Fig. 52).

(2) It is easy to show that the function

$$a \sin (qt + \epsilon) + b \cos (qt + \epsilon) \qquad . \qquad (7)$$

is equal to $A \sin (qt + \epsilon_1)$ by expanding (7) as indicated in formulæ (23) and (24), page 612. Thus we get

$$\sin qt(a \cos \epsilon - b \sin \epsilon) + \cos qt(b \cos \epsilon + a \sin \epsilon) = A \sin (qt + \epsilon_1),$$

provided we collect the constant terms as indicated below.

$$A \cos \epsilon_1 = a \cos \epsilon - b \sin \epsilon;\ A \sin \epsilon_1 = b \cos \epsilon + a \sin \epsilon. \qquad . \qquad (8)$$

Square equations (8) and add

$$\therefore A^2 = a^2 + b^2. \qquad . \qquad . \qquad . \qquad . \qquad (9)$$

Divide equations (8), rearrange terms and show that

$$\frac{\sin (\epsilon - \epsilon_1)}{\cos (\epsilon - \epsilon_1)} = \tan (\epsilon - \epsilon_1) = - \frac{b}{a}. \qquad . \qquad . \qquad . \qquad (10)$$

(3) Draw the graphs of the two curves,

$$y = a \sin (qt + \epsilon);\ \text{and}\ y_1 = a_1 \sin (qt + \epsilon_1).$$

Compare the result with the graph of

$$y_2 = a \sin (qt + \epsilon) + a_1 \sin (qt + \epsilon_1).$$

(4) Draw the graphs of

$$y_1 = \sin x;\ y_2 = \tfrac{1}{3} \sin 3x;\ y_3 = \tfrac{1}{5} \sin 5x;\ y = \sin x + \tfrac{1}{3} \sin 3x + \tfrac{1}{5} \sin 5x.$$

(5) There is an interesting relation between $\sin x$ and e^x. Thus, show that if

$$y = a \sin qt + b \sin qt;\ \frac{d^2y}{dt^2} = - q^2y;\ \frac{d^4y}{dt^4} = q^4y;\ldots$$

$$y = e^{qt};\ \frac{d^2y}{dt^2} = q^2y;\ \frac{d^4y}{dt^4} = q^4y;\ldots$$

The motion of M (Fig. 51), that is to say, the projection of the moving point on the diameter of the circle xOx' is a good illustration of the periodic motion discussed in § 21. The motion of an oscillating pendulum, of a galvanometer needle, of a tuning fork, the up and down motion of a water wave, the alternating electric current, sound, light, and electromagnetic waves are all periodic motions.   Many of the properties of the chemical elements are also periodic functions of their atomic weights (Newlands-Mendeléeff law).

Some interesting phenomena have recently come to light which indicate that chemical action may assume a periodic character. The evolution of hydrogen gas, when hydrochloric acid acts on one of the allotropic forms of chromium, has recently been studied by W. Ostwald (*Zeit. phys. Chem.*, **35**, 33, 204, 1900).   He found that if the rate of evolution of gas evolved during the action be plotted as ordinate against the time as abscissa, a curve is

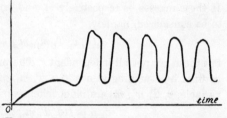

FIG. 54.—Ostwald's Curve of Chemical Action.

obtained which shows regularly alternating periods of slow and rapid evolution of hydrogen.   The particular form of these " waves " varies with the conditions of the experiment.   One of Ostwald's curves is shown in Fig. 54 (see J. W. Mellor's *Chemical Statics and Dynamics*, London, 348, 1904).

§ 50. Generalized Forces and Coordinates.

When a mass of any substance is subject to some physical change, certain properties—mass, chemical composition—remain fixed and invariable, while other properties—temperature, pressure, volume—vary.   When the value these variables assume in any given condition of the substance is known, we are said to have a complete knowledge of the state of the system.   These variable properties are not necessarily independent of one another.   We have just seen, for instance, that if two of the three variables defining the state of a perfect gas are known, the third variable can be determined from the equation

$$pv = RT,$$

where R is a constant.   In such a case as this, the third variable is said to be a dependent variable, the other two, independent variables.   When the state of any material system can be defined in terms of n independent variables, the system is said to possess n **degrees of freedom,** and the n independent variables are called **generalized coordinates.**   For the system just considered $n = 2$, and the system possesses two degrees of freedom.

Again, in order that we may possess a knowledge of some systems, say gaseous nitrogen peroxide, not only must the variables given by the gas equation

$$\phi(p, v, T) = 0$$

be known, but also the mass of the N_2O_4 and of the NO_2 present. If these masses be respectively m_1 and m_2, there are five variables to be considered, namely,

$$\phi_1(p, v, T, m_1, m_2) = 0,$$

but these are not all independent.   The pressure, for instance, may be fixed by assigning values to v, T, m_1, m_2 ; p is thus a dependent variable, v, T, m_1, m_2 are independent variables.   Thus

$$p = f(v, T, m_1, m_2).$$

We know that the dissociation of N_2O_4 into $2NO_2$ depends on the volume, temperature and amount of NO_2 present in the system under consideration.   At ordinary temperatures

$$m_1 = f_1(v, T, m_2),$$

and the number of independent variables is reduced to three.   In this case the system is said to possess three degrees of freedom. At temperatures over 135°—138° the system contains NO_2 alone, and behaves as a perfect gas with two degrees of freedom.

In general, if a system contains m dependent and n independent variables, say

$$x_1, x_2, x_3, \ldots x_{n + m}$$

variables, the state of the system can be determined by $m + n$ equations.   As in the familiar condition for the solution of simultaneous equations in algebra, n independent equations are required for finding the value of n unknown quantities.   But the state of the system is *defined* by the m dependent variables ; the remaining n independent variables can therefore be determined from n independent equations.

Let a given system with n degrees of freedom be subject to external forces

$$X_1, X_2, X_3, \ldots X_n,$$

so that no energy enters or leaves the system except in the form of heat or work, and such that the n independent variables are displaced by amounts

$$dx_1, \ dx_2, \ dx_3, \ldots dx_n.$$

Since the amount of work done on or by a system is measured by the product of the force and the displacement, these external forces $X_1 X_2 \ldots$ perform a quantity of work dW which depends on the nature of the transformation.   Hence

$$dW = X_1 dx_1 + X_2 dx_2 + \ldots X_n dx_n$$

where the coefficients X_1, X_2, $X_3 \ldots$ are called the **generalized forces** acting on the system.   P. Duhem, in his work, *Traité Élémentaire de Mécanique Chimique fondée sur la Thermodynamique*, Paris, 1897-99, makes use of generalized forces and generalized coordinates.

CHAPTER III.

FUNCTIONS WITH SINGULAR PROPERTIES.

"Although a physical law may never admit of a perfectly abrupt
change, there is no limit to the approach which it may make
to abruptness."—W. STANLEY JEVONS.

§ 51. Continuous and Discontinuous Functions.

THE law of continuity affirms that no change can take place
abruptly. The conception involved will have been familiar to the
reader from the second section of this work. It was there
shown that the amount of substance, x, transformed in a chemical
reaction in a given time becomes smaller as the interval of time, t,
during which the change occurs, is diminished, until finally, when
the interval of time approaches zero, the amount of substance
transformed also approaches zero. In such a case x is not only a
function of t, but it is a **continuous function** of t. The course of
such a reaction may be represented by the motion of a point along
the curve

$$x = f(t).$$

If the two states of a substance subjected to the influence of two
different conditions of temperature be represented, say, by two
neighbouring points on a plane, the principle of continuity affirms
that the state of the substance at any intermediate temperature
will be represented by a point lying between the two points just
mentioned; and in order that the moving point may pass from one
point, a, on the curve to another point. b, on the same curve, it
must successively assume all values intermediate between a and b,
and never move off the curve. This is a characteristic property of
continuous functions. Several examples have been considered in
the preceding chapters. Most natural processes, perhaps all, can
be represented by continuous functions. Hence the old empiricism :
Natura non agit per saltum.

The law of continuity, though tacitly implied up to the present,

142

does not appear to be always true.   Even in some of the simplest phenomena exceptions seem to arise.   In a general way, we can divide discontinuous functions into two classes : first, those in which the graph of the function suddenly stops to reappear in some other part of the plane—in other words a **break** occurs ; second, those in which the graph suddenly changes its direction without exhibiting a break [1]—in that case a **turning point or point of inflexion** appears.

Other kinds of discontinuity may occur, but do not commonly arise in physical work.   For example, a function is said to be discontinuous when the value of the function $y = f(x)$ becomes infinite for some particular value of x.   Such a discontinuity occurs when $x = 0$ in the expression $y = 1/x$.   The differential coefficient of this expression,

$$\frac{dy}{dx} = -\frac{1}{x^2},$$

is also discontinuous for $x = 0$.   Other examples, which should be verified by the reader are, $\log x$, when $x = 0$; $\tan x$, when $x = \frac{1}{2}\pi$, ... The graph for Boyle's equation, $pv = \text{constant}$, is also said to be discontinuous at an infinite distance along both axes.

§ 52. Discontinuity accompanied by "Breaks".

If a cold solid be exposed to a source of heat, heat appears to be absorbed, and the temperature, θ, of the solid is a function of the amount of heat, Q, apparently absorbed by the solid.   As soon as the solid begins to melt, it absorbs a great amount of heat (latent heat of fusion), unaccompanied by any rise of temperature.   When the

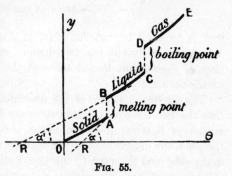

Fig. 55.

substance has assumed the fluid state of aggregation, the tem-

---

[1] Sometimes the word "break" is used indiscriminately for both kinds of discontinuity.   It is, indeed, questionable if ever the "break" is real in natural phenomena.   I suppose we ought to call turning points "singularities," not "discontinuities" (see S. Jevon's *Principles of Science*, London, 1877).

perature is a function of the amount of heat absorbed by the fluid, until, at the boiling point, similar phenomena recur. Heat is absorbed unaccompanied by any rise of temperature (latent heat of vaporization) until the liquid is completely vaporized. The phenomena are illustrated graphically by the curve $OABCDE$ (Fig. 55). If the quantity of heat, Q, supplied be regarded as a function of the temperature, θ, the equation of the curve $OABCED$ (Fig. 55) will be

$$Q = f(\theta).$$

This function is said to be discontinuous between the points A and B, and between C and D. Breaks occur in these positions. $f(\theta)$ is accordingly said to be a **discontinuous function**, for, if a small quantity of heat be added to a substance, whose state is represented by a point, between A and B, or C and D, the temperature is not affected in a perceptible manner. The geometrical signification of the phenomena is as follows: There are two generally different, tangents to the curve at the points A and B corresponding to the one abscissa, namely, tan α and tan α'. In other words, see page 102, we have

$$\frac{dQ}{d\theta} = f'(\theta) = \tan\alpha = \tan\text{ angle } \theta RA \ ;$$

$$\frac{dQ}{d\theta} = f'(\theta) = \tan\alpha' = \tan\text{ angle } \theta R'A,$$

that is to say, the function $f'(\theta)$ is discontinuous because the differential coefficient has two distinct values determined by the slope of the tangent to each curve at the point where the discontinuity occurs.

The physical meaning of the discontinuity in this example, is that the substance may have two values for its specific heat—the amount of heat required to raise the temperature of one gram of the solid one degree—at the melting point, the one corresponding to the solid and the other to the liquid state of aggregation. The tangent of the angle represented by the ratio $dQ/d\theta$ obviously represents the specific heat of the substance. An analogous set of changes occurs at the boiling point.

It is necessary to point out that the alleged discontinuity in the curve $OABC$ may be only apparent. The "corners" may be rounded off. It would perhaps be more correct to say that the curve is really continuous between A and B, but that the *change* of temperature with the addition of heat is discontinuous.

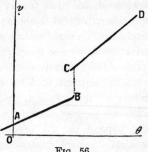

Again, Fig. 56 shows the result of plotting the variations in the volume of phosphorus with temperatures in the neighbourhood of its melting point. AB represents the expansion curve of the solid, CD that of the liquid. A break occurs between B and C. Phosphorus at its melting point may thus have two distinct coefficients of ex-

FIG. 56.

pansion, the one corresponding to the solid and the other to the liquid state of aggregation.   Similar changes take place during the passage of a system from one state to another, say of rhombic to monoclinic sulphur; of a mixture of magnesium and sodium sulphates to astracanite, etc.   The temperature at which this change occurs is called the "transition point".

§ 53. The Existence of Hydrates in Solution.

Another illustration.   If p denotes the percentage composition of an aqueous solution of ethyl alcohol and s the corresponding specific gravity *in vacuo* at 15° (sp. gr. H_2O at 15° = 9991·6), we have the following table compiled by Mendeléeff:—

p	s	p	s	p	s	p	s
5	9904·1	30	9570·2	55	9067·4	80	8479·8
10	9831·2	35	9484·5	60	8953·8	85	8354·8
15	9768·4	40	9389·6	65	8838·6	90	8225·0
20	9707·9	45	9287·8	70	8714·5	95	8086·9
25	9644·3	50	9179·0	75	8601·4	100	7936·6

It was found empirically that the experimental results are fairly well represented by the equation

$$s = a + bp + cp^2, \qquad . \qquad . \qquad . \qquad (1)$$

which is the general expression for a parabolic curve, a, b and c being constants, page 99, or the equation may embody two straight lines, page 121.   By plotting the experimental data the curve shown in Fig. 57 is obtained.

It is urged that just as compounds may be formed and decomposed at temperatures higher than that at which their dissociation *commences*, and that for any given temperature a definite relation exists between the amounts of the original compound and of the products of its dissociation, so may definite but unstable hydrates exist in solutions at temperatures above their dissociation temperature. If the dissolved substance really enters into combination with the solvent to form different compounds according to the nature of the solution, many of the physical properties of the solution—density, thermal conductivity and such like—will naturally depend on the amount and nature of these compounds, because chemical combination is usually accompanied by volume, density, thermal and other changes.

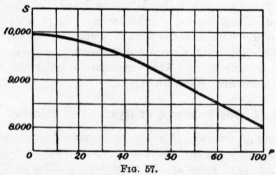

FIG. 57.

Assuming that the *amount* of such a definite compound is proportional to the concentration of the solution, the rate of change of, say, the density, s, with change of concentration, p, will be a linear function of p, in other words, ds/dp will be represented by the equation for a straight line. From the differentiation of (1), we obtain,

$$\frac{ds}{dp} = b + 2cp, \qquad . \qquad . \qquad . \qquad (2)$$

where ds is the difference in the density of two experimental values corresponding with a difference dp in the percentage composition of the two solutions. The second member of (2) corresponds with the equation of a straight line, page 90. On treating the experimental data by this method, Mendeléeff [1] found that ds/dp

[1] D. Mendeléeff, *Journ. Chem. Soc.*, **51**, 778, 1887; S. U. Pickering, *ib.*, **57**, 64, 331, 1890; *Phil. Mag.* [5], **29**, 427, 1890; *Watt's Dict. Chem.*, art. "Solutions" ii., 1894; H. Crompton, *Journ. Chem. Soc.*, **53**, 116, 1888; S. Arrhenius, *Phil. Mag.* [5], **28**, 36, 1889; E. H. Hayes, *ib.* [5], **32**, 99, 1891; A. W. Rücker, *ib.* [5], **32**, 306, 1891; S. Lupton, *ib.* [5], **31**, 418, 1891; T. M. Lowry, *Science Progress*, **3**, 124, 1908.

was discontinuous.   Breaks were obtained by plotting ds/dp as ordinates against abscissa p for concentrations corresponding to 17·56, 46·00 and 88·46 per cent. of ethyl alcohol. These concentrations coincide

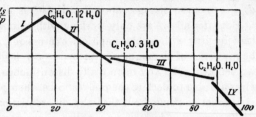

FIG. 58.—After Mendeléeff.

with chemical compounds having the composition $C_2H_5OH . 12H_2O$, $C_2H_5OH . 3H_2O$ and $3C_2H_5OH . H_2O$ as shown in Fig. 58. The curves between the breaks are supposed to represent the "zone" in which the corresponding hydrates are present in the solution.

The mathematical argument is that the differential coefficient of a continuous curve will differentiate into a straight line or another continuous curve ; while if a curve is really discontinuous, or made up of a number of different curves, it will yield a series of straight lines. Each line represents the rate of change of the particular physical property under investigation with the amount of *hypothetical* unstable compound existing in solution at that concentration. An abrupt change in the direction of the curve leads to a breaking up of the first differential coefficient of that curve into two curves which do not meet. This argument has been extensively used by Pickering in the treatment of an elaborate and painstaking series of determinations of the physical properties of solutions. Crompton found that if the electrical conductivity of a solution is regarded as a function of its percentage composition, such that

$$K = a + bp + cp^2 + fp^3, \quad \cdot \quad \cdot \quad \cdot \quad (3)$$

the first differential coefficient gives a parabolic curve of the type of (1) above, while the second differential coefficient, instead of being a continuous function of p,

$$\frac{d^2K}{dp^2} = A + Bp, \quad \cdot \quad \cdot \quad \cdot \quad (4)$$

was found to consist of a series of straight lines, the position of the breaks being identical with those obtained from the first differential coefficient ds/dp. The values of the constants A and B are readily obtained if c and p are known. If the slope of the (p, s)-curve changes abruptly, ds/dp is discontinuous ; if the slope of the $(ds/dp, p)$-curve changes abruptly, d^2s/dp^2 is discontinuous.

But after all we are only working with empirical formulæ, and "no juggling with feeble empirical expressions, and no appeal to the mysteries of elementary mathematics can legitimately make experimental results any more really discontinuous than they themselves are able to declare themselves to be when properly plotted ".[1]

It must be pointed out that the differentiation of experimental results very often furnishes quantities of the same order of magnitude as the experimental errors themselves.[2] This is a very serious objection. Pickering has tried to eliminate the experimental errors, to some extent, by differentiating the results obtained by "smoothing" the curve obtained by plotting the experimental results. On the face of it this "smoothing" of experimental results is a dangerous operation even in the hands of the most experienced workers. Indeed, it is supposed that that prince of experimenters, Regnault, overlooked an important phenomenon in applying this very smoothing process to his observations on the vapour pressure of saturated steam. Regnault supposed that the curve OPQ (Fig. 64) showed no singular point at P (Fig. 64) when water passed from the liquid to the solid state at 0°. It was reserved for J. Thomson to prove that the ice-steam curve has a different slope from the water-steam curve.

§ 54. The Smoothing of Curves.

The results of observations of a series of corresponding changes

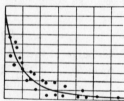

FIG. 59.—Smoothed Curve.

in two variables are represented by light dots on a sheet of squared paper. The dots in Fig. 59 represent the vapour pressures of dissociating ammonium carbonate at different temperatures. A curve is drawn to pass as nearly as possible through all these points. The resulting curve is assumed to be a graphic representation of the general formula (known or unknown) connecting the two variables. Points devi-

---

[1] O. J. Lodge, *Nature*, **40**, 273, 1889 ; S. U. Pickering, *ib.*, **40**, 343, 1889.
[2] This paragraph will be better understood after Chapter V., § 106, has been studied. The reader may then return to this section.

ating from the curve are assumed to be affected with errors of observation. As a general rule the curve with the least curvature is chosen to pass through or within a short distance of the greatest number of dots, so that an equal number of these dots (representing experimental observations) lies on each side of the curve. Such a curve is said to be a **smoothed curve** (see also page 320).

One of the commonest methods of smoothing a curve is to pin down a flexible lath to points through which the curve is to be drawn and draw the pen along the lath. It is found impossible in practice to use similar laths for all curves. The lath is weakest where the curvature is greatest. The selection and use of the lath is a matter of taste and opinion. The use of " French curves " is still more arbitrary. Pickering used a bent spring or steel lath held near its ends. Such a lath is shown in statical works to give a line of constant curvature. The line is called an "elastic curve" (see G. M. Minchin's *A Treatise on Statics*, Oxford, 2, 204, 1886).

§ 55. Discontinuity accompanied by a Sudden Change of Direction.

The vapour pressure of a solid increases continuously with rising temperature until, at its melting point, the vapour pressure " suddenly " begins to increase more rapidly than before. This is shown graphically in Fig. 60. The substance melts at the point of intersection of the " solid " and " liquid " curves. The vapour pressure itself is not discontinuous. It has the same value at the melting point for both solid and liquid states of aggregation. It is, however, quite clear that the tangents of the two curves differ from each other at the transition point, because

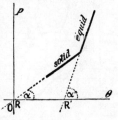

FIG. 60.

$\tan a = f(\theta) = \dfrac{dp}{d\theta}$ is less than $\tan a' = f(\theta) = \dfrac{dp}{d\theta}$.

There are two tangents to the $p\theta$-curve at the transition point. The value of $dp/d\theta$ for solid benzene, for example, is greater than for the liquid. The numbers are 2·48 and 1·98 respectively.

If the equations of the two curves were respectively $ax + by = 1$; and $bx + ay = 1$, the roots of these two equations,

$$x = \frac{1}{a+b}; \; y = \frac{1}{a+b},$$

would represent the coordinates of the point of intersection, as indicated on page 94. To illustrate this kind of discontinuity we shall examine the following phenomena :—

I. Critical temperature. Cailletet and Collardeau have an ingenious method for finding the **critical temperature** of a substance without seeing the liquid.[1] By plotting temperatures as abscissæ against the vapour pressures of different weights of the same substance heated at constant volume, a series of curves are obtained which are coincident as long as *part* of the substance is liquid, for " the pressure exerted by a saturated vapour depends

FIG. 61.

on temperature only and is independent of the quantity of liquid with which it is in contact ". Above the critical temperature the different masses of the substance occupying the same volume give different pressures. From this point upwards the pressure-temperature curves are no longer superposable. A series of curves are thus obtained which coincide at a certain point *P* (Fig. 61), the abscissa, *OK*, of which denotes the critical temperature. As before, the tangent of each curve *Pa*, *Pb* . . . is different from that of *OP* at the point *P*.

II. Cooling curves. If the temperature of cooling of pure liquid bismuth be plotted against time, the resulting curve, called a **cooling curve** (*ab*, Fig. 62), is continuous, but the moment a part of the

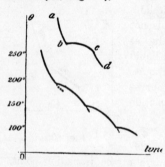

FIG. 62.—Cooling Curves.

metal solidifies, the curve will take another direction *bc*, and continue so until all the metal is solidified, when the direction of the curve again changes, and then continues quite regularly along *cd*. For bismuth the point *b* is at 268°.

If the cooling curve of an alloy of bismuth, lead and tin (Bi, 21 ; Pb, 5·5 ; Sn, 75·5) is similarly plotted, the first change of direction is observed at 175°, when solid bismuth is deposited ; at 125° the curve again changes its direction,

---

[1] L. P. Cailletet and E. Collardeau, *Ann. Chim. Phys.*, [6], **25**, 522, 1891. Note that the *critical temperature* is the temperature above which a substance cannot exist other than in the gaseous state.

with a simultaneous deposition of solid bismuth and tin; and finally at 96° another change occurs corresponding to the solidification of the eutectic alloy of these three metals.

These cooling curves are of great importance in investigations on the constitution of metals and alloys.   The cooling curve of iron from a white heat is particularly interesting, and has given rise to much discussion.   The curve shows changes of direction at about 1,130°, at about 850° (called Ar_3 critical point), at about 770° (called Ar_2 critical point), at about 500° (called the Ar_1 critical point), at about 450°—500° C., and at about 400° C.   The magnitude of these changes varies according to the purity of the iron.   Some are very marked even with the purest iron.   This sudden evolution of heat (recalescence) at different points of the cooling curve has led many to believe that iron exists in some

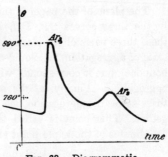

FIG. 63.—Diagrammatic.

allotropic state in the neighbourhood of these temperatures.[1]   Fig. 63 shows part of a cooling curve of iron in the most interesting region, namely, the Ar_3 and Ar_2 critical points.

§ 56. The Triple Point.

Another example, which is also a good illustration of the beauty and comprehensive nature of the graphic method of representing natural processes, may be given here.

(a) When water, partly liquid, partly vapour, is enclosed in a vessel, the relation between the pressure and the temperature can be represented by the curve PQ (Fig. 64), which gives the pressure corresponding with any given tempera-

FIG. 64.—Triple Point.

ture when the liquid and vapour are in contact and in equilibrium. This curve is called the **steam line**.

(b) In the same way if the enclosure were filled with solid ice,

---

[1] W. C. Roberts-Austen's papers in the *Proc. Soc. Mechanical Engineers*, 543, 1891 ; 102, 1893 ; 238, 1895 ; 31, 1897 ; 35, 1899, may be consulted for fuller details.

and liquid water, the pressure of the mixture would be completely determined by the temperature. The relation between pressure and temperature is represented by the curve *PN*, called the **ice line**.

(*c*) Ice may be in stable equilibrium with its vapour, and we can plot the variation of the vapour pressure of ice with its temperature. The curve *OP* so obtained represents the variation of the vapour pressure of ice with temperature. It is called the **hoar frost line**.

The plane of the paper is thus divided into three parts bounded by the three curves *OP*, *PN*, *PQ*. If a point falls within one of these three parts of the plane, it represents water in one particular state of aggregation, ice, liquid or steam.[1] When a point falls on a boundary line it corresponds with the coexistence of two states of aggregation. Finally, at the point *P*, and only at this point, the three states of aggregation, ice, water, and steam may coexist together. This point is called the **triple point**. For water the coordinates of the triple point are

$$p = 4 \cdot 58 \text{ mm.,} \quad T = 0 \cdot 0076° \text{ C.}$$

1. Influence of pressure on the melting-point of a solid. The two formulæ, $dQ = Td\phi$; $(\partial Q/\partial v)_T = T(\partial p/\partial T)_v$, were discussed on pages 81 and 82. Divide the former by dv and substitute the result in the latter. We thus obtain,

$$\left(\frac{\partial \phi}{\partial v}\right)_T = \left(\frac{\partial p}{\partial T}\right)_v, \quad \cdot \quad \cdot \quad \cdot \quad (1)$$

which states that the change of entropy, ϕ, per unit change of volume, v, at a constant temperature ($T°$ absolute), is equal to the change of pressure per unit change of temperature at constant volume. If a small amount of heat, dQ, be added to a substance existing partly in one state, "1," and partly in another state, "2," a proportional quantity, dm, of the mass changes its state, such that

$$dQ = L_{12}dm,$$

where L_{12} is a constant representing the latent heat of the change from state "1" to state "2". From the definition of entropy, ϕ,

---

[1] Certain unstable conditions (*metastable states*) are known in which a liquid may be found in the solid region. A supercooled liquid, for instance, may continue the *QP* curve along to *S* instead of changing its direction along *PM*.

$$dQ = Td\phi \; ; \; \text{hence} \; d\phi = \frac{L_{12}}{T}dm. \quad . \quad . \quad (2)$$

If v_1, v_2 be the specific volumes of the substance in the first and second states respectively

$$dv = v_2 dm - v_1 dm = (v_2 - v_1)dm.$$

From (2) and (1)

$$\therefore \left(\frac{\partial\phi}{\partial v}\right)_T = \frac{L_{12}}{T(v_2 - v_1)}\; ; \; \left(\frac{\partial p}{\partial T}\right)_v = \frac{L_{12}}{T(v_2 - v_1)}. \quad . \quad (3)$$

This last equation tells us at once how a change of pressure will change the temperature at which two states of a substance can coexist, provided that we know v_1, v_2, T and L_{12}.

EXAMPLES.—(1) If the specific volume of ice is 1·087, and that of water unity, find the lowering of the freezing point of water when the pressure increases one atmosphere (latent heat of ice = 80 cal.). Here $v_2 - v_1 = 0·087$, $T = 273$, $dp = 76$ cm. mercury. The specific gravity of mercury is 13·5, and the weight of a column of mercury of one square cm. cross section is $76 \times 13·5 = 1,033$ grams. Hence $dp = 1,033$ grams? $L_{12} = 80$ cal.$= 80 \times 47,600$ C.G.S. or dynamical units. From (3), $dT = 0·0064°$ C. per atmosphere.

(2) For naphthalene $T = 352·2$, $v_2 - v_1 = 0·146$; $L_{12} = 35·46$ cal. Find the change of melting point per atmosphere increase of pressure. $dT = 0·031$.

II. *The slopes of the pT-curves at the triple point.* Let L_{12}, L_{23}, L_{31} be the latent heats of conversion of a substance from states 1 to 2; 2 to 3; 3 to 1 respectively; v_1, v_2, v_3 the respective volumes of the substance in states 1, 2, 3 respectively; let T denote the absolute temperature at the triple point. Then dp/dT is the slope of the tangent to these curves at the triple point, and

$$\left(\frac{\partial p}{\partial T}\right)_{12} = \frac{L_{12}}{T(v_2 - v_1)}\; ; \; \left(\frac{\partial p}{\partial T}\right)_{23} = \frac{L_{23}}{T(v_3 - v_2)}\; ; \; \left(\frac{\partial p}{\partial T}\right)_{31} = \frac{L_{31}}{T(v_1 - v_3)}. \quad (4)$$

The specific volumes and the latent heats are generally quite different from the three changes of state, and therefore the slopes of the three curves at the triple point are also different. The difference in the slopes of the tangents of the solid-vapour (hoar frost line), and the liquid-vapour (steam line) curves of water (Fig. 39) is

$$\left(\frac{\partial p}{\partial T}\right)_{13} - \left(\frac{\partial p}{\partial T}\right)_{23} = \frac{1}{T}\left(\frac{L_{13}}{v_3 - v_1} - \frac{L_{23}}{v_3 - v_2}\right). \quad . \quad (5)$$

At the triple point

$$L_{13} = L_{12} + L_{23}\; ; \; \text{and} \; (v_3 - v_1) = (v_2 - v_1) + (v_3 - v_2). \quad (6)$$

EXAMPLE.—As a general rule, the change of volume on melting, $(v_2 - v_1)$, is very small compared with the change in volume on evaporation, $(v_3 - v_2)$, or sublimation, $(v_3 - v_1)$; hence $v_2 - v_1$ may be neglected in comparison with the other volume changes.   Then, from (5) and (6),

$$\left(\frac{\partial p}{\partial T}\right)_{13} - \left(\frac{\partial p}{\partial T}\right)_{23} = \frac{L_{12}}{T(v_3 - v_2)} . \quad \cdot \quad \cdot \quad \cdot \quad (7)$$

Hence calculate the difference in the slope of the hoar frost and steam lines for water at the triple point.   Latent heat of water = 80 ; $L_{12} = 80 \times 42,700$; $T = 273, v_3 - v_2 = 209,400$ c.c.   Substitute these values on the right-hand side of the last equation.   Ansr. 0·059.

The above deductions have been tested experimentally in the case of water, sulphur and phosphorus ; the results are in close agreement with theory.

§ 57. Maximum and Minimum Values of a Function.

By plotting the rates, V, at which illuminating gas flows through the gasometer of a building as ordinates, with time, t, as abscissæ, a curve resembling the adjoining diagram (Fig. 65) is obtained.

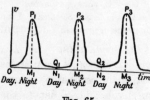

FIG. 65.

It will be seen that very little gas is consumed in the day time, while at night there is a relatively great demand.   Observation shows that as t changes from one value to another, V changes in such a way that it is sometimes increasing and sometimes decreasing.   In consequence, there must be certain values of the function for which V, which had previously been increasing, begins to decrease, that is to say, V is greater for this particular value of t than for any adjacent value ; in this case V is said to have a **maximum value.** Conversely, there must be certain values of $f(t)$ for which V, having been decreasing, begins to increase.   When the value of V, for some particular value of t, is less than for any adjacent value of t, V is said to be a **minimum value.**

Imagine a variable ordinate of the curve to move perpendicularly along Ot, gradually increasing until it arrives at the position M_1P_1, and afterwards gradually decreasing.   The ordinate at M_1P_1 is said to have a maximum value.   The decreasing ordinate, continuing its motion, arrives at the position N_1Q_1, and after that gradually increases.   In this case the ordinate at N_1Q_1 is said to have a minimum value.

The terms "maximum" and "minimum" do not necessarily

denote the greatest and least possible values which the function can assume, for the same function may have several maximum and several minimum values, any particular one of which may be greater or less than another value of the same function. In walking across a mountainous district every hill-top would represent a maximum, every valley a minimum.

The mathematical form of the function employed in the above illustration is unknown, the curve is an approximate representation of corresponding values of the two variables determined by actual measurements.

EXAMPLE.—Plot the curve represented by the equation $y = \sin x$. Give x a series of values $\frac{1}{2}\pi$, π, $\frac{3}{2}\pi$, 2π, and so on. Show that

Maximum values of y occur for $x = \frac{1}{2}\pi$, $\frac{5}{2}\pi$, $\frac{9}{2}\pi$, ...

Minimum values of y occur for $x = -\frac{1}{2}\pi$, $\frac{3}{2}\pi$, $\frac{7}{2}\pi$, ...

The resulting curve is the harmonic or sine curve shown in Fig. 52, page 136.

One of the most important applications of the differential calculus is the determination of maximum and minimum values of a function. Many of the following examples can be solved by special algebraic or geometric devices. The calculus, however, offers a sure and easy method for the solution of these problems.

§ 58. How to find Maximum and Minimum Values of a Function.

If a cricket ball be thrown up into the air, its velocity, ds/dt, will go on diminishing until the ball reaches the highest point of its ascent. Its velocity will then be zero. After this, the velocity of the ball will increase until it is caught in the hand. In other words, ds/dt is first positive, then zero, and then negative. This means that the distance, s, of the ball from the ground will be greatest when ds/dt is least; s will be a maximum when ds/dt is zero.

We generally reckon distances up as positive, and distances down as negative. We naturally extend this to velocities by making velocities directed upwards positive, and velocities directed downwards negative. Thus the velocity of a falling stone is negative although it is constantly getting numerically greater (*i.e.*, algebraically less). We also extend this convention to directed acceleration; but we frequently call an increasing velocity positive, and a decreasing velocity negative as indicated on page 18.

NUMERICAL ILLUSTRATION.—The distance, s, of a body from the ground at any instant, t, is given by the expression

$$s = \tfrac{1}{2}gt^2 + v_0t,$$

where v_0 represents the velocity of the body when it started its upward or downward journey; g is a constant equal to -32 when the body is going upwards, and to $+32$ when the body is coming down. Now let a cricket ball be sent up from the hand with a velocity of 64 feet per second, it will attain its highest point when ds/dt is zero, but

$$\frac{ds}{dt} = -32t + v_0 \; ; \; \therefore t = \frac{v_0}{32} = \frac{64}{32}, \text{ when } \frac{ds}{dt} = 0.$$

Let us now trace the different values which the tangent to the curve at any point X (Fig. 66) assumes as X travels from A to P;

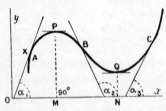

FIG. 66.—Maximum and Minimum.

from P to B; from B to Q; and from Q to C; let a denote the angle made by the tangent at any point on the curve with the x-axis. Remember that $\tan 0° = 0$; $\tan 90° = \infty$; when a is less than 90°, $\tan a$ is positive; and when a is greater than 90° and less than 180° $\tan a$ is negative.

First, as P travels from A to P, x increases, y increases. The tangent to the curve makes an acute angle, a_1, with the x-axis. In this case, $\tan a$ is positive, and also

$$\frac{dy}{dx} = +. \qquad . \qquad . \qquad . \qquad . \qquad (1)$$

At P, the tangent is parallel to the x-axis; y is a maximum, that is to say, $\tan a$ is zero, and

$$\frac{dy}{dx} = 0 ; \qquad . \qquad . \qquad . \qquad . \qquad (2)$$

Secondly, immediately after passing P, the tangent to the curve makes an *obtuse* angle, a_2, with the x-axis, that is to say, $\tan a$ is negative, and

$$\frac{dy}{dx} = -. \qquad . \qquad . \qquad . \qquad . \qquad (3)$$

The tangent to the curve reaches a minimum value at NQ; at Q the tangent is again parallel to x-axis, y is a minimum and $\tan a$, as well as

$$\frac{dy}{dx} = 0. \qquad . \qquad . \qquad . \qquad . \qquad (4)$$

After passing Q, again we have an acute angle, a_3, and,

$$\frac{dy}{dx} = +. \quad . \quad . \quad . \quad . \quad (5)$$

Thus we see that every time dy/dx becomes zero, y is either a maximum or a minimum.   Hence the rule : When the first differential coefficient changes its sign from a positive to a negative value the function has a maximum value, and when the first differential coefficient changes its sign from a negative to a positive value the function has a minimum value.

There are some curves which have maximum and minimum values very much resembling P' and Q' (Fig. 67).   These curves are said to have cusps at P' and Q'.

It will be observed, in Fig. 67, that x increases and y approaches a maximum value while the tangent $M'P'$ makes an acute angle with the x-axis, that is to say, dy/dx is positive.   At P' the tangent becomes perpendicular to the x-axis, and in consequence the ratio dy/dx becomes *infinite*.   The point P' is called a **cusp**. After passing P', dy/dx is negative.   In

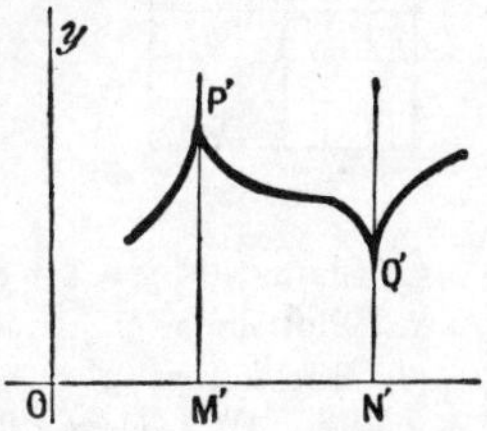

Fig. 67.—Maximum and Minimum Cusps.

the same way it can be shown that as the tangent approaches $N'Q'$, dy/dx is negative, at Q', dy/dx becomes *infinite*, and after passing Q', dy/dx is positive.   Now plot $y = x^{\frac{2}{3}}$, and you will get a cusp at O.

A function may thus change its sign by becoming zero or infinity, it is therefore necessary for the first differential coefficient of the function to assume either of these values in order that it may have a maximum or a minimum value.   Consequently, in order to find all the values of x for which y possesses a maximum or a minimum value, the first differential coefficient must be equated to zero or infinity and the values of x which satisfy these conditions determined.

EXAMPLES.—(1) Consider the equation $y = x^2 - 8x$, $\therefore$ $dy/dx = 2x - 8$. Equating the first differential coefficient to zero, we have $2x - 8 = 0$; or $x = 4$. Add ± 1 to this root and substitute for x in the original equation,

$$\text{when } x = 3, y = \quad 9 - 24 = -15;$$
$$x = 4, y = 16 - 32 = -16;$$
$$x = 5, y = 25 - 40 = -15.$$

y is therefore a minimum when $x = 4$, since a slightly greater or a slightly less value of x makes y assume a greater value.   The addition of ± 1 to the root gives only a first approximation.   The minimum value of the function might have been between 3 and 4; or between 4 and 5. The approximation may be carried as close as we please by using less and less numerical values in the above substitution. Suppose we substitute in place of $\pm 1, \pm h$, then

$$\text{when } x = 4 - h,\ y = h^2 - 16;$$
$$x = 4,\qquad y = \quad -16;$$
$$x = 4 + h,\ y = h^2 - 16.$$

Therefore, however small h may be, the corresponding value of y is greater than -16. That is to say, $x = 4$ makes the function a minimum, Q (Fig. 68). You can easily see that this is so by plotting the original equation as in Fig. 68.

FIG. 68.

FIG. 69.

FIG. 70.

(2) Show that $y = 1 + 8x - 2x^2$, has a maximum value, P (Fig. 69), for $x = 2$. Plot the original equation as in Fig. 69.

(3) Show that y has neither a maximum nor a minimum when $y = 2 + (x - 1)^3$. Here $dy/dx = 3(x - 1)^2 = 0$; $\therefore x = 1$. But $x = 1$ does not make y a maximum nor a minimum. If $x = 1, y = 2$; if $x = 0, y = 1$; if $x = 2, y = 3$, the graph is shown in Fig. 70. The critical point is at P.

§ 59. Turning Points or Points of Inflexion.

Let us now return to the subject of § 58. The fact that

$$\frac{dy}{dx} = 0 ;\ \text{or},\ \frac{dy}{dx} = \infty,$$

is not a *sufficient* condition to establish the existence of maximum and minimum values of a function, although it is a rough practical

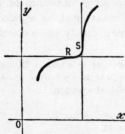

test. Some of the values thus obtained do not necessarily make the function a maximum or a minimum, since a variable may become zero or infinite without changing its sign. This will be obvious from a simple inspection of Fig. 71, where

$$\frac{dy}{dx} = 0 \text{ at } R ;\ \text{and},\ \frac{dy}{dx} = \infty \text{ at } S.$$

FIG. 71.—Points of Inflexion.

Yet neither maximum nor minimum values of the function exist. A further test is therefore required in order to decide whether individual values of x correspond to maximum or minimum values of the function. This is all the more essential in practical work where the function, not the curve, is to be operated upon.

By reference to Fig. 71 it will be noticed that the tangent crosses the curve at the points R and S. Such a point is called a **turning point or point of inflexion.** You will get a point of inflexion by plotting $y = x^3$. The point of inflexion marks the spot where the curve passes from a convex to a concave, or from a concave to a convex configuration with regard to one of the co-ordinate axes. The terms concave and convex have here their ordinary meaning.

§ 60. How to Find whether a Curve is Concave or Convex.

Referring to Fig. 72, along the concave part from A to P, the numerical value of $\tan a$, regularly decreases to zero. At P the highest point of the curve $\tan a = 0$; from this point to B the tangent to the angle continually decreases. You will see this better if you take numbers. Let $a_1 = 45°$, $a_2 = 135°$; $\therefore \tan a_1 = +1$, and $\tan a_2 = -1$. Hence as you pass along the curve from A to P to B, the numerical value of the tangent of the curve ranges from

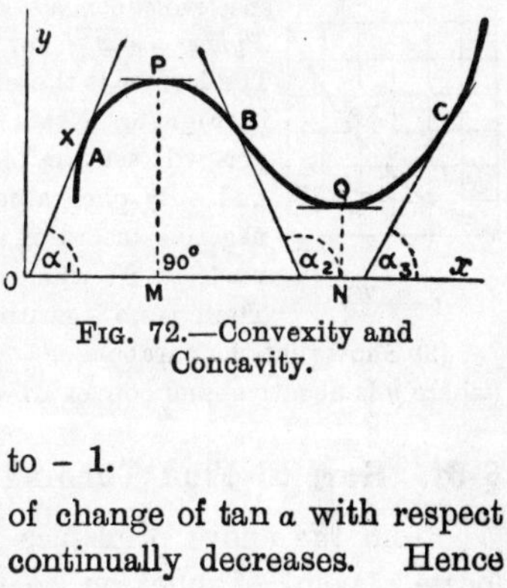

FIG. 72.—Convexity and Concavity.

$$+ 1, \text{ to } 0, \text{ to } - 1.$$

The differential coefficient, or rate of change of $\tan a$ with respect to x for the concave curve APB continually decreases. Hence $d(\tan a)/dx$ is negative, or

$$\frac{d(\tan a)}{dx} = \frac{d^2y}{dx^2} = \text{negative value} = < 0. \quad . \quad . \quad \textbf{(1)}$$

If a function, $y = f(x)$, increases with increasing values of x, dy/dx is positive; while if the function, $y = f(x)$, decreases with increasing values of x, dy/dx is negative.

Along the convex part of the curve BQC, $\tan a$ regularly increases in value. Let us take numbers. Suppose $a_2 = 135°$, $a_3 = 45°$, then $\tan a_2 = -1$ and $\tan a_3 = +1$. Hence as you pass along the curve from B to Q, $\tan a$ increases in value from -1 to 0. At the point Q, $\tan a = 0$, and from Q to C, $\tan a$ continually increases in value from 0 to + 1. The differential coefficient of tan α with respect to the convex curve BQC is, therefore, positive, or

$$\frac{d(\tan \alpha)}{dx} = \frac{d^2y}{dx^2} = \text{ positive value } = > 0. \quad . \quad . \quad (2)$$

Hence *a curve is concave or convex upwards, according as the second differential coefficient is negative or positive.*

I have assumed that the curve is on the positive side of the x-axis; when the curve lies on the negative side, assume the x-axis to be displaced parallel with itself until the above condition is attained. A more general rule, which evades the above limitation, is proved in the regular text-books. The proof is of little importance for our purpose. The rule is to the effect that " a curve is concave or convex upwards according as the product of the ordinate of the curve and the second differential coefficient, *i.e.*, according as yd^2y/dx^2 is positive or negative ".

EXAMPLES.—(1) Show that the curves $y = \log x$ and $y = x \log x$ are respectively concave and convex towards the x-axis. Hint. $d^2y/dx^2 = - x^{-2}$ for the former; and $+ x^{-1}$ for the latter. The former is therefore concave, the latter convex, as shown in Fig. 73. Note: If you plot $y = \log x$ on a larger scale you will see that for every positive value of x there is one and only one value of y; the value of y will be positive or negative according as x is greater or less than unity. When $x = 1$, $y = 0$; when $x = 0$, $y = - \infty$; when $x = + \infty$, $y = + \infty$. There is no logarithmic function for negative values of x.

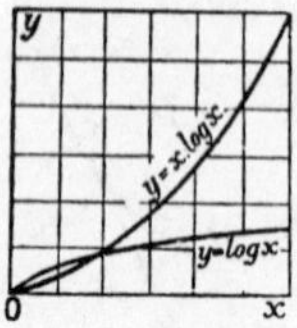

FIG. 73.

(2) Show that the parabola, $y^2 = 4ax$, is concave upwards below the x-axis (where y is negative) and convex upwards above the x-axis.

§ 61. How to Find Turning Points or Points of Inflexion.

From the above principles it is clearly necessary, in order to locate a point of inflexion, to find a value of x, for which tan α assumes a maximum or a minimum value. But

$$\tan \alpha = \frac{dy}{dx}; \; \therefore \frac{d(\tan \alpha)}{dx} = \frac{d^2y}{dx^2} = 0. \quad . \quad . \quad (3)$$

Hence the rule : In order to find a point of inflexion we must equate the second differential coefficient of the function to zero; find the value of x which satisfies these conditions; and test if the second differential coefficient does really change sign by substituting in the second differential coefficient a value of x a little greater and one a little less than the critical value. If there is no change of sign we are not dealing with a point of inflexion

EXAMPLES.—(1) Show that the curve $y = a + (x - b)^3$ has a point of inflexion at the point $y = a$, $x = b$. Differentiating twice we get $d^2y/dx^2 = 6(x - b)$. Equating this to zero we get $x = b$; by substituting $x = b$ in the original equation, we get $y = a$. When $x = b - 1$ the second differential coefficient is negative, when $x = b + 1$ the second differential coefficient is positive. Hence there is an inflexion at the point (b, a). See Fig. 70, page 158.

(2) For the special case of the harmonic curve, Fig. 52, page 136, $y = \sin x$; $\therefore d^2y/dx^2 = - \sin x = - y$, that is to say, at the point of inflexion the ordinate y changes sign. This occurs when the curve crosses the x-axis, and there are an infinite number of points of inflexion for which $y = 0$.

(3) Show that the probability curve, $y = ke^{-h^2x^2}$, has a point of inflexion for $x = \pm \sqrt{\frac{1}{2}}/h$. (Fig. 168, page 513.)

(4) Show that Roche's vapour pressure curve $p = ab^{\theta^{-1}(m+n\theta)}$ has a point of inflexion when $\theta = m(\log b - 2n)/2n^2$; and $p = ab^{(\log b - 2n)/n\log b}$. See Ex. (6), page 67; and Fig. 88, page 172.

§ 62. Six Problems in Maxima and Minima.

It is first requisite, in solving problems in maxima and minima, to express the relation between the variables in the form of an algebraic equation, and then to proceed as directed on page 157. In the majority of cases occurring in practice, it only requires a little common-sense reasoning on the nature of the problem, to determine whether a particular value of x corresponds with a maximum or a minimum. The very nature of the problem generally tells us whether we are dealing with a maximum or a minimum, so that we may frequently dispense with the labour of investigating the sign of the second derivative.

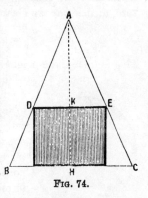

FIG. 74.

I. Divide a line into any two parts such that the rectangle having these two parts as adjoining sides may have the greatest possible area. If a be the length of the line, x the length of one part, $a - x$ will be the length of the other part; and, in consequence, the area of the rectangle will be

$$y = (a - x)x.$$

Differentiate, and

$$\frac{dy}{dx} = a - 2x.$$

Equate to zero, and, $x = \frac{1}{2}a$; that is to say, the line a must be divided into two equal parts, and the greatest possible rectangle is a square.

II. Find the greatest possible rectangle that can be inscribed in a given triangle. In Fig. 74, let b denote the length of the base of the triangle ABC, h its altitude, x the altitude of the inscribed rectangle. We must first find the relation between the area of the rectangle and of the triangle. By similar triangles, page 603,

$$AH : AK = BC : DE ; \; h : h - x = b : DE,$$

but the area of the rectangle is obviously $y = DE \times KH$, and

$$DE = \frac{b}{h}(h - x), \; KH = x ; \; \therefore y = \frac{b}{h}(hx - x^2).$$

It is the rule, when seeking maxima and minima, to simplify the process by omitting the constant factors, since, whatever makes the variable $hx - x^2$ a maximum will also make $b(hx - x^2)/h$ a maximum.[1] Now differentiate the expression obtained above for the area of the rectangle neglecting b/h, and equate the result to zero, in this way we obtain

$$\frac{dy}{dx} = h - 2x = 0; \; \text{or } x = \frac{h}{2}.$$

That is to say, the height of the rectangle must be half the altitude of the triangle.

Fig. 75.

III. To cut a sector from a circular sheet of metal so that the remainder can be formed into a conical-shaped vessel of maximum capacity. Let ACB (Fig. 75) be a circular plate of radius, r, it is required to cut out a portion AOB such that the conical vessel formed by joining OA and OB together may hold the greatest possible amount of fluid. Let x denote the angle remaining after the sector AOB has been removed. We must first find a relation between x and the volume, v, of the cone.[2]

The length of the arc ACB is $\frac{1}{180}x\pi r$, (3), page 603, and when

---

[1] This is easily proved, for let $y = cf(x)$, where c has any arbitrary constant value. For a maximum or minimum value $dy/dx = cf'(x) = 0$, and this can only occur where $f'(x) = 0$.

[2] Mensuration formulæ (1), (3), (4), (27), § 191, page 603; and (1), page 606, will be required for this problem.

the plate is folded into a cone, this is also the length of the perimeter of the circular base of the cone.   Let R denote the radius of
the circular base.   The perimeter of the base is therefore equal to
$2\pi R$.   Hence,

$$2\pi R = \frac{x}{\pi}\pi r ; \text{ or, } R = \frac{xr}{2\pi}. \qquad \qquad (1)$$

If h is the height of the vertical cone,

$$r^2 = R^2 + h^2 ; \text{ or, } h = \sqrt{r^2 - R^2}. \qquad \quad (2)$$

The volume of the cone is therefore

$$v = \frac{\pi}{3}R^2 h = \frac{\pi}{3}\left(\frac{xr}{2\pi}\right)^2 \sqrt{r^2 - \left(\frac{xr}{2\pi}\right)^2} \qquad \quad (3)$$

Rejecting the constants, v will be a maximum when $x^2\sqrt{4\pi^2 - x^2}$,
or when $x^4(4\pi^2 - x^2)$ is a maximum.   That is, when

$$\frac{d}{dx}\{x^4(4\pi^2 - x^2)\} = (16\pi^2 - 6x^2)x^3 = 0.$$

If $x = 0$, we have a vertical line corresponding with a cone of minimum volume.   Hence, if x is not zero, we must have

$$16\pi^2 - 6x^2 = 0 ; \text{ or, } x = 2\sqrt{\tfrac{2}{3}} \times 180° = 294°.$$

Hence the angle of the removed sector is about $360° - 294° = 66°$.
The application to funnels is obvious.   Of course the sides of the
chemists' funnel has a special slope for other reasons.

*IV. At what height should a light be placed above my writing table
in order that a small portion of the surface of the table, at a given
horizontal distance away from the foot of
the perpendicular dropped from the light
on to the table, may receive the greatest
illumination possible ?*   Let S (Fig. 76)
be the source of illumination whose distance, x, from the table is to be determined in such a way that B may receive
the greatest illumination.   Let $AB = a$,
and a the angle made by the incident
rays $SB = r$ on the surface B.

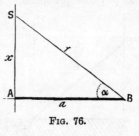

Fig. 76.

It is known that the intensity of illumination, y, varies inversely
as the square of the distance of SB, and directly as the sine of the
angle of incidence.   Since, by Pythagoras' theorem (Euclid, i., 47),
$r^2 = a^2 + x^2$; and $\sin a = x/r$, in order that the illumination may
be a maximum,

$$y = \frac{\sin a}{r^2} = \frac{x}{r^3} = \frac{x}{r^2\sqrt{a^2 + x^2}} = \frac{x}{(a^2 + x^2)^{\frac{3}{2}}}$$

L *

must be a maximum.   By differentiation, we get

$$\frac{dy}{dx} = \frac{a^2 - 2x^2}{(a^2 + x^2)^{\frac{5}{2}}} = 0 \; ; \; \therefore x = a \sqrt{\tfrac{1}{2}}.$$

The interpretation is obvious.   The height of the light must be 0·707 times the horizontal distance of the writing table from the " foot " A.   Negative and imaginary roots have no meaning in this problem.

V. To arrange a number of voltaic cells to furnish a maximum current against a known external resistance.   Let the electromotive force of each cell be E, and its internal resistance r.   Let R be the external resistance, n the total number of cells.   Assume that x cells are arranged in series and n/x in parallel.   The electromotive force of the battery is xE.   Its internal resistance $x^2 r/n$.   The current C, according to the text-books on electricity, is given by the relation

$$C = \frac{xE}{R + \dfrac{r}{n}x^2} \; ; \; \therefore \frac{dC}{dx} = \frac{\left(R - \dfrac{r}{n}x^2\right)E}{\left(B + \dfrac{r}{n}x^2\right)^2}.$$

Equate to zero, and simplify, $R = rx^2/n$, remains.   This means that the battery must be so arranged that its internal resistance shall be as nearly as possible equal to the external resistance.

The theory of maxima and minima must not be applied blindly to physical problems.   It is generally necessary to take other things into consideration   An arrangement that satisfies one set of conditions may not be suitable for another.   For instance, while the above arrangement of cells will give the maximum current, it is by no means the most economical.

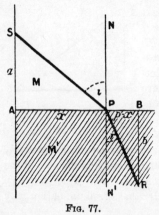

FIG. 77.

VI. To find the conditions which must subsist in order that light may travel from a given point in one medium to a given point in another medium in the shortest possible time.   Let SP (Fig. 77) be a ray of light incident at P on the surface of separation of the media M and M'; let PR be the refracted ray in the same plane as the incident ray. If PN is normal (perpendicular) to the surface of incidence, then the angle $NPS = i$, is the angle of incidence; and the angle $N'PR = r$, is the angle of refraction. Drop perpendiculars from S and R on to A and B, so that $SA = a$, $RB = b$. Now the light will travel from S to R, according to Fermat's principle, in the shortest possible time, with a uniform velocity different in the different media M and M'. The ray passes through the surface separating the two media at the point P, let $AP = x$, $BP = p - x$. Let the velocity of propagation of the ray of light in the two media be respectively V_1 and V_2 units per second. The ray therefore travels from S to P in PS/V_1 seconds, and from P to R in RP/V_2 seconds, and the total time, t, occupied in transit from S to R is the sum

$$t = \frac{PS}{V_1} + \frac{RP}{V_2}. \qquad \qquad (1)$$

From the triangles SAP and PBR, as indicated in (1), page 603, it follows that $PS = \sqrt{a^2 + x^2}$; and $RP = \sqrt{b^2 + (p - x)^2}$. Substituting these values in (1), and differentiating in the usual way, we get

$$\frac{dt}{dx} = \frac{x}{V_1\sqrt{a^2 + x^2}} - \frac{p - x}{V_2\sqrt{b^2 + (p - x)^2}} = 0. \qquad (2)$$

Consequently, by substituting for PS, RP, AP, and BP as above, we get from the preceding equation (2), solved for V_1/V_2,

$$\frac{\sin i}{\sin r} = \frac{\dfrac{AP}{PS}}{\dfrac{BP}{RP}} = \frac{\dfrac{x}{\sqrt{a^2 + x^2}}}{\dfrac{p - x}{\sqrt{b^2 + (p - x)^2}}} = \frac{V_1}{V_2}.$$

This result, sometimes called Snell's law of refraction, shows that the sines of the angles of incidence and refraction must be proportional to the velocity of the light in the two given media in order that the light may pass from one point to the other in the shortest possible interval of time. Experiment justifies Fermat's guess. The ratio of the sines of the two angles, therefore, is constant for the same two media. The constant is usually denoted by the symbol μ, and called the index of refraction.

EXAMPLES.—(1) The velocity of motion of a wave, of length λ, in deep water is $V = \sqrt{(\lambda/a + a/\lambda)}$, a is a constant. Required the length of the wave when the velocity is a minimum. (N. Z. Univ. Exam. Papers.) Ansr. $\lambda = a$.

(2) The contact difference of potential, E, between two metals is a function of the temperature, θ, such that $E = a + b\theta + c\theta^2$. How high

must the temperature of one of the metals be raised in order that the difference of potential may be a maximum or a minimum. a, b, c are constants.   Ansr. $\theta = -b/2c$.

(3) Show that the greatest rectangle that can be inscribed in the circle $x^2 + y^2 = r^2$ is a square. Hint. Draw a circle of radius r, Fig. 78. Let the sides of the rectangle be $2x$ and $2y$ respectively; $\therefore$ area $= 4xy$, $x^2 + y^2 = r^2$.

Solve for y, and substitute in the former equation. Differentiate, etc., and then show that both x and y are equal to $r\sqrt{\frac{1}{2}}$, etc.

(4) If v_0 be the volume of water at $0°$ C., v the volume at $\theta°$ C., then, according to Hällstrom's formula, for temperatures between $0°$ and $30°$,

$$v = v_0(1 - 0.000057,577\theta + 0.000007,5601\theta^2 - 0.000000,03509\theta^3).$$

Fig. 78.

Show that the volume is least and the density greatest when $\theta = 3.92$. The graph is shown in Fig. 79. In the working of this example, it will be found simplest to use $a, b, c \ldots$ for the numerical coefficients,

differentiate, etc., for the final result, restore the numerical values of $a, b, c \ldots$, and simplify. Probably the reader has already done this.

(5) Later on I shall want the student to show that the expression $\sqrt{(q^2 - n^2)^2 + 4f^2n^2}$ is a minimum when $n^2 = q^2 - 2f^2$.

(6) An electric current flowing round a coil of radius r exerts a force F on a small magnet whose axis is at some point on a line drawn through the centre and perpendicular to the plane of the coil. If x is the distance of the magnet from the plane of the coil, $F = x/(r^2 + x^2)^{5/2}$. Show that the force is a maximum when $x = \frac{1}{2}r$.

Fig. 79.

(7) Draw an ellipse whose area for a given perimeter shall be a maximum. Hint. Although the perimeter of an ellipse can only be represented with perfect accuracy by an infinite series, yet for all practical purposes the perimeter may be taken to be $\pi(x + y)$ where x and y are the semi-major and semi-minor axes. The area of the ellipse is $z = \pi xy$. Since the perimeter is to be constant, $a = \pi(x + y)$ or $y = a/\pi - x$. Substitute this value of y in the former expression and $z = ax - \pi x^2$. Hence, $x = a/2\pi$ when z is a maximum. Substitute this value of x in $y = a/\pi - x$, and $y = a/2\pi$, that is to say, $x = y = a/2\pi$, or of all ellipses the circle has the greatest area. Boys' leaden water-pipes designed not to burst at freezing temperatures, are based on this principle. The cross section of the pipe is elliptical. If the contained water freezes, the resulting expansion makes the tube tend to become circular in cross section. The increased capacity allows the ice to have more room without putting a strain on the pipe.

(8) If A, B be two sources of heat, find the position of a point O on the line $AB = a$, such that it is heated the least possible. Assume that the intensity of the heat rays is proportional to the square of the distance from the source of heat. Let $AO = x$, $BO = a - x$. The intensity of each source of heat at unit distance away is α and β. The total intensity of the heat which reaches O is $I = \alpha x^{-2} + \beta(a - x)^{-2}$. Find dI/dx. I is a minimum when $x = \sqrt[3]{\alpha} \cdot a/(\sqrt[3]{\alpha} + \sqrt[3]{\beta})$.

(9) The weight, W (lbs. per sec.), of flue gas passing up a chimney at different temperatures T, is represented by $W = A(T - T_0)(1 + \alpha T)^{-2}$, where A is a constant, T the absolute temperature of the hot gases passing within the chimney, T_0 the temperature (°C) of the outside air, $\alpha = \frac{1}{273}$ the co-efficient of expansion of the gas. Hence show that the greatest amount of gas will pass up the chimney—the "best draught" will occur—when the temperature of the "flue gases" is nearly 333° C. and the temperature of the atmosphere is 15° C.

(10) If VC denotes the "input" of a continuous current dynamo; σ the fixed losses due to iron, friction, excitation, etc.; τC^2, the variable losses; C, the current, then the efficiency, E, is given by $E = 1 - (\sigma - \tau C^2)/VC$. Show that the efficiency will be a minimum when $\sigma = \tau C^2$. Hint. Find dE/dC, etc.

(11) Show that $x^{\frac{1}{x}}$ is a maximum when $x = e$. Hint. $dy/dx = x^{\frac{1}{x}}(1 - \log x)/x^2$; $\therefore \log x = 1$, etc.

(12) A submarine telegraph cable consists of a circular core surrounded by a concentric circular covering. The speed of signalling through this varies as $1 : x^2 \log x^{-1}$, where x denotes the ratio of the radius of the core to that of the covering. Show that the fastest signalling can be made when this ratio is 0·606 ... Hint. $1 : \sqrt{e} = 0·606$.

(13) The velocity equations for chemical reactions in which the normal course is disturbed by autocatalysis are, for reactions of the first order, $dx/dt = kx(a - x)$; or, $dx/dt = k(b + x)(a - x)$. Hence show that the velocity of the reaction will be greatest when $x = \frac{1}{2}a$ for the former reaction, and $x = \frac{1}{2}(a - b)$ for the latter.

(14) A privateer has to pass between two lights, A and B, on opposite headlands. The intensity of each light is known and also the distance between them. At what point must the privateer cross the line joining the lights so as to be illuminated as little as possible. Given the intensity of the light at any point is equal to its illuminating power divided by the square of the distance of the point from the source of light. Let p_1 and p_2 respectively denote the illuminating power of each source of light. Let a denote the distance from A to B. Let x denote the distance from A to the point on AB where the intensity of illumination is least; hence the ship must be illuminated $p_1/x^2 + p_2/(a - x)^2$. This function will be a minimum when $(p_1/p_2)^{\frac{1}{3}} = x/(a - x)$; $\therefore x = ap_1^{\frac{1}{3}}(p_1^{\frac{1}{3}} + p_2^{\frac{1}{3}})^{-1}$.

(15) Assuming that the cost of driving a steamer through the water varies as the cube of her speed, show that her most economical speed through the water against a current running V miles per hour is $\frac{3}{2}V$. Let x denote the speed of the ship in still water, $x - V$ will then denote the speed against the current. But the distance traversed is equal to the velocity multiplied by the time. Hence, the time taken to travel s miles will be $s/(x - V)$. The cost in fuel per hour is ax^3, where a is the constant of proportion. Hence: Total cost $= asx^3/(x - V)$. Hence, $x^3/(x - V)$ is to be a minimum. Differentiate as usual, and we get $x = \frac{3}{2}V$. The captain of a river steamer must be always applying this fact subconsciously.

(16) The stiffness of a rectangular beam of any given material is proportional to its breadth, and to the cube of its depth, find the stiffest beam that

can be cut from a circular tree 12 in. in diameter. Let x denote the breadth of the beam, and y its depth; obviously, $12^2 = x^2 + y^2$. Hence, the depth of the beam is $\sqrt{12^2 - x^2}$; $\therefore$ stiffness is proportional to $x(12^2 - x^2)^{\frac{3}{2}}$. This is a maximum when $x = 6$. Hence the required depth, y, must be $6\sqrt{3}$.

(17) Suppose that the total waste, y, due to heat, depreciation, etc., which occurs in an electric conductor with a resistance R ohms per mile with an electric current, C, in ampères is $C^2R + (17)^2/R$, find the relation between C and R in order that the waste may be a minimum. Ansr. $CR = 17$, which is known as Lord Kelvin's rule. Hint. Find dy/dR, assuming that C is constant. Given the approximation formula, resistance of conductor of cross sectional area a is $R = 0.04/a$; $\therefore$ $C = 425a$, or, for a minimum cost, the current must be 425 ampères per square inch of cross sectional area of conductor.

§ 63. Singular Points.

The following table embodies the relations we have so far deduced between the shape of the curve $y = f(x)$ and the first four differential coefficients. Some relations have been " brought forward " from a later chapter. The symbol " . . " means that the value of the corresponding derivative does not affect the result :—

TABLE I.—SINGULAR VALUES OF FUNCTIONS.

Property of Curve.	$\dfrac{dy}{dt}$	$\dfrac{d^2y}{dt^2}$	$\dfrac{d^3y}{dt^3}$	$\dfrac{d^4y}{dt^4}$
Tangent parallel to x-axis	0	..	..	..
Tangent parallel to y-axis	∞	..	..	..
Maximum . . {	0	−	..	..
	0	0	0	−
Minimum . . {	0	+	..	..
	0	0	0	+
Point of inflexion . .	..	0	not zero	..
Convex downwards . .	not zero	+	..	..
Concave downwards .	not zero	−	..	..

It is perhaps necessary to add a few more remarks so as to give the beginner an inkling of the vastness of the subject we are about to leave behind. P. Frost's *An Elementary Treatise on Curve Tracing*, London, 1872, is the text-book on this subject. Before you proceed to the actual plotting, look out for symmetrical axes; maxima and minima ordinates; points of inflexion; and asymptotes. Does the curve cut the axes at any points? There may be other singular points besides points of inflexion, and maxima and minima.

Two or more branches of the same curve will intersect or cross one another, as shown at O, Fig. 80, when the first differential coefficient has two or more real unequal values, and y has at least two equal values. The number of intersecting branches is denoted by the number of real roots of the first differential coefficient. The point of intersection is called a **multiple point**. If two branches of the curve cross each other the point is called a **node**; Cayley calls it a **crunode**.

EXAMPLES.—(1) In the lemniscate curve, familiar to students of crystallography, $y^2 = a^2x^2 - x^4$; $y = \pm x\sqrt{a^2 - x^2}$. y has two values, of opposite sign, for every value of x between $\pm a$; the curve is therefore symmetrical with respect to the x-axis. When $x = \pm a$, these two values of y become zero; but these are not multiple points since the curve does not extend beyond these limits, and therefore cannot satisfy the above conditions. When $x = 0$, the two values of y become zero, and since there are two values of y, one on each side of the point $x = 0$, $y = 0$, this is a multiple point. Since $dy/dx = \pm (a^2 - 2x^2)(a^2 - x^2)^{-\frac{1}{2}}$ becomes $\pm a$ when $x = 0$, it follows that there are two tangents to the curve at this point, such that $\tan a = \pm a$. In order to plot the curve, give a some numerical value, say 5. The graph is shown in Fig. 80. The node is at O. Notice

FIG. 80.

that if the numerical value of x is greater than that of a you have to extract the square root of a negative quantity. This cannot be done because we do not know a number which will give a negative quantity when multiplied by itself. Mathematicians have agreed to call the square root of a negative number an "imaginary number" in contrast with a "real number".

(2) The curve $y = b \pm (x - a)\sqrt{x}$ has a node at the point $P(a, b)$. For every value of x there are two unequal values of y, but when $x = 0$, the two values of $y = b$, and when $x = a$, also, $y = b$. There are two real values of y on each side of the point $P(a, b)$; this can be determined by substituting $a + h$, and $a - h$ successively in place of x. $dy/dx = \pm\frac{1}{2}(3x - a)x^{-\frac{1}{2}}$. For $x = a$, $dy/dx = \pm\sqrt{a}$. Hence the tangents to the curve at the node make angles with the x-axis whose tangents are $\pm\sqrt{a}$. The point $x = 0$, $y = b$ is not a multiple point because when x is negative, y is imaginary. This shows that the curve does not go to the left of the y-axis. The singular point is shown in Fig. 81.

FIG. 81.

A **cusp or spinode** (Cayley) is a point where two branches of a curve have a common tangent and stop at that point, as shown in Figs. 82 and 83. The branches terminate at the point of contact and do not pass beyond. Hence the values of y on one side of the point are real; and on the other imaginary.

EXAMPLES.—(1) In the cissoid curve, $y = b \pm \sqrt{(x^2 - a^2)^3}$; y is imaginary for all values of x between $\pm a$. When $x = \pm a$, y has one value; for any point to the right of $x = + a$, or to the left of $x = - a$, y has two values; $dy/dx = \pm 3x(x^2 - a^2)^{\frac{1}{2}}$ vanishes when $x = a$. The two branches of the curve have therefore a common tangent parallel to the x-axis and there is a cusp. The cusp is said to be of the first species, or a ceratoid cusp. We now find that there are two real and equal values for the second differential coefficient,

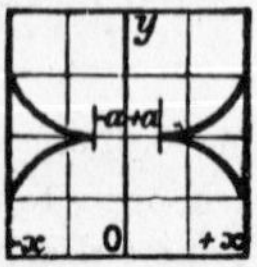

FIG. 82.—Single Cusps   FIG. 83.—Single Cusp   FIG. 84.
    (First Species).   (Second Species).

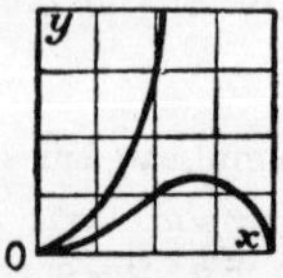

namely, $d^2y/dx^2 = \pm 3(2x^2 - a^2) (x^2 - a^2)^{-\frac{1}{2}}$. The upper branch is convex towards the x-axes; and the lower branch is concave towards the x-axis, as shown in Fig. 82.

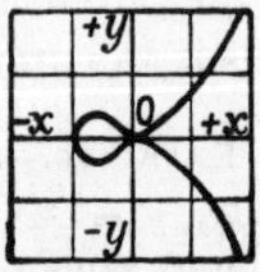

(2) The second differential coefficient of the curve $(y - x^2)^2 = x^5$ has two different values of the same sign. The cusp is then said to be a cusp of the second species, or a rhamphoid cusp. The lower curve also has a maximum when $x = \frac{1}{2}\frac{5}{6}$. The general form of the curve is shown in Fig. 83.

The cusps which have just been described are called **single cusps** in contradistinction to **double cusps or points of osculation in** which the curves extend to both sides of the point of contact. These are what Cayley calls **tacnodes**. The differential coefficient has now two or more equal roots and y has at least two equal values. The different branches of the curve have a common tangent.

To distinguish cusps from points of osculation : compare the ordinate of the curve for that point with the ordinates of the curve on each side. For a cusp, y and the first differential coefficient have only one real value.

EXAMPLES.—(1) The curve $y^2 = x^4(x + 5)$; or what is the same thing $y = \pm x^2 \sqrt{x + 5}$, has a tacnode at the origin, as shown in Fig. 84. $dy/dx = \pm \frac{5}{2}x(x + 4) (x + 5)^{-\frac{1}{2}}$, which becomes zero when $x = 0$. The two branches of the curve are tangent to one another at this point when $x = - 5$, $dy/dx = \infty$ and $y = 0$. The tangent cuts the axis at right angles at the point $x = - 5$, and when x is less than 5, y is imaginary. In Fig. 82, each cusp at the tacnode is of the first species, but sometimes the cusps are of the second species, as shown in Fig. 85.

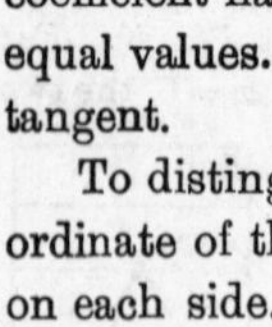

FIG. 85.

the second species, as shown in Fig. 85.

(2) The curve $y^2 - 6xy = x^5$ has another kind of tacnode shown in Fig. 86. The cusp is of the first species on one side and of the second species on the other.

After the student has investigated the fifth chapter he may be able to show that when $u = 0$; $(\partial u/\partial x)_y = 0$; and $(\partial u/\partial y)_x = 0$, then if

FIG. 86.

$$\left(\frac{\partial^2 u}{\partial x^2}\right)_y \left(\frac{\partial^2 u}{\partial y^2}\right)_x - \left(\frac{\partial^2 u}{\partial x\partial y}\right)^2 = \begin{cases} - = \text{node.} \\ 0 = \text{cusp.} \\ + = \text{conjugate point.} \end{cases}$$

A conjugate point or acnode is one whose coordinates satisfy the equation of the curve and yet is itself quite detached from the curve. On each side of a conjugate point, real values of one coordinate give a pair of imaginary values of the other. On plotting the graph of $y^2 = x^2(x - 2)$, for example, it will be found that there is a point at the origin whose coordinates satisfy the equation of the curve, and yet the curve itself does not pass through the origin as shown in Fig. 87. There are

FIG. 87.

no real values of y when x is less than 2 (except when $x = 0, y = 0$) so that the curve does not go to the left of $x = 2$.

One branch of the curve $y = x \log x$ suddenly stops at the origin (Fig. 73, page 160). This is said to be a *point d'arrêt* or a **terminal point**. When $x = 0$, $y = 0$; when x is negative, y has no real value because negative numbers have no logarithms. Do not waste any time trying to show that $y = 0$, when $x = 0$. There is a difficulty which you will easily master later on.

De la Roche has published a "proof" that the vapour pressure, p, of water at any temperature, θ, is given by the expression

$$p = ab^{\frac{\theta}{m + n\theta}},$$

where a, b, m, and n are constants. August, Regnault, and Magnus found that the expression represented their experimental results fairly well. But Regnault (*Ann. Chim. Phys.*, [3], **11**, 273, 1844) has pointed out that Roche's formula can only be regarded as an empirical interpolation formula pure and simple. The properties of this equation do not agree with the actual phenomena. See Ex. (4), page 161. The curve has a point of inflexion, E, Fig. 88, when θ is equal to $\frac{1}{2}m(\log b - 2n)n^{-2}$. The curve has two branches, GAB, and DC. The portion AB alone applies to the observed relations between p and θ. For this branch there is a terminal point,

G, when $\theta = - m/n$, provided b is greater than unity. This curve

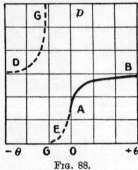

is also asymptotic to a line $p = ab^{1/n}$ parallel to the θ-axis. The other branch of the curve, I may notice *en passant*, is asymptotic to the same straight line and also to the straight line $\theta = - m/n$ parallel to the p-axis. I have asked a class of students to *plot* the above equation and all missed the point of inflexion at E. As a matter of fact you should try to get as much information as you can by applying the above principles before actual plotting is attempted. You

Fig. 88.

will now see that if you know the formula of a curve, the calculus gives you a method of finding all the critical points without going to the trouble of plotting.

§ 64. *pv*-Curves.

We have already had something to say about van der Waals' equation for the relation between the pressure, p, the volume, v, and the temperature, $T°$ abs., of a gas

$$\left(p + \frac{a}{v^2}\right)(v - b) = RT. \qquad . \qquad . \qquad . \qquad (1)$$

Now try and plot this equation for any gas from the published values of a, b, R. For example, for ethylene $a = 0.00786$, $b = 0.0024$, $R = 0.0037$; for carbon dioxide, van der Waals gives

$$\left(p + \frac{0.00874}{v^2}\right)(v - 0.0023) = 0.00369(273 + \theta), . \qquad (2)$$

where θ denotes $°$ C. First fix the values for θ, and calculate a set of corresponding values of p and v, thus, for $0°$ C., when
$v = 0.1, \quad 0.05, \quad 0.025, \quad 0.01, \quad 0.0075, \quad 0.005, \quad 0.004, \quad 0.003, \ldots;$
$p = 9.4, 19.7, \quad 30.3, \quad 43.3, \quad 37.9, \quad \quad 23.2, \quad 45.8, \quad 466.8, \ldots$
Make the successive increments in v small when in the neighbourhood of a singular point. Plot these numbers on squared paper. Note the points of inflexion. Now do the same thing with $\theta = 32°$ C., and $\theta = 91°$ C. The set of curves shown in the adjoining diagram (Fig. 89) were so obtained. In this way you

will get a better insight into the "inwardness" of van der Waals'
equation than if pages of
descriptive matter were
appended. Notice that
the a/v^2 term has no appreciable influence on the
value of p when v becomes
very great, and also that
the difference between v
and $v - b$ is negligibly
small, as v becomes very
large. What does this
signify? When the gas

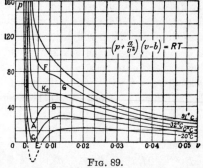

FIG. 89.

is rarefied, it will follow Boyle's law $pv = $ constant. What would
be the state of the gas when $v = 0\cdot0023$?

For convenience, solve (1) in terms of p, and treat RT as if it
were one constant,

$$p = \frac{RT}{v - b} - \frac{a}{v^2}; \text{ or, } p = \frac{1}{v - b}\left(RT - \frac{a(v - b)}{v^2}\right). \qquad (3)$$

This enables us to see that p will become zero when the fraction
$a(v - b)/v^2$ becomes equal to RT. This fraction attains the
maximum value $a/2^2b$, when v becomes $2b$; and obviously, when
$v = b$, this fraction is zero. Hence, p will become zero when RT
is equal to $a/2^2b$, and $v = 2b$. The curve for $- 20°$ C. (Fig. 89)
cuts the x-axis in two real points D and E when RT is less than
$a/2^2b$. If $RT = a/2^2b$, Ov is tangent to the curve at C.

Let us now differentiate (3) with respect to v,

$$\frac{dp}{dv} = -\frac{RT}{(v-b)^2} + \frac{2a}{v^3}; \text{ or, } \frac{dp}{dv} = -\frac{1}{(v-b)^2}\left(RT - \frac{2a(v-b)^2}{v^3}\right). \qquad (4)$$

If T be great enough, dp/dv will always be negative, that is to say,
the curve, or rather its tangent, will slope from left to right downwards, like the hyperbola for 91° C. (Fig. 89). If v be small
enough $(v - b)^2$ also becomes very small, the curve will retain its
negative slope because dp/dv will be negative; and when $v = b$,
$(v - b)^2/v^3 = 0$. When dp/dv becomes zero, the tangent to the
curve is horizontal. This means that we may have maximum or
minimum values of p. If T is small enough, dp/dv will have a
positive value for certain values of v. The curve then slopes from
left to right upwards, as at AB (Fig. 89).

You can now show that $2a(v - b)^2/v^3$ has the maximum value

$2^3a/3^3b$, when $v = 3b$; and gradually approaches zero, as v becomes very great. If, therefore, RT is greater than $2^3a/3^3b$, the maximum value of $2a(v - b)^2/v^3$, then v will increase as p decreases. When RT is less than $2^3a/3^3b$, p will decrease for small and large values of v, but it will increase in the neighbourhood of $v = 3b$. Consequently, p has a maximum or a minimum value for any value of v which makes $2a(v - b)^2/v^3 = RT$. This curve resembles that for 0° C. (Fig. 89), for all values of RT between $a/2^2b$ and $2^3a/2^3b$; when $RT = 2^3a/3^3b$, we have the point of inflexion K_0 (Fig. 89).

Let us now see what we can learn from the second differential coefficient

$$\frac{d^2p}{dv^2} = \frac{2RT}{(v - b)^3} - \frac{6a}{v^4} ; \text{ or, } \frac{d^2p}{dv^2} = \frac{2}{(v - b)^3}\left(RT - \frac{3a(v - b)^3}{v^4}\right). \quad (5)$$

The curve will have a point of inflexion when the fraction $3a(v - b)^3/v^4 = RT$. By the methods already described you can show that $3a(v - b)^3/v^4$ will be zero when $v = b$; and that it will attain the maximum value $3^4a/4^4b$ when $v = 4b$. Every value of v which makes (5) zero will correspond with a point of inflexion. RT may be equal to, greater, or less than $3^4a/4^4b$. For all values of RT between $2^3a/3^3b$ and $3^4a/4^4b$, there will be two points of inflexion, as shown at F and G (Fig. 89). When RT exceeds the value $3^4a/4^4b$, we have a branch of the rectangular hyperbola as shown for 91°.

If we take the experimental curves obtained by Andrews for the relation between the pressure, p, and volume, v, of carbon dioxide at different temperatures T, T_0, T_1, T_2, ... we get a set of curves resembling Fig. 90. At any temperature T above the critical temperature, the relation between p and v is given by the curve pT. The gas will not liquefy. Below the critical temperature, say T_1, the volume decreases as the pressure increases, as shown by the curve T_1K_1 ; at K_1 the gas begins to liquefy and the pressure remains constant although the volume of the system diminishes from K_1 to M_1. At M_1 all the gas will have liquefied and the curve M_1p_1 will represent the relation between the pressure

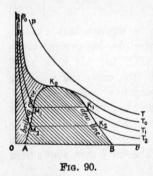

Fig. 90.

and volume of the liquid. Similar curves $T_2K_2M_2P_2$, $T_3K_3M_3P_3$,

.. are obtained at the different temperatures below the critical temperature T_0.

The lines K_0A, K_0p_0 and K_0B divide the plane of the paper into three regions. Every point to the left of AK_0p_0 represents a homogeneous liquid; every point to the right of BK_0p_0 represents a homogeneous gaseous phase; while every point in the region AK_0B represents a heterogeneous liquid-gas phase.

By gradually increasing the pressure, at any assigned temperature below T_0, the gas will begin to liquefy at some point along the line BK_0; this is called the **dew curve**—*ligne de rosée*. If the pressure on a liquid whose state is represented by a point in the region OAK_0p, be gradually diminished, the substance will begin to assume the gaseous state at some point along the line K_0A. This is called the **boiling curve**—*ligne d'ébullition*. At K_0 there is a tacnodal point or double cusp of the mixed species.

A remarkable phenomenon occurs when a mixture of two gases is treated in a similar manner. If a mixture of one volume of air and nine volumes of carbon dioxide be subjected to a gradually increasing pressure at about 2° C., the gas begins to liquefy at a pressure of 72 atm.; and on increasing the pressure, still keeping the temperature constant, the liquid again passes into the gaseous state when the pressure reaches 149 atm.; and the liquid does not reappear again however great the pressure. If the pressure at which the liquid appears and disappears be plotted with the corresponding temperature, we get the dew curve BKC, shown in Fig. 91. For the same abscissa T_1, there are two ordinates, p_1 and p_1', between which the mixture is in a heterogeneous condition. At temperatures above T_0, no condensation will occur at all; below T_1 only normal condensation takes place; at temperatures between T_1 and T_0 both normal

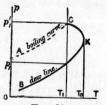

FIG. 91.

and **retrograde condensation** will occur. The dotted line AC represents the boiling curve; above AC the system will be in the liquid state. K corresponds with the critical temperature of the mixture. C is called the **plait-point**.

The phenomenon only occurs with mixtures of a certain composition. Above and below these limits the dew curves are quite normal. This is shown by the curves DC and OC_5 in Fig. 92. C is the plait-point; and the line joining the plait-points C_2, C_3, C_4, ..

176 HIGHER MATHEMATICS. § 65.

for different mixtures is called the **plait-point curve.** The dotted
lines in the same diagram represent boiling curves. Note the
gradual narrowing of the border curves and their transit into or-

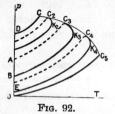

FIG. 92.

dinary vapour pressure curves DC and OC_5
at the two extremes. You must notice that
we are really working in three dimensions.
The variables are p, v and T.

The plait-point curve appears to form
a double cusp of the second species at a
plait-point. There is some discussion as to
whether, say, AC_3K_3B really forms a con-
tinuous curve line, so that at C_3 the line CC_5 is tangent to AC_3K_3B;
or separate lines each forming a spinode or cusp with the line CC_5
at the point C_3. But enough has been said upon the nature of
these curves to carry the student through this branch of mathematics in, say, J. D. van der Waals' *Binäre Gemische*, Leipzig, 1900.

EXAMPLE.—Show that the product pv for van der Waals' equation furnishes a minimum when

$$v = \frac{ab}{a - RbT} - \sqrt{\left(\frac{ab}{a - RbT}\right)^2 - \frac{ab^2}{a - RbT}}$$

Hint. Multiply the first of equations (3) through with v; differentiate to get
$d(pv)/dv = 0$, etc. The conclusion is in harmony with M. Amagat's experiments (*Ann. Chim. Phys.*, [5] 22, 353, 1881) on carbon dioxide, ethylene,
nitrogen and methane. For hydrogen, a, in (3), is negligibly small, hence
show that pv has no minimum.

§ 65. Imaginary Quantities.

We have just seen that no number is known which has a
negative value when multiplied by itself. The square root of a
negative quantity cannot, therefore, be a real number. In spite of
this fact, the square roots of negative quantities frequently occur in
mathematical investigations. Again, logarithms of negative numbers, inverse sines of quantities greater than unity, ..., cannot have
real values. These, too, sometimes crop up in our work and we
must know what to do with them.

Let $\sqrt{-a^2}$ be such a quantity. If $-a^2$ is the product of a^2
and -1, $\pm\sqrt{-a^2}$ may be supposed to consist of two parts, *viz.*,
$\pm a$ and $\sqrt{-1}$. Mathematicians have agreed to call a the real
part of $\sqrt{-a^2}$ and $\sqrt{-1}$, the imaginary part. Following Gauss,

$\sqrt{-1}$ is written ι (or i). It is assumed that $\sqrt{-1}$, or ι obeys all the rules of algebra.[1] Thus,

$$\sqrt{-1} \times \sqrt{-1} = -1; \quad \sqrt{-4} = 2\sqrt{-1}; \quad \sqrt{-a} \times \sqrt{b} = \sqrt{-ab}; \quad \iota^4 = 1.$$

We know what the phrase " the point x, y " means   If one or both of x and y are imaginary, the point is said to be imaginary. An **imaginary point** has no geometrical or physical meaning   If an equation in x and y is affected with one or more imaginary co-efficients, the non-existent graph is called an **imaginary curve;** while a similar equation in x, y and z will furnish an **imaginary surface.**

EXAMPLES.—(1) Show $\iota^{4n} = 1$; $\iota^{4n+1} = \iota$; $\iota^{4n+2} = -1$; $\iota^{4n+3} = -\iota$.

(2) Prove that $a^2 + b^2 = (a + \iota b)(a - \iota b)$.

(3) The quadratic $x^2 + bx + c = 0$, has imaginary roots only when $b^2 - 4c$ is less than zero (5), page 354. If a and β are the roots of this equation, show that $a = -\tfrac{1}{2}b + \tfrac{1}{2}\iota\sqrt{b^2 - 4c}$; and $\beta = -\tfrac{1}{2}b - \tfrac{1}{2}\iota\sqrt{b^2 - 4c}$, satisfy the equation.

(4) Show $(a + \iota b)(c + \iota d) = (ac - bd) + (ad + bc)\iota$.

(5) Show by multiplying numerator and denominator by $c + \iota d$ that $\dfrac{a + \iota b}{c - \iota d} = \dfrac{ac - bd}{c^2 + d^2} + \dfrac{bc + ad}{c^2 + d^2}\iota$.

To illustrate the periodic nature of the symbol ι, let us suppose that ι represents the symbol of an operation which when repeated twice changes the sign of the subject of the operation, and when repeated four times restores the subject of the operation to its original form   For instance, if we twice operate on x with ι, we get $-x$, or

$$(\sqrt{-1})^2 x = \sqrt{-1} \times \sqrt{-1} \times x = -x; \quad \text{and } (\sqrt{-1})^4 a = x,$$

and so on in cycles of four. If the imaginary quantities ιx, $-\iota x$, ... are plotted on the y-axis—axis of imaginaries—and the real quantities x, $-x$, ... on the x-axis—axis of reals—the operation of ι on x will rotate x through 90°, two operations will rotate x through 180°, three operations will rotate x through 270°, and four operations will carry x back to its original position.

---

[1] The so-called **fundamental laws of algebra** are : *I. The law of association :* The number of things in any group is independent of the order. *II. The commutative law :* (a) Addition. The number of things in any number of groups is independent of the order. (b) Multiplication. The product of two numbers is independent of the order. *III. The distributive law :* (a) Multiplication. The multiplier may be distributed over each term of the multiplicand, *e.g.*, $m(a + b) = ma + mb$. (b) Division. $(a + b)/m = a/m + b/m$. *IV. The index law :* (a) Multiplication. $a^m a^n = a^{m+n}$. (b) Division. $a^m/a^n = a^{m-n}$.

We shall see later on that $2\iota \sin x = e^{\iota x} - e^{-\iota x}$; hence, if $x = \pi$, $\sin \pi = 0$, and we have

$$e^{\iota \pi} - e^{-\iota \pi} = 0 \; ; \; \text{or}, \; e^{\iota \pi} = e^{-\iota \pi},$$

meaning that the function $e^{\iota x}$ has the same value whether $x = \pi$, or $x = -\pi$. From the last equation we get the remarkable connection between the two great incommensurables π and e discovered by Euler:

$$e^{2\iota \pi} = 1.$$

EXAMPLE.—Show $x = x \times 1 = x \times e^{2\iota \pi} = e^{\log x + 2\iota \pi}$. This means that the addition of $2\iota \pi$ to the logarithm of any quantity has the effect of multiplying it by unity, and will not change its value. Every real quantity therefore, has one real logarithm and an infinite number of imaginary logarithms differing by $2\iota n \pi$, where n is an integer.

Do not confuse irrational with **imaginary** quantities. Numbers like $\sqrt{2}$, $\sqrt[3]{5}$, ... which cannot be obtained in the form of a whole number or finite fraction are said to be **irrational or surd numbers**. On the contrary, $\sqrt{4}$, $\sqrt[3]{27}$, ... are rational numbers. Although we cannot get the absolutely correct value of an irrational number, we can get as close an approximation as ever we please; but we cannot even say that the imaginary quantity is entitled to be called a quantity.

§ 66. Curvature.

The curvature **at** any point of a plane curve is the rate at which the curve is bending. Of two curves AC, AD, that has the greater curvature which departs the more rapidly from its tangent AB

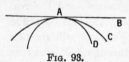

FIG. 93.

(Fig. 93). In passing from P (Fig. 94) to another neighbouring point P_1 along any arc δs of the plane curve AB, the tangent at P turns through the angle δa, where a is the angle made by the intersection of the tangent at P with the t-axis. The .curvature of the curve at the point P is defined as the limiting value of the ratio $\delta a/\delta s$ when P_1 coincides with P. When the points P and P_1 are not infinitely close together, this ratio may be called the mean or average curvature of the curve between A and B. We might now say that

$$R = \frac{da}{ds} = \text{Rate of bending of curve.} \qquad . \qquad . \qquad (1)$$

I. The curvature of the circumference of all circles of equal radius is the same at all points, and varies inversely as the radius.

This is established in the following way : Let AB (Fig. 94) be a part of a circle ; Q, the centre ; $QP = QP_1 =$ radius $= R$. The two angles marked δa are obviously equal. The angle PQP_1 is measured in circular measure, page 606, by the ratio of the arc PP_1 to the radius, *i.e.*, the angle $PQP_1 =$ arc PP_1/R ; or, $\delta a/\delta s = 1/R$. The

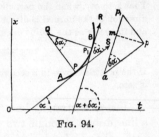

Fig. 94.

curvature of a circle is therefore the reciprocal of the radius, or, in symbols,

$$\frac{da}{ds} = \frac{1}{R}. \qquad . \qquad . \qquad . \qquad . \qquad (2)$$

EXAMPLE.—An illustration from mechanics. If a particle moves with a variable velocity on the curve AB (Fig. 94) so that at the time t, the particle is at P, the particle would, by Newton's first law of motion, continue to move in the direction of the tangent PS, if it were not acted upon by a central force at Q which compels the particle to keep moving on the curvilinear path PP_1B. Let P_1 be the position of the particle at the end of a short interval of time dt. The direction of motion of the particle at P_1 may similarly be represented by the tangent P_1R. Let the length of the two straight lines ap and ap_1 represent, in direction and magnitude, the respective velocities of the particle at P and at P_1. Join pp_1. The angle pap_1 is evidently equal to the angle δa. Since ap represents in direction and magnitude the velocity of the particle at P, and ap_1, the velocity of the particle at P_1, pp_1 will represent the increment in the velocity of the particle as it passes from P to P_1, for the parallelogram of velocities tells us that ap_1 is the resultant of the two component velocities ap and pp_1, in direction and magnitude. The **total acceleration** of the particle in passing from P to P_1 is therefore

$$\text{Total acceleration} = \frac{\text{Velocity gained}}{\text{Time occupied}} = \frac{pp_1}{dt}.$$

Now drop a perpendicular from the point p to meet ap_1 at m. The infinitely small change of velocity pp_1 may be regarded as the resultant of two changes pm and p_1m, or the acceleration pp_1/dt is the resultant of two accelerations pm/dt and mp_1/dt represented in direction and magnitude by the lines mp and p_1m respectively. pm/dt is called the **normal acceleration**. p_1m/dt, the **tangential acceleration**. If dt be made small enough, the direction of mp coincides with the direction of the normal QP to the tangent of the curve at the point P; just as RP_1 ultimately coincides with SP if δa be taken small enough. But $mp = ap \sin \delta a$. If δa is small enough, we may write $\sin \delta a = \delta a$ (11), page 602. Let V denote the velocity of the particle at the point P, then $mp = Vda$. From (2), $\delta a = \delta s/R$; and $\delta s/\delta t = V$, hence,

$$\text{Normal acceleration} = \frac{mp}{dt} = \frac{V}{R} \cdot \frac{ds}{dt} = \frac{V^2}{R}.$$

That is to say, when the particle moves on the curve, the acceleration in the direction of the normal is directly proportional to the square of the velocity, and inversely as the radius of curvature. Similarly the

$$\text{Tangential acceleration} = \frac{dV}{dt}.$$

If the particle moves in a straight line, $R = \delta a$, and the normal acceleration is zero.

Just as a straight line touching a curve, may be regarded as a line drawn through two points of the curve infinitely close to each other (definition of tangent), so a circle in contact with a

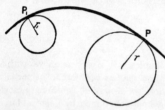

curve may be considered to pass through three consecutive points of the curve infinitely near each other. Such a circle is called an "osculatory circle" or a "circle of curvature". The osculatory circle of a curve has the same curvature as the curve itself *at*

FIG. 95.

the point of contact. The curvature of different parts of a curve may be compared by drawing osculatory circles through these points. If r be the radius of an osculatory circle at P (Fig. 95) and r_1 that at P_1, then

$$\text{Curvature at } P \; : \; \text{Curvature at } P_1 = \frac{1}{r} : \frac{1}{r_1} . \qquad (3)$$

In other words, the curvature at any two points on a curve varies inversely as the radius of the osculatory circles at these points. The radius of the osculatory circle at different points of a curve is called the "radius of curvature" at that point. The centre of the osculatory circle is the "centre of curvature".

II. To find the radius of curvature of a curve. Let the co-ordinates of the centre of the circle be a and b, R the radius, then the equation of the circle is, page 98,

$$(x - a)^2 + (y - b)^2 = R^2. \qquad . \qquad . \qquad (4)$$

Differentiating this equation twice; and, dividing by 2, we get

$$(x - a) + (y - b)\frac{dy}{dx} = 0 ; \text{ and, } 1 + (y - b)\frac{d^2y}{dx^2} + \left(\frac{dy}{dx}\right)^2 = 0. \qquad (5)$$

Let $u = dy/dx$ and $v = d^2y/dx^2$, for the sake of ease in manipulation, (5) then becomes

$$y - b = -\frac{1 + u^2}{v} \; ; \; \text{and,} \; x - a = \frac{1 + u^2}{v}u \quad . \quad . \quad (6)$$

by substituting for $y - b$ in the first of equations (5). Now u, v, x and y at any point of the curve are the same for both the curve and the osculating circle at that point, and therefore a, b[1] and R can be determined from x, y, u, v. By substituting equation (6) in (4), we get

$$\frac{1}{R} = \frac{v}{\sqrt{(1 + u^2)^3}} . \quad . \quad . \quad . \quad (7)$$

The standard equation for the radius of curvature at the point (x, y) is

$$\frac{1}{R} = \frac{da}{ds} = \frac{\dfrac{d^2y}{dx^2}}{\left\{1 + \left(\dfrac{dy}{dx}\right)^2\right\}^{\frac{3}{2}}} \; ; \; \text{or,} \; R = \frac{\left\{1 + \left(\dfrac{dy}{dx}\right)^2\right\}^{\frac{3}{2}}}{\dfrac{d^2y}{dx^2}}. \quad (8)$$

When the curve is but slightly inclined to the x-axis, dy/dx is practically zero, and the radius of curvature is given by the expression

$$R = \frac{1}{\dfrac{d^2y}{dx^2}} . \quad . \quad . \quad . \quad (9)$$

a result frequently used in physical calculations involving capillarity, superficial tension, theory of lenses, etc.

III. The direction of curvature has been discussed in § 60. It was there shown that a curve is concave or convex upwards at a point (x, y) according as $d^2y/dx^2 >$ or < 0.

EXAMPLES.—(1) Find the radius of curvature at any point (x, y) on the ellipse

$$\frac{x^2}{a^2} + \frac{y^2}{b^2} = 1 \quad \therefore \frac{dy}{dx} = -\frac{b^2x}{a^2y}; \; \frac{d^2y}{dx^2} = -\frac{b^4}{a^2y^3}; \; R = -\frac{(a^4y^2 + b^4x^2)^{\frac{3}{2}}}{a^4b^4}.$$

At the point $x = a$, $y = 0$, $R = b^2/a$. Hint. The steps for d^2y/dx^2 are :

$$\frac{d^2y}{da^2} = \frac{b^4}{a^2y^3} = -\frac{b^2}{a^2} \cdot \frac{y - x.dy/dx}{y^3} = -\frac{b^2}{a^2} \cdot \frac{a^2y^2 + b^2x^2}{a^2y^3} = -\frac{b^2}{a^2} \cdot \frac{a^2b^2}{y^3}.$$

(2) The radius of curvature on the curve $xy = a$, at any point (x, y), is $(x^2 + y^2)^{\frac{3}{2}}/2a$.

---

[1] The determination of a and b is of little use in practical work. They give equations to the evolute of the curve under consideration. The *evolute* is the curve drawn through the centres of the osculatory circles at every part of the curve, the curve itself is called the *involute*. Example : the osculatory circle has the equation $(x - a)^2 + (y - b)^2 = R$. a and b may be determined from equations (4), (7) and (8). The evolute of the parabola $y^2 = mx$ is $27my^2 = 8(2x - m)^3$.

§ 67. Envelopes.

The equation $\qquad y = \dfrac{m}{a} + ax,$

represents a straight line cutting the y-axis at m/a, and making an angle $\tan^{-1}a$ with the x-axis. If a varies by slight increments, the equation represents a series of straight lines so near together that their consecutive intersections may be considered to lie upon a continuous curve. a is said to be the **variable parameter** of the family, since the different members of the family are obtained by assigning arbitrary values for a. Let the equations

$$y_1 = \frac{m}{a} + ax \qquad . \quad . \quad . \quad . \quad . \quad (1)$$

$$y_2 = \frac{m}{a + \delta a} + (a + \delta a)x \quad . \quad . \quad . \quad (2)$$

$$y_3 = \frac{m}{a + 2\delta a} + (a + 2\delta a)x \quad . \quad . \quad . \quad (3)$$

be three successive members of the family. As a general rule two

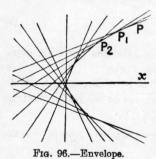

distinct curves in the same family will have a point of intersection. Let P (Fig. 96) be the point of intersection of curves (1) and (2); P_1 the point of intersection of curves (2) and (3), then, since P_1 and P_2 are both situated on the curve (2), PP_1 is part of the locus of a curve whose arc PP_1 coincides with an equal part of the curve (2). It can be proved, in fact, that the curve $PP_1 \ldots$ touches the whole family of curves represented by the original equation. Such a curve is said to be an **envelope** of the family.

FIG. 96.—Envelope.

To find the equation of the envelope, bring all the terms of the original equation to one side,

$$y - \frac{m}{a} - ax = 0.$$

Then differentiate with respect to the variable parameter, and put

$$\frac{m\,da}{a^2} - x\,da = 0 ; \quad \therefore \quad \frac{m}{a^2} - x = 0.$$

Eliminate a between these equations,

$$y - \sqrt{m \cdot x} - x\sqrt{\frac{m}{x}} = 0, \text{ or } y - 2\sqrt{m \cdot x} = 0.$$
$$\therefore y^2 = 4mx.$$

EXAMPLES.—(1) Find the envelope of the family of circles
$$(x - a)^2 + y^2 = r^2,$$
where a is the variable parameter.   Differentiate with respect to a, equate

to 0, and we get $x - a = 0$; then
eliminating a, we get $y = \pm r$, which
is the required envelope. The envelope $y = \pm r$ represents two straight
lines parallel to the x-axis, AB, and
at a distance $+ r$ and $- r$ from it.
Shown Fig. 97.

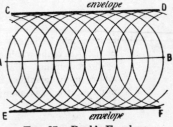

(2) Show that the envelope of the
family of curves $x/a + y/\beta = 1$, where
a and β are variable parameters subject to the condition that $a\beta = 4m^2$,
is the hyperbola $xy = m^2$.   Hint.

FIG. 97.—Double Envelope.

Differentiate each of the given equations with respect to the given parameters, and we get $xda/a^2 + yd\beta/\beta^2 = 0$ from the first, and $\beta da + ad\beta = 0$,
from the second.   Eliminate da and $d\beta$.   Hence $x/a = y/\beta = \frac{1}{2}$; $\therefore a = 2x$;
$\beta = 2y$.   Substitute in $a\beta = 4m^2$, etc.

If a given system of rays be incident upon a bright curve, the
envelope of the reflected rays is called a *caustic* by reflection.

CHAPTER IV.

THE INTEGRAL CALCULUS.

" Mathematics may be defined as the economy of counting. There is
no problem in the whole of mathematics which cannot be solved
by direct counting. But with the present implements of mathematics many operations of counting can be performed in a few
minutes, which, without mathematics, would take a lifetime."—
E. MACH.

§ 68. The Purpose of Integration.

In the first chapter, methods were described for finding the momentary rate of progress of any uniform or continuous change in
terms of a limiting ratio, the so-called "differential coefficient"
between two variable magnitudes. The fundamental relation
between the variables must be accurately known before one can
form a quantitative conception of the process taking place at any
moment of time. When this relation or law is expressed in the
form of a mathematical equation, the "methods of differentiation"
enable us to determine the character of the continuous physical
change at any instant of time. These methods have been
described.

Another problem is even more frequently presented to the
investigator. Knowing the momentary character of any natural
process, it is asked : "What is the fundamental relation between
the variables?" "What law governs the whole course of the
physical change?"

In order to fix this idea, let us study an example. The conversion of cane sugar—$C_{12}H_{22}O_{11}$—into invert sugar—$C_6H_{12}O_6$—
in the presence of dilute acids, takes place in accordance with the
reaction :

$$C_{12}H_{22}O_{11} + H_2O = 2C_6H_{12}O_6.$$

Let x denote the amount of invert sugar formed in the time t;
the amount of sugar remaining in the solution will then be $1 - x$,

provided the solution originally contained one gram-molecule of cane sugar. The amount of invert sugar formed in the time dt, will be dx. From the law of mass action, "the velocity of the chemical reaction *at* any moment is proportional to the amount of cane sugar actually present in the solution". That is to say,

$$\frac{dx}{dt} = k(1 - x), \quad . \quad . \quad . \quad . \quad (1)$$

where k is the "constant of proportion," page 23. The meaning of k is obtained by putting $x = 0$. Thus, $dx/dt = k$, or, k denotes the rate of transformation of unit mass of sugar, or

$$V = \frac{dx}{dt}, \quad . \quad . \quad . \quad . \quad (2)$$

where V denotes the velocity of the reaction. This relation is strictly true only when we make the interval of time so short that the velocity has not had time to vary during the process. But the velocity is not really constant during any finite interval of time, because the amount of cane sugar remaining to be acted upon by the dilute acid is continually decreasing. For the sake of simplicity, let $k = \frac{1}{10}$, and *assume* that the action takes place in a series of successive stages, so that dx and dt have finite values, say δx and δt respectively. Then,

$$V = \frac{\text{Amount of cane sugar transformed}}{\text{Interval of time}} = \frac{\delta x}{\delta t}. \quad . \quad (3)$$

Let δt be one second of time. Let $\frac{1}{10}$ of the cane sugar present be transformed into invert sugar in each interval of time, at the same uniform rate that it possessed at the beginning of the interval. At the commencement of the first interval, when the reaction has just started, the velocity will be at the rate of 0·100 grams of invert sugar per second. This rate will be maintained until the commencement of the second interval, when the velocity suddenly slackens down, because only 0·900 grams of cane sugar are then present in the solution.

During the second interval, the rate of formation of invert sugar will be $\frac{1}{10}$ of the 0·900 grams actually present at the beginning. Or, 0·090 grams of invert sugar are formed during the second interval.

At the beginning of the third interval, the velocity of the reaction is again suddenly retarded, and this is repeated every second for say five seconds.

Now let δx_1, δx_2, ... denote the amounts of invert sugar formed in the solution during each second, δt. Assume, for the sake of simplicity, that one gram of cane sugar yields one gram of invert sugar.

Cane sugar transformed.

During the 1st second, $\delta x_1 = 0\cdot 100$

,,　　,, 2nd　　,,　　$\delta x_2 = 0\cdot 090$

,,　　,, 3rd　　,,　　$\delta x_3 = 0\cdot 081$

,,　　,, 4th　　,,　　$\delta x_4 = 0\cdot 073$

,,　　,, 5th　　,,　　$\delta x_5 = 0\cdot 066$

Total,　　　$0\cdot 410$

This means that if the chemical reaction proceeds during each successive interval with a uniform velocity equal to that which it possessed at the commencement of that interval, then, $0\cdot 410$ gram of invert sugar would be formed at the end of five seconds. As a matter of fact, $0\cdot 3935$ gram is formed.

But $0\cdot 410$ gram is evidently too great, because the retardation is a uniform, not a jerky process. We have resolved it into a series of elementary stages and *pretended* that the rate of formation of invert sugar remained uniform during each elementary stage. We have ignored the retardation which takes place from moment to moment. If we shorten the interval and determine the amounts of invert sugar formed during intervals of say half a second, we shall have ten instead of five separate stages to sum up, thus :

Cane sugar transformed.

During the 1st half second, $\delta x_1 = 0\cdot 0500$

,,　　,, 2nd　　,,　　$\delta x_2 = 0\cdot 0475$

,,　　,, 3rd　　,,　　$\delta x_3 = 0\cdot 0451$

,,　　,, 4th　　,,　　$\delta x_4 = 0\cdot 0429$

,,　　,, 5th　　,,　　$\delta x_5 = 0\cdot 0407$

,,　　,, 6th　　,,　　$\delta x_6 = 0\cdot 0387$

,,　　,, 7th　　,,　　$\delta x_7 = 0\cdot 0367$

,,　　,, 8th　　,,　　$\delta x_8 = 0\cdot 0349$

,,　　,, 9th　　,,　　$\delta x_9 = 0\cdot 0332$

,,　　,, 10th　　,,　　$\delta x_{10} = 0\cdot 0315$

Total,　　　$0\cdot 4012$

The quantity of invert sugar calculated on the supposition that the velocity is retarded every half second instead of every second, corresponds more closely with the actual change. The smaller we make the interval of time the more accurate the result. Finally, by making δt infinitely small, although we should have

an infinite number of equations to add up, the actual summation
would give a perfectly accurate result. To add up an infinite
number of equations is, of course, an arithmetical impossibility,
but, by the "methods of integration" we can actually perform
this operation.

$x =$ Sum of all the terms $V.dt$, between $t = 0$, and $t = 5$;

$\therefore x = V.dt + V.dt + V.dt + \dots$ to infinity.

This is more conveniently written,

$$x = \Sigma_0^5(V.dt) ; \text{ or, better still, } x = \int_0^5 V.dt.$$

The signs "Σ" and "$\int$" are abbreviations for "the sum of all
the terms containing..."; the subscripts and superscripts denote

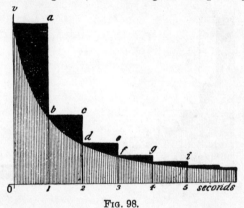

Fig. 98.

the limits between which the time has been reckoned. The second
member of the last equation is called, on Bernoulli's suggestion,
an **integral**. "$\int f(x).dx$" is read "the integral of $f(x).dx$".
When the limits between which the integration (evidently another
word for "summation") is to be performed, are stated, the
integral is said to be **definite**; when the limits are omitted, the
integral is said to be **indefinite**. The superscript to the symbol
"$\int$" is called the **upper or superior limit**; the subscript, the
lower or inferior limit. For example, $\int_{v_1}^{v_2} p.dv$ denotes the sum
of an infinite number of terms $p.dv$, when v is taken between the
limits v_2 and v_1. In order that the "limit" of integration may not
be confounded with the "limiting value" of a function, some
writers call the former the "end-values of the integral".

To prevent any misunderstanding, I will now give a graphic

representation of the above process. Take Ot and Ov as co-ordinate axes (Figs. 98 and 99). Mark off, along the abscissa axis, intervals 1, 2, 3,..., corresponding to the intervals of time δt. Let the ordinate axis represent the velocities of the reaction during these different intervals of time. Let the curve $vbdfh...$ represent the actual velocity of the transformation on the supposi-tion that the rate of formation of invert sugar is a uniform and continuous process of retardation. This is the real nature of the change. But we have pretended that the velocity remains con-stant during a short but finite interval of time say $\delta t = 1$ second. The amount of cane sugar inverted during the first second is,

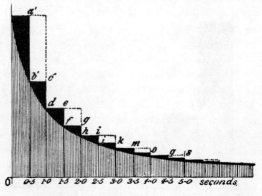

Fig. 99.

therefore, represented by the area $va1O$ (Fig. 98); during the second interval by the area $bc21$, and so on.

At the end of the first interval the velocity at a is supposed to suddenly fall to b, whereas, in reality, the decrease should be represented by the gradual slope of the curve vb.

The error resulting from the inexact nature of this " simplifying assumption" is graphically represented by the blackened area vab; for succeeding intervals the error is similarly represented by bcd, $def, ...$ In Fig. 99, by halving the interval, we have considerably reduced the magnitude of the error. This is shown by the dimin-ished area of the blackened portions for the first and succeeding seconds of time. *The smaller we make the interval, the less the error, until, at the limit, when the interval is made infinitely small, the result is absolutely correct.* The amount of invert sugar formed during the first five seconds is then represented by the area $vbdf \ldots 5O$.

The above reasoning will repay careful study; once mastered, the "methods of integration" are, in general, mere routine work.

The operation[1] denoted by the symbol "$\int$" is called **integration.** When this sign is placed before a differential function, say dx, it means that the function is to be integrated with respect to dx. *Integration is essentially a method for obtaining the sum of an infinite number of infinitely small quantities.* This does not mean, as some writers have it, "if enough nothings be taken their sum is something". The integral itself is not exactly what we usually understand by the term "sum," but it is rather "the limit of a sum when the number of terms is infinitely great".

Not only can the amount of substance formed in a chemical reaction during any given interval of time be expressed in this manner, but all sorts of varying magnitudes can be subject to a similar operation. The *distance* passed over by a train travelling with a known velocity, can be represented in terms of a definite integral. The *quantity of heat* necessary to raise the temperature, θ, of a given mass, m, of a substance from $\theta°_1$ to $\theta°_2$, is given by the integral $\int_{\theta_1}^{\theta_2} m\sigma . d\theta$, where σ denotes the specific heat of the substance. The *work* done by a variable force, F, when a body changes its position from s_0 to s_1 is $\int_{s_0}^{s_1} F . ds$. This is called a **space integral.** The impulse of a variable force F, acting during the interval of time $t_2 - t_1$, is given by the **time integral** $\int_{t_1}^{t_2} F . dt$. By Newton's second law, "the change of momentum of any mass, m, is equal to the impulse it receives". Momentum is defined as the product of the mass into the velocity. If, when t is t_1, $v = v_1$; and, when t is t_2, $v = v_2$, Newton's law may be written

$$\int_{v_1}^{v_2} m . dv = \int_{t_1}^{t_2} F . dt.$$

The quantity of heat developed in a conductor during the passage of an electric current of intensity C, for a short interval of time dt is given by the expression $kC . dt$ (Joule's law), where k is a constant depending on the nature of the circuit. If the current remains constant during any short interval of time, the amount of

---

[1] The symbol "$\int$" is supposed to be the first letter of the word "sum". "Omn," from *omnia*, meaning "all," was once used in place of "$\int$". The first letter of the differential dx is the initial letter of the word "difference".

heat generated by the current during the interval of time $t_2 - t_1$, is given by the integral $\int_{t_1}^{t_2} kC \cdot dt$. The quantity of gas, q, consumed in a building during any interval of time $t_2 - t_1$, may be represented as a definite integral,

$$q = \int_{t_1}^{t_2} v \cdot dt,$$

where v denotes the velocity of efflux of the gas from the burners. The value of q can be read off on the dial of the gas meter at any time. The gas meter performs the integration automatically. The cyclometer of a bicycle can be made to integrate,

$$s = \int_{t_1}^{t_2} v dt.$$

Differentiation and integration are reciprocal operations in the same sense that multiplication is the inverse of division, addition of subtraction. Thus,

$$a \times b \div b = a; \ a + b - b = a; \ \sqrt{a^2} = a;$$
$$d \int a \cdot dx = a \cdot dx; \ \int dx = x;$$

$3x^2 dx$ is the differential of x^3, so is x^3 the integral of $3x^2 dx$. The differentiation of an integral, or the integration of a differential always gives the original function. The signs of differentiation and of integration mutually cancel each other. The integral, $\int f'(x) dx$, is sometimes called an *anti-differential*. Integration reverses the operation of differentiation and restores the differentiated function to its original value, but with certain limitations to be indicated later on.

While the majority of mathematical functions can be differentiated without any particular difficulty, the reverse operation of integration is not always so easy, in some cases it cannot be done at all. If, however, the function from which the differential has been derived, is known, the integration can always be performed. Knowing that $d(\log x) = x^{-1} dx$, it follows at once that $\int x^{-1} dx = \log x$. The differential of x^n is $nx^{n-1} dx$, hence $\int nx^{n-1} dx = x^n$. In order that the differential of x^n may assume the form of x^{-1}, we must have $n - 1 = -1$, or $n = 0$. In that case x^n becomes $x^0 = 1$. This has no differential. The algebraic function x^n cannot therefore give rise to a differential of the form $x^{-1} dx$. Nor can any other known function except $\log x$ give rise to $x^{-1} dx$. If logarithms had not been invented we could not have integrated $\int x^{-1} dx$. The integration of algebraic functions may also give rise to transcendental functions. Thus, $(1 - x)^{-\frac{1}{2}}dx$ becomes $\sin^{-1}x$; and $(1 + x^2)^{-1}dx$ becomes $\tan^{-1}x$. Still further, the integration of many expressions can only be effected when new functions corresponding with these forms have been invented. The integrals $\int e^{x^2}. dx$, and $\int (x^3 + 1)^{-\frac{1}{2}}dx$, for example, have not yet been evaluated, because we do not know any function which will give either of these forms when differentiated.

The nature of mathematical reasoning may now be defined with greater precision than was possible in § 1. There, stress was laid upon the search for constant relations between observed facts. But the best results in science have been won by anticipating Nature by means of the so-called working hypothesis. The investigator first endeavours to reproduce his ideas in the form of a differential equation representing the momentary state of the phenomenon. Thus Wilhelmy's law (1850) is nothing more than the mathematician's way of stating an old, previously unverified, speculation of Berthollet (1779) ; while Guldberg and Waage's law (1864-69) is still another way of expressing the same thing.

To test the consequences of Berthollet's hypothesis, it is clearly necessary to find the amount of chemical action taking place during intervals of time accessible to experimental measurement. It is obvious that Wilhelmy's equation in its present form will not do, but by "methods of integration" it is easy to show that if

$$\frac{dx}{dt} = k(1 - x), \text{ then, } k = \frac{1}{t} \cdot \log \frac{1}{1 - x},$$

where x denotes the amount of substance transformed during the time t. x is measurable, t is measurable. We are now in a position to compare the fundamental assumption with observed facts. If Berthollet's guess is a good one, k, above, must have a constant value. But this is work for the laboratory, not the study, as indicated in connection with Newton's law of cooling, § 20.

Integration, therefore, bridges the gap between theory and fact by reproducing the hypothesis in a form suitable for experimental verification, and, at the same time, furnishes a direct answer to the two questions raised at the beginning of this section. The idea was represented in my *Chemical Statics and Dynamics* (1904), thus :—

Hypothesis → Differential Equation → Integration → Observation.

We shall return to the above physical process after we have gone through a drilling in the methods to be employed for the integration of expressions in which the variables are so related that all the x's and dx's can be collected to one side of the equation, all the y's and

dy's to the other. In a later chapter we shall have to study the integration of equations representing more complex natural processes.

If the mathematical expression of our ideas leads to equations which cannot be integrated, the working hypothesis will either have to be verified some other way,[1] or else relegated to the great repository of unverified speculations.

§ 69. Table of Standard Integrals.

Every differentiation in the differential calculus, corresponds with an integration in the integral calculus. Sets of corresponding functions are called "Tables of Integrals". Table II., page 193, contains the more important; handy for reference, better still for memorizing.

§ 70. The Simpler Methods of Integration.

I. Integration of the product of a constant term and a differential. On page 38, it was pointed out that "the differential of the product of a variable and a constant, is equal to the constant multiplied by the differential of the variable". It follows directly that the integral of the product of a constant and a differential, is equal to the constant multiplied by the integral of the differential. *E.g.*, if a is constant,

$$\int a \cdot dx = a\int dx = ax; \quad \int \log a \cdot dx = \log a\int dx = x \cdot \log a.$$

On the other hand, the value of an integral is altered if a term containing one of the variables is placed *outside* the integral sign. For instance, the reader will see very shortly that while

$$\int x^2 dx = \tfrac{1}{3}x^3; \quad x\int x dx = \tfrac{1}{2}x^3.$$

II. A constant term must be added to every integral. It has been shown that a constant term always disappears from an expression during differentiation, thus,

$$d(x + C) = dx.$$

This is equivalent to stating that there is an infinite number of expressions, differing only in the value of the constant term, which, when differentiated, produce the same differential. In

---

[1] Say, by slipping in another "simplifying assumption". Clairaut expressed his ideas of the moon's motion in the form of a set of complicated differential equations, but left them in this incomplete stage with the invitation, "Now integrate them who can".

TABLE II.—STANDARD INTEGRALS.

Function.	Differential Calculus.	Integral Calculus.	
$u = x^n.$	$\dfrac{du}{dx} = nx^{n-1}.$	$\displaystyle\int x^n dx = \dfrac{x^{n+1}}{n+1}$	(1)
$u = a^x.$	$\dfrac{du}{dx} = a^x \log_e a.$	$\displaystyle\int a^x dx = \dfrac{a^x}{\log_e a}.$	(2)
$u = e^x.$	$\dfrac{du}{dx} = e^x.$	$\displaystyle\int e^x dx = e^x.$	(3)
$u = \log_e x.$	$\dfrac{du}{dx} = \dfrac{1}{x}.$	$\displaystyle\int \dfrac{dx}{x} = \log_e x.$	(4)
$u = \sin x.$	$\dfrac{du}{dx} = \cos x.$	$\displaystyle\int \cos ax\,dx = \dfrac{\sin ax}{a}.$	(5)
$u = \cos x.$	$\dfrac{du}{dx} = -\sin x.$	$\displaystyle\int \sin ax\,dx = -\dfrac{\cos ax}{a}.$	(6)
$u = \tan x.$	$\dfrac{du}{dx} = \sec^2 x.$	$\displaystyle\int \sec^2 ax\,dx = \dfrac{\tan ax}{a}.$	(7)
$u = \cot x.$	$\dfrac{du}{dx} = -\operatorname{cosec}^2 x.$	$\displaystyle\int \operatorname{cosec}^2 ax . dx = -\dfrac{\cot ax}{a}.$	(8)
$u = \sec x.$	$\dfrac{du}{dx} = \dfrac{\sin x}{\cos^2 x}.$	$\displaystyle\int \dfrac{\sin x}{\cos^2 x}dx = \sec x.$	(9)
$u = \operatorname{cosec} x.$	$\dfrac{du}{dx} = -\dfrac{\cos x}{\sin^2 x}.$	$\displaystyle\int \dfrac{\cos x}{\sin^2 x}dx = -\operatorname{cosec} x.$	(10)
$u = \sin^{-1} x.$	$\dfrac{du}{dx} = \dfrac{1}{\sqrt{(1-x^2)}}.$	$\displaystyle\int \dfrac{dx}{\sqrt{(a^2-x^2)}}\begin{cases} = \sin^{-1}\dfrac{x}{a}. \end{cases}$	(11)
$u = \cos^{-1} x.$	$\dfrac{du}{dx} = -\dfrac{1}{\sqrt{(1-x^2)}}.$	$\begin{cases} = -\cos^{-1}\dfrac{x}{a}. \end{cases}$	(12)
$u = \tan^{-1} x.$	$\dfrac{du}{dx} = \dfrac{1}{1+x^2}.$	$\displaystyle\int \dfrac{dx}{a^2+x^2}\begin{cases} = \dfrac{1}{a}\tan^{-1}\dfrac{x}{a}. \end{cases}$	(13)
$u = \cot^{-1} x.$	$\dfrac{du}{dx} = -\dfrac{1}{1+x^2}.$	$\begin{cases} = -\dfrac{1}{a}\cot^{-1}\dfrac{x}{a}. \end{cases}$	(14)
$u = \sec^{-1} x.$	$\dfrac{du}{dx} = \dfrac{1}{x\sqrt{(x^2-1)}}.$	$\displaystyle\int \dfrac{dx}{x\sqrt{(x^2-a^2)}}\begin{cases} = \dfrac{1}{a}\sec^{-1}\dfrac{x}{a}. \end{cases}$	(15)
$u = \operatorname{cosec}^{-1} x.$	$\dfrac{du}{dx} = -\dfrac{1}{x\sqrt{(x^2-1)}}.$	$\begin{cases} = -\dfrac{1}{a}\operatorname{cosec}^{-1}\dfrac{x}{a}. \end{cases}$	(16)
$u = \operatorname{vers}^{-1} x.$	$\dfrac{du}{dx} = \dfrac{1}{\sqrt{(2x-x^2)}}.$	$\displaystyle\int \dfrac{dx}{\sqrt{(2x-x^2)}}\begin{cases} = \operatorname{vers}^{-1} x. \end{cases}$	(17)
$u = \operatorname{covers}^{-1} x.$	$\dfrac{du}{dx} = -\dfrac{1}{\sqrt{(2x-x^2)}}.$	$\begin{cases} = -\operatorname{covers}^{-1} x. \end{cases}$	(18)

stating the result of any integration, therefore, we must provide
for any possible constant term, by adding on an undetermined,
" empirical," or " arbitrary " constant, called the **constant of
integration**, and usually represented by the letter C. Thus,

$$\int du = u + C.$$

If we are given

$$dy = dx,$$

N

or, if we put $C = C_2 - C_1$, we get $\int dy + C_1 = \int dx + C_2$; $y + C_1 = x + C_2$;

$$y = x + C.$$

The geometrical signification of this constant is analogous to that of " b " in the tangent form of the equation of the straight line, formula (8), page 94; thus, the equation

$$y = mx + b,$$

represents an infinite number of straight lines, each one of which has a slope m to the x-axis and cuts the y-axis at some point b. An infinite number of values may be assigned to b. Similarly, an infinite number of values may be assigned to C in $\int \ldots dx + C$.

EXAMPLE.—Find a curve with the slope, at any point (x, y), of $2x$ to the x-axis. Since dy/dx is a measure of the slope of the curve at the point (x, y), $dy/dx = 2x$; $\therefore y = x^2 + C$. If $C = 0$, we have the curve $y = x^2$; if $C = 1$, another curve, $y = x^2 + 1$; if $C = 3$, $y = x^2 + 3 \ldots$ In the given problem we do not know enough to be able to say what particular value C ought to possess.

According to (5), (6), (7), (8), Table II., which are based upon (1), (2), (3), (4), page 48,

$$\int \frac{dx}{\sqrt{1 - x^2}} = \sin^{-1}x = -\cos^{-1}x \; ; \; \int \frac{dx}{\sqrt{1 + x^2}} = \tan^{-1}x = -\cot^{-1}x,$$

etc. This means that $\sin^{-1}x$, $\cos^{-1}x$; or $\tan^{-1}x$, $\cot^{-1}x, \ldots$ *only differ by a constant term.* This agrees with the trigonometrical properties of these functions illustrated on page 48. The following remarks are worth thinking over :

" Fourier's theorem is a most valuable tool of science, practical and theoretical, but it necessitates adaptation to any particular case by the provision of exact data, the use, that is, of definite figures which mathematicians humorously call ' constants,' because they vary with every change of condition. A simple formula is $n + n = 2n$, so also $n \times n = n^2$. In the concrete, these come to the familiar statement that 2 and 2 equals 4. So in the abstract, $40 + 40 = 80$. but in the concrete two 40 ft. ladders will in no way correspond to one 80 ft, ladder. They would require something else to join them end to end and to strengthen them. That something would correspond to a ' constant' in the formula. But even then we could not climb 80 ft. into the air unless there was something to secure the joined ladder. We could not descend 80 ft. into the earth unless there was an opening, nor could we cross an 80 ft. gap. For each of these uses we need something which is a ' constant' for the special case. It is in this way that all mathematical demonstrations and assertions need to be examined. They mislead people by their very definiteness and apparent exactness...."—J. T. SPRAGUE.

III. Integration of a sum and of a difference. Since

$$d(x + y + z + \ldots) = dx + dy + dz + \ldots,$$

it follows that

$$\int(dx + dy + dz + \ldots) = \int dx + \int dy + \int dz + \ldots,$$
$$= x + y + z + \ldots,$$

plus the arbitrary constant of integration. It is customary to append the integration constant to the final result, not to the intermediate stages of the integration. Similarly,

$$\int(dx - dy - dz - \ldots) = \int dx - \int dy - \int dz - \ldots,$$
$$= x - y - z - \ldots + C.$$

In words, the integral of the sum or difference of any number of differentials is equal to the sum of their respective integrals.

EXAMPLES.—(1) Remembering that $\log xy = \log x + \log y$, show that

$$\int\{\log (a + bx) (1 + 2x)\}dx = \int \log (a + bx)dx + \int \log (1 + 2x)dx + C.$$

(2) Show $\int \log \dfrac{a + bx}{1 + 2x}dx = \int \log(a + bx)dx - \int \log (1 + 2x)dx + C.$

IV Integration of $x^n dx$. Since the differential calculus, page 37, teaches us that

$$d(x^{n+1}) = (n + 1)x^n dx \; ; \; x^n . dx = d\left(\frac{x^{n+1}}{n + 1}\right) ;$$

we infer that

$$\therefore \int x^n dx = \frac{x^{n+1}}{n + 1} + C. \quad . \quad . \quad . \quad (1)$$

Hence, to integrate any expression of the form $ax^n . dx$, it is necessary to increase the index of the variable by unity, multiply by any constant term that may be present, and divide the product by the new index. An apparent exception occurs when $n = -1$, for then

$$\int x^{-1} . dx = \frac{x^{-1+1}}{1 - 1} = \frac{1}{0} = \infty.$$

But we can get at the integration by remembering that

$$d(\log x) = \frac{dx}{x} = x^{-1} . dx \; ; \; \therefore \int \frac{dx}{x} = \log x + C. \quad . \quad (2)$$

If, therefore, the numerator of a fraction can be obtained by the differentiation of its denominator, the integral is the natural logarithm of the denominator.

I want the beginner to notice that instead of writing $\log x + C$, we may put $\log x + \log a = \log ax$, for $\log a$ is an arbitrary constant as well as C. Hence $\log a = C$.

EXAMPLES.—(1) One of the commonest equations in physical chemistry is, $dx = k(a - x)dt$. Rearranging terms, we obtain

$$k \int dt = \int \frac{dx}{a - x} \; ; \; \therefore \; kt = - \int \frac{d(a - x)}{a - x} \; ;$$

Hence $kt = - \log (a - x)$; but $\log 1 = 0$, $\therefore kt = \log 1 - \log(a - x)$; or,

$$k = \frac{1}{t} \log \frac{1}{a - x} + C.$$

(2) Wilhelmy's equation, $dy/dt = - \alpha y$, already discussed in connection with the "compound interest law," page 63, may be written

$$\frac{dy}{y} = - \alpha dt \; ; \; \therefore \int \frac{dy}{y} = - \alpha t.$$

Remembering that $\log e = 1$; $\log y = \log b - \alpha t \log e = \log e^{-\alpha t} + \log b$, where $\log b$ is the integration constant, hence, $\log be^{-\alpha t} = \log y$; and, $y = be^{-\alpha t}$. A meaning for the constants will be deduced in the next section.

(3) Show $\int 4x^{-5} dx = 4\int x^{-5} . dx = - x^{-4} + C.$ Here n of (1) $= - 5$, and $n + 1 = - 5 + 1 = - 4.$

(4) Show $\int ax^3 . dx = \frac{1}{4}ax^4 + C.$

(5) Show $\int 4ax^{-\frac{3}{5}} . dx = 5ax^{\frac{2}{5}} + C.$

(6) Show $\int 2bx . dx/(a - bx^2) = - \log(a - bx^2) + C.$

(7) By a similar method to that employed for evaluating $\int x^n dx$; $\int x^{-1} dx$; show that

$$\int a^x dx = \frac{a^x}{\log_e a} + C \; ; \; \int e^x dx = e^x + C \; ; \; \int e^{-ax} dx = - \frac{1}{a} e^{-ax} + C. \quad (3)$$

(8) Prove that

$$- \int \frac{dx}{x^n} = \frac{1}{n - 1} \cdot \frac{1}{x^{n-1}} + C, \quad . \quad . \quad . \quad . \quad (4)$$

by differentiating the right-hand side.   Keep your result for use later on.

(9) Evaluate $\int \sin^4 x . \cos x . dx$.   Note that $\cos x . dx = d(\sin x)$, and that $\sin^4 x$ is the mathematician's way [1] of writing $(\sin x)^4$.   Ansr. $\frac{1}{5} \sin^5 x + C.$

$$\therefore \int \sin^4 x . \cos x . dx = \int \frac{1}{5} \sin^4 x . d(\sin x) = \frac{1}{5} \sin^5 x . + C.$$

(10) What is wrong with this problem : "Evaluate the integral $\int x^3$"? Hint. The symbol "$\int$" has no meaning apart from the accompanying "dx". For brevity, we call "$\int$" the symbol of integration, but the integral must be written or *understood* to mean $\int \dots dx$.

(11) If $y = a + bt + ct^2$; show that $\int y dt = at + \frac{1}{2}bt^2 + \frac{1}{3}ct^3 + C.$ (Heilborn, *Zeit. phys. Chem.*, **7**, 367, 1891).

V. Integration of the product of a polynomial and its differential. Since, page 39,

$$d(ax^m + b)^n = n(ax^m + b)^{n-1} amx^{m-1} dx,$$

where $amx^{m-1} dx$ has been obtained by differentiating the expression within the brackets,

$$\therefore n \int (ax^m + b)^{n-1} amx^{m-1} dx = (ax^m + b)^n + C. \quad . \quad (5)$$

In words, integrate the product of a polynomial with its differ-

---

[1] But we must *not* write $\sin^{-1} x$ for $(\sin x)^{-1}$, nor $(\sin x)^{-1}$ for $\sin^{-1} x$. $\sin^{-1}$, $\cos^{-1}$, $\tan^{-1}$, ... have the *special* meaning pointed out in § 17.

ential, increase the index of the polynomial by unity and divide the result by the new exponent.

EXAMPLES.—(1) Show $\int (3ax^3 + 1)^2 9ax^2 . dx = \frac{1}{3}(3ax^3 + 1)^3 + C$.

(2) Show $\int (x + 1)^{-\frac{2}{3}} dx = 3(x + 1)^{\frac{1}{3}} + C$.

VI. Integration of expressions of the type :

$$(a + bx + cx^2 + \ldots)^m x dx, \quad . \quad . \quad . \quad (6)$$

where m is a positive integer. Multiply out and integrate each term separately.

EXAMPLES.—(1) $\int (1 + x)^2 x^3 dx = \int (x^3 + 2x^4 + x^5) dx = (\frac{1}{4} + \frac{2}{5}x + \frac{1}{6}x^2)x^4 + C$.

(2) Show that $\int (a + x^{\frac{1}{2}})^2 x^{\frac{1}{2}} dx = (\frac{2}{3}a^2 + ax^{\frac{1}{2}} + \frac{2}{5}x)x^{\frac{3}{2}} + C$

Here are a few simple though useful " tips " for special notice :

(i) Any constant term or a number may be added to the numerator of a fraction provided the differential sign is placed before it. The object of this is usually to show that the numerator of the given integral has been obtained by the differentiation of the denominator. If successful the integral reduces to the logarithm of the denominator. *E.g.*,

$$2\int \frac{xdx}{1 - x^2} = -\int \frac{d(1 - x^2)}{1 - x^2} = -\log (1 - x^2) = \log \frac{1}{1 - x^2} + C.$$

H. Danneel (*Zeit. phys. Chem.*, **33**, 415, 1900) used an integral like this in studying the " free energy of chemical reactions ".

(ii) Note the addition of log 1 makes no difference to the value of an expression, because $\log 1 = 0$; similarly, multiplication by $\log_e e$ makes no difference to the value of any term, because $\log_e e = 1$.

(iii) $\int \sin nx . dx$ may be made to depend on the known integral $\int \sin nx . d(nx)$ by multiplying and dividing by n. *E.g.*,

$$\int \cos nx . dx = \frac{1}{n}\int \cos nx . d(nx) = \frac{1}{n}\sin nx + C.$$

(iv) It makes no difference to the value of any term if the same quantity be added and then subtracted from it; or if the term be multiplied with and then divided by the same quantity. *E.g.*,

$$\int \frac{x . dx}{1 + 2x} = \int \frac{(\frac{1}{2} + x) - \frac{1}{2}}{1 + 2x} dx = \int \left(\frac{1}{2} - \frac{1}{2} \cdot \frac{1}{1 + 2x}\right) dx = \frac{x}{2} - \frac{1}{4}\int \frac{d(1 + 2x)}{1 + 2x}.$$

EXAMPLES.—(1) Show by (16), page 44, and (2) above,

$$\int \frac{dx}{(x^2 \log x - x^2)^{\frac{1}{2}}} = \int \frac{d(\log x)}{(\log x - 1)^{\frac{1}{2}}} = \int \frac{d(\log x - 1)}{(\log x - 1)^{\frac{1}{2}}} = 2(\log x - 1)^{\frac{1}{2}} + C.$$

(2) The following equation occurs in the theory of electrons (*Encyc. Brit.*,

26, 61, 1902): $dx/dt = (ua/D) \sin pt$; hence show $x = - (ua/pD) \cos pt + C$ where u, a, p and D are constants. Use (iv) above.

(3) Show that $\int x(1 + 2x)^{-1}dx = \frac{1}{2}x - \frac{1}{4} \log (1 + 2x) + C$. Use (iv) and (i).

The favourite methods for integration are by processes known as " the substitution of a new variable," " integration by parts " and by " resolution into partial fractions ". The student is advised to pay particular attention to these operations. Before proceeding to the description of these methods, I will return once more to the integration constant.

§ 71. How to find a Value for the Integration Constant.

It is perhaps unnecessary to remind the reader that integration constants must not be confused with the constants belonging to the original equation. For instance, in the law of descent of a falling body

$$\frac{dV}{dt} = g \; ; \; \int dV = g \int dt \; ; \; \text{or,} \; V = gt + C. \quad (1)$$

Here g is a constant representing the increase of velocity due to the earth's attraction, C is the constant of integration. There are two methods in general use for finding the value of the integration constant.

FIRST METHOD.—Returning to the falling body, and to its equation of motion,

$$V = gt + C.$$

On attempting to apply this equation to an actual experiment, we should find that, at the moment we began to calculate the velocity, the body might be moving upwards or downwards, or starting from a position of rest. All these possibilities are included in the integration constant C. Let V_0 denote the initial velocity of the body. The computation begins when $t = 0$, hence

$$V_0 = g \times 0 + C \; ; \; \text{or,} \; C = V_0.$$

If the body starts to fall from a position of rest, $V_0 = C = 0$, and

$$\int dv = gt \; ; \; \text{or,} \; V = gt.$$

This suggests a method for evaluating the constant whenever the nature of the problem permits us to deduce the value of the function for particular values of the variable. If possible, therefore, substitute particular values of the variables in the equation containing the integration constant and solve the resulting expression for C.

EXAMPLES.—(1) Find the value of C in the equation

$$t = \frac{1}{k} \log \frac{1}{a-x} + C, \qquad . \qquad . \qquad . \qquad (2)$$

which is the integral of a standard "velocity equation" of physical chemistry. t represents the time required for the formation of an amount of substance x. When the reaction is just beginning, $x = 0$ and $t = 0$. Substitute these values of x and t in (2).

$$\frac{1}{k} \log \frac{1}{a} + C = 0 \text{ ; or, } C = -\frac{1}{k} \log \frac{1}{a}.$$

Substitute this value of C in the given equation and we get

$$t = \frac{1}{k}\left(\log \frac{1}{a-x} - \log \frac{1}{a}\right) = \frac{1}{k} \log \frac{a}{a-x}.$$

(2) If $\dfrac{d(\log K)}{dT} = -\dfrac{10232 - 0\cdot1685T - 0\cdot00101T^2}{2T^2}$, and $K = 6\cdot25$, when $T = 3100$, show that the integration constant is $-2\cdot0603$. Hint. $\log k = 5116/T + 0\cdot08425 \log T + 0\cdot000505T + C$. Use natural logs. Substitute the above values of k and T in this equation. We get $1\cdot8326 = 1\cdot65 + 0\cdot6774 + 1\cdot5655 + C$; etc.

(3) If the temperature of a substance be raised $dT(^\circ \text{ abs.})$ it is commonly said that it has gained the entropy $d\phi = dT/T$. Show that the entropy, ϕ, of one gram of water at T° is $\log T - \log 273$ if the entropy at 0° C. be taken as zero. Hint. When $\phi = 0$, $T = 273$, etc.

(4) In Soret's experiments "On the Density of Ozone" (*Ann. Chim. Phys.* [4], **7**, 113, 1866 ; **13**, 257, 1868) a vessel A containing v_0 volumes of ozone mixed with oxygen was placed in communication with another vessel B containing oxygen, but no ozone. The volume, dv, of ozone which diffused from A to B during the given interval of time, dt, is proportional to the difference in the quantity of ozone present in the two vessels, and to the duration of the interval dt. If v volumes of ozone have passed from A to B at the time t, the vessel A, at the time t, will have $v_0 - v$ volumes of ozone in it, and the vessel B will have v volumes. The difference in the amount of ozone in the two vessels is therefore $v_0 - 2v$. By Graham's law, the rate of diffusion of ozone from A to B is inversely proportional to the square root of the density, ρ, of the ozone. Hence, by the rules of variation, page 22,

$$dv = \frac{a}{\sqrt{\rho}}(v_0 - 2v)dt \text{ ; or, } \frac{dv}{dt} = \frac{a}{\sqrt{\rho}}(v_0 - 2v),$$

where a is a constant whose numerical value depends upon the nature of the vessels used in the experiment, etc. Now, remembering that v_0 is a constant,

$$\int \frac{dv}{v_0 - 2v} = \frac{1}{2}\int \frac{d(2v)}{v_0 - 2v} = -\frac{1}{2}\int \frac{d(v_0 - 2v)}{v_0 - 2v} = -\frac{\log(v_0 - 2v)}{2} + C.$$

But when $t = 0$, $v = 0$, $\therefore C = \frac{1}{2} \log v_0$. Consequently,

$$\log \frac{v_0}{v_0 - 2v} = \frac{2a}{\sqrt{\rho}}t \text{ ; or, } \frac{v}{v_0} = \frac{1}{2}\left(1 - e^{-\frac{2at}{\sqrt{\rho}}}\right).$$

For the same gas, the same apparatus, and the same interval of time, ρ, t, and a will all be constant, and therefore,

$$\frac{v_n}{v_0} = \text{Constant.}$$

With different gases, under the same conditions, any difference in the value of v_n/v_0 must be due to the different densities of the gases. The mean of a series of experiments with chlorine (density, 35·5), carbon dioxide (density, 22), and ozone (density, x), gave the following for the value of this ratio:—

$$CO_2, \; 0·29; \quad \text{Ozone, } 0·271; \quad Cl_2, \; 0·227.$$

Compare chlorine with ozone. Let x denote the density of ozone. Then, by Graham's law,

$$\frac{v_n}{v_0}(O_3) : \frac{v_n}{v_0}(Cl_2) = \sqrt{35·5} : \sqrt{x} \; ; \; \therefore (0·271)^2 : (0·227)^2 = 35·5 : x \; ; \; \therefore x = 24·9,$$

which agrees with the triatomic molecule, O_3.

SECOND METHOD.—Another way is to find the values of x corresponding to two different values of t. Substitute the two sets of results in the given equation. The constant can then be made to disappear by subtraction. The result of this method is to *eliminate*, not *evaluate* the constant.

EXAMPLES.—(1) In the above equation, (2), assume that when $t = t_1$, $x = x_1$, and when $t = t_2$, $x = x_2$; where x_1, x_2, t_1 and t_2 are numerical measurements. Substitute these results in (2).

$$t_1 = \frac{1}{k} \log \frac{1}{a - x_1} + C \; ; \; t_2 = \frac{1}{k} \log \frac{1}{a - x_2} + C.$$

By subtraction and rearrangement of terms

$$k = \frac{1}{t_2 - t_1} \log \frac{a - x_1}{a - x_2}.$$

(2) If the specific heat, σ, of a substance at $\theta°$ is given by the expression $\sigma = a + b\theta$, and the quantity of heat, dQ, required to raise the temperature of unit mass of the substance is $dQ = \sigma d\theta$, show that the amount of heat required to heat the substance from $\theta_1°$ to $\theta_2°$ is

$$Q = \int_{\theta_1}^{\theta_2} (a + b\theta) d\theta = a(\theta_2 - \theta_1) + \tfrac{1}{2}b(\theta_2{}^2 - \theta_1{}^2).$$

Numerous examples of both methods will occur in the course of this work. Some have already been given in the discussion on the "Compound Interest Law in Nature," page 56.

§ 72. Integration by the Substitution of a New Variable.

When a function can neither be integrated by reference to Table II., nor by the methods of § 71, a suitable change of variable may cause the function to assume a less refractory form. The new variable is, of course, a known function of the old. This method of integration is, perhaps, best explained by the study of a few typical examples.

I. *Evaluate* $\int(a + x)^n dx$. Put $a + x = y$; therefore, $dx = dy$

Substitute y and dy in place of their equivalent values $a + x$ and dx in the given integral. We thus obtain an integral with a new variable y, in place of x, namely, $\int(a + x)^n dx = \int y^n dy$. From (1), page 195, $\int y^n dy = y^{n+1}/(n + 1) + C$. Restore the original values of y and dy, and we get

$$\int (a + x)^n dx = \frac{(a + x)^{n+1}}{n + 1} + C. \quad \cdot \quad \cdot \quad (1)$$

When the student has become familiar with integration he will find no particular difficulty in doing these examples mentally.

EXAMPLES.—(1) Integrate $\int(a - bx)^n dx$. Ansr. $-(a - bx)^{n+1}/b(n+1) + C$.
(2) Integrate $\int(a^2 + x^2)^{-1/2} x dx$. Ansr. $\sqrt{(a^2 + x^2)} + C$.
(3) Show

$$\int \frac{dx}{(a+x)^n} = -\frac{1}{n-1} \cdot \frac{1}{(a+x)^{n-1}} + C \; ; \; \int \frac{dx}{(a-x)^n} = \frac{1}{n-1} \cdot \frac{1}{(a-x)^{n-1}} + C.$$

(4) Show that $\int \dfrac{dx}{x \cdot \log x} = \dfrac{d(\log x)}{\log x} = \log(\log x) + C.$

II. Integrate $(1 - ax)^m x^n dx$, where m or n is a positive integer, and the x within the brackets has unit index. Put $y = 1 - ax$, therefore, $x = (1 - y)/a$; and $dx = -dy/a$. Substitute these values of x and dx in the original equation, and we get

$$\int (1 - ax)^m x^n dx = \frac{1}{a^{n+1}} \int (1 - y)^n (-y^m) dy,$$

which has the same form as (6), page 197. The rest of the work is obvious—expand $(1 - y)^n$ by the binomial theorem, page 36; multiply through with $-y^m dy$; and integrate as indicated in III., page 194.

EXAMPLE.—Show $\int x(a+x)^{\frac{1}{3}} dx = \frac{3}{28}(4x - 3a)(a + x)^{\frac{4}{3}} + C$. Hint. Put $a + x = y$, etc.

III.—Trigonometrical functions can often be integrated by these methods. For example, required the value of $\int \tan x \, dx$.

$$\int \tan x \, dx = \int \frac{\sin x}{\cos x} dx. \quad \cdot \quad \cdot \quad \cdot \quad (2)$$

Let $\cos x = u$, $-\sin x \, dx = du$. Since $-\int du/u = -\log u$, and $\log 1 = 0$, therefore,

$$\int \tan x \, dx = \log \frac{1}{\cos x} = \log \sec x + C.$$

Or, remembering that $-d(\cos x) = \sin x \cdot dx$, we can go straight on without any substitution at all,

$$\int \frac{\sin x}{\cos x} dx = - \int \frac{d(\cos x)}{\cos x} = - \log \cos x, \text{ etc.}$$

EXAMPLES.—(1) Show that $\int \sin x . \cos x . dx = \tfrac{1}{2}\sin^2 x + C$. Put $\sin x = u$.

(2) Show $\int \cot x dx = \log \sin x + C$. Hint. $\cot x = \cos x/\sin x$, etc.

(3) Show $\int \sin x . dx/\cos^2 x = \sec x + C$. Hint. Put $\cos x = u$; or go the short cut as in (2) above.

(4) Show that $\int \cos x . dx/\sin^2 x = - \operatorname{cosec} x + C$.

(5) Show that $\int e^{-x^2} x dx = - \tfrac{1}{2}\int e^{-x^2} . 2x dx = + \tfrac{1}{2}\int e^{-x^2} d(x^2) = -\tfrac{1}{2}e^{-x^2} + C$.

Some expressions require a little "humouring". Facility in this art can only be acquired by practice. A glance over the collection of formulæ on pages 611 to 612 will often give a clue. In this way, we find that $\sin x = 2 \sin \tfrac{1}{2}x . \cos \tfrac{1}{2}x$. Hence integrate

$$\int \frac{dx}{\sin x} ; \; i.e. \int \frac{dx}{2 \sin \tfrac{1}{2}x . \cos \tfrac{1}{2}x} \text{ or } \int \frac{\sec \tfrac{1}{2}x . dx}{2 \sin \tfrac{1}{2}x}.$$

Divide the numerator and denominator by $\cos \tfrac{1}{2}x$, then, since $1/\cos^2\tfrac{1}{2}x = \sec^2\tfrac{1}{2}x$; and $d(\tan x) = \sec^2 x . dx$, page 49, (3),

$$\therefore \int \frac{dx}{\sin x} = \int \frac{\sec^2\tfrac{1}{2}x . d(\tfrac{1}{2}x)}{\tan \tfrac{1}{2}x} = \int \frac{d(\tan \tfrac{1}{2}x)}{\tan \tfrac{1}{2}x} = \log \tan \frac{x}{2} + C.$$

The substitutions may be difficult to one not familiar with trigonometry.

EXAMPLES.—(1) Remembering that $\cos x = \sin (\tfrac{1}{2}\pi + x)$, (9), page 611, show that $\int dx/\cos x = \log \tan (\tfrac{1}{4}\pi + \tfrac{1}{2}x) + C$. Hint. Proceed as in the illustration just worked out in the text.

(2) Integrate $\int \dfrac{dx}{\sin x . \cos x}$. Hint, see (19), page 611; $\cos x dx = d(\sin x)$; etc.

$$\therefore \int \frac{\cos^2 x + \sin^2 x}{\sin x \cos x} dx = \int \frac{\cos x}{\sin x} dx + \int \frac{\sin x}{\cos x} dx = \log \tan x + C.$$

(3) Integrate $\int (a^2 - x^2)^{-\tfrac{1}{2}} dx$. Put $y = x/a$; $\therefore x = ay$; $\therefore dx = a dy$; $\therefore \sqrt{(a^2 - x^2)} = a \sqrt{1 - y}$;

$$\therefore \int \frac{dx}{\sqrt{a^2 - x^2}} = \int \frac{dy}{\sqrt{1 - y^2}} = \sin^{-1}y = \sin^{-1}\frac{x}{a} + C.$$

(4) Show $\int \dfrac{\sqrt{a^2 - x^2}}{x^4} dx = - \dfrac{(a^2 - x^2)^{\tfrac{3}{2}}}{3a^2 x^3} + C$. Hint. Put $x = \dfrac{1}{y}$.

IV. *Expressions involving the square root of a quadratic binomial* can very often be readily solved by the aid of a lucky trigonometrical substitution. The form of the inverse trigonometrical functions (Table II.) will sometimes serve as a guide in the right choice. If the binomial has the forms :

$\sqrt{x^2 + 1}$; or, $\sqrt{x^2 + a^2}$; try $x = \tan \theta$; or, $a \tan \theta$; or, $\cot \theta$.   (3)

$\sqrt{1 - x^2}$; or, $\sqrt{a^2 - x^2}$; try $x = \sin \theta$; or, $a \sin \theta$; or, $\cos \theta$.   (4)

$\sqrt{x^2 - 1}$; or, $\sqrt{x^2 - a^2}$; try $x = \sec \theta$; or, $a \sec \theta$; or, $\mathrm{cosec}\, \theta$, (5)

$$\sqrt{a^2 - (x + b)^2}; \text{ try } x + b = a \sin \theta.   .   .   (6)$$

EXAMPLES.—(1) Find the value of $\int \sqrt{(a^2 - x^2)} dx$.   In accordance with the above rule (4), put $x = a \sin \theta$, $\therefore\ dx = a \cos \theta \cdot d\theta$.   Consequently, by substitution,

$$\int \sqrt{(a^2 - x^2)} dx = a^2 \int \cos^2\theta d\theta = \tfrac{1}{2}a^2 \int (1 + \cos 2\theta) d\theta = \tfrac{1}{2}a^2(\theta + \tfrac{1}{2} \sin 2\theta);$$

since $2 \cos^2\theta = 1 + \cos 2\theta$, (31), page 612.   But $x = a \sin \theta$, $\theta = \sin^{-1} x/a$, and

$$\therefore \tfrac{1}{2} \sin 2\theta = \sin \theta \cdot \cos \theta = \sin \theta \sqrt{(1 - \sin^2\theta)} = \sqrt{a^2 - x^2} \cdot x/a^2,$$

$$\therefore \int \sqrt{(a^2 - x^2)} dx = \tfrac{1}{2}a^2 \sin^{-1} x/a + \tfrac{1}{2}x \sqrt{a^2 - x^2} + C.$$

(2) The integration of $\int x^2 \sqrt{a^2 - x^2} \cdot dx$ arises in the study of molecular dynamics (Helmholtz's *Vorlesungen über theoretische Physik*, **2**, 176, 1902). Rule (4). Put $x = a \sin \theta$; $\therefore\ x^2 = a^2 \sin^2\theta$; $dx = a \cos \theta \cdot d\theta$; $\sqrt{(a^2 - x^2)} = a \sqrt{(1 - \sin^2\theta)}$. Remembering that $\cos \theta = \sqrt{(1 - \sin^2\theta)}$, and $\sin 2x = 2 \sin x \cdot \cos x$, (19) and (29), pages 611 and 612, we get the expression

$$\int x^2 \sqrt{a^2 - x^2} \cdot dx = a^4 \int \sin^2\theta \cdot \cos^2\theta \cdot d\theta = \tfrac{1}{8}a^4 \int \sin^2 2\theta \cdot d(2\theta);$$

which will be integrated very shortly.

(3) Show $\int \dfrac{dx}{(1 - x)\sqrt{1 - x^2}} = \sqrt{\dfrac{1 + x}{1 - x}} + C$.   Put $x = \cos \theta$. Rule (4).   If the beginner has forgotten his "trig." he had better verify these steps from the collection of trigonometrical formulæ in Appendix I., page 611.   The substitutions are here very ingenious, but difficult to work out *de novo*.

$$= -\int \frac{\sin \theta d\theta}{(1 - \cos \theta)\sqrt{1 - \cos^2\theta}} = -\int \frac{d\theta}{1 - \cos \theta} = -\tfrac{1}{2}\int \frac{d\theta}{\sin^2\tfrac{1}{2}\theta} = -\int \mathrm{cosec}^2\frac{\theta}{2} \cdot d\left(\frac{\theta}{2}\right);$$

$$= \cot \tfrac{1}{2}\theta = \frac{\cos \tfrac{1}{2}\theta}{\sin \tfrac{1}{2}\theta} = \sqrt{\frac{2 \cos^2\tfrac{1}{2}\theta}{2 \sin^2\tfrac{1}{2}\theta}} = \sqrt{\frac{1 + \cos \theta}{1 - \cos \theta}} = \sqrt{\frac{1 + x}{1 - x}}.$$

(4) Show $\int \dfrac{dx}{\sqrt{(x^2 + 1)}} = \log (x + \sqrt{x^2 + 1}) + C$.   Put $x = \tan \theta$. Rule (3). Given $\tan (\tfrac{1}{4}\pi + \tfrac{1}{2}\theta) = \tan \theta + \sec \theta$; $\therefore\ = x + \sqrt{(x^2 + 1)}$; see Ex. (1), preceding set.

(5) Show $\int \dfrac{dx}{\sqrt{(x^2 - 1)}} = \log (x + \sqrt{x^2 - 1}) + C$.   Put $x = \sec \theta$. Rule (5).

It may be here remarked that whenever there is a function of the second degree included under a root sign, such, for instance, as $\sqrt{x^2 + px + q}$, the substitution of

$$z = x + \sqrt{x^2 + px + q}, \quad . \quad . \quad . \quad (7)$$

will enable the integration to be performed.   For the sake of ease, let us take the integral discussed in Ex. (4), above, for illustrative purposes.   Obviously, on reference to (7), $p = 0$, $q = 1$.   Hence, put $z = x + \sqrt{x^2 + 1}$;

$$\therefore z^2 - 2zx + x^2 = x^2 + 1 \; ; \; x = \tfrac{1}{2}(z^2 - 1)z^{-1} \; ;$$

$$\sqrt{x^2 + 1} = z - x = \tfrac{1}{2}(z^2 + 1)z^{-1} \; ; \; dx = \tfrac{1}{2}(z^2 + 1)z^{-2}dz \; ;$$

$$\therefore \int \frac{dx}{\sqrt{x^2 + 1}} = \int \frac{dz}{z} = \log z = \log (x + \sqrt{x^2 + 1}) + C.$$

V. The integration of expressions containing fractional powers of x and of $x^m(a + bx^n)^p.dx$. Here m, n, or p may be fractional. In this case the expression can be made rational by substituting $x = z^r$, or $a + bx = z^r$, where r is the least common multiple—L.C.M.—of the denominators of the several fractions.

EXAMPLES.—(1) Evaluate $\int x^5(1 + x^2)^{\frac{1}{2}}dx$. Here the L.C.M. of the denominators of the fractional parts is 2   Put $1 + x^2 = z^2$; then, $x^2 = z^2 - 1$; $\therefore z = \sqrt{1 + x^2}$; $x.dx = z.dz$. Substitute these values as required in the original expression, and

$$\int x^5(1 + x^2)^{\frac{1}{2}}dx = \int (z^2 - 1)^2 z^2 dz = \int (z^6 - 2z^4 + z^2)dz = \tfrac{1}{7}z^7 - \tfrac{2}{5}z^5 + \tfrac{1}{3}z^3 \; ;$$

$$\therefore \int x^5(1 + x^2)^{\frac{1}{2}}dx = \tfrac{1}{105}(1 + x^2)^{\frac{3}{2}}\{15(1 + x^2)^2 - 42(1 + x^2) + 35\} + C.$$

(2) Evaluate $\int x^{-4}(1 + x^2)^{-\frac{1}{2}}dx$. Here again $r = 2$. Put $1 + x^2 = z^2 x^2$; $\therefore x^{-2} = z^2 - 1$; $\therefore x^{-4} = (z^2 - 1)^2$; $\therefore x = (z^2 - 1)^{-\frac{1}{2}}$; $dx = -(z^2 - 1)^{-\frac{3}{2}}zdz$; $(1 + x^2)^{-\frac{1}{2}} = 1/zx = \sqrt{(z^2 - 1)}/z$. Consequently, we get the expression $\int x^{-4}(1 + x^2)^{-\frac{1}{2}}dx = -\int (z^2 - 1)dz = -\tfrac{1}{3}z^3 + z$; and hence,

$$\int \frac{dx}{x^4(1 + x^2)^{\frac{1}{2}}} = \frac{(2x^2 - 1)(1 + x^2)^{\frac{1}{2}}}{3x^3} + C.$$

(3) Evaluate $\int (1 + x^{\frac{1}{3}})^{-1}x^{\frac{1}{2}}dx$. Here, the L.C.M. is 6.   Hence, put $x = z^6$. The final result is $\tfrac{2}{7}x^{\frac{7}{6}} - \tfrac{6}{5}x^{\frac{5}{6}} + \tfrac{3}{2}x^{\frac{3}{6}} - \tfrac{6}{1}x^{\frac{1}{6}} + 6\tan^{-1}x^{\frac{1}{6}} + C$.   Hint. To integrate $(1 + z^2)^{-1}z^3dz$; first divide z^3 by $1 + z^2$, and multiply through with dz.

(4) Show $\displaystyle\int \frac{x^{\frac{1}{2}} - x^{\frac{3}{3}}}{x^{\frac{1}{4}}}dx = \frac{12}{15}x^{1\frac{4}{4}} - \frac{12}{13}x^{1\frac{1}{3}} + C$.   The least common multiple is 12.   Hence, put $x = z^{12}$, etc.

I have no doubt that the reader is now in a position to understand why the study of differentiation must precede integration. "Common integration," said A. de Morgan, "is only the *memory of differentiation*, the different artifices by which integration is effected are changes, not from the known to the unknown, but from forms in which memory will not serve us to those in which it will" (*Trans. Cambridge Phil. Soc.*, **8**, 188, 1844).   The purpose of the substitution of a new variable is to transform the given integral into another integral which has been obtained by the differentiation of a known function. The integration of any function therefore ultimately resolves itself into the direct or indirect comparison of the given integral with a tabulated list of the results of the differentiation of known functions. The reader will find it an advantage to keep such a list of known integrals at hand. A set of standard types is given in Table II., page 193, but this list should be extended by the student himself; or *A Short Table of Integrals* by B. O. Pierce, Boston, 1898, can be purchased.

When an expression cannot be rationalised or transformed into a known integral by the foregoing methods, we proceed to the so-called "methods of reduction" which will be discussed in the three succeeding sections. These may also furnish alternative methods for transforming some of the integrals which have just been discussed.

§ 73. Integration by Parts.

The differentiation of the product uv, furnishes

$$d(uv) = vdu + udv.$$

By integrating both sides of this expression we obtain

$$uv = \int vdu + \int udv.$$

Hence, by a transposition of terms, we have

$$\int udv = uv - \int vdu + C. \quad . \quad . \quad . \quad \textbf{(A)}$$

that is to say, the integral of udv can be obtained provided vdu can be integrated. This procedure is called **integration by parts.** The geometrical interpretation will be apparent after **A** has been deduced from Fig. 7, page 41. Since equation **A** is used for reducing involved integrals to simpler forms, it may be called a **reduction formulæ.** More complex reduction formulæ will come later.

EXAMPLES.—(1) Evaluate $\int x \log x dx$. Put

$$u = \log x, \quad \bigg| \quad dv = x \, . \, dx;$$
$$du = dx/x, \quad \bigg| \quad v = \tfrac{1}{2}x^2.$$

Substitute in **A**, and we obtain

$$\int u \, . \, dv = \int x \log x \, . \, dx = uv - \int v \, . \, du,$$
$$= \tfrac{1}{2}x^2 \log x - \int \tfrac{1}{2}x \, . \, dx = \tfrac{1}{2}x^2 \log x - \tfrac{1}{4}x^2$$
$$= \tfrac{1}{2}x^2(\log x - \tfrac{1}{2}) + C.$$

(2) Show that $\int x \cos x \, . \, dx = x \sin x + \cos x + C$. Put

$$u = x, \quad \bigg| \quad dv = \cos x \, . \, dx;$$
$$du = dx, \quad \bigg| \quad v = \sin x.$$

From **A**, $\int x \cos x \, . \, dx = x \sin x - \int \sin x \, . \, dx$; etc.

(3) Evaluate $\int \sqrt{(a^2 - x^2)}dx$, by "integration by parts". Put

$$u = \sqrt{(a^2 - x^2)}, \quad \bigg| \quad dv = dx;$$
$$du = - x . dx/\sqrt{(a^2 - x^2)}, \quad \bigg| \quad v = x.$$

$$\therefore \int \sqrt{(a^2 - x^2)}dx = x\sqrt{a^2 - x^2} + \int \frac{x^2 dx}{\sqrt{(a^2 - x^2)}},$$

$$= x\sqrt{a^2 - x^2} + \int \frac{\{a^2 - (a^2 - x^2)\}dx}{\sqrt{(a^2 - x^2)}}$$

$$= x\sqrt{a^2 - x^2} + \int \frac{a^2 dx}{\sqrt{(a^2 - x^2)}} - \int \sqrt{(a^2 - x^2)}dx.$$

Transpose the last term to the left-hand side :

$$2\int \sqrt{a^2 - x^2} \ dx = x\sqrt{a^2 - x^2} + a^2\sin^{-1}x/a \text{ (page 193)},$$

$$\therefore \int \sqrt{(a^2 - x^2)}dx = \tfrac{1}{2}a^2 \sin^{-1}x/a + \tfrac{1}{2}x \sqrt{(a^2 - x^2)} + C.$$

(4) Show that $\int xe^x dx = (x - 1)e^x + C$. Take $u = x$; $dv = e^x dx$.

(5) Show $\int x^2 e^x dx = (x^2 - 2x + 2)e^x + C$. Take $dv = e^x dx$ and use the result of the preceding example for vdu.

(6) Show, integrating by parts, that $\int \log x . dx = x(\log x - 1) + C$.

(7) Show that the result of integrating $\int x^{-1}dx$ by parts is $\int x^{-1}dx$ itself.

The selection of the proper values of u and v is to be determined by trial. A little practice will enable one to make the right selection instinctively. The rule is that the integral $\int v . du$ must be more easily integrated than the given expression. In dealing with Ex. (4), for instance, if we had taken $u = e^x$, $dv = xdx$, $\int v . du$ would have assumed the form $\tfrac{1}{2}\int x^2 e^x dx$, which is a more complex integral than the one to be reduced.

§ 74. Successive Integration by Parts.

A complex integral can often be reduced to one of the standard forms by the "method of integration by parts". By a repeated application of this method, complicated expressions may often be integrated, or else, if the expression cannot be integrated, the non-integrable part may be reduced to its simplest form. This procedure is sometimes called **integration by successive reduction**. See Ex. (5), above.

EXAMPLES.—(1) Evaluate $\int x^2\cos nxdx$. Put

$$u = x^2, \quad \bigg| \quad dv = \{\cos nx . d(nx)\}/n ;$$
$$du = 2x .\,dx, \quad \bigg| \quad v = (\sin nx)/n.$$

Hence, on integration by parts,

$$\int x^2\cos nxdx = \frac{x^2\sin nx}{n} - \frac{2}{n}\int x \sin nx . dx. \qquad . \qquad . \qquad (1)$$

Now put

$$u = x, \quad \bigg| \quad dv = \sin nx . dx ;$$
$$du = dx, \quad \bigg| \quad v = - (\cos nx)/n.$$

Hence,

$$\int x \sin nx . dx = - \frac{x \cos nx}{n} - \int \frac{- \cos nx . dx}{n} = - \frac{x \cos nx}{n} + \frac{\sin nx}{n^2}, \quad (2)$$

Now substitute (2) in (1) and we get,

$$\int x^2 \cos nx . dx = \frac{x^2 \sin nx}{n} + \frac{2x \cos nx}{n^2} - \frac{2 \sin nx}{n^3} + C.$$

(2) In the last example, we made the integral $\int x^2 \cos nx . dx$ depend on that of $x \sin nx . dx$, and this, in turn, on that of $- \cos nx . d(nx)$, thus reducing the given integral to a known standard form. The integral $\int x^4 \cos x . dx$ is a little more complex. Put

$$u = x^4, \quad \Big| \quad dv = \cos x dx;$$
$$du = 4x^3 dx, \quad \Big| \quad v = \sin x.$$
$$\therefore \int x^4 \cos x . dx = x^4 \sin x - 4 \int x^3 \sin x . dx.$$

In a similar way,

$$4 \int x^3 \sin x . dx = 4x^3 \cos x - 3 . 4 \int x^2 \cos x . dx.$$

Similarly,

$$3 . 4 \int x^2 \cos x . dx = 3 . 4 . x^2 \sin x + 2 \ 3 . 4 \int x \sin x . dx,$$

and finally,

$$2 . 3 . 4 \int x \sin x dx = 2 . 3 . 4 x \cos x + 1 . 2 . 3 . 4 \sin x.$$

All these values must be collected together, as in the first example. In this way, the integral is reduced, by successive steps, to one of simpler form. The integral $\int x^4 \cos x . dx$ was made to depend on that of $x^3 \sin x . dx$, this, in turn, on that of $x^2 \cos x . dx$, and so on until we finally got $\int \cos x . dx$, a well-known standard form.

(3) It is an advantage to have two separate sheets of paper in working through these examples; on one work as in the preceding examples and on the other enter the results as in the next example. Show that

$$\int x^3 e^x dx = x^3 e^x - 3 \int x^2 e^x dx;$$
$$= x^3 e^x - 3(x^2 e^x - 2 \int x e^x dx);$$
$$= x^3 e^x - 3x^2 e^x + 2 . 3(x e^x - \int e^x dx;$$
$$= (x^3 - 3x^2 + 6x - 6) e^x + C.$$

It is also interesting to notice that we sometimes obtain different results with different substitutions. For instance, we get either

$$\int x^{-\frac{1}{2}} e^x . dx = \frac{e^x}{x^{\frac{1}{2}}} \Big\{ 1 + \frac{1}{2x} + \frac{3}{(2x)^2} + \frac{3.5}{(2x)^3} + \dots \Big\} + C_1; \quad (3)$$

$$\int x^{-\frac{1}{2}} e^x . dx = \frac{e^x}{x^{\frac{1}{2}}} \Big\{ 2x - \frac{(2x)^2}{3} + \frac{(2x)^3}{3.5} - \dots \Big\} + C_2, . \quad (4)$$

according as we take $u = x^{-\frac{1}{2}}$, etc., or, $u = e^x$. In the last series, (4), the numerator and denominator of each term has been multiplied by $x^{\frac{1}{2}}$. Differences of this kind can generally be traced to differences in the range of the variable, or to differences in the value of the integration constants. Another example occurs during the integration of $(1 - x)^{-2} dx$. In one case,

$$\int (1-x)^{-2}dx = -\int (1-x)^{-2}d(1-x) = (1-x)^{-1} + C_1 ; \quad (5)$$

but if we substitute $x = z^{-1}$ before integration, then

$$\int (1-x)^{-2}dx = -\int (z-1)^{-2}dz = (z-1)^{-1} = x(1-x)^{-1} + C_2. \quad (6)$$

The two solutions only differ by the constant "-1". By adding -1 to (5), (6) is obtained. C_1 is not therefore equal to C_2, $C_1 = C_2 - 1$.

§ 75. Reduction Formulæ (*for reference*).

We found it convenient, on page 205, to refer certain integrals to a "standard formula" **A**; and on page 206 reduced complex integrals to known integrals by a repeated application of the same formula, namely, Ex. (1), page 206, etc. Such a formula is called a **reduction formula**. The following are standard reduction formulæ convenient for the integration of binomial integrals of the type :—

$$\int x^m(a + bx^n)^p dx. \quad \bullet \quad \bullet \quad \bullet \quad \bullet \quad (1)$$

These expressions can always be integrated if $(m + 1)/n$ be a positive integer. Four cases present themselves according as m, or p are positive or negative.

I.—m is positive.

The integral $\int x^m(a + bx^n)^p . dx$, may be made to depend on that of $\int x^{m-n}(a + bx^n)^{p+1} . dx$, through the following reduction formula. The integral (1) is equal to

$$\frac{x^{m-n+1}(a+bx^n)^{p+1}}{b(m + np + 1)} - \frac{a(m - n + 1)}{b(m + np + 1)} \int x^{m-n}(a + bx^n)^p dx. \quad \textbf{(B)}$$

when m is a positive integer. This formula may be applied successively until the factor outside the brackets, under the integral sign, is less than n. Then proceed as on page 204. **B** can always be integrated if $(m - n + 1)/n$ is a positive integer. See Ex. (7), below.

II.—m is negative.

In **B**, m must be the positive, otherwise the index will increase, instead of diminish, by a repeated application of the formula. When m is negative, it can be shown that the integral (1) is equal to

$$\frac{x^{m+1}(a + bx^n)^{p+1}}{a(m + 1)} - \frac{b(np + m + n + 1)}{a(m + 1)} \int x^{m+n}(a + bx^n)^p dx, \quad \textbf{(C)}$$

where m is negative. This formula diminishes m by the number of units in n. If $np + m + n + 1 = 0$, the part to be integrated will disappear, and the integration will be complete. **C** can always be integrated if $(m + n + 1)/n$ is a positive integer. See Ex. (7), below.

III.—p is positive.

Another useful formula diminishes the exponent of the bracketed term, so that the integral (1) is equal to

$$\frac{x^{m+1}(a + bx^n)^p}{m + np + 1} + \frac{anp}{m + np + 1}\int x^m(a + bx^n)^{p-1}dx, \quad \textbf{(D)}$$

where p is positive. By a repeated application of this formula the exponent of the binomial, if positive, may be reduced to a positive or negative fraction less than unity.

IV.—p is negative.

If p is negative, the integral (1) is equal to

$$-\frac{x^{m+1}(a + bx^n)^{p+1}}{an(p + 1)} + \frac{(np + m + n + 1)}{an(p + 1)}\int x^m(a + bx^n)^{p+1}dx. \quad \textbf{(E)}$$

Formulæ **B, C, D, E** have been deduced from (1), page 208, by the method of integration by parts. Perhaps the student can do this for himself. The reader will notice that formula **B** *decreases* (algebraically) the exponent of the monomial factor from m to $m - n + 1$, while **C** *increases* the exponent of the same factor from m to $m + 1$. Formula **D** *decreases* the exponent of the binomial factor from p to $p - 1$, while **E** *increases* the exponent of the binomial factor from p to $p + 1$. **B** and **D** fail when $np + m + 1 = 0$; **C** fails when $m + 1 = 0$; **E** fails when $p + 1 = 0$. When **B, C,** and **D** fail use V, page 204; if **E** fails $p = -1$ and the preceding methods apply.

EXAMPLES.—Evaluate the following integrals:—

(1) $\int \sqrt{(a+x^2)}dx$. Hints. Use **D**. Put $m = 0$, $b = 1$, $n = 2$, $p = \frac{1}{2}$. Ansr. $\frac{1}{2}[x\sqrt{(a + x^2)} + a \log \{x + \sqrt{(a + x^2)}\}] + C$. See bottom of page 206.

(2) $\int x^4dx/\sqrt{(a^2 - x^2)}$. Hints. Put $m = 4$, $b = -1$, $n = 2$, $p = -\frac{1}{2}$. Use **B** twice. Ansr. $\frac{1}{8}\{3a^4\sin^{-1}x/a - x(2x^2 + 3a^2)\sqrt{(a^2 - x^2)}\} + C$.

(3) $\int \sqrt{(1 - x^2)}x^3dx$. Hint. Use **B**. Ansr. $-\frac{1}{5}(x^2 + 2)\sqrt{(1 - x^2)} + C$.

(4) $\int \sqrt{(a + bx^2)}^{-3}dx$. Ansr. $x(a + bx^2)^{-1/2}/a + C$ Use **E**.

(5) $\int \frac{dx}{x^3\sqrt{x^2 - a^2}}$, i.e. $\int x^{-3}(-a^2 + x^2)^{-\frac{1}{2}}dx$. Hint. Use **C**. $m = -3$, $b = 1$, $n = 2$, $p = -\frac{1}{2}$. Ansr. $\frac{\sqrt{x^2 - a^2}}{2a^2x^2} + \frac{1}{2a^3}\sec^{-1}\frac{x}{a}$.

(6) Renyard (*Ann. Chim. Phys.*, [4], **19**, 272, 1870), in working out a theory of electro-dynamic action, integrated $\int (a^2 + x^2)^{-\frac{3}{2}} dx$. Hence $m = 0$, $n = 2$, $b = 1$, $a = a^2$, $p = -\frac{3}{2}$. Use **E**. Ansr. $x(a^2 + x^2)^{-\frac{1}{2}}/a^2 + C$.

(7) To show that it is possible to integrate the expression

$$\int (a^{n-1} - x^{n-1})^{-\frac{1}{2}} x^{\frac{1}{2}(n-1)} dx, \quad . \quad . \quad . \quad (2)$$

when $n = \dots \frac{3}{5}, \frac{1}{3} - 1, \frac{3}{1}, \frac{5}{3}, \dots$; and when $n = \dots \frac{3}{4}, \frac{2}{3}, \frac{1}{2}, 0, 2, \frac{3}{2}, \dots$, substitute $z = a + bx^n$ in (1). We get

$$n^{-1} b^{-\frac{m+1}{n}} \int (z-a)^{\frac{m+1}{n}-1} z^p dz. \quad . \quad . \quad . \quad (3)$$

If $(m + 1)/n$ be a positive integer, the expression in brackets can be expanded by the binomial theorem, and integrated in the usual manner. By comparing (2) with (3), it is easy to see that (2) can be integrated when

$$\frac{m+1}{n} = \frac{\frac{1}{2}(n-1)+1}{n-1} = \frac{1}{n-1} + \frac{1}{2}, \quad . \quad . \quad . \quad (4)$$

is a positive integer. From **B** and **C**, the integral (2) depends upon the integral

$$\int x^{m-n}(a + bx^n)^p dx; \text{ or, } \int x^{m+n}(a + bx^n)^p dx. \quad . \quad . \quad (5)$$

By the substitution of $m - n$, and $m + n$ respectively for m in $(m + 1)/n$, and comparison with (2), we find that (2) can be integrated when

$$\frac{m-n+1}{n} = \frac{\frac{1}{2}(n-1) - (n-1) + 1}{n-1} = \frac{1}{n-1} - \frac{1}{2}, \quad . \quad . \quad (6)$$

is a positive integer ; or else when

$$\frac{m+n+1}{n} = \frac{\frac{1}{2}(n-1) + (n-1) + 1}{n-1} = \frac{1}{n-1} + \frac{3}{2}, \quad . \quad . \quad (7)$$

is a positive integer. But (7) can be reduced to either (4) or (6) by subtracting unity, and since integration by parts can be performed a finite number of times, we have the condition that

$$\frac{1}{n-1} - \frac{1}{2} \quad . \quad . \quad . \quad . \quad . \quad (8)$$

be a positive or negative integer, or zero, in order that (2) may be integrated ; in other words, we must have

$$\frac{1}{n-1} - \frac{1}{2} = 0, 1, 2, 3, \dots; = -1, -2, -3, \dots \quad . \quad (9)$$

Similarly, by substituting $x = z^{-1}$, in (1), we obtain $-z^{-np-m-2}(az^n + b)^p dz$. As with (3) and (4), this can be integrated when

$$\frac{m+1}{n} = \frac{-np - m - 2 + 1}{n} = -\frac{m+1}{n} - p \quad . \quad . \quad (10)$$

is a positive integer. From **D** and **E**, and with the method used in deducing (8), we can extend this to cases where

$$-\frac{m+1}{n} - (p \pm 1) = -\frac{\frac{1}{2}(n-1)+1}{n+1} - \left(-\frac{1}{2} \pm 1\right); \quad . \quad (11)$$

or, where $-(n-1)^{-1}$ is a positive or negative integer. Equating this to $1, 2, 3, \dots$; and to $-1, -2, -3, \dots$ we get, with (9), the desired values of n. Notice that we have not proved that these are the only values of n which will allow (2) to be integrated.

The remainder of this section may be omitted until required. If n be a positive integer, we can integrate $\int \sin^n x \, . \, dx$ by putting,

$$u = \sin^{n-1} x \quad \bigg| \quad v = -\cos x.$$
$$du = (n-1)\sin^{n-2} x \cos x \, . \, dx \quad \bigg| \quad dv = \sin x \, . \, dx.$$

$\therefore \int \sin^n x \, . \, dx = -\sin^{n-1} x \, . \, \cos x + (n-1) \int \sin^{n-2} x \, . \, \cos^2 x \, . \, dx ;$

$= -\sin^{n-1} x \, . \, \cos x + (n-1) \int \sin^{n-2} x (1 - \sin^2 x) dx ;$

$= -\sin^{n-1} x \, . \, \cos x + (n-1) \int \sin^{n-2} x \, . \, dx - (n-1) \int \sin^n x \, . \, dx.$

Transpose the last term to the first member ; combine, and divide by n. The result is

$$\int \sin^n x \, . \, dx = -\frac{\sin^{n-1} x \, . \, \cos x}{n} + \frac{n-1}{n} \int \sin^{n-2} x \, . \, dx. \qquad (12)$$

Integrating $\int \cos^n x \, . \, dx$ by parts, by putting $u = \cos^{n-1} x$; $dv = \cos x \, . \, dx$, we get

$$\int \cos^n x \, . \, dx = \frac{\sin x \, . \, \cos^{n-1} x}{n} + \frac{n-1}{n} \int \cos^{n-2} x \, . \, dx. \qquad (13)$$

Remembering that $\cos \frac{1}{2}\pi = \cos 90° = 0$; and that $\sin 0° = 0$, we can proceed further

$$\int_0^{\frac{1}{2}\pi} \sin^n x \, . \, dx = \frac{n-1}{n} \int_0^{\frac{1}{2}\pi} \sin^{n-2} x \, . \, dx.$$

Now treat $n - 2$ the same as if it were a single integer n.

$$\therefore \int_0^{\frac{1}{2}\pi} \sin^{n-2} x \, . \, dx = \frac{n-3}{n-2} \int_0^{\frac{1}{2}\pi} \sin^{n-4} x \, . \, dx.$$

Combine the last two equations, and repeat the reduction. Thus. we get finally

$$\int_0^{\frac{1}{2}\pi} \sin^n x \, dx = \frac{(n-1)(n-3)\ldots 3.1}{n(n-2)\ldots 4.2} \int_0^{\frac{1}{2}\pi} dx = \frac{(n-1)(n-3)\ldots 3.1}{n(n-2)\ldots 4.2} \cdot \frac{\pi}{2}. \quad \textbf{(F)}$$

when n is even

$$\int_0^{\frac{1}{2}\pi} \sin^n x \, dx = \frac{(n-1)(n-3)\ldots 2}{n(n-2)\ldots 3} \int_0^{\frac{1}{2}\pi} \sin x \, dx = \frac{(n-1)(n-3)\ldots 2}{n(n-2)\ldots 3}, \quad \textbf{(G)}$$

when n is odd. If we take the cosine integral (3) above, and work in the same way, we get

$$\int_0^{\frac{1}{2}\pi} \cos^n x \, dx = \frac{(n-1)(n-3)\ldots 3.1}{n(n-2)\ldots 4.2} \cdot \frac{\pi}{2}; \quad \cdot \quad \cdot \quad \textbf{(H)}$$

if n is even, and

$$\int_0^{\frac{1}{2}\pi} \cos^n x \, dx = \frac{(n-1)(n-3)\ldots 4.2}{n(n-2)\ldots 5.3}, \quad \cdot \quad \cdot \quad \textbf{(I)}$$

if n is odd. Test this by actual integration and by substituting $n = 1, 2, 3, \ldots$ Note the resemblance between **H** with **F**, and **I** with **G**. The last four reduction formulæ are rather important in physical work. They can be employed to reduce $\int \cos^n x dx$ or $\int \sin^n x dx$ to an index unity, or $\frac{1}{2}\pi$.

If n is greater than unity, we can show that

$$\int_0^{\frac{1}{2}\pi} \sin^m x \cdot \cos^n x dx = \frac{n-1}{m+n}\int_0^{\frac{1}{2}\pi} \sin^m x \cdot \cos^{n-2} x dx; \quad . \quad \textbf{(J)}$$

by integration by parts, using $u = \sin^{m-1} x$, $dv = \cos^n x \cdot d(\cos x)$. If m is greater than unity, it also follows that

$$\int_0^{\frac{1}{2}\pi} \sin^m x \cdot \cos^n x dx = \frac{m-1}{m+n}\int_0^{\frac{1}{2}\pi} \sin^{m-2} x \cdot \cos^n x dx. \quad . \quad \textbf{(K)}$$

EXAMPLES.—(1) Show $\int_0^{\frac{1}{2}\pi} \sin x \cdot \cos x dx = \frac{1}{2}$; $\int_0^{\frac{1}{2}\pi} \sin^2 x \cdot \cos x dx = \frac{1}{3}$.

(2) $\int_0^{\frac{1}{2}\pi} \sin^6 x dx = \frac{5}{32}\pi$; $\int_0^{\frac{1}{2}\pi} \sin^3 \theta \cdot d\theta = \frac{2}{3}$.

(3) $\int_0^{\frac{1}{2}\pi} \sin x \cdot \cos^2 x dx = \frac{1}{3}$; $\int_0^{\frac{1}{2}\pi} \sin^2 x \cdot \cos^2 x dx = \frac{\pi}{16}$.

§ 76. Integration by Resolution into Partial Fractions.

Fractions containing higher powers of x in the numerator than in the denominator may be reduced to a whole number and a fractional part. Thus, by division,

$$\int \frac{x^5 \cdot dx}{x^2 + 1} = \int \left(x^3 - x + \frac{x}{x^2 + 1}\right)dx.$$

The integral part may be differentiated by the usual methods, but the fractional part must often be resolved into the sum of a number of fractions with simpler denominators, before integration can be performed.

We know that $\frac{4}{9}$ may be represented as the sum of two other fractions, namely $\frac{1}{6}$ and $\frac{1}{3}$, such that $\frac{4}{9} = \frac{1}{6} + \frac{1}{3}$. Each of these parts is called a **partial fraction**. If the numerator is a compound quantity and the denominator simple, the partial fractions may be deduced, at once, by assigning to each numerator its own denominator and reducing the result to its lowest terms. *E.g.*,

$$\frac{x^2 + x + 1}{x^3} = \frac{x^2}{x^3} + \frac{x}{x^3} + \frac{1}{x^3} = \frac{1}{x} + \frac{1}{x^2} + \frac{1}{x^3}.$$

When the denominator is a compound quantity, say $x^2 - x$, it is obvious, from the way in which the addition of fractions is performed, that the denominator is some multiple of the denominator of the partial fractions and contains no other factors. We therefore expect the denominators of the partial fractions to be factors of the given denominator. Of course, this latter may have been reduced after the addition of the partial fractions, but, in practice, we proceed as if it had not been so treated.

To reduce a fraction to its partial fractions, the denominator must first be split into its factors, thus : $x^2 - x$ is the product of the two factors : x, and $x - 1$. Then assume each factor to be the denominator of a partial fraction, and assign a certain indeterminate quantity to each numerator. These quantities may, or may not, be independent of x. The procedure will be evident from the following examples. There are four cases to be considered.

Case i. — *The denominator can be resolved into real unequal factors of the type :*

$$\frac{1}{(a - x)(b - x)}. \qquad . \qquad . \qquad . \qquad (1)$$

By resolution into partial fractions, (1) becomes

$$\frac{1}{(a - x)(b - x)} = \frac{A}{a - x} + \frac{B}{b - x} = \frac{A(b - x) + B(a - x)}{(a - x)(b - x)},$$

$$\therefore \frac{1}{(a - x)(b - x)} = \frac{Ab + Ba - Ax - Bx}{(a - x)(b - x)}.$$

We now assume—and it can be proved if necessary—that the numerators on the two sides of this last equation are identical,[1]

---

[1] An **identical equation** is one in which the two sides of the equation are either identical, or can be made identical by reducing them to their simplest terms. *E.g.*,

$$ax^2 + bx + c = ax^2 + bx + c \; ; \; (a - x)/(a - x)^2 = 1/(a - x),$$

or, in general terms,

$$a + bx + cx^2 + \ldots = a' + b'x + c'x^2 + \ldots$$

An identical equation is satisfied by each or any value that may be assigned to the variable it contains. The coefficients of like powers of x, in the two numbers, are also equal to each other. Hence, if $x = 0$, $a = a'$. We can remove, therefore, a and a' from the general equation. After the removal of a and a', divide by x and put $x = 0$, hence $b = b'$; similarly, $c = c'$, etc. For fuller details, see any elementary text-book on algebra. The symbol " $\equiv$ " is frequently used in place of "=" when it is desired to emphasize the fact that we are dealing with identities, not equations of condition. While an *identical equation* is satisfied by *any* value we may choose to assign to the variable it contains, an *equation of condition* is only satisfied by *particular* values of the variable. As long as this distinction is borne in mind, we may follow customary usage and write "=" when " $\equiv$ " is intended. For " $\equiv$ " we may read, " may be transformed into... whatever value the variable x may assume " ; while for " =," we must read, " is equal to... when the variable x satisfies some *special* condition or assumes some particular value ".

$$Ab + Ba - Ax - Bx = 1.$$

Pick out the coefficients of like powers of x, so as to build up a series of equations from which A and B can be determined. For example,

$$Ab + Ba = 1; \; x(A + B) = 0; \; \therefore A + B = 0; \; \therefore A = - B;$$

$$\therefore A = \frac{1}{b - a}, \; \therefore B = - \frac{1}{b - a}.$$

Substitute these values of A and B in (1).

$$\frac{1}{(a - x)(b - x)} = \frac{1}{b - a} \cdot \frac{1}{a - x} - \frac{1}{b - a} \cdot \frac{1}{b - x}. \quad (2)$$

An ALTERNATIVE METHOD, much quicker than the above, is indicated in the following example: Find the partial fractions of the function in example (3) below.

$$\frac{1}{(a - x)(b - x)(c - x)} = \frac{A}{a - x} + \frac{B}{b - x} + \frac{C}{c - x} \cdots$$

Consequently,

$$(b - x)(c - x)A + (a - x)(c - x)B + (a - x)(b - x)C = 1.$$

This identical equation is true for all values of x, it is, therefore, true

$$\text{when } x = a, \; \therefore (b - a)(c - a)A = 1; \; \therefore A = \frac{1}{(b - a)(c - a)};$$

$$\text{when } x = b, \; \therefore (c - b)(a - b)B = 1; \; \therefore B = \frac{1}{(c - b)(a - b)};$$

$$\text{when } x = c, \; \therefore (a - c)(b - c)C = 1; \; \therefore C = \frac{1}{(a - c)(b - c)}.$$

EXAMPLES.—(1) In studying bimolecular reactions we meet with

$$\int \frac{dx}{(a - x)(b - x)} = \int \frac{dx}{(b - a)(a - x)} - \int \frac{dx}{(b - a)(b - x)} = \frac{1}{b - a} \cdot \log \frac{b - x}{a - x} + C.$$

(2) J. J. Thomson's formula for the rate of production of ions by the Röntgen rays is $dx/dt = q - ax^2$. Remembering that $a - x^2 = (\sqrt{a} - x)(\sqrt{a} + x)$; show that if we put $q/a = b^2$, for the sake of brevity, then

$$2b = \frac{1}{t} \log_e \frac{b + x}{b - x} + C.$$

(3) Evaluate $\int \dfrac{dx}{(a - x)(b - x)(c - x)}$. Keep your answer for use later on.

(4) Show that $\int \dfrac{dx}{a^2 - b^2x^2} = \dfrac{1}{2ab} \log \dfrac{a + bx}{a - bx} + C.$

(5) If the velocity of the reaction between bromic and hydrobromic acids is represented by the equation: $dx/dt = k(na + x)(a - x)$, then show that

$$k = \frac{1}{(n + 1)at} \cdot \log \frac{na + x}{a - x} + C.$$

(6) If $\dfrac{dx}{dt} = k(a + x)(na - x)$; show that $k = \dfrac{2\cdot3026}{(n + 1)at} \cdot \log_{10}\dfrac{a + x}{na - x}$.

(7) S. Arrhenius, in studying the hydrolysis of ethyl acetate, employed the integral.

$$\int \frac{1 + mx - nx^2}{(a - x)(b - x)}dx; \; \therefore = \int\left[- n + \frac{1 + nab + \{m - n(a + b)\}x}{(a - x)(b - x)}\right]dx.$$

Substitute $p = 1 + nab$; $q = m - n(a + b)$, then, by the method of partial fractions, show that

$$\int \frac{p + qx}{(a - x)(b - x)}dx = \frac{p + aq}{a - b}\log (a - x) - \frac{p + bq}{a - b}\log (b - x) + C.$$

(8) Integrals like $\int \dfrac{dx}{x(a - x)} = \dfrac{1}{a}\log\dfrac{x}{a - x} + C$ are very common in chemi cal dynamics—autocatalysis.

(9) H. Danneel (*Zeit. phys. Chem.*, **33,** 415, 1900) has the integral

$$kt = \int \frac{xdx}{a^2 - x^2}; \; \therefore \frac{1}{2}\log\frac{a^2 - x_1^2}{a^2 - x_2^2} = k(t_2 - t_1)$$

if $x = x_1$, when $t = t_1$; and $x = x_2$, when $t = t_2$.

(10) R. B. Warder's equation for the velocity of the reaction between chloroacetic acid and ethyl alcohol is

$$\frac{dy}{dt} = ak\{1 - (1 + b)y\}\{1 - (1 - b)y\}. \; \therefore \log\frac{1 - (1 - b)y}{1 - (1 + b)y} = 2abkt.$$

Case ii.—*The denominator can be resolved into real factors some of which are equal. Type:*

$$\frac{1}{(a - x)^2(b - x)}.$$

The preceding method cannot be used here because, if we put

$$\frac{1}{(a - x)^2(b - x)} = \frac{A}{a - x} + \frac{B}{a - x} + \frac{C}{b - x} = \frac{A + B}{a - x} + \frac{C}{b - x},$$

$A + B$ must be regarded as a single constant. Reduce as before and pick out coefficients of like powers of x. We thus get three independent equations containing two unknowns. The values of A, B and C cannot, therefore, be determined by this method. To overcome the difficulty, assume that

$$\frac{1}{(a - x)^2(b - x)} = \frac{A}{(a - x)^2} + \frac{B}{a - x} + \frac{C}{b - x}.$$

Multiply out and proceed as before, the final result is that

$$A = \frac{1}{b - a}; \; B = -\frac{1}{b - a}; \; C = -\frac{1}{(b - a)^2}.$$

EXAMPLES.—(1) H. Goldschmidt represents the velocity of the chemical reaction between hydrochloric acid and ethyl alcohol, by the relation $dx/dt = k(a - x)(b - x)^2$. Hence,

$$k\int dt = \int \frac{dx}{(a-x)(b-x)^2} = \frac{1}{(a-b)^2}\left\{\int \frac{(a-b)dx}{(b-x)^2} - \int \frac{dx}{b-x} + \int \frac{dx}{a-x}\right\}.$$

Integrate. To find a value for C, put $x = 0$ when $t = 0$. The final result is

$$kt(a-b)^2 = \frac{(a-b)x}{b(b-x)} + \log \frac{a(b-x)}{b(a-x)}.$$

(2) Show $\int \frac{dx}{x^2(a+bx)} = \frac{b}{a^2}\log \frac{a+bx}{a} - \frac{1}{ax} + C.$

(3) Show $\int \frac{dx}{(x-1)^2(x+1)} = \frac{1}{4}\log \frac{x+1}{x-1} - \frac{1}{2}\cdot\frac{1}{x-1} + C.$ An expression

used by W. Meyerhofer, *Zeit. phys. Chem.*, **2**, 585, 1888.

(4) Show $\int \frac{xdx}{(a-x)(b-x)^2} = \frac{1}{b(a-b)^2}\left\{a\log \frac{a(b-x)}{b(a-x)} + \frac{x(a-b)}{(b-x)}\right\},$

for values of x from $x = x$ to $x = 0$.   (H. Kühl, *Zeit. phys. Chem.*, **44**, 385, 1903.)

(5) P. Henry (*Zeit. phys. Chem.*, **10**, 96, 1892) in studying the phenomenon of autocatalysis employed the expression

$$\frac{dx}{dt} = k(a-x)\left(\sqrt{4K(a-x) + K^2} - K\right).$$

To integrate, put $4K(a-x) + K^2 = z^2$; $\therefore a - x = (z^2 - K^2)/4K$; $dx = -z.dz/2K$.

$$\therefore \frac{z.dz}{(z-K)(z^2-K^2)} = -\frac{kdt}{2}; \therefore \frac{1}{4K}\log \frac{z-K}{z+K} - \frac{1}{2}\frac{1}{z-K} = -\frac{kt}{2} + C.$$

Now put $P = \sqrt{4K(a-x) + K^2}$; $Q = \sqrt{4Ka + K^2}$, and show that if $x = 0$ when $t = 0$,

$$\frac{1}{t}\left\{\frac{Q-P}{(P-K)(Q-K)} + \frac{1}{2K}\log \frac{(P+K)(Q-K)}{(P-K)(Q+K)}\right\} = k.$$

For a more complex example see T. S. Price, *Journ. Chem. Soc.*, **79**, 314, 1901.

(6) J. W. Walker and W. Judson's equation for the velocity of the chemical reaction between hydrobromic and bromic acids, is

$$\frac{dx}{dt} = k(a-x)^4. \therefore 3k = \frac{1}{t}\left\{\frac{1}{(a-x)^3} - \frac{1}{a^3}\right\}.$$

The reader is probably aware of the fact that he can always prove whether his integration is correct or not, by differentiating his answer. If he gets the original integral the result is correct.

Case iii. — *The denominator can be resolved into imaginary factors all unequal. Type:*

$$\frac{1}{(a^2+x^2)(b+x)}.$$

Since imaginary roots always occur in pairs (page 353), the product of each pair of imaginary factors will give a product of the form, $x^2 + a^2$. Instead of assigning a separate partial fraction to each imaginary factor, we assume, for each pair of imaginary factors, a partial fraction of the form :

$$\frac{Ax + B}{a^2 + x^2}.$$

Hence we must write

$$\frac{1}{(a^2 + x^2)(b + x)} = \frac{Ax + B}{a^2 + x^2} + \frac{C}{b + x}.$$

Now get (13), page 193, fixed upon your mind.

EXAMPLES.—(1) $\int \dfrac{dx}{(x-1)^2(x^2+1)} = \int \left(\dfrac{A}{(x-1)^2} + \dfrac{B}{x-1} + \dfrac{Cx+D}{x^2+1} \right) dx.$ Here

$A = \frac{1}{2}$; $B = -\frac{1}{2}$; $C = \frac{1}{2}$; $D = 0$. Ansr $\frac{1}{4} \log (x^2+1)(x-1)^{-2} - \frac{1}{2}(x-1)^{-1} + C.$

(2) Show $\int \dfrac{dx}{1-x^4} = \dfrac{1}{2} \tan^{-1}x + \dfrac{1}{4} \log \dfrac{1+x}{1-x} + C.$

(3) H. Danneel (*Zeit. phys. Chem.*, **33**, 415, 1900) used a similar expression in his study of the " Free Energy of Chemical Reactions ". Thus, he has

$$\frac{x^2 dx}{a^4 - x^4} = k dt. \; \therefore \; 2k(t_2 - t_1) = \frac{1}{a}\left(\tan^{-1}\frac{x_2}{a} - \tan^{-1}\frac{x_1}{a} \right) + \frac{1}{2a} \log \frac{(x_2 - a)(x_1 + a)}{(x_2 + a)(x_1 - a)},$$

in an experiment where $x = x_1$ when $t = t_1$; and $x = x_2$ when $t = t_2$.

(4) The integral $\int \dfrac{dx}{(a-bx)^{2/3}(c-x)}$ has to be solved when the rate of dissolution of a spheroidal solid is under discussion. Put $a - bx = z^3$; $a - bc = n^3$; $\therefore x = (a - z^3)/b$; $dx = -3z^2 dz/b$. Substitute these results in the given integral, and we get

$$3 \int \frac{dz}{n^3 - z^3} = 3 \int \frac{dz}{(n-z)(n^2 + nz + z^2)} = \frac{1}{n^2}\int \frac{dz}{n-z} + \frac{1}{n^2}\int \frac{(z+2n)dz}{n^2 + nz + z^2};$$

by resolution into partial fractions. Let me make a digression. Obviously, we may write

$$\int \frac{(y+2b)dy}{a+by+y^2} = \frac{1}{2}\int \left(\frac{2y+b}{a+by+y^2} + \frac{3b}{a+by+y^2} \right) dy.$$

The numerator of the first fraction on the right is the differential coefficient of the denominator; and hence, its integral is $\frac{1}{2} \log (a+by+y^2)$; the integral of the second term of the right member is got by the addition and subtraction of $\frac{1}{4}b^2$ in the denominator. Hence,

$$\int \frac{dy}{a+by+y^2} = \int \frac{dy}{(a-\frac{1}{4}b^2)+(y+\frac{1}{2}b)^2} = \frac{2}{\sqrt{4a-b^2}} \tan^{-1}\frac{2y+b}{\sqrt{4a-b^2}}.$$

Returning to the original problem, we see at once that

$$3 \int \frac{dz}{n^3 - z^3} = \frac{1}{n^2}\left(\log \frac{\sqrt{n^2 + nz + z^2}}{n - z} \right) + \sqrt{3} \tan^{-1}\frac{2z+n}{\sqrt{3}\,n} + C.$$

Now restore the original values, $z = (a - bx)^{\frac{1}{3}}$, and $n = (a - bc)^{\frac{1}{3}}$.

In most of the examples which I have selected to illustrate my text, the denominator of the integral has been split up into factors so as not to divert the student's attention from the point at issue. If the student feels weak on this subject a couple of hours' drilling with W. T. Knight's booklet on *Algebraic Factors*, London, 1888, will probably put things right.

Case iv.—*The denominator can be resolved into imaginary factors, some of which are equal to one another. Type:*

$$\frac{1}{(a^2 + x^2)^2(b + x)}.$$

Combining the preceding results,

$$\frac{1}{(a^2 + x^2)^2(b + x)} = \frac{Ax + B}{(a^2 + x^2)^2} + \frac{Cx + D}{a^2 + x^2} + \frac{E}{b + x}.$$

In this expression, there are just sufficient equations to determine the complex system of partial fractions, by equating the coefficients of like powers of x. The integration of many of the resulting expressions usually requires the aid of one of the reduction formulæ (§ 76).

EXAMPLE. — Prove $\int \frac{(x^3 + x - 1)dx}{(x^2 + 1)^2} = \int \frac{xdx}{x^2 + 1} - \int \frac{dx}{(x^2 + 1)^2}.$

Integrate. Ansr. $\frac{1}{2}\log(x^2 + 1) - \frac{1}{2}x/(1 + x^2) + \frac{1}{2}\tan^{-1}x + C$. Use formula **E**, page 209, for evaluating the last term.

Consequently, if the denominator of any fractional differential can be resolved into factors, the differential can be integrated by one or other of these processes. The remainder of this chapter will be mainly taken up with practical illustrations of integration processes. A number of geometrical applications will also be given because the accompanying figures are so useful in helping one to form a mental picture of the operation in hand.

§ 77. The Velocity of Chemical Reactions.

The time occupied by a chemical reaction is dependent, among other things, on the nature and concentration of the reacting substances, the presence of impurities, and on the temperature. With some reactions these several factors can be so controlled, that measurements of the velocity of the reaction agree with theoretical results. But a great number of chemical reactions have hitherto defied all attempts to reduce them to order. For instance, the mutual action of hydriodic acid and bromic acid ; of hydrogen and oxygen ; of carbon and oxygen ; and the oxidation of phosphorus.

The magnitude of the disturbing effects of secondary and catalytic actions obscures the mechanism of such reactions. In these cases more extended investigations are required to make clear what actually takes place in the reacting system.

Chemical reactions are classified into uni- or mono-molecular, bi-molecular, ter- or tri-molecular, and quadri-molecular reactions according to the number of molecules which are supposed to take part in the reaction. Uni-, bi-, ter-, ... molecular reactions are often called reactions of the first, second, third, ... order.

I.—Reactions of the first order. Let a be the concentration of the reacting molecules at the beginning of the action when the time $t = 0$. The concentration, after the lapse of an interval of time t, is, therefore, $a - x$, where x denotes the amount of substance transformed during that time. Let dx denote the amount of substance formed in the time dt. The velocity of the reaction, at any moment, is proportional to the concentration of the reacting substance—**Wilhelmy's law**—hence we have

$$\frac{dx}{dt} = k(a - x); \text{ or, } k = \frac{1}{t} \cdot \log \frac{a}{a - x}; \qquad (1)$$

or, what is the same thing, $x = a(1 - e^{-kt})$, where k is a constant depending on the nature of the reacting system. Reactions which proceed according to this equation are said to be reactions of the first order.

II.—Reactions of the second order. Let a and b respectively denote the concentration of two different substances, say, in such a reacting system as occurs when acetic acid acts on alcohol, or bromine on fumaric acid, then, according to the law of mass action, the velocity of the reaction at any moment is proportional to the product of concentration of the reacting substances. For every gram molecule of acetic acid transformed, the same amount of alcohol must also disappear. When the system contains $a - x$ gram molecules of acetic acid it must also contain $b - x$ gram molecules of alcohol. Hence

$$\frac{dx}{dt} = k(a - x)(b - x); \therefore k = \frac{1}{t} \cdot \frac{1}{a - b} \log \frac{(a - x)b}{(b - x)a}. \qquad (2)$$

Reactions which progress according to this equation are called reactions of the second order. If the two reacting molecules are the same, then $a = b$. From (2), therefore, we get $\log 1 \times \frac{1}{0} = 0 \times \infty$. Such indeterminate fractions will be discussed later on. But if we start from the beginning, we get, by the integration of

$$\frac{dx}{dt} = k(a - x)^2; \quad k = \frac{1}{t} \cdot \frac{x}{a(a - x)}. \qquad (3)$$

In the hydrolysis of cane sugar,

$$C_{12}H_{22}O_{11} + H_2O = 2C_6H_{12}O_6,$$

let a denote the amount of cane sugar, b the amount of water present at the beginning of the action. The velocity of the reaction can therefore be represented by the equation (3), when x denotes the amount of sugar which actually undergoes transformation. If the sugar be dissolved in a large excess of water, the concentration of the water, b, is practically constant during the whole process, because b is very large in comparison with x, and a small change in the value of x will have no appreciable effect upon the value of b; $b - x$ may, therefore, be assumed constant. $\therefore k' = k(b - x)$, where k' and k are constant. Hence equation (1) should represent the course of this reaction. Wilhelmy's measurements of the rate of this reaction shows that the above supposition corresponds closely with the truth. The hydrolysis of cane sugar in presence of a large excess of water is, therefore, said to be a reaction of the first order, although it is really bimolecular.

EXAMPLE.—Proceed as on page 59 with the following pairs of values of x and t:—

$$t = \quad 15, \qquad 30, \qquad 45, \qquad 60, \qquad 75,\dots$$
$$x = 0{\cdot}046, \quad 0{\cdot}088, \quad 0{\cdot}130, \quad 0{\cdot}168, \quad 0{\cdot}206,\dots$$

Substitute these numbers in (1); show that k' is constant. Make the proper changes for use with common logs. Put $a = 1$.

III.—Reactions of the third order. In this case three molecules take part in the reaction. Let a, b, c, denote the concentration of the reacting molecules of each species at the beginning of the reaction, then,

$$\frac{dx}{dt} = k(a - x)(b - x)(c - x). \qquad (4)$$

Integrate this expression and put $x = 0$ when $t = 0$ in order to find the value of C. The final equation can then be written in the form,

$$k = -\frac{\log\left\{\left(\frac{a}{a - x}\right)^{b-c}\left(\frac{b}{b - x}\right)^{c-a}\left(\frac{c}{c - x}\right)^{a-b}\right\}}{t(a - b)(b - c)(c - a)}, \qquad (5)$$

where a, b, c, are all different. If we make $a = b = c$, in equation

(4) and integrate the resulting expression

$$\frac{dx}{dt} = k(a - x)^3 \; ; \;\; k = \frac{1}{2t}\left\{\frac{1}{(a - x)^2} - \frac{1}{a^2}\right\} = \frac{x(2a - x)}{2ta^2(a - x)^2}. \qquad (6)$$

By rearranging the terms of equation (6) so that,

$$x = a\left(1 - \frac{1}{\sqrt{2a^2kt + 1}}\right), \quad . \quad . \quad . \quad (7)$$

we see that the reaction can only come to an end ($x = a$) after the elapse of an infinite time, $t = \infty$. If $c = b$ when a is not equal to b,

$$k = \frac{1}{t} \cdot \frac{1}{(a - b)^2}\left\{\frac{(a - b)x}{b(b - x)} + \log\frac{a(b - x)}{b(a - x)}\right\}. \quad . \quad (8)$$

Among reactions of the third order we have the polymerization of cyanic acid, the reduction of ferric by stannous chloride, the oxidation of sulphur dioxide, and the action of benzaldehyde upon sodium hydroxide. For full particulars J. W Mellor, *Chemical Statics and Dynamics*, might be consulted.

IV.—Reactions of the fourth order. These are comparatively rare. The reaction between hydrobromic and bromic acids is, under certain conditions, of the fourth order. So is the reaction between chromic and phosphorous acids; the action of bromine upon benzene; and the decomposition of potassium chlorate. The general equation for an *n*-molecular reaction, or a reaction of the *n*th order is

$$\frac{dx}{dt} = k(a - x)^n \; ; \;\; k = \frac{1}{t} \cdot \frac{1}{n - 1}\left\{\frac{1}{(a - x)^{n-1}} - \frac{1}{a^{n-1}}\right\}. \quad . \quad (9)$$

The intermediate steps of the integration are, Ex. (3) and Ex. (4), page 196. The integration constant is evaluated by remembering that when $x = 0$, $t = 0$. We thus obtain

$$\frac{1}{(n - 1)(a - x)^{n-1}} = kt + C \; ; \; C = +\frac{1}{(n - 1)a^{n-1}},$$

V.—To find the order of a chemical reaction. Let C_1, C_2 respectively denote the concentration of the reacting substance in the solution, at the end of certain times t_1 and t_2. From (9), if $C = C_1$, when $t = t_1$, etc.,

$$-\frac{dC}{dt} = kC^n \; ; \; \therefore \; \frac{1}{n - 1}\left\{\frac{1}{C_2^{n-1}} - \frac{1}{C_1^{n-1}}\right\} = k(t_2 - t_1), \qquad (10)$$

where *n* denotes the number of molecules taking part in the reaction.   It is required to find a value for n.   From (10)

$$-\int_{c_1}^{c_2}\frac{dC}{C^n} = kt \; ; \; \text{or,} \; n = 1 + \frac{\log t_1 - \log t_2}{\log C_2 - \log C_1}. \quad . \quad (11)$$

Why the negative sign ?   The answer is that (10) denotes the rate of formation of the products of the reaction, (11) the rate at which the original substance disappears. $C = a - x$, $\therefore dC = - dx$.

NUMERICAL ILLUSTRATION.—W. Judson and J. W. Walker (*Journ. Chem. Soc.*, **73**, 410, 1898) found that while the time required for the decomposition of a mixture of bromic and hydrobromic acids of concentration 77, was 15 minutes ; the time required for the transformation of a similar mixture of substances in a solution of concentration 51·33, was 50 minutes.   Substituting these values in (11),

$$n = 1 + \frac{\log 3\cdot 333}{\log 1\cdot 5} = 3\cdot 97.$$

The nearest integer, 4, represents the order of the reaction.   Use the Table of Natural Logarithms, page 627.

The intervals of time required for the transformation of equal fractional parts m of a substance contained in two solutions of different concentration C_1 and C_2, may be obtained by graphic interpolation from the curves whose abscissæ are t_1 and t_2 and whose ordinates are C_1 and C_2 respectively.

Another convenient formula for the order of a reaction, is

$$n = \frac{\log \dfrac{dC_1}{dt} - \log \dfrac{dC_2}{dt}}{\log C_1 - \log C_2}. \quad . \quad . \quad . \quad (12)$$

The reader will probably be able to deduce this formula for himself.

The mathematical treatment of velocity equations here outlined is in no way difficult, although, perhaps, some practice is still requisite in the manipulation of laboratory results.   The following selection illustrates what may be expected in practical work if the reaction is not affected by disturbing influences.

EXAMPLES.—(1) M. Bodenstein (*Zeit. phys. Chem.*, **29**, 315, 1899) has the equation

$$\frac{dx}{dt} = k(a - x)(b - x)^{\frac{1}{2}}$$

for the rate of formation of hydrogen sulphide from its elements.   To integrate this expression put $b - x = z^2$, $\therefore dx = - 2zdx$, and therefore

$$\int \frac{dz}{z^2 + A^2} = - \frac{kt}{2} : \text{or,} \; \frac{2}{A} \tan^{-1} \frac{z}{A} + C = - kt$$

where $A^2 = a - b$.   For the integration, see (13), page 193.   This presupposes that $a > b$; if $a < b$ the integration is Case i. of page 213. We get a similar expression for the rate of dissolution of a solid cylinder of metal in an acid. To evaluate C, note that $x = 0$ when $t = 0$.

(2) L. T. Reicher (*Zeit. phys. Chem.*, **16**, 203, 1895) in studying the action of bromine on fumaric acid, found that when $t = 0$, his solution contained 8·8 of fumaric acid, and when $t = 95$, 7·87; the concentration of the acid was then altered by dilution with water, it was then found that when $t = 0$, the concentration was 3·88, and when $t = 132$, 3·51. Here $dC_1/dt = (8\cdot88 - 7\cdot87)/95 = 0\cdot0106$; $dC_2/dt = 0\cdot00227$; $C_1 = (8\cdot88 + 7\cdot87)/2 = 8\cdot375$; $C_2 = 3\cdot7$, $n = 1\cdot87$ in (12) above The reaction is, therefore, of the second order.

(3) In the absence of disturbing side reactions, arrange velocity equations for the reaction (A. A. Noyes and G. J. Cottle, *Zeit. phys. Chem.*, **27**, 578, 1898):—$2CH_3 . CO_2Ag + H . CO_2Na = CH_3 . COOH + CH_3 . CO_2Na + CO_2 + 2Ag$. Assuming that the silver, sodium and hydrogen salts are completely dissociated in solution, the reaction is essentially between the ions:

$$2Ag^+ + H . COO^- = 2Ag + CO_2 + H^+,$$

therefore, the reaction is of the third order. Verify this from the following data. When a (sodium formate) $= 0\cdot050$, b (silver acetate) $= 0\cdot100$; and when

$t =$	2,	4,	7,	11,	17, …
$(b-x) \times 10^3 =$	81·03,	71·80,	63·95,	59·20,	56·25,…

Show that if the reaction be of the second order, k varies from 1·88 to 2·67, while if the reaction be of the third order, k varies between 31·2 and 28·0.

(4) For the conversion of acetochloranilide into p-chloracetanilide, J. J. Blanksma (*Rec. Trav. Pays-Bas.*, **21**, 366, 1902 ; **22**, 290, 1903) has

$t =$	0,	1,	2,	3,	4,	6,	8,…;
$a - x =$	49·3,	35·6,	25·75,	18·5,	13·8,	7·3,	4·8,…

Show that the reaction is of the first order.

(5) An homogeneous spheroidal solid is treated with a solvent which dissolves layer after layer of the substance of the sphere. To find the rate of dissolution of the solid. Let r_0 denote the radius of the sphere at the beginning of the experiment, when $t = 0$; and r the radius of the time t; let ϕ denote the volume of one gram molecule of the solid ; and let x denote the number of gram molecules of the sphere which have been dissolved at the time t. The rate of dissolution of the sphere will obviously be proportional to the surface s, and to the amount of acid, $a - x$, present in the solution at the time t. But, remembering that the volume of the sphere is $\frac{4}{3}\pi r^3$, the volume of the x gram molecules of the sphere dissolved at the time t will be

$$\phi x = \frac{4\pi}{3}\left(r_0^3 - r^3\right); \; \therefore \; r = \left(r_0^3 - \frac{3\phi x}{4\pi}\right)^{\frac{1}{3}},$$

and the surface s of the sphere at the time t will be $4\pi r^2$.

$$\therefore \; s = 4\pi\left(r_0^3 - \frac{3\phi x}{4\pi}\right)^{\frac{2}{3}}. \; \; \therefore \; \frac{dx}{dt} = ks(a-x) \; ; \; \text{or,} \; \frac{dx}{dt} = 4\pi k\left(r_0^3 - \frac{3\phi x}{4\pi}\right)^{\frac{2}{3}}(a-x),$$

an expression resembling that integrated on page 217, Ex. (4).

(6) L. T. Reicher (*Liebig's Ann.*, **228**, 257, 1885 ; **232**, 103, 1886) measuring the rate of hydrolysis of ethyl acetate by sodium hydroxide, found that

when

$t =$	0,	393,	669,	1010,	1265, ... units,
$a - x =$	0·5638,	0·4866,	0·4467,	0·4113,	0·3879, ...
$b - x =$	0·3114,	0·2342,	0·1943,	0·1589,	0·1354, ...

Now apply these results to equation (2), page 219, and show that k is approximately constant and that, in consequence, the reaction is of the second order.

(7) Ethyl acetate is hydrolized in the presence of acidified water forming alcohol and acetic acid. Suppose a gram molecules of acetic acid are used to acidify the water, and that we start an experiment with b gram molecules of ethyl acetate, show that Wilhelmy's law leads to

$$\frac{dx}{dt} = k_1(a + x) \ (b - x); \ \text{or,} \ \frac{1}{t} \cdot \log_{10}\frac{b(a + x)}{a(b - x)} = \text{constant} ;$$

with the additional assumption that the velocity of the reaction is proportional to the amount of acetic acid present in the system. If a gram molecules of some other acid are used as "catalytic" agent,

$$\frac{dx}{dt} = (k_2 a + k_1 x) \ (b - x); \ \text{or,} \ \frac{1}{t} \cdot \log_{10}\left(\frac{b}{b - x} \cdot \frac{k_2 a + k_1 x}{k_2 a}\right) = \text{constant}.$$

See W. Ostwald, *Journ. prakt. Chem.*, [2], **28**, 449, 1883, for experimental numbers. Hint. There is a of catalyzing acid present and the velocity of the reaction due to this agent will be $k_2 a(b - x)$; but x of acetic acid has also been produced; so that the velocity of the reaction due to the catalyzing action of acetic acid is equal to $k_1 x(b - x)$. Now apply the principle of the mutual independence of different reactions of page 70.

(8) It was once thought that the decomposition of phosphine by heat was in accordance with the equation, $4PH_3 = P_4 + 6H_2$; now, it is believed that the reaction is more simple, *viz.*, $PH_3 = P + 3H$, and that the subsequent formation of the P_4 and H_2 molecules has no perceptible influence on the rate of the decomposition. Show that these suppositions respectively lead to the following equations :

$$\frac{dx}{dt} = k(1 - x)^4; \ \therefore \ k = \frac{1}{t}\left\{\frac{1}{(1 - x)^3} - 1\right\}. \quad \frac{dx}{dt} = k'(1 - x); \ \therefore \ k' = \frac{1}{t} \cdot \log\frac{1}{1 - x}.$$

In other words, if the reaction be of the fourth order, k will be constant, and if of the first order, k' will be constant. To put these equations into a form suitable for experimental verification let a gram molecules of PH_3 per unit volume be taken. Let the fraction x of a be decomposed in the time t. Hence, $(1 - x)a$ gram molecules of phosphine and $\frac{3}{2}ax$, of hydrogen remain. Since the pressure of the gas is proportional to its density, if the original pressure of PH_3 be p_0 and of the mixture of hydrogen and phosphine p_1, then,

$$\frac{p_1}{p_0} = \frac{(1 - x)a + \frac{3}{2}xa}{a} = 1 + \tfrac{1}{2}x; \ x = \frac{2p_1}{p_0} - 2; \ (1 - x)a = \frac{1}{a}\left(3 - \frac{2p_1}{p_0}\right);$$

and

$$k = \frac{1}{t}\left\{\left(\frac{p_0}{3p_0 - 2p_1}\right)^3 - 1\right\}; \ k' = \frac{1}{t} \log\frac{p_0}{3p_0 - 2p_1}.$$

where the constants are not necessarily the same as before. D. M. Kooij

(Zeit. phys. Chem., **12**, 155, 1892) has published the following data:—

$$t = \quad 0, \qquad 4, \qquad 14, \qquad 24, \qquad 46\cdot3. \; \ldots$$
$$p = 758\cdot01, \quad 769\cdot34 \quad 795\cdot57, \quad 819\cdot16, \quad 865\cdot22, \ldots$$

Hence show that k', not k satisfies the required condition. The decomposition of phosphine is, therefore, said to be a reaction of the first order. Of course this does not *prove* that a reaction is really unimolecular. It only proves that the velocity of the reaction is proportional to the pressure of the gas—quite another matter. See J. W. Mellor's *Chemical Statics and Dynamics.*

In experimental work in the laboratory, the investigator proceeds by the method of trial and failure in the hope that among many wrong guesses, he will at last hit upon one that will " go ". So in mathematical work, there is no royal road.   We proceed by instinct, not by rule. For instance, we have here made three guesses. The first appeared the most probable, but on trial proved unmistakably wrong.   The second, least probable guess, proved to be the one we were searching for.   In his celebrated quest for the law of descent of freely falling bodies, Galileo first tried if V, the velocity of descent was a function of s, the distance traversed. He found the assumption was not in agreement with facts.   He then tried if V was a function of t, the time of descent, and so established the familiar law $V = gt$. So Kepler is said to have made nineteen conjectures respecting the form of the planetary orbits, and to have given them up one by one until he arrived at the elliptical orbit which satisfied the required conditions.

§ 78. Chemical Equilibria—Incomplete or Reversible Reactions.

Whether equivalent proportions of sodium nitrate and potassium chloride, or of sodium chloride and potassium nitrate, are mixed together in aqueous solution at constant temperature, each solution will, after the elapse of a certain time, contain these four salts distributed in the same proportions.   Let m and n be positive integers, then

$$(m+n)\text{NaNO}_3 + (m+n)\text{KCl} = m\text{NaCl} + m\text{KNO}_3 + n\text{NaNO}_3 + n\text{KCl} ;$$
$$(m+n)\text{NaCl} + (m+n)\text{KNO}_3 = m\text{NaCl} + m\text{KNO}_3 + n\text{NaNO}_3 + n\text{KCl}.$$

This is more concisely written,

$$\text{NaCl} + \text{KNO}_3 \rightleftharpoons \text{NaNO}_3 + \text{KCl}.$$

The phenomenon is explained by assuming that the products of the reaction interact to reform the original components simul-

taneously with the direct reaction. That is to say, two independent and antagonistic changes take place simultaneously in
the same reacting system. When the speeds of the two opposing
reactions are perfectly balanced, the system appears to be in a
stationary state of equilibrium. This is another illustration of the
principle of the coexistence of different actions. The special case
of the law of mass action dealing with these "incomplete" or
reversible reactions is known as **Guldberg and Waage's law.**
Consider a system containing two reacting substances A_1 and A_2
such that

$$A_1 \rightleftharpoons A_2.$$

Let a_1 and a_2 be the respective concentrations of A_1 and A_2. Let
x of A_1 be transformed in the time t, then by the law of mass action,

$$\frac{\partial x}{\partial t} = k_1(a_1 - x).$$

Further, let x' of A_2 be transformed in the time t. The rate of
transformation of A_2 to A_1 is then

$$\frac{\partial x'}{\partial t} = k_2(a_2 - x').$$

But for the mutual transformation of x of A_1 to A_2 and x' of A_2
to A_1, we must have, for equilibrium, $x = -x'$; and, $dx = -dx'$;

$$\therefore \frac{\partial x}{\partial t} = -k_2(a_2 + x).$$

The net, or total velocity of the reaction is obviously the algebraic
sum of these "partial" velocities, or

$$\frac{dx}{dt} = k_1(a_1 - x) - k_2(a_2 + x). \qquad . \qquad . \qquad (1)$$

It is usual to write $K = k_1/k_2$. When the system has attained the
stationary state $dx/dt = 0$. "Equilibrium," says Ostwald, "is a
state which is not dependent upon time." Consequently

$$K = \frac{(a_2 + x)}{(a_1 - x)}, \qquad . \qquad . \qquad . \qquad (2)$$

where x is to be determined by chemical analysis, a_1 is the amount
of substance used at the beginning of the experiment, a_2 is made
zero when $t = 0$. This determines K. Now integrate (1) by
the method of partial fractions and proceed as indicated in the
subjoined examples.

EXAMPLES.—(1) In aqueous solution γ-oxybutyric acid is converted into γ-butyrolactone, and γ-butyrolactone is transformed into γ-oxybutyric acid according to the equation,

$$CH_2OH . CH_2 . CH_2 . COOH \rightleftharpoons CH_2 . CH_2 . CH_2 . CO + H_2O.$$

Use the preceding notation and show that the velocity of formation of the lactone is, $dx/dt = k_1(a_1 - x) - k_2(a_2 + x)$, and $K = k_1/k_2 = (a_2 + x)/(a_1 - x)$. Now integrate the first equation by the method of partial fractions. Evaluate the integration constant for $x = 0$ when $t = 0$ and show that

$$\frac{1}{t} \cdot \log \frac{Ka_1 - a_2}{(Ka_1 - a_2) - (1 + K)x} = \text{Constant.} \quad . \quad . \quad (3)$$

P. Henry (Zeit. phys. Chem., 10, 116, 1892) worked with $a_1 = 18\cdot23$, $a_2 = 0$; analysis showed that when $dx/dt = 0$, $x = 13\cdot28$; $a_1 - x = 4\cdot95$; $a_2 + x = 13\cdot28$; $K = 2\cdot68$. Substitute these values in (3); reduce the equation to its lowest terms and verify the constancy of the resulting expression when the following pairs of experimental values are substituted for x and t,

$$t = 21, \qquad 50, \qquad 65, \qquad 80, \qquad 160 \dots;$$
$$x = 2\cdot39, \qquad 4\cdot98, \qquad 6\cdot07, \qquad 7\cdot14, \qquad 10\cdot28 \dots$$

(2) A more complicated example than the preceding reaction of the first order, occurs during the esterification of alcohol by acetic acid:

$$CH_3 . COOH + C_2H_5 . OH \rightleftharpoons CH_3 . COOC_2H_5 + H . OH,$$

a reaction of the second order. Let a_1, b_1 denote the initial concentrations of the acetic acid and alcohol respectively, a_2, b_2 of ethyl acetate and water. Show that, $dx/dt = k_1(a_1 - x)(b_1 - x) - k_2(a_2 + x)(b_2 + x)$. Here, as elsewhere, the calculation is greatly simplified by taking gram molecules such that $a_1 = 1$, $b_1 = 1$, $a_2 = 0$, $b_2 = 0$. The preceding equation thus reduces to

$$\frac{dx}{dt} = k_1(1 - x)^2 - k_2 x^2. \quad . \quad . \quad . \quad (4)$$

For the sake of brevity, write $k_1/(k - k_2) = m$ and let a, β be the roots of the equation $x^2 - 2mx + m = 0$. Show that (7) may be written

$$\frac{dx}{(x - a)(x - \beta)} = (k_1 - k_2)dt.$$

Integrate for $x = 0$ when $t = 0$, in the usual way. Show that since $a = m + \sqrt{m^2 - m}$ and $\beta = m - \sqrt{m^2 - m}$, page 353,

$$\frac{1}{t} \log \frac{(m - \sqrt{m^2 - m})(m + \sqrt{m^2 - m} - x)}{(m + \sqrt{m^2 - m})(m - \sqrt{m^2 - m} - x)} = 2(k_1 - k_2)\sqrt{m^2 - m}. \quad (5)$$

K is evaluated as before. Since $m = k_1/(k_1 - k_2)$; $m = 1/(1 - k_2/k_1)$. M. Berthelot and L. Péan St. Gilles' experiments show that for the above reaction, $k_1/k_2 = 4$; $m = \frac{4}{3}$; $\sqrt{m^2 - m} = \frac{2}{3}$; $\frac{4}{3}(k_1 - k_2) = 0\cdot00575$; or, using common logs, $\frac{4}{3}(k_1 \times 0\cdot4343 - k_2) = 0\cdot0025$. The corresponding values of x and t were

$$t = 64, \qquad 103, \qquad 137, \qquad 167 \dots;$$
$$x = 0\cdot250, \qquad 0\cdot345, \qquad 0\cdot421, \qquad 0\cdot474 \dots;$$
$$\text{constant} = 0\cdot0023, \qquad 0\cdot0022, \qquad 0\cdot0020, \qquad 0\cdot0021 \dots$$

Verify this last line from (5). For smaller values of t, side reactions are supposed to disturb the normal reaction, because the value of the constant deviates somewhat from the regularity just found.

(3) Let one gram molecule of hydrogen iodide in a v litre vessel be heated, decomposition takes place according to the equation: $2HI \rightleftharpoons H_2 + I_2$. Hence show that for equilibrium,

$$\frac{dx}{dt} = k_1 \left(\frac{1 - 2x}{v} \right)^2 - \left(k_2 \frac{x}{v} \right)^2 . \quad \cdots \quad (6)$$

and that $(1 - 2x)/v$ is the concentration of the undissociated acid. Put $k_1/k_2 = K$ and verify the following deductions,

$$\int \frac{dx}{K(1 - 2x)^2 - x^2} = \frac{1}{2\sqrt{K}} \cdot \log \frac{\sqrt{K}(1 - 2x) + x}{\sqrt{K}(1 - 2x) - x} = \frac{k_2 t}{v^2}$$

Since, when $t = 0$, $x = 0$, $C = 0$. M. Bodenstein (*Zeit. phys. Chem.*, **13**, 56, 1894; **22**, 1, 1897) found K, at $440° = 0.02$, hence $\sqrt{K} = 0.141$,

$$\therefore \frac{1}{t} \cdot \log \frac{1 + 5 \cdot 1x}{1 - 9 \cdot 1x} = \text{constant,}$$

provided the volume remains constant. The corresponding values of x and t are to be found by experiment. *E.g.*, when $t = 15$, $x = 0.0378$, constant $= 0.0171$; and when $t = 60$, $x = 0.0950$, constant $= 0.0173$, etc.

(4) The "active mass" of a solid is independent of its quantity. Hence, if c is a constant, show that for $CaCO_3 \rightleftharpoons CaO + CO_2$, $Kc = p$, where p denotes the pressure of the gas.

(5) Prove that the velocity equation of a complete reaction of the first order, $A_1 = A_2$, has the same general form as that of a reversible reaction, $A_1 \rightleftharpoons A_2$, of the same order when the concentration of the substances is referred to the point of equilibrium instead of to the original mass. Let ξ denote the value of x at the point of equilibrium, then, $dx/dt = k_1(a_1 - x) - k_2 x$; becomes $dx/dt = k_1(a_1 - \xi) - k_2 \xi$. Substitute for k_2 its value $k_1(a_1 - \xi)/\xi$, when $dx/dt = 0$,

$$\therefore \frac{dx}{dt} = \frac{k_1 a_1 (\xi - x)}{\xi}; \text{ or, } \frac{dx}{dt} = k(\xi - x), \quad \cdots \quad (7)$$

where the meanings of a, k, k_1 will be obvious.

(6) Show that k is the same whether the experiment is made with the substance A_1, or A_2. It has just been shown that starting with A_1, $k = k_1 a_1/\xi$; starting with A_2, it is evident that there is $a_1 - \xi$ of A_2 will exist at the point of equilibrium. Hence show $dx/dt = k_2 a_1\{(a_1 - \xi) - x\}/(a_1 - \xi)$; $k_2 \xi = k_1(a_1 - \xi)$, therefore, as before, $k_2 a_1/(a_1 - \xi) = k_1 a_1/\xi$. $dx/dt = k_1 a_1(a_1 - \xi - x)/\xi$. Integrate between the limits $t = 0$ and $t = t$, $x = x_0$ and $x = x_1$; then show, from (7), that

$$\frac{1}{t} \log \frac{\xi - x_1}{\xi - x_2} = \frac{1}{t} \log \frac{a_1 - \xi - x_1}{a_1 - \xi - x_2} = \frac{k_1 a_1}{\xi} = k_1 + k_2. \quad \cdots \quad (8)$$

C. Tubandt has measured the rate of inversion of l-menthone into d-menthone, and *vice versâ* (Dissertation, Halle, 1904). In the first series of experiments x denotes the amount of d-menthone present at the time t; and in the second series, the amount of l-menthone present at the time t; ξ is the value of x when the system is in a state of equilibrium, that is when t is infinite. First, the conversion of l-menthone into d-menthone.

$$t = 0, \quad 15, \quad 30, \quad 45, \quad 60, \quad 75, \quad 90, \quad 105, \quad \infty;$$
$$x = 0, \quad 0.73, \quad 1.31, \quad 1.74, \quad 2.06, \quad 2.30, \quad 2.48, \quad 2.62, \quad 3.09.$$

Second, the conversion of d-menthone into l-menthone.

$$t = 0, \quad 15, \quad 30, \quad 45, \quad 60, \quad 75, \quad 90, \quad 105, \quad \infty;$$
$$x = 0, \quad 0.45, \quad 0.76, \quad 1.03, \quad 1.22, \quad 1.37, \quad 1.47, \quad 1.56, \quad 1.84.$$

Show that the "velocity constant" is nearly the same in each case. $k = 0.008$ nearly.

§ 79. Fractional Precipitation.

If to a solution of a mixture of two salts, A and B, a third substance C, is added, in an amount insufficient to precipitate all A and B in the solution, more of one salt will be precipitated, as a rule, than the other. By redissolving the mixed precipitate and again partially precipitating the salts, we can, by many repetitions of the process, effect fairly good separations of substances otherwise intractable to any known process of separation.

Since Mosander thus fractioned the gadolinite earths in 1839, the method has been extensively employed by W. Crookes (*Chem. News*, **54**, 131, 155, 1886), in some fine work on the yttria and other earths. The recent separations of polonium, radium and other curiosities have attracted some attention to the process. The "mathematics" of the reactions follows directly from the law of mass action. Let only sufficient C be added to partially precipitate A and B and let the solution originally contain a of the salt A, b of the salt B. Let x and y denote the amounts of A and B precipitated at the end of a certain time t, then $a - x$ and $b - y$ will represent the amounts of A and B respectively remaining in the solution. The rates of precipitation are, therefore,

$$\frac{dx}{dt} = k_1(a - x)(c - z); \quad \frac{dy}{dt} = k_2(b - y)(c - z),$$

where $c - z$ denotes the amount of C remaining in the solution at the end of a certain time t.

$$\therefore \frac{dx}{dt} : \frac{dy}{dt} = k_1(a - x) : k_2(b - y);$$

or, multiplying through with dt, we get

$$k_2 \frac{dx}{a - x} = k_1 \frac{dy}{b - y}; \quad \therefore k_2 \int \frac{d(a - x)}{a - x} = k_1 \int \frac{d(b - y)}{b - y}$$

On integration, $k_2\log(a - x) = k_1\log(b - y) + \log C$, where $\log C$ is the integration constant. To find C notice that when $x = 0$, $y = 0$, and consequently $\log a^{k_2} = \log Cb^{k_1}$; or, $C = a^{k_2}/b^{k_1}$.

$$\therefore \frac{k_1}{k_2} = \frac{\log \dfrac{a}{a - x}}{\log \dfrac{b}{b - y}}. \qquad . \qquad . \qquad . \qquad (1)$$

The ratio $(a - x)/a$ measures the amount of salt remaining in the solution, after x of it has been precipitated. The less this ratio, the greater the amount of salt A in the precipitate. The same thing may be said of the ratio $(b - y)/b$ in connection with the salt B. The more k_2 exceeds k_1, the less will A tend to accumulate in the precipitate and, the more k_1 exceeds k_2, the more will A tend to accumulate in the precipitate. If the ratio k_1/k_2 is nearly unity, the process of fractional precipitation will be a very long one, because the ratio of the quantities of A and B in the precipitate will be nearly the same. In the limiting case, when $k_1 = k_2$, or $k_1/k_2 = 1$, the ratio of A to B in the mixed precipitate will be the same as in the solution. In such a case, the complex nature of the "earth" could never be detected by fractional precipitation. The application to gravimetric analysis has not yet been worked out.

§ 80. Areas enclosed by Curves. To Evaluate Definite Integrals.

Let AB (Fig. 100) be any curve whose equation is known. It

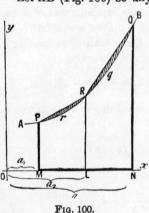

FIG. 100.

is required to find the area of the portion bounded by the curve; the two coordinates PM, QN; and that portion of the x-axis, MN, included between the ordinates at the extremities of that portion of the curve under investigation. The area can be approximately determined by supposing $PQMN$ to be cut up into small strips—called **surface elements**—perpendicular to the x-axis; finding the area of each separate strip on the assumption that the curve bounding one end of the strip is a straight

line ; and adding the areas of all the trapezoidal-shaped strips
together. Let the surface $PrqQNM$ be cut up into two strips by
means of the line LR. Join PR, RQ.

Area $PQMN$ = Area $PRLM$ + Area $RQNL$.

But the area so calculated is greater than that of the required
figure. The shaded portion of the diagram represents the magnitude of the error. It is obvious that the narrower each strip is
made, the greater will be the number of trapeziums to be included
in the calculation and the smaller will
be the error. If we could add up the
areas of an infinite number of such strips,
the actual error would become vanishingly small. Although we are unable
to form any distinct conception of this
process, we feel assured that such an
operation would give a result absolutely
correct. But enough has been said on
this matter in § 68. We want to know
how to add up an infinite number of infinitely small strips.

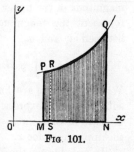

FIG. 101.

In order to have some concrete image before the mind, let
us find the area of $PQNM$ in Fig. 101. Take any small strip
$PRSM$; let $PM = y$, $RS = y + \delta y$; $OM = x$; and $OS = x + \delta x$.
Let δA represent the area of the small strip under consideration.
If the short distance, PR, were straight and not curved, the area,
δA, of the trapezium $PRSM$ would be, (11), page 604,

$$\delta A = \tfrac{1}{2}\delta x(PM + RS) = \delta x(y + \tfrac{1}{2}\delta y).$$

By making δx smaller and smaller, the ratio, $\delta A/\delta x = y + \tfrac{1}{2}\delta y$,
approaches, and, at the limit, becomes equal to

$$\mathrm{Lt}_{\delta x = 0} \frac{\delta A}{\delta x} = \frac{dA}{dx} = y ; \; \therefore \; dA = y \, . \, dx. . \qquad (1)$$

This formula represents the area of an infinitely narrow strip, say,
PM. The total area, A, can be determined by adding up the
areas of the infinite number of infinitely narrow strips ranged side
by side from MP to NQ. The area of any strip is obviously length
× width, or $y × dx$. Before we can proceed any further, we must
know the relation between the length, y, of any strip in terms of its
distance, x, from the point O. In other words, we must have the
equation of the curve PQ. For instance, the area of any indefinite

portion of the curve, is

$$A = \int y \cdot dx + C, \quad . \quad . \quad . \quad _u \quad (2)$$

and the area bounded by the portion situated between the ordinates having the abscissæ a_2 and a_3 (Fig. 100) is

$$A = \int_{a_2}^{a_3} y \cdot dx + C. \quad . \quad . \quad . \quad (3)$$

Equation (2) is an indefinite integral, equation (3) a definite integral. The value of the definite integral is determined by the magnitude of the upper and lower limits. In Fig. 100, if a_1, a_2, a_3 represent the magnitudes of three abscissæ, such that a_2 lies between a_1 and a_3,

$$A = \int_{a_1}^{a_3} y \cdot dx + C = \int_{a_1}^{a_2} y \cdot dx + \int_{a_2}^{a_3} y \cdot dx + C.$$

When the limits are known, the value of the integral is found by subtracting the expression obtained by substituting the lower limit in place of x, from a similar expression obtained by substituting the upper limit for x.

In order to fix the idea, let us take a particular case. Suppose $y = 2x$, and we want to deal with that portion of the curve between the ordinates a and b. From (3),

$$\int_a^b 2x \cdot dx = \Big|_a^b x^2 + C; \quad . \quad . \quad . \quad (4)$$

The vertical line in the preceding equation, (4), resembles Sarraus' **symbol of substitution.** The same idea is sometimes expressed by square brackets, thus,

$$\int_a^b 2x \cdot dx = \Big[x^2 + C \Big]_a^b = (b^2 + C) - (a^2 + C) = (b^2 - a^2).$$

The process of finding the area of any surface is called, in the regular text-books, the **quadrature of surfaces,** from the fact that the area is measured in terms of a square—sq. cm., sq. in., or whatever unit is employed. In applying these principles to specific examples, the student should draw his own diagrams. If the area bounded by a portion of an ellipse or of an hyperbola is to be determined, first sketch the curve, and carefully note the limits of the integral.

EXAMPLES.—(1) To find the area bounded by an ellipse, origin at the centre   Here

$$\frac{x^2}{a^2} + \frac{y^2}{b^2} = 1; \text{ or, } y = \pm \frac{b}{a} \sqrt{a^2 - x^2}.$$

Refer to Fig. 22, page 100. The sum of all the elements perpendicular to the x-axis, from OP_1 to OP_4, is given by the equation

$$A = \int_0^a y \cdot dx,$$

for, when the curve cuts the x-axis, $x = a$, and when it cuts the y-axis, $x = 0$. The positive sign in the above equation, represents ordinates above the x-axis. The area of the ellipse is, therefore,

$$A = 4\int_0^a y \cdot dx.$$

Substitute the above value of y in this expression and we get for the sum of this infinite number of strips,

$$A = 4\frac{b}{a}\int_0^a \sqrt{(a^2 - x^2)}dx,$$

which may be integrated by parts, thus

$$A = 4\frac{b}{a}\left[\frac{x}{2}\sqrt{(a^2 - x^2)} + \frac{a^2}{2}\sin^{-1}\frac{x}{a} + C\right]_0^a.$$

The term within the brackets is yet to be evaluated between the limits $x = a$ and $x = 0$

$$A = 4\frac{b}{a}\left[\left\{\frac{a}{2}\sqrt{(a^2 - a^2)} + \frac{a^2}{2}\sin^{-1}\frac{a}{a} + C\right\} - \left\{\frac{0}{2}\sqrt{(a^2 - 0^2)} + \frac{a^2}{2}\sin^{-1}\frac{0}{a} + C\right\}\right]$$

$$\therefore A = 4\frac{b}{a} \times \frac{a^2}{2}\sin^{-1}1 ;$$

remembering that $\sin 90° = 1$, $\sin^{-1}1 = 90°$ and $2\sin^{-1}1 = 180 = \pi$. The area of the ellipse is, therefore, πab. If the major and minor axes are equal, $a = b$, the ellipse becomes a circle whose area is πa^2. It will be found that the constant always disappears in this way when evaluating a definite integral.

(2) Find the area bounded by the rectangular hyperbola, $xy = a$; or, $y = a/x$, between the limits $x = x_1$ and $x = x_2$.

$$A = \int_{x_1}^{x_2} y \cdot dx = \int_{x_1}^{x_2}\frac{a}{x}dx ;$$

$$\therefore A = a\bigg|_{x_1}^{x_2}\log x + C = a\{(\log x_2 + C) - (\log x_1 + C)\} = a \log\frac{x_2}{x_1}.$$

If $x_1 = 1$, and $x_2 = x$; $A = a\log_e x$. This simple relation appears to be the reason natural logarithms are sometimes called hyperbolic logarithms.

(3) Find the area bounded by the curve $y = 12(x - 1)/x$, when the limits are 12 cm. and 3 cm. Ansr. 91·36 sq. cm. The integral is $12\int(x - 1)x^{-1}dx$; or $12[x - \log x]_3^{12} = 12(9 - \log 4)$, etc. Use the table of natural logarithms, page 627.

(4) Show that the area bounded by the logarithmic curve, $x = \log y$, is $y - 1$. Hint. $A = \int dy = y + C$. Evaluate C by noting that when $x = 0$, $y = -1$, $A = 0$. If $y = 1$, $A = 0$; if $y = 2$, $A = 1$; etc.

If polar coordinates are employed, the differential of the area assumes the form

$$dA = \tfrac{1}{2}r^2 d\theta. \quad . \quad . \quad . \quad . \quad (5)$$

EXAMPLE.—Find the area of the hyperbolic spiral between 0 and $+ r$. See Ex. (2), page 117. $r\theta = a$; $d\theta = -a \cdot dr/r^2$; consequently,

$$A = -\int_r^0 \frac{a}{r^2} \cdot dr = -\frac{1}{2}\Big|_r^0 \frac{ar}{2} = \frac{ar}{4}.$$

After this the integration constant is not to be used at any stage of the process of integration between limits. It has been retained in the above discussion to further emphasize the rule: *The integration constant of a definite integral disappears during the process of integration. The absence of the indefinite integration constant is the mark of a definite integral.*

§ 81. Mean Values of Integrals.

The curve

$$y = r\sin x,$$

represents the sinusoid curve for the electromotive force, y, of an alternating current; r denotes the maximum current; x denotes the angular displacement made in the time t, such that $x = 2\pi t/T$, where T denotes the time of a complete revolution of the coil in seconds. The value of y, at any instant of time, is proportional to the corresponding ordinate of the curve. When $x = 90°$, $t = \tfrac{1}{4}T$, the coil has made a quarter revolution, and the ordinate is a maximum.

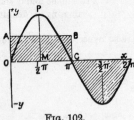

FIG. 102.

When $x = 270°$, or when $t = \tfrac{3}{4}T$, that is, in three-quarters of a revolution, the ordinate is a minimum. The curve cuts the x-axis when $x = 0°$, 180°, and 360°, that is, when $t = 0$, $\tfrac{1}{2}T$, and T. For half revolution, the average electromotive force beginning when $x = 0$, is equal to the area bounded by the curve OPC (Fig. 102), and the x-axis, cut off at $\tfrac{1}{2}T$, that is, at π. This area, A_1, is evidently

$$A_1 = \int_0^{\pi} r\sin x \cdot dx = -\Big[r\cos x\Big]_0^{\pi} = -r\cos \pi + r\cos 0 = 2r,$$

because $\cos \pi = \cos 180° = -1$, and $\cos 0° = 1$.

The area, A_2, bounded by the sine curve during the second half revolution of the coil lies below the x-axis, and it has the same numerical value as in the first half. This means that the average

electromotive force during the second half revolution is numerically
equal to that of the first half, but of opposite sign. It is easy to
see this.

$$A_2 = \int_\pi^{2\pi} r \sin x \, . \, dx = - \Big[r \cos x \Big]_\pi^{2\pi} = - r \cos 2\pi + r \cos \pi = - 2r,$$

since $\cos 360° = \cos 0° = 1$. The total area, A, bounded by the
sine curve and the x-axis during a complete revolution of the coil
is zero, since

$$A = A_1 + A_2 = 0.$$

The area bounded by the sine curve and the x-axis for a whole
period 2π, or for any number of whole periods, is zero.

If now $y_1, y_2, y_3, \ldots, y_n$ be the values of $f(x)$ when the space
from a to b is divided into n equal parts each δx wide, $b - a = n\delta x$,
and if

$$y = f(x) ;$$

$y_1 = f(a) ; \ y_2 = f(a + \delta x) ; \ y_3 = f(a + 2\delta x) ; \ldots ; \ y_n = f(b - \overline{n-1}\delta x)$.
The **arithmetical mean** of these n values of y is, by definition,
the nth part of their sum. Hence,

$$\frac{y_1 + y_2 + y_3 + \ldots + y_n}{n} = \frac{(y_1 + y_2 + y_3 + \ldots + y_n)\delta x}{b - a},$$

since $n\delta x = b - a$. If x now assumes every possible value lying
in the interval between b and a, n must be infinitely great. Hence
the sum of this infinite number of indefinitely small quantities is
expressed by the symbol

$$\int_a^b f(x)dx,$$

as indicated on page 189. The arithmetical mean of all the values
which $f(x)$ can assume in the interval $b - a$ is, therefore,

$$\frac{\int_a^b f(x)dx}{b - a} \ ; \ \text{or,} \ \frac{1}{b - a} \int_a^b f(x)dx.$$

This is called the **mean or average value** of $f(x)$ over the range
$b - a$. Geometrically, the mean value is the altitude of a rectangle,
on the base $b - a$, whose area is equal to that bounded by the curve
$y = f(x)$, the two ordinates and the x-axis. In Fig. 102, OA is the
mean value of y, that is, of $r \sin x$, for all values of x which may
vary continuously from 0 to π. This is easy to see,

$$\int_0^\pi r \sin x \, . \, dx = \text{Area } OPC = \text{Area of rectangle } OABC;$$
$$= OC \times OA = (b - a) \times OA,$$

where a denotes the abscissa at the point O, and b the abscissa at C. But $b - a = \pi$, and $OA = y_1$, consequently,

$$\text{Mean value of ordinate} = \frac{1}{\pi} \int_0^\pi r \sin x \, . \, dx = \frac{2r}{\pi} = 0 \cdot 6366r.$$

Instruments for measuring the average strength, y_1, of an alternating current during half a complete period, that is to say, during the time the current flows in one direction, are called electrodynamometers. The electrodynamometer, therefore, measures $y_1 = OA$ (Fig. 102) $= 2r/\pi = 0 \cdot 6366r$. But $MP = r$ denotes the maximum current, because $\sin x$ is greatest when $x = 90°$, and $\sin 90° = 1$. Hence, $y = r \sin 90° = r$.

$$\text{Maximum current} = r \; ; \quad \text{Average current} = 0 \cdot 6366r.$$

There is another variety of mean of no little importance in the treatment of alternating currents, namely, the square root of the mean of the squares of the ordinates for the range from $x = 0$ to $x = \pi$. This magnitude is called the **mean square value** of $f(x)$. With the preceding function, $y = r \sin x$, the

$$\text{Mean value of } y^2 = \frac{1}{\pi} \int_0^\pi r^2 \sin^2 x \, . \, dx = \frac{r^2}{2};$$

on integration by parts as in (12), page 205. Again

$$\text{Mean square value of } y^2 = \sqrt{\tfrac{1}{2}r^2} = 0 \cdot 7071r.$$

EXAMPLES.—(1) In calculations involving mean values care must be taken not to take the wrong independent variable. Find the mean velocity of a particle falling from rest with a constant acceleration, the velocities being taken at equal distances of time. When a body falls from rest, $V = gt$,

$$\frac{1}{t} \int_0^t V dt = \frac{1}{t} \int_0^t gt \, . \, dt = \frac{gt}{2} = \frac{V}{2},$$

that is to say, the mean velocity, Vt, with respect to equal intervals of time is one half the final velocity. On the other hand, if we seek the mean velocity which the body had after describing equal intervals of space, s, and remembering that $V^2 = 2gs$,

$$\frac{1}{s} \int_0^s V ds = \frac{\sqrt{2g}}{s} \int_0^s \sqrt{s} \, . \, ds = \frac{2\sqrt{2gs}}{3} = \frac{2V}{3},$$

that is, two-thirds of the final velocity.

(2) Show that if a particle moves with a constant acceleration, the mean square of the velocities at equal infinitely small intervals of time, is $\frac{1}{3}(V_0^2 + V_0 V_1 + V_1^2)$, where V_0 and V_1 respectively denote the initial and final velocities.

(3) The relation between the amount, x, of a substance transformed at the time, t, in a unimolecular chemical reaction may be written $x = a(1 - e^{-kt})$ where a denotes the amount of substance present at the beginning of the reaction, and k is a constant. Show that $V = ake^{-kt}$; or, $V = k(a - x)$ according as we refer the velocity to equal intervals of time, t; or to equal amounts of substance transformed, x. Also show that the mean velocity with respect to equal intervals of time in the interval $t_1 - t_0$, is

$$V_t = \frac{1}{t_1 - t_0} \int_{t_0}^{t_1} ake^{-kt} dt = \frac{a(e^{-kt_1} - e^{-kt_0})}{t_1 - t_0} = \frac{V_0 - V_1}{\log V_0 - \log V_1},$$

and the mean velocity, V_x, with respect to equal amounts of substance transformed, is

$$V_x = \frac{1}{x_1 - x_0} \int_{x_0}^{x_1} k(a - x) dx = \frac{k(x_1 - x_0)(2a - x_1 - x_0)}{2(x_1 - x_0)} = \frac{V_0 + V_1}{2}.$$

If $t_0 = 0$, and t_1 is infinite, the mean velocity, V_t, converges towards zero. Several interesting relations can be deduced from this equation.

Problems connected with mean densities, centres of mass, moments of inertia, mean pressures, and centres of pressure are treated by the aid of the above principles.

§ 82. Areas Bounded by Curves. Work Diagrams.

I.—The area enclosed between two different curves. Let $PABQ$ and $PA'B'Q$ (Fig. 103) be two curves, it is required to find the area $PABQB'A'$. Let $y_1 = f_1(x)$ be the equation of one curve, $y_2 = f_2(x)$, the equation of the other. First find the abscissæ of the points of intersection of the two curves. Find separately the

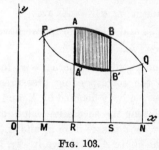

Fig. 103.   Fig. 104.

areas $PABQMN$ and $PA'B'QMN$, by the preceding methods. Let a and b respectively denote the abscissæ OM, and ON (Fig. 103), of the points of intersection, P and Q, of the two curves. The required area, A, is, therefore,

Area $PABQB'A'$ = Area $PABQMN$ − Area $PA'B'QMN$

$$\therefore A = \int_a^b y_1 dx - \int_a^b y_2 . dx. \quad \cdot \quad \cdot \quad \cdot \quad (1)$$

To find the area of the portion $ABB'A'$, let x_1 be the abscissa of AR and x_2 the abscissa of BS, then,

$$A = \int_{x_1}^{x_2} y_1 \cdot dx - \int_{x_1}^{x_2} y_2 \cdot dx = \int_{x_1}^{x_2} (y_1 - y_2) dx. \qquad (2)$$

In illustration let us consider the area included between the two parabolas whose equations are $y^2 = 4x$; and $x^2 = 4y$. The curves obviously meet at the origin, and at the point $x = 4$, cm., say, $y = 4$ cm. (16), page 95. Consequently,

$$A = \int_0^4 \frac{x^2}{4} dx - \int_0^4 2\sqrt{x} \cdot dx = 2 \int_0^4 \left(\frac{x^2}{8} - \sqrt{x} \right) dx = -5\frac{1}{3} \text{ sq. cm.} \qquad (3)$$

Why the negative sign? On plotting it will be seen that we first integrated along the line OCB (Fig. 104), and then subtracted from this the result of integrating along the line OAP. We ought to have gone along OAP first. It is therefore necessary to pay some attention to this matter.

Let a given volume, x, of a gas be contained in a cylindrical vessel in which a tightly fitting piston can be made to slide (Fig.

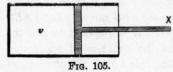

FIG. 105.

105). Let the sectional area of the piston be unity. Now let the volume of gas change dx units when a slight pressure X is applied to the free end of the piston. Then, by definition of work, W,

Work = Force × Displacement; or, $dW = X \cdot dx$.

If p denotes the pressure of the gas and v the volume, we have,

$$dW = p \cdot dv.$$

Now let the gas pass from one condition where $x = x_1$ to another state where $x = x_2$. Let the corresponding pressures to which the gas was subjected be respectively denoted by X_1 and X_2.

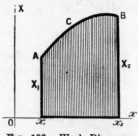

FIG. 106.—Work Diagram.

By plotting the successive values of X and x, as x passes from x_1 and x_2, we get the curve ACB, shown in Fig. 106. The shaded part of the figure represents the total work done *on* the system during the change.

If the gas returns to its original state through another series of successive values of X and x we have the curve ADB (Fig. 107). The total work done *by* the system will then be represented by the area $ABDx_2x_1$. If we agree to call the work done *on* the system *positive;* and work done *by* the system *negative*, then (Fig. 107),

$$W_1 - W_2 = \text{Area } ACBx_2x_1 - \text{Area } ADBx_2x_1 = \text{Area } ACBD.$$

The shaded part in Fig. 107, therefore, represents the work done on the system during the above cycle of changes. A series of operations by which a substance, after leaving a certain state, finally returns to its original condition, is called a **cycle**, or a **cyclic process**. A cyclic process is represented graphically by a closed curve. In any cyclic change, the work done on the system is equal to the "area of the cycle".

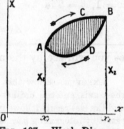

FIG. 107.—Work Diagram.

Work is done *on* the system while x is increasing and *by* the system when x is decreasing. Therefore, if the curve is described by a point moving round the area $ACBD$ in the direction of the hands of a clock, the total work done on the system is positive; if done in the opposite direction, negative. We can now understand the negative sign in the comparatively simple example, Fig. 104, above. We should have obtained a positive value if we had started from the origin and taken the curves in the direction of the hands of a clock.

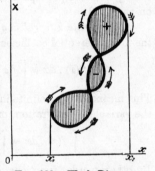

FIG. 108.—Work Diagram.

If the diagram has several loops as shown in Fig. 108, the total work is the sum of the areas of the several loops developed by the point travelling in the same direction as the hands of a clock, minus the sum of the areas developed when the point travels in a contrary direction. This graphic mode of representing work was first used by Clapeyron. The diagrams are called **Clapeyron's Work Diagrams**.

In Watt's indicator diagrams, the area enclosed by the curve represents the excess of the work done by the steam *on* the piston during a forward stroke, over the work done by the piston when ejecting the steam in the return stroke. The total energy communicated to the piston is thus represented by the area enclosed by the curve. This area may be determined by one of the methods described in the next chapter, page 335, § 110.

II. The area bounded by two branches of the same curve is but a simple application of Equation (1). Thus the area, A, enclosed between the two limbs of the curve $y^2 = (x^2 + 6)^2$ and the ordinates $x = 1$, $x = 2$ is

$$A = \pm \int_1^2 (x^2 + 6)dx = \pm 16\tfrac{2}{3} \text{ units,}$$

as you will see by the method adopted in the preceding example.

EXAMPLE.—Show that the area between the parabola $y = x^2 - 5x + 6$, the x-axis, and the ordinates $x = 1$, $x = 5$, is $5\tfrac{1}{3}$ units. Hint. Plot the curve and the last result follows from the diagram. Of course you can get the same result by integrating ydx between the limits $x = 5$, and $x = 1$.

§ 83. Definite Integrals and their Properties.

There are some interesting properties of definite integrals worth noting, and it is perhaps necessary to further amplify the remarks on page 232.

I. A definite integral is a function of its limits. If $f'(x)$ denotes the first differential coefficient of $f(x)$,

$$\int_a^b f'(x) . dx = \left[f(x) \right]_a^b, \text{ or, } \Big|_a^b f(x) = f(b) - f(a).$$

This means that a definite integral is a function of its limits, not of the variable of integration, or

$$\int_a^b f(x) . dx = \int_a^b f(y) . dy = \int_a^b f(z) . dz . \qquad . \qquad (1)$$

In other words, functions of the same form, when integrated between the same limits have the same value.

EXAMPLES.—(1) Show $\int_b^a e^{-x}dx = \int_b^a e^{-z}dz = e^{-b} - e^{-a}$.

(2) Prove $\int_{-1}^3 x^2 . dx = \frac{1}{3}\{(3)^3 - (-1)^3\} = 9\tfrac{1}{3}$.

By way of practice verify the following results:—

(3) $\int_0^{\frac{1}{2}\pi} \sin x . dx = - \Big|_0^{\frac{1}{2}\pi} \cos x = - \left(\cos \frac{\pi}{2} - \cos 0^{\circ} \right) = 1.$

(4) $\int_0^{\frac{1}{2}\pi} \sin^2x . dx = \frac{\pi}{4}$; $\int_0^{\frac{1}{2}\pi} \sin^2x . dx = \frac{1}{4}\left(\frac{\pi}{2} - 1 \right)$; $\int_0^{\pi} \sin^2x . dx = \frac{\pi}{2}.$

Hint for the indefinite integral. Integrate by parts. Put $u = \sin x$, $dv = \sin x \, . \, dx$. From (1), § 74,

$$\int \sin^2 x \, . \, dx = \sin x \, . \, \cos x + \int \cos^2 x \, . \, dx = \sin x \, . \, \cos x + \int (1 - \sin^2 x) dx.$$

Transpose the last term to the left-hand side, and divide by 2.

$$\therefore \int \sin^2 x \, . \, dx = \tfrac{1}{2}(\sin x \, . \, \cos x + x) + C.$$

II. The interchange of the limits of a definite integral causes the integral to change its sign. It is evident that

$$\int_b^a f'(x)dx = f(a) - f(b) = -\int_a^b f'(x)dx, \qquad (2)$$

or, when the upper and lower limits of an integral are interchanged, only the sign of the definite integral changes. This means that if the change of the variable from b to a is reckoned positive, the change from a to b is negative. That is to say, if motion in one direction is reckoned positive, motion in the opposite direction is to be reckoned negative.

III. The decomposition of the integration limits. If m is any interval between the limits a and b, it follows directly from what has been said upon page 232, that

$$\int_b^a f'(x)dx = \int_m^a f'(x)dx + \int_b^m f'(x)dx = f(a) - f(m) + f(m) - f(b). \quad (3)$$

Or we can write

$$\int_b^a f'(x)dx = \int_b^m f'(x)dx - \int_a^m f'(x)dx = f(m) - f(b) - f(m) + f(a). \quad (4)$$

In words, a definite integral extending over any given interval is equal to the sum of the definite integrals extending over the partial intervals. Consequently, if $f'(x)$ is a finite and single-valued function between $x = a$, and $x = b$, but has a finite discontinuity at some point m (Fig. 109), we can evaluate the integral by taking the sum of the partial integrals extending from a to m, and from m to b.

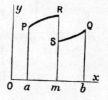

FIG. 109.

When any function has two or more values for any assigned real or imaginary value of the independent variable, it is said to be a multi-valued function. Such are logarithmic, irrational algebraic, and inverse trigonomet-

FIG. 110.

rical functions. For example, $y = \tan^{-1}x$ is a multiple-valued function, because the ordinates corresponding to the same value of x differ by multiples of π. Verify this by plotting. Obviously, if $x = a$ and $x = b$ are the limits of integration of a multiple-valued function, we must make sure that the ordinates $x = a$ and $x = b$ belong to the same branch of the curve $y = f(x)$. In Fig. 110, if $x = OM$, y is multi-valued, for y may be MP, MQ, or MR. The imaginary values in no way interfere with the ordinary arithmetical ones. A single-valued

function assumes one single value for any assigned (real or imaginary) value of the independent variable. For example, rational algebraic, exponential and trigonometrical functions are single-valued functions.

IV. *If $f'(x)dx$ be one function of y, and $f'(a - x)dx$ be another function of y,*

$$\int_0^a f'(x)dx = \int_0^a f'(a - x)dx. \quad . \quad . \quad . \quad (5)$$

For, if we put $a - y = x$; $\therefore dx = - dy$, and substitute $x = a$, we see at once that $y = 0$; and similarly, if $x = 0$, $y = a$.

$$\therefore \int_0^a f'(x)dx = - \int_0^a f'(a - y)dy = \int_0^a f'(a - x)dx,$$

from (2) and (1) above, or we can see this directly, since

$$\int_0^a f'(x)dx = \int_0^a f'(a-x)dx = - \int_0^a f'(a-x)d(a-x) = f(a) - f(0).$$

This result simply means that the area of $OPP'O'$ (Fig. 111)

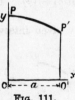

FIG. 111.

can be determined either by taking the origin at O and calling OO' the positive direction of the x-axis; or by transferring the origin to the point O', a distance a from the old origin O, and calling $O'O$ the positive direction of the x-axis. The following result is an important application of this,

$$\int_0^{\frac{1}{2}\pi} \sin^n x \, . \, dx = \int_0^{\frac{1}{2}\pi} \sin^n \left(\frac{\pi}{2} - x\right)dx = \int_0^{\frac{1}{2}\pi} \cos^n x \, . \, dx. \quad (6)$$

EXAMPLES.—(1) Verify the following results:—

$$\int_0^{\frac{1}{2}\pi} \cos x \, . \, dx = \int_0^{\frac{1}{2}\pi} \sin x \, . \, dx = 1 \, ; \, \int_0^{\frac{1}{2}\pi} \cos^2 x \, . \, dx = \int_0^{\frac{1}{2}\pi} \sin^2 x \, . \, dx = \frac{\pi}{4}.$$

(2) Show that $\int_{-a}^a f(x^2)dx = 2\int_0^a f(x^2)dx.$

(3) Evaluate $\int_0^\pi \sin mx \,.\, \sin nx dx$. By (28), page 612,

$$- 2 \sin mx \,.\, \sin nx = \cos(m - n)x - \cos(m + n)x.$$

$$\therefore \int \sin mx \,.\, \sin nx dx = \tfrac{1}{2}\int \cos(m - n)x dx - \tfrac{1}{2}\int \cos(m + n)x dx\,;$$

$$\therefore \int \sin mx \,.\, \sin nx dx = \frac{\sin(m - n)x}{2(m - n)} - \frac{\sin(m + n)x}{2(m + n)}.$$

Therefore, if m and n are integral,

$$\int_0^\pi \sin mx \,.\, \cos nx dx = 0.$$

Remembering that $\sin \pi = \sin 180° = 0$, and $\sin 0° = 0$, if $m = n$, show that

$$\int_0^\pi \sin^2 nx dx = \frac{1}{2}\int_0^\pi (1 - \cos 2nx) dx = \left[\frac{x}{2} - \frac{\sin 2nx}{4n} \right]_0^\pi = \frac{\pi}{2}.$$

(4) Show that the integral of $\cos mx \,.\, \cos nx \,.\, dx$, between the limits π and 0, is zero when m and n are whole numbers and that the integral is $\tfrac{1}{2}\pi$, when $m = n$. Hints. From (27), page 612,

$$2 \cos mx \,.\, \cos nx = \cos(m - n)x + \cos(m + n)x.$$

(5) Evaluate $\int_0^\pi a \sin \dfrac{x}{2} \,.\, \cos \dfrac{x}{2} \,.\, dx$. Ansr.

$$2a\int_0^\pi \sin \frac{x}{2} \,.\, d\left(\sin \frac{x}{2} \right) = \frac{2a}{2} \Big|_0^\pi \sin^2\frac{x}{2} = a.$$

(6) Show that $\int_{-\pi}^{+\pi} \cos mx \,.\, \cos nx \,.\, dx = 0\,; \int_{-\pi}^{+\pi} \sin mx \,.\, \sin nx \,.\, dx = 0,$

$\int_{-\pi}^{+\pi} \cos mx \,.\, \sin nx \,.\, dx = 0.$ Hint. Use the results of Ex. (3) and (4).

(7) Integrate $\int_{-1}^1 \dfrac{dx}{x^2} = \int_{-1}^1 x^{-2} dx = \left[-\dfrac{1}{x} \right]_{-1}^{+1}$, and is the answer -2?

V. The function may become infinite at or between the limits of integration. We have assumed that the integrals are continuous between the limits of integration. I dare say that the beginner has given an affirmative answer to the question at the end of the last example. The integral $\int x^{-2} dx$, between the limits 1 and -1 ought to be given by the area bounded by the curve $y = x^{-2}$, the x-axis and the ordinates corresponding with $x = 1$, and $x = -1$. Plot the curve and you will find that this result is erroneous. The curve sweeps through infinity, whatever that may mean, as x passes from $+1$ to -1 (Fig. 112). *The method of integration is, therefore, unreliable when the function to be integrated becomes infinite or otherwise discontinuous at or between the limits of integration.* Consequently, it is necessary to examine

FIG. 112.

certain functions in order to make sure that they are finite and continuous between the given limits, or that the functions either continually increase or decrease, or alternately increase and decrease a finite number of times.

This subject is discussed in the opening chapters of B. Riemann and H. Weber's *Die Partiellen Differential-Gleichungen der mathematischen Physik*, Braunschweig, 1900-1901, to which the student must refer if he intends to go exhaustively into this subject. I can, however, give a few hints on the treatment of these integrals. It is easy to see that

$$\int_0^n e^{-x}dx = \left[- e^{-x}\right]_0^n = -\left[\frac{1}{e^n} - \frac{1}{e^0}\right] = 1 - \frac{1}{e^n},$$

and if n is made infinitely great, the integral tends towards the limit unity. Hence we say that

$$\int_0^\infty e^{-x}dx = 1.$$

If the function is continuous for all values of x between a and b, except when $x = b$, at the upper limit, it is obvious that

$$\int_a^b f'(x)dx = \mathrm{Lt}_{h=0}\int_a^{b-h} f'(x)dx \qquad . \qquad . \qquad (7)$$

if h is diminished indefinitely. h, of course, is a positive number. And in a similar manner, if $f(x)$ is continuous for all values of x except when $x = a$, at the lower limit,

$$\int_a^b f'(x)dx = \mathrm{Lt}_{h'=0}\int_{a+h'}^b f'(x)dx. \qquad . \qquad . \qquad (8)$$

EXAMPLES.—(1) $\int_0^1 \dfrac{dx}{\sqrt{1-x}} = \mathrm{Lt}_{h=0}\int_0^{1-h} \dfrac{dx}{\sqrt{1-x}} = \mathrm{Lt}_{h=0}\left[- 2\sqrt{1-x}\right]_0^{1-h}$

$= \mathrm{Lt}_{h=0}\{- 2\sqrt{1-1+h} - (-2)\} = 2 - 2\sqrt{h}.$

As h is made indefinitely small, the integral tends towards the limit 2.

$$\therefore \int_0^1 \frac{dx}{\sqrt{1-x}} = 2.$$

(2) Show that $\int_0^1 \dfrac{dx}{x^2} = \mathrm{Lt}_{h=0}\int_h^1 \dfrac{dx}{x^2} = \mathrm{Lt}_{h=0}\left(\dfrac{1}{h} - 1\right).$

As h is made very small, the expression on the right becomes infinite. A definite numerical value for the integral does not exist.

(3) Show that $\int_0^a \dfrac{dx}{\sqrt{a^2-x^2}} = \mathrm{Lt}_{h=0}\int_0^{a-h} \dfrac{dx}{\sqrt{a^2-x^2}} = \mathrm{Lt}_{h=0}\sin^{-1}\left(1 - \dfrac{h}{a}\right).$

Since when h is made very small the limit [1] approaches $\sin^{-1}1$, or $\frac{1}{2}\pi$.

(4) Show that $\int_{0}^{1}\frac{dx}{x} = \text{Lt}_{h=0}\int_{h}^{1}\frac{dx}{x} = \log 1 - \log h = \log\frac{1}{h} = \infty$.

When the function $f'(x)$ becomes infinite *between* the limits, we write

$$\int_{a}^{b}f'(x)dx = \text{Lt}_{h=0}\int_{a}^{m-h}f'(x)dx \,+\, \text{Lt}_{h'=0}\int_{m+h'}^{b}f'(x)dx. \qquad (9)$$

if $f'(x)$ only becomes infinite at the one point.   If there are n discontinuities, we must obviously take the sum of n integrals.

EXAMPLES.—(1) $\int_{-1}^{1}\frac{dx}{x^2} = \text{Lt}_{h=0}\int_{h}^{1}\frac{dx}{x^2} + \text{Lt}_{h'=0}\int_{-1}^{-h'}\frac{dx}{x^2}$,

$= \text{Lt}_{h=0}\Big[-\frac{1}{x}\Big]_{h}^{1} + \text{Lt}_{h'=0}\Big[-\frac{1}{x}\Big]_{-1}^{-h'} = \text{Lt}_{h=0}\Big(1 - \frac{1}{h}\Big) + \text{Lt}_{h'=0}\Big(\frac{1}{h'} - 1\Big)$,

The integral thus approaches infinity as h and h' are made very small.

(2) $\int_{0}^{2}\frac{dx}{(x-1)^2} = \text{Lt}_{h=0}\int_{1+h}^{2}\frac{dx}{(x-1)^2} + \text{Lt}_{h'=0}\int_{0}^{1-h}\frac{dx}{(x-1)^2}$,

$= \text{Lt}_{h=0}\Big[-\frac{1}{x-1}\Big]_{1+h'}^{2} + \text{Lt}_{h'=0}\Big[-\frac{1}{x-1}\Big]_{0}^{1-h} = \text{Lt}_{h=0}\Big(\frac{1}{h} - 1\Big) + \text{Lt}_{h'=0}\Big(\frac{1}{h'} - 1\Big)$,

as h and h' become indefinitely small, the limit becomes indefinitely great, and the integral is indeterminate.

(3) Show that $\int_{-1}^{1}\frac{dx}{\sqrt[3]{x}} = \frac{6}{2}$.

It would now do the beginner good to revise the study of limits by the aid of say J. J. Hardy's pamphlet, *Infinitesimals and Limits*, Easton, 1900, or the discussions in the regular text-books.

§ 84. To find the Length of any Curve.

To find the length, l, of the curve AB (Fig. 113) when the equation of the curve is known.   This is equivalent to finding the length of a straight line of the same length as the curve if the curve were flattened out or rectified, hence the process is called the **rectification of curves.**   Let the coordinates of A be (x_0, y_0), and of B, (x_n, y_n).   Take any two points, P, Q, on the curve.   Make the construction shown in the figure.   Then, by Euclid, i., 47, if P and Q are sufficiently close, we have, very nearly

$$(PQ)^2 = (\delta x)^2 + (\delta y)^2 \text{ ; or, } dl = \sqrt{(dx)^2 + (dy)^2}$$

---

[1] Note the equivocal use of the word limit.   There is a difference between the "limit" of the differential calculus and the "limit" of the integral calculus.

at the limit when the length of the chord PQ is equal to the length of the arc PQ, (1), page 15. Hence, the sum, l, of all the small elements dl ranging side by side from x_1 to x_2 will be

$$l = \int_{x_1}^{x_2} \sqrt{1 + \left(\frac{dy}{dx}\right)^2} \cdot dx. \quad . \quad . \quad . \quad (1)$$

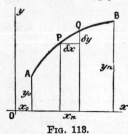

In order to apply this result it is only necessary to differentiate the equation of the curve and substitute the values of dx and dy, so obtained, in equation (1). By integrating this equation, we obtain a general expression between the assigned limits, we get the length of the given portion of the curve.

If the equation is expressed in polar coordinates, the length of a small element, dl, is deduced in a similar manner. Thus,

Fig. 113.

$$dl = \sqrt{(dr)^2 + r^2(d\theta)^2}. \quad . \quad . \quad . \quad (2)$$

The mechanical rectification of curves in practical work is frequently done by running a wheel along the curve and observing how much it travels. In the *opisometer* this is done by starting the wheel from a stop, running it along the path to be measured; and then applying it to the scale of the diagram, running it backwards until the stop is felt.

EXAMPLES.—(1) If the curve is a common parabola $y^2 = 4ax$, $\therefore ydy = 2adx$; or, $(dx)^2 = y^2(dy)^2/4a^2$; $\therefore dl = \sqrt{(y^2 + 4a^2)}dy/2a$, from (1); now integrate, as in Ex. (1), page 203, and we get $l = \frac{1}{2}y\sqrt{y^2 + 4a^2} + 2a_2 \log\{(y + \sqrt{y^2 + 4a^2})/2a\} + C$. To find C, put $y = 0$, when $l = 0$; $\therefore C = -2a^2 \log 2a$.

(2) Show that the perimeter of the circle, $x^2 + y^2 = r^2$, is $2\pi r$. Let l be the length of the arc in the first quadrant, then $dy/dx = -x/y$.

$$\therefore l = \int_0^r \sqrt{1 + \left(\frac{dy}{dx}\right)^2} \cdot dx = \int_0^r \left(\frac{x^2 + y^2}{y^2}\right)^{\frac{1}{2}} dx = r \int_0^r \frac{dx}{\sqrt{r^2 - x^2}} =$$

$$\left[r \sin^{-1}\frac{x}{r}\right]_0^r = \frac{\pi r}{2}.$$

$\therefore$ Whole perimeter $= 4 \times \frac{1}{2}\pi r = 2\pi r$.

(3) Find the length of the equiangular spiral, page 116, whose equation is $r = e^\theta$; or, $\theta = \log r/\log e$. Ansr. $l = \sqrt{2} \cdot r$. Hint. Differentiate; $\therefore d\theta = dr/r$, $\therefore dl = \sqrt{2} \cdot dr$. $\therefore l = \sqrt{2} \cdot r + C$; when $r = 0$, $l = 0$, $C = 0$.

(4) The length of the first whorl of Archimedes' spiral $2\pi r = a\theta$ is $3 \cdot 3885a$. Verify this. Hint. First show that the length of the spiral from the origin to any value of θ is $\frac{1}{4}a/\pi \times \{\theta\sqrt{1 + \theta^2} + \log_e(\theta + \sqrt{1 + \theta^2})\}$. For the first whorl, $\theta = 2\pi = 6 \cdot 2832$; $\sqrt{1 + \theta^2} = 6 \cdot 363$; $\theta + \sqrt{1 + \theta^2} = 12 \cdot 6462$; $\log_e(\theta + \sqrt{1 + \theta^2}) = \log_e 12 \cdot 6462 = 2 \cdot 5373$. Ansr. $= a(3 \cdot 1865 + 0 \cdot 202)$.

(5) Find the value of the ratio

$$u = \frac{l}{r} = \frac{\text{Length of hyperbolic arc from } x = a \text{ to } x = x}{\text{Distance of a point } P(x, y) \text{ from the origin}}.$$

The equation of the rectangular hyperbola is $x^2 - y^2 = a^2$, $\therefore y = \sqrt{x^2 - a^2}$; $\therefore dy/dx = x/\sqrt{x^2 - a^2}$. By substitution in (1), remembering that $r = \sqrt{x^2 + y^2}$; $y^2 = x^2 - a^2$; $\therefore r = \sqrt{2x^2 - a^2}$.

$$l = \int_a^x \sqrt{\frac{2x^2 - a^2}{x^2 - a^2}} dx; \quad \therefore \frac{l}{r} = \int_a^x \frac{dx}{\sqrt{x^2 - a^2}} = \log \frac{x + \sqrt{x^2 - a^2}}{a}.$$

We shall want to refer back to this result when we discuss hyperbolic functions, and also to show that

$$e^u = \frac{x + \sqrt{x^2 - a^2}}{a}; \quad \left(e^u - \frac{x}{a}\right)^2 = \frac{x^2}{a^2} - 1; \quad \frac{2xe^u}{a} = e^{2u} + 1; \quad \therefore \frac{x}{a} = \frac{e^u + e^{-u}}{2}.$$

The reader may have noticed the remarkable analogy between the chemist's "atom," the physicist's "particle," and "molecule," and the mathematician's "differential".   When the chemist wishes to understand the various transformations of matter, he resolves matter into minute elements which he calls atoms; so here, we have sought the form of a curve by resolving it into small elements.   Both processes are temporary and arbitrary auxiliaries designed to help the mind to understand in parts what it cannot comprehend as a whole.   But once the whole concept is builded up, the scaffolding may be rejected.

§ 85. To find the Area of a Surface of Revolution.

A surface of revolution is a surface generated by the rotation of a line about a fixed axis, called the *axis of revolution*.   The quadrature of surfaces of revolution is sometimes styled the **complanation of surfaces.**   Let the curve APQ (Fig. 114) generate a surface of revolution as it rotates about the fixed axis Ox.   It is required to find the area of this surface. If dx and dy be made sufficiently small, we may assume that the portion $(PQ)^2$, or

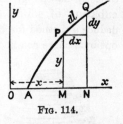

FIG. 114.

$$(dl)^2 = (dx)^2 + (dy)^2, \qquad (1)$$

as indicated above.   The student is supposed to know that the area of the side of a circular cylinder is $2\pi rh$, where r denotes the radius of the base of the cylinder, and h the height of the cylinder. The surface, ds, of the cylinder generated by the revolution of the

line dl, will approach the limit

$$ds = 2\pi y dl \quad . \quad . \quad . \quad . \quad (2)$$

as the length, dl, at P is made infinitesimally small. Hence, from (1), and (2),

$$ds = 2\pi y \sqrt{(dx)^2 + (dy)^2}. \quad . \quad . \quad . \quad (3)$$

All the elements, dl, revolving around the x-axis, will together cut out a surface having an area

$$s = 2\pi \int_{x_1}^{x_2} y \sqrt{1 + \left(\frac{dy}{dx}\right)^2} dx, \quad . \quad . \quad . \quad (4)$$

where x_1 and x_2 respectively denote the abscissæ of the portion of the curve under investigation.

EXAMPLES.—(1) Find the surface generated by the revolution of the slant side of a triangle. Hints. Equation of the line OC (Fig. 115) is $y = mx$; ∴ $dy = mdx$, $ds = 2\pi y \sqrt{1+m^2} . dx$, $s = \int 2\pi m \sqrt{1+m^2} . x dx = \pi m x^2 \sqrt{1+m^2} + C$.

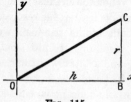

Reckon the area from the apex, where $x = 0$, therefore $C = 0$. If $x = h =$ height of cone $= OB$ and the radius of the base $= r = BC$, then, $m = r/h$ and

$$= \pi r \sqrt{h^2 + r^2} = 2\pi r \times \tfrac{1}{2} \text{ slant height.}$$

This is a well-known rule in mensuration.

FIG. 115.

(2) Show that the surface generated by the revolution of a circle is $4\pi r^2$. Hint. $x^2 + y^2 = r^2$; $dy/dx = -x/y$; $y = \sqrt{(r^2 - x^2)}$; ∴ $2\pi \int y \sqrt{(1 + x^2/y^2)} dx$ becomes $2\pi r \int dx$ by substituting $r^2 = x^2 + y^2$. The limits of the integral for half the surface are $x_2 = r$, and $x_1 = 0$.

§ 86. To find the Volume of a Solid of Revolution.

This is equivalent to finding the volume of a cube of the same capacity as the given solid. Hence the process is named the **cubature of solids.** The notion of differentials will allow us to deduce a method for finding the volume of the solid figure swept out by a curve rotating about an axis of revolution. At the same time, we can obtain a deeper insight into the meaning of the process of integration.

We can, in imagination, resolve the solid into a great number of elementary parallel planes, so that each plane is part of a small cylinder. Fig. 116 will, perhaps, help us to form a mental picture of the process. It is evident that the total

FIG. 116.—After Cox.

volume of the solid is the sum of a number of such elementary cylinders about the same axis. If δx be the height of one cylinder, y the radius of its base, the area of the base is πy^2. But the area of the base multiplied by the height of the cylinder is the volume of each elementary cylinder, that is to say, $\pi y^2 \delta x$. The less the height of each cylinder, the more nearly will a succession of them form a figure with a continuous surface. At the limit, when $\delta x = 0$, the volume, v, of the solid is

$$v = \pi \int_{x_1}^{x_2} y^2 . dx, \quad . \quad . \quad . \quad . \quad (1)$$

where x and y are the coordinates of the generating curve ; x_1 and x_n the abscissæ of the two ends of the revolving curve ; and the x-axis is the axis of revolution.

The methods of limits can be used in place of the method of infinitesimals to deduce this expression, as well as (4) of the preceding section. The student can, if he wishes, look this up in some other text-book.

EXAMPLES.—(1) Find the volume of the cone generated by the revolution of the slant side of the triangle in Ex. 1 of the preceding section. Here $y = mx$; $dv = \pi y^2 dx = \pi m^2 x^2 dx$. ∴ $v = \frac{1}{3}\pi m^2 x^3 + C$. If the volume be reckoned from the apex of the cone, $x = 0$, and therefore $C = 0$. Let $x = h$ and $m = r/h$, as before, and the

Volume of the entire cone $= \frac{1}{3}\pi r^2 h$.

(2) Show that the volume generated by the revolving parabola, $y^2 = 4ax$, is $\frac{1}{2}\pi y^2 x$, where $x =$ height and $y =$ radius of the base.

(3) Required the volume of the sphere generated by the revolution of a circle, with the equation : $x^2 + y^2 = r^2$. Volume of sphere $= \frac{4}{3}\pi r^3$. Hint. $v = \pi \int (r^2 - x^2) dx$; use limits for half the surface $x_2 = r$, $x_1 = 0$.

§ 87. Successive Integration. Multiple Integrals.

Just as it is sometimes necessary, or convenient, to employ the second, third or the higher differential coefficients d^2y/dx^2, $d^3y/dx^3 \ldots$, so it is often just as necessary to apply successive integration to reverse these processes of differentiation. Suppose that it is required to reduce, $d^2y/dx^2 = 2$, to its original primitive form. We can write for the first integration

$$\frac{d^2y}{dx^2} = 2 \; ; \frac{d}{dx}\Big(\frac{dy}{dx}\Big) = 2 \; ; \quad \text{or,} \quad d\Big(\frac{dy}{dx}\Big) = 2dx \; ; \; \therefore \; \frac{dy}{dx} = 2\int dx = 2x + C_1.$$

$$\therefore \; dy = (2x + C_1)dx \; ; \quad \text{or,} \; y = \int(2x + C_1)dx \; ; \; \therefore \; y = x^2 + C_1 x + C_2.$$

In order to show that d^2y/dx^2 is to be integrated twice, we affix two symbols of integration.

$$y = \iint 2dx \cdot dx, \; \therefore \; y = x^2 + C_1x + C_2.$$

Notice that there are as many integration constants, C_1, C_2, as there are symbols of integration.

EXAMPLES.—(1) Find the value of $y = \iiint x^3 \cdot dx \cdot dx \cdot dx$. Ansr.

$$\tfrac{1}{4} \cdot \tfrac{1}{3} \cdot \tfrac{1}{2}x^6 + \tfrac{1}{2}C_1x^2 + C_2x + C_3.$$

(2) Integrate $d^2s/dt^2 = g$, where g is a constant due to the earth's gravitation, t the time and s the space traversed by a falling body.

$$\therefore s = \iint \frac{d\left(\dfrac{ds}{dt}\right)}{dt} = \frac{gt^2}{2} + C_1t + C_2.$$

To evaluate the constants C_1 and C_2, when the body starts from a position of rest, $s = 0$, $t = 0$, $C_1 = 0$, $C_2 = 0$.

In finding the area of a curve $y = f(x)$, the same result will be obtained whether we divide the area Oab into a number of strips parallel to the y-axis, as in Fig. 117, or strips parallel to the x-axis, Fig. 118. In the second case, the reader will no doubt be able to satisfy himself that the area

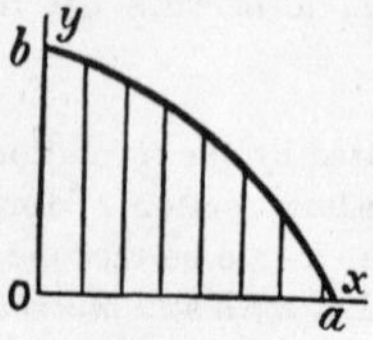

FIG. 117.—Surface Elements.

$$A = \int_0^b x \cdot dy ; \qquad . \qquad . \qquad (1)$$

and, in the former case, that

$$A = \int_0^a y \cdot dx. \qquad . \qquad . \qquad . \qquad (2)$$

There is another way of looking at the matter. Suppose the surface is divided up into an infinite number of infinitely small rectangles as illustrated in Fig. 119. The area of each rectangle will

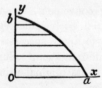

FIG. 118.—Surface Elements.

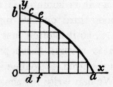

FIG. 119.—Surface Elements.

be $dx \cdot dy$. The area of the narrow strip $Obcd$ is the sum of the areas of the infinite number of rectangles ranged side by side along this strip from O to b. The length of this strip, $y = b$, and the width, dx, is constant; consequently,

$$\text{Area of strip } ObcO = dx \int_0^b dy.$$

The total area of the surface $Obcd$ is obviously the sum of the areas of the infinite number of similar strips ranged along Oa. The height of the second strip, say, $dcef$ obviously depends upon the nature of the curve ba. If the equation of this line be represented by the equation,

$$\frac{x}{a} + \frac{y}{b} = 1, \quad . \quad . \quad . \quad . \quad (3)$$

the height y of any strip at a distance x from O is obtained by solving (3) for y. Consequently,

$$y = \frac{b}{a}(a - x). \quad . \quad . \quad . \quad (4)$$

The area of any strip lying between O and a is therefore

$$\text{Area of any strip} = dx \int_0^{\frac{b(a-x)}{a}} dy = dx \left[\int_0^{\frac{b(a-x)}{a}} dy \right] = \frac{b}{a}(a-x)dx \quad (5)$$

and it follows naturally that the area of all the strips, when each strip has an area $b(a - x)dx/a$, will be

$$\text{Area of all the strips} = \int_0^a \frac{b(a-x)}{a} dx = \left[\frac{abx - \frac{1}{2}bx^2}{a} \right]_0^a = \frac{a^2 b}{a} - \frac{\frac{1}{2}a^2 b}{a} = \frac{ab}{2} \quad (6)$$

Combining (5) and (6), into one expression, we get

$$A = \int_0^a dx \int_0^{\frac{b(a-x)}{a}} dy = \int_0^a \int_0^{\frac{b(a-x)}{a}} dx \cdot dy, \quad . \quad (7)$$

which is called a **double integral**. This integral means that if we divide the surface into an infinite number of small rectangles—**surface elements**—and take their sum, we shall obtain the required area of the surface.

To evaluate the double integral, first integrate with respect to one variable, no matter which, and afterwards integrate with respect to the other. If we begin by keeping x constant and integrating with respect to y, as y passes from O to b, we get the area of the vertical strip $Obcd$ (Fig. 119); we then take the sum of the rectangles in each vertical strip as x passes from O to a in such a way as to include the whole surface $ObaO$. When there can be any doubt as to which differential the limits belong, the integration is performed in the following order : the right-hand element is taken with the first integration sign on the right, and so on with the next element. It just happens that there is no special advantage in resorting to double integration in the above example because the single integration involved in (1) or (2) would have been sufficient. In some cases double integration is alone practicable. The application of the integral calculus to this simple problem in mensuration may seem as incongruous as the employment of a hundred-ton steam hammer to crack nuts. But I have done this in order that the attention might be alone fixed upon the mechanism of the hammer.

EXAMPLES.—(1) Show that if the curve ab (Fig. 119) be represented by equation (3), then the area of the surface bounded by ab, and the two co-ordinate axes, may be variously represented by the integrals

$$\frac{a}{b}\int_0^b (b - y)dy \; ; \; \frac{b}{a}\int_0^a (a - x)dx \; ; \; \int_0^a \int_0^{b(a - x)/a} dy \, . \, dx \; ; \; \int_0^b \int_0^{a(b - y)/b} dx \, . \, dy.$$

(2) Show $\displaystyle\int_2^3 \int_2^5 x \, . \, dx \, . \, dy = \int_2^3 x \, . \, dx \left[y \right]_2^5 = 3 \int_2^3 x \, . \, dx = 3 \left|\begin{matrix}3\\2\end{matrix}\frac{x^2}{2}\right. = 7\tfrac{1}{2}.$

(3) Show $\displaystyle\int_0^a \int_0^b xy^2 \, . \, dx \, . \, dy = \frac{a^2 b^3}{6_1}.$

(4) Show that the area bounded by the two parabolas $3y^2 = 25x$; and $5x^2 = 9y$ is 5 units.

The areas of curves in polar coordinates may be obtained in a similar manner. Divide the given surfaces up into slices by drawing radii vectores at an angle $d\theta$ apart, and subdivide these slices by drawing arcs of circles with origin as centre. Consider any little

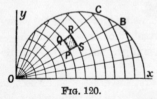

FIG. 120.

surface element, say, $PQRS$ (Fig. 120). OPQ may be regarded as a triangle in which $PQ = OQ \sin (d\theta)$. But the limiting value of the sine of a very small angle is the angle itself, and since $OQ = r$, we have $QP = rd\theta$. Now PS is, by construction, equal to dr. The area of each little segment is, at the limit, equal to $PQ \times PS$, or

$$dA = r \, . \, dr \, . \, d\theta. \qquad . \qquad . \qquad . \qquad (8)$$

The total area will be found by first adding up all the surface elements in the sector OBC, and then adding up all the sectors like COB which it contains, or,

$$A = \int_{r_1}^{r_2}\int_{\theta_1}^{\theta_2} r \, . \, dr \, . \, d\theta. \quad . \quad . \quad . \quad (9)$$

EXAMPLE.—Find the area of the circle whose equation is $r = 2a\cos\theta$, where r denotes the radius of the circle. Ansr.

$$A = \int_0^{2a\cos\theta}\int_{-\frac{\pi}{2}}^{\frac{1}{2}\pi} r \, . \, dr \, . \, d\theta = \pi a^2.$$

We can also imagine a solid to be split up into an infinite number of little parallelopipeds along the three dimensions x, y, z. These infinitesimal figures may be called **volume elements.** The capacity of each little element $dx \times dy \times dz$. The total volume, v, of the solid is represented by the triple integral

$$v = \iiint dx \, . \, dy \, . \, dz. \quad . \quad . \quad . \quad (10)$$

The first integration along the x-axis gives the length of an infinitely narrow strip; the integration along the y-axis gives the area of the surface of an infinitely thin slice, and a third integration along the z-axis gives the total volume of all these little slices, in other words, the volume of the body.

In the same way, quadruple and higher integrals may occur. These, however, are not very common. Multiple integration rarely extends beyond triple integrals.

EXAMPLES.—(1) Evaluate the following triple integrals :—

$$\int_1^4\int_1^5\int_1^6 yz^2 \, . \, dx \, . \, dy \, . \, dz \, ; \quad \int_1^4\int_1^5\int_1^6 yz^2 \, . \, dy \, . \, dz \, . \, dx \, ; \quad \int_1^4\int_1^5\int_1^6 yz^2 \, . \, dz \, . \, dx \, . \, dy.$$

Ansrs. 2580, 1550, 1470 respectively.

(2) Show

$$\int_0^a\int_0^b\left(\frac{x^2}{2p} + \frac{y^2}{2q}\right)dx \, . \, dy = \frac{b}{2}\int_0^a\left(\frac{x^2}{p} + \frac{b^2}{3q}\right)dx = \frac{ab}{6}\left(\frac{a^2}{p} + \frac{b^2}{q}\right).$$

(3) Evaluate $8\displaystyle\int_0^r\int_0^{\sqrt{(r^2-x^2)}}\int_0^{\sqrt{(r^2-x^2-y^2)}} dx \, . \, dy \, . \, dz.$ Ansr. $\dfrac{4\pi r^3}{3}.$

Note $\sin\frac{1}{2}\pi = 1$. Show that this integral represents the volume of a sphere whose equation is $x^2 + y^2 + z^2 = r^2$. Hint. The " dy " integration is the most troublesome. For it, put $r^2 - x^2 = c$, say, and use Ex. (1), p. 203. As a result, $\frac{1}{2}y\sqrt{r^2 - x^2 - y^2} + \frac{1}{2}(r^2 - x^2)\sin^{-1}\{y/\sqrt{r^2 - x^2}\}$ has to be evaluated between the limits $y = \sqrt{(r^2 - x^2)}$ and $y = 0$. The result is $\frac{1}{4}(r^2 - x^2)\pi$. The rest is simple enough.

§ 88. The Isothermal Expansion of Gases.

To find the work done during the isothermal expansion of a gas, that is, the work done when the gas changes its volume, by expansion or compression, at a constant temperature. A contraction may be regarded as a negative expansion. There are three interesting applications.

I.—*The gas obeys Boyle's law*, pv = constant, say, c. We have seen that the work done when a gas expands against any external pressure is represented by the product of the pressure into the change of volume. The work performed during any small change of volume, is

$$dW = p \cdot dv. \quad \text{.} \quad \text{.} \quad \text{.} \quad \text{.} \quad (1)$$

But by Boyle's law,

$$p = f(v) = \frac{c}{v}. \quad \text{.} \quad \text{.} \quad \text{.} \quad (2)$$

Substitute this value of p in (1), and we get $dW = c \cdot dv/v$. If the gas expands from a volume v_1 to a new volume v_2, it follows

$$W = c\int_{v_1}^{v_2}\frac{dv}{v} = c\Big|_{v_1}^{v_2}\log v + C. \quad \therefore W = p_1 v_1 \log\frac{v_2}{v_1}. \quad (3)$$

From (2), $v_1 = c/p_1$, and also $v_2 = c/p_2$, consequently

$$W = p_1 v_1 \log\frac{p_1}{p_2}. \quad \text{.} \quad \text{.} \quad \text{.} \quad (4)$$

Equations (3) and (4) play a most important part in the theory of gases, in thermodynamics and in the theory of solutions. The value of c is equal to the product of the initial volume, v_1, and pressure, p_1, of the gas. Hence we may also put

$$W = 2\cdot3026 p_1 v_1 \log_{10}\frac{v_1}{v_2} = 2\cdot3026 p_1 v_1 \log_{10}\frac{p_2}{p_1},$$

for the work done in compressing the gas.

EXAMPLE.—In an air compressor the air is drawn in at a pressure of 14·7 lb. per square inch, and compressed to 77 lb. per square inch. The volume drawn in per stroke is 1·52 cubic feet, and 133 strokes are made per minute. What is the work of isothermal compression? Hint. The work done is the compression of 1·52 cubic feet × 133 = 202·16 cubic feet of air at 14·7 lb. to 77 lb. per square inch, or 14·7 × 144 = 2116·8 lb. to 77 × 144 = 11088 lb. per square foot. From Boyle's law, $p_1 v_1 = p_2 v_2$; $\therefore v_2 \times 77 = 14·7 \times 202·16$; or, $v_2 = 38·598$. From the above equation, therefore, the work = 2·3026 × 2116·8 × 202·16 (log 202·16 − log 38·598) = 708757·28 foot pounds per minute; or, since a "horse power" can work 33,000 foot pounds per minute, the work of isothermal compression is 21·48 H.P.

II.—The gas obeys van der Waals' law, that is to say,

$$\left(p + \frac{a}{v^2}\right)(v - b) = \text{constant, say, } c.$$

As an exercise on what precedes, prove that

$$W = c \log \frac{v_2 - b}{v_1 - b} - a\left(\frac{1}{v_1} - \frac{1}{v_2}\right); \qquad . \qquad . \qquad (5)$$

This equation has occupied a prominent place in the development of van der Waals' theories of the constitution of gases and liquids.

EXAMPLE.—Find the work done when two litres of carbon dioxide are compressed isothermally to one litre; given van der Waals' $a = 0.00874$; $b = 0.0023$; $c = 0.00369$. Substitute in (5), using a negative sign for contraction.

III.—The gas dissociates during expansion. By Guldberg and Waage's law, in the reaction:

$$N_2O_4 \rightleftharpoons 2NO_2,$$

for equilibrium, if x denotes that fraction of unit mass of N_2O_4 which exists as NO_2, we must have

$$K \frac{1 - x}{v} = \frac{x}{v} \cdot \frac{x}{v}.$$

where $(1 - x)/v$ represents the concentration of the undissociated nitrogen peroxide. The relation between the volume and degree of dissociation is, therefore,

$$Kv = \frac{x^2}{1 - x}. \qquad . \qquad . \qquad . \qquad . \qquad (6)$$

If n represents the original number of molecules; $(1 - x)n$ will represent the number of undissociated molecules; and $2xn$ the number of dissociated molecules. If the relation $pv = c$ does not vary during the expansion, the pressure will be proportional to the number of molecules actually present, that is to say, if p denotes the pressure when there was no dissociation, and p' the actual pressure of the gas,

$$\frac{p}{p'} = \frac{n}{(1 - x)n + 2xn} = \frac{1}{1 + x}.$$

The actual pressure of the gas is, therefore, $p' = (1 + x)p$; and the work done is,

$$dW = p' . dv = (1 + x)p . dv = p . dv + xp . dv. \qquad . \qquad (7)$$

From Boyle's law, and (6), we see that

$$\therefore p = \frac{c}{v} = \frac{cK(1 - x)}{x^2}.$$

Substitute this value of p in (7). Differentiate (6) and we obtain

$$\frac{dv}{dx} = \frac{2(1 - x)x + x^2}{K(1 - x)^2} \; ; \therefore \; dv = \frac{x(2 - x)}{K(1 - x)^2}dx.$$

Now substitute this value of dv in (7); simplify, and we get

$$W = c\int_{v_1}^{v_2}\frac{dv}{v} + c\int_{x_1}^{x_2}\Big(1 + \frac{1}{1 - x}\Big)dx,$$

where x_1 and x_2 denote the values of x corresponding with v_1 and v_2. On integration, therefore,

$$W = c\Big(\log\frac{v_2}{v_1} + x_2 - x_1 - \log\frac{1 - x_2}{1 - x_1}\Big) \; . \quad . \quad (8)$$

It follows directly from (6), that

$$v_1 = \frac{x_1{}^2}{K(1 - x_1)} \; ; \; \text{and,} \; v_2 = \frac{x_2{}^2}{K(1 - x_2)}.$$

Substitute these values of v in (8), and the work of expansion

$$W = c\Big\{x_2 - x_1 - 2\log\frac{x_1(1 - x_2)}{x_2(1 - x_1)}\Big\}. \quad . \quad . \quad (9)$$

EXAMPLES.—(1) Find the work done during the isothermal expansion of dissociating ammonium carbamate (gas): $NH_2COONH_4 \rightleftharpoons 2NH_3 + CO_2$.

(2) In calculating the work done during the isothermal expansion of dissociating hydrogen iodide, $2HI \rightleftharpoons H_2 + I_2$, does it make any difference whether the hydrogen iodide dissociates or not?

(3) A particle of mass m moves towards a centre of force F which varies inversely as the square of the distance. Determine the work done by the force as it moves from one place r_2 to another place r_1. Work = force × displacement

$$\therefore \; W = \int_{r_1}^{r_2}F \, . \, dr = \int_{r_1}^{r_2}\frac{m}{r^2}dr = m\Big(\frac{1}{r_2} - \frac{1}{r_1}\Big).$$

If r is infinite, $W = m/r$. If the body moves towards the centre of attraction work is done by the force; if away from the centre of attraction, work is done against the central force.

(4) If the force of attraction, F, between two molecules of a gas, varies inversely as the fourth power of the distance, r, between them, show that the work, W, done against molecular attractive forces when a gas expands into a vacuum, is proportional to the difference between the initial and final pressures of the gas. That is, $W = A(p_1 - p_2)$, where A is the variation constant. By hypothesis, $F = a/r^4$; and $dW = F \, . \, dr$, where a is another variation constant. Hence,

$$W = \int_{r_1}^{r_2}F \, . \, dr = a\int_{r_1}^{r_2}\frac{dr}{r^4}.$$

But r is linear, therefore, the volume of the gas will vary as r^3. Hence, $v = br^3$, where b is again constant.

$$\therefore W = \frac{a}{3}\left(\frac{1}{r_1^3} - \frac{1}{r_2^3}\right); \therefore W = \frac{ab}{3}\left(\frac{1}{v_1} - \frac{1}{v_2}\right).$$

But by Boyle's law, $pv = $ constant, say, c. Hence if $A = ab/3c = $ constant,

$$W = A(p_1 - p_2).$$

(5) *If the work done against molecular attractive forces when a gas expands into a vacuum, is*

$$W = \int_{v_1}^{v_2} \frac{a}{v^2}\,dv = a\left(\frac{1}{v_1} - \frac{1}{v_2}\right),$$

where a is constant; v_1, v_2, refer to the initial and final volumes of the gas, show that "any two molecules of a gas will attract one another with a force inversely proportional to the fourth power of the distance between them". For the meaning of a/v^2, see van der Waals' equation.

§ 89. The Adiabatic Expansion of Gases.

When the gas is in such a condition that no heat can enter or leave the system during the change of volume—expansion or contraction—the temperature will generally change during the operation. This alters the magnitude of the work of expansion. Let us first find the relation between p and v when no heat enters or leaves the gas while the gas changes its volume. Boyle's relation is obscured if the gas be not kept at a constant temperature.

I.—The relation between the pressure and the volume of a gas when the volume of the gas changes adiabatically. In example (5) appended to § 27, we obtained the expression,

$$dQ = \left(\frac{\partial Q}{\partial v}\right)_p dv + \left(\frac{\partial Q}{\partial p}\right)_v dp. \qquad . \qquad . \qquad (1)$$

As pointed out on page 44, we may, without altering the value of the expression, multiply and divide each term within the brackets by ∂T. Thus,

$$dQ = \left(\frac{\partial Q}{\partial T}\frac{\partial T}{\partial v}\right)_p dv + \left(\frac{\partial Q}{\partial T}\frac{\partial T}{\partial p}\right)_v dp. \qquad . \qquad . \qquad (2)$$

But $(\partial Q/\partial T)_p$ is the amount of heat added to the substance at a constant pressure for a small change of temperature; this is none other than the specific heat at constant pressure, usually written C_p. Similarly $(\partial Q/\partial T)_v$ is the specific heat at constant volume, written C_v. Consequently,

$$dQ = C_p\left(\frac{\partial T}{\partial v}\right)_p dv + C_v\left(\frac{\partial T}{\partial p}\right) dp. \qquad . \qquad . \qquad (3)$$

This equation tells that when a certain quantity of heat is added
to a substance, one part is. spent in raising the temperature while
the volume changes under constant pressure, and the other part is
spent in raising the temperature while the pressure changes under
constant volume.   For an ideal gas obeying Boyle's law,

$$pv = RT; \quad \therefore \frac{v}{R} = \left(\frac{\partial T}{\partial p}\right)_v; \quad \frac{p}{R} = \left(\frac{\partial T}{\partial v}\right)_p.$$

Substitute these values in (3), and we get

$$dQ = C_p \frac{p}{R} dv + C_v \frac{v}{R} dp; \quad \therefore \frac{dQ}{\theta} = C_p \frac{dv}{v} + C_v \frac{dp}{p}, \quad (4)$$

after dividing through with $\theta = pv/R$.   By definition, an adiabatic
change takes place when the system neither gains nor loses heat.
Under these conditions, $dQ = 0$; and remembering that the ratio
of the two specific heats C_p/C_v is a constant, usually written γ;

$$\therefore \frac{C_p}{C_v} \cdot \frac{dv}{v} + \frac{dp}{p} = 0; \text{ or, } \gamma \int \frac{dv}{v} + \int \frac{dp}{p} = \text{Constant.}$$

or, $\gamma \log v + \log p = \text{const.}$; or, $\log v\gamma + \log p = \text{const.}$; $\therefore \log (pv\gamma) = \text{const.}$

$$\therefore pv\gamma = c. \qquad \cdot \qquad \cdot \qquad \cdot \qquad \cdot \qquad (5)$$

A most important relation sometimes called Poisson's equation.

By integrating between the limits p_1, p_2; and v_1, v_2 in the above
equation, we could have eliminated the constant and obtained (5)
in another form, namely,

$$\frac{p_2}{p_1} = \left(\frac{v_1}{v_2}\right)^\gamma. \qquad \cdot \qquad \cdot \qquad \cdot \qquad \cdot \qquad (6)$$

The last two equations tell us that the adiabatic pressure of a gas
varies inversely as the γth power of the volume.   Now substitute
$v_1 = T_1R/p_1$; and $v_2 = T_2R/p_2$, in (6), the result is that

$$\left(\frac{p_2}{p_1} \cdot \frac{T_1}{T_2}\right)^\gamma = \frac{p_2}{p_1}; \text{ or, } \left(\frac{T_1}{T_2}\right)^\gamma = \left(\frac{p_2}{p_1}\right)\left(\frac{p_1}{p_2}\right)^\gamma; \text{ i.e., } \left(\frac{T_1}{T_2}\right)^\gamma = \left(\frac{p_1}{p_2}\right)^{\gamma-1} \quad (7)$$

and the relation between the volume and temperature of a gas under
adiabatic conditions assumes the form,

$$\frac{T_2}{T_1} = \left(\frac{v_1}{v_2}\right)^{\gamma-1}. \qquad \cdot \qquad \cdot \qquad \cdot \qquad (8)$$

This equation affirms that for adiabatic changes, the absolute temperature of a gas varies inversely as the $(\gamma - 1)$th power of the
volume.   A well-known thermodynamic law.

Again, since "weight varies directly as the volume," if w_1

denotes the weight of v volumes of the gas at a pressure p_1 and w_2 the weight of the same volume, at a pressure p_2, we see at once, from (6), that

$$\frac{w_2}{w_1} = \left(\frac{p_2}{p_1}\right)^{\frac{1}{\gamma}} \quad . \quad . \quad . \quad . \quad (9)$$

II.—*The work performed when a gas is compressed under adiabatic conditions.* From (5), $p = c/v^\gamma$; and we know that the work done when v volumes of a gas are compressed from v_1 to v_2, is

$$W = - \int_{v_1}^{v_2} p \,.\, dv = - \int_{v_1}^{v_2} c \frac{dv}{v^\gamma} = - c \left[\frac{v^{-(\gamma-1)}}{-(\gamma-1)} \right]_{v_1}^{v_2},$$

$$\therefore W = \frac{c}{\gamma-1}\left(\frac{1}{v_2^{\gamma-1}} - \frac{1}{v_1^{\gamma-1}}\right). \quad . \quad . \quad (10)$$

From (5), $c = p_1 v_1^\gamma = p_2 v_2^\gamma$. We may, therefore, represent this relation in another form, *viz.* :

$$\frac{c}{\gamma-1}\left(\frac{1}{v_2^{\gamma-1}} - \frac{1}{v_1^{\gamma-1}}\right) = \frac{1}{\gamma-1}\left(\frac{p_1 v_1^\gamma}{v_2^{\gamma-1}} - \frac{p_1 v_1^\gamma}{v_1^{\gamma-1}}\right) = \frac{1}{\gamma-1}\left(\frac{p_2 v_2^\gamma}{v_2^{\gamma-1}} - \frac{p_1 v_1^\gamma}{v_1^{\gamma-1}}\right).$$

$$\therefore W = \frac{1}{\gamma-1}(p_2 v_2 - p_1 v_1). \quad . \quad . \quad (11)$$

If a gas *expands* adiabatically from a pressure p_1 to a pressure p_2, we get, from (5) and (11),

$$W = \frac{1}{\gamma-1}\left(p_1^{1-\frac{1}{\gamma}} - p_2^{1-\frac{1}{\gamma}}\right)c^{\frac{1}{\gamma}} = \frac{1}{\gamma-1}\left(p_1^{1-\frac{1}{\gamma}} - p_2^{1-\frac{1}{\gamma}}\right)p_1^{\frac{1}{\gamma}}, \quad (12)$$

provided we work with unit volume, $v_1 = 1$, of gas, so that $p_1 = c$.

If $p_1 v_1 = RT_1$; and $p_2 v_2 = RT_2$, are the isothermal equations for T_1° and T_2°, we may write,

$$W = \frac{R}{\gamma-1}(T_2 - T_1), \quad . \quad . \quad . \quad (13)$$

which states in words, that the work required to compress a mass of gas adiabatically while the temperature changes from T_1° to T_2°, will be independent of the initial pressure and volume of the gas. In other words, the work done by a perfect gas in passing along an adiabatic curve, from one isothermal to another, page 111, is constant and independent of the path.

EXAMPLES.—(1) Two litres of a gas are compressed adiabatically to one litre. What is the work done? Given $\gamma = 1.4$; atmospheric pressure $p = 1.03$ kilograms per sq. cm. Ansr. 16.48 kilogram metres. Hint. $v_2 = \frac{1}{2}v_1$; from (6), $p_2 = p_1 2^\gamma$; $v_1 = 2000$ c.c. From a table of common logs, $\log 2^\gamma = \log 2^{1.4} = 0.30103 \times 1.4 = 0.4214$; or $2^{1.4} = 2.64$. From (11),

$$W = \frac{v_2 p_1 \cdot 2^{1\cdot4} - v_1 p_1}{\gamma - 1} = \frac{v_1 p_1 (\frac{1}{2} \times 2^{1\cdot4} - 1)}{1\cdot4 - 1} = \frac{1\cdot03 \times 2000}{0\cdot4}(1\cdot32 - 1), \text{ etc.}$$

(2) To continue illustration 3, § 20, page 62. We have assumed Boyle's law $p_2 p_1 = p_1 p_2$. This is only true under isothermal conditions. For a more correct result, use (5) above. For a constant mass, m, of gas, $m = \rho v$, hence show that for adiabatic conditions,

$$\frac{p_2}{p_1} = \left(\frac{\rho_2}{\rho_1}\right)^{\gamma} ; \quad \therefore p_2^{1-\frac{1}{\gamma}} = p_1^{1-\frac{1}{\gamma}} e^{-\frac{\gamma-1}{\gamma} ch} \qquad . \quad . \qquad (14)$$

is the more correct form of Halley's law for the pressure, p_2, of the atmosphere at a height h above sea-level. Atmospheric pressure at sea-level $= p_1$.

(3) From the preceding example proceed to show that the rate of diminution of temperature, T, is constant per unit distance, h, ascent. In other words, prove and interpret

$$T_0 - T = \frac{1}{R} \cdot \frac{\gamma - 1}{\gamma} h \; . \qquad . \quad . \quad . \quad . \qquad (15)$$

(4) A litre of gas at 0° C. is allowed to expand adiabatically to two litres. Find the fall of temperature given $\gamma = 1\cdot4$. Ansr. 66° C. (nearly). Hints. $v_1 = 2v_2$; from (8). $T_2 \times 2^{0\cdot4} = 273$; $2^{0\cdot4} = 1\cdot32$, $\therefore T_2 = 207°$; there is therefore a fall of $273 - 207°$ absolute, $= 66°$ C.

(5) To continue the discussion §§ 15 and 64, suppose the gas obeys van der Waals' law :

$$\left(p + \frac{a}{v^2}\right)(v - b) = RT. \qquad . \quad . \quad . \qquad (16)$$

where R, a, b, are known constants. The first law of thermodynamics may be written

$$dQ = C_v \cdot dT + (p + a/v^2)dv, \qquad . \quad . \quad (17)$$

where the specific heat at constant volume has been assumed constant. To find a value for C_p, the specific heat at constant pressure. Expand (16). Differentiate the result. Cancel the term $2ab \cdot dv/v^3$ as a very small order of magnitude (§ 4). Solve the result for dv. Multiply through with $p + a/v^2$. Since a/v^2 is very small, show that the fraction $(p + a/v^2)/(p - a/v^2)$ is very nearly $1 + 2a/pv^2$. Substitute the last result in (17), and

$$dQ = \left\{ C_v + R\left(1 + \frac{2a}{pv^2}\right)\right\} dT - \left(1 + \frac{2a}{pv^2}\right)(v - b)dp.$$

By hypothesis C_v is constant,

$$\therefore \frac{C_p}{C_v} = 1 + \frac{R}{C_v}\left(1 + \frac{2a}{pv^2}\right). \qquad . \quad . \quad . \qquad (18)$$

For ideal gases $a = 0$, and we get Mayer's equation, § 27. From Boynton, p. 114;

For.	Air.	Hydrogen.	Carbon Dioxide.
a.	0·002812	0·0000895	0·00874
R/C_v	0·4	0·4	0·2857
γ Calculated (18)	1·40225	1·40007	1·2907
γ Observed	1·403	1·4017	1·2911

(6) Show van der Waals' equation for adiabatic conditions is

$$\left(p + \frac{a}{v^2}\right)(v - b)^\gamma = RT, \quad \cdot \quad \cdot \quad \cdot \quad \cdot \quad (19)$$

and the work of adiabatic expansion is

$$W = R(T_1 - T_2)\left\{\frac{1}{\gamma - 1} - a\left(\frac{1}{v_1} - \frac{1}{v_2}\right)\right\}. \quad \cdot \quad \cdot \quad (20)$$

(7) Calculate the work done by a gas which is compressed adiabatically from a state represented by the point A (Fig. 121) along the path AB until a state B is reached. It is then allowed to expand isothermally along the path BC until a state C is reached. This is followed by an adiabatic expansion along CD; and by an isothermal contraction along DA until the original state A is reached. The total work done is obviously represented by the sum of

$$- AabB + BCcb + CDdc - DdaA.$$

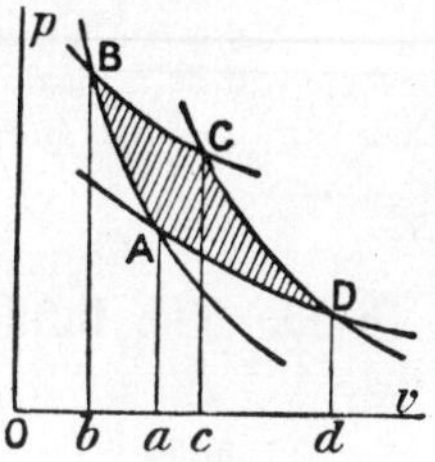

By evaluating the work in each operation as indicated in the last two sections, on the assumption that the equation of AB is $pv^\gamma = c_1$; of BC, $pv = c_2$; CD

FIG. 121.

$pv^\gamma = c_3$; DA, $pv = c_4$. Hence show that the external work, W, done by the gas, is

$$W = \frac{c_2 - c_4}{\gamma - 1} \log \frac{c_3}{c_1}.$$

(8) Compare the work of isothermal and adiabatic compression in the example on page 254. Take γ for air $= 1\cdot408$. Hint. From (6), $14\cdot7 \times 206\cdot16^{1\cdot408} = 77 \times v_2^{1\cdot408}$; $\therefore v_2 = 62\cdot36$ cubic feet; and from (10), $(62\cdot36 \times 11,088 - 202\cdot16 \times 2116\cdot8)/0\cdot408 = 645\cdot871$ foot lbs. per minute $= 19\cdot75$ H.P. The required ratio is therefore as $1 : 0\cdot91$.

(9) If a gas flows adiabatically from one place where the pressure is p_1 to another place where the pressure is p_2, the work of expansion is spent in communicating kinetic energy to the gas. Let V be the velocity of flow. The kinetic energy gained by the gas is equal to the work done. But kinetic energy is, by definition, $\frac{1}{2}mV^2$, where m is the mass of the substance set in motion; but we know that mass = weight $\div$ g, hence, if w_1 denotes the weight of gas flowing per second from a pressure p_1 to a pressure p_2,

$$\therefore \frac{mV^2}{2} = \frac{w_1 V^2}{2g} = W; \quad \therefore V = \sqrt{\frac{2g}{w_1}W}.$$

If a denotes the cross sectional area of the flowing gas, obviously, $w_1 = aVw_2$, where w_2 denotes the weight of unit volume of the gas at a pressure p_2. Let $p_2/p_1 = q$. From (9), $w_2 = w_1 q^{1/\gamma}$. Hence the weight of gas

$$w_1 = aVw_2 = a\sqrt{\frac{2gw_2^2}{w_1(\gamma - 1)}\left(p_1^{1 - \frac{1}{\gamma}} - p_2^{1 - \frac{1}{\gamma}}\right)p^{\frac{1}{\gamma}}}.$$

Now multiply through with $p^{1/\gamma}$; then with the denominator of p_1/p_1; then with w_2/w_1, or, what is the same thing, with $q^{1/\gamma}$; substitute $w_2 = w_1 q^{1/\gamma}$, and multiply through with the last result. The weight of gas which passes per second from a pressure p_1 to a pressure p_2 is then

$$w_1 = a\sqrt{\frac{2gw_2p_1}{\gamma - 1}\left(q^{\frac{2}{\gamma}} - q^{1 + \frac{1}{\gamma}}\right)}.$$

w_1 will be a maximum when

$$q = \tfrac{1}{2}(\gamma + 1)^{\frac{\gamma}{1 - \gamma}}.$$

For dry steam, $\gamma = 1\cdot13$, and hence,

$$\log_e q = -8\cdot7 \times \log_e 1\cdot065 = 1\cdot762 \,; \therefore q = 0\cdot58\,; \text{ or, } p_2 = 0\cdot58p_1\,;$$

or there will be a maximum flow when the external pressure is a little more than half the supply pressure. This conclusion was verified by the experiments of Navier.

§ 90. The Influence of Temperature on Chemical and Physical Changes.

On page 82, (18), we deduced the formula,

$$\left(\frac{\partial Q}{\partial v}\right)_T = T\left(\frac{\partial p}{\partial T}\right)_v, \qquad \cdot \quad \cdot \quad \cdot \qquad (1)$$

by a simple process of mathematical reasoning. The physical signification of this formula is that the change in the quantity of heat communicated to any substance per unit change of volume at constant temperature, is equal to the product of the absolute temperature into the change of pressure per unit change of temperature at constant volume.

Suppose that $1 - x$ grams of one system A is in equilibrium with x grams of another system B. Let v denote the total volume, and T the temperature of the two systems. Equation (1) shows that $(\partial Q/\partial v)_T$ is, the heat absorbed when the very large volume of system A is increased by unity at constant temperature T, less the work done during expansion. Suppose that during this change of volume, a certain quantity $(\partial x/\partial v)_T$ of system B is formed, then, if q be the amount of heat absorbed when unit quantity of the first system is converted into the second, the quantity of heat absorbed during this transformation is $q(\partial x/\partial v)_T$. q is really the molecular heat of the reaction.

The work done during this change of volume is $p \cdot dv$; but dv is unity, hence the external work of expansion is p. Under these circumstances,

$$q\left(\frac{\partial x}{\partial v}\right)_T = \left(\frac{\partial Q}{\partial v}\right)_T - p = T\left(\frac{\partial p}{\partial T}\right)_v - p = \frac{T\partial p - p\partial T}{\partial T}, \qquad (2)$$

from (1). Now multiply and divide the numerator by the integrating factor, T^2;

$$\therefore q\left(\frac{\partial x}{\partial v}\right)_T = T^2\left(\frac{\partial \frac{p}{T}}{\partial T}\right). \qquad . \quad . \quad (3)$$

If, now, n_1 molecules of the system A ; and n_2 molecules of the
system B, take part in the reaction, we must write, instead of
$pv = RT$,

$$pv = RT\{n_1(1 - x) + n_2 x\}; \text{ or, } \frac{p}{T} = \frac{R\{n_1 + (n_2 - n_1)x\}}{v}.$$

The reason for this is well worth puzzling out. Differentiate with
respect to (p/T) and x ; divide by ∂T; and

$$\left(\frac{\partial \frac{p}{T}}{\partial T}\right) = \frac{R}{v}(n_2 - n_1)\left(\frac{\partial x}{\partial T}\right).$$

Substitute this result in equation (3), and we obtain

$$q\left(\frac{\partial x}{\partial v}\right)_\theta = \frac{T^2 R}{v}(n_2 - n_1)\left(\frac{\partial x}{\partial T}\right). \qquad . \quad . \quad (4)$$

By Guldberg and Waage's statement of the mass law, when n_1
molecules of the one system react with n_2 molecules of the other,

$$\left(\frac{x}{v}\right)^{n_2} = K\left(\frac{1 - x}{v}\right)^{n_1}.$$

Hence, taking logarithms,

$$\log K + (n_2 - n_1) \log v = n_2 \log x - n_1 \log (1 - x).$$

Differentiate this last expression with respect to T, at constant
volume ; and with respect to v, at constant temperature,

$$\left(\frac{\partial x}{\partial v}\right)_T = \frac{n_2 - n_1}{v\left(\frac{n_2}{x} + \frac{n_1}{1 - x}\right)}; \left(\frac{\partial x}{\partial T}\right)_v = \frac{\frac{\partial \log K}{\partial T}}{\frac{n_2}{x} + \frac{n_1}{1 - x}}.$$

Introduce these values in (4) and reduce the result to its simplest
terms, thus,

$$\frac{\partial \log K}{\partial T} = \frac{q}{RT^2}. \qquad . \quad . \quad (5)$$

This fundamental relation expresses the change of the equilibrium
constant K with temperature at constant volume in terms of the
molecular heat of the reaction.

Equation (5), first deduced by van't Hoff, has led to some of the most important results of physical chemistry. Since R and T are positive, K and q must always have the same sign. Hence *van't Hoff's principle of mobile equilibrium* follows directly, viz., If the reaction absorbs heat, it advances with rise of temperature ; if the reaction evolves heat it retrogrades with rise of temperature ; and if the reaction neither absorbs nor evolves heat, the state of equilibrium is stationary with rise of temperature.

According to the particular nature of the systems considered q may represent the so-called heat of sublimation, heat of vaporization, heat of solution, heat of dissociation, or the thermal value of strictly chemical reactions when certain simple modifications are made in the interpretation of the " concentration " K. If, at temperature T_1 and T_2, K becomes K_1 and K_2, we get, by the integration of (5),

$$\log \frac{K_2}{K_1} = \frac{q}{2}\left(\frac{1}{T_1} - \frac{1}{T_2}\right). \quad \cdot \quad \cdot \quad \cdot \quad (6)$$

The thermal values of the different molecular changes, calculated by means of this equation, are in close agreement with experiment. For instance :

	q in calories.	
Heat of	Calculated.	Observed.
Vaporization of water . . .	10100	10296
Solution of benzoic acid in water .	6700	6500
Sublimation of NH_4SH . . .	21550	21640
Combination of $BaCl_2 + 2H_2O$ . .	3815	3830
Dissociation of N_2O_4 . . .	12900	12500
Precipitation of $AgCl$ . . .	15992	15850

A sufficiently varied assortment to show the profound nature of the relation symbolized by equations (5) and (6).

NUMERICAL EXAMPLE.—Calculate the heat of solution of mercuric chloride from the change of solubility with change of temperature. If c_1, c_2 denote the solubilities corresponding to the respective absolute temperatures T_1 and T_2,

$c_1 = 6\cdot57$ when $T_1 = 273^\circ + 10^\circ$; $c_2 = 11\cdot84$ when $T_2 = 273^\circ + 50^\circ$.

Since the solubility of a salt in a given solvent is constant at any fixed temperature, we may write c in place of the equilibrium constant K. From (6), therefore,

$$\log \frac{c_2}{c_1} = \frac{q}{2}\left(\frac{1}{T_1} - \frac{1}{T_2}\right); \therefore \log \frac{11 \cdot 84}{6 \cdot 57} = \frac{q}{2}\left(\frac{1}{283} - \frac{1}{323}\right).$$

$\therefore q = \log 1 \cdot 8 \times 45,704 \cdot 5 = 2,700$ (nearly); q (observed) $= 3,000$ (nearly). Use the Table of Natural Logarithms, Appendix II., for the calculation.

Le Chatelier has extended van't Hoff's law and enunciated the important generalization : "any change in the factors of equilibrium from outside, is followed by a reversed change within the system". This rule, known as "Le Chatelier's theorem," enables the chemist to foresee the influence of pressure and other agents on physical and chemical equilibria.

CHAPTER V.

INFINITE SERIES AND THEIR USES.

"In abstract mathematical theorems, the approximation to truth is
perfect. ... In physical science, on the contrary, we treat of
the least quantities which are perceptible."—W. STANLEY JEVONS.

§ 91. What is an Infinite Series?

MARK off a distance AB (Fig. 122) of unit length. Bisect AB at
O_1; bisect O_1B at O_2; O_2B at O_3; etc.

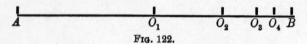

FIG. 122.

By continuing this operation, we can approach as near to B as we
please. In other words, if we take a sufficient number of terms
of the series,

$$AO_1 + O_1O_2 + O_2O_3 + \ldots,$$

we shall obtain a result differing from AB by as small a quantity
as ever we please. This is the geometrical meaning of the infinite
series of terms,

$$1 = \tfrac{1}{2} + (\tfrac{1}{2})^2 + (\tfrac{1}{2})^3 + (\tfrac{1}{2})^4 + \ldots \text{ to infinity.} \qquad (1)$$

Such an expression, in which the successive terms are related
according to a known law, is called a **series**.

EXAMPLE.—I may now be pardoned if I recite the old fable of Achilles
and the tortoise. Achilles goes ten times as fast as the tortoise and the latter
has ten feet start. When Achilles has gone ten feet the tortoise is one foot
in front of him; when Achilles has gone one foot farther the tortoise is $\tfrac{1}{10}$ ft.
in front; when Achilles has gone $\tfrac{1}{10}$ ft. farther the tortoise is $\tfrac{1}{100}$ ft. in front;
and so on without end; therefore Achilles will never catch the tortoise. There
is a fallacy somewhere of course, but where?

When the sum of an infinite series approaches closer and closer
to some definite finite value, as the number of terms is increased

without limit, the series is said to be a **convergent series.** The sum of a convergent series is the "limiting value" of § 6. On the contrary, if the sum of an infinite series obtained by taking a sufficient number of terms can be made greater than any finite quantity, however large, the series is said to be a **divergent series.** For example,

$$1 + 2 + 3 + 4 + \dots \text{ to infinity.} \qquad . \qquad . \qquad (2)$$

Divergent series are not much used in physical work, while converging series are very frequently employed.[1]

The student should be able to discriminate between convergent and divergent series. I shall give tests very shortly. To simplify matters, it may be assumed that the series discussed in this work satisfy the tests of convergency. It is necessary to bear this in mind, otherwise we may be led to absurd conclusions. E. W. Hobson's *On the Infinite and Infinitesimal in Mathematical Analysis*, London, 1902, is an interesting pamphlet to read at this stage of our work.

Let S denote the limiting value or sum of the converging series,

$$S = a + ar + ar^2 + \dots + ar^n + ar^{n+1} + \dots \text{ ad inf.} \qquad (3)$$

When r is less than unity, cut off the series at some assigned term, say the nth, $i.e.$, all terms after ar^{n-1} are suppressed. Let s_n denote the sum of the n terms retained, σ_n the sum of the suppressed terms. Then,

$$s_n = a + ar + ar^2 + \dots + ar^{n-1}. \qquad . \qquad . \qquad (4)$$

Multiply through by r,

$$rs_n = ar + ar^2 + ar^3 + \dots + ar^n.$$

Subtract the last expression from (4),

$$s_n(1 - r) = a(1 - r^n)\,;\ \text{or,}\ s_n = a\frac{1 - r^n}{1 - r}. \qquad . \qquad (5)$$

Obviously we can write series (3), in the form,

$$S = s_n + \sigma_n. \qquad . \qquad . \qquad . \qquad . \qquad (6)$$

The error which results when the first n terms are taken to represent the series, is given by the expression

$$\sigma_n = S - s_n.$$

This error can be made to vanish by taking an infinitely great

---

[1] A prize was offered in France some time back for the best essay on the use of diverging series in physical mathematics.

numbei of terms, or, $\mathrm{Lt}_{n=\infty}\sigma_n = 0$. But,

$$s_n = a\frac{1 - r^n}{1 - r} = \frac{a}{1 - r} - \frac{ar^n}{1 - r}.$$

When n is made infinitely great, the last term vanishes,

$$\therefore \mathrm{Lt}_{n=\infty}\frac{ar^n}{1 - r} = 0.$$

The sum of the infinite series of terms (3), is, therefore, given by the expression

$$S = \frac{a}{1 - r}. \quad \cdot \quad \cdot \quad \cdot \quad \cdot \quad (7)$$

Series (3) is generally called a **geometrical series**. If r is either equal to or greater than unity, S is infinitely great when $n = \infty$, the series is then divergent.

To determine the magnitude of the error introduced when only a finite number of terms of an infinite series is taken. Take the infinite number of terms,

$$S = \frac{1}{1 - r} = 1 + r + r^2 + \ldots + r^{n-1} + \frac{r^n}{1 - r}. \quad \cdot \quad (8)$$

The error introduced into the sum S, by the omission of all terms after the nth, is, therefore,

$$\sigma_n = \frac{r^n}{1 - r}. \quad \cdot \quad \cdot \quad \cdot \quad \cdot \quad (9)$$

When r is positive, σ_n is positive, and the result is a little too small; but if r is negative

$$\sigma_n = \pm\frac{r^n}{1 - r}, \quad \cdot \quad \cdot \quad \cdot \quad (10)$$

which means that if all terms after the nth are omitted, the sum obtained will be too great or too small, according as n is odd or even.

EXAMPLES.—(1) Suppose that the electrical conductivity of an organic acid at different concentrations has to be measured and that the first measurement is made on 50 c.c. of solution of concentration c. 25 c.c. of this solution are then removed and 25 c.c. of distilled water added instead. This is repeated five more times. What is the then concentration of the acid in the electrolytic cell? Obviously we are required to find the 7th term in the series $c\{1 + \frac{1}{2} + (\frac{1}{2})^2 + (\frac{1}{2})^3 + \ldots\}$, where the nth term is $c(\frac{1}{2})^{n-1}$. Ansr. $(\frac{1}{2})^6 c$.

(2) If the receiver of an air pump and connections have a volume a, and the cylinder with the piston at the top has a volume b, the first stroke of the pump will remove b of the air. Hence show that the density of the air in the receiver after the third stroke will be 0·75 of its original density if $a = 1000$ c.c., and $b = 100$ c.c. Hint. After the first stroke the density of the

air, ρ_1, will be $\rho_1(a + b) = \rho_0 a$, when ρ_0 denotes the original density of the air; after the second stroke the density will be ρ_2, and $\rho_2(a+b)=\rho_1 a$; $\therefore \rho_2(a+b)^2=\rho_0 a$. After the nth stroke, $\rho_n(a+b)^n=\rho_0 a^n$; or $\rho_n(1000+100)^3 = 1000^3$; $\therefore \rho_n = 0.73$.

§ 92. Washing Precipitates.

Applications of the series to the washing of organic substances with ether; to the washing of precipitates; to Mallet's process for separating oxygen from air by shaking air with water, etc., are obvious. We can imagine a precipitate placed upon a filter paper, and suppose that C_0 represents the concentration of the mother liquid which is to be washed from the precipitate; let v denote the volume of the liquid which remains behind after the precipitate has drained; v_1 the volume of liquid poured on to the precipitate in the filter paper.

EXAMPLES.—(1) A precipitate at the bottom of a beaker which holds v c.c. of mother liquid is to be washed by decantation, *i.e.*, by repeatedly filling the beaker up to say the v_1 c.c. mark with distilled water and emptying. Suppose that the precipitate and vessel retain v c.c. of the liquid in the beaker at each decantation, what will be the percentage volume of mother liquor about the precipitate after the nth emptying, assuming that the volume of the precipitate is negligibly small? Ansr. $100(v/v_1)^{n-1}$. Hint. The solution in the beaker, after the first filling, has v/v_1 c.c. of mother liquid. On emptying, v of this v/v_1 c.c. is retained by the precipitate. On refilling, the solution in the beaker has $(v^2/v_1)/v_1$ of mother liquor, and so we build up the series,

$$v\left\{1 + \frac{v}{v_1} + \left(\frac{v}{v_1}\right)^2 + \left(\frac{vl}{v_1}\right)^3 + \dots\right\}.$$

(2) Show that the residual liquid which remains with the precipitate after the first, second and nth washings is respectively

$$vC_1 = \frac{v}{v + v_1}vC_0; \; vC_2 = \left(\frac{v}{v + v_1}\right)^2 vC_0; \; vC_n = \left(\frac{v}{v + v_1}\right)^n vC_0.$$

It is thus easy to see that the residue of mother liquid vC_n which contaminates the precipitate, as impurity, is smaller the less the value of $v/(v + v_1)$; this fraction, in turn, is smaller the less the value of v, and the greater the value of v_1. Hence it is inferred that (i) the more perfectly the precipitate is allowed to drain— lessening v; and (ii) the greater the volume of washing liquid employed—increasing v_1—the more perfectly effective will be the washing of the precipitate.

EXAMPLE.—Show that if the amount of liquid poured on to the precipitate at each washing is nine times the amount of residual liquid retained by the precipitate on the filter paper, then, if the amount of impurity contaminating the original precipitate be one gram, show that 0.0001 gram of impurity will remain after the fourth washing.

What simplifying assumptions have been made in this discussion?
We have assumed that the impurity on the filter paper is reduced
a v_1th part when v_1 volumes of the washing liquid is poured on to
the precipitate, and the latter is allowed to drain. We have neglected the amount of impurity which adheres very tenaciously, by
surface condensation or absorption. The washing is, in consequence, less thorough than the simplified theory would lead us to
suppose. Here is a field for investigation. Can we make the
plausible assumption that the amount of impurity absorbed is proportional to the concentration of the solution? Let us find how
this would affect the amount of impurity contaminating the precipitate after the nth washing.

Let a denote the amount of solution retained as impurity by
surface condensation, let b denote the concentration of the solution.
If we make the above-mentioned assumption, then

$$b = ka,$$

where k is the constant of proportion. Let v c.c. of washing liquid
be added to the precipitate which has absorbed a c.c. of mother
liquid. Then $a_0 - a_1$ c.c. of impurity passes into solution, and with
the v c.c. of solvent gives a solution of concentration $(a_0 - a_1)/v$;
the amount of impurity remaining with the precipitate will be

$$\frac{a_0 - a_1}{v} = ka_1. \qquad . \qquad . \qquad . \qquad (11)$$

When this solution has drained off, and v more c.c. of washing
liquid is added, the amount of impurity remaining with the precipitate will be

$$\frac{a_1 - a_2}{v} = ka_2. \qquad . \qquad . \qquad . \qquad (12)$$

Eliminate a_1 from this by the aid of (11), and we get

$$a_2 = \frac{a_0}{kv + 1}$$

for the second washing; and for the nth washing,

$$a_n = \frac{1}{kv + 1}a_0.$$

But all this is based upon the unverified assumption as to the constancy of k, a question which can only be decided by an appeal to
experiment. See R. Bunsen, *Liebig's Ann.*, **148**, 269, 1868.

§ 93. Tests for Convergent Series.

Mathematicians have discovered some very interesting facts in their investigations upon the properties of infinite series.   Many of these results can be employed as tests for the convergency of any given series.   I shall not give more than three tests to be used in this connection.

I. If the series of terms are alternately positive and negative, and the numerical value of the successive terms decreases, the series is convergent.   For example, the series

$$1 - \tfrac{1}{2} + \tfrac{1}{3} - \tfrac{1}{4} + \tfrac{1}{5} - \ldots$$

may be expressed in either of the following forms:—

$$(1 - \tfrac{1}{2}) + (\tfrac{1}{3} - \tfrac{1}{4}) + (\tfrac{1}{5} - \tfrac{1}{6}) + \ldots; \quad 1 - (\tfrac{1}{2} - \tfrac{1}{3}) - (\tfrac{1}{4} - \tfrac{1}{5}) - (\tfrac{1}{6} - \tfrac{1}{7}) - \ldots$$

Every quantity within the brackets is of necessity positive.   The sum of the former series is greater than $1 - \tfrac{1}{2}$, and the sum of the latter is less than 1; consequently, the sum of the series must have some value between 1 and $\tfrac{1}{2}$.   In other words, the series is convergent.   If a series in which all the terms are positive is convergent, the series will also be convergent when some or all of the terms have a negative value.   Otherwise expressed, a series with varying signs is convergent if the series derived from it by making all the signs positive is convergent.

II. If there be two infinite series.

$$u_0 + u_1 + u_2 + \ldots u_n + \ldots; \quad \text{and } v_0 + v_1 + v_2 + \ldots v_n + \ldots$$

the first of which is known to be convergent, and if each term of the other series is not greater than the corresponding term of the first series, the second series is also convergent.   If the first series is divergent, and each term of the second series is greater than the corresponding term of the first series, the second series is divergent.   This is called the **comparison test.**   The series most used for reference are the geometrical series

$$a + ar + ar^2 + \ldots + ar^n + \ldots$$

which is known to be convergent when r is less than unity, and divergent when r is greater than or equal to unity; and

$$1 + \frac{1}{2^m} + \frac{1}{3^m} + \frac{1}{4^m} + \ldots$$

which is known to be convergent when m is greater than unity; and divergent, if m is equal to or less than unity.

EXAMPLE.—Show that the series $1 + \frac{1}{4} + \frac{1}{18} + \frac{1}{64} + \dots$ is convergent by comparison with the geometrical series $1 + \frac{1}{4} + \frac{1}{16} + \frac{1}{64} + \dots$

III. *An infinite series is convergent if from and after some fixed term the ratio of each term to the preceding term is numerically less than some quantity which is itself less than unity.* For instance, let the series, beginning from the fixed term, be

$$a_1 + a_2 + a_3 + \dots$$

Let s_n denote the sum of the first n terms. We can therefore write

$$s_n = a_1 + a_2 + a_3 + a_4 + \dots$$

By rearranging the terms of the series, we get

$$s_n = a_1\left(1 + \frac{a_2}{a_1} + \frac{a_3}{a_2}.\frac{a_2}{a_1} + \frac{a_4}{a_3}.\frac{a_3}{a_1} + \dots\right)$$

The fraction $\dfrac{a_{n+1}}{a_n}$ is called the **ratio test.** Suppose the ratio test

$$\frac{a_2}{a_1} \text{ be less than } r\ ;\ \ \frac{a_3}{a_2} \text{ be less than } r\ ;\ \ \frac{a_4}{a_3} \text{ be less than }\ r\ ;\ \dots$$

that is, from (3) and (5), page 267,

$$s_n \text{ be less than } a_1\frac{1 - r^n}{1 - r}.$$

Hence, from (7), if r is less than unity,

$$s_n \text{ be less than } \frac{a_1}{1 - r}.$$

Thus the sum of as many terms as we please, beginning with a, is less than a certain finite quantity r, and therefore the series beginning with a_1 is convergent.

EXAMPLES.—(1) The series $1 + \frac{1}{1}x + \frac{'1}{2!}x^2 + \frac{1}{3!}x^3 + \dots$, is convergent because the test-ratio $= x/n$ becomes zero when $n = \infty$.

(2) The series $1 + \frac{1}{2}x + \frac{1}{2}.\frac{3}{4}x^2 + \frac{1}{2}.\frac{3}{4}.\frac{5}{6}x^3 + \dots$ is convergent when x is less than unity.

It is possible to have a series in which the terms increase up to a certain point, and then begin to decrease. In the series

$$1 + 2x + 3x^2 + 4x^3 + \dots + nx^{n+1} + \dots,$$

for example, we have

$$\frac{a_n}{a_{n-1}} = \frac{nx}{n - 1} = \left(1 + \frac{1}{n - 1}\right)x.$$

If n be large enough, the series can be made as nearly equal to x as we please. Hence, if x is less than unity, the series is convergent. The ratio will not be less than unity until

$$\frac{n-1}{nx}- \text{ be less than } 1 \; ; \; i.e., \text{ until } n > \frac{1}{1-x}.$$

If $x = \frac{9}{10}$, for example, $\frac{1}{1-x} = 10$, and the terms only begin to decrease after the 10th term.

These tests will probably be found sufficient for all the series the student is likely to meet in the ordinary course of things. If the test-ratio is greater than unity, the series is divergent; and if this ratio is equal to unity, the test fails.

§ 94. Approximate Calculations in Scientific Work.

A good deal of the tedious labour involved in the reduction of experimental results to their final form, may be avoided by attention to the degree of accuracy of the measurements under consideration. It is one of the commonest of mistakes to extend the arithmetical work beyond the degree of precision attained in the practical work. Thus, Dulong calculated his indices of refraction to eight digits when they agreed only to three. When asked " Why?" Dulong returned the ironical answer: "I see no reason for suppressing the last decimals, for, if the first are wrong, the last may be all right"!

In a memoir "On the Atomic Weight of Aluminium," at present before me, I read, "0·646 grm. of aluminium chloride gave 2·0549731 grms. of silver chloride...." It is not clear how the author obtained his seven decimals seeing that, in an earlier part of the paper, he expressly states that his balance was not sensitive to more than 0·0001 grm. A popular book on "The Analysis of Gases," tells us that 1 c.c. of carbon dioxide weighs 0·00196633 grm. The number is calculated upon the assumption that carbon dioxide is an ideal gas, whereas this gas is a notorious exception. Latitude also might cause variations over a range of $\pm$ 0·000003 grm. The last three figures of the given constant are useless. "Superfluitas," said R. Bacon, "impedit multum...reddit opus abominabile."

Although the measurements of a Stas, or of a Whitworth, may require six or eight decimal figures, few observations are correct to more than four or five. But even this degree of accuracy is only obtained by picked men working under special conditions. Observations which agree to the second or third decimal place are comparatively rare in chemistry.

Again, the best of calculations is a more or less crude approximation on account of the "simplifying assumptions" introduced when deducing the formula to which the experimental results are referred. It is, therefore, no good extending the "calculated results" beyond the reach of experimental verification. "It is unprofitable to demand a greater degree of precision from the calculated than from the observed results—but one ought not to demand a less" (H. Poincaré's *Mécanique Céleste*, Paris, 1892).

The general rule in scientific calculations is to use one more decimal figure than the degree of accuracy of the data. In other words, reject as superfluous all decimal figures beyond the first doubtful digit. The remaining digits are said to be **significant figures.**

EXAMPLES.—In 1·540, there are four significant figures, the cypher indicates that the magnitude has been measured to the thousandth part; in 0·00154, there are three significant figures, the cyphers are added to fix the decimal point; in 15,400, there is nothing to show whether the last two cyphers are significant or not, there may be three, four, or five significant figures.

In "casting off" useless decimal figures, the last digit retained must be increased by unity when the following digit is greater than four. We must, therefore, distinguish between 9·2 when it means exactly 9·2, and when it means anything between 9 14 and 9·25. In the so-called "exact sciences," the latter is the usual interpretation. Quantities are assumed to be equal when the differences fall within the limits of experimental error.

LOGARITHMS.—There are very few calculations in practical work outside the range of four or five figure logarithms. The use of more elaborate tables may, therefore, be dispensed with. There are so very many booklets and cards containing "Tables of Logarithms" upon the market that one cannot be recommended in preference to another.

ADDITION AND SUBTRACTION.—In adding such numbers as 9·2 and 0·4913, cast off the 3 and the 1, then write the answer, 9·69, not 9·6913. Show that $5·60 + 20·7 + 103·193 = 129·5$, with an error of about 0·01, that is about 0·08 per cent.

MULTIPLICATION AND DIVISION.—The product $2·25\pi$ represents the length of the perimeter of a circle whose diameter is 2·25 units; π is a numerical coefficient whose value has been calculated by Shanks (*Proc. Roy. Soc.*, **22**, 45, 1873), to over seven hundred decimal places, so that $\pi = 3\cdot141592,653589,793\ldots$. Of these two numbers, therefore, $2\cdot25$ is the less reliable. Instead of the ludicrous $7\cdot0685808625\ldots$, we simply write the answer, $7\cdot07$. Again, although W. H. Colvill has run out $\sqrt{2}$ to 110 decimal places we are not likely to want more than half a dozen significant figures.

It is no doubt unnecessary to remind the reader that in scientific computations the standard arithmetical methods of multiplication and division are abbreviated so as to avoid writing down a greater number of digits than is necessary to obtain the desired degree of accuracy. The following scheme for " **shortened multiplication and division**," requires little or no explanation :—

Shortened Multiplication.	Shortened Division.
$9\cdot774$	$365\cdot4)3571\cdot3(9\cdot774$
$365\cdot4$	$3288\cdot6$
$2932\cdot2$	$282\cdot7$
$586\cdot4$	$255\cdot8$
$48\cdot\overline{9}$	
$3\cdot9$	$26\cdot9$
	$25\cdot5$
$3571\cdot\overline{4}$	
	$1\cdot4$

The digits of the multiplier are taken from left to right, not right to left. One figure less of the divisor is used at each step of the division. The last figure of the quotient is obtained mentally. A "bar" is usually placed over strengthened figures so as to allow for an excess or defect of them in the result.

W. Ostwald, in his *Hand- und Hilfsbuch zur Ausführung physikochemiker Messungen,* Leipzig, 1893, has said that "the use of these methods cannot be too strongly emphasized. The ordinary methods of multiplication and division must be termed unscientific." Full details are given in E. M. Langley's booklet, *A Treatise on Computation,* London, 1895.

The error introduced in approximate calculations by the " casting off" of decimal figures.

Some care is required in rounding off decimals to avoid an excess or defect of strengthened figures by making the positive and negative errors neutralize each other in the final result. It is sometimes advisable, in dealing with the 5 in a " train" of arithmetical operations, to leave the last figure an even number. *E.g.,* $3\cdot75$ would become $3\cdot8$, while $3\cdot85$ would be written $3\cdot8$.

The percentage error of the product of two approximate numbers is very nearly the algebraic sum of the percentage error of each. If the positive error in the one be numerically equal to the negative error in the other, the product will be nearly correct, the errors neutralize each other.

EXAMPLE.—$19 \cdot 8 \times 3 \cdot 18$. The first factor may be written 20 with a + error of 1 %, and, therefore, $20 \times 3 \cdot 18 = 63 \cdot 6$, with a + error of 1 %. This excess must be deducted from $63 \cdot 6$. We thus obtain $62 \cdot 95$. The true result is $62 \cdot 964$.

The percentage error of the quotient of two approximate numbers is obtained by subtracting the percentage error of the numerator from that of the denominator. If the positive error of the numerator is numerically equal to the positive error of the denominator, the error in the quotient is practically neutralized.

There is a well-defined distinction between the approximate values of a physical constant, which are seldom known to more than three or four significant figures, and the approximate value of the incommensurables π, e, $\sqrt{2}$, ... which can be calculated to any desired degree of accuracy. If we use $\frac{22}{7}$ in place of $3 \cdot 1416$ for π, the **absolute error** is greater than or equal to $3 \cdot 1429 - 3 \cdot 1416$, and equal to or less than $3 \cdot 1428 - 3 \cdot 1416$; that is, between $\cdot 0012$ and $\cdot 0014$. In scientific work we are rarely concerned with absolute errors.

§ 95. Approximate Calculations by Means of Infinite Series.

The reader will, perhaps, have been impressed with the frequency with which experimental results are referred to a series formula of the type:

$$y = A + Bx + Cx^2 + Dx^3 + \ldots, \qquad . \qquad . \qquad (1)$$

in physical or chemical text-books. For instance, I have counted over thirty examples in the first volume of Mendeléeff's *The Principles of Chemistry*, and in J. W. Mellor's *Chemical Statics and Dynamics* it is shown that all the formulæ which have been proposed to represent the relation between the temperature and the velocity of chemical reactions have been derived from a similar formula by the suppression of certain terms. The formula has no theoretical significance whatever. It does not pretend to accurately represent the whole course of any natural phenomena. All it postulates is that the phenomena in question proceed continuously. In the absence of any knowledge as to the proper setting of the "law" connecting two variables, this formula may be used to express the relation between the two phenomena to any required degree of approximation. It is only to be looked upon as an arbitrary device which is used for calculating corresponding values of the two variables where direct measurements have not been obtained. $A, B, C, \ldots$ are constants to be determined from the experimental data by methods to be described later on. There are several interesting features about this expression.

I. *When the progress of any physical change is represented by the above formula, the approximation is closer to reality the greater the number of terms included in the calculation.* This is best shown by an example. The specific gravity s of an aqueous solution of hydrogen chloride is an unknown function of the amount of gas p per cent. dissolved in the water. (Unit: water at $4° = 10,000$.)

The first two columns of the following table represent corresponding values of p and s, determined by Mendeléeff. It is desired to find a mathematical formula to represent these results with a fair degree of approximation, in order that we may be able to calculate p if we know s, or, to determine s if we know p. Let us suppress all but the first two terms of the above series,

$$s = A + Bp,$$

where A and B are constants, found, by methods to be described later, to be $A = 9991\cdot6$, $B = 50\cdot5$. Now calculate s from the given values of p by means of the formula,

$$s = 9991\cdot6 + 50\cdot5p, \quad . \quad . \quad . \quad . \quad (2)$$

and compare the results with those determined by experiment. See the second and third columns of the following table :—

Percentage Composition p.	Specific Gravity s.		
	Found.	Calculated.	
		1st Approx.	2nd Approx.
5	10242	10244	10240
10	10490	10497	10492
15	10744	10749	10746
20	11001	11002	11003
25	11266	11254	11263

Formula (2), therefore, might serve all that is required in, say, a manufacturing establishment, but, in order to represent the connection between specific gravity and percentage composition with a greater degree of accuracy, another term must be included in the calculation, thus we write

$$s = A + Bp + Cp^2,$$

where B is found to be equivalent to 49·43, and C to 0·0571. The agreement between the results calculated according to the formula:

$$s = 9991·6 + 49·43p + 0·0571p^2, \qquad . \qquad . \qquad (3)$$

and those actually found by experiment is now very close. This will be evident on comparing the second with the fourth columns of the above table. The term $0·0571p^2$ is to be looked upon as a **correction term.** It is very small in comparison with the preceding terms.

If a still greater precision is required, another correction term must be included in the calculation, we thus obtain

$$y = A + Bx + Cx^2 + Dx^3.$$

Such an expression was employed by T. E. Thorpe and A. W. Rücker (*Phil. Trans.*, **166**, ii., 1, 1877) for the relation between the volume and temperature of sea-water; by T. E. Thorpe and A. E. Tutton (*Journ. Chem. Soc.*, **57**, 545, 1890) for the relation between the temperature and volume of phosphorous oxide; and by Rapp for the specific heat of water, σ, between 0° and 100°. Thus Rapp gives

$$\sigma = 1·039935 - 0·007068\theta + 0·00021255\theta^2 - 0·00000154\theta^3,$$

and Hirn (*Ann. Chim. Phys.* [4], **10**, 32, 1867) used yet a fourth term, namely,

$$v = A + B\theta + C\theta^2 + D\theta^3 + E\theta^4,$$

in his formula for the volume of water, between 100° and 200°.

The logical consequence of this reasoning, is that by including every possible term in the approximation formula, we should get absolutely correct results by means of the infinite converging series:

$$y = A + Bx + Cx^2 + Dx^3 + Ex^4 + Fx^5 + \ldots + \text{ad infin.} \quad (4)$$

It is the purpose of Maclaurin's theorem to determine values of $A, B, C, \ldots$ which will make this series true.

II. *The rapidity of the convergence of any series determines how many terms are to be included in the calculation in order to obtain any desired degree of approximation.* It is obvious that the smaller the numerical value of the "correction terms" in the preceding series, the less their influence on the calculated result. If each correction term is very small in comparison with the preceding one, very good approximations can be obtained by the use of comparatively simple formulæ involving two, or, at most, three terms, e.g., p. 87.   On the other hand, if the number of correction terms is very great, the series becomes so unmanageable as to be practically useless.

Equation (1) may be written in the form,

$$y = A(1 + bx + cx^2 + \ldots),$$

where A, b, c, ... are constants ; A is the value of y when $x = 0$.

As a general rule, when a substance is heated, it increases in volume, v ; its mass, m, remains constant, the density, ρ, therefore, must necessarily decrease.   But,

Mass = Density × Volume; or, $m = \rho v$.

The volume of a substance at $\theta°$ is given by the expression

$$v = v_0(1 + a\theta),$$

where v_0 represents the volume of the substance when θ is $0°$ C. a is the coefficient of cubical expansion.   Evidently,

$$\frac{\rho_0}{\rho} = \frac{v}{v_0} = \frac{v_0(1 + a\theta)}{v_0} = 1 + a\theta \; ; \; \therefore \rho = \frac{\rho_0}{1 + a\theta}.$$

True for solids, liquids, and gases.   For simplicity, put $\rho_0 = 1$.   By division, we obtain

$$\rho = 1 - a\theta + (a\theta)^2 - (a\theta)^3 + \ldots$$

For solids and some liquids a is very small in comparison with unity.   For example, with mercury $a = 0\cdot00018$.   Let θ be small enough

$$\rho = 1 - 0\cdot00018\theta + (0\cdot00018\theta)^2 - \ldots$$
$$\therefore \rho = 1 - 0\cdot00018\theta + 0\cdot000000,0324\theta^2 - \ldots$$

If the result is to be accurate to the second decimal place (1 per 100), terms smaller than $0\cdot01$ should be neglected ; if to the third decimal place (1 per 1000), omit all terms smaller than $0\cdot001$, and so on. It is, of course, necessary to extend the calculation a few decimal places beyond the required degree of approximation.   How many, naturally depends on the rapidity of convergence of the series. If, therefore, we require the density of mercury correct to the sixth decimal place, the omission of the third term can make no perceptible difference to the result.

EXAMPLES.—(1) If h_0 denotes the height of the barometer at $0°$ C. and h its height at $\theta°$, what terms must be included in the approximation formula, $h = h_0(1 + 0\cdot00018\theta)$, in order to reduce a reading at $20°$ to the standard temperature, correct to 1 in 100,000?

(2) In accurate weighings a correction must be made for the buoyancy of the air by reducing the "observed weight in air" to "weight in vacuo".[1] Let W denote the true weight of the body (*in vacuo*), w the observed weight in air, ρ the density of the body, ρ_1 the density of the weights, ρ_2 the density of the air at the time of weighing. Hence show that if

$$W\left(1 - \frac{\rho_2}{\rho}\right) = w\left(1 - \frac{\rho_2}{\rho_1}\right); \quad W = w\frac{1 - \frac{\rho_2}{\rho_1}}{1 - \frac{\rho_2}{\rho}} = w\left(1 - \frac{\rho_2}{\rho_1} + \frac{\rho_2}{\rho}\right) = w + 0\cdot0012w\left(\frac{1}{\rho} - \frac{1}{\rho_1}\right);$$

which is the standard formula for reducing weighings in air to weighings in vacuo. The numerical factor represents the density of moderately moist air at the temperature of a room under normal conditions.

(3) If α denotes the coefficient of cubical expansion of a solid, the volume of a solid at any temperature θ is, $v = v_0(1 + \alpha\theta)$, where v_0 represents the volume of the substance at $0°$. Hence show that the relation between the volumes, v_1 and v_2, of the solid at the respective temperatures of θ_1 and θ_2 is $v_1 = v_2(1 + \alpha\theta_1 - \alpha\theta_2)$. Why does this formula fail for gases?

(4) Since

$$\frac{1}{x - a} = \frac{1}{x} + \frac{a}{x^2} + \frac{a^2}{x^3} + \dots,$$

the reciprocals of many numbers can be very easily obtained correct to many decimal places. Thus

$$\frac{1}{97} = \frac{1}{100 - 3} = \frac{1}{100} + \frac{3}{10,000} + \frac{9}{1,000,000} + \dots = 0\cdot01 + 0\cdot0003 + 0\cdot000009 + \dots$$

(5) We require an accuracy of 1 per 1,000. What is the greatest value of x which will permit the use of the approximation formula $(1 + x)^3 = 1 + 3x$? There is a collection of approximation formulæ on page 601.

(6) From the formula, $(1 \pm x)^n = 1 \pm nx$, where n may be positive or negative, integral or fractional, calculate the approximate values of $\sqrt{999}$, $1/\sqrt{1\cdot02}$, $(1\cdot001)^3$, $\sqrt{1\cdot05}$, mentally. Hints. In the first case $n = \frac{1}{2}$; in the second, $n = -\frac{1}{2}$; in the third, $n = 3$. In the first, $x = -1$; in the second, $x = 0\cdot02$; in the third, $x = 0\cdot001$, etc.

§ 96. Maclaurin's Theorem.

Maclaurin's theorem determines the law for the expansion of a function of a SINGLE *variable in a series of ascending powers of that variable.* Let the variable be denoted by x, then,

$$u = f(x).$$

---

[1] A difference of 45 mm. in the height of a barometer during an organic combustion analysis, may cause an error of $0\cdot6$ % in the determination of the CO_2, and an error of $0\cdot4$ % in the determination of the H_2O. See W. Crookes, "The Determination of the Atomic Weight of Thallium," *Phil. Trans.*, **163**, 277, 1874.

Assume that $f(x)$ can be developed in ascending powers of x, like the series used in the preceding section, namely,

$$u = f(x) = A + Bx + Cx^2 + Dx^3 + \ldots, \qquad . \qquad (1)$$

where A, B, C, $D \ldots$, are constants independent of x, but dependent on the constants contained in the original function. It is required to determine the value of these constants, in order that the above assumption may be true for all values of x.

There are several methods for the development of functions in series, depending on algebraic, trigonometrical, or other processes. The one of greatest utility is known as Taylor's theorem. Maclaurin's [1] theorem is but a special case of Taylor's. We shall work from the special to the general.

By successive differentiation of (1),

$$\frac{du}{dx} = \frac{df(x)}{dx} = B + 2Cx + 3Dx^2 + \ldots; \quad . \qquad . \qquad (2)$$

$$\frac{d^2u}{dx^2} = \frac{df'(x)}{dx} = 2C + 2 \cdot 3Dx + \ldots; \qquad . \qquad . \qquad (3)$$

$$\frac{d^3u}{dx^3} = \frac{df''(x)}{dx} = 2 \cdot 3 \cdot D + \ldots \qquad . \qquad . \qquad . \qquad (4)$$

By hypothesis, (1) is true whatever be the value of x, and, therefore, the constants A, B, C, $D, \ldots$ are the same whatever value be assigned to x. Now substitute $x = 0$ in equations (2), (3), (4). Let v denote the value assumed by u when $x = 0$. Hence, from (1),

$$\left.\begin{array}{lll} v = f(0) = A, & \therefore A = v; \\[2mm] \text{from (2),} \quad \dfrac{dv}{dx} = f'(0) = 1 \cdot B, & \therefore B = \dfrac{dv}{dx}; \\[2mm] \text{from (3),} \quad \dfrac{d^2v}{dx^2} = f''(0) = 1 \cdot 2C, & \therefore C = \dfrac{1}{2\,!}\dfrac{d^2v}{dx^2}; \\[2mm] \text{from (4),} \quad \dfrac{d^3v}{dx^3} = f'''(0) = 1 \cdot 2 \cdot 3D, & \therefore D = \dfrac{1}{3\,!}\dfrac{d^3v}{dx^3}. \end{array}\right\} \quad . \qquad (5)$$

Substitute the above values of A, B, $C, \ldots$, in (1) and we get

$$u = v + \frac{dv}{dx}\frac{x}{1} + \frac{d^2v}{dx^2}\frac{x^2}{2\,!} + \frac{d^3v}{dx^3}\frac{x^3}{3\,!} + \ldots \qquad . \qquad (6)$$

---

[1] The name is here a historical misnomer. Taylor published his series in 1715. In 1717, Stirling showed that the series under consideration was a special case of Taylor's. Twenty-five years after this Maclaurin independently published Stirling's series. But then "both Maclaurin and Stirling," adds De Morgan, "would have been astonished to know that a particular case of Taylor's theorem would be called by either of their names".

The series on the right-hand side is known as **Maclaurin's Series.** The first term is what the series becomes when $x = 0$; the second term is what the first derivative of the function becomes when $x = 0$, multiplied by x; the third term is the product of the second derivative of the function when $x = 0$, into x^2 divided by factorial 2 ...

"$f^n(0)$" means that $f(x)$ is to be differentiated n times, and x equated to zero in the resulting expression. Using this notation the series assumes the form

$$u = f(0) + f'(0)\frac{x}{1} + f''(0)\frac{x^2}{1 \cdot 2} + f'''(0)\frac{x^3}{1 \cdot 2 \cdot 3} + \ldots \qquad (7)$$

§ 97. Useful Deductions from Maclaurin's Theorem.

The following may be considered as a series of examples of the use of the formula obtained in the preceding section. Many of the results now to be established will be employed in our subsequent work.

I. Binomial Series.

In order to expand any function by Maclaurin's theorem, the successive differential coefficients of u are to be computed and x then equated to zero. This fixes the values of the different constants.

Let $$u = (a + x)^n,$$

$du/dx = n(a+x)^{n-1},$ $\qquad \therefore f'(0) = na^{n-1};$

$d^2u/dx^2 = n(n-1)(a+x)^{n-2},$ $\qquad \therefore f''(0) = n(n-1)a^{n-2};$

$d^3u/dx^3 = n(n-1)(n-2)(a+x)^{n-3},$ $\therefore f'''(0) = n(n-1)(n-2)a^{n-3},$

and so on. Now substitute these values in Maclaurin's series (6),

$$(a + x)^n = a^n + \frac{n}{1}a^{n-1}x + \frac{n(n-1)}{1 \cdot 2}a^{n-2}x^2 + \ldots, \qquad (1)$$

a result known as the **binomial series,** true for positive, negative, or fractional values of n.

EXAMPLES.—(1) Prove that

$$(a - x)^n = a^n - \frac{n}{1}a^{n-1}x + \frac{n(n-1)}{1 \cdot 2}a^{n-2}x^2 - \ldots \qquad (2)$$

When n is a positive integer, and $n = m$, the infinite series is cut off at a point where $n - m = 0$. A finite number of terms remains.

(2) Establish $(1 + x^2)^{1/2} = 1 + x^2/2 - x^4/8 + x^6/16 - \ldots$

(3) Show $(1 - x^2)^{-1/2} = 1 + x^2/2 + 3x^4/8 + 5x^6/16 + \ldots$

(4) Show $(1 + x^2)^{-1} = 1 - x^2 + x^4 - \ldots$ Verify this result by actual division.

II. *Trigonometrical Series.*

Suppose $u = f(x) = \sin x$.   Note that $du/dx = d(\sin x)/dx = \cos x$; $d^2u/dx^2 = d^2(\sin x)/dx^2 = d(\cos x)/dx = - \sin x$, etc.; and that $\sin 0 = 0$, $- \sin 0 = 0$, $\cos 0 = 1$, $- \cos 0 = - 1$.

Hence, we get the **sine series,**

$$\sin x = \frac{x}{1} - \frac{x^3}{3!} + \frac{x^5}{5!} - \frac{x^7}{7!} + \dots \quad . \quad . \quad (3)$$

In the same manner we find the **cosine series**

$$\cos x = 1 - \frac{x^2}{2!} + \frac{x^4}{4!} - \frac{x^6}{6!} + \dots \quad . \quad . \quad (4)$$

These series are employed for calculating the numerical values of angles between 0 and $\frac{1}{4}\pi$.   All the other angles found in "trigonometrical tables of sines and cosines," can be then determined by means of the formulæ, page 611,

$$\sin(\tfrac{1}{2}\pi - x) = \cos x ; \; \cos(\tfrac{1}{2}\pi - x) = \sin x.$$

Now let

$$u = f(x) = \tan x. \quad \therefore u \cos x = \sin x.$$

From page 67, by successive differentiation of this expression, remembering that $u_1 = du/dx$, $u_2 = d^2u/dx^2$, ..., as in § 8,

$$\therefore u_1 \cos x - u \sin x = \cos x \; ;$$
$$\therefore u_2 \cos x - 2u_1 \sin x - u \cos x = - \sin x \; ;$$
$$\therefore u_3 \cos x - 3u_2 \sin x - 3u_1 \cos x + u \sin x = - \cos x.$$

By analogy with the coefficients of the binominal development (1), or Leibnitz' theorem, § 21,

$$u_n \cos x - \frac{n}{1} u_{n-1} \sin x - \frac{n(n-1)}{1 . 2} u_{n-2} \cos x + \dots = n\text{th deriv. } \sin x.$$

Now find the values of u, u_1, u_2, u_3 ... by equating $x = 0$ in the above equations, thus,

$$f(0) = f''(0) = \dots = 0 ; f'(0) = 1, f'''(0) = 2, \dots$$

Substitute these values in Maclaurin's series (7), preceding section. The result is, the **tangent series :**

$$\tan x = \frac{x}{1} + \frac{2x^3}{3!} + \frac{16x^5}{5!} + \dots; \text{ or, } \tan x = \frac{x}{1} + \frac{x^3}{3} + \frac{2x^5}{15} + \dots \; (5)$$

III. *Inverse Trigonometrical Series.*

Let $\theta = \tan^{-1}x$.   By (3), § 17 and Ex. (4) above,

$$\therefore d\theta/dx = (1 + x^2)^{-1} = 1 - x^2 + x^4 - x^6 + \dots$$

By successive differentiation and substitution in the usual way, we find that

$$\tan^{-1}x = x - \frac{x^3}{3} + \frac{x^5}{5} - \ldots, \qquad \cdot \quad \cdot \quad (6)$$

or, from the original equation,

$$\theta = \tan \theta - \tfrac{1}{3}\tan^3\theta + \tfrac{1}{5}\tan^5\theta - \ldots, \qquad \cdot \quad \cdot \quad (7)$$

which is known as **Gregory's series.** This series is known to be converging when θ lies between $-\tfrac{1}{4}\pi$ and $\tfrac{1}{4}\pi$; and it has been employed for calculating the numerical value of π. Let $\theta = 45° = \tfrac{1}{4}\pi$, $\therefore x = 1$. Substitute in (6),

$$\frac{\pi}{4} = 1 - \frac{1}{3} + \frac{1}{5} - \frac{1}{7} + \frac{1}{9} - \frac{1}{11} + \frac{1}{13} - \ldots$$

The so-called **Leibnitz series.** We can obtain the **inverse sine series**

$$\sin^{-1}x = x + \frac{1}{2}\frac{x^3}{3} + \frac{3}{8}\frac{x^5}{5} + \frac{5}{16}\frac{x^7}{7} + \ldots, \qquad \cdot \quad (8)$$

in a similar manner. Now write $x = \tfrac{1}{2}$, $\sin^{-1}x = \tfrac{1}{6}\pi$. Substitute these values in (8). The resulting series was used by Newton for the computation of π.

IV. *The Numerical value of* π.

This is a convenient opportunity to emphasize the remarks on the unpracticable nature of a slowly converging series. It would be an extremely laborious operation to calculate π accurately by means of this series. A little artifice will simplify the method, thus,

$$\frac{\pi}{4} = \left(1 - \frac{1}{3}\right) + \left(\frac{1}{5} - \frac{1}{7}\right) + \left(\frac{1}{9} - \frac{1}{11}\right) + \ldots; \frac{\pi}{4} = \frac{2}{1.3} + \frac{2}{5.7} + \frac{2}{9.11} + \ldots$$

$$\therefore \frac{\pi}{8} = \frac{1}{1.3} + \frac{1}{5.7} + \frac{1}{9.11} + \ldots,$$

which does not involve quite so much labour. It will be observed that the angle x is not to be referred to the degree-minute-second system of units, but to the unit of the circular system (page 606), namely, the radian. Suppose $x = \sqrt{\tfrac{1}{3}}$, then $\tan^{-1}x = 30° = \tfrac{1}{6}\pi$. Substitute this value of x in (6), collect the positive and negative terms in separate brackets, thus

$$\frac{\pi}{6} = \left(\frac{1}{\sqrt{3}} + \frac{1}{5\sqrt{3^3}} + \ldots\right) - \left(\frac{1}{3\sqrt{3^3}} + \frac{1}{7\sqrt{3^5}} + \ldots\right).$$

To further illustrate, we shall compute the numerical value of π to five correct decimal places. At the outset, it will be obvious that (1) we must include two or three more decimals in each term than is required in the final result, and (2) we must evaluate term after term until the subsequent terms can no longer influence the numerical value of the desired result.   Hence :

Terms enclosed in the first brackets.	Terms enclosed in the second brackets.
0·57735 03	0·06415 01
0·01283 00	0·00305 48
0·00079 20	0·00021 60
0·00006 09	0·00001 76
0·00000 52	0·00000 15
0·00000 05	0·00000 02
0·59103 89	0·06744 02

$$\therefore \pi = 6(0\cdot59103\ 89 - 0\cdot06744\ 02) = 3\cdot14159\ 22.$$

The number of unreliable figures at the end obviously depends on the rapidity of the convergence of the series.   Here the last two figures are untrustworthy.   But notice how the positive errors are, in part, balanced by the negative errors.   The correct value of π to seven decimal places is $3\cdot1415926$.   There are several shorter ways of evaluating π.   See *Encyc. Brit.*, Art. " Squaring the Circle ".

V. Exponential Series.

Show that

$$e^x = 1 + \frac{x}{1} + \frac{x^2}{2!} + \frac{x^3}{3!} + \ldots, \quad e = 1 + 1 + \frac{1}{2!} + \frac{1}{3!} + \ldots \quad (9)$$

by Maclaurin's series.   An **exponential series** expresses the development of e^x, a^x, or some other exponential function in a series of ascending powers of x and coefficients independent of x.

EXAMPLES.—(1) Show that if $k = \log a$,

$$a^x = 1 + kx + \frac{k^2 x^2}{2!} + \frac{k^3 x^3}{3!} + \ldots \quad \quad \quad (10)$$

(2) Represent Dalton's and Gay Lussac's laws, from the footnote, page 91, in symbols. Show by mathematical reasoning that if second and higher powers of $a\theta$ are outside the range of measurement, as they are supposed to be in ordinary gas calculations, Dalton's law, $v = v_0 e^{a\theta}$, is equivalent to Gay Lussac's, $v = v_0(1 + a\theta)$.

(3) Show $e^{-x} = 1 - \frac{x}{1} + \frac{x^2}{2!} - \frac{x^3}{3!} + \frac{x^4}{4!} - \ldots$.   .   .   (11)

VI. Euler's Sine and Cosine Series.

If we substitute $\sqrt{-1}\,.\,x$, or, what is the same thing, ιx in place of x, we obtain,

$$e^{\iota x} = 1 + \frac{\iota x}{1} - \frac{x^2}{2!} - \frac{\iota x^3}{3!} + \frac{x^4}{4!} + \frac{\iota x^5}{5!} - \dots;$$

$$\therefore e^{\iota x} = \left(1 - \frac{x^2}{2!} + \frac{x^4}{4!} - \dots\right) + \iota\left(\frac{x}{1} - \frac{x^3}{3!} + \frac{x^5}{5!} - \dots\right). \quad (12)$$

By reference to page 283, we shall find that the first expression in brackets, is the cosine series, the second the sine series. Hence,

$$e^{\iota x} = \cos x + \iota \sin x. \quad \cdot \quad \cdot \quad \cdot \quad (13)$$

In the same way, it can be shown that

$$e^{-\iota x} = 1 - \frac{\iota x}{1} - \frac{x^2}{2!} + \frac{\iota x^3}{3!} + \frac{x^4}{4!} - \frac{\iota x^5}{5!} - \dots;$$

$$\therefore e^{-\iota x} = \left(1 - \frac{x^2}{2!} + \frac{x^4}{4!} - \dots\right) - \iota\left(\frac{x}{1} - \frac{x^3}{3!} + \frac{x^5}{5!} - \dots\right). \quad (14)$$

Or,

$$e^{-\iota x} = \cos x - \iota \sin x. \quad \cdot \quad \cdot \quad \cdot \quad (15)$$

Combining equations (13) and (15), we get

$$\tfrac{1}{2}(e^{\iota x} - e^{-\iota x}) = \iota \sin x; \ \tfrac{1}{2}(e^{\iota x} + e^{-\iota x}) = \cos x. \ . \quad (16)$$

The development by Maclaurin's series cannot be used if the function or any of its derivatives becomes infinite or discontinuous when x is equated to zero. For example, the first differential coefficient of $f(x) = \sqrt{x}$, is $\tfrac{1}{2}x^{-\frac{1}{2}}$, which is infinite for $x = 0$, in other words, the series is no longer convergent. The same thing will be found with the functions $\log x$, $\cot x$, $1/x$, $a^{1/x}$ and $\sec^{-1}x$. Some of these functions may, however, be developed as a fractional or some other simple function of x, or we may use Taylor's theorem.

§ 98. Taylor's Theorem.

Taylor's theorem determines the law for the expansion of a function of the sum, or difference of TWO *variables into a series of ascending powers of one of the variables.* Now let

$$u_1 = f(x + y).$$

Assume that

$$u_1 = f(x + y) = A + By + Cy^2 + Dy^3 + \dots, \quad \cdot \quad (1)$$

where $A, B, C, D, \dots$ are constants, independent of y, but dependent upon x and also upon the constants entering into the original equation. It is required to find values for $A, B, C, \dots$ which will make the series true. Since the proposed development is true for all values of x and y, it will also be true for any given value of x, say a. Now let $A', B', C', \dots$ be the respective values of A, B, C, ... in (1) when $x = a$. Hence, we start with the assumption that

$$u' = f(a + y) = A' + B'y + C'y^2 + D'y^3 + \ldots \quad . \quad (2)$$

Put $z = a + y$, hence, $y = z - a$, and Maclaurin's theorem gives us

$$u' = f(z) = A' + B'(z - a) + C'(z - a)^2 + D'(z - a)^3 + \ldots$$

Now write down the successive derivatives with respect to z.

$$\frac{du'}{dz} = f'(z) = B' + 2C'(z - a) + 3D'(z - a)^2 + \ldots$$

$$\frac{d^2u'}{dz^2} = f''(z) = 2C' + 2.3D'(z - a) + 3.4E(z - a)^2 + \ldots$$

$$\frac{d^3u'}{dz^3} = f'''(z) = 2.3D' + 2.3.4E'(z - a) + \ldots$$

While Maclaurin's theorem evaluates the series upon the assumption that the variable becomes zero, Taylor's theorem deduces a value for the series when $x = a$. Let $z = a$, then $y = 0$, and we get

$$f(a) = A' ; \ f'(a) = B' ; \ f''(a) = 2C' ; \ \therefore \ C' = \tfrac{1}{2}f''(a) ; \ f'''(a) = 2.3D' ;$$
$$\therefore D' = \tfrac{1}{2}f'''(a).$$

Substitute these values of A', B', C', ... in equation (2), and we get

$$u' = f(a + y) = f(a) + f'(a)\frac{y}{1} + f''(a)\frac{y^2}{2!} + f'''(a)\frac{y^3}{3!} + \ldots \quad (3)$$

for the proposed development when x assumes a given particular value. But a is any value of x; hence, if

$$u = f(x). \quad . \quad . \quad . \quad (4)$$

Substitute these values of A, B, C, D in the original equation and we obtain

$$u_1 = f(x + y) = u + \frac{du}{dx}\frac{y}{1} + \frac{d^2u}{dx^2}\frac{y^2}{1.2} + \frac{d^3u}{dx^3}\frac{y^3}{1.2.3} + \ldots \quad (5)$$

The series on the right-hand side is known as **Taylor's series.** The first term is what the given function becomes when $y = 0$; the second term is the product of the first derivative of the function when $y = 0$, into y; the third term is the product of the second derivative of the function when $y = 0$, into y^2 divided by factorial 2 ... In (5), $u = f(x)$ is obtained by putting $y = 0$. Thus, in the development of $(x + y)^5$ by Taylor's theorem,

$$u = f(x) = x^5 ; \ du/dx = f'(x) = 5x^4 ; \ d^2u/dx^2 = f''(x) = 4.5x^3 ; \ \ldots$$
$$\therefore (x + y)^5 = x^5 + 5x^4y + 10x^3y^2 + 10x^2y^3 + 5xy^4 + y^5.$$

Instead of (5), we may write Taylor's series in the form,-

$$u_1 = f(x + y) = f(x) + f'(x)\frac{y}{1} + f''(x)\frac{y^2}{1 \cdot 2} + f'''(x)\frac{y^3}{1 \cdot 2 \cdot 3} + \cdots \quad (6)$$

Or, interchanging the variables,

$$u_1 = f(x + y) = f(y) + f'(y)\frac{x}{1} + f''(y)\frac{x^2}{1 \cdot 2} + f'''(y)\frac{x^3}{1 \cdot 2 \cdot 3} + \cdots \quad (7)$$

I leave the reader to prove that

$$f(x - y) = f(x) - f'(x)\frac{y}{1} + f''(x)\frac{y^2}{2!} - f'''(x)\frac{y^3}{3!} + \cdots \quad (8)$$

Maclaurin's and Taylor's series are slightly different expressions for the same thing. The one form can be converted into the other by substituting $f(x + y)$ for $f(x)$ in Maclaurin's theorem, or by putting $y = 0$ in Taylor's.

EXAMPLES.—(1) Expand $u_1 = (x + y)^n$ by Taylor's theorem. Put $y = 0$ and $u = x^n$, as indicated above,

$$\therefore \frac{du}{dx} = nx^{n-1}; \quad \frac{d^2u}{dx^2} = n(n-1)x^{n-2}, \text{ etc.}$$

Substitute the values of these derivatives in (7).

$$\therefore u_1 = (x + y)^n = x^n + nx^{n-1}y + \tfrac{1}{2}n(n-1)x^{n-2}y^2 + \cdots$$

(2) If $k = \log a$; $u_1 = a^{x+y} = a^x(1 + ky + \tfrac{1}{2}k^2y^2 + \tfrac{1}{6}k^3y^3 + \cdots)$.

(3) Show $(x + y + a)^{\frac{1}{2}} = (x + a)^{\frac{1}{2}} + \tfrac{1}{2}y(x + a)^{-\frac{1}{2}} - \cdots$ If $x = -a$, the development fails.

(4) Show $\sin(x + y) = \sin x\left(1 - \dfrac{y^2}{2!} + \dfrac{y^4}{4!} - \cdots\right) + \cos x\left(y - \dfrac{y^3}{3!} + \cdots\right)$.

(5) The numerical tables of the trigonometrical functions are calculated by means of Taylor's or by Maclaurin's theorems. For example, by Maclaurin's theorem,

$$\sin x = x - \frac{x^3}{3!} + \frac{x^5}{5!} - \cdots; \quad \cos x = 1 - \frac{x^2}{2!} + \frac{x^4}{4!} - \cdots$$

But $35° = {\cdot}610865$ radians, and $\therefore \sin 35° = \sin {\cdot}610865$. Consequently,

$$\sin 35° = {\cdot}610865 - \tfrac{1}{6}({\cdot}610865)^3 + \tfrac{1}{120}({\cdot}610865)^5 - \cdots = {\cdot}57357\ldots$$

In the same way, show that $\cos 35° = {\cdot}81915\ldots$ Again by Taylor's theorem, $\sin 36° = \sin(35° + 1°)$:

$$\therefore \sin 36° = \sin 35° + \frac{\cos 35°}{1!}({\cdot}017453) - \frac{\sin 35°}{2!}({\cdot}017453)^2 - \cdots = {\cdot}58778\ldots$$

(6) Taylor's theorem is used in tabulating the values of a function for different values of the variable. Suppose we want the value of $y = x(24 - x^2)$ for values of x ranging from 2·7 to 3·3. First draw up a set of values of the successive differential coefficients of y.

$$f(x) = f(3) = x(24 - x^2) = 45 ; \quad f'(x) = f'(3) = 24 - 3x^2 = -3 ;$$
$$f''(x) = f''(3) = -6x = -18 ; \quad f'''(x) = f'''(3) = -6.$$

By Taylor's theorem,

$$f(3 \pm h) = f(3) \pm f'(3)h + \tfrac{1}{2}f''(3)h^2 \pm \tfrac{1}{6}f'''(3)h^3 = 45 \mp 3h - 9h^2 \mp h^3.$$

But $2\cdot7 = 3 - 0\cdot3$; $2\cdot8 = 3 - 0\cdot2$;..., $3\cdot3 = 3 + 0\cdot3$. Hence,

$$f(2\cdot7) = 45 + 0\cdot9 - 0\cdot81 + 0\cdot027 = 45\cdot117.$$
$$f(2\cdot8) = 45 + 0\cdot6 - 0\cdot36 + 0\cdot008 = 45\cdot148.$$
$$f(2\cdot9) = 45 + 0\cdot3 - 0\cdot09 + 0\cdot001 = 45\cdot211.$$
$$f(3\cdot0) = 45 \qquad\qquad\qquad\quad = 45\cdot000.$$
$$f(3\cdot1) = 45 - 0\cdot3 - 0\cdot09 - 0\cdot001 = 44\cdot609.$$
$$f(3\cdot2) = 45 - 0\cdot6 - 0\cdot36 - 0\cdot008 = 44\cdot032.$$
$$f(3\cdot3) = 45 - 0\cdot9 - 0\cdot81 - 0\cdot027 = 43\cdot263.$$

(7) Show $\log (x + y) = \log x + \dfrac{y}{x} - \dfrac{y^2}{2x^2} + \dfrac{y^3}{3x^3} - \cdots$

(8) Expand $\log (n + h)$ and also $\log (n + 1)$. Observe that we can neglect terms containing second powers of h, if h is less than unity, and n is large. Thus, if $h < 1$, and n is 10,000, $h/n < 0\cdot0001$; the second term of the expansion is less than $0\cdot000000,005$; and the next term still less again. By division of the two expansions, we get the important result,

$$\frac{\log (n + h) - \log n}{\log (n + 1) - \log n} = \frac{h}{1}. \qquad \cdot \qquad \cdot \qquad \cdot \qquad (9)$$

or,

Incr. when $\log n$ becomes $\log(n + h)$: Incr. when $\log n$ becomes $\log(n + 1) = h : 1$, provided the differences between two numbers n and h are such that n is of the order of 10,000 when x is less than unity. This formula, known as the **rule of proportional parts**, is used for finding the exact logarithm of a number containing more digits than the table of logarithms allows for, or for finding the number corresponding to a logarithm not exactly coinciding with those in the tables. The following examples wil make this clear :—

(9) Find the logarithm of $46502\cdot32$, having given
$\log 46501 = 4\cdot6674623$; $\log 46502 = 4\cdot6674716$; difference $= 0\cdot0000093$. Let h denote the quantity to be added to the smaller of the given logs. The problem may be stated thus,

$$\log n \qquad = \log 46501 \qquad\quad = 4\cdot6674623;$$
$$\log (n + 1) = \log (46501 + 1) \quad = 4\cdot6674623 + 0\cdot0000093;$$
$$\log (n + h) = \log (46501 + 0\cdot32) = 4\cdot6674623 + x.$$

By (9), that is, by simple rule of three : if a difference of 1 unit in a number corresponds with a difference of $0\cdot0000093$ in the logarithm, what difference in the logarithm will arise when the number is augmented by $0\cdot32$?

$$\therefore 1 : 0\cdot32 = 0\cdot0000093 : x, \therefore x = 0\cdot00000298 \ldots$$

The required logarithm is, therefore, $4\cdot6674653$.

Again, find the number whose logarithm is $4\cdot6816223$, having given

$$\log 48042 = 4\cdot6816211; \quad \log 48043 = 4\cdot6816301.$$

Since a difference of unity in the number causes a difference of $0\cdot0000090$ in the logarithm, what will be the difference in the number when the logarithms differ by $0\cdot0000012$?

$$\therefore 1 : h = 0\cdot0000090 : 0\cdot0000012; \therefore h = 0\cdot13. \quad \text{The number is } 48042\cdot13.$$

(10) Show $\log (1 + y) = y - \tfrac{1}{2}y^2 + \tfrac{1}{3}y^3 - \tfrac{1}{4}y^4 + \cdots$

T

This series may be employed for evaluating log 2, but as the series happens to be divergent for numbers greater than 2, and very slowly convergent for numbers less than 2, it is not suited for general computations.

(11) Show $\log (1 - y) = - (y + \frac{1}{2}y^2 + \frac{1}{3}y^3 + \frac{1}{4}y^4 + \ldots)$.

If $y = 4$, the development gives a divergent series and the theorem is then said to fail. The last four examples are **logarithmic series**.

A series suitable for finding the numerical values of logarithms may here be indicated as a subject of general interest, but of no particular utility since we can purchase "ready-made tables from a penny upwards". But the principle involved has useful applications.

Subtract the series in Ex. (11) from that in Ex. (10) and we get

$$\log \frac{1 + y}{1 - y} = 2\left(y + \frac{y^3}{3} + \frac{y^5}{5} + \frac{y^7}{7} + \ldots\right),$$

a series slowly convergent when y is less than unity. Let n have a value greater than unity. Put

$$\frac{n + 1}{n} = \frac{1 + y}{1 - y}, \text{ so that } y = \frac{1}{2n + 1}.$$

Hence, when n is greater than unity, y is less than unity. By substitution, therefore,

$$\log (n + 1) = \log n + 2\left(\frac{1}{2n + 1} + \frac{1}{3(2n + 1)^3} + \ldots\right).$$

This series is rapidly convergent. It enables us to compute the numerical value of $\log (n + 1)$ when the value of $\log n$ is known. Thus starting with $n = 1$, $\log n = 0$, the series then gives the value of log 2, hence, we get the value of log 3, then of log 4, etc.

(12) Put $y = - x$ in Taylor's expansion, and show that

$$f(x) = f(0) + f'(x) . x - \frac{1}{2}f''(x) . x^2 + \ldots,$$

known as **Bernoulli's series** (of historical interest, published 1694).

Mathematical text-books, at this stage, proceed to discuss the conditions under which the sum of the individual terms of Taylor's series is really equal to $f(x+y)$. When the given function $f(x+y)$ is finite, the sum of the corresponding series must also be finite, in other words, the series must either be finite or convergent. The development is said to fail when the series is divergent.

It is not here intended to show how mathematicians have succeeded in placing Taylor's series on a satisfactory basis. That subject belongs to the realms of pure mathematics.[1] The reader may exercise "belief based on suitable evidence outside personal experience," otherwise known as faith. This will require no great mental effort on the part of the student of the physical sciences. He has to apply the very highest orders of faith to the fundamental

---

[1] If the student is at all curious, Todhunter, or Williamson on "Lagrange's Theorem on the Limits of Taylor's Series," is always available.

principles—the inscrutables—of these sciences, namely, to the theory of atoms, stereochemistry, affinity, the existence and properties of interstellar ether, the origin of energy, etc., etc. What is more, "reliance on the *dicta* and *data* of investigators whose very names may be unknown, lies at the very foundation of physical science, and without this faith in authority the structure would fall to the ground ; not the blind faith in authority of the unreasoning kind that prevailed in the Middle Ages, but a rational belief in the concurrent testimony of individuals who have recorded the results of their experiments and observations, and whose statements can be verified...".[1]

The rest of this chapter will be mainly concerned with direct or indirect applications of infinite converging series.

§ 99. The Contact of Curves.

The following is a geometrical illustration of one meaning of the different terms in Taylor's development. If four curves Pa, Pb, Pc, Pd, ... (Fig. 123) have a common point P, any curve, say Pc, which passes between two others, Pb, Pd, is said to have a closer contact with Pb than Pd. Now let two curves P_0P and P_0P_1 (Fig. 124) referred to the same rectangular axes, have equations,

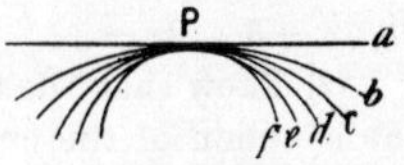

FIG. 123.—Contact of Curves.

$$y = f(x) ; \text{ and, } y_1 = f_1(x_1). \qquad . \qquad . \qquad (1)$$

Let the abscissa of each curve at any given point, be increased by a small amount h, then, by Taylor's theorem,

$$f(x + h) = y + \frac{dy}{dx}h + \frac{d^2y}{dx^2}\frac{h^2}{2!} + \cdots$$

$$f_1(x_1 + h) = y_1 + \frac{dy_1}{dx_1}h + \frac{d^2y_1}{dx_1^2}\frac{h^2}{2!} + \cdots \qquad . \qquad (2)$$

If the curves have a common point P_0, $x = x_1$, and $y = y_1$ at the point of contact. Since the first differential coefficient represents the angle made by a tangent with the x-axis, if, at the point P_0,

$$x = x_1 ; \ y = y_1, \text{ and } \frac{dy}{dx} = \frac{dy_1}{dx_1},$$

---

[1] Excerpt from the Presidential Address of Dr. Carrington Bolton to the Washington Chemical Society, *English Mechanic*, 5th April, 1901.

the curves will have a common tangent at P_0. This is called a **contact of the first order.** If, however,

$$x = x_1,\ y = y_1;\ \frac{dy}{dx} = \frac{dy_1}{dx^1};\ \text{and}\ \frac{d^2y}{dx^2} = \frac{d^2y_1}{dx_1{}^2},$$

the curves are said to have a **contact of the second order,** and so on for the higher orders of contact.

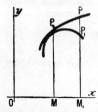

If all the terms in the two equations are equal the two curves will be identical; the greater the number of equal terms in the two series, the closer will be the order of contact of the two curves. If the order of contact is even, the curves will intersect at their common point; if the order of contact is odd, the curves will not cross each other at the point of contact.

FIG. 124.—Contact of Curves.

EXAMPLES.—(1) Show that the curves $y = -x^2$, and $y = 3x - x^2$ intersect at the point $x = 0$, $y = 0$. Hint. The first differential coefficients are not equal to one another when we put $x = 1$. Thus, in the first case, $dy/dx = -2x = -2 = 0$; and in the second, $dy/dx = 3 - 2x = 1$.

(2) Show that the tangent crosses a curve at a point of inflexion. Let the equation of the curve be $y = f(x)$; of the tangent, $Ax + By + C = 0$. The necessary condition for a point of inflexion in the curve $y = f(x)$ is that $d^2y/dx^2 = 0$. But for the equation of the tangent, d^2y/dx^2 is also zero. Hence, there is a contact of the second order at the point of inflexion, and the tangent crosses the curve.

§ 100. Extension of Taylor's Theorem.

Taylor's theorem may be extended so as to include the expansion of functions of two or more independent variables. Let

$$u = f(x, y),\ \ .\ \ \ \ .\ \ \ \ .\ \ \ \ .\ \ \ \ (1)$$

where x and y are independent of each other. Suppose each variable changes independently so that x becomes $x + h$, and y becomes $y + k$. First, let $f(x, y)$ change to $f(x + h, y)$. By Taylor's theorem

$$f(x + h, y) = u + \frac{\partial u}{\partial x}h + \frac{\partial^2 u}{\partial x^2}\frac{h^2}{2!} + \cdots\ \ \ .\ \ \ \ (2)$$

If y now becomes $y + k$, each term of equation (2) will change so that

$$u \text{ becomes } u + \frac{\partial u}{\partial y}k + \frac{\partial^2 u}{\partial y^2}\frac{k^2}{2!} + \cdots;$$

$$\frac{\partial u}{\partial x} \text{ becomes } \frac{\partial u}{\partial x} + \frac{\partial^2 u}{\partial x \partial y}k + \ldots; \quad \frac{\partial^2 u}{\partial x^2} \text{ becomes } \frac{\partial^2 u}{\partial x^2} + \frac{\partial^3 u}{\partial x^2 \partial y}k + \ldots,$$

by Taylor's theorem. Now substitute these values in (2) and we obtain, if u' denotes the value of u when x becomes $x + h$, and y becomes $y + k$,

$$u' = f(x + h,\ y + k);$$

$$u' = u + \frac{\partial u}{\partial y}k + \frac{\partial^2 u}{\partial y^2}\frac{k}{2!} + \ldots + \frac{\partial^2 u}{\partial x \partial y}hk + \ldots + \frac{\partial u}{\partial x}h + \frac{\partial^2 u}{\partial x^2}\frac{h}{2!} + \ldots$$

$$\delta u = u' - u = f(x + h,\ y + k) - f(x,\ y);$$

$$\delta u = \frac{\partial u}{\partial x}h + \frac{\partial u}{\partial y}k + \frac{1}{2}\left(\frac{\partial^2 u}{\partial x^2}h^2 + 2\frac{\partial^2 u}{\partial x \partial y}hk + \frac{\partial^2 u}{\partial y^2}k^2\right) + \ldots \qquad (3)$$

The final result is exactly the same whether we expand first with respect to y or in the reverse order.

By equating the coefficients of hk in the identical results obtained by first expanding with regard to h, (2) above, and by first expanding with regard to k, we get

$$\frac{\partial^2 u}{\partial x \partial y} = \frac{\partial^2 u}{\partial y \partial x},$$

which was obtained another way in page 77. The investigation may be extended to functions of any number of variables.

§ 101. The Determination of Maximum and Minimum Values of a Function by means of Taylor's Series.

I. *Functions of one variable.*

Taylor's theorem is sometimes useful in seeking the maximum and the minimum values of a function, say,

$$u = f(x).$$

It is required to find particular values of x in order that y may be a maximum or a minimum. If x changes by a small amount h, Taylor's theorem tells us that

$$f(x \pm h) - f(x) = \pm \frac{du}{dx}h + \frac{1}{2}\frac{d^2u}{dx^2}h^2 \pm \frac{1}{6}\frac{d^3u}{dx^3}h^3 + \ldots, \qquad (1)$$

according as h is added to or subtracted from x.

First, it must be proved that h can be made so small that the term $\frac{du}{dx}h$ will be greater than the sum of all succeeding terms of either series. Assume that Taylor's series may be written,

$$f(x + h) = u + Ah + Bh^2 + Ch^3 + \ldots,$$

where A, B, C, ... are coefficients independent of h but dependent upon x, then, if $Rh = Bh + Ch^2 + \ldots = (B + Ch + \ldots)h$, and

$$f(x + h) = u + h(A + Rh). \qquad . \qquad . \qquad (2)$$

Consequently, for sufficiently small values of h, it will be obvious that Rh must be less than A.

Let us put

$$\delta u = f(x \pm h) - f(x).$$

If u is really a maximum, ever so small a change—increase or decrease—in the value of x will diminish the value of u; and $f(x)$ must be greater than $f(x \pm h)$. Hence, for a maximum,

$$\delta u = f(x \pm h) - f(x) \text{ must be negative.}$$

Again, if u is really a minimum, then u will be augmented when x is increased or diminished by h. In other words, if u is a minimum,

$$\delta u = f(x \pm h) - f(x) \text{ must be positive.}$$

ILLUSTRATION.—The function $u = 4x^3 - 3x^2 - 18x$ will be a maximum when $x = -1$. In that case, $f(x) = 11$; if we put some small quantity, say $\frac{1}{2}$, in place of h, then $f(x + h) = + \frac{5}{4}$, and $f(x - h) = + \frac{2\frac{3}{4}}{}$. Hence, $f(x \pm h) - f(x)$ will be either $- \frac{13}{4}$, or $- \frac{1}{4}$. You can also show in the same manner that u will be a minimum when $x = \frac{3}{2}$.

Now if h is made small enough, we have just proved that the higher derivatives in equations (1) will become vanishingly small; and so long as the first derivative, du/dx, remains finite, the algebraic sign of δu will be the same as

$$\delta u = \frac{du}{dx} h.$$

At a turning point—maximum or minimum—we must have, as explained in an earlier chapter,

$$\frac{du}{dx} = 0.$$

Substituting this in the above series,

$$\delta u = \frac{1}{2} \cdot \frac{d^2 u}{dx^2} h^2 \pm \frac{1}{6} \cdot \frac{d^3 u}{dx^3} h^3 + \ldots$$

remains. Now h may be taken so small that the derivatives higher than the second become vanishingly small, and so long as $d^2 u/dx^2$ remains finite, the sign δu will be the same as that of

$$\delta u = \frac{d^2 u}{dx^2} \cdot \frac{h^2}{2}.$$

But h^2, being the square of a number, must be positive. The sign of the second differential coefficient will, in consequence, be the same as that of δu. But $u = f(x)$ is a maximum or a minimum according as δu is negative or positive. This means that y will be a maximum when $dy/dx = 0$ and d^2y/dx^2 is negative, and a minimum, if d^2y/dx^2 is positive.

If, however, the second differential coefficient vanishes, the reasoning used in connection with the first differential must be applied to the third differential coefficient. If the third derivative vanishes, a similar relation holds between the second and fourth differential coefficients. See Table I., page 168. Hence the rules:—

1. *y is either a maximum or a minimum for a given value of x only when the first non-vanishing derivative, for this value of x, is even.*

2. *y is a maximum or a minimum according as the sign of the non-vanishing derivative of an even order, is negative or positive.*

In practice, if the first derivative vanishes, it is often convenient to test by substitution whether y changes from a positive to a negative value. If there is no change of sign, there is neither a maximum nor a minimum. For example, in

$$y = x^3 - 3x^2 + 3x + 7 \; ; \; \therefore \; \frac{dy}{dx} = 3x^2 - 6x + 3.$$

For a maximum or a minimum, we must have

$$x^2 - 2x + 1 = 0 \; ; \; \therefore x = 1.$$

If $x = 0$, $y = 7$; if $x = 1$, $y = 8$; if $x = 2$, $y = 9$. There is no change of sign and $x = 1$ will not make the function a maximum or a minimum.

EXAMPLES.—(1) Test $y = x^3 - 12x^2 - 60x$ for maximum or minimum values. $dy/dx = 3x^2 - 24x - 60$; $\therefore$ $x^2 - 8x - 20 = 0$, or $x = -2$, or $+10$. $d^2y/dx^2 = 6x - 24$; or, $x = +4$. Since d^2y/dx^2 is positive when $x = 10$ is substituted, $x = 10$ will make y a minimum. When -2 is substituted, d^2y/dx^2 becomes negative, hence $x = -2$ will make y a maximum. This can easily be verified by plotting (Fig. 125), for, if

FIG. 125.

$x = -3, \quad -2, \qquad -1, \quad \dots +9, \quad +10, \qquad +11, \dots$
$y = +45, \quad +64\text{ (max.)}, \quad +48, \quad \dots -783, \quad -800\text{ (min.)}, \quad -781, \dots$

(2) What value of x will make y a maximum or a minimum in the expression, $y = x^3 - 6x^2 + 11x + 6$? $dy/dx = 3x^2 - 12x + 11 = 0$; $\therefore$ $x = 2 \pm \sqrt{\frac{1}{3}}$; $d^2y/dx^2 = 6x - 12$. If $x = 2 + \sqrt{\frac{1}{3}}$, $d^2y/dx^2 = 6\sqrt{\frac{1}{3}} = +2\sqrt{3}$; and if $x = 2 - \sqrt{\frac{1}{3}}$, $d^2y/dx^2 = -2\sqrt{3}$. Hence $2 + \sqrt{\frac{1}{3}}$ makes y a minimum, and $2 - \sqrt{\frac{1}{3}}$ makes y a maximum (see Fig. 126).

(3) Show that $x^3 - 9x^2 + 15x - 3$ is a

FIG. 126.

FIG. 127.

maximum when $x = 1$, and a minimum when $x = 5$. The graph is shown in Fig. 127.

II. *Functions of two variables.*

To find particular values of x and y which will make the function,

$$u = f(x, y),$$

a maximum or a minimum. As before, when x changes by a small amount h, and y by a small amount k, if $f(x, y)$ is greater than $f(x \pm h, y \pm k)$, for all values of h or k, then $f(x, y)$ is a maximum. Hence, if

$$\delta u = f(x \pm h, y \pm k) - f(x, y) \text{ is negative,}$$

u will be a maximum; whereas when $f(x, y)$ is less than $f(x \pm h, y \pm k)$,

$$\delta u = f(x \pm h, y \pm k) - f(x, y) \text{ is positive,}$$

and u will be a minimum.

ILLUSTRATION.—The function $u = x^2y + xy^2 - 3xy$ will be a minimum when $x = 1$ and $y = 1$. In that case $f(x, y) = -1$; and if we put $h = \frac{1}{2}$, and $k = \frac{1}{2}$—any other small quantity will do just as well—then $f(x+h, y+k) = 0$; and $f(x - h, y - k) = -\frac{1}{2}$. Hence, $f(x \pm h, y \pm k) - f(x, y) = +1$, or $+\frac{1}{2}$.

Also, let

$$\delta u = f(x + h, y + k) - f(x, y).$$

Let us now expand this function as indicated in the preceding section, and we get

$$\delta u = \frac{\partial u}{\partial x}h + \frac{\partial u}{\partial y}k + \frac{1}{2}\left(\frac{\partial^2 u}{\partial x^2}h^2 + 2\frac{\partial^2 u}{\partial x \partial y}hk + \frac{\partial^2 u}{\partial y^2}k^2\right) + \ldots \quad (3)$$

By making the values of h and k small enough, the higher orders of differentials become vanishingly small. But as long as $\partial u/\partial x$ and $\partial u/\partial y$ remain finite, the algebraic sign of δu will be that of

$$\left(\frac{\partial u}{\partial x}\right)_y h + \left(\frac{\partial u}{\partial y}\right)_x k.$$

At a turning point—maximum or a minimum—we must have

$$\frac{\partial u}{\partial x}h + \frac{\partial u}{\partial y}k = 0, \quad . \quad . \quad . \quad . \quad (4)$$

and, since h and k are independent of each other, and the sign of δu, in (4), depends on the signs of h and k, u can have a maximum or a minimum value only when

$$\left(\frac{\partial u}{\partial x}\right)_y = 0; \text{ and } \left(\frac{\partial u}{\partial y}\right)_x = 0. \quad . \quad . \quad . \quad (5)$$

We can perhaps get a clearer mental picture of what we are talking about if we imagine an undulating surface lying above the xy-plane. At the top of an *isolated* hill, P (Fig. 128), u will be a maximum; at the bottom of a valley or lake, Q, u will be a minimum. The surface can only be horizontal at the point where $\partial u/\partial x$ and $\partial u/\partial y$ are both zero. At this point, u will be either a maximum or a minimum. It is easy to see that if $APBC$ is a surface represented by $u = f(x, y)$, $\partial u/\partial x$ is the slope of the surface along AP, and $\partial u/\partial y$, the slope along BP.

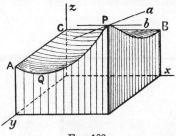

FIG. 128.

The line Pb represents the slope $\partial u/\partial x$ at P, and Pa the slope $\partial u/\partial y$ at P.

If u is really a maximum, it follows from our previous work, page 159, that $\partial^2 u/\partial x^2$ and $\partial^2 u/\partial y^2$ must be negative, just as surely as if P is really the top of a hill, movement in the directions Pb, or Pa must be down hill. And similarly, if we are really at the bottom of a valley, $\partial^2 u/\partial x^2$ and $\partial^2 u/\partial y^2$ must be both positive.

Let us now examine the sign of δu in (3) when $\partial u/\partial x$ and $\partial u/\partial y$ are made zero; h and k can be made so small that

$$\delta u = \frac{1}{2}\left(\frac{\partial^2 u}{\partial x^2}h^2 + 2\frac{\partial^2 u}{\partial x \partial y}hk + \frac{\partial^2 u}{\partial y^2}k^2\right) \quad . \quad . \quad (6)$$

remains. For the sake of brevity, write the homogeneous quadratic (6) in the form

$$ah^2 + 2bhk + ck^2. \quad . \quad . \quad . \quad (7)$$

Add and subtract b^2k^2/a; rearrange terms, and we get the equivalent form

$$\frac{1}{a}\left\{(ah + bk)^2 + (ac - b^2)k^2\right\}, \quad . \quad . \quad (8)$$

which enables us to see at a glance that for small values of h and k the sign of (7), or (6), is independent of h and k only when $ac - b^2$ is positive or zero, for if $ac - b^2$ is negative, the expression will be positive when $k = 0$, and negative when $ah + bk$ is zero. Consequently, in order that we may have a real maximum or minimum, ac must be greater than b^2; or what is the same thing,

$$\frac{\partial^2 u}{\partial x^2} \times \frac{\partial^2 u}{\partial y^2} \text{ must be greater than } \left(\frac{\partial^2 u}{\partial x \partial y}\right)^2. \quad . \quad (9)$$

This is called **Lagrange's criterion for maximum and minimum values of a function of two variables.** When this criterion is satisfied $f(x, y)$ will either be a maximum or a minimum. To summarize, in order that $u = f(x, y)$ may be a maximum or a minimum, we must have

(1) $\dfrac{\partial u}{\partial x} = 0$; $\dfrac{\partial u}{\partial y} = 0$.

(2) $\dfrac{\partial^2 u}{\partial x^2}$ negative, if u is a maximum; positive, if u is a minimum.

(3) $\dfrac{\partial^2 u}{\partial x^2} \times \dfrac{\partial^2 u}{\partial y^2} - \left(\dfrac{\partial^2 u}{\partial x \partial y}\right)^2$ must not be negative.

If $$\dfrac{\partial^2 u}{\partial x^2} \times \dfrac{\partial^2 u}{\partial y^2} \text{ is less than } \left(\dfrac{\partial^2 u}{\partial x \partial y}\right)^2, \qquad . \quad . \quad (10)$$

or $\partial^2 u/\partial x^2$ and $\partial^2 u/\partial y^2$ have different signs, the function is neither a maximum nor a minimum. If a man were travelling across a mountain pass he might reach a maximum height in the direction in which he was travelling, yet if he were to diverge on either side of the path he would ascend to higher ground. This is not therefore a true maximum. A similar thing might be said of a "bar" across a valley for a minimum. If

$$\dfrac{\partial^2 u}{\partial x^2} \times \dfrac{\partial^2 u}{\partial y^2} = \left(\dfrac{\partial^2 u}{\partial x \partial y}\right)^2, \qquad . \quad . \quad . \quad (11)$$

there will probably be neither a maximum nor a minimum, but the higher derivatives must be examined before we can definitely decide this question.

EXAMPLES.—(1) Show that the velocity of a bimolecular chemical reaction $V = k(a - x)(b - x)$ is greatest when $a = b$. Here $\partial V/\partial a = - k(b - x)$; $\partial V/\partial b = - k(a - x)$. Hence if $k(b - x) = 0$; and $k(a - x) = 0$, $a = b$, etc.

(2) Test the function $u = x^3 + y^3 - 3axy$ for maxima or minima. Here $\partial u/\partial x = 3x^2 - 3ay = 0$, $\therefore y = x^2/a$; $\partial u/\partial y = 3y^2 - 3ax = 0$, $\therefore y^2 - ax = x^4/a^2 - ax = 0$; $\therefore x = 0$, $x^3 - a^3 = 0$, or $x = a$. The other roots, being imaginary, are neglected; $\therefore y = x^2/a = a$, or $y = 0$;

$$\therefore \dfrac{\partial^2 u}{\partial x^2} = 6x; \quad \dfrac{\partial^2 u}{\partial x \partial y} = - 3a; \quad \dfrac{\partial^2 u}{\partial y^2} = 6y.$$

Call these derivatives (a), (b), and (c) respectively, then if $x = 0$, $(a) = 0$, $(b) = - 3a$, $(c) = 0$; if $x = a$, $(a) = 6a$, $(b) = - 3a$, $(c) = 6a$;

$$\therefore \dfrac{\partial^2 u}{\partial x^2}; \quad \dfrac{\partial^2 u}{\partial y^2} = 36a^2; \quad \left(\dfrac{\partial^2 u}{\partial x \partial y}\right)^2 = 9a^2.$$

This means that $x = y = a$ will make the function a minimum because $\partial^2 u/\partial x^2$ is positive; $x = 0$ will give neither a maximum nor a minimum.

(3) Find the condition that the rectangular parallelopiped whose edges are x, y, and z shall have a minimum surface u when its volume is v^3. Since

$v^3 = xyz$, $u = xy + yz + zx = xy + v^3/x + v^3/y$. When $\partial u/\partial x = 0$, $x^2 y = v^3$; when $\partial u/\partial y = 0$, $xy^2 = v^3$. The only real roots of these equations are $x = y = v$, therefore $z = v$. The sides of the box are, therefore, equal to each other.

(4) Show that $u = x^3 y^2 (1 - x - y)$ is a maximum when $x = \frac{1}{2}$, $y = \frac{1}{3}$.

(5) Find the maximum value of u in $u = x^3 - 3ax^2 - 4ay^2$. $\partial u/\partial x = 3x(x - 2a)$; $\partial u/\partial y = -8ay$; $\partial^2 u/\partial x^2 = 6(x - a)$; $\partial^2 u/\partial x \partial y = 0$; $\partial^2 u/\partial y^2 = -8a$. Condition (5) is satisfied by $x = 0, y = 0$ and by $x = 2a, y = 0$. The former alone satisfies Lagrange's condition (9), the latter comes under (10).

(6) In Fig. 129, let P_1 be a luminous point; OM_1, OM_2 are mirrors at right angles to each other. The image of P_1 is reflected at N_1 and N_2 in such a way that (i) the angles of incidence and reflection are equal, (ii) the length of the path $P_1 N_1 N_2 P_2$ is the shortest possible. (Fermat's principle: " a ray of light passes from one point to another by the path which makes the time of transit a minimum ".) Let $i_1 = r_1$, $i_2 = r_2$ be the angles of incidence and reflection as shown in the figure. To find the position of N_1 and N_2:

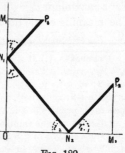

FIG. 129.

Let $ON_2 = x$; $ON_1 = y$; $OM_2 = a_1$; $M_1 P_1 = a_2$; $M_2 P_2 = b_2$; $OM_1 = b_1$. Let
$s = P_1 N_1 + N_1 N_2 + N_2 P_2 = \sqrt{a^2_2 + (b_1 - y)^2} + \sqrt{x^2 + y^2} + \sqrt{(a_1 - x)^2 + b_2^2}$.
Find $\partial s/\partial x$ and $\partial s/\partial y$. Equate to zero, etc. The final result is
$$x = (a_2 b_1 - a_1 b_2)/(b_1 + b_2); \; y = (a_2 b_1 - a_1 b_2)/(a_1 + a_2).$$
Note that $x/y = (a_1 + a_2)/(b_1 + b_2)$. Work out the same problem when the angle $M_2 O M_1 = a$.

(7) Required the volume of the greatest rectangular box that can be sent by " Parcel Post " in accord with the regulation: " length plus girth must not exceed six feet ". Ansr. 1 ft. × 1 ft. × 2 ft. = 2 c.ft. Hint. $V = xyz$ is to be a maximum when $V = x + 2(y + z) = 6$. But obviously $y = z$, ∴ $V = xy^2$ is to be a maximum, etc.

(8) Required the greatest cylindrical case that can be sent under the same regulation. Ansr. Length 2 ft., diameter 4/π ft., capacity 2·55 c.ft. Hint. Volume of cylinder = area of base × height, or, $\frac{1}{4}\pi l D^2$ is to be a maximum when the length + the perimeter of the cylinder = 6, i.e., $l + \pi D = 6$. Obviously l and D denote the respective length and diameter of the cylinder.

(9) Prove that the sum of three positive quantities, x, y, z, whose product is constant, is greatest when those quantities are equal. Hint. Let $xyz = a$; $x + y + z = u$. Hence $u = a/yz + y + z$; ∴ $\partial u/\partial y = -a/y^2 z + 1 = 0$; $\partial u/\partial z = -a/yz^2 + 1 = 0$; ∴ $y = x, u = x$; ∴ $x = y = z = \sqrt[3]{a}$. To show that u is a minimum, note $\partial^2 u/\partial x^2 = +3a/x^4$.

III. Functions of three variables.

Without going into details I shall simply state that if we are dealing with three variables x, y, and z, such that

$$u = f(x, y, z), \qquad . \qquad . \qquad . \qquad (12)$$

there will be a maximum or a minimum if the first partial derivatives are each equal to zero; and Lagrange's criterion, $u_{xx}u_{yy} > (u_{xy})^2$, is satisfied; and if

$$u_{xx}(u_{xx}u_{yy}u_{zz} + 2u_{yz}u_{xz}u_{xy} - u_{xx}u^2_{yz} - u_{yy}u^2_{xz} - u_{zz}u^2_{xy}) > 0. \qquad (13)$$

For a maximum u_{xx} will be negative, and positive for a minimum. The meaning of the notation used will be understood from page 19. $u_{xx} = \partial^2 u/\partial x^2$; $u_{xy} = \partial^2 u/\partial x \partial y$.

EXAMPLES.—(1) If $u = x^2 + y^2 + z^2 + x - 2z - xy$, $u_x = 2x - y + 1 = 0$; $u_y = 2y - x$; $u_z = 2z - 2 = 0$; $\therefore x = -\frac{2}{3}$; $y = -\frac{1}{3}$; $z = 1$; $u = -\frac{4}{3}$. $u_{xx} = 2$; $u_{yy} = 2$; $u_{zz} = 2$; $u_{xy} = -1$; $u_{xz} = 0$; $u_{yz} = 0$. Hence, Lagrange's criterion furnishes $+3$; and criterion (13) furnishes $2(8 + 0 - 0 - 0 - 2) = 12$. Hence, since u_{xx} is positive, $-\frac{4}{3}$ is a minimum value of u.

(2) If we have an implicit function of three variables, and seek the maximum value of say z in $u = 2x^2 + 5y^2 + z^2 - 4xy - 2x - 4y - \frac{1}{2} = 0$, we proceed as follows: $u_x = 4x - 4y - 2 = 0$; $u_y = 10y - 4x - 4 = 0$; $\therefore x = \frac{3}{2}$; $y = 1$; $z = \pm 2$. $u_z = 2z = \pm 4$; $u_{xx} = 4$; $u_{yy} = 10$; $u_{xy} = -4$. Lagrange's criterion furnishes the value $40 - 16 = 24$. z is therefore a maximum when $x = -\frac{3}{2}$ and $y = 1$.

IV. Conditional Maxima and Minima.

If the variables

$$u = f(x, y, z) = 0, \qquad . \qquad . \qquad . \qquad (14)$$

are also connected by the condition

$$v = \phi(x, y, z) = 0, \qquad . \qquad . \qquad . \qquad (15)$$

we must also have, for a maximum or a minimum,

$$\frac{\partial u}{\partial x}dx + \frac{\partial u}{\partial y}dy + \frac{\partial u}{\partial z}dz = 0. \qquad . \qquad . \qquad (16)$$

From (15), we have by partial differentiation

$$\frac{\partial v}{\partial x}dx + \frac{\partial v}{\partial y}dy + \frac{\partial v}{\partial z}dz = 0. \qquad . \qquad . \qquad (17)$$

Multiply (17) by an arbitrary constant λ, called an undetermined multiplier, and add the result to (16).

$$\left(\frac{\partial u}{\partial x} + \lambda\frac{\partial v}{\partial x}\right)dx + \left(\frac{\partial u}{\partial y} + \lambda\frac{\partial v}{\partial y}\right)dy + \left(\frac{\partial u}{\partial z} + \lambda\frac{\partial v}{\partial z}\right)dz = 0. \qquad (18)$$

But λ is arbitrary, and it can be so chosen that

$$\frac{\partial u}{\partial x} + \lambda\frac{\partial v}{\partial x} = 0.$$

Substitute the result in (18), and we obtain

$$\left(\frac{\partial u}{\partial y} + \lambda\frac{\partial v}{\partial y}\right)dy + \left(\frac{\partial u}{\partial z} + \lambda\frac{\partial v}{\partial z}\right)dz = 0.$$

But if y and z are independent, we also have

$$\left(\frac{\partial u}{\partial y} + \lambda \frac{\partial v}{\partial y}\right)dy = 0\,;\ \left(\frac{\partial u}{\partial z} + \lambda \frac{\partial v}{\partial z}\right)dz = 0.$$

Hence, we have the three equations

$$\frac{\partial u}{\partial x} + \lambda\frac{\partial v}{\partial x} = 0\,;\ \frac{\partial u}{\partial y} + \lambda\frac{\partial v}{\partial y} = 0\,;\ \frac{\partial u}{\partial z} + \lambda\frac{\partial v}{\partial z} = 0,$$

together with $\phi(x, y, z) = 0$, for evaluating x, y, z, and λ. This is called **Lagrange's method of undetermined multipliers.** To illustrate the application of these facts in the determination of maxima and minima, let us turn to the following examples :—

EXAMPLES.—(1) Find the greatest value of $V = 8xyz$, subject to the condition that $x^2 + y^2 + z^2 = 1$. By differentiation,

$$x\,dx + y\,dy + z\,dz = 0\,;\text{ and }yz\,dx + xz\,dy + xy\,dx = 0.$$

For a maximum, we must have

$$yz + \lambda x = 0\,;\ xz + \lambda y = 0\,;\ xy + \lambda z = 0.$$

Multiply these equations respectively by x, y, and z, so that

$$xyz + \lambda x^2 = 0\,;\ xyz + \lambda y^2 = 0\,;\ xyz + \lambda z^2 = 0. \quad . \quad . \quad (19)$$

By addition

$$3xyz + \lambda(x^2 + y^2 + z^2) = 0. \quad \therefore \tfrac{3}{8}V + \lambda = 0\,;\text{ or, }\lambda = -\tfrac{3}{8}V.$$

Substitute this value of λ in equation (19), and we get

$$x = \sqrt{3}\,;\ y = \sqrt{3}\,;\ z = \sqrt{3}\,;\ \therefore V = 8/3\sqrt{3}.$$

(2) Find the rectangular parallelopiped of maximum surface which can be inscribed in a sphere whose equation is $x^2 + y^2 + z^2 = r^2$. The surface of the parallelopiped is $s = 8(xy + xz + yz)$, where $2x$, $2y$, and $2z$ are the lengths of its three coterminous edges. By differentiation, $x\,dx + y\,dy + z\,dz = 0$; $(y+z)dx + (x+z)dy + (y+x)dz = 0$. For a maximum, therefore, $y + z + \lambda x = 0$; $x + z + \lambda y = 0$; $x + y + \lambda z = 0$. Proceed as before, and we get finally $x = y = z$. Ansr. Cube with edges $2x = 2r\sqrt{\tfrac{1}{3}}$.

(3) Find the dimensions of a cistern of maximum capacity that can be formed out of 300 sq. ft. of sheet iron, when there is no lid. Let x, y, z, respectively = length, breadth and depth. Then, $xy + 2xz + 2yz = 300$; and, $u = xyz$, is to be a maximum. Proceed as before, and we get $x = y = 2z$. Substitute in the first equation, and we get $x = y = 10$, $z = 5$. Hence the cistern must be 10 ft. long, 10 ft. broad, and 5 ft. deep.

§ 102. Lagrange's Theorem.

Just as Maclaurin's theorem is a special case of Taylor's, so the latter is a special form of the more general Lagrange's theorem, and the latter, in turn, a special form of Laplace's theorem. There is no need for me to enter into extended details, but I shall have something to say about Lagrange's theorem.

If we have an implicit function of three variables,

$$z = y + x\phi(z), \quad . \quad . \quad . \quad . \quad (1)$$

such that x and y have no other relation than is given by the equation (1), each may vary independently of the other. It is required to develop another function of z, say $f(z)$, in ascending powers of x. Let

$$u = f(z);$$

then, by Maclaurin's theorem,

$$u = u_0 + \left(\frac{du}{dx}\right)_0\frac{x}{1} + \left(\frac{d^2u}{dx^2}\right)_0\frac{x^2}{2!} + \left(\frac{d^3u}{dx^3}\right)_0\frac{x^3}{3!} + \dots$$

Without going into details, it is found that after evaluating the respective differential coefficients indicated in this series from (1), we get as a final result

$$f(z) = f(y) + \frac{df(y)}{dy}\phi(y)\frac{x}{1} + \frac{d}{dy}\left[\frac{df(y)}{dy}\left\{\phi(y)\right\}^2\right]\frac{x^2}{2!} + \dots, \qquad (2)$$

which is known as **Lagrange's theorem.** The application of this series to specific problems is illustrated by the following set of examples :—

EXAMPLES.—(1) Given $a - by + cy^2 = 0$, find y.
Rearranging the given equation, we get

$$y = \frac{a}{b} + \frac{c}{b}y^2; \qquad \cdot \qquad \cdot \qquad \cdot \qquad \cdot \qquad \cdot \qquad (3)$$

and on comparing this with the typical equations (1) and (2), we have
$$f(z) = y, \therefore f(y) = z; \ \phi(z) = y^2, \ \phi(y) = z^2; \ z = a/b; \ x = c/b.$$
From (2), $df(y)/dy = 1$; $dz/dz = 1$, etc., z of (1) is y of (3), therefore,

$$y = z + z^2\frac{x}{1} + \frac{d(z^4)}{dz}\cdot\frac{x^2}{2!} + \frac{d^2(z^6)}{dz^2}\cdot\frac{x^3}{3!} + \dots;$$

$$\therefore y = z + z^2\frac{x}{1} + 4z^3\frac{x^2}{2!} + 6.5z^4\frac{x^3}{3!} + \dots;$$

$$\therefore y = \frac{a}{b} + \frac{a^2}{b^2}\cdot\frac{c}{b} + \frac{4}{2!}\cdot\frac{a^3}{b^3}\cdot\frac{c^2}{b^2} + \frac{6.5}{3!}\cdot\frac{a^4}{b^4}\cdot\frac{c^3}{b^3} + \dots;$$

$$\therefore y = \frac{a}{b}\left(1 + \frac{ac}{b^2} + \frac{4}{2!}\cdot\frac{a^2c^2}{b^4} + \frac{6.5}{3!}\cdot\frac{a^3c^3}{b^6} + \dots\right),$$

a series which is identical with that which arises when the least of the two roots of equation (3) is expanded by Taylor's theorem.

(2) Given $y^3 - ay + b = 0$, find y^n. On comparing the given equation

$$y = \frac{b}{a} + \frac{1}{a}y^3,$$

with the typical forms, we see that

$$f(z) = y^n, \therefore f(y) = z^n; \ \phi(z) = y^3, \therefore \phi(y) = z^3; \ z = b/a; \ x = 1/a.$$

$$\therefore y^n = z^n + nz^{n-1}z^3\frac{x}{1} + \frac{d(nz^{n-1}z^6)}{dz}\cdot\frac{x^2}{2!} + \dots;$$

$$\therefore y^n = \frac{b^n}{a^n}\left(1 + n\frac{b^2}{a^2}\cdot\frac{1}{a} + \frac{n(n+5)}{2!}\cdot\frac{b^4}{a^4}\cdot\frac{1}{a^2} + \dots\right).$$

(3) In solving the velocity equations

$$\frac{dx}{dt} = k_1(a - x)(a - x - \xi);\ \frac{d\xi}{dt} = k_2(a - x)(a - x - \xi),$$

for the reaction between propyl iodide and sodium ethylate, W. Hecht, M. Conrad, and C. Brückner (*Zeit. phys. Chem.*, **4**, 273, 1889) found that by division of the two equations, and integration,

$$1 - \frac{x}{a} = \left(1 - \frac{\xi}{a}\right)^K,$$

where a denotes the amount of substance at the beginning of the reaction; x and ξ are the amounts decomposed at the time t; $K = k_1/k_2$; when $t = 0$, $x = 0$, and $\xi = 0$. If K is small, Maclaurin's theorem furnishes the expression

$$1 - \frac{x}{a} = \left(1 - \frac{\xi}{a}\right)^K = 1 - K\frac{\xi}{a};\ \text{or,}\ x = K\xi. \qquad (4)$$

If we put $x + \xi = y$, we can get a straightforward relation between y and t; for obviously,

$$K\xi + \xi = y;\ (1 + K)\xi = y;\ \therefore (1 + K)d\xi = dy;$$

$$\therefore \frac{d\xi}{dt} = k_2(a - \xi)(a - x - \xi);\ \text{becomes}\ \frac{dy}{dt} = k_1(aK + a - y)(a - y),$$

which can be integrated in the ordinary way. But K was usually too large to allow of the approximation (4). We have therefore to solve the problem: Given

$$1 - \frac{x}{a} = 1 - \frac{y}{a} + \frac{\xi}{a} = \left(1 - \frac{\xi}{a}\right)^K,\ \text{find}\ \frac{\xi}{a}.$$

For the sake of brevity write this:

$$1 - x + z = (1 - z)^K, \therefore 1 - x + z = 1 - Kz + \tfrac{1}{2}K(K-1)z^2 - \ldots;$$
$$\therefore x = (K+1)z - K(K-1)z^2 + \ldots = f_1(z). \qquad (5)$$

$$\therefore zx = zf_1(z);\ \therefore z = x\frac{z}{f_1(z)} = x\phi(z). \qquad (6)$$

On referring to the fundamental types (1) and (2), we see that

$$f(z) = z, f(y) = y;\ \phi(z) = \phi(z), \phi(y) = \phi(y);\ y = 0, x = y;$$

$$\therefore z = y + \frac{\partial f(y)}{\partial y}\phi(y)\frac{x}{1} + \frac{\partial}{\partial y}\left[\frac{\partial f(y)}{\partial y}\{\phi(y)\}^2\right]\frac{x^2}{2!} + \ldots \qquad (7)$$

We must now evaluate the separate terms.

$$\frac{\partial}{\partial y}f(y) = \frac{\partial y}{\partial y} = 1. \qquad (8)$$

From (5) and (6),

$$\phi(y) = \frac{y}{f_1(y)} = \frac{y}{(K+1)y - \tfrac{1}{2}K(K-1)y^2 + \ldots} = \frac{1}{K+1}, \qquad (9)$$

since $y = 0$; again, from (5), (6), (7), and (8),

$$\frac{\partial}{\partial y}\left[\frac{\partial f(y)}{\partial y}\{\phi(y)\}^2\right] = \frac{\partial}{\partial y}\{\phi(y)\}^2 = \frac{\partial}{\partial y}\left\{\frac{1}{(K+1) - \tfrac{1}{2}K(K-1)y + \ldots}\right\}^2$$
$$= \frac{2K(K-1)}{\{(K+1) - \tfrac{1}{2}K(K-1)y + \ldots\}^3} = \frac{K(K-1)}{(K+1)^3}, \qquad (10)$$

since y is zero. Hence, the required development, from (7), is

$$z = \frac{1}{K+1} \cdot \frac{x}{1} + \frac{1}{2} \cdot \frac{K(K-1)}{(K+1)^3} \cdot \left(\frac{x}{2!}\right)^2 + \ldots \qquad . \qquad . \quad (11)$$

We have put z for ξ/a, and x for y/a. On restoring the proper values of z and x into the given velocity equations, we can get, by integration, a relation between y, t, and constants.

§ 103. Functions requiring special Treatment before Substituting Numbers.

In discussing the velocity of reactions of the second order, we found that if the concentration of the two species of reacting molecules is the same, the expression

$$kt = \frac{1}{a-b} \log \frac{a-x}{b-x} \cdot \frac{a}{b},$$

assumes the indeterminate form

$$kt = \infty \times 0,$$

by substituting $a = b$. We are constantly meeting with the same sort of thing when dealing with other functions, which may reduce to one or other of the forms: $\frac{0}{0}$, $\frac{\infty}{\infty}$, $\infty - \infty$, 1^∞, ∞^0, 0^0 ... We can say nothing at all about the value of any one of these expressions, and, consequently, we must be prepared to deal with them another way so that they may represent something instead of nothing. They have been termed *illusory*, *indeterminate* and *singular* forms. In one sense, the word "indeterminate" is a misnomer, because it is the object of this section to show how values of such functions may be determined.

Sometimes a simple substitution will make the value apparent at a glance. For instance, the fraction $(x+a)/(x+b)$ is indeterminate when x is infinite. Now substitute $x = y^{-1}$ and it is easy to see that when x is infinite, y is zero and consequently,

$$\mathrm{Lt}_{x=\infty} \frac{x+a}{x+b} = \mathrm{Lt}_{y=0} \frac{1+ay}{1+by} = 1.$$

Fractions which assume the form $\frac{0}{0}$ are called vanishing fractions, thus, $(x^2 - 4x + 3)/(x^2 - 1)$ reduces to $\frac{0}{0}$, when $x = 1$. The trouble is due to the fact that the numerator and denominator contain the common factor $(x-1)$. If this be eliminated before the substitution, the true value of the fraction for $x = 1$ can be obtained. Thus,

$$\frac{x^2 - 4x + 3}{x^2 - 1} = \frac{(x-1)(x-3)}{(x-1)(x+1)} = \frac{x-3}{x+1} = -\frac{2}{2} = -1.$$

These indeterminate functions may often be evalued by algebraic or trigonometrical methods, but not always. Taylor's theorem furnishes a convenient means of dealing with many of these functions. The most important case for discussion is "$\frac{0}{0}$," since this form most frequently occurs and most of the other forms can be referred to it by some special artifice.

I. The function assumes the form $\frac{0}{0}$.

This form is the so-called **vanishing fraction**. As already pointed out, the numerator and denominator here contain some common factor which vanishes for some particular value of x, say. These factors must be got rid of. One of the best ways of doing this, short of factorizing at sight, is to substitute $a + h$ for x in the numerator and denominator of the fraction and then reduce the fraction to its simplest form. In this way, some power of h will appear as a common factor of each. After reducing the fraction to its simplest form, put $h = 0$ so that $a = x$. The true value of the fraction for this particular value of the variable x will then be apparent.

For cases in which x is to be made equal to zero, the numerator and denominator may be expanded at once by Maclaurin's theorem without any preliminary substitution for x. For instance, the trigonometrical function $(\sin x)/x$ approaches unity when x converges towards zero. This is seen directly. Develop $\sin x$ in ascending powers of x by Taylor's or Maclaurin's theorems. We thus obtain

$$\frac{\sin x}{x} = \frac{\left(\dfrac{x}{1} - \dfrac{x^3}{3!} + \dfrac{x^5}{5!} - \dfrac{x^7}{7!} + \cdots\right)}{x} = 1 - \frac{x^2}{3!} + \frac{x^4}{5!} - \frac{x^6}{7!} + \cdots$$

The terms to the right of unity all vanish when $x = 0$, therefore,

$$\mathrm{Lt}_{x=0}\frac{\sin x}{x} = 1.$$

EXAMPLES.—(1) Show $\mathrm{Lt}_{x=0}(a^x - b^x)/x = \log a/b$.

(2) Show $\mathrm{Lt}_{x=0}(1 - \cos x)/x^2 = \frac{1}{2}$.

(3) The fraction $(x^n - a^n)/(x - a)$ becomes $\frac{0}{0}$ when $x = a$. Put $x = a + h$ and expand by Taylor's theorem in the usual way. Thus,

$$\mathrm{Lt}_{x=a}\frac{x^n - a^n}{x - a} = \mathrm{Lt}_{h=a}\frac{(a+h)^n - a^n}{h} = na^{n-1}.$$

It is rarely necessary to expand more than two or three of the lowest powers of h. The intermediate steps are

$$\mathrm{Lt}_{h=0}\frac{(a^n + na^{n-1}h + \frac{1}{2}n(n-1)a^{n-2}h^2 + \cdots) - a^n}{a + h - a}.$$

U

Cancel out a^n in the numerator, and a in the denominator; divide out the h's and put $h = O$.

(4) The velocity, V, of a body falling from rest in a resisting medium after an interval of time t, is

$$V = \frac{1}{\beta} \cdot \frac{e^{2g\beta t} - 1}{e^{2g\beta t} + 1}; \therefore V = gt,$$

when the coefficient of resistance, β, is made zero. Hint. Expand the numerator only before substituting $\beta = 0$.

(5) Show that $\mathrm{Lt}_{h=0} \frac{1}{h} \log\left(1 + \frac{h}{x}\right) = \frac{1}{x}$, as on page 51.

(6) If H denotes the height which a body must fall in order to acquire a velocity, V, then

$$H = \frac{1}{2gk^2} \log \frac{1}{1 - k^2 V^2}, \therefore H = \frac{V^2}{2g}\left(1 + \frac{(kV)^2}{2} + \frac{(kV)^4}{4} + \dots\right),$$

where k is the coefficient of resistance. If $k=0$, show that $H = \frac{1}{2}V^2/g$.

We can generalize the preceding discussion. Let

$$\mathrm{Lt}_{x=a} \frac{f_1(x)}{f_2(x)} = \frac{f_1(a)}{f_2(a)} = \frac{0}{0}. \quad \cdot \quad \cdot \quad \cdot \quad (1)$$

Obviously,

$$f_1(a) = f_2(a) = 0. \quad \cdot \quad \cdot \quad \cdot \quad (2)$$

Expand the two given functions by Taylor's theorem,

$$\frac{f_1(x + h)}{f_2(x + h)} = \frac{f_1(x) + f_1'(x)h + \frac{1}{2}f_1''(x)h^2 + \dots}{f_2(x) + f_2'(x)h + \frac{1}{2}f_2''(x)h^2 + \dots}. \quad \cdot \quad (3)$$

Now substitute $x = a$, and $f_1(a) = f_2(a) = 0$ as in (2); divide by h; and

$$\frac{f_1(a + h)}{f_2(a + h)} = \frac{f_1'(a) + \frac{1}{2}f_1''(a)h + \dots}{f_2'(a) + \frac{1}{2}f_2''(a)h + \dots} \quad \cdot \quad \cdot \quad (4)$$

remains.

$$\mathrm{Lt}_{x=a} \frac{f_1(a + h)}{f_2(a + h)} = \mathrm{Lt}_{x=a} \frac{f_1'(a) + \frac{1}{2}f_1''(a)h + \dots}{f_2'(a) + \frac{1}{2}f_2''(a)h + \dots}. \quad (5)$$

$$\therefore \frac{f_1(a)}{f_2(a)} = \frac{f_1'(a)}{f_2'(a)}; \text{ and } \mathrm{Lt}_{x=a} \frac{f_1(a)}{f_2(a)} = \mathrm{Lt}_{x=a} \frac{f_1'(a)}{f_2'(a)}. \quad (6)$$

In words, if the fraction $f_1(x)/f_2(x)$ becomes $\frac{0}{0}$, when $x = a$, the fraction can be evaluated by dividing the first derivative of the numerator by the first derivative of the denominator, and substituting $x = a$ in the result. This leaves us with three methods for dealing with indeterminate fractions.

1. *Division Method.*—i.e., by dividing out the common factors.
2. *Expansion Method.*—i.e., by substituting $x + h$ for x, etc.
3. *Differentiation Method.*—i.e., by the method just indicated.

EXAMPLES.—(1) Prove that $\int \frac{dx}{x} = \log x$, by means of the general formula

$\int x^n dx = \dfrac{x^{n+1}}{n+1}$.   Hint. Show that

$$\mathrm{Lt}_{n=-1}\frac{x^{n+1}}{n+1} = \mathrm{Lt}_{n=-1}\frac{x^{n+1}\log x \,.\, dn}{dn} = \mathrm{Lt}_{n=-1}x^{n+1}\log x = \log x,$$

by differentiating the numerator and denominator separately with regard to n and substituting $n = -1$ in the result.

(2) Show $\mathrm{Lt}_{\gamma=1}\dfrac{c}{\gamma-1}\left(\dfrac{1}{v_2{}^{\gamma-1}} - \dfrac{1}{v_1{}^{\gamma-1}}\right) = c\log\dfrac{v_1}{v_2}$.   See (10), p. 259, (3), p. 254.

II. *The function assumes the form* $\frac{\infty}{\infty}$.

Functions of this type can be converted into the preceding "$\frac{0}{0}$" case by interchanging the numerator and denominator, but it is not difficult to show that (6) applies to both $\frac{0}{0}$ and to $\frac{\infty}{\infty}$; and generally, if the ratio of the first derivatives vanishes, use the second; if the second vanishes, use the third, etc. Or, symbolically,

$$\mathrm{Lt}_{x=a}\frac{f_1(x)}{f_2(x)} = \mathrm{Lt}_{x=a}\frac{f_1'(x)}{f_2'(x)} = \mathrm{Lt}_{x=a}\frac{f_1''(x)}{f_2''(x)} = \mathrm{Lt}_{x=a}\frac{f_1'''(x)}{f_2'''(x)} = \dots \text{ (7)}$$

This is the so-called **rule of l'Hopital.**

EXAMPLES.—(1) Show that $\mathrm{Lt}_{x=0}\dfrac{\log x}{x^{-1}} = \mathrm{Lt}_{x=0}\dfrac{x^{-1}}{-x^{-2}} = \mathrm{Lt}_{x=0}-x = 0$.

(2) The nth derivative of x^n is $n!$ and the nth derivative of e^x is e^x by Leibnitz' theorem, when n is positive. Hence show that

$$\mathrm{Lt}_{x=\infty}\frac{e^x}{x^n} = \mathrm{Lt}_{x=\infty}\frac{e^x}{1\,.\,2\,\dots\,n} = \infty.$$

III. *The function assumes the form* $\infty \times 0$.

Obviously, such a fraction can be converted into the "$\frac{0}{0}$" form by putting the infinite expression as the denominator of the fraction; or into the $\frac{\infty}{\infty}$ form by putting the zero factor as the denominator of the fraction as shown in the subjoined examples.

EXAMPLES.—(1) The reader has already encountered the problem: what does $x\log x$ become when $x = 0$? We are evidently dealing with the $0 \times \infty$ case. Obviously, as in a preceding example,

$$\mathrm{Lt}_{x=0}x\log x = \mathrm{Lt}_{x=0}\frac{\log x}{\frac{1}{x}} = 0.$$

(2) Show $\mathrm{Lt}_{a=b}\dfrac{1}{a-b}\log\dfrac{(a-x)b}{(b-x)a} = \dfrac{x}{a(a-x)}$, as indicated on page 220.

(3) Show $\mathrm{Lt}_{x=\infty}e^{-x}\log x = 0 \times \infty = 0$.

IV. *The function assumes the form* $\infty - \infty$, *or* $0 - 0$.

First reduce the expression to a single fraction and treat as above.

EXAMPLES.—(1) Show by differentiating twice, etc., that

$$\mathrm{Lt}_{x=1}\frac{x}{x-1} - \frac{1}{\log x} = \mathrm{Lt}_{x=1}\frac{x\log x - x + 1}{(x-1)\log x} = \mathrm{Lt}_{x=1}\frac{x}{x+1} = \frac{1}{2},\text{ etc.}$$

(2) Show that $\mathrm{Lt}_{x=1}\dfrac{x}{\log x} - \dfrac{1}{\log x} = 1$.

(3) W. Hecht, M. Conrad and C. Brückner (*Zeit. phys. Chem.*, 4, 273, 1889) wanted the limiting value of the following expression in their work on chemical kinetics :—

$$\mathrm{Lt}_{n=1}\frac{1}{n-1}\left(\log\frac{na-x}{a-x} - \log n\right).\quad\text{Ansr. }\frac{x}{a-x},$$

V. The function assumes one of the forms 1^{∞}, ∞^0, 0^0.

Take logarithms and the expression reduces to one of the preceding types.

EXAMPLES.—(1) $\mathrm{Lt}_{x=0}x^x = 0^0$. Take logs and noting that $y = x^x$, $\log y = x\log x$. But we have just found that $x\log x = 0$ when $x = 0$; ∴ $\log y = 0$ when $x = 0$; ∴ $y = 1$. Hence, $\mathrm{Lt}_{x=0}x^x = 1$.

(2) Show $\mathrm{Lt}_{x=0}(1 + mx)^{1/x} = 1^{\infty} = e^m$. Here $\log y = x^{-1}\log(1 + mx)$. But when $x = 0$, $\log y = \frac{0}{0}$; by the differential method, we find that $\log(1 + mx)x^{-1}$ becomes m when $x = 0$; hence $\log y = m$; or $y = e^m$, when $x = 0$.

§ 104. The Calculus of Finite Differences.

The calculus of finite differences deals with the changes which take place in the value of a function when the independent variable suffers a finite change. Thus if x is increased a finite quantity h, the function x^2 increases to $(x + h)^2$, and there is an increment of $(x + h)^2 - x^2 = 2xh + h^2$ in the given function. The independent variable of the differential calculus is only supposed to suffer infinitesimally small changes. I shall show in the next two sections some useful results which have been obtained in this subject; meanwhile let us look at the notation we shall employ.

In the series

$$1^3,\ 2^3,\ 3^3,\ 4^3,\ 5^3,\ \ldots,$$

subtract the first term from the second, the second from the third, the third from the fourth, and so on. The result is a new series,

$$7,\ 19,\ 37,\ 61,\ 91,\ \ldots$$

called the **first order of differences**. By treating this new series in a similar way, we get a third series,

$$12,\ 18,\ 24,\ 30,\ \ldots,$$

called the **second order cf differences**. This may be repeated as long as we please, unless the series terminates or the differences become very irregular.

The different orders of differences are usually arranged in the form of a "table of differences". To construct such a table, we can begin with the first member of series of corresponding values of the two variables. Let the different values of one variable, say, x_0, x_1, x_2, ... correspond with y_0, y_1, y_2, ... The differences between the dependent variables are denoted by the symbol "Δ," with a superscript to denote the order of difference, and a subscript to show the relation between it and the independent variable. Thus, in general symbols :—

Argument.	Function.	Orders of Differences.			
		First.	Second.	Third.	Fourth.
x_a	y_a				
x_{a+h}	y_{a+h}	Δ^1_a	Δ^2_a		
x_{a+2h}	y_{a+2h}	Δ^1_{a+h}	Δ^2_{a+h}	Δ^3_a	
x_{a+3h}	y_{a+3h}	Δ^1_{a+2h}	Δ^2_{a+2h}	Δ^3_{a+h}	Δ^4_a
x_{a+4h}	y_{a+4h}	Δ^1_{a+3h}			

If we apply this to the function $y = x^3$ we get the table of differences :

x.	y.	Δ^1.	Δ^2.	Δ^3.	Δ^4.
1	$(1)_0$				
2	$(8)_1$	$(7)_0$	$(12)_0$		
3	$(27)_2$	$(19)_1$	$(18)_1$	$(6)_0$	
4	$(64)_3$	$(37)_2$	$(24)_2$	$(6)_1$	0
5	$(125)_4$	$(61)_3$			

Such a table will often furnish a good idea of any sudden change which might occur in the relative values of the variables with a view to expressing the experimental results in terms of an empirical or interpolation formula. It is not uncommon to find faulty measurements, and other mistakes in observation or calculation, shown up in an unmistakable manner by the appearance of a marked irregularity in a member of one of the difference columns. It is, of course, quite possible that these irregularities are due to something of the nature of a discontinuity in the phenomenon under consideration.

§ 105. Interpolation.

In one method of fixing the order of a chemical reaction it is necessary to find the time which is required for the transformation of equal fractional parts of a given substance in two separate systems. Let x denote the concentration of the reacting substance at the time t; a, the initial concentration of the reacting substance; and suppose that the following numbers were obtained :—

System I., $a = 0·1$.		System II., $a = 0·0625$.	
t.	x.	t.	x.
1·0	0·0581	1	0·04816
1·5	0·0490	3	0·03564
2·5	0·0382	7	0·02638
4·0	0·0300	17	0·01748

In one system, $\frac{3}{10}$ths of the substance were transformed in four minutes; it is required to find in what time $\frac{3}{10}$ths of the reacting substance were transformed in the second system.

Expressed in more general terms, given a definite number of observations, to calculate any required intermediate values. This kind of problem frequently confronts the practical worker, particularly in dealing with isolated and discontinuous observations, and measurements in which time is one of the variables. The process of computation of the numerical values of two variables *intermediate* between those actually determined by observation and measurement, is called **interpolation**. When we attempt to obtain values lying *beyond* the limits of those actually measured, the process is called **extrapolation**. The term "interpolation" is also applied to both processes. See page 92.

It is apparent that the correct formula connecting the two variables must be known before exact interpolation can be performed. If the relation between the mass, m, and volume, v, of a substance be represented by the expression $m = \frac{1}{2}v$, we can readily calculate the value of m for any value of v we might desire. Moreover, the method of testing a supposed formula is to compare the experimental values with those furnished by interpolation. Interpolation, therefore, is based on the assumption that when a law is known

with fair exactness, we can, by the principle of continuity, anticipate the results of any future measurements.

When the form of the function connecting the two variables is
known, the determination of the value of one variable corresponding with any assigned value of the other is simple arithmetic.
When the form of the function is quite unknown, and the definite
values set out in the table alone are known, the problem loses its
determinate character, and we must then resort to the methods now
to be described.

I. *Interpolation by proportional parts.*

If the differences between the succeeding pairs of values are
small and regular, any intermediate value can be calculated by
simple proportion on the assumption that the change in the value
of the function is proportional to that of the variable. This is
obviously nothing more than the rule of proportional parts illustrated on page 289, by the interpolation of $\log(n + h)$ when $\log n$
and $\log(n + 1)$ are known. The rule is in very common use. For
example, *weighing by the method of vibrations* is an example of
interpolation. Let x denote the zero point of the balance, let w_0
be the true weight of the body in question. This is to be measured
by finding the weight required to bring the index of the balance to
zero point. Let x_1 be the position of rest when a weight w_1 is
added and x_2 the position of rest when a weight w_2 is added. Assuming that for small deflections of the beam the difference in the
two positions of rest will be proportional to the difference of the
weights, the weight, w_0, necessary to bring the pointer to zero will
be given by the simple proportion :

$$(w_0 - w_1) : (x_0 - x_1) = (w_2 - w_1) : (x_2 - x_1).$$

When the intervals between the two terms are large, or the
differences between the various members of the series decrease
rapidly, simple proportion cannot be used with confidence. To take
away any arbitrary choice in the determination of the intermediate
values, it is commonly assumed that the function can be expressed
by a limited series of powers of one of the variables. Thus we have
the interpolation formulæ of Newton, Bessel, Stirling, Lagrange,
and Gauss.

II. *Newton's interpolation formula.*

Let us now return to fundamentals. If y_x denotes a function of
x, say

$$y_x = f(x),$$

then, if x be increased by h,

$$y_{x+h} = f(x+h),$$

and consequently,

$$\text{Increment } y_x = y_{x+h} - y_x = f(x+h) - f(x) = \Delta^1{}_x. \qquad (1)$$

Similarly, the increment

$$\Delta^1 y_x = \Delta^1{}_{x+h} - \Delta^1{}_x = \Delta^1(\Delta^1{}_x) = \Delta^2{}_x, \qquad . \qquad (2)$$

where $\Delta^1{}_x$ is the first difference in the value of y_x, when x is increased to $x+h$; $\Delta^2{}_x$ is the first difference of the first difference of y_x, that is, the second difference of y_x when x is increased to $x+h$. It will now be obvious that Δ^1 is the symbol of an operation—the taking of the increment in the value of $f(x)$ when the variable is increased to $x+h$. For the sake of brevity, we generally write Δ_x for Δy_x. From (1) and (2), it follows that

$$y_{x+h} = y_x + \Delta^1 y_x; \qquad . \qquad . \qquad (3)$$

$$y_{x+2h} = y_{x+h} + \Delta^1 y_{x+h} = y_x + \Delta^1 y_x + \Delta^1(y_x + \Delta^1 y_x);$$

$$\therefore y_{x+2h} = y_x + 2\Delta^1 y_x + \Delta^2 y_x. \qquad . \qquad . \qquad (4)$$

Similarly,

$$y_{x+3h} = y_x + 3\Delta^1 y_x + 3\Delta^2 y_x + \Delta^3 y_x. \qquad . \qquad (5)$$

We see that the numerical coefficients of the successive orders of differences follow the binomial law of page 36. This must also be true of y_{x+nh} if n is a positive integer, consequently,

$$y_{x+nh} = y_x + n\Delta y_x + \tfrac{1}{2}n(n-1)\Delta^2 y_x + \ldots$$

This is **Newton's interpolation formula** (Newton's *Principia*, **3**, lem. 5, 1687) employed in finding or interpolating one or more terms when n particular values of the function are known. Let us write y_0 in place of y_x for the first term, then

$$y_{nh} = y_0 + n\Delta^1{}_0 + \frac{n(n-1)}{2!}\Delta^2{}_0 + \frac{n(n-1)(n-2)}{3!}\Delta^3{}_0 + \ldots \quad (6)$$

continued until the differences become negligibly small or irregular. If we write $nh = x$, $n = x/h$, and (6) assumes the form

$$y_x = y_0 + \frac{x}{h}\cdot\frac{\Delta^1{}_0}{1} + \frac{x(x-h)}{h^2}\cdot\frac{\Delta^2{}_0}{2!} + \frac{x(x-h)(x-2h)}{h^3}\cdot\frac{\Delta^3{}_0}{3!} + \ldots \quad (7)$$

where h denotes the increment in the successive values of the independent variable; and x is the total increment of the interpolated term. The application is best illustrated by example.

EXAMPLES.—(1) If $y_0 = 2,844$; $y_1 = 2,705$; $y_2 = 2,501$; $y_3 = 2,236$, find $y_{\frac{1}{5}}$ (Inst. of Actuaries Exam., 1889). First set up the difference table, paying particular attention to the algebraic signs of the differences.

x.	y.	Δ^1.	Δ^2.	Δ^3.
0	2,844	$(-139)_0$	$(-65)_0$	$(+4)_0$
1	2,705	$(-204)_1$	$(-61)_1$	
2	2,501	$(-265)_2$		
3	2,236			

Now substitute these values in (6) or (7), $h = 1$, and if $n = \frac{1}{5}$, we have $x = \frac{1}{5}$.

$$\therefore y_{\frac{1}{5}} = y_0 + \tfrac{1}{5}\Delta^1_0 + \frac{\tfrac{1}{5}(\tfrac{1}{5} - 1)}{2!}\Delta^2_0 + \frac{\tfrac{1}{5}(\tfrac{1}{5} - 1)(\tfrac{1}{5} - 2)}{3!}\Delta^3_0.$$

$$\therefore y_{\frac{1}{5}} = 2844 - \tfrac{1}{5} \times 139 + \tfrac{2}{25} \times 65 + \tfrac{9}{125} \times 4 = 2821{\cdot}592.$$

(2) The amount of £1 in 50 years at $2\frac{1}{2}\,°/_\circ = 3{\cdot}4371090$; at $3\,°/_\circ = 4{\cdot}3839061$; at $3\frac{1}{2}\,°/_\circ = 5{\cdot}5849264$; at $4\,°/_\circ = 7{\cdot}1066845$ (Inst. Actuaries Exam., 1888). Find the amount at $3\frac{3}{4}\,°/_\circ$. Here $\Delta^1_0 = 0{\cdot}9467971$; $\Delta^2_0 = 0{\cdot}2542232$; $\Delta^3_0 = 0{\cdot}0665146$; $y_0 = 3{\cdot}4371090$; let $y_0,\ y_2,\ y_4,$ and y_6 denote the respective values of y here given; $h = 2$. Required y_5.

$$\therefore y_5 = y_0 + \tfrac{5}{2}\Delta^1_0 + \frac{5 \cdot 3}{8}\Delta^2_0 + \frac{5 \cdot 3 \cdot 1}{48}\Delta^3_0,$$

$$\therefore y = 3{\cdot}4371090 + 2{\cdot}3669928 + 0{\cdot}4766685 + 0{\cdot}0207858 = 6{\cdot}3015561.$$

The correct value is $6{\cdot}30094$. The discrepancy is due to the fact that the order of difference above the third ought not to be neglected. But we can only get $n - 1$ orders of differences from n consecutive terms and equidistant terms values of a function. If more terms had been given we could have got a more exact result.

(3) Given $y_0 = 89,685$; $y_1 = 88,994$; $y_2 = 88,294$; $y_3 = 87,585$, find y_9 (Inst. Actuaries Exam., 1902). Here $\Delta^1_0 = -691$; $\Delta^2_0 = -9$; the succeeding differences $\Delta^3,\ \Delta^4,\ \ldots$ are all zero. Here (6) becomes

$$y_9 = y_0 + 9\Delta^1_0 + 36\Delta^2_0 = 89,685 - 6,219 - 324 = 83,142.$$

(4) Given $\log 4{\cdot}22 = 0{\cdot}6253125$; $\log 4{\cdot}23 = 0{\cdot}6263404$; $\log 4{\cdot}24 = 0{\cdot}6273659$; $\log 4{\cdot}25 = 0{\cdot}6283889$, find $\log 4{\cdot}21684$. Here $y_0,\ y_1,\ y_2,\ y_3$ denotes the given quantities, we want $y_x = y_{-0{\cdot}00316}$; $h = 0{\cdot}01$. Hence, from (7),

$$y_{-0{\cdot}00316} = y_0 - \frac{0{\cdot}00316}{0{\cdot}01} \cdot \frac{\Delta^1_0}{1} - \frac{0{\cdot}00316(-0{\cdot}00316 - 1)}{0{\cdot}0001} \cdot \frac{\Delta^2_0}{2!};$$

$$= 0{\cdot}6253125 - 0{\cdot}0003248 - 0{\cdot}0000005 = 0{\cdot}6249872.$$

(5) What is the cube root of $60{\cdot}25$, given the cube root of $60 = 3{\cdot}914868$; $61 = 3{\cdot}936497$; $62 = 3{\cdot}957891$; $63 = 3{\cdot}979057$; $64 = 4{\cdot}000000$? Here, $\Delta^1_0 = +0{\cdot}021629$; $\Delta^2_0 = -0{\cdot}000235$. Substitute $x = \frac{1}{4}$; $h = 1$.

$$\therefore y = y_0 + \tfrac{1}{4}\Delta^1_0 - \tfrac{3}{32}\Delta^2_0 = 3{\cdot}914868 + 0{\cdot}005407 + 0{\cdot}000022 = 3{\cdot}920297.$$

The number obtained by simple proportion is $3{\cdot}920295$. The correct number is a little greater than $3{\cdot}920297$.

III. Lagrange's interpolation formula.

We have assumed that the n given values are all equidistant. This need not be. A new problem is now presented : Given n consecutive values of a function, which are not equidistant from one another, to find any other intermediate value.

Let y become $y_a, y_b, y_c, \ldots y_n$ when x becomes $a, b, c, \ldots n$. Lagrange has shown that the value of y corresponding with any given value of x, can be determined from the formula

$$y_x = \frac{(x-b)(x-c)\ldots(x-n)}{(a-b)(a-c)\ldots(a-n)}y_a + \frac{(x-a)(x-c)\ldots(x-n)}{(b-a)(b-c)\ldots(b-n)}y_b + \ldots, \quad (8)$$

where each term is of the nth degree in x. This is generally known as **Lagrange's interpolation formula,** although it is said to be really due to Euler.

EXAMPLES.—(1) Find the probability that a person aged 53 will live a year having given the probability that a person aged 50 will live a year $= 0\cdot98428$; for a person aged 51 $= 0\cdot98335$; 54, $0\cdot98008$; 55, $0\cdot97877$ (Inst. Actuaries Exam., 1890). Here, $y_a = 0\cdot98428$, $a = 0$; $y_b = 0\cdot98335$, $b = 1$; $y_c = 0\cdot98008$, $c = 4$; $y_d = 0\cdot97877$, $d = 5$; $\therefore x = 3$.

$$(x-b)(x-c)(x-d) = (3-1)(3-4)(3-5) = +4;$$
$$(x-a)(x-c)(x-d) = (3-0)(3-4)(3-5) = +6;$$
$$(x-a)(x-b)(x-d) = (3-0)(3-1)(3-5) = -12;$$
$$(x-a)(x-b)(x-c) = (3-0)(3-1)(3-4) = -6;$$
$$(a-b)(a-c)(a-d) = (0-1)(0-4)(0-5) = -20;$$
$$(b-a)(b-c)(b-d) = (1-0)(1-4)(1-5) = +12;$$
$$(c-a)(c-b)(c-d) = (4-0)(4-1)(4-5) = -12;$$
$$(d-a)(d-b)(d-c) = (5-0)(5-1)(5-4) = +20.$$

$$y_x = -\frac{4}{20}y_a + \frac{6}{12}y_b + \frac{12}{12}y_c - \frac{6}{20}y_d = -\frac{0\cdot98428}{5} + \frac{0\cdot98335}{2} + \frac{0\cdot98008}{1} - \frac{3\times0\cdot97877}{10};$$

$$y_x = -0\cdot196856 + 0\cdot491675 + 0\cdot98008 - 0\cdot29361 = 0\cdot98127.$$

(2) Given $\log 280 = 2\cdot4472$; $\log 281 = 2\cdot4487$; $\log 283 = 2\cdot4518$; $\log 286 = 2\cdot4564$, find $\log 282$ by Lagrange's formula (Inst. Actuaries Exam., 1890). $x = 2$, $a = 0$, $b = 1$, $c = 3$, $d = 6$. Hence show that

$$y_x = -\tfrac{2}{9}y_a + \tfrac{4}{5}y_b + \tfrac{4}{9}y_c - \tfrac{1}{45}y_d = 2\cdot4502.$$

(3) Find by Lagrange's formula $\log x = 2\tfrac{1}{3}$, given $\log 200 = 2\cdot30103$; $\log 210 = 2\cdot32222$; $\log 220 = 2\cdot34242$; $\log 230 = 2\cdot36173$ (Inst. Actuaries Exam., 1891). Here $a = 0$, $b = 1$, $c = 2$, $d = 3$. Substitute in the interpolation formula and we get

$$y_x = \frac{(x-1)(x-2)(x-3)}{(0-1)(0-2)(0-3)}y_a + \frac{(x-0)(x-2)(x-3)}{(1-0)(1-2)(1-3)}y_b + \ldots;$$

$$\therefore y_x = -\frac{x^3 - 6x^2 + 11x - 6}{6}y_a + \frac{x^3 - 5x^2 + 6x}{2}y_b + \ldots;$$

the student must fill in the other terms himself.   Collect together the different terms in x, x^2, x^3, etc., and

$$2\text{·}33333 = 2\text{·}30103 + 0\text{·}02171x - 0\text{·}00055x^2 + 0\text{·}00001x^3.$$

When this equation is solved by the approximation methods described in a later chapter, we get $x = 215\text{·}462$ (nearly).

(4) Ammonium sulphate has the electrical conductivities : 552, 1010, 1779 units at the respective concentrations : $0\text{·}778$, $1\text{·}601$, $3\text{·}377$ grm. molecules per litre.   Calculate the conductivity of a solution containing one grm. molecule of the salt per litre.   Ansr. $684\text{·}5$ units nearly.   Hint.   By Lagrange's formula, (8),

$$x = \frac{(1 - 1\text{·}601)\,(1 - 3\text{·}377)}{(0\text{·}778 - 1\text{·}601)\,(0\text{·}778 - 3\text{·}377)}552 + \frac{(1 - 0\text{·}778)\,(1 - 3\text{·}377)}{(1\text{·}601 - 0\text{·}778)\,(1\text{·}601 - 3\text{·}377)}1010 + \dots$$

$$= \frac{0\text{·}601 \cdot 2\text{·}377}{0\text{·}823 \cdot 2\text{·}599}552 + \frac{0\text{·}222 \cdot 2\text{·}377}{0\text{·}823 \cdot 1\text{·}776}1010 - \frac{0\text{·}222 \cdot 0\text{·}601}{2\text{·}599 \cdot 1\text{·}776}1779.$$

Simple proportion gives 680 units.   But we have only selected three observations ; if we used all the known data in working out the conductivity there would be a wider difference between the results furnished by proportion and by Lagrange's formula.   The above has been selected to illustrate the use of the formula.

(5) From certain measurements it is found that if $x = 618$, $y = 3\text{·}927$; $x = 588$, $y = 3\text{·}1416$; $x = 452$, $y = 1\text{·}5708$.   Apply Lagrange's formula, in order to find the best value to represent y when $x = 617$.   Ansr. $3\text{·}898$.

If the function is periodic, **Gauss' interpolation formula** may be used.   This has a close formal analogy with Lagrange's.[1]

$$y_x = \frac{\sin \tfrac{1}{2}(x - b)\,.\,\sin \tfrac{1}{2}(x - c)\dots\sin \tfrac{1}{2}(x - n)}{\sin \tfrac{1}{2}(a - b)\,.\,\sin \tfrac{1}{2}(a - c)\dots\sin \tfrac{1}{2}(a - n)}y_a + \dots \qquad (9)$$

IV. Interpolation by central differences.

A comparison of the difference table, page 309, with Newton's formula will show that the interpolated term y_x is built up by taking the algebraic sum of certain proportions of each of the terms employed.   The greatest proportions are taken from those terms nearest the interpolated term.   Consequently we should expect more accurate results when the interpolated term occupies a central position among the terms employed rather than if it were nearer the beginning or end of the given series of terms.

Let us take the series y_0, y_1, y_2, y_3, y_4 so that the term, y_x, to be interpolated lies nearest to the central term y_2.   Hence, with our former notation, Newton's expression assumes the form

---

[1] For the theoretical bases of these reference interpolation formulæ the reader must consult Boole's work, *A Treatise on the Calculus of Finite Differences*, London, 38, 1880.

$$y_{2+x} = y_0 + (2+x)\Delta^1 y_0 + \frac{(2+x)(1+x)}{2!}\Delta^2 y_0 + \ldots \quad (10)$$

It will be found convenient to replace the suffixes of y_0, y_1, y_2, y_3, y_4, respectively by $y_{-2}, y_{-1}, y_0, y_1, y_2$. The table of differences then assumes the form

$$
\begin{array}{llllll}
x_{-2} & y_{-2} & & & & \\
& & \Delta^1_{-2} & \Delta^2_{-2} & & \\
x_{-1} & y_{-1} & \Delta^1_{-1} & & \Delta^3_{-2} & \\
x_0 & y_0 & \Delta^1 & \Delta^2_{-1} & \Delta^3_{-1} & \Delta^4_{-3} \\
& & \Delta^1_0 & \Delta^2_{-0} & & \\
x_1 & y_1 & \Delta^1_1 & & & \\
x_2 & y_2 & & & &
\end{array}
$$

Equation (10) must now be written

$$y_x = y_{-2} + (2+x)\Delta^1_{-2} + \frac{(2+x)(1+x)}{2!}\Delta^2_{-2} + \ldots \quad (11)$$

Let us now try to convert this formula into one in which only the central differences, blackened in the above table, appear. It will be good practice in the manipulation of difference columns. First assume that

$$\Delta^1 = \tfrac{1}{2}(\Delta^1_{-1} + \Delta^1_0); \quad \Delta^3 = \tfrac{1}{2}(\Delta^3_{-2} + \Delta^3_{-1}). \quad (12)$$

$$\therefore \Delta^3_{-2} = 2\Delta^3 - \Delta^3_{-1}. \quad \cdot \quad \cdot \quad \cdot \quad (13)$$

Again from the table of differences

$$\Delta^4_{-2} = \Delta^3_{-1} - \Delta^3_{-2}; \therefore \Delta^3_{-2} = \Delta^3_{-1} - \Delta^4_{-2}. \quad (14)$$

By adding together (13) and (14),

$$\Delta^3_{-2} = \Delta^3 - \tfrac{1}{2}\Delta^4_{-2}. \quad \cdot \quad \cdot \quad \cdot \quad (15)$$

In a similar manner, from the table, and (15), we have

$$\Delta^2_{-2} = \Delta^2_{-1} - \Delta^3_{-2} = \Delta^2_{-1} - \Delta^3 + \tfrac{1}{2}\Delta^4_{-2}. \quad \cdot \quad (16)$$

And also from the first of equations (12), and the fact that $\Delta^2_{-1} = \Delta^1_0 - \Delta^1_{-1}; \ \Delta^1_{-1} = \Delta^1 - \tfrac{1}{2}\Delta^2_{-1}$, it follows that

$$\Delta^1_{-2} = \Delta^1_{-1} - \Delta^2_{-2} = (\Delta^1 - \tfrac{1}{2}\Delta^2_{-1}) - (\Delta^2_{-1} - \Delta^3 + \tfrac{1}{2}\Delta^4_{-2});$$

$$\therefore \Delta^1_{-2} = \Delta^1 - \tfrac{3}{2}\Delta^2_{-1} + \Delta^3 - \tfrac{1}{2}\Delta^4_{-2}. \quad \cdot \quad (17)$$

Still further, from the table of differences, (16), and the fact that $\Delta^1_{-1} = y_0 - y_{-1}$, we get

$$y_{-2} = y_{-1} - \Delta^1_{-2} = (y_0 - \Delta^1_{-1}) - \Delta^1_{-2};$$

$$= (y_0 - \Delta^1_{-1}) - (\Delta^1 - \tfrac{3}{2}\Delta^2_{-1} + \Delta^3 - \tfrac{1}{2}\Delta^4_{-2}).$$

But Δ^1_{-1} is equal to $\Delta^1 - \tfrac{1}{2}\Delta^2_{-1}$, as just shown, therefore,

$$y_{-2} = y_0 - 2\Delta^1 + 2\Delta^2_{-1} - \Delta^3 + \tfrac{1}{2}\Delta^4_{-2}. \quad (18)$$

Now substitute these values of $y_{-2}, \Delta^1_{-2}, \Delta^2_{-2}, \Delta^3_{-2}$, from (15), (16), (17), and (18), in (11); rearrange terms and we get a new formula (19).

$$y = y_0 + \frac{x}{1} \cdot \frac{\Delta^1{}_0 + \Delta^1{}_{-1}}{2} + \frac{x^2}{2!}\Delta^2{}_{-1} + \frac{x(x^2-1)}{3!} \cdot \frac{\Delta^3{}_{-1} + \Delta^3{}_{-2}}{2} + \dots \quad (19)$$

which is called **Stirling's interpolation formula** (J. Stirling, *Methodus Differentialis*, London, 1730), when we are given a set of corresponding values of x and y, we can calculate the value y corresponding to any assigned value x, lying between x_0 and x_1. Stirling's interpolation formula supposes that the intervals $x_1 - x_0$, $x_0 - x_{-1}, \dots$ are unity. If, however, h denotes the equal increments in the values $x_1 - x_0, x_0 - x_{-1} \dots$, Stirling's formula becomes

$$\left. \begin{aligned} y = y_0 &+ \frac{x}{h} \cdot \frac{\Delta^1{}_0 + \Delta^1{}_{-1}}{2} + \frac{x^2}{2! h^2}\Delta^2{}_{-1} + \frac{(x+h)x(x-h)}{3! h^3} \cdot \frac{\Delta^3{}_{-1} + \Delta^3{}_{-2}}{2} \\ &+ \frac{(x+h)x^2(x-h)}{4! h^4}\Delta^4{}_{-2} \\ &+ \frac{(x+2h)(x+h)x(x-h)(x-2h)}{5! h^5} \cdot \frac{\Delta^5{}_{-2} + \Delta^5{}_{-3}}{2} + \dots, \end{aligned} \right\} (20)$$

where y is written in place of y_x.

EXAMPLE.—The 3 % annuities on lives aged 21, 25, 29, 33, and 37 are respectively 21·857, 21·025, 20·132, 19·145, and 18·057. Find the annuity for age 30. Set up the table of differences, $h = 4$.

x.	y.	Δ^1.	Δ^2.	Δ^3.	Δ^4.
21	$(21·857)_{-2}$	$(-0·832)_{-2}$			
25	$(21·025)_{-1}$	$(-0·893)_{-1}$	$(-0·061)_{-2}$	$(-0·033)_{-2}$	
29	$(20·132)_0$	$(-0·987)_0$	$(-0·094)_{-1}$	$(-0·007)_{-1}$	$(+0·026)_{-2}$
33	$(19·145)_1$	$(-1·088)_1$	$(-0·101)_0$		
37	$(18·057)_2$				

$$\therefore y = 20·132 - \frac{0·940}{4} - \frac{0·094}{2! \times 4^2} + \frac{15 \times 0·02}{3! \times 4^3} - \frac{15 \times 0·026}{4! \times 4^4}.$$
$$= 20·132 - 0·235 - 0·003 + 0·0008 - 0·0001 = 19·895.$$

By Newton's formula, we get 19·895.

The central difference formula of Stirling thus furnishes the same result as the ordinary difference formula of Newton. We get different results when the higher orders of differences are neglected. For instance, if we neglect differences of the second order in formulæ (7) and (20), Stirling's formula would furnish more accurate results, because, in virtue of the substitution $\Delta^1{}_{-1} = \Delta^1 - \frac{1}{2}\Delta^2{}_{-1}$, we have really retained a portion of the second order of differences. If, therefore, we take the difference formula as far as the first, third, or some odd order of differences, we get the same results with the central and the ordinary difference formulæ. One more term is required to get an odd order of differences when central differences are employed. Thus, five terms are required to get third order differences in the one case, and four terms in the other. For practical purposes I do not see that any advantage is to be gained by the use of central differences.

V. Graphic interpolation.

Intermediate values may be obtained from the graphic curve by measuring the ordinate corresponding to a given abscissa or *vice versâ*.

In measuring high temperatures by means of the Le Chatelier-Austin pyrometer, the deflection of the galvanometer index on a millimetre scale is caused by the electromotive force generated by the heating of a thermo-couple (Pt – Pt with 10 °/₀ Rd) in circuit with the galvanometer. The displacement of the index is nearly proportional to the temperature. The scale is calibrated by heating the junction to well-defined temperatures and plotting the temperatures as ordinates, the scale readings as abscissæ. The resulting graph or "*calibration curve*" is shown in Fig. 130. The ordinate to the curve corresponding to any scale reading, gives the desired temperature. For example, the scale reading "160" corresponds with the temperature 1300°.

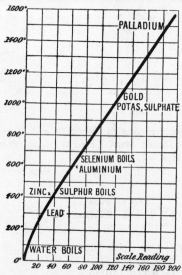

FIG. 130.—Calibration Chart °C.

§ 106. Differential Coefficients from Numerical Observations.

It is sometimes necessary to calculate the value of dy/dx and d^2y/dx^2 from the relation $y = f(x)$. Three methods are available :—

I. Differentiation of a known function.

If corresponding values of two variables can be represented in the form of a mathematical equation, the differential coefficient of the one variable with respect to the other can be easily obtained.

In illustration, A. Horstmann (*Liebig's Ann. Ergbd.*, **8**, 112, 1872), wished to compare the experimental values of the heats of vaporization, Q, of ammonium chloride with those calculated from the expression : $Q = T(dp/dT)dv$, which had been deduced from the principles of thermodynamics. He found that the observed vapour pressure, p, at different temperatures, θ, could be represented well enough by Biot's formula : $\log_{10}p = a + ba^{\theta - 258 \cdot 5}$. Hence, the value of $dp/d\theta$, or dp/dT, for the vapour pressure at any particular temperature could be obtained by differentiating this formula and substituting the observed values of p and t in the result. It is assumed, of course, that the numerical values of a, b and a are known. Following Horstmann $a = 5 \cdot 15790$, $b = -3 \cdot 34598$, and $\log_{10}a = 0 \cdot 9979266 - 1$. Suppose it be required to find the value of $dp/d\theta$ at 300°. When $\theta = 300$, $\theta - 258 \cdot 5 = 41 \cdot 5$; and $a^{41 \cdot 5} = 0 \cdot 819$, because $\log_{10}a^{41 \cdot 5} = 41 \cdot 5 \log_{10}a = 41 \cdot 5 \times -0 \cdot 0020734 = -0 \cdot 086046$; consequently, $0 \cdot 086046 = -41 \cdot 5 \log_{10}a = \log_{10}a^{-41 \cdot 5} = \log_{10}1 \cdot 221$. Hence, $a^{-41 \cdot 5} = 1 \cdot 221$; $\therefore a^{41 \cdot 5} = 0 \cdot 819$; and $ba^{41 \cdot 5} = -3 \cdot 34598 \times 0 \cdot 8192 = -2 \cdot 74036$. Hence, $\log_{10}p = 5 \cdot 1579 - 2 \cdot 7403$; or, $\log_{10}p = 2 \cdot 4175 = \log_{10}261 \cdot 5$; or, $p = 261.5$. By differentiation of $\log_{10}p = a + ba^{\theta - 258 \cdot 5}$

$$\frac{dp}{d\theta} = pba^{41 \cdot 5}\log_{10}a = 261 \cdot 5 \times -2 \cdot 74035 \times -0 \cdot 0020734 = 1 \cdot 5.$$

EXAMPLES.—(1) Assuming that the pressure, p, of steam at $\theta°$ C. in lbs. per square foot is given by the law $\theta = 29 \cdot 77p^{\frac{1}{5}} - 37 \cdot 6$, show that when $p = 290$, $dp/d\theta = 15 \cdot 67$. Hint. $d\theta/dp = -\frac{1}{5}(29 \cdot 77)p^{-4/5}$; $\therefore dp/d\theta = 0 \cdot 168p^{4/5}$; $\therefore dp/d\theta = 0 \cdot 168 \times 290^{4/5}$ lbs. per square foot per ° C.

(2) The volume, v_s, of a cubic foot of saturated steam at $T°$ abs. is given by the formula $L = T(v_s + v_w)dp/dT$, where v_w the volume of one pound of water which may be taken as negligibly small in comparison with v_s ; L is the latent heat of one pound of steam in mechanical units, i.e., 740,710 ft. lbs. Given also the formula of the preceding example, show that when $\theta = 127°$ C., $p = \{(127 + 37 \cdot 6)/29 \cdot 77\}^5$; $\therefore \log p = 3 \cdot 71365$; $\therefore dp/d\theta$, or, what is the same thing, $dp/dT = 0 \cdot 168 \times 935 = 157$ lbs. per square foot per degree absolute. Hence, $740710 = 157 \times v_s \times 400$; $\therefore v_s = 11 \cdot 8$.

II. *Graphic interpolation.*

In the above-quoted investigation, Horstmann sought the value of dp/dT for the dissociation pressure of aqueous vapour from crystalline disodium hydrogen phosphate at different temperatures. Here the form of $p = f(T)$ was not known, and it became necessary to deal directly with the numerical observations, or with the curve expressing these measurements. In the latter case, the tangent to the "smoothed" or "faired" curve obtained by plotting corresponding values of p and T on squared paper will sometimes allow the required differential coefficient to be obtained. Suppose, for example, we seek the numerical value of $dp/d\theta$ at 150° when it is known that when

$$p = 8\cdot698, \quad 9\cdot966, \quad 11\cdot380 \text{ lbs. per sq. ft. ;}$$
$$\theta = 145, \quad 150, \quad 155° \text{ C.}$$

These numbers are plotted on squared paper as in Fig. 131. To

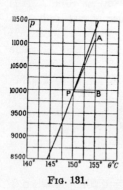

Fig. 131.

find $dp/d\theta$ at the point P corresponding with 150°, and 9·966 lbs. per square foot, first draw the tangent PA; from P draw PB parallel with the θ-axis. If now the pressure were to increase throughout 5° from 150° to 155° at the same rate as it is increasing at P, the increase in pressure for 5° rise of temperature would be equal to the length BA, or to 1300 lbs. per square foot. Consequently, the increase of pressure per degree rise of temperature is equal to $1300 \div 5 = 260$ lbs. per sq. ft. Hence $dp/dT = 260$.

The graphic differentiation of an experimental curve is avoided if very accurate results are wanted, because the errors of the experimental curve are greatly exaggerated when drawing tangents. If the measurements are good better results can be obtained, because the curve does not then want smoothing. Graphic interpolation was accurate enough for Horstmann's work. See also O. W. Richardson, J. Nicol, and T. Parnell, *Phil. Mag.* [6], **8**, 1, 1904, for another illustration.

We now seek a more exact method for finding the differential coefficient of one variable, say y, with respect to another, say x, from a set of corresponding values of x and y obtained by actual measurement.

III. *From the difference formulæ.*

Let us now return to Stirling's interpolation formula. Differentiate (19), page 317, with respect to x, and if we take the difference between y_0 and y_x to be infinitely small, we must put $x = 0$ in the result. In this way, we find that

$$\frac{dy}{dx} = \frac{1}{h}\left(\frac{\Delta^1_{\,0} + \Delta^1_{\,-1}}{2} - \frac{1}{6}\cdot\frac{\Delta^3_{\,-1} + \Delta^3_{\,-2}}{2} + \frac{1}{30}\cdot\frac{\Delta^5_{\,-2} + \Delta^5_{\,-3}}{2} - \ldots\right). \quad \textbf{(1)}$$

This series may be written in the form

$$\frac{dy}{dx} = \frac{1}{h}\left(\frac{\Delta^1_{\,0} + \Delta^1_{\,-1}}{2} - \frac{1^2}{3!}\cdot\frac{\Delta^3_{\,-1} + \Delta^3_{\,-2}}{2} + \frac{1^2\cdot 2^2}{5!}\cdot\frac{\Delta^5_{\,-2} + \Delta^5_{\,-3}}{2} + \ldots\right). \quad \textbf{(2)}$$

To illustrate the use of formula (2), let the first two columns of the following table represent a set of measurements obtained in the laboratory. It is required to find the value of dy/dx corresponding to $x = 5\cdot2$. First set up the table of central differences.

x.	y.	Δ^1.	Δ^2.	Δ^3.	Δ^4.	Δ^5.
4·9	$(134\cdot290)_{-3}$					
		$(14\cdot123)_{-3}$				
5·0	$(148\cdot413)_{-2}$		$(1\cdot486)_{-3}$			
		$(15\cdot609)_{-2}$		$(0\cdot155)_{-3}$		
5·1	$(164\cdot022)_{-1}$		$(1\cdot641)_{-2}$		$(0\cdot019)_{-3}$	
		$(17\cdot250)_{-1}$		$(0\cdot174)_{-2}$		$(-0\cdot004)_{-3}$
5·2	$(181\cdot272)_0$		$(1\cdot815)_{-1}$		$(0\cdot015)_{-2}$	
		$(19\cdot065)_0$		$(0\cdot189)_{-1}$		$(+0\cdot009)_{-2}$
5·3	$(200\cdot337)_1$		$(2\cdot004)_0$		$(0\cdot024)_{-1}$	
		$(21\cdot069)_1$		$(0\cdot213)_0$		
5·4	$(221\cdot406)_2$		$(2\cdot217)_1$			
		$(23\cdot286)_2$				
5·5	$(244\cdot692)_3$					

Make the proper substitutions in (2). In the case of $5\cdot2$ only the block figures in the above table are required. Thus,

$$\frac{dy}{dx} = \frac{1}{0\cdot1}\left(\frac{17\cdot250 + 19\cdot065}{2} - \frac{1}{6}\cdot\frac{0\cdot174 + 0\cdot189}{2} + \frac{1}{30}\cdot\frac{0\cdot009 - 0\cdot004}{2}\right).$$

$$\therefore \frac{dy}{dx} = 181\cdot273.$$

The student may now show that by differentiating Stirling's formula twice, and putting $x = 0$ in the result, we obtain the second differential coefficient

$$\frac{d^2y}{dx^2} = \frac{1}{h^2}\left(\Delta^2_{\,-1} - \frac{1}{12}\Delta^4_{\,-2} + \frac{1}{90}\Delta^6_{\,-3} - \ldots\right), \quad \textbf{(3)}$$

which may also be writtten

$$\frac{d^2y}{dx^2} = \frac{1}{h^2}\left(\frac{2}{2!}\Delta^2_{\,-1} - \frac{2}{4!}\Delta^4_{\,-2} + \frac{2\cdot2^2}{6!}\dot{\Delta}^6_{\,-3} - \frac{2\cdot2^2\cdot3^2}{8!}\Delta^8_{\,-4} + \ldots\right). \quad \textbf{(4)}$$

The difference columns should not be carried further than is consistent with the accuracy of the data, otherwise the higher approximations will be *less* accurate than the first. Do not carry the differences further than the point at which they begin to exhibit marked irregularities. The Δ^5 differences in the above table, for instance, are "out of bounds". The first two terms generally suffice for all practical requirements.

EXAMPLES.—(1) From Horstmann's observations on the dissociation pressure, p, of the ammonio-chlorides of silver at different temperatures, θ:

$$\theta = 8, \qquad 12, \qquad 16, \ldots \ °C.$$
$$p = 43\cdot2, \qquad 52\cdot0, \qquad 65\cdot3, \ldots cm. \ Hg.$$

show that at 12°, $dp/d\theta = 2\cdot76$.

(2) Show that $ds/d\theta = -4\cdot7 \times 10^{-6}$, at 0° C, from the following data :—

$$\theta = 1, \qquad 0\cdot5, \qquad 0, \qquad -0\cdot5, \qquad -1\cdot0, \ldots ;$$
$$10^6 \times s = 1288\cdot3, \qquad 1290\cdot7, \qquad 1293\cdot1, \qquad 1295\cdot4, \qquad 1297\cdot8, \ldots$$

(3) Find the value of d^2y/dx^2 for $y = 5\cdot2$ from the above table. Ansr. 181·4.

(4) The variation in the pressure of saturated steam, p, with temperature θ has been found to be as follows :—

$$\theta = 90, \qquad 95, \qquad 100, \qquad 105, \qquad 110, \qquad 115, \qquad 120, \ldots ;$$
$$p = 1463, \qquad 1765, \qquad 2116, \qquad 2524, \qquad 2994, \qquad 3534, \qquad 4152, \ldots$$

Hence show that at 105° $dp/d\theta = 87\cdot58$, $d^2p/d\theta^2 = 2\cdot48$. Hint. $dy/dx = \frac{1}{5}\{\frac{1}{2}(408 + 470) - \frac{1}{12}(5 + 8)\} = \frac{1}{5}(437\cdot917) = 87\cdot583$.

§ 107. How to Represent a Set of Observations by Means of a Formula.

After a set of measurements of two independent variables has been made in the laboratory, it is necessary to find if there is any simple relation between them, in other words, to find if a general expression of the one variable can be obtained in terms of the other so as to abbreviate in one simple formula the whole set of observations, as well as intermediate values not actually measured.

The most satisfactory method of finding a formula to express the relation between the two variables in any set of measurements, is to deduce a mathematical expression in terms of variables and constants, from known principles or laws, and then determine the value of the constants from the experimental results themselves. Such expressions are said to be **theoretical formulæ** as distinct from **empirical formulæ**, which have no well-defined relation with known principles or laws.

The terms "formula" and "function" are by no means synonymous. The function is the relation or law involved in the process. The relation *may* be represented in a formula by symbols which stand for numbers. The formula is not the function, it is only its dress. The fit may or may not be a good one. This must be borne in mind when the formal relations of the symbols are made to represent some physical process or concrete thing.

It is, of course, impossible to determine the correct form of a function from the experimental data alone. An infinite number of formulæ might satisfy the numerical data, in the same sense that an infinite number of curves might be drawn through a series of points. For instance, over thirty empirical formulæ have been proposed to express the unknown relation between the pressure and temperature of saturated steam.

As a matter of fact, empirical formulæ frequently originate from a lucky guess. Good guessing is a fine art. A hint as to the most plausible form of the function is sometimes obtained by plotting the experimental results. It is useful to remember that if the curve increases or decreases regularly, the equation is probably algebraic ; if it alternately increases and decreases, the curve is probably expressed by some trigonometrical function.

If the curve is a straight line, the equation will be of the form, $y = mx + b$. If not, try $y = ax^n$, or $y = ax/(1 + bx)$. If the rate of increase (or decrease) of the function is proportional to itself we have the compound interest law. In other words, if dy/dx varies proportionally with y, $y = be^{-ax}$ or be^{ax}. If dy/dx varies proportionally with x/y, try $y = bx^a$. If dy/dx varies as x, try $y = a + bx^2$. Other general formulæ may be tried when the above prove unsatisfactory, thus,

$$y = \frac{a + x}{b - x}; \; y = 10^{a + bx}; \; y = a + b \log x; \; y = a + bc^x, \text{ etc.}$$

Otherwise we may fall back upon Maclaurin's expansion in ascending powers of x, the constants being positive, negative or zero. This series is particularly useful when the terms converge rapidly.

When the results exhibit a periodicity, as in the ebb and flow of tides ; annual variations of temperature and pressure of the atmosphere ; cyclic variations in magnetic declination, etc., we refer the results to a trigonometrical series as indicated in the chapter on Fourier's series.

Empirical formulæ, however closely they agree with facts, do not pretend to represent the true relation between the variables under consideration. They do little more than follow, more or less closely, the course of the graphic curve representing the relation between the variables within a more or less restricted range. Thus, Regnault employed three interpolation formulæ for the vapour pressure of water between − 32° F. and 230° F.[1] For example, from − 32° F. to 0° F., he used $p = a + ba^\theta$, from 0° to 100° F.,

[1] Rankine was afterwards lucky enough to find that $\log p = a - \beta\theta^{-1} - \gamma\theta^{-2}$, represented Regnault's results for the vapour pressure of water throughout the whole range − 32° F. to 230° F.

$\log p = a + ba^\theta + c\beta^\theta$; from 100° to 230° F., $\log p = a + ba^\theta - c\beta^\theta$. Kopp required four formulæ to represent his measurements of the thermal expansion of water between 0° and 100° C. Each of Kopp's formulæ was only applicable within the limited range of 25° C.

If all attempts to deduce or guess a satisfactory formula are unsuccessful, the results are simply tabulated, or preferably plotted on squared paper, because then "it is the thing itself that is before the mind instead of a numerical symbol of the thing".

§ 108. To Evaluate the Constants in Empirical or Theoretical Formulæ.

Before a formula containing constants can be adapted to any *particular* process, the numerical values of the constants must be accurately known.   For instance, the volume, v, to which unit volume of *any* gas expands when heated to $\theta°$, may be represented by

$$v = 1 + a\theta,$$

where a is a constant.   The law embodied in this equation can only be applied to a particular gas when a assumes *the* numerical value characteristic of that gas.   If we are dealing with hydrogen, $a = 0\cdot00366$; if carbon dioxide, $a = 0\cdot00371$; and if sulphur dioxide $a = 0\cdot00385$.

Again, if we want to apply the law of definite proportions, we must know exactly what the definite proportions are before it can be decided whether any particular combination is comprised under the law.   In other words, we must not only know the general law, but also particular numbers appropriate to particular elements. In mathematical language this means that before a function can be used practically, we must know :

   (i) The form of the function ;

   (ii) The numerical values of the constants.

The determination of the form of the function has been discussed in the preceding section, the evaluation of the constants remains to be considered.

Is it legitimate to deduce the numerical values of the constants from the experiments themselves ?   The answer is that the numerical data are determined from experiments purposely made by different methods under different conditions.   When all independently furnish the same result it is fair to assume that the experimental numbers includes the values of the constants under discussion.[1]

In some determinations of the volume, v, of carbon dioxide dissolved in one volume of water at different temperatures, θ, the following pairs of values were obtained :—

$$\theta = \quad 0, \qquad 5, \qquad 10, \qquad 15 ;$$
$$v = 1 \cdot 80, \qquad 1 \cdot 45, \qquad 1 \cdot 18, \qquad 1 \cdot 00.$$

As Herschel has remarked, in all cases of "direct unimpeded action," we may expect the two quantities to vary in a simple proportion, so as to obey the linear equation,

$$y = a + bx ; \text{ we have, } v = a + b\theta, \qquad . \qquad . \qquad (1)$$

which, be it observed, is obtained from Maclaurin's series by the rejection of all but the first two terms.

It is required to find from these observations the values of the constants, a and b, which will represent the experimental data in the best possible manner.   The above results can be written,

$$\left. \begin{array}{l} \text{(i) } 1 \cdot 80 = a, \\ \text{(ii) } 1 \cdot 45 = a + 5b, \\ \text{(iii) } 1 \cdot 18 = a + 10b, \\ \text{(iv) } 1 \cdot 00 = a + 15b, \end{array} \right\} \qquad . \qquad . \qquad . \qquad (2)$$

which is called a set of **observation equations.**   We infer, from

(i) and (ii) $a = 1 \cdot 80$, $b = - 0 \cdot 07$,
(ii) and (iii) $a = 1 \cdot 62$, $b = - 0 \cdot 054$,
(iii) and (iv) $a = 1 \cdot 54$, $b = - 0 \cdot 036$, etc.

The want of agreement between the values of the constants obtained from different sets of equations is due to errors of observation, and, of course, to the fact that the particular form of the function chosen does not fit the experimental results.   It nearly always occurs when the attempt is made to calculate the constants in this manner.

The numerical values of the constants deduced from any arbitrary set of observation equations can only be absolutely correct when the measurements are perfectly accurate.   The problem here presented is to pick the best representative values of the constants from the experimental numbers.   Several methods are available.

---

[1] J. F. W. Herschel's *A Preliminary Discourse on the Study of Natural Philosophy*, London, 1831, is worth reading in this connexion.

I. Solving the equations by algebraic methods.

Pick out as many observation equations as there are unknowns and solve for a, b, c by ordinary algebraic methods. The different values of the unknown corresponding with the different sets of observation arbitrarily selected are thus ignored.

EXAMPLE.—Corresponding values of the variables x and y are known, say, x_1, y_1; x_2, y_2; x_3, y_3; ... Calculate the constants a, b, c, in the interpolation formula

$$y = a \cdot 10^{\frac{bx}{1 + cx}}.$$

When $x_1 = 0$, $y_1 = a$. Thus b and c remain to be determined. Take logarithms of the two equations in x_2, y_2 and x_3, y_3 and show that,

$$b = \frac{\log_{10}\frac{y_3}{a}\left(\frac{1}{x_2} - \frac{1}{x_3}\right)\log_{10}\frac{y_2}{a}}{\log_{10}\frac{y_3}{a} - \frac{1}{x_3}\log_{10}\frac{y_2}{a}}; \quad c = \frac{\frac{1}{x^2}\log_{10}\frac{y_2}{a} - \frac{1}{x_3}\log_{10}\frac{y_3}{a}}{\log_{10}\frac{y_3}{a} - \log_{10}\frac{y_2}{a}}.$$

This method may be used with any of the above formulæ when an exact determination of the constants is of no particular interest, or when the errors of observation are relatively small. V. H. Regnault used it in his celebrated "Mémoire sur les forces élastiques de la vapeur d'eau" (*Ann. Chim. Phys.*, [3], **11**, 273, 1844) to evaluate the constants mentioned in the formula, page 323; so did G. C. Schmidt (*Zeit. phys. Chem.*, **7**, 433, 1891); and A. Horstmann (*Liebig's Ann. Ergbd.*, **8**, 112, 1872).

II. Method of Least Squares.

The constants must satisfy the following criterion : The differences between the observed and the calculated results must be the smallest possible with small positive and negative differences. One of the best ways of fixing the numerical values of the constants in any formula is to use what is known as the method of least squares. This rule proceeds from the assumption that the most probable values of the constants are those for which the sum of the squares of the differences between the observed and the calculated results are the smallest possible. We employ the rule for computing the maximum or minimum values of a function.

In this work we usually pass from the special to the general. Here we can reverse this procedure and take the general case first. Let the observed magnitude y depend on x in such a way that

$$y = a + bx. \qquad \qquad \qquad (3)$$

It is required to determine the most probable values of a and b. For perfect accuracy, we should have the following observation equations:

$$a + bx_1 - y_1 = 0 ; \; a + bx_2 - y_2 = 0 ; \; \ldots a + bx_n - y_n = 0.$$

In practice this is unattainable.   Let $v_1, v_2, \ldots v_n$ denote the actual deviations so that

$$a + bx_1 - y_1 = v_1 ; \; a + bx_2 - y_2 = v_2 ; \; \ldots a + bx_n - y_n = v_n.$$

It is required to determine the constants so that,

$$\Sigma(v^2) = v_1{}^2 + v_2{}^2 + \ldots + v_n{}^2 \text{ is a minimum.}$$

With observations affected with errors the smallest value of v^2 will generally differ from zero; and the sum of the squares will therefore always be a positive number.   We must therefore choose such values of a and b as will make

$$\Sigma_{n=1}^{n=n}(a + bx_n - y_n)^2$$

the smallest possible.   This condition is fulfilled, page 156, by equating the partial derivatives of $\Sigma(v^2)$ with respect to a and b to zero.   In this way, we obtain,

$$\frac{\partial}{\partial a}\Sigma(a + bx - y)^2 = 0 ; \text{ hence, } \Sigma(a + bx - y) = 0 ;$$

$$\frac{\partial}{\partial b}\Sigma(a + bx - y)^2 = 0 ; \text{ hence, } \Sigma x(a + bx - y) = 0.$$

If there are n observation equations, there are n a's and $\Sigma(a) = na$, therefore,

$$na + b\Sigma(x) - \Sigma(y) = 0 ; \; a\Sigma(x) + b\Sigma(x^2) - \Sigma(xy) = 0.$$

Now solve these two simultaneous equations for a and b,

$$a = \frac{\Sigma(x) \cdot \Sigma(xy) - \Sigma(x^2) \cdot \Sigma(y)}{[\Sigma(x)]^2 - n\Sigma(x^2)} ; \; b = \frac{\Sigma(x)\Sigma(y) - n\Sigma(xy)}{[\Sigma(x)]^2 - n\Sigma(x^2)}, \quad (4)$$

which determines the values of the constants.

Returning to the special case at the commencement of this section, to find the best representative value of the constants a and b in formula (1).   Previous to substitution in (4), it is best to arrange the data according to the following scheme :—

θ.	v.	θ^2.	θv.
0	1·80	0	0
5	1·45	25	7·25
10	1·18	100	11·80
15	1·00	225	15·00
$\Sigma(\theta) = 30$	$\Sigma(v) = 5\cdot43$	$\Sigma(\theta^2) = 350$	$\Sigma(\theta v) = 34\cdot05$

Substitute these values in equation (4), n, the number of observations, $= 4$, hence we get

$$a = 1 \cdot 758 \, ; \quad b = - \, 0 \cdot 0534.$$

The amount of gas dissolved at $\theta°$ is therefore obtained from the interpolation formula,

$$v = 1 \cdot 758 - 0 \cdot 0534 \theta.$$

To show that this is the best possible formula to employ, in spite of $1 \cdot 758$ volumes obtained at $0°$, proceed in the following manner:—

Temp. $= \theta$.	Volume of gas $= v$.		Difference between Calculated and Observed.	Square of Difference between Calculated and Observed.
	Calculated.	Observed.		
0	1·758	1·80	− 0·042	0·00176
5	1·491	1·45	+ 0·041	0·00168
10	1·224	1·18	+ 0·044	0·00194
15	0·957	1·00	− 0·043	0·00185
				0·00723

The number $0 \cdot 00723$, the sum of the squares of the differences between the observed and the calculated results, is a minimum. Any alteration in the value of either a or b will cause this term to increase. This can easily be verified. For example, if we try the very natural $a = 1 \cdot 80$, $b = - \, 0 \cdot 065$, we get $0 \cdot 039$; if $a = 1 \cdot 772$, $b = - \, 0 \cdot 056$ we get $0 \cdot 0082$, etc.

EXAMPLES.—(1) Find the law connecting the length, l, of a rod with temperature, θ, when the length of a metre bar at $0°$ elongates with rise of temperature according to the following scheme:—

$$\theta = \quad 20°, \qquad 48°, \qquad 50°, \qquad 60° \, \text{C.} \, ;$$
$$l = 1000 \cdot 22, \quad 1000 \cdot 65, \quad 1000 \cdot 90, \quad 1001 \cdot 05 \, \text{mm.}$$

(F. Kohlrausch's *Leitfaden der praktischen Physik*, Leipzig, 12, 1896.) During the calculation, for the sake of brevity, use $l = \cdot 22$, $\cdot 65$, $\cdot 9$ and $1 \cdot 05$. Assume $l = a + b\theta$, and show that $a = 999 \cdot 804$, $b = 0 \cdot 0212$, or $l = 999 \cdot 804 + 0 \cdot 01212 \theta$.

(2) According to G. J. W. Bremer's measurements (*Zeit. phys. Chem.*, 3, 423, 1889), aqueous solutions of sodium carbonate containing $p \, °/_{0}$ of the salt expand by an amount v as indicated in the following table:—

$$p = 3 \cdot 2420 \qquad 4 \cdot 8122 \qquad 7 \cdot 4587 \qquad 10 \cdot 1400 \, ;$$
$$10^{4} \times v = 1 \cdot 766, \qquad 2 \cdot 046, \qquad 2 \cdot 342, \qquad 2 \cdot 732.$$

Hence show that $v = 0 \cdot 0001354 + 0 \cdot 00001360 p$.

Suppose that instead of the general formula (3), we had started with

$$y = a + bx + cx^2, \quad . \qquad . \qquad . \qquad . \qquad (5)$$

where a, b and c are constants to be determined. The resulting formulæ for b and c (omitting a), analogous to (4), are,

$$b = \frac{\Sigma(x^4) \cdot \Sigma(xy) - \Sigma(x^3) \cdot \Sigma(x^2y)}{\Sigma(x^2) \cdot \Sigma(x^4) - [\Sigma(x^3)]^2} \, ; \, c = \frac{\Sigma(x^2) \cdot \Sigma(x^2y) - \Sigma(x^3) \cdot \Sigma(xy)}{\Sigma(x^2) \cdot \Sigma(x^4) - [\Sigma(x^3)]^2}. \quad (6)$$

These two formulæ have been deduced by a similar method to that employed in the preceding case. a is a constant to be determined separately by arranging the experiment so that when $x = 0$, $a = y_0$.

EXAMPLES.—(1) The following series of measurements of the temperature, θ, at different depths, x, in an artesian well, were made at Grenelle (France):—

$x =$ 28,   66,   173,   248,   298,   400,   505,   548;
$\theta =$ 11·71,   12·90,   16·40,   20·00,   22·20,   23·75,   26·45,   27·70.

The mean temperature at the surface, where $x = 0$, was 10·6°. Hence show that at a depth of x metres, $\theta = 10·6 + 0·042096x - 0·000020558x^2$.

(2) If, when $x = 0$, $y = 1$ and when

$x =$ 8·97,   20·56,   36·10,   49·96,   62·38,   83·73;
$y =$ 1·0078,   1·0184,   1·0317,   1·0443,   1·0563,   1·0759.

Hence show that $y = 1 + 0·00084x + 0·0000009x^2$.

Thomson (*Wied. Ann.*, **44**, 553, 1891) employed the general formulæ for a, b, c, when still another correction term is included, namely,

$$y = ax + bx^2 + cx^3. \quad . \quad . \quad . \quad (7)$$

Illustrations will be found in the original paper

If three variables are to be investigated, we may use the general formula

$$z = ax + by. \quad . \quad . \quad . \quad (8)$$

The reader may be able to prove, on the above lines, that

$$a = \frac{\Sigma(x^2) \cdot \Sigma(xz) - \Sigma(xy) \cdot \Sigma(yz)}{\Sigma(x^2) \cdot \Sigma(y^2) - [\Sigma(xy)]^2} \, ; \, b = \frac{\Sigma(x^2) \cdot \Sigma(yz) - \Sigma(xy) \cdot \Sigma(xz)}{\Sigma(x^2) \cdot \Sigma(y^2) - [\Sigma(xy)]^2}. \quad (9)$$

M. Centnerszwer (*Zeit. phys. Chem.*, **26**, 1, 1896) referred his observations on the partial pressure of oxygen during the oxidation of phosphorus in the presence of different gases and vapours to the empirical formula

$$p_x = p_o - a \log (1 + bx); \, \text{or to} \, p_o - p_x = a \log (1 + bx),$$

where p_o denotes the pressure of pure oxygen. p_x the partial pressure of oxygen mixed with x °/$_o$ of foreign gas or vapour. Show with Centnerszwer, that if $y = p_o - p_x$

$$a = \frac{\Sigma(xy) \cdot \Sigma(x^4) - \Sigma(x^2y) \cdot \Sigma(x^3)}{\Sigma(x^2) \cdot \Sigma(x^4) - [\Sigma(x^3)]^2}; \; b = \frac{\Sigma(xy) \cdot \Sigma(x^3) - \Sigma(x^2y) \cdot \Sigma(x^2)}{\Sigma(x^2) \cdot \Sigma(x^4) - [\Sigma(x^3)]^2}, \quad (10)$$

EXAMPLE.—Show, with Centnerszwer, that $a = 184$, $b = 113$ for chlor-
benzene when it is known that when

$$p_x = 561, \quad 549, \quad 536, \quad 523, \quad 509, \quad 485;$$
$$x = 0, \quad 0\cdot054, \quad 0\cdot108, \quad 0\cdot215, \quad 0\cdot430, \quad 0\cdot858.$$

The method of least squares *assumes* that the observations are
all equally reliable. The reader will notice that we have assumed
that one variable is quite free from error, and very often we can
do so with safety, especially when the one variable can be
measured with a much greater degree of accuracy than the other.
We shall see later on what to do when this is not the case.

III. Graphic methods.

Returning to the solubility determinations at the beginning of
this section, prick points corresponding to pairs of values of v and
θ on squared paper. The points lie approximately on a straight
line. Stretch a black thread so as to get *the* straight line which
lies most evenly among the points. Two points lying on the
black thread are $v = 1\cdot0$, $\theta = 14\cdot5$, and $v = 1\cdot7$, $\theta = 1\cdot5$.

$$\therefore \; a + 14\cdot5b = 1; \; a + 1\cdot5b = 1\cdot7.$$

By subtraction, $b = -0\cdot54$, $\therefore a = 1\cdot78$. It is here assumed that
the curve which goes most evenly among the points represents the
correct law, see page 148. But the number of observations is,
perhaps, too small to show the method to advantage. Try
these:

$$p = 2, \quad 4, \quad 6, \quad 8, \quad 10, \quad 20, \quad 25, \quad 30, \quad 35, \quad 40,$$
$$s = 1\cdot02, \; 1\cdot03, \; 1\cdot06, \; 1\cdot07, \; 1\cdot09, \; 1\cdot18, \; 1\cdot23, \; 1\cdot29, \; 1\cdot34, \; 1\cdot40,$$

where s denotes the density of aqueous solutions containing $p\,\%$
of calcium chloride at $15°\,C$. The selection of the best "black
thread" line is, in general, more uncertain the greater the magnitude of the errors of observation affecting the measurements.
The values deduced for the constants will differ slightly with
different workers or even with the same worker at different times.
With care, and accurately ruled paper, the results are sufficiently
exact for most practical requirements.

When the " best " curve has to be drawn freehand, the results are still more uncertain. For example, the amount of "active" oxygen, y, contained in a solution of hydrogen dioxide in dilute sulphuric acid was found, after the lapse of t days, to be :

$t = $ 6,   9,   10,   14,   18,   27,   34,   38,   41,   54,   87,
$y = $ 3·4,   3·1,   3·1,   2·6,   2·2,   1·3,   0·9,   0·7,   0·6,   0·4,   0·2,

where $y = 3·9$ when $t = 0$. We leave these measurements with the reader as an exercise.

In J. Perry's *Practical Mathematics*, London, 1899, a trial plotting on "logarithmic paper " is recommended in certain cases. On *squared paper*, the distances between the horizontal and vertical lines are in fractions of a metre or of a foot. On *logarithmic paper* (Fig. 132), the distances between the lines, like the divisions on the slide rule, are proportional to the

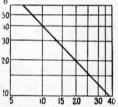

logarithms of the numbers. If, therefore, the experimental numbers follow a law like $\log_{10}x + a\log_{10}y = $ constant, the function can be plotted as easily as on squared paper. If the resulting graph is a straight line, we may be sure that we are dealing with some such law as $xy^a = $ constant; or, $(x + a) (y + b)^a = $ constant.

FIG. 132.—Log. Paper.

EXAMPLE.—The pressure, p, of saturated steam in pounds per square inch when the volume is v cubic feet per pound is

$p = $ 10,   20,   30,   40,   50,   60,
$v = $ 37·80, 19·72, 13·48, 10·29, 8·34, 6·62.

Hence, by plotting corresponding values of p and v on logarithmic paper, we get the straight line :

$\log_{10}p + \gamma\log_{10}v = \log_{10}b$; hence, $pv^{1·065} = 382$, since $\log_{10}b = 2·5811$, ∴ $b = 382$ and $\gamma = 1·065$. The graph is shown on log paper in Fig. 132, and on ordinary squared paper in Fig. 134.

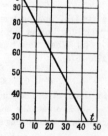

A *semi-logarithmic paper* (Fig. 133) may be made with distances between say the horizontal columns in fractions of a metre, while the distances between the vertical columns

FIG. 133.—Semi-log. Paper.

are proportional to the logarithms of the numbers. Functions obeying the compound interest law will plot, on such paper, as a straight line. One advantage of logarithmic paper is that the

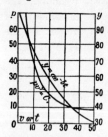

skill required for drawing an accurate freehand curve is not required. The stretched
black thread will be found sufficient. With
semi-logarithmic paper, either $x + \log_{10}y =$
constant ; or, $y + \log_{10}x =$ constant will give
a straight line.

According to C. Runge and Paschen's law,
if the logarithms of the atomic weights are
plotted as ordinates with the distances between the brightest spectral lines in the

FIG. 134.

magnetic field as abscissæ, chemically allied elements lie on the
same straight line. This, for example, is the case with magnesium,
calcium, strontium, and barium. Radium, too, lies on the same
line, hence C. Runge and J. Precht (*Ber. deut. phys. Ges.*, 313,
1903) infer the atomic weight of radium to be 257·8. Obviously
we can plot atomic weights and the other data directly on the
logarithmic paper. Another example will be found in W. N.
Hartley and E. P. Hedley's study (*Journ. Chem. Soc.*, **91**, 1010,
1907), of the absorption spectra solutions of certain organic compounds where the oscillation frequencies were plotted against the
logarithms of the thicknesses of the solutions.

EXAMPLES.—(1) Plot on semi-logarithmic paper Harcourt and Esson's
numbers (*l.c.*) :

$t =$ 2,   5,   8,   11,   14,   17,   27,   31,   35,   44,
$y = $ 94·8, 87·9, 81·3, 74·9, 68·7, 64·0, 49·3, 44·0, 39·1, 31·6,

for the amount of substance y remaining in a reacting system after the elapse
of an interval of time t. Hence determine values for the constants a and b in

$$y = ae^{-bt} ; \ i.e., \ \text{in} \ \log_{10}y + bt = \log_{10}a,$$

a straight line on "semi-log" paper. The graph is shown in Fig. 133 on
"semi-log" paper and in Fig. 134 on ordinary paper.

(2) What "law" can you find in J. Perry's numbers (*Proc. Roy. Soc.*, **23**,
472, 1875),

$\theta =$ 58,   86,   148,   166,   188,   202,   210,
$C = $ 0,   ·004,   ·018,   ·029,   ·051,   ·073,   ·090,

for the electrical conductivity C of glass at a temperature of $\theta°$ F. ?

(3) Evaluate the constant a in S. Arrhenius' formula, $\eta = a^x$, for the viscosity η of an aqueous solution of sodium benzoate of concentration x, given

$\eta = $ 1·6498,   1·2780,   1·1303,   1·0623,
$x =$ 1, $\frac{1}{2}$, $\frac{1}{4}$, $\frac{1}{8}$.

Several other methods have been proposed. Gauss' method,
for example, will be taken up later on. See also Hopkinson,

§ 109. Substitutes for Integration.

It may not always be convenient, or even possible, to integrate the differential equation; in that case a less exact method of verifying the theory embodied in the equation must be adopted. For the sake of illustration, take the equation

$$\frac{dx}{dt} = k(a - x); \quad \cdot \quad \cdot \quad \cdot \quad (1)$$

used to represent the velocity of a chemical reaction, x denotes the amount of substance transformed at the time t; and a denotes the initial concentration. Let dt denote unit interval of time, and let Δx denote the difference between the initial and final quantity of substance transformed in unit interval of time, then $\frac{1}{2}\Delta x$ denotes the average amount of substance transformed during the same interval of time. Hence, for the first interval, we write

$$\Delta x = k_1(a - \tfrac{1}{2}\Delta x),$$

which, by algebraic transformation, becomes

$$\Delta x = \frac{k_1 a}{1 + \tfrac{1}{2}k_1}. \quad \cdot \quad \cdot \quad \cdot \quad (2)$$

For the next interval,

$$\Delta x = k_1(a - x - \tfrac{1}{2}\Delta x), \text{ etc.}$$

These expressions may be used in place of the integral of (1), namely

$$k = \frac{1}{t}\log\frac{a}{a - x}, \quad \cdot \quad \cdot \quad \cdot \quad (3)$$

for the verification of (1).

With equations of the second order

$$\frac{dx}{dt} = k_2(a - x)^2, \quad \cdot \quad \cdot \quad \cdot \quad (4)$$

we get, in the same way,

$$\Delta x = \frac{k_2 a^2}{1 + k_2 a}; \quad \Delta x = \frac{k_2(a - x)^2}{1 + k_2(a - x)}, \text{ etc.,} \quad \cdot \quad (5)$$

by putting, as before, Δx in place of dx, $dt = 1$, $x = \frac{1}{2}\Delta x$, and remembering that the second power of Δx is negligibly small. The regular integral of (4) is

$$k_2 = \frac{1}{at} \cdot \frac{x}{a - x}. \quad \cdot \quad \cdot \quad \cdot \quad (6)$$

NUMERICAL ILLUSTRATION.—Let us suppose that k_1 and k_2 are both equal to 0.1, and that $a = 100$.   From (2)

$$\Delta x = \frac{0.1 \times 100}{1.05} = 9.52; \therefore a - x = 100 - 9.52 = 90.48;$$

$$\Delta x = \frac{0.1 \times 90.48}{1.05} = 8.62; \therefore a - x = 90.48 - 8.62 = 81.87.$$

Again from (5), for reactions of the second order

$$\Delta x = \frac{0.1 \times 10,000}{1 + 0.1 \times 100} = 90.99; \therefore a - x = 100 - 90.09 = 9.09;$$

$$\Delta x = \frac{(9.09)^2 \times 0.1}{1 + 0.1 \times 9.09} = 4.33; \therefore a - x = 9.09 - 4.33 = 4.76.$$

The following table shows that the results obtained by this method of approximation compare very favourably with those obtained from the regular integrals (3) and (6).   There is, of course, a slight error, but that is usually within the limits of experimental error.

	First Order.			Second Order.	
		$a - x$.			$a - x$.	
t.	by (2).	by (3).	t.	by (5).	by (6).
0	100	100	0	100	100
1	90·48	90·48	1	9·09	9·09
2	81·86	81·86	2	4·76	4·76
3	74·08	74·06	3	3·23	3·23
4	67·03	67·01	4	2·44	2·44
5	60·65	60·63	5	1·96	1·96
6	54·88	54·86	6	1·64	1·64
7	49·66	49·64	7	1·41	1·41
8	44·93	44·91	8	1·23	1·24

This method of integration was used by W. Federlin (*Zeit. phys. Chem.*, **41**, 565, 1902) in his study of the reaction between phosphorous acid, potassium iodide, and potassium persulphate; and by R. Wegscheider (*Zeit. phys. Chem.*, **41**, 52, 1902) for the saponification of the sulphonic esters.

The student should always be on the lookout for short cuts and simplifications.   Thus, it may be possible to transform the integral into a simpler form before evaluating by the methods of approximation.   For example, let

$$u = \int y \, . \, dx$$

be the integral.   In one investigation (R. A. Lehfeldt, *Phil. Mag.*, [5], **46**, 42, 1898; [6], **1**, 377, 403, 1901), y represented the concentration, x the electromotive force, and u the osmotic pressure of a solution. y was a known function, hence, dy could be readily calculated. Integrate by parts, and we get

$$u = xy - \int x \cdot dy,$$

which can be evaluated by the planimeter, or any other means.

Again, to calculate the vapour pressure, p_2, in the expression

$$x \frac{\partial \log p_1}{\partial x} + (1 - x) \frac{\partial \log p_2}{\partial x} = 0,$$

where p_1 and p_2 denote the vapour pressure of two components of a mixture; x is the fractional composition of the mixture. Suppose that p_1 and x are known, it is required to calculate p_2. Here also, on integration by parts,

$$\log p_2 = - \int \frac{x}{1 - x} \cdot \frac{\partial \log p_1}{\partial x} dx = - \frac{x \log p_1}{1 - x} + \int \frac{\log p_1}{(1 - x)^2} dx.$$

The second setting is much better adapted for numerical computation.

§ 110. Approximate Integration.

We have seen that the area enclosed by a curve can be estimated by finding the value of a definite integral. This may be reversed. The numerical value of a definite integral can be determined from measurements of the area enclosed by the curve. For instance, if the integral $\int f(x) \cdot dx$ is unknown, the value of $\int_b^a f(x) \cdot dx$ can be found by plotting the curve $y = f(x)$; erecting ordinates to the curve on the points $x = a$ and $x = b$; and then measuring the surface bounded by the x-axis, the two ordinates just drawn and the curve itself.

This area may be measured by means of the planimeter, an instrument which automatically registers the area of any plane figure when a tracer is passed round the boundary lines. A good description of these instruments by O. Henrici will be found in the *British Association's Reports*, 496, 1894.

Another way is to cut the figure out of a sheet of paper, or other uniform material. Let w_1 be the weight of a known area a_1 and w the weight of the piece cut out. The desired area x can then be obtained by simple proportion,

$$w_1 : a = w : x.$$

Other methods may be used for the finding the approximate value of an integral between certain limits. First plot the curve.

Divide the curve into n portions bounded by $n + 1$ equidistant ordinates $y_0, y_1, y_2, \ldots, y_n$, whose magnitude and common distance apart is known, it is required to find an approximate expression for the area so divided, that is to say, to evaluate the integral

$$\int_0^n f(x) \cdot dx.$$

Assuming Newton's interpolation formula

$$f(x) = y_0 + x\Delta^1_0 + \tfrac{1}{2!}x(x-1)\Delta^2_0 + \ldots, \qquad (1)$$

we may write,

$$\therefore \int_0^n f(x) \cdot dx = y_0\int_0^n dx + \Delta^1_0\int_0^n x \cdot dx + \int_0^n \frac{\Delta^2_0}{2!}x(x-1)dx + \ldots, \quad (2)$$

which is known as the **Newton-Cotes integration formula.** We may now apply this to special cases, such as calculating the value of a definite integral from a set of experimental measurements, etc.

I. Parabolic Formulæ.

Take three ordinates. There are two intervals. Reject all terms after Δ^2_0. Remember that $\Delta^1_0 = y_1 - y_0$ and $\Delta^2_0 = y_2 - 2y_1 + y_0$. Let the common difference be unity,

$$\int_0^2 f(x) \cdot dx = 2y_0 + 2\Delta^1_0 + \tfrac{1}{3}\Delta^2_0 = \tfrac{1}{3}(y_0 + 4y_1 + y_2). \qquad (3)$$

If h represents the common distance of the ordinates apart, we have the familiar result known as **Simpson's one-third rule,** thus,

$$\int_0^2 f(x) \cdot dx = \tfrac{1}{3}h(y_0 + 4y_1 + y_2). \qquad . \qquad . \qquad (4)$$

A graphic representation will perhaps make the assumptions in-

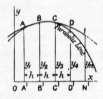

FIG. 135.

volved in this formula more apparent. Make the construction shown in Fig. 135. We seek the area of the portion $ANN'A'$ corresponding to the integral $f(x) \cdot dx$ between the limits $x = x_0$ and $x = x_n$, where $f(x)$ represents the equation of the curve $ABCDN$. Assume that each strip is bounded on one side by a parabolic curve. The area of the portion

$ABCC'A' = $ Area trapezium $ACC'A' + $ Area parabolic segment $ABCA$,
From well-known mensuration formulæ (16), page 604, the area of the portion

$$ABCC'A' = A'C[\tfrac{1}{2}(A'A + C'C) + \tfrac{2}{3}\{B'B - \tfrac{1}{2}(A'A + C'C)\}];$$
$$= 2h(\tfrac{1}{6}A'A + \tfrac{2}{3}B'B + \tfrac{1}{6}C'C) = \tfrac{1}{3}h(A'A + 4B'B + C'C). \qquad (5)$$

Extend this discussion to include the whole figure,

Area $ANN'A' = \frac{1}{3}h(1 + 4 + 2 + 4 + \ldots + 2 + 4 + 1)$,   (6)

where the successive coefficients of the perpendiculars AA', BB', . . . alone are stated ; h represents the distance of the strips apart. The greater the number of equal parts into which the area is divided, the more closely will the calculated correspond with true area.

Put $OA' = x_0$; $ON = x_n$; $A'N' = x_n - x_0$ and divide the area into n parts ; $h = (x_n - x_0)/n$. Let y_0, y_1, y_2, . . . y_n denote the successive ordinates erected upon Ox, then equation (6) may be written in the form,

$$\int_{x_0}^{x_n} f(x) \, . \, dx = \frac{1}{3}h\{(y_0 + y_n) + 4(y_1 + y_3 + \ldots + y_{n-1}) \\ + 2(y_2 + y_4 + \ldots + y_{n-2}).$$ (7)

In practical work a great deal of trouble is avoided by making the measurements at equal intervals $x_1 - x_0$, $x_2 - x_1$, . . ., $x_n - x_{n-1}$. R. Wegscheider (*Zeit. phys. Chem.*, **41**, 52, 1902) employed Simpson's rule for integrating the velocity equations for the speed of hydrolysis of sulphonic esters; and G. Bredig and F. Epstein (*Zeit. anorg. Chem.*, **42**, 341, 1904) in their study of the velocity of adiabatic reactions.

EXAMPLES.—(1) Evaluate the integral $\int x^3 \, . \, dx$ between the limits 1 and 11 by the aid of formula (6), given $h = 1$ and y_0, y_1, y_2, y_3, . . . y_8, y_9, y_{10} are respectively 1, 8, 27, 64, . . . 1000, 1331. Compare the result with the absolutely correct value. From (6),

$$\int_1^3 x^3 \, . \, dx = \frac{1}{3}(10980) = 3660 ; \text{ and } \int_1^3 x \, . \, dx = \frac{1}{4}(11)^4 - \frac{1}{4}(1)^4 = 3660,$$

is the perfect result obtained by actual integration.

(2) In measuring the magnitude of an electric current by means of the hydrogen voltameter, let C_0, C_1, C_2, . . . denote the currents passing through the galvanometer at the times t_0, t_1, t_2, . . . minutes. The volume of hydrogen liberated, v, will be equal to the product of the "intensity" of the current, C ampères, the time, t, and the electrochemical equivalent of the hydrogen, x ; $\therefore v = xCt$. Arrange the observations so that the galvanometer is read after the elapse of equal intervals of time. Hence $t_1 - t_0 = t_2 - t_1 = t_3 - t_2 = \ldots = h$. From (7),

$$\int_{t_0}^{t_n} C \, . \, dt = \frac{1}{3}h\{(C_0 + C_n) + 4(C_1 + C_3 + \ldots + C_{n-1}) + 2(C_2 + C_4 + \ldots + C_{n-2})\}.$$

In an experiment, $v = 0.22$ when $t = 3$, and

$$t = 1.0, \quad 1.5, \quad 2.0, \quad 2.5, \quad 3.0, \quad \ldots;$$
$$C = 1.53, \quad 1.03, \quad 0.90, \quad 0.84, \quad 0.57, \ldots$$

$$\therefore \int_0^4 C \, . \, dt = \frac{0.5}{3}\{(1.53 + 0.57) + 4(1.03 + 0.84) + 2 \times 0.90\} = 1.897.$$

$$\therefore x = \frac{0.22}{1.897} = 0.1159.$$

Y

This example also illustrates how the value of an integral can be obtained from a table of numerical measurements. The result 0·1159, is better than if we had simply proceeded by what appears, at first sight, the more correct method, namely,

$$\int_0^4 C \,.\, dt = (t_1 - t_0)\frac{C_0 + C_1}{2} + (t_2 - t_1)\frac{C_1 + C_2}{2} + \ldots = 1\text{·}91,$$

for then $x = \dfrac{0\text{·}22}{1\text{·}91} = 0\text{·}1152$. The correct value is 0·116 nearly.

(3) If $\int dz = \int e^{a/x}(b - x)^{-1}dx$, where b is the end value of x, then, in the interval $z_2 - z_1$, show that the integrals will assume the form

$$z_2 - z_1 = \frac{x_2 - x_1}{6}\left(\frac{e^{\frac{a}{x_1}}}{b - x_1} + 4\frac{e^{\frac{a}{\frac{1}{2}(x_1 + x_2)}}}{b - \frac{1}{2}(x_1 + x_2)} + \frac{e^{\frac{a}{x_2}}}{b - x_2}\right),$$

between the limits x_1 and x_2. Hint. Use (4); $h = \frac{1}{2}(x_1 + x_2)$.

If we take four ordinates and three intervals, (4) assumes the form

$$\int_0^3 f(x) \,.\, dx = \tfrac{3}{8}h(y_0 + 3(y_1 + y_2) + y_3)\,;\,. \qquad . \qquad (8)$$

where h denotes the distance of the ordinates apart, y_0, y_1, ... the ordinates of the successive perpendiculars, in the preceding diagram. This formula is known as **Simpson's three-eighths rule.** If we take seven ordinates and neglect certain small differences, we get

$$\int_0^6 f(x) \,.\, dx = \tfrac{3}{10}h(y_0 + 5y_1 + y_2 + 6y_3 + y_4 + 5y_5 + y_6) \qquad (9)$$

which is known as **Weddle's rule** (*Math. Journ.*, **11**, 79, 1854). J. E. H. Gordon (*Proc. Roy. Soc.*, **25**, 144, 1876 ; or *Phil. Trans.*, **167**, i., 1, 1877) employed Weddle's rule to find the intensity of the magnetic field in the axis of a helix of wire through which an electric current was flowing. The intensity of the field was measured at seven equidistant points along the axis by means of a dynamometer, and the total force was computed from (9).

EXAMPLES.—(1) Compare Simpson's one-third rule and the three-eighths rule when $h = 1$, with the result of the integration of

$$\int_{-3}^{+3} x^4 dx. \quad \text{Ansr. } \tfrac{1}{5}\{(+3)^5 - (-3)^5\} = 97\text{·}2,$$

by actual integration ; for Simpson's one-third rule,

$$\tfrac{1}{3}[(+3)^4 + (-3)^4 + 4\{(+2)^4 + 0^4 + (-2)^4\} + 2(1 + 1)] = 98.$$

The three-eighths rule gives

$$\int_{-3}^{+3} f(x)dx = \tfrac{3}{8}h(y_0 + 3y_1 + 3y_2 + 2y_3 + 3y_4 + 3y_5 + y_6),$$

$$\tfrac{3}{8}[(+3)^4 + (-3)^4 + 3\{(+2)^4 + 1^4 + (-1)^4 + (-2)^4\} + 2 \times 0] = 99.$$

The errors are thus as 8 : 18, or as 4 : 9. A great number of cases has been tried and it is generally agreed that *the parabolic rule with an odd number of ordinates always gives a better arithmetical result than if one more ordinate is employed.* Thus, Simpson's rule with five ordinates gives a better result than if six ordinates are used.

(2) On plotting $f(x)$ in $\int f(x)dx$, it is found that the lengths of the ordinates 3 cm. apart were: 14·2, 14·9, 15·3, 15·1, 14·5, 14·1, 13·7 cm. Find the numerical value of the integral. Ansr. 263·9 sq. cm. by Simpson's one-third rule. Hint. From (7),

$$\int_0^{x_n} f(x)dx = (14\cdot2 + 13\cdot7) + 4(14\cdot9 + 15\cdot1 + 14\cdot1) + 2(15\cdot3 + 14\cdot5).$$

An objection to these rules is that more weight is attached to some of the measurements than to others. *E.g.*, more weight is attached to y_1, y_3, and y_5 than to y_2 and y_4 in applying Weddle's rule.

II. *Trapezoidal Formulæ.*

Instead of assuming each strip to be the sum of a trapezium and a parabolic segment, we may *suppose that each strip is a complete trapezium.* In Fig. 136, let AN be a curve whose equation is $y = f(x)$; AA', BB', ... perpendiculars drawn from the x-axis. The area of the portion $ANN'A'$ is to be determined. Let $OB' - OA' = OC' - OB' = \ldots = h$. It follows from known mensuration formulæ, (11), page 604,

FIG. 136.

Area $ANN'A' = \frac{1}{2}h(AA' + BB') + \frac{1}{2}h(B'B + C'C) + \ldots;$

$\qquad = \frac{1}{2}h(AA' + 2BB' + 2CC' + \ldots + 2MM' + NN');$

$\qquad = h(\frac{1}{2} + 1 + 1 + \ldots + 1 + 1 + \frac{1}{2}),$ . . **(10)**

where the coefficients of the successive ordinates alone are written. The result is known as the **trapezoidal rule.**

Let $x_0, x_1, x_2, \ldots, x_n$, be the values of the abscissæ corresponding with the ordinates $y_0, y_1, y_2, \ldots, y_n$, then,

$$\int_{x_0}^{x_n} f(x) \cdot dx = \tfrac{1}{2}(x_1 - x_0)(y_0 + y_1) + \ldots + \tfrac{1}{2}(x_n - x_{n-1})(y_{n-1} + y_n). \quad (11)$$

If $x_1 - x_0 = x_2 - x_1 = \ldots = h$, we get, by multiplying out,

$$\int_{x_0}^{x_n} f(x) \cdot dx = h\{\tfrac{1}{2}(y_0 + y_n) + y_2 + y_3 + \ldots + y_{n-1}\}. \quad (12)$$

The trapezoidal rule, though more easily manipulated, is not quite so accurate as those rules based on the parabolic formula of Newton and Cotes.

The expression,

Area $ANN'A' = h(\frac{5}{12} + \frac{13}{12} + 1 + 1 + \ldots + 1 + 1 + \frac{13}{12} + \frac{5}{12}),$ (13) or,

$$\int_{x_0}^{x_n} f(x) \cdot dx = h\{0\cdot4(y_0 + y_n) + 1\cdot1(y_1 + y_{n-1}) + y_2 + y_3 + \ldots + y_{n-2}\}, \quad (14)$$

is said to combine the accuracy of the parabolic rule with the simplicity of the trapezoidal. It is called **Durand's rule.**

EXAMPLES.—(1) Evaluate the integral $\int_2^{10} \frac{dx}{x}$, by the approximation formulæ (7), (10) and (13), assuming $h = 1$, $n = 8$. Find the absolute value of the result and show that these approximation formulæ give more accurate results when the interval h is made smaller. Ansr. (7) gives 1·611, (10) gives 1·629, (13) gives 1·616. The correct result is 1·610.

(2) Now try what the trapezoidal formula would give for the integration of Ex. (2), page 339. Ansr. 263·55. Hint. From (12)

$$3\{\tfrac{1}{2}(14\cdot2 + 13\cdot7) + 14\cdot9 + 15\cdot3 + 15\cdot1 + 14\cdot5 + 14\cdot1\}.$$

G. Lemoine (*Ann. Chim. Phys.*, [4], **27**, 289, 1872) encountered some non-integrable equations during his study of the action of heat on red phosphorus. In consequence, he adopted these methods of approximation. The resulting tables "calculated" and "observed" were very satisfactory.

Double integrals for the calculation of volumes can be evaluated by a double application of the formula. For illustrations, see C. W. Merrifield's report "On the present state of our knowledge of the application of quadratures and interpolation to actual calculation," *B. A. Reports*, 321, 1880.

III. Mid-section Formula.

A shorter method is sometimes used. Suppose the indicator

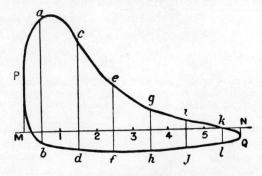

FIG. 137.

diagram (Fig. 137) to be under investigation. Drop perpendiculars *PM* and *QN* on to the "Atmospheric line" *MN*; divide *MN* into *n* equal parts. In the diagram $n = 6$. Then measure the middle length ab, cd, ef, ... of each strip; add, and divide by n.   Algebraically, if the length of $ab = y_1$; $cd = y_3$; $ef = y_5$; ...

$$\text{Total area} = \frac{1}{n}(y_1 + y_3 + y_5 + \ldots).MN. \tag{15}$$

§ 111. Integration by Infinite Series.

Some integrations tax, and even baffle, the resources of the most expert.   It is, indeed, a common thing to find expressions which cannot be integrated by the methods at our disposal.   We may then resort to the methods of the two preceding sections, or, if the integral can be expanded in the form of a converging series of ascending or descending powers of x, we can integrate each term of the expanded series separately and thus obtain any desired degree of accuracy by summing up a finite number of these terms.

If $f(x)$ can be developed in a converging series of ascending powers of x, that is to say, if

$$f(x) = a_0 + a_1x + a_2x^2 + a_3x^3 + \ldots \quad . \quad . \quad (1)$$

By integration, it follows that

$$\int f(x)dx = \int(a_0 + a_1x + a_2x^2 + \ldots)dx;$$
$$= \int a_0 dx + \int a_1 x dx + \int a_2 x^2 dx + \ldots;$$
$$= a_0x + \tfrac{1}{2}a_1x^2 + \tfrac{1}{3}a_2x^3 + \ldots;$$
$$= x(a_0 + \tfrac{1}{2}a_1x + \tfrac{1}{3}a_2x^2 + \ldots) + C. \quad . \quad (2)$$

Again, if $f(x)$ is a converging series, $\int f(x).dx$ is also convergent.   Thus, if

$$f(x) = 1 + x + x^2 + x^3 + \ldots + x^{n-1} + x^n + \ldots, \tag{3}$$

$$\int f(x).dx = x + \frac{1}{2}x^2 + \frac{1}{3}x^3 + \ldots + \frac{1}{n}x^n + \frac{1}{n+1}x^{n+1} + \ldots \tag{4}$$

Series (3) is convergent when x is less than unity, for all values of n.   Series (4) is convergent when $\frac{n}{n+1}x$, and therefore when x is less than unity.   The convergency of the two series thus depends on the same condition, $x > 1$.   If the one is convergent, the other must be the same.

If the reader is able to develop a function in terms of Taylor's series, this method of integration will require but few words of explanation.   One illustration will suffice.   By division, or by Taylor's theorem,

$$(1 + x^2)^{-1} = 1 - x^2 + x^4 - x^6 + \ldots$$

Consequently.

$$\int \frac{dx}{1 + x^2} = \int dx - \int x^2 \cdot dx + \int x^4 \cdot dx - \int x^6 \cdot dx + \dots;$$

$$\therefore \int (1 + x^2)^{-1} dx = x - \tfrac{1}{3}x^3 + \tfrac{1}{5}x^5 - \dots = \tan^{-1}x + C,$$

from (6), page 284.

EXAMPLES.—(1) Show $\displaystyle\int \frac{dx}{(1 - x^2)^{\frac{1}{2}}} = x + \frac{x^3}{2 \cdot 3} + \frac{1 \cdot 3\, x^5}{2 \cdot 4 \cdot 5} + \dots = \sin^{-1}x + C$

(2) Show $\displaystyle\int \frac{dx}{\sqrt{\sin x}} = 2\sqrt{\sin x}\left(1 + \frac{1}{2} \cdot \frac{\sin^2 x}{5} + \frac{1 \cdot 3}{2 \cdot 4} \cdot \frac{\sin^4 x}{9} + \dots \right) + C.$

(3) Show $\displaystyle\int e^{-x^2} dx = x - \frac{x^3}{1 \cdot 3} + \frac{x^5}{1 \cdot 2 \cdot 5} - \frac{x^7}{1 \cdot 2 \cdot 3 \cdot 7} + \dots + C.$

The two following integrals will be required later on. k_2 is less than unity.

(4) $\displaystyle\int_0^{\pi/2} \frac{d\phi}{\sqrt{1 - k^2\sin^2\phi}} = \frac{\pi}{2}\left\{1 + \left(\frac{1}{2}k\right)^2 + \left(\frac{1 \cdot 3}{2 \cdot 4}k^2\right)^2 + \left(\frac{1 \cdot 3 \cdot 5}{2 \cdot 4 \cdot 6}k^3\right)^2 + \dots \right\}.$

(5) $\displaystyle\int_0^{\pi/2} (1 - k^2\sin^2\phi)^{\frac{1}{2}} d\phi = \frac{\pi}{2}\left\{1 - \frac{1}{1}\left(\frac{1}{2}k\right)^2 + \frac{1}{3}\left(\frac{1 \cdot 3}{2 \cdot 4}k^2\right)^2 + \dots \right\}.$

(6) How would you propose to integrate $\int_0^1 (1 - x)^{-1} \log x \cdot dx$ in series?
Hint. Develop $(1 - x)^{-1}$ in series. Multiply through with $\log x \cdot dx$. Then integrate term by term. The quickest plan for the latter operation will be to first integrate $\int x^n \log x \cdot dx$ by parts, and show that

$$\int x^n \log x \cdot dx = \frac{x^{n+1}}{n + 1}\left(\log x - \frac{1}{n + 1}\right).$$

$$\therefore \int_0^1 \frac{\log x}{1 - x} dx = -\left(\frac{1}{1^2} + \frac{1}{2^2} + \frac{1}{3^2} + \frac{1}{4^2} + \dots \right)$$

(7) Show that $\dfrac{1}{\sin \frac{1}{2}x} = \dfrac{2}{x} + \dfrac{1}{3!} \cdot \dfrac{x}{2} + \dfrac{14}{6!}\left(\dfrac{x}{2}\right)^3 + \dots$

Then, remembering that $2 \sin^2 \frac{1}{2}x = 1 - \cos x$, (35) page 612, show that

$$\int \frac{x \cdot dx}{\sqrt{1 - \cos x}} = \frac{1}{\sqrt{2}}\left(2x + \frac{x^3}{36} + \frac{7x^5}{14,400} + \dots \right) + C.$$

(8) Show $\displaystyle\int_0^1 \sin \frac{\pi x^2}{2} dx = \left[\frac{\pi}{2} \cdot \frac{x^3}{3} - \frac{1}{6}\left(\frac{\pi}{2}\right)^3 \frac{x^7}{7} + \frac{1}{120}\left(\frac{\pi}{2}\right)^5 \frac{x^{11}}{11} - \dots \right]_0^1;$

$= 0{\cdot}5236 - 0{\cdot}0875 + 0{\cdot}0069 - 0{\cdot}0003 + \dots = 0{\cdot}446.$

We often integrate a function in series when it is a comparatively simple matter to express the integral in a finite form. The finite integral may be unfitted for numerical computations. Thus, instead of

$$-\frac{dC}{dt} = kC(C + x); \therefore kt = \int_{c_1}^{c_n} \frac{dC}{C(C + x)} = \frac{1}{x}\left[\log \frac{C + x}{C}\right]_{c_1}^{c_n}, \quad (5)$$

S. Arrhenius (*Zeit. phys. Chem.*, **1**, 110, 1887) used

$$kt = \frac{1}{C_n} - \frac{1}{C_1} - \frac{x}{2}\left(\frac{1}{C_n{}^2} - \frac{1}{C_1{}^2}\right) \quad \cdot \quad \cdot \quad (6)$$

because x being small in comparison with C, (5) would not give accurate results in numerical work, on account of the factor x^{-1}, and in (6) the higher terms are negligibly small. Again, the ordinary integral of

$$\frac{dx}{dt} = k(a - x)(b - x)^2; \quad kt = \frac{1}{(a - b)^2}\left\{\frac{(a - b)x}{b(b - x)} + \log\frac{a(b - x)}{b(a - x)}\right\},$$

from (9), page 221, does not give accurate results when a is nearly equal to b, for the factor $(a - b)^{-2}$ then becomes very great. We can get rid of the difficulty by integration in series. Add and subtract $(b - x)^{-3} dx$ to the denominator of

$$\frac{dx}{(a - x)(b - x)^2} = \left[\frac{1}{(b - x)^3} + \frac{1}{(a - x)(b - x)^2} - \frac{1}{(b - x)^3}\right]dx;$$

$$= \left[\frac{1}{(b - x)^3} - \frac{a - b}{b - x}\left\{\frac{1}{(a - x)(b - x)^2}\right\}\right]dx;$$

$$= \left[\frac{1}{(b - x)^3} - \frac{a - b}{b - x}\left\{\frac{1}{(b - x)^3} - \frac{a - b}{b - x}\cdot\frac{1}{(a - x)(b - x)^2}\right\}\right]dx;$$

$$= \left[\frac{1}{(b - x)^3} - \frac{a - b}{(b - x)^4} + \frac{(a - b)^2}{(b - x)^5} - \frac{(a - b)^3}{(b - x)^6} + \ldots\right]dx.$$

This is a geometrical series with a quotient $(a - b)/(b - x)$ and convergent when $(a - b) < (b - x)$; that is when $a < b$, or when a is only a little greater than b. Now integrate term by term; evaluate the constant when $x = 0$ and $t = 0$; we get

$$k = \frac{1}{t}\left[\frac{1}{2}\left\{\frac{1}{(b - x)^2} - \frac{1}{b^2}\right\} - \frac{a - b}{3}\left\{\frac{1}{(b - x)^3} - \frac{1}{b^3}\right\} + \ldots\right].$$

The first term is independent of $a - b$, and it will be sufficiently exact for practical work.

Integrals of the form

$$\int_0^x e^{-x^2}dx; \quad \text{or,} \quad \int_0^\infty e^{-x^2}dx \quad \cdot \quad \cdot \quad \cdot \quad (7)$$

are extensively employed in the solution of physical problems. *E.g.*, in the investigation of the path of a ray of light through the atmosphere (Kramp); the conduction of heat (Fourier); the secular cooling of the earth (Kelvin), etc. One solution of the important differential equation

$$\frac{\partial V}{\partial t} = \kappa\frac{\partial^2 V}{\partial x^2},$$

is represented by this integral. Errors of observation may also be represented by similar integrals. Glaisher calls the first of equations (7) the *error function complement*, and writes it, "erfc x";

and the second, he calls the **error function**, and writes it, "erf x".
J. W. L. Glaisher (*Phil. Mag.* [4], **42**, 294, 421, 1871) and R.
Pendlebury (*ib.*, p. 437) have given a list of integrals expressible
in terms of the error function. The numerical value of any integral which can be reduced to the error function, may then be
read off directly from known tables. See also J. Burgess, *Trans.
Roy. Soc. Edin.*, **39**, 257, 1898.

We have deduced the fact, on page 240, that functions of the
same form, when integrated between the same limits, have the same
value. Hence, we may write

$$\int_0^\infty e^{-x^2}dx = \int_0^\infty e^{-y^2}dy \,;$$

$$\therefore \int_0^\infty e^{-x^2}dx \int_0^\infty e^{-y^2}dy = \int_0^\infty\int_0^\infty e^{-(x^2+y^2)}dxdy = \left[\int_0^\infty e^{-x^2}dx\right]^2. \quad (8)$$

Now put

$$y = vx \,; \ i.e., \ dy = xdv.$$

Our integral becomes

$$\int_0^\infty\int_0^\infty xe^{-x^2(1+v^2)}dxdv. \quad \cdot \quad \cdot \quad \cdot \quad (9)$$

It is a common device when integrating exponential functions to
first differentiate a similar one. Thus, to integrate $\int xe^{-ax^2}dx$, first
differentiate e^{-ax^2}, and we have $d(e^{-ax^2}) = -2axe^{-ax^2}dx$. From
this we infer that

$$\int d(e^{-ax^2}) = -2a\int xe^{-ax^2}dx \,; \ \text{or}, \int xe^{-ax^2}dx = -\frac{1}{2a}e^{-ax^2} + C.$$

Applying this result to the "dx" integration of (9), we get

$$\int_0^\infty xe^{-x^2(1+v^2)}dx = \left[\frac{-e^{-x^2(1+v^2)}}{2(1+v^2)}\right]_0^\infty = \frac{1}{2(1+v^2)}\,;$$

since the function vanishes when x is ∞. Again, from (13),
page 193, the "dv" integration becomes

$$\int_0^\infty \frac{dv}{2(1+v^2)} = \left[\frac{1}{2}\tan^{-1}v\right]_0^\infty = \frac{\pi}{4}.$$

Consequently, by combining the two last results with (8) and (9),
it follows that

$$\left[\int_0^\infty e^{-x^2}dx\right]^2 = \frac{\pi}{4}\,; \ \text{or}, \int_0^\infty e^{-x^2}dx = \frac{\sqrt{\pi}}{2}. \quad \cdot \quad (10)$$

This fact seems to have been discovered by Euler about 1730.
There is another ingenious method of integration, due to Gauss,

in which the penultimate integral of equations (8) is transformed into polar coordinates and the limits are made so as to just cover one quadrant.

$$\therefore \int_0^\infty \int_0^\infty e^{-(x^2+y^2)}dxdy = \int_0^{\frac{\pi}{2}}\int_0^\infty e^{-r^2}r\,.\,d\theta\,.\,dr = \frac{\pi}{2}\int_0^\infty e^{-r^2}r\,.\,dr = \frac{\pi}{4}, \text{etc.}$$

This important result enables us to solve integrals of the form $\int e^{-x^2}x^n dx$, for by successive reduction

$$\int_0^\infty e^{-x^2}x^n\,.\,dx = \frac{(n-1)(n-3)\ldots 2}{2^{(n-1)/2}}\int_0^\infty e^{-x^2}x\,.\,dx, \quad (11)$$

when n is odd; and, when n is even

$$\int_0^\infty e^{-x^2}x^n\,.\,dx = \frac{(n-1)(n-3)\ldots 1}{2^{n/2}}\int_0^\infty e^{-x^2}dx. \quad (12)$$

All these integrals are of considerable importance in the kinetic theory of gases, and in the theory of probability. In the former we shall meet integrals like

$$\frac{2Nma^2}{\sqrt{\pi}}\int_0^\infty e^{-x^2}x^4\,.\,dx\;;\text{ and, }\frac{2Na}{\sqrt{\pi}}\int_0^\infty e^{-x^2}x^3\,.\,dx. \quad (13)$$

From (12), the first one may be written $\frac{3}{4}Nma^2$; the latter $2Na/\sqrt{\pi}$.

If the limits are finite, as, for instance, in the probability integral,

$$P = \frac{2}{\sqrt{\pi}}\int_0^{hx} e^{-h^2x^2}d(hx)\;;\;\therefore\;P = \frac{2}{\sqrt{\pi}}\int_0^t e^{-t^2}dt,$$

by putting $hx = t$. Develop e^{-t^2} into a series by Maclaurin's theorem, as just done in Ex. (3) above. The result is that

$$P = \frac{2}{\sqrt{\pi}}\Big(t - \frac{t^3}{1\,.\,3} + \frac{t^5}{1\,.\,2\,.\,5} - \cdots\Big) \quad (14)$$

may be used for small values of t. For large values, integrate by parts,

$$\int e^{-t^2}dt = -\frac{1}{2t}e^{-t^2} - \frac{1}{2}\int\frac{e^{-t^2}}{t^2}dt = -\frac{1}{2t}e^{-t^2} + \frac{1}{2^2t^3}e^{-t^2} + \frac{3}{2^3}\int\frac{e^{-t^2}}{t^4}dt,$$

$$\therefore -\int e^{-t^2}dt = e^{-t^2}\Big(\frac{1}{2t} - \frac{1}{4t^3} + \frac{3}{8t^5} - \frac{15}{16t^7} + \cdots\Big)$$

By the decomposition of the limits, (4), page 241, we get

$$\int_0^t e^{-t^2}dt = \int_0^\infty e^{-t^2}dt - \int_t^\infty e^{-t^2}dt$$

The first integral on the right-hand side $= \frac{1}{2}\sqrt{\pi}$. Integrating the second between the limits ∞ and t

$$P = 1 - \frac{e^{-t^2}}{t\sqrt{\pi}}\Big(1 - \frac{1}{x^2} + \frac{1.3}{(2t^2)^2} - \frac{1.3.5}{(2t^2)^3} + \dots\Big). \qquad (15)$$

This series converges rapidly for large values of t. From this expression the value of P can be found with any desired degree of accuracy. These results are required later on.

§ 112. The Hyperbolic Functions.

I shall now explain the origin of a new class of functions, and show how they are to be used as tools in mathematical reasoning. We all know that every point on the perimeter of a circle is equidistant from the centre; and that the radius of any given circle has a constant magnitude, whatever portion of the arc be taken. In plane trigonometry, an angle is conveniently measured as a function of the arc of a circle. Thus, if l' denotes the length of an arc of a circle subtending an angle θ at the centre, r' the radius of the circle, then

$$\theta = \frac{\text{Length of arc}}{\text{Length of radius}} = \frac{l'}{r'}.$$

This is called the circular measure of an angle and, for this reason, trigonometrical functions are sometimes called **circular functions.** This property is possessed by no plane curve other than the circle. For instance, the hyperbola, though symmetrically placed with respect to its centre, is not at all points equidistant from it. The same thing is true of the ellipse. The parabola has no centre.

If l denotes the length of the arc of any hyperbola which cuts the x-axis at a distance r from the centre, the ratio

$$u = \frac{l}{r},$$

is called an **hyperbolic function** of u, just as the ratio l'/r' is a circular function of θ. If the reader will refer to Ex. (5), page 247, it will be found that if l denotes the length of the arc of the rectangular hyperbola

$$x^2 - y^2 = a^2, \qquad \cdot \qquad \cdot \qquad \cdot \qquad (1)$$

between the ordinates having abscissæ a and x,

$$\frac{x}{a} = \tfrac{1}{2}(e^u + e^{-u}).$$

But this relation is practically that developed for $\cos x$, on page 286, ιx, of course, being written for u. The ratio x/a is defined as the **hyperbolic cosine** of u. It is usually written cosh u, or hycos u, and pronounced "cosh u," or "h-cosine u". Hence,

$$\cosh u = \tfrac{1}{2}(e^u + e^{-u}) = 1 + \frac{u^2}{2!} + \frac{u^4}{4!} + \dots \quad . \quad (2)$$

In the same way, proceeding from (1), it can be shown that

$$\frac{y}{a} = \sqrt{\frac{x^2}{a^2} - 1} = \sqrt{\frac{e^{2u} + 2 + e^{-2u}}{4} - 1} = \sqrt{\frac{e^{2u} - 2 + e^{-2u}}{4}};$$

which reduces to

$$\frac{y}{a} = \tfrac{1}{2}(e^u - e^{-u}),$$

a relation previously developed for $\iota \sin x$. The ratio y/a is called the **hyperbolic sine** of u, written sinh u, or hysin u. As before

$$\sinh u = \tfrac{1}{2}(e^u - e^{-u}) = u + \frac{u^3}{3!} + \frac{u^5}{5!} + \dots \quad . \quad (3)$$

The remaining four hyperbolic functions, analogous to the remaining four trigonometrical functions, are tanh u, cosech u, sech u and coth u. Values for each of these functions may be deduced from their relations with sinh u and cosh u. Thus,

$$\left. \begin{array}{l} \tanh u = \dfrac{\sinh u}{\cosh u}; \ \operatorname{sech} u = \dfrac{1}{\cosh u}; \\[2mm] \coth u = . \dfrac{1}{\tanh u}; \ \operatorname{cosech} u = \dfrac{1}{\sinh u} \end{array} \right\} . \quad (4)$$

Unlike the circular functions, the ratios x/a, y/a, when referred to the hyperbola, do not represent angles. *An hyperbolic function expresses a certain relation between the coordinates of a given portion on the arc of a rectangular hyperbola.*

Let O (Fig. 138) be the centre of the hyperbola APB, described about the coordinate axes Ox, Oy. From any point $P(x, y)$ drop a perpendicular PM on to the x-axis. Let $OM = x$, $MP = y$, $OA = a$.

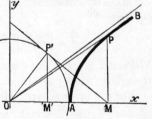

FIG. 138.

$$\therefore \cosh u = x/a; \ \sinh u = y/a.$$

For the rectangular hyperbola, $x^2 - y^2 = a^2$. Consequently,

$$a^2\cosh^2 u - a^2\sinh^2 u = a^2; \ \text{or, } \cosh^2 u - \sinh^2 u = 1.$$

The last formula thus resembles the well-known trigonometrical relation: $\cos^2 x + \sin^2 x = 1$. Draw $P'M$ a tangent to the circle AP' at P'. Drop a perpendicular $P'M$ on to the x-axis. Let the angle $M'OP' = \theta$.

$$\therefore x/a = \sec\theta = \cosh u \,; \; y/a = \tan\theta = \sinh u. \quad . \quad (6)$$

I. Conversion Formulæ.—Corresponding with the trigonometrical formulæ there are a great number of relations among the hyperbolic functions, such as (5) above, also

$$\cosh 2x = 1 + 2\sinh^2 x = 2\cosh^2 x + 1. \quad . \quad (7)$$

$$\sinh x - \sinh y = 2\cosh \tfrac{1}{2}(x + y).\sinh \tfrac{1}{2}(x - y), \; . \quad (8)$$

and so on. These have been summarized in the Appendix, "Collection of Reference Formulæ".

II. Graphic representation of hyperbolic functions.—We have seen that the trigonometrical sine,

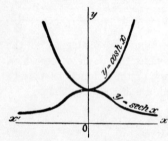

FIG. 139.—Graphs of cosh x and sech x.

cosine, etc., are periodic functions. The hyperbolic functions are exponential, not periodic. This will be evident if the student plots the six hyperbolic functions on squared paper, using the numerical values of x and y given in Tables IV. and V. I have done this for $y = \cosh x$, and $y = \mathrm{sech}\,x$ in Fig. 139. The graph of $y = \cosh x$, is known in statics as the "catenary".

III. Differentiation of the hyperbolic functions.—It is easy to see that

$$\frac{d(\sinh x)}{dx} = \frac{d\{\tfrac{1}{2}(e^x - e^{-x})\}}{dx} = \tfrac{1}{2}(e^x + e^{-x}) = \cosh x.$$

We could get the same result by treating sinh u exactly as we treated sin x on page 48, using the reference formulæ of page 611.

For the inverse hyperbolic functions, let

$$y = \sinh^{-1} x \,; \; \therefore \; dx/dy = \cosh y.$$

From (5) above, it follows that

$$\cosh y = \sqrt{\sinh^2 y + 1} \,; \; \therefore \; \cosh y = \sqrt{x^2 + 1} \,;$$

and, from the original function, it follows that

$$\frac{dy}{dx} = \frac{1}{\sqrt{x^2 + 1}}.$$

IV. Integration of the hyperbolic functions.—A standard collection of results of the differentiation and integration of hyperbolic functions, is set forth in the following table :—

TABLE III.—STANDARD INTEGRALS.

Function.	Differential Calculus.	Integral Calculus.	
$y = \sinh x.$	$\dfrac{dy}{dx} = \cosh x.$	$\displaystyle\int \cosh x\, dx = \sinh x.$	(9)
$y = \cosh x.$	$\dfrac{dy}{dx} = \sinh x.$	$\displaystyle\int \sinh x\, dx = \cosh x.$	(10)
$y = \tanh x.$	$\dfrac{dy}{dx} = \operatorname{sech}^2 x.$	$\displaystyle\int \operatorname{sech}^2 x\, dx = \tanh x.$	(11)
$y = \coth x.$	$\dfrac{dy}{dx} = -\operatorname{cosech}^2 x.$	$\displaystyle\int \operatorname{cosech}^2 x\, dx = -\coth x$	(12)
$y = \operatorname{sech} x.$	$\dfrac{dy}{dx} = -\dfrac{\sinh x}{\cosh^2 x}.$	$\displaystyle\int \dfrac{\sinh x}{\cosh^2 x}\, dx = -\operatorname{sech} x.$	(13)
$y = \operatorname{cosech} x.$	$\dfrac{dy}{dx} = -\dfrac{\cosh x}{\sinh^2 x}.$	$\displaystyle\int \dfrac{\cosh x}{\sinh^2 x}\, dx = -\operatorname{cosech} x.$	(14)
$y = \sinh^{-1} x.$	$\dfrac{dy}{dx} = \dfrac{1}{\sqrt{x^2+1}}.$	$\displaystyle\int \dfrac{dx}{\sqrt{x^2+1}} = \sinh^{-1} x.$	(15)
$y = \cosh^{-1} x.$	$\dfrac{dy}{dx} = \dfrac{1}{\sqrt{x^2-1}}.$	$\displaystyle\int \dfrac{dx}{\sqrt{x^2-1}} = \cosh^{-1} x.$	(16)
$y = \tanh^{-1} x.$	$\dfrac{dy}{dx} = \dfrac{1}{1-x^2}, x<1.$	$\displaystyle\int \dfrac{dx}{1-x^2} = \tanh^{-1} x.$	(17)
$y = \coth^{-1} x.$	$\dfrac{dy}{dx} = \dfrac{1}{x^2-1}, x>1.$	$\displaystyle\int \dfrac{dx}{x^2-1} = \coth^{-1} x.$	(18)
$y = \operatorname{sech}^{-1} x.$	$\dfrac{dy}{dx} = -\dfrac{1}{x\sqrt{1-x^2}}.$	$\displaystyle\int \dfrac{dx}{x\sqrt{1-x^2}} = -\operatorname{sech} x.$	(19)
$y = \operatorname{cosech}^{-1} x.$	$\dfrac{dy}{dx} = -\dfrac{1}{x\sqrt{x^2+1}}.$	$\displaystyle\int \dfrac{dx}{x\sqrt{x^2+1}} = -\operatorname{cosech} x.$	(20)

EXAMPLES.—When integrating algebraic expressions involving the square root of a quadratic, hyperbolic functions may frequently be substituted in place of the independent variable. Such equations are very common in electrotechnics. It is convenient to remember that $x = a\tanh u$, or $x = \tanh u$ may be put in place of $a^2 - x^2$, or $1 - x^2$; similarly, $x = a\cosh u$ may be tried in place of $\sqrt{x^2 - a^2}$; $x = a\sinh u$, for $\sqrt{x^2 + a^2}$.

(1) Evaluate $\int \sqrt{x^2 + a^2}\,.\, dx$. Substitute $x = a\sinh u$ for $\sqrt{x^2+a^2}$, $dx = a\cosh u\,.\,du$. From (5), above; and (22) and (24), page 613,

$$\therefore \int \sqrt{x^2 + a^2}\,.\, dx = \int \sqrt{a^2(1 + \sinh^2 u)}\,.\, a\cosh u\,.\, du = a^2\int \cosh^2 u\,.\, du$$
$$= \tfrac{1}{2}a^2\int(\cosh 2u + 1)\,.\, du ;$$
$$= \tfrac{1}{4}a^2\sinh 2u + \tfrac{1}{2}a^2 u = \tfrac{1}{2}a\sinh u\,.\, a\cosh u + \tfrac{1}{2}a^2 u.$$
$$= \tfrac{1}{2}x\sqrt{(x^2 + a^2)} + \tfrac{1}{2}a^2 \sinh^{-1} x/a.$$

And since we are given $\sinh^{-1} y = \log(y + \sqrt{y^2 + 1})$ on page 613, (31),

$$\therefore \int \sqrt{x^2 + a^2}\,.\, dx = \frac{x\sqrt{a^2 + x^2}}{2} + \frac{a^2}{2}\log \frac{x + \sqrt{x^2 + a^2}}{a} + C.$$

(2) Now try and show that $\int \sqrt{x^2 - a^2} \, . \, dx$ furnishes the result $\frac{1}{2}x\sqrt{x^2 - a^2} - \frac{1}{2}a^2\log(x + \sqrt{x^2 - a^2})/a + C$, when treated in a similar manner by substituting $x = a \cosh u$.

(3) Find the area of the segment OPA (Fig. 138) of the rectangular hyperbola $x^2 - y^2 = 1$. Put $x = \cosh u$; $y = \sinh u$. From (6),

$$\therefore \text{Area } APM = \int_1^x y \, . \, dx = \int_0^u \sinh^2 u \, . \, du = \frac{1}{2}\int_0^u (\cosh 2u - 1) \, . \, du.$$

Area $APM = \frac{1}{4}\sinh 2u - \frac{1}{2}u$. $\therefore$ Area $OPA = \frac{1}{2}$ Area $PM \, . \, OM -$ Area $APM = \frac{1}{2}u$. Note the area of the circular sector $OP'A$ (same figure) $= \frac{1}{2}\theta$, where θ is the angle AOP'.

(4) Rectify the catenary curve $y = c \cosh x/c$ measured from its lowest point Ansr. $l = c \sinh (x/c)$. Note $l = 0$ when $x = 0$, $\therefore C = 0$. Hint. (26), page 613.

(5) Rectify the curve $y^2 = 4ax$ (see Ex. (1), page 246). The expression $\sqrt{(1 + a/x)}dx$ has to be integrated. Hint. Substitute $x = a \sinh^2 u$. $2a\int \cosh^2 u \, . \, du$ remains. Ansr. $= a\int(1 + \cosh 2u)du$, or $a(u + \frac{1}{2}\sinh 2u)$. At vertex, where $x = 0$, $\sinh u = 0$, $C = 0$. Show that the portion bounded by an ordinate passing through the focus has $l = 2\cdot296a$. Hint. Diagrams are a great help in fixing limits. Note $x = a$, $\therefore \sinh u = 1$, $\cosh u = \sqrt{2}$, from (5). From (31), page 613, $\sinh^{-1}1 = u = \log(1 + \sqrt{2})$. From (20), page 613, $\sinh 2u = 2\sinh u \, . \, \cosh u$.

$$l = a\left[u + \frac{1}{2}\sinh 2u\right]_0^u = a(u + \sinh u \, . \, \cosh u) = a\left[\log(1 + \sqrt{2}) + \sqrt{2}\right].$$

Use Table of Natural Logarithms, Appendix II. Ansr. $2\cdot296a$.

(6) Show that $y = A \cosh mx + B \sinh mx$, satisfies the equation of $d^2y/dx^2 = m^2y$, where m, A and B are undetermined constants. Hint. Differentiate twice, etc. Note the resemblance of this result with $y = A \cos nx + B \sin nx$, which furnishes $d^2y/dx^2 = -n^2y$ when treated in the same way.

(7) In studying the rate of formation of carbon monoxide in gas producers, J. K. Clement and C. N. Haskins (1909), obtained the equation

$$\frac{dx}{dt} = \frac{a}{\beta}(\beta^2 - x^2)$$

with the initial condition that $x = 0$ when $t = 0$. Integrating, and

$$\log \frac{\beta + x}{\beta - x} = 2at.$$

Solving for x, we get

$$x = \beta \frac{e^{at} - e^{-at}}{e^{at} + e^{-at}} = \beta \tanh at.$$

V. Numerical Values of hyperbolic functions.—Table IV. (pages 616, 617, and 618) contains numerical values of the hyperbolic sines and cosines for values of x from 0 to 5, at intervals of 0·01. They have been checked by comparison with *Des Ingenieurs Taschenbuch*, edited by the Hütte Academy, Berlin, 1877. The tables are used exactly like ordinary logarithm tables. Numerical values of the other functions can be easily deduced from those of $\sinh x$ and $\cosh x$ by the aid of equations (4).

EXAMPLE.—The equation $l = x(e^{s/2x} - e^{-s/2x})$, represents the relation between the length l of the string hanging from two points at a distance s apart when the horizontal tension of the string is equal to a length x of the string. Show that the equation may be written in the form $11u - 10 \sinh u = 0$ by writing $u = 10/x$ and solved by the aid of Table IV., page 616. Given $l = 22$, $s = 20$. ∴ $x = 13.16$. Hint. Substitute $s = 20$, $l = 22$, $u = 10/x$, and we get $22u - 10(e^u - e^{-u}) = 0$; ∴ $11u - 10 \times \frac{1}{2}(e^u - e^{-u}) = 0$; etc. u is found by the method described in a later chapter; the result is $u = 0.76$. But $x = 10/u$, etc.

VI. Demoivre's theorem.—We have seen that

$$\cos x = \tfrac{1}{2}(e^{\iota x} + e^{-\iota x}); \quad \iota \sin x = \tfrac{1}{2}(e^{\iota x} - e^{-\iota x}),$$
$$e^{\iota x} = \cos x + \iota \sin x; \quad \text{and } e^{-\iota x} = \cos x - \iota \sin x.$$

If we substitute nx for x, where n is any real quantity, positive or negative, integral or fractional,

$$\cos nx = \tfrac{1}{2}(e^{\iota nx} + e^{-\iota nx}); \, i \sin nx = \tfrac{1}{2}(e^{\iota nx} - e^{-\iota nx}).$$

By addition and subtraction and a comparison with the preceding expressions; we get

$$\left.\begin{array}{l} \cos nx + \iota \sin nx = e^{\iota nx} = (\cos x + \iota \sin x)^n \\ \cos nx - \iota \sin nx = e^{-\iota nx} = (\cos x - \iota \sin x)^n \end{array}\right\} \quad (21)$$

which is known as **Demoivre's theorem.** The theorem is useful when we want to express an imaginary exponential in the form of a trigonometrical series, in certain integrations, and in solving certain equations.

EXAMPLES.—(1) Verify the following result and compare it with Demoivre's theorem : $(\cos x + \iota \sin x)^2 = (\cos^2 x - \sin^2 x) + 2\iota \sin x . \cos x = \cos 2x + \iota \sin 2x$.

(2) Show $e^a + {}^{\iota\beta} = e^a e^{\iota\beta} = e^a(\cos \beta + \iota \sin \beta)$.

(3) Show $\int e^{ax}(\cos \beta x + \iota \sin \beta x)dx = e^{ax}(\cos \beta x + \iota \sin \beta x)/(a + \iota\beta)$;

$$= e^{ax}\frac{(\cos \beta x + \iota \sin \beta x)\,(a - \iota\beta)}{a^2 + \beta^2};$$

$$= e^{ax}\frac{(a \cos \beta x + \beta \sin \beta x) + \iota(-\beta \cos \beta x + a \sin \beta x)}{a^2 + \beta^2} + C,$$

by separating the real and imaginary parts.

For a fuller discussion on the properties and uses of hyperbolic functions, consult G. Chrystal's *Algebra*, Part ii., London, 1890; and A. G. Greenhill's *A Chapter in the Integral Calculus*, London, 1888.

CHAPTER VI.

HOW TO SOLVE NUMERICAL EQUATIONS.

"The object of all arithmetical operations is to save direct enumeration. Having done a sum once, we seek to preserve the answer for future use; so too the purpose of algebra, which, by substituting relations for values, symbolizes and definitely fixes all numerical operations which follow the same rule."—E. MACH.

§ 113. Some General Properties of the Roots of Equations.

THE mathematical processes culminating in the integral calculus furnish us with a relation between the quantities under investigation. For example, in § 20, we found a relation between the temperature of a body and the time the body has been cooling. This relation was represented symbolically: $\theta = be^{-at}$, where a and b are constants. I have also shown how to find values for the constants which invariably affect formulæ representing natural phenomena. It now remains to compute one variable when the numerical values of the other variable and of the constants are known. Given b, a, and θ to find t, or given b, a, and t to find θ. The operation of finding the numerical value of the unknown quantity is called **solving the equation.** The object of solving an equation is to find what value or values of the unknown will satisfy the equation, or will make one side of the equation equal to the other. Such values of the unknown are called **roots,** or **solutions** of the equation.

The reader must distinguish between **identical equations** like

$$(x + 1)^2 = x^2 + 2x + 1,$$

which are true for *all* values of x, and **conditional equations** like

$$x + 1 = 8 \; ; \; x^2 + 2x + 1 = 0,$$

which are only true when x has some particular value or values, in the former case, when $x = 7$, and in the latter when $x = -1$.

352

An equation like

$$x^2 + 2x + 2 = 0,$$

has no real roots because no real values of x will satisfy the equation. By solving as if the equation had real roots, the imaginary again forces itself on our attention. The *imaginary roots* of this equation are $-1 \pm \sqrt{-1}$, or $-1 \pm \iota$. Imaginary roots in an equation with real coefficients occur in pairs. *E.g.*, if $a + \beta \sqrt{-1}$ is one root of the equation, $a - \beta \sqrt{-1}$ is another.

The general equation of the nth degree is

$$x^n + ax^{n-1} + bx^{n-2} + \ldots + qx + R = 0. \qquad . \qquad (1)$$

The term R is called the *absolute term*. If $n = 2$, the equation is a *quadratic*, $x^2 + ax + R = 0$; if $n = 3$, the equation is said to be a *cubic*; if $n = 4$, a *biquadratic*, etc. If x^n has any coefficient, we can divide through by this quantity, and so reduce the equation to the above form. When the coefficients $a, b, \ldots$, instead of being literal, are real numbers, the given relation is said to be a **numerical equation**. Every equation of the nth degree has n equal or unequal roots and no more—**Gauss' law.** *E.g.*, $x^5 + x^4 + x + 1 = 0$, has five roots and no more.

General methods for the solution of algebraic equations of the first, second and third degree are treated in regular algebraic textbooks; it is, therefore, unnecessary to give more than a brief *résumé* of their most salient features. We nearly always resort to the approximation methods for finding the roots of the numerical equations found in practical calculations.

After suitable reduction, every quadratic may be written in the form :

$$ax^2 + bx + c = 0; \text{ or, } x^2 + \frac{b}{a}x + \frac{c}{a} = 0. \qquad . \qquad (2)$$

If a and β represent the roots of this equation, x must be equal to a or β, where

$$a = \frac{-b + \sqrt{b^2 - 4ac}}{2a}; \text{ and, } \beta = \frac{-b - \sqrt{b^2 - 4ac}}{2a}. \qquad (3)$$

The sum and product of the roots in (3) are therefore so related that $a + \beta = -b/a$; $a\beta = c/a$. Hence $x^2 - (a + \beta)x + a\beta = 0$; or, $x^2 - $ (sum of roots) $x + $ product of roots $= 0$; (4) if one of the roots is known, the other can be deduced directly. From the second of equations (2), and (4) we see that the sum of the roots is equal to the coefficient of the second term with its sign changed, the product of the roots is equal to the absolute term. If a is a root of the given equation, the equation can be divided by $x - a$ without remainder. If $\beta, \gamma, \ldots$ are roots of the equation, the equation can be divided by $(x - \beta)(x - \gamma) \ldots$ without remainder. From Gauss' law, therefore, (2) may be written

$$(x - a)(x - \beta) = 0. \qquad . \qquad . \qquad (5)$$

From (3), and (4), we can deduce many important particulars respecting the nature of the roots [1] of the quadratic. These are:

RELATIONS BETWEEN THE COEFFICIENTS OF EQUATIONS AND THEIR ROOTS.

Relation between the Coefficients.		The Nature of the Roots.	
$b^2 - 4ac$ is	positive, . . .	real and unequal. . .	(6)
	zero, ...	real and equal. . .	(7)
	negative, . .	imaginary and unequal. .	(8)
	perfect square, . .	rational and unequal. .	(9)
	not a perfect square, .	irrational and unequal. .	(10)
$a, b, c,$ have the same sign, . .		negative. . . .	(11)
$a, b,$ differ in sign from $c,$ . .		opposite sign. . .	(12)
$a, c,$ differ in sign from $b,$ . .		positive. . . .	(13)
$a = 0,$		one root infinite. . .	(14)
$b = 0,$		equal and opposite in sign. .	(15)
$c = 0,$		one root zero. . .	(16)
$c = 0, b = 0,$		both roots zero. . .	(17)

On account of the important *rôle* played by the expression $b^2 - 4ac$, in fixing the character of the roots, "$b^2 - 4ac$," is called the **discriminant** of the equation.

EXAMPLES.—(1) In the familiar equation of Guldberg and Waage
$$K(a - x)(b - x) = (c + x)(d + x)$$
found in most text-books of theoretical chemistry, show that
$$x = \frac{K(a + b) + d + c}{2(K - 1)} \pm \sqrt{\left\{ \frac{K(a + b) + d + c}{2(K - 1)} \right\}^2 + \frac{cd + Kab}{K - 1}}.$$
Hint. Expand the given equation; rearrange terms in descending powers of x; and substitute in the above equations (2) and (3).

(2) If $v^2 - 516 \cdot 17v + 1852 \cdot 6 = 0$, find v. This equation arises in Ex. (4), page 362. On reference to equations (2) and (3), $a = 1$; $b = -516 \cdot 17$; $c = 1852 \cdot 6$. Hence show that $v = \frac{1}{2}(516 \cdot 17 \pm 508 \cdot 94)$.

(3) The thermal value, q, of the reaction between hydrogen and carbon dioxide is represented by $q = -10232 + 0 \cdot 1685T + 0 \cdot 00101T^2$, where T denotes the absolute temperature. Show $T = 3100°$ when $q = 0$. Hint. You will have to reject the negative root. To assist the calculation, note $(0 \cdot 1685)^2 = 0 \cdot 02839$; $4 \times 10232 \times 0 \cdot 00101 = 41 \cdot 33728$; $\sqrt{41 \cdot 36567} = 6 \cdot 432$.

---

[1] In the table, the words "equal" and "unequal" refer to the numerical values of the roots.

§ 114. Graphic Methods for the Approximate Solution of Numerical Equations.

In practical work, it is generally most convenient to get *approximate* values for the real roots of equations of higher degree than the second. Cardan's general method—found in the regular text-books—for equations of the third degree, is generally so unwieldy as to be almost useless. Trigonometrical methods are better. For the numerical equations pertaining to practical work, one of the most instructive methods for locating the real roots, is to trace the graph of the given function. Every point of intersection of the curve with the x-axis, represents a root of the equation. The location of the roots of the equation thus reduces itself to the determination of the points of intersection of the graph of the equation with the x-axis. The accuracy of the graphic method depends on the scale of the diagram and the skill of the draughtsman. The larger the " scale " the more accurate the results.

EXAMPLES.—(1) Find the root of the equation $x + 2 = 0$. At sight, of course, we know that the root is -2. But plot the. curve $y = x + 2$, for values of y when $-3, -2, -1, 0, 1, 2, 3$, are successively assigned to x. The curve (Fig. 140) cuts the x-axis when $x = -2$. Hence, $x = -2$, is a root of the equation.

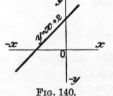

(2) Locate the roots of $x^2 - 8x + 9 = 0$. Proceed as before by assigning successive values to x. Roots occur between 6 and 7 and 1 and 2.

(3) Show that $x^3 - 6x^2 + 11x - 6 = 0$ has roots in the neighbourhood of 1, 2, and 3.

FIG. 140.

(4) Show, by plotting, that an equation of an odd degree with real coefficients, has either one or an odd number of real roots. For large values of x, the graph must lie on the positive side of the x-axis, and on the opposite side for large negative values of x. Therefore the graph must cut the x-axis at least once; if twice, then it must cut the axis a third time, etc.

(5) Prove by plotting if the results obtained by substituting two numbers are of opposite signs, at least one root lies between the numbers substituted.

(6) Solve $x^3 + x - 2 = 0$. Here $x^3 = -x + 2$. Put $y = x^3$ and $y = -x + 2$. Plot the graph of each of these equations, using a Table of Cubes, The abscissa of the point of intersection of these two curves is one root of the given equation. $x = OM$ (Fig. 141) is the root required.

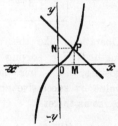

FIG. 141.

(7) Show, by plotting, that an equation of an even degree with real coefficients, has either 2, 4, . . . or an even number of roots, or else no real roots at all.

(8) Plot $x^2 - 2x + 1 = 0$. The curve touches but does not cut the x-axis.

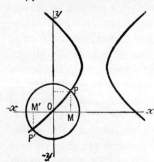

This means that the point of contact of the curve with the x-axis, corresponds to two points infinitely close together. That is to say, that there are at least two equal roots.

(9) Solve $x^2 + y^2 = 1$; $x^2 - 4x = y^2 - 3y$. Plot the two curves as shown in Fig. 142 hence $x = OM$ or OM' are the roots required.

The graphic method can also be employed for transcendental equations.

(10) If $x + \cos x = 0$, we may locate the roots by finding the point of intersection of the two curves $y = -x$ and $y = \cos x$.

FIG. 142.

(11) If $x + e^x = 0$, plot $y = e^x$ and $y = -x$. Table IV., page 616, for e^x.

In his *Die Thermodynamik in der Chemie* (Leipzig, 61, 1893), J. J. van Laar tabulates the values of b calculated from the expression

$$\log \frac{v_2 - b}{v_1 - b} - 2 = \frac{1 \cdot 82}{v_1 - b},$$

for corresponding values of v_1 and v_2. Here is part of the table :

v_1.	v_2.	b.
7754	1·0169	0·804
1688	1·0432	0·775
196·5	1·1268	0·700

Operations like this are very tedious. There are no general methods for solving equations containing logarithms, sines, cosines, etc. There is nothing for it but to educe the required value by successive approximations. Thus, substitute for v_2 and v_1, so as to get

$$\log (196 \cdot 5 - b) - \log (1 \cdot 1268 - b) - 2 = \frac{1 \cdot 82}{196 \cdot 5 - b} \qquad (1)$$

Now set up the following table containing values of b computed on the right and on the left sides of equation (1):—

$b.$	Right Side.	Left Side.
1·0	14·5	5·3
0·8	5·6	4·1
0·6	3·4	3·9
0·4	2·5	3·6

In the first pair, b is greater on the right side than on the left; in the second pair, b is greater on the left side than on the right. Hence, we see that the desired value of b lies between 0·8 and 0·6. Having thus located the root, further progress depends upon the patience of the computer. Closer approximations are got by proceeding in the same way for values of v between 0·8 and 0·6. By plotting the assigned values of b, as ordinates, with the computed values on the right and left sides of (1), as abscissæ, it is possible to abbreviate the work very considerably. Very often the physical conditions of the problem furnish us with an approximate idea of the magnitude of the desired root.

EXAMPLES.—(1) M. Planck (*Wied. Ann.*, **40**, 561, 1890) in his study of the potential difference between two dilute solutions of binary electrolytes, developed the equation

$$\frac{xU_2 - U_1}{V_2 - xV_1} = \frac{\log k - \log x}{\log k + \log x} \cdot \frac{xC_2 - C_1}{C_2 - xC_1}.$$

By plotting x as abscissa and y as ordinate in the two equations

$$y = \frac{xU_2 - U_1}{V_2 - xV_1} ; \ y = \frac{\log k - \log x}{\log k + \log x} \cdot \frac{xC_2 - C_1}{C_2 - xC_1},$$

the point of intersection of the two curves will be found to give the desired value of x. In one experiment the constants assumed the following values : $U_1 = 5 \cdot 2$; $U_2 = 272$; $V_1 = 5 \cdot 4$; $V_2 = 54$; $C_1 = 0 \cdot 1$; $C_2 = 1 \cdot 0$. It is required to find the corresponding value of x. The alternative method just described furnishes $x = 0 \cdot 1139$.

(2) W. Hecht, M. Conrad and C. Brückner (*Zeit. phys. Chem.*, **4**, 273, 1889) in their study of "affinity constants" solved the equations

$$0 \cdot 3537 = \log \frac{25}{25 - x} - \log \frac{25}{20 - x} ; \ 0 \cdot 3537 = \log \frac{25}{20 - y} - \log \frac{25}{25 - y},$$

"with an accuracy up to 0·01 of the units employed". Ansrs. $x = 36 \cdot 78$; $y = 8 \cdot 217$.

§ 115. Newton's Method for the Approximate Solution of Numerical Equations.

According to the above method, the equation

$$f(x) = y = x^3 - 7x + 7, \quad . \quad . \quad . \quad (1)$$

has a root lying somewhere between -3 and -4. We can keep on assigning intermediate values to x until we get as near to the exact value of the root as our patience will allow. Thus, if $x = -3$, $y = +1$, if $x = -3.2$, $y = -3.3$. The desired root thus lies somewhere between -3 and -3.2. Assume that the actual value of the root is -3.1. To get a close approximation to the root by plotting is a somewhat laborious operation. Newton's method based on Taylor's theorem, allows the process to be shortened.

Let a be the desired root, then

$$f(a) = a^3 - 7a + 7. \quad . \quad . \quad . \quad (2)$$

As a first approximation, assume that $a = -3.1 + h$, is the required root. From (1), by differentiation,

$$\frac{dy}{dx} = 3x^2 - 7; \quad \frac{d^2y}{dx^2} = 6x; \quad \frac{d^3y}{dx^3} = 6. \quad . \quad . \quad (3)$$

All succeeding derivatives are zero. By Taylor's theorem

$$f(x + h) = y + h\frac{dy}{dx} + \frac{h^2}{2!} \cdot \frac{d^2y}{dx^2} + \frac{h^3}{3!} \cdot \frac{d^3y}{dx^3}.$$

Put $v = -3.1$ and $a = v + h$.

$$f(a) = f(v + h) = f(v) + h\frac{dv}{dx} + \frac{h^2}{2!} \cdot \frac{d^2v}{dx^2} + \frac{h^3}{3!} \cdot \frac{d^3v}{dx^3}.$$

Neglecting the higher powers of h, in the first approximation,

$$f(v) + h\frac{dv}{dx} = 0; \quad \text{or,} \quad h = -\frac{f(v)}{f'(v)}, \quad . \quad . \quad (4)$$

where $f'(v) = dv/dx$. The value of $f(v)$ is found by substituting -3.1, in (2), and the value of $f'(v)$ by substituting -3.1, in the first of equations (3), thus, from (4),

$$h = -\frac{f(v)}{f'(v)} = \frac{1.091}{21.83} = 0.04999.$$

Hence the first approximation to the root is -3.05.

As a second approximation, assume that

$$a = -3.05 + h_1 = v_1 + h_1.$$

As before,

$$h_1 = -\frac{f(v_1)}{f'(v_1)} = +\frac{0.022625}{20.9081} = +0.001082.$$

The second approximation, therefore, is − 3·048918. We can, in this way, obtain third and higher degrees of approximation. The first approximation usually gives all that is required for practical work.

EXAMPLES.—(1) In the same way show that the first approximation to one of the roots of $x^3 - 4x^2 - 2x + 4 = 0$, is $a = 4·2491$ ... and the second $a = 4·2491405....$

(2) If $x^3 + 2x^2 + 3x - 50 = 0$; $x = 2·9022834....$

(3) The method can sometimes be advantageously varied as follows. Solve

$$\left(\frac{0·795}{1 + x}\right)^x = 0·398. \quad . \quad . \quad . \quad . \quad (5)$$

Put $x = 1$, and the left side becomes 0·3975—a number very nearly 0·398. If, therefore, we put $1 + a$ for x, a will be a very small magnitude.

$$\therefore \left(\frac{0·795}{2 + a}\right)^{1 + a} = f(a). \quad . \quad . \quad . \quad (6)$$

By Maclaurin's theorem,

$$f(a) = f(0) + af'(0) + \text{remaining terms.} \quad . \quad . \quad (7)$$

As a first approximation, omit the remaining terms since they include higher powers of a small quantity a. If $f(0) = 0·3975$, by differentiation of the left side of (6), $f'(0) = - 0·5655$. Hence,

$$f(a) = 0·3975 - 0·5655a.$$

But by hypothesis, $f(a) = 0·398$,

$$\therefore 0·398 = 0·3975 - 0·5655a; \text{ or, } a = - 0·0008842.$$

Since, $x = 1 + a$, it follows that $x = 0·9991158$. By substituting this value of x in the left side of (5), the expression reduces to 0·39801 which is sufficiently close to 0·398 for all practical requirements. But, if not, a more exact result will be furnished by treating $0·9991158 + \rho = x$ exactly as we have done $1 + a = x$.

§ 116. How to Separate Equal Roots from an Equation.

This is a preliminary operation to the determination of the roots by a process, perhaps simpler than the above. From (5), page 354, we see that if a, β, γ, ... are the roots of an equation of the nth degree,

$$x^n + ax^{n-1} + \ldots + sx + R = 0,$$

becomes

$$(x - a)(x - \beta) \ldots (x - \eta) = 0.$$

If two of the roots are equal, two factors, say $x - a$ and $x - \beta$, will be identical and the equation will be divisible by $(x - a)^2$; if there are three equal roots, the equation will be divisible by $(x - a)^3$, etc. If there are n equal roots, the equation will contain a factor

$(x - a)^n$, and the first derivative will contain a factor $n(x - a)^{n-1}$, or $x - a$ will occur $n - 1$ times. The highest common factor of the original equation and its first derivative must, therefore, contain $x - a$, repeated once less than in the original equation. If there is no common factor, there are no equal roots.

EXAMPLES.—(1) $x^3 - 5x^2 - 8x + 48 = 0$ has a first derivative $3x^2 - 10x - 8$. The common factor is $x - 4$. This shows that the equation has two roots equal to $x = 4$.

(2) $x^4 + 7x^3 - 3x^2 - 55x + 50 = 0$ has two roots each equal to $x - 5$.

§ 117. Sturm's Method of Locating the Real and Unequal Roots of a Numerical Equation.

Newton's method of approximation does not give satisfactory results when the two roots have nearly equal values. For instance, the curve

$$y = x^3 - 7x + 7$$

has two nearly equal roots between 1 and 2, which do not appear if we draw the graph for the corresponding values of x and y, viz.:

$$x = 0, \quad 1, \quad 2, \quad 3, \ldots;$$
$$y = 7, \quad 1, \quad 1, \quad 13, \ldots$$

The problem of separating the real roots of a numerical equation is, however, completely solved by what is known as Sturm's theorem. It is clear that if x assumes every possible value in succession from $+ \infty$ to $- \infty$, every change of sign will indicate the proximity of a real root. The total number of roots is known from the degree of the equation, therefore the number of imaginary roots can be determined by difference.

Number of real roots + Number of imaginary roots = Total number of roots.

Sturm's theorem enables these changes of sign to be readily detected. The process is as follows :—

First remove the real equal roots, as indicated in the preceding section, let

$$y = x^3 - 7x + 7, \qquad . \quad . \quad . \quad (1)$$

remain. Find the first differential coefficient,

$$\dot{y} = 3x^2 - 7. \qquad . \quad . \quad . \quad (2)$$

Divide the primitive (1) by the first derivative (2), thus,

$$\frac{x^3 - 7x + 7}{3x^2 - 7},$$

and we get $\frac{1}{3}x$ with the remainder $- \frac{1}{3}(14x - 21)$. Change the sign of the remainder and multiply by $\frac{3}{7}$, the result

$$R = 2x - 3, \quad . \quad . \quad . \quad . \quad (3)$$

is now to be divided into (2). Change the sign of the remainder and we obtain,

$$R = 1. \quad . \quad . \quad . \quad (4)$$

The right-hand sides of equations (1), (2), (3), (4),

$$x^3 - 7x + 7; \; 3x^2 - 7; \; 2x - 3; \; 1,$$

are known as **Sturm's functions.**

Substitute $- \infty$ for x in (1), the sign is negative;

,,	,,	(2),	,, positive;
,,	,,	(3),	,, negative;
,,	,,	(4),	,, positive.

Note that the last result is independent of x. The changes of sign may, therefore, be written

$$- + - +.$$

In the same way,

Value of x.	Corresponding Signs of Sturm's Functions.	Number of Changes of Sign.
$- \infty$	$- + - +$	3
$- 4$	$- + - +$	3
$- 3$	$+ + - +$	2
$- 2$	$+ + - +$	2
$- 1$	$+ - - +$	2
$+ 0$	$+ - - +$	2
$+ 1$	$+ - - +$	2
$+ 2$	$+ + + +$	0
$+ \infty$	$+ + + +$	0

There is, therefore, no change of sign caused by the substitution of any value of x less than $- 4$, or greater than $+ 2$; on passing from $- 4$ to $- 3$, there is one change of sign; on passing from 1 to 2, there are two changes of sign. The equation has, therefore, one real root between $- 4$ and $- 3$, and two between 1 and 2.

It now remains to determine a sufficient number of digits, to distinguish between the two roots lying between 1 and 2. First reduce the value of x in the given equation by 1. This is done by substituting $u + 1$ in place of x, and then finding Sturm's functions for the resulting equation. These are,

$$u^3 + 3u^2 - 4u + 1; \; 3u^2 + 6u - 4; \; 2u - 1; \; 1.$$

As above, noting that if $x = +1.1$, $u = + 0.1$, etc.,

Value of x.	Corresponding Signs of Sturm's Functions.	Number of Changes of Sign.
1·1	+ − − +	2
1·2	+ − − +	2
1·3	+ − − +	2
1·4	− − − +	1
1·5	− − + +	1
1·6	− + + +	1
1·7	+ + + +	0

The second digits of the roots between 1 and 2 are, therefore, 3 and 6, and three real roots of the given equation are approximately − 3, 1·3, 1·6.

EXAMPLES.—Locate the roots in the following equations:

(1) $x^3 - 3x^2 - 4x + 13$. Ansr. Between −3 and −2; 2 and 2·5; 2·5 and 3

(2) $x^3 - 4x^2 - 6x + 8$. Ansr. Between 0 and 1; 5 and 6; −1 and −2.

(3) $x^4 + x^3 - x^2 - 2x + 4$. We have five Sturm's functions for this equation. Call the original equation (1), the first derivative, $4x^3 + 3x^2 - 2x - 2$, (2); divide (1) by (2) and $x^2 + 2x - 6$ (3) remains; divide (2) by (3) and $-x + 1$ (4) remains; divide (3) by (4) and change the sign of the result for + 1 (5). Now let $x = + \infty$ and $- \infty$, we get

$$+ + + - + \ (2 \text{ variations of sign}); \ + - + + + \ (2 \text{ variations}).$$

This means that there are no real roots. All the roots are imaginary.

(4) Calculate the volume, v, of one gram of carbon dioxide at 0° C. and one megadyne pressure per sq. cm., given van der Waals' equation

$$\left(p + \frac{1852.6}{v^2}\right)(v - 0.9565) = 1.8824T.$$

0° C. = $273.7°T$; $p = 1$. Expand the equation and arrange terms in descending powers of v. Substitute the numerical values of the constants and reduce to

$$v^3 - 516.17v^2 + 1852.6v - 1772.0 = 0.$$

The only admissible root of this cubic is 512·5. The labour of solving this equation can sometimes be reduced by neglecting a/v^2 when it is small.

(5) The equation, $x^3 - 3rx^2 + 4r^3\rho = 0$, is obtained in problems referring to the depth to which a floating sphere of radius r and density ρ sinks in water. Solve this equation for the case of a wooden ball of unit radius and specific gravity 0·65. Hence, $x^3 - 3x^2 + 2.6 = 0$. The three roots, by Sturm's theorem, are—a negative root, a positive root between 1 and 2, and one over 2. The depth of the sphere in the water cannot be greater than its diameter 2. A negative root does not represent a physical reality. The two negative roots must, therefore, be excluded from the solution. The other root, by Newton's method of approximation, is $x = 1.204....$

In this last example we have rejected two roots because they were inconsistent with the physical conditions of the problem under consideration. This is a very common thing to do. Not all the solutions to which an equation may lead are solutions of the problem. Of course, every solution has some meaning, but this may be quite outside the requirements of the problem. A mathematical equation often expresses more than Nature allows. In the physical world only changes of a certain kind take place. If the velocity of a falling body is represented by the expression $v^2 = 64s$, then, if we want to calculate the velocity when s is 4, we get $v^2 = 256$, or, $v = \pm 16$. In other words, the velocity is either positive or negative. We must therefore limit the generality of the mathematical statement by rejecting those changes which are physically inadmissible. Thus we may have to reject imaginary roots when the problem requires real numbers; and negative or fractional roots, when the problem requires positive or whole numbers. Sometimes, indeed, none of the solutions will satisfy the conditions imposed by the problem, in this case the problem is indeterminate. The restrictions which may be imposed by the application of mathematical equations to specific problems, introduces us to the idea of **limiting conditions**, which is of great importance in higher mathematics. The ultimate test of every solution is that it shall satisfy the equation when substituted in place of the variable. If not it is no solution.

EXAMPLES.—(1) A is 40 years, B 20 years old. In how many years will A be three times as old as B? Let x denote the required number of years.

$$\therefore 40 + x = 3(20 + x); \text{ or } x = -10.$$

But the problem requires a positive number. The answer, therefore, is that A will never be three times as old as B. (The negative sign means that A *was* three times as old as B, 10 years ago.)

(2) A number x is squared; subtract 7; extract the square root of the result; add twice the number, 5 remains. What was the number x?

$$\therefore 2x + \sqrt{(x^2 - 7)} = 5.$$

Solve in the usual way, namely, square $5 - 2x = \sqrt{x^2 - 7}$; rearrange terms and use (2), § 113. Hence $x = 4$ or $\frac{8}{3}$. On trial both solutions, $x = 4$ and $x = 2\frac{2}{3}$, fail to satisfy the test. These *extraneous solutions* have been introduced during rationalization (by squaring).

§ 118. Horner's Method for Approximating to the Real Roots of Numerical Equations.

When the first significant digit or digits of a root have been obtained, by, say, Sturm's theorem, so that one root may be distinguished from all the other roots nearly equal to it, Horner's method is one of the simplest and best ways of carrying the approximation as far as may be necessary. So far as practical requirements are concerned, Horner's process is perfection. The arithmetical methods for the extraction of square and cube roots are special cases of Horner's method, because to extract $\sqrt{9}$, or $\sqrt[3]{9}$, is equivalent to finding the roots of the equation $x^2 - 9 = 0$, or $x^3 - 9 = 0$.

"Considering the remarkable elegance, generality, and simplicity of the method, it is not a little surprising that it has not taken a more prominent place in current mathematical text-books. Although it has been well expounded by several English writers, . . . it has scarcely as yet found a place in English curricula. Out of five standard Continental text-books where one would have expected to find it we found it mentioned in only one, and there it was expounded in a way which showed little insight into its true character. This probably arises from the mistaken notion that there is in the method some algebraic profundity. As a matter of fact, its spirit is purely arithmetical; and its beauty, which can only be appreciated after one has used it in particular cases, is of that indescribably simple kind which distinguishes the use of position in the decimal notation and the arrangement of the simple rules of arithmetic. It is, in short, one of those things whose invention was the creation of a commonplace."—G. Chrystal, *Text-book of Algebra* (London, i., 346, 1898).

In outline, the method is as follows : Find by means of Sturm's theorem, or otherwise, the integral part of a root, and transform the equation into another whose roots are less than those of the original equation by the number so found. Suppose we start with the equation

$$x^3 - 7x + 7 = 0, \quad . \quad . \quad . \quad . \quad (1)$$

which has one real root whose first significant figures we have found to be 1·3. Transform the equation into another whose roots are less by 1·3 than the roots of (1). This is done by substituting $u + 1·3$ for x. In this way we obtain,

$$u + 3·90u^2 - 1·93u^3 + ·097 = 0. \quad . \quad . \quad (2)$$

The first significant figure of the root of this equation is 0·05. Lower the roots of (2) by the substitution of $v + 0·05$ for u in (2). Thus,

$$v^3 + 4·05v^2 - 1·5325v + ·010375 = 0.. \quad . \quad (3)$$

The next significant figure of the root, deduced from (3), is ·006. We could have continued in this way until the root had been obtained of any desired degree of accuracy.

Practically, the work is not so tedious as just outlined. Let $a, b, c,$

be the coefficients of the given equation, R the absolute term,

$$ax^3 + bx^2 + cx + R = 0.$$

1. Multiply a by the first significant digits of the root and add the product to b.   Write the result under b.

2. Multiply this sum by the first figure of the root, add the product to c.   Write the result under c.

3. Multiply this sum by the first figure of the root, add the product to R, and call the result the **first dividend.**

4. Again multiply a by the root, add the product to the last number under b.

5. Multiply this sum by the root and add the product to the last number under c, call the result the **first trial divisor.**

6. Multiply a by the root once more, and add the product to the last number under b.

7. Divide the first dividend by the first trial divisor, and the first significant figure in the quotient will be the second significant of the root.   Thus starting from the old equation (1), whose root we know to be about 1.

a	b	c	R	(Root
1	+ 0	− 7	+ 7	(1·3
	1	1	− 6	
	—	—		
	1	− 6	1 First dividend	
	1	2		
	—	—		
	2	− 4 First trial divisor.		
	1			
	—			
	3			

8. Proceed exactly as before for the second trial divisor, using the second digit of the root, viz., ·3.

9. Proceed as before for the second dividend.   We finally obtain the result shown in the next scheme.   Note that the black figures in the preceding scheme are the coefficients of the second of the equations reduced on the supposition that $x = 1·3$ is a root of the equation.

a'	b'	c'	R'	(Root
1	3	− 4	1	(1·35
	0·3	0·99	− 0·903	
	—	—		
	3·3	− 3·01	0·097 Second dividend.	
	0·3	1·08		
	—	—		
	3·6	− 1·93 Second trial divisor.		
	0·3			
	—			
	3·9			

Once more repeating the whole operation, we get,

a''	b''	c''	R''	(Root
1	3·9	− 1·93	0·097	(1·356
	0·05	0·1975	− 0·086625	
	3·95	− 1·7325	**0·010375** Third dividend.	
	0·05	0·2000		
	4·00	− **1·5325** Third trial divisor.		
	0·05			
	4·05			

Having found about five or seven decimal places of the root in this way, several more may be added by dividing, say the fifth trial dividend by the fifth trial divisor. Thus, we pass from 1·356895, to 1·356895867 ... a degree of accuracy more than sufficient for any practical purpose.

Knowing one root, we can divide out the factor $x - 1\!\cdot\!3569$ from equation (1), and solve the remainder like an ordinary quadratic.

If any root is finite, the dividend becomes zero, as in one of the following examples. If the trial divisor gives a result too large to be subtracted from the preceding dividend, try a smaller digit.

To get the other root whose significant digits are 1·6, proceed as above, using 6 instead of 3 as the quotient from the first dividend and trial divisor. Thus we get 1·692 ... Several ingenious short cuts have been devised for lessening the labour in the application of Horner's method, but nothing much is gained, when the method has only to be used occasionally, beyond increasing the probability of error. It is usual to write down the successive steps as indicated in the following example.

EXAMPLES.—(1) Find the root between 6 and 7 in

$$4x^3 - 13x^2 - 31x = 275.$$

4	− 13	− 31	− 275	(6·25
	24	66	210	
	11	35	− 65	
	24	210	51·392	
	35	245	− 13·608	
	24	11·96	13·608	
	59	256·96	0	
	0·8	12·12		
	59·8	269·08		
	0·8	3·08		
	60·6	272·16		
	0·8			
	61·4			

The steps mark the end of each transformation.   The digits in black letters are the coefficients of the successive equations.

(2) There is a positive root between 4 and 5 in $x^3 + x^2 + x - 100$.   Ansr. 4·2644 ...

(3) Find the positive and negative roots in $x^4 + 8x^2 + 16x = 440$.   Ansr. + 3·976 ..., − 4·3504.   To find the negative roots, proceed as before, but first transform the equation into one with an opposite sign by changing the sign of the absolute term.

(4) Show that the root between − 3 and − 4, in equation (1), is − 3·0489173396 ... Work from $a = 1$, $b = − 0$, $c = − 7$, $R = − 7$.

§ 119. Van der Waals' Equation.

The relations between the roots of equations, discussed in this chapter, are interesting in many ways ; for the sake of illustration, let us take the van der Waals' relation between the pressure, p, volume, v, and temperature, T, of a gas.

$$\left(p + \frac{a}{v^2}\right)(v - b) = RT; \text{ or, } v^3 - \left(b + \frac{RT}{p}\right)v^2 + \frac{a}{p}v - \frac{ab}{p} = 0. \quad (1)$$

This equation of the third degree in v, must have three roots, a, β, γ, equal or unequal, real or imaginary.   In any case,

$$(v - a)(v - \beta)(v - \gamma) = 0. \quad \quad \quad (2)$$

Imaginary roots have no physical meaning ; we may therefore confine our attention to the real roots.   Of these, we have seen that there must be one, and there may be three.   This means that there may be one or three (different) volumes, corresponding with every value of the pressure, p, and temperature, T.   There are three interesting cases :

I. *There is only one real root present.*   This implies that there is one definite volume, v, corresponding to every assigned value of pressure, p, and temperature, T. This is realized in the pv-curve, of all gases under certain physical conditions ; for instance, the graph of carbon dioxide at 91° has only one value of p corresponding with each value of v.   See curve GH, Fig. 143.

II. *There are three real unequal roots present.*   The pv-curve of carbon dioxide at temperatures be-

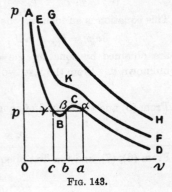

Fig. 143.

low 32°, has a wavy curve BC (Fig. 143). This means that at this temperature and a pressure of Op, carbon dioxide ought to have three different volumes corresponding respectively with the abscissæ Oc, Ob, Oa. Only two of these three volumes have yet been observed, namely for gaseous CO_2 at a and for liquid CO_2 at γ, the third, corresponding to the point β, is unknown. The curve $A\gamma\beta aD$, has been realized experimentally. The abscissa of the point a represents the volume of a given mass of gaseous carbon dioxide, the abscissa of the point γ represents the volume occupied by the same mass of liquid carbon dioxide at the same pressure.

Under special conditions, parts of the sinuous curve $\gamma B\beta Ca$ have been realized experimentally. $A\gamma$ has been carried a little below the line γa, and Da has been extended a little above the line γa. This means that a liquid may exist at a pressure less than that of its own vapour, and a vapour may exist at a pressure higher than the "vapour pressure" of its own liquid.

III. *There are three real equal roots present.* At and above the point where $a = \beta = \gamma$, there can only be one value of v for any assigned value of p. This point K (Fig. 143) is no other than the well-known critical point of a gas. Write p_c, v_c, T_c, for the critical pressure, volume, and temperature of a gas. From (2),

$$(v - a)^3 = 0; \text{ or, } v = a; \quad . \quad . \quad . \quad (3)$$

let v_c denote the value of v at the critical point when $a = v = v_c$. Therefore, if p_c denotes the pressure corresponding wiih $v = v_c$, from (1), and the expansion of (3),

$$v^3 - \left(b + \frac{RT_c}{p_c}\right)v^2 + \frac{a}{p_c}v - \frac{ab}{p_c} = v^3 - 3v_c v^2 + 3v_c^2 v - v_c^3. \quad (4)$$

This equation is an identity, therefore, from page 213,

$$3v_c p_c = bp_c + RT_c; \quad 3v_c^2 p_c = a; \quad v_c^3 p_c = ab, \quad . \quad (5)$$

are obtained by equating the coefficients of like powers of the unknown v. From the last two of equations (5),

$$v_c = 3b. \quad . \quad . \quad . \quad (6)$$

From (6) and the second of equations (5),

$$p_c = \frac{1}{27} \cdot \frac{a}{b^2} \quad . \quad . \quad . \quad (7)$$

From (6), (7), and the first of equations (5),

$$T_c = \frac{8}{27} \cdot \frac{a}{bR}. \quad . \quad . \quad . \quad (8)$$

From these results, (6), (7), (8), van der Waals has calculated the values of the constants a and b for different gases.   Let $p = p/p^c$, $v = v/v_c$, $T = T/T_c$.   From (1), (6), (7) and (8), we obtain

$$\left(p + \frac{3}{v^2}\right)(3v - 1) = 8T, \quad . \quad . \quad . \quad (9)$$

which appears to be van der Waals' equation freed from arbitrary constants.   This result has led van der Waals to the belief that all substances can exist in states or conditions where the corresponding pressures, volumes and temperatures are equivalent. These he calls *corresponding states*—uebereinstimmende Zustände. The deduction has only been verified in the case of ether, sulphur dioxide and some of the benzene halides.

CHAPTER VII.

HOW TO SOLVE DIFFERENTIAL EQUATIONS.

"Theory always tends to become more abstract as it emerges success-
fully from the chaos of facts by processes of differentiation and
elimination, whereby the essentials and their connections become recognized, while minor effects are seen to be secondary
or unessential, and are ignored temporarily, to be explained by
additional means."—O. HEAVISIDE.

§ 120. The Solution of a Differential Equation by the Separation of the Variables.

THIS chapter may be looked upon as a sequel to that on the
integral calculus, but of a more advanced character. The
"methods of integration" already described will be found ample
for most physico-chemical processes, but more powerful methods
are now frequently required.

I have previously pointed out that in the effort to find the
relations between phenomena, the attempt is made to prove that
if a limited number of hypotheses are prevised, the observed facts
are a necessary consequence of these assumptions. The *modus
operandi* is as follows:—

1. To "anticipate Nature" by means of a "working hypothesis," which is possibly nothing more than a "convenient fiction".

"From the practical point of view," said A. W. Rücker (Presidential
Address to the B. A. meeting at Glasgow, September, 1901), "it is a matter of
secondary importance whether our theories and assumptions are correct, if
only they guide us to results in accord with facts. . . . By their aid we can
foresee the results of combinations of causes which would otherwise elude us."

2. Thence to deduce an equation representing the momentary
rate of change of the two variables under investigation.

3. Then to integrate the equation so obtained in order to
reproduce the "working hypothesis" in a mathematical form
suitable for experimental verification.

So far as we are concerned this is the ultimate object of our integration. By the process of integration we are said to solve the equation. For the sake of convenience, any equation containing differentials or differential coefficients will, after this, be called a **differential equation.**

I.—*The variables can be separated directly.*

The different equations hitherto considered have required but little preliminary arrangement before integration. For example, the equations representing the velocity of chemical reactions have the general type :

$$\frac{dx}{dt} = kf(x), \quad . \quad . \quad . \quad . \quad (1)$$

We have invariably collected all the x's on one side, the t's, on the other, before proceeding to the integration. This separation of the variables is nearly always attempted before resorting to other artifices for the solution of the differential equation, because the integration is then comparatively simple.

EXAMPLES.—(1) Integrate the equation, $y \cdot dx + x \cdot dy = 0$. Rearrange the terms so that

$$\frac{dx}{x} + \frac{dy}{y} = 0; \text{ or, } \int \frac{dx}{x} + \int \frac{dy}{y} = C,$$

by multiplying through with $1/xy$. Ansr. $\log x + \log y = C$. Two or more apparently different answers may mean the same thing. Thus, the solution of the preceding equation may also be written, $\log xy = \log e^C$; *i.e.*, $xy = e^C$; or $\log xy = \log C'$; *i.e.*, $xy = C'$. C and $\log C'$ are, of course, the arbitrary constants of integration.

(2) F. A. H. Schreinemaker (*Zeit. phys. Chem.*, **36**, 413, 1901) in his study of the distillation of ternary mixtures, employed the equation $dy/dx = ay/x$. Hence show that $y = Cx^a$. He calls the graph of this equation the "distillation curve".

(3) The equation for the rectilinear motion of a particle under the influence of an attractive force from a fixed point is $v \cdot dv/dx + ax^{-2} = 0$; $\therefore$ $\frac{1}{2}v^2 = a/x + C$.

(4) In consequence of imperfect insulation, the charge on an electrified body is dissipated at a rate proportional to the magnitude E of the charge. Hence show that if a is a constant depending on the nature of the body, and E_0 represents the magnitude of the charge when t (time) $= 0$, $E = E_0 e^{-at}$. Hint. Compound interest law. Integrate by the separation of the variables. Interpret your result in words.

(5) Solve $(1 + x^2)dy = \sqrt{y} \cdot dx$. Ansr. $2\sqrt{y} - \tan^{-1}x = C$.

(6) Soive $y - x \cdot dy/dx = a(y + dy/dx)$. Ansr. $y = C(a + x)^{(1-a)}$.

(7) Abegg's formula for the relation between the dielectric constant, D, of

a fluid and temperature θ, is $- dD/d\theta = \frac{1}{150}D$. Hence show that $D = Ce^{-\frac{\theta}{150}}$, where C is a constant whose value is to be determined from the conditions of the experiment. Put the answer into words.

(8) What curves have a slope $- y/x$ to the x-axis? Ansr. The rectangular hyperbolas $xy = C$. Hint. Set up the proper differential equation and solve.

(9) The relation between small changes of pressure and volume of a gas under adiabatic conditions, is $\gamma pdv + vdp = 0$. Hence show that $pv^\gamma = $ constant.

(10) A lecturer discussing the physical properties of substances at very low temperatures, remarked " it appears that the specific heat, σ, of a substance decreases with decreasing temperatures, θ, at a rate proportional to the specific heat of the substance itself ". Set up the differential equation to represent this "law" and put your result in a form suitable for experimental verification. Ansr. $(\log \sigma_0 - \log\sigma)/\theta = $ const.

(11) Helmholtz's equation for the strength of an electric current, C, at the time t, is $C = E/R - (L/R)dC/dt$, where E represents the electromotive force in a circuit of resistance R and self-induction L. If E, R, L, are constants, show that $RC = E(1 - e^{-Rt/L})$ provided $C = 0$, when $t = 0$.

(12) The distance x from the axis of a thick cylindrical tube of metal is related to the internal pressure p as indicated in the equation $(2p - a)dx + xdp = 0$, where a is a constant. Hence show that $p = \frac{1}{2}a + Cx^{-2}$.

(13) A substitution will often enable an equation to be treated by this simple method of solution. Solve $(x - y^2)dx + 2xydy = 0$. Ansr. $xe^{y^2/x} = C$. Hint. Put $y^2 = v$, divide by x^2, $\therefore dx/x + d(y/x) = 0$, etc.

(14) Solve Dulong and Petit's equation: $d\theta/dt = b(c^\theta - 1)$, page 60. Put $c^\theta - 1 = x$ and differentiate for $d\theta$ and dx. Hence $dx = c^\theta \log c . d\theta$, $d\theta = dx/c^\theta \log c$; and page 213, Case 1.

$$\int \frac{d\theta}{c^\theta - 1} = \int \frac{dx}{x(x + 1) \log c}; \therefore bt \log c = \log \frac{x}{x + 1} + C; \text{ etc.}$$

(15) Solve Stefan's equation: $d\theta/dt = a\{(273 + \theta)^4 - 273^4\}$, page 60. Put $x = 273 + \theta$ and $c = 273$. Hence the given equation can be written $dx/dt = a(x^4 - c^4) = a(x + c) (x - c) (x^2 + c^2)$ which can be solved by Case 3, page 216. Thus, $at = \frac{1}{4c^3}\left\{ \log \frac{x - c}{x + c} - 2 \tan^{-1} \frac{x}{c}\right\} + c$.

(16) Solve $du/dr - u/r = C_1/r^2 - \frac{1}{4}ar^2$. Substitute $v = u/r$; $\therefore rdv/dr = du/dr - u/r$. $\therefore dv/dr = C_1/r^3 - \frac{1}{4}ar$; $\therefore u/r = C_2 - \frac{1}{2}C_1/r^2 - \frac{1}{8}ar^2$.

(17) According to the *Glasgow Herald* the speed of H.M.S. *Sapphire* was V when the engines indicated the horse-power P. When

$P = 5012$,	7281,	10200,	12650;
$V = 18\cdot47$,	20·60,	22·43,	23·63.

Do these numbers agree with the law $dP/dV = aP$, where a is constant? Ansr. Yes. Hint. On integration, remembering that $V = 0$ when $P = 0$, we get $\log_{10}P - \log_{10}C = aV$, where C is constant. Evaluate the constants as indicated on page 324, we get $C = 181$, $a = 0\cdot07795$, etc.

II.—*The equation is homogeneous in x and y.*

If the equation be homogeneous in x and y, that is to say, if the sum of the exponents of the variables in each term is of the same degree, a preliminary substitution of $x = ty$, or $y = tx$, according to convenience, will always enable variables to be separated. The rule for the substitution is to treat the differential which involves the smallest number of terms.

EXAMPLES.—(1) Solve $x + y \,.\, dy/dx - 2y = 0$.   Substitute $y = zx$; or $dy = xdz + zdx$, and rearrange terms. We get $(1 - 2z + z^2)dx + xzdz = 0$; or $(1 - z)^2dx + xzdz = 0$; and

$$\int \frac{zdz}{(1-z)^2} + \int \frac{dx}{x} = C \,;\, \therefore \frac{1}{1 - z} + \log(1 - z) + \log x = C' \,.\, (x - y)e^{\frac{z}{x - y}} = C.$$

(2) F. A. H. Schreinemaker (*Zeit. phys. Chem.*, **36**, 413, 1901) in studying the vapour pressure of ternary mixtures used the equation $dy/dx = my/x + n$ This becomes homogeneous when $x = ty$ is substituted.   Hence show that $Cx^m - nx/(m - 1) = y$, where C is the integration constant.

(3) Show that if $(y - x)dy + ydx = 0$; $y = Ce^{-x/y}$.
(4) Show that if $x^2dy - y^2dx - xydx = 0$; $x = e^{-x/y} + C$.
(5) Show that if $(x^2 + y^2)dx = 2xydy$; $x^2 - y^2 = Cx$.

III.—The equation is non-homogeneous in x and y.

Non-homogeneous equations in x and y can be converted into the homogeneous form by a suitable substitution.   The most general type of a non-homogeneous equation of the first degree is,

$$(ax + by + c)dx + (a'x + b'y + c')dy = 0, \qquad (2)$$

where x and y are of the first degree.   To convert this into an homogeneous equation, assume that $x = v + h$; and $y = w + k$, and substitute in the given equation (2).   Thus, we obtain

$$\{av + bw + (ah + bk + c)\}dv + \{a'v + b'w + (a'h + b'k + c')\}dw = 0. \quad (3)$$

Find h and k so that $ah + bk + c = 0$; $a'h + b'k + c' = 0$.

$$\therefore h = \frac{b'c - bc'}{a'b - ab'}\,;\, k = \frac{ac' - a'c}{a'b - ab'}. \qquad \cdot \qquad (4)$$

Substitute these values of h and k in (3).   The resulting equation

$$(av + bw)dv + (a'v + b'w)dw = 0, \qquad \cdot \qquad (5)$$

is homogeneous and, therefore, may be solved as just indicated.

EXAMPLES.—(1) Solve $(3y - 7x - 7)dx + (7y - 3x - 3)dy = 0$. Ansr. $(y - x - 1)^2(y + x + 1)^5 = C$. Hints. From (2), $a = -7$, $b = 3$, $c = -7$: $a' = -3$, $b' = 7$, $c' = -3$. From (4), $h = -1$, $k = 0$. Hence, from (3), we get $3wdv - 7vdv + 7wdw - 3vdw = 0$. To solve this homogeneous equation, substitute $w = vt$, as above, and separate the variables.

$$\therefore 7\frac{dv}{v} = \frac{3 - 7t}{t^2 - 1}dt \,;\, \therefore 7\int\frac{dv}{v} + \int\frac{2dt}{t - 1} + \int\frac{5dt}{t + 1} = C.$$

$\therefore 7 \log v + 2 \log(t - 1) + 5 \log(t + 1) = C$; or, $v^7(t - 1)^2(t + 1)^5 = C$.

But $x = v + h$, $\therefore v = x + 1$; $y = w + k$, $\therefore y = w$; $\therefore t = w/v = y/(x + 1)$, etc.

(2) If $(2y - x - 1)dy + (2x - y + 1)dx = 0$; $x^2 - xy + y^2 + x - y = C$.

IV.—Non-homogeneous equations in which the constants have the special relation $ab' = a'b$.

If $a : b = a' : b' = 1 : m$ (say), then h and k are indeterminate, since (2) then becomes

$$(ax + by + c)dx + \{m(ax + by) + c'\}dy = 0.$$

The denominators in equations (4) also vanish. In this case put $z = ax + by$, and eliminate y, thus, we obtain,

$$a - b\frac{z + c}{mz + c'} - \frac{dz}{dx} = 0, \quad . \quad . \quad . \quad (6)$$

an equation which allows the variables to be separated.

EXAMPLES.—(1) Solve $(2x + 3y - 5)dy + (2x + 3y - 1)dx = 0$.

Ansr. $x + y - 4 \log(2x + 3y + 7) = C$.

(2) Solve $(3y + 2x + 4)dx - (4x + 6y + 5)dy = 0$.

Ansr. $9 \log\{(21y + 14x + 22)\}21(2y - x) = C$.

When the variables cannot be separated in a satisfactory manner, special artifices must be adopted. We shall find it the simplest plan to adopt the routine method of referring each artifice to the particular class of equation which it is best calculated to solve. These special devices are sometimes far neater and quicker processes of solution than the method just described. We shall follow the conventional x and y rather more closely than in the earlier part of this work. The reader will know, by this time, that his x and y's, his p and v's and his s and t's are not to be kept in "water-tight compartments". It is perhaps necessary to make a few general remarks on the nomenclature.

§ 121. What is a Differential Equation?

We have seen that the straight line,

$$y = mx + b, \quad . \quad . \quad . \quad . \quad (1)$$

fulfils two special conditions : (i) It cuts one of the coordinate axes at a distance b from the origin ; (ii) It makes an angle $\tan a = m$, with the x-axis. By differentiation,

$$\frac{dy}{dx} = m. \quad . \quad . \quad . \quad . \quad (2)$$

This equation has nothing at all to say about the constant b.

That condition has been eliminated.   Equation (2), therefore, represents a straight line fulfilling one condition, namely, that it makes an angle $\tan^{-1}m$ with the x-axis.   Now substitute (2) in (1), the resulting equation,

$$y = \frac{dy}{dx}x + b, \quad . \quad . \quad . \quad . \quad (3)$$

in virtue of the constant b, satisfies only one definite condition, (3), therefore, is the equation of any straight line passing through b.   Nothing is said about the magnitude of the angle $\tan^{-1}m$. Differentiate (2).   The resulting equation,

$$\frac{d^2y}{dx^2} = 0, \quad . \quad . \quad . \quad . \quad (4)$$

represents any straight line whatever.   The special conditions imposed by the constants m and b in (1), have been entirely eliminated.   Equation (4) is the most general equation of a straight line possible, for it may be applied to any straight line that can be drawn in a plane.

Let us now find a physical meaning for the differential equation. In § 7, we have seen that the third differential coefficient, d^3s/dt^3 represents "the rate of change of acceleration from moment to moment".   Suppose that the acceleration d^2s/dt^2, of a moving body does not change or vary in any way.   It is apparent that the rate of change of a constant or uniform acceleration must be zero. In mathematical language, this is written,

$$d^3s/dt^3 = 0. \quad . \quad . \quad . \quad (5)$$

By integration we obtain,

$$d^2s/dt^2 = \text{Constant} = g. \quad . \quad . \quad . \quad (6)$$

Equation (6) tells us not only that the acceleration is constant, but it fixes that value to the definite magnitude g ft. per sec. per sec. Remembering that acceleration measures the rate of change of velocity, and integrating (6), we get,

$$ds/dt = gt + C_1. \quad . \quad . \quad . \quad (7)$$

From § 71, we have learnt how to find the meaning of C_1.   Put $t = 0$, then $ds/dt = C_1$.   This means that when we begin to reckon the velocity, the body may have been moving with a definite velocity C_1.   Let $C_1 = v_0$ ft. per second.   Of course if the body started from a position of rest, $C_1 = 0$.   Now integrate (7) and find the value of C_2 in the result,

$$s = \tfrac{1}{2}gt^2 + v_0t + C_2, \quad . \quad . \quad . \quad (8)$$

by putting $t = 0$. It is thus apparent that C_2 represents the space which the body had traversed when we began to study its motion. Let $C_2 = s_0$ ft. The resulting equation

$$s = \tfrac{1}{2}gt^2 + v_0t + s_0, \quad . \quad . \quad . \quad (9)$$

tells us three different things about the moving body at the instant we began to take its motion into consideration.

1. It had traversed a distance of s_0 ft. To use a sporting phrase, if the body is starting from " scratch," $s_0 = 0$.

2. The body was moving with a velocity of v_0 ft. per second.

3. The velocity was increasing at the *uniform* rate of g ft. per second per second.

Equation (7) tells us the two latter facts about the moving body; equation (6) only tells us the third fact; equation (5) tells us nothing more than that the acceleration is constant. (5), therefore, is true of the motion of any body moving with a uniform acceleration.

EXAMPLES.—(1) A body falls from rest. Show that it travels 400 ft. in 5 sec. Hint. Use $g = 32$.

(2) A body starting with a velocity of 20 ft. per sec. falls in accord with equation (7); what is its velocity after 6 seconds? Ansr. 212 ft.

(3) A body dropped from a balloon hits the ground with a velocity of 384 ft. per sec. How long was it falling? Ansr. 12 seconds.

(4) A particle is projected vertically upwards with a velocity of 100 ft. per sec. Find the height to which it ascends and the time of its ascent. Here $d^2s/dt^2 = -g$; multiply by $2ds/dt$, and integrate

$$2\frac{ds}{dt}\cdot\frac{d^2s}{dt^2} = \frac{d\left(\frac{ds}{dt}\right)^2}{dt} = -2g\frac{ds}{dt}; \therefore \left(\frac{ds}{dt}\right)^2 - v_0{}^2 = -2gs,$$

when the particle has reached its maximum height $ds/dt = 0$; and, therefore, $s = \tfrac{1}{2}v_0{}^2/g = \frac{10,000}{64}$; from (7), since $C_1 = 100 = v_0$, $t = v_0/g = \frac{100}{32}$.

(5) If a body falls in the air, experiment shows that the retarding effect of the resisting air is proportional to the square of the velocity of the moving body. Instead of g, therefore, we must write $g - bv^2$, where b is the variation constant of page 22. For the sake of simplicity, put $b = g/a^2$ and show that

$$v = a\frac{e^{gt/a} - e^{-gt/a}}{e^{gt/a} + e^{-gt/a}}; \; s = \frac{a^2}{g}\log\frac{e^{gt/a} + e^{-gt/a}}{2} = \frac{a^2}{g}\log\cosh\frac{gt}{a},$$

since $v = 0$, when $t = 0$, and $s = 0$ when $t = 0$. Hint. The equation of motion is $dv/dt = g - bv^2$.

Similar reasoning holds good from whatever sources we may draw our illustrations. We are, therefore, able to say that a **differential equation, freed from constants, is the most general way of expressing a natural law.**

Any equation can be freed from its constants by combining it with the various equations obtained by differentiation of the given equation as many times as there are constants. The operation is called **elimination**. Elimination enables us to discard the accidental features associated with any natural phenomenon and to retain the essential or general characteristics. It is, therefore, possible to study a theory by itself without the attention being distracted by experimental minutiæ. In a great theoretical work like "Maxwell" or "Heaviside," the differential equation is ubiquitous, experiment a rarity. And this not because experiments are unimportant, but because, as Heaviside puts it, they are fundamental, the foundations being always hidden from view in well-constructed buildings.

EXAMPLES.—(1) Eliminate the arbitrary constants a and b, from the relation $y = ax + bx^2$. Differentiate twice; evaluate a and b; and substitute the results in the original equation. The result,

$$x^2\frac{d^2y}{dx^2} - 2x\frac{dy}{dx} + 2y = 0,$$

is quite free from the arbitrary restrictions imposed in virtue of the presence of the constants a and b in the original equation.

(2) Eliminate m from $y^2 = 4mx$. Ansr. $y = 2x . dy/dx$.

(3) Eliminate a and b from $y = a\cos x + b\sin x$. Ansr. $d^2y/dx^2 + y = 0$.

We always *assume* that every differential equation has been obtained by the elimination of constants from a given equation called the **primitive**. In practical work we are not so much concerned with the building up of a differential equation by the elimination of constants from the primitive, as with the reverse operation of finding the primitive from which the differential equation has been derived. In other words, we have to find some relation between the variables which will satisfy the differential equation. Given an expression involving x, y, dx/dy, $d^2x/dy^2, \ldots$, to find an equation containing only x, y and constants which can be reconverted into the original equation by the elimination of the constants.

This relation between the variables and constants which satisfies the given differential equation is called a **general solution**, or a **complete solution**, or a **complete integral** of the differential equation. A solution obtained by giving particular values to the arbitrary constants of the complete solution is a **particular solution**. Thus $y = mx$ is a complete solution of $y = x . dy/dx$; $y = x\tan 45°$, is a particular solution.

A differential equation is **ordinary** or **partial**, according as there is one or more than one independent variables present. Ordinary differential equations will be treated first.   Equations like (2) and (3) above are said to be of the first order, because the highest derivative present is of the first order.   For a similar reason (4) and (6) are of the second order, (5) of the third order. The **order of a differential equation**, therefore, is fixed by that of the highest differential coefficient it contains.   The **degree of a differential equation** is the highest power of the highest order of of differential coefficient it contains.   This equation is of the second order and first degree :

$$\frac{d^2y}{dx^2} + k\left(\frac{dy}{dx}\right)^3 + \mu x^4 = 0.$$

It is not difficult to show that *the complete integral of a differential equation of the nth order, contains n, and no more than n, arbitrary constants*.   As the reader acquires experience in the representation of natural processes by means of differential equations, he will find that the integration *must* provide a sufficient number of undetermined constants to define the initial conditions of the natural process symbolized by the differential equation.   The complete solution must provide so many particular solutions (containing no undetermined constants) as there are definite conditions involved in the problem.   For instance, equation (5), page 375, is of the third order, and the complete solution, equation (9), requires three initial conditions, g, s_0, v_0 to be determined.   Similarly, the solution of equation (4), page 375, requires two initial conditions, m and b, in order to fix the line.

§ 122. Exact Differential Equations of the First Order.

The reason many differential equations are so difficult to solve is due to the fact that they have been formed by the elimination of constants as well as by the elision of some common factor from the primitive.   Such an equation, therefore, does not actually represent the complete or total differential of the original equation or primitive.   The equation is then said to be inexact.   On the other hand, an **exact differential equation** is one that has been obtained by the differentiation of a function of x and y and performing no other operation involving x and y.

Easy tests have been described, on page 77, to determine

whether any given differential equation is exact or inexact.   It
was pointed out that the differential equation,

$$M . dx + N . dy = 0, \qquad . \qquad . \qquad . \qquad (1)$$

is the direct result of the differentiation of any function u, provided,

$$\frac{\partial M}{\partial y} = \frac{\partial N}{\partial x}. \qquad . \qquad . \qquad . \qquad . \qquad (2)$$

This last result was called " the criterion of integrability," because,
if an equation satisfies the test, the integration can be readily performed by a direct process.   This is not meant to imply that only
such equations can be integrated as satisfy the test, for many equations which do not satisfy the test can be solved in other ways.

EXAMPLES.—(1) Apply the test to the equations, $ydx + xdy = 0$, and
$ydx - xdy = 0$. In the former, $M = y$, $N = x$; $\therefore$ $\partial M/\partial y = 1$, $\partial N/\partial x = 1$;
$\therefore$ $\partial M/\partial y = \partial N/\partial x$. The test is, therefore, satisfied and the equation is exact.
In the other equation, $M = y$, $N = - x$, $\therefore$ $\partial M/\partial y = 1$, $\partial N/\partial x = - 1$. This
does not satisfy the test. In consequence, the equation cannot be solved by
the method for exact differential equations.

(2) Show that $(a^2y + x^2)dx + (b^3 + a^2x)dy = 0$, is exact.

(3) Is the equation, $(x + 2y)xdx + (x^2 - y^2)dy = 0$, exact ? $M = x(x + 2y)$,
$N = x^2 - y^2$; $\therefore$ $\partial M/\partial y = 2x$, $\partial N/\partial x = 2x$. The condition is satisfied, the
equation is exact.

(4) Show that $(\sin y + y \cos x)dx + (\sin x + x \cos y)dy = 0$, is exact.

I. Equations which satisfy the criterion of integrability.

We must remember that M is the differential coefficient of u
with respect to x, y being constant, and N is the differential coefficient of u with respect to y, x being constant.   Hence we may
integrate Mdx on the supposition that y is constant and then treat
Ndy as if x were a constant.   The complete solution of the whole
equation is obtained by equating the sum of these two integrals to
an undetermined constant.   The complete integral is

$$u = C. \qquad . \qquad . \qquad . \qquad . \qquad (3)$$

EXAMPLE.—Integrate $x(x + 2y)dx + (x^2 - y^2)dy = 0$, from the preceding
set of examples.   Since the equation is exact, $M = x(x + 2y)$; $N = x^2 - y^2$;
$\therefore$ $\int Mdx = \int x(x + 2y)dx = \frac{1}{3}x^3 + x^2y = Y$, where Y is the integration constant
which may, or may not, contain y, because y has here been regarded as a con-
stant.   Now the result of differentiating $\frac{1}{3}x^3 + x^2y = Y$, should be the original
equation.   On trial, $x^2dx + 2xydx + x^2dy = dY$.   On comparison with the
original equation, it is apparent that $dY = y^2dy$; $\therefore$ $Y = \frac{1}{3}y^3 + C$.   Substitute this in the preceding result.   The complete solution is, therefore,
$\frac{1}{3}x^3 + x^2y - \frac{1}{3}y^3 = C$.   The method detailed in this example can be put into a
more practical shape.

To integrate an exact differential equation of the type

$$M . dx + N . dy = 0,$$

first find $\int M . dx$ on the assumption that y is constant and substitute the result in

$$\int M dx + \int \left(N - \frac{\partial}{\partial y} \int M dx \right) dy = C. \quad . \quad . \quad (4)$$

E.g., in $x(x + 2y)dx + (x^2 - y^2)dy = 0$, it is obvious that $\int M dx$ is $\frac{1}{3}x^3 + x^2 y$, and we may write down at once

$$\frac{1}{3}x^3 + x^2 y + \int \left\{ x^2 - y^2 - \frac{\partial}{\partial y}\left(\frac{1}{3}x^3 + x^2 y \right) \right\} dy = C.$$

$\therefore \frac{1}{3}x^3 + x^2 y + \int(x^2 - y^2 - x^2)dy = C$; or, $\frac{1}{3}x^3 + x^2 y - \frac{1}{3}y^3 = C$
If we had wished we could have used

$$\int N dy + \int \left(M - \frac{\partial}{\partial x} \int N dy \right) dx = C,$$

in place of (4), and integrated $\int N . dy$ on the assumption that x is constant.

In practice it is often convenient to modify this procedure. If the equation satisfies the criterion of integrability, we can easily pick out terms which make $M dx + N dy = 0$, and get

$$M dx + Y; \text{ and } N dy + X,$$

where Y cannot contain x and X cannot contain y. Hence if we can find $M dy$ and $N dx$, the functions X and Y will be determined. In the above equation, the only terms containing x and y are $2xy dx + x^2 dy$, which obviously have been derived from $x^2 y$. Hence integration of these and the omitted terms gives the above result.

EXAMPLES.—(1) Solve $(x^2 - 4xy - 2y^2)dx + (y^2 - 4xy - 2x^2)dy = 0$. Pick out terms in x and y, we get $- (4xy + 2y^2)dx - (4xy + 2x^2)dy = 0$. Integrate. $\therefore - 2x^2 y - 2xy^2 =$ constant. Pick out the omitted terms and integrate for the complete solution. We get,
$\int x^2 dx + \int y^2 dy - 2x^2 y - 2xy^2 = C$; $\therefore x^3 - 6x^2 y - 6xy^2 + y^3 =$ constant.
(2) Show that the solution of $(a^2 y + x^2)dx + (b^3 + a^2 x)dy = 0$, furnishes the relation $a^2 xy + b^3 y + \frac{1}{3}x^3 = C$. Use (4).
(3) Solve $(x^2 - y^2)dx - 2xy dy = 0$. Ansr. $\frac{1}{3}x^2 - y^2 = C/x$. Use (4).

II. Equations which do not satisfy the criterion of integrability.

As just pointed out, the reason any differential equation does not satisfy the criterion of exactness, is because the "integrating factor" has been cancelled out during the genesis of the equation from its primitive. If, therefore, the equation

$$M dx + N dy = 0,$$

does not satisfy the criterion of integrability, it will do so when the factor, previously divided out, is restored. Thus, the preceding equation is made exact by multiplying through with the integrating factor μ.   Hence,

$$\mu(Mdx + Ndy) = 0,$$

satisfies the criterion of exactness, and the solution can be obtained as described above.

§ 123. How to find Integrating Factors.

Sometimes integrating factors are so simple that they can be detected by simple inspection.

EXAMPLES.—(1) $ydx - xdy = 0$ is inexact. It becomes exact by multiplication with either x^{-2}, $x^{-1}.y^{-1}$, or y^{-2}.

(2) In $(y - x)dy + ydx = 0$, the term containing $ydx - xdy$ is not exact, but becomes so when multiplied as in the preceding example.

$$\therefore \frac{dy}{y} - \frac{xdy - ydx}{y^2} = 0; \text{ or, } \log y - \frac{x}{y} = C.$$

We have already established, in § 26, that an integrating factor always exists which will make the equation

$$Mdx + Ndy = 0,$$

an exact differential.   Moreover, there is also an infinite number of such factors, for if the equation is made exact when multiplied by μ, it will remain exact when multiplied by any function of μ. The different integrating factors correspond to the various forms in which the solution of the equation may present itself.   For instance, the integrating factor $x^{-1}y^{-1}$, of $ydx + xdy = 0$, corresponds with the solution $\log x + \log y = C$.   The factor y^{-2} corresponds with the solution $xy = C'$.   Unfortunately, it is of no assistance to know that every differential equation has an infinite number of integrating factors.   No general practical method is known for finding them; and the reader must consult some special treatise for the general theorems concerning the properties of integrating factors.   Here are four elementary rules applicable to special cases.

Rule I. Since

$$d(x^m y^n) = x^{m-1}y^{n-1}(mydx + nxdy),$$

an expression of the type $mydx + nxdy = 0$, has an integrating factor $x^{m-1}y^{n-1}$; or, the expression

$$x^a y^\beta(mydx + nxdy) = 0, \quad . \quad . \quad . \quad (1)$$

has an integrating factor

$$x^{m-1-a}y^{n-1-\beta},$$

or more generally still,

$$x^{km-1-a}y^{kn-1-\beta}, \qquad \cdot \quad \cdot \quad \cdot \quad (2)$$

where k may have any value whatever.

EXAMPLE.—Find an integrating factor of $ydx - xdy = 0$. Here, $a = 0$, $\beta = 0$, $m = 1$, $n = -1$ ∴ y^{-2} is an integrating factor of the given equation.

If the expression can be written

$$x^a y^\beta (mydx + nxdy) + x^{a'} y^{\beta'} (m'ydx + n'xdy) = 0, \qquad . \quad (3)$$

the integrating factor can be readily obtained, for

$$x^{km-1-a}y^{kn-1-\beta}; \text{ and } x^{k'm'-1-a'}y^{k'n'-1-\beta'},$$

are integrating factors of the first and second members respectively. In order that these factors may be identical,

$$km - 1 - a = k'm' - 1 - a'; \quad kn - 1 - \beta = k'n' - 1 - \beta'.$$

Values of k and k' can be obtained to satisfy these two conditions by solving these two equations. Thus,

$$k = \frac{n'(a - a') - m'(\beta - \beta')}{mn' - m'n}; \quad k' = \frac{n(a - a') - m(\beta - \beta')}{mn' - m'n}. \quad (4)$$

EXAMPLES.—(1) Solve $y^3(ydx - 2xdy) + x^4(2ydx + xdy) = 0$. Hints. Show that $a = 0$, $\beta = 3$, $m = 1$, $n = -2$; $a' = 4$, $\beta' = 0$, $m' = 2$, $n' = 1$; ∴ $x^{k-1}y^{-2k-4}$ is an integrating factor of the first, $x^{2k'-5}y^{k'-1}$ of the second member. Hence, from (4), $k = -2$, $k' = 1$, ∴ x^{-3} is an integrating factor of the whole expression. Multiply through and integrate for $2x^4y - y^4 = Cx^2$.

(2) Solve $(y^3 - 2yx^2)dx + (2xy^2 - x^3)dy = 0$. Ansr. $x^2y^2(y^2 - x^2) = C$. Integrating factor deduced after rearranging the equation is xy.

Rule II. *If the equation is homogeneous and of the form:* $Mdx + Ndy = 0$, *then* $(Mx + Ny)^{-1}$ *is an integrating factor.*

Let the expression

$$Mdx + Ndy = 0$$

be of the mth degree and μ an integrating factor of the nth degree,

$$\therefore \mu Mdx + \mu Ndy = du, \qquad . \qquad . \qquad . \qquad (5)$$

is of the $(m+n)$th degree, and the integral u is of the $(m+n+1)$th degree. By Euler's theorem, § 23,

$$\therefore \mu Mx + \mu Ny = (m + n + 1)u. \qquad . \qquad . \qquad (6)$$

Divide (5) by (6),

$$\frac{Mdx + Ndy}{Mx + Ny} = \frac{1}{m + n + 1} \cdot \frac{du}{u}.$$

The right side of this equation is a complete differential, consequently, the left side is also a complete differential.   Therefore, the factor $(Mx + Ny)^{-1}$ has made $Mdx + Ndy = 0$ an exact differential equation.

EXAMPLES.—(1) Show that $(x^3y - xy^3)^{-1}$ is an integrating factor of $(x^2y + y^3)dx - 2xy^2dy = 0$.

(2) Show that $1/(x^2 - nyx + y^2)$ is an integrating factor of $ydy + (x - ny)dx = 0$.

The method, of course, cannot be used if $Mx + Ny$ is equal to zero.   In this case, we may write $y = Cx$, a solution.

Rule III. *If the equation is homogeneous and of the form* .

$$f_1(x, y)ydx + f_2(x, y)xdy = 0,$$

then $(Mx - Ny)^{-1}$ *is an integrating factor.*

EXAMPLE.—Solve $(1 + xy)ydx + (1 - xy)xdy = 0$.   Hint. Show that the integrating factor is $1/2x^2y^2$.   Divide out $\frac{1}{2}$. $\therefore \int Mdx = -1/xy + \log x$.   Ansr.

$$x = Cye - \frac{x}{y}.$$

If $Mx - Ny = 0$, the method fails and $xy = C$ is then a solution of the equation.   *E.g.*, $(1 + xy)ydx + (1 + xy)xdy = 0$.

Rule IV. *If* $\dfrac{1}{N}\left(\dfrac{\partial M}{\partial y} - \dfrac{\partial N}{\partial x}\right)$ *is a function of* x *only,* $e^{\int f(x)dx}$ *is an integrating factor.*   *Or, if* $\dfrac{1}{M}\left(\dfrac{\partial N}{\partial x} - \dfrac{\partial M}{\partial y}\right) = f(y)$, *then* $e^{\int f(y)dy}$ *is an integrating factor.*   These are important results.

EXAMPLES.—(1) Solve $(x^2 + y^2)dx - 2xydy = 0$.   Ansr. $x^2 - y^2 = Cx$. Hint. Show $f(x) = -2x^{-1}$.   The integrating factor is $e^{-\int 2x^{-1}dx} = e^{-2\log x} = x^{-2}$.   Prove that this is an integrating factor, and solve as in the preceding section.

(2) Solve $(y^4 + 2y)dx + (xy^3 + 2y^4 - 4x)dy = 0$.   Ansr. $xy^3 + y^4 + 2x = Cy^2$.

We may now illustrate this rule for a special case, as we shall want the result later on.   The steps will serve to recall some of the principles established in some earlier chapters.   Let

$$\frac{dy}{dx} + Py = Q, \qquad . \qquad . \qquad . \qquad . \qquad (7)$$

where P and Q are either constants or functions of x.   Let μ be an integrating factor which makes

$$dy + (Py - Q)dx = 0, \qquad . \qquad . \qquad . \qquad (8)$$

an exact differential.

$$\therefore \mu dy + \mu(Py - Q)dx \equiv Ndy + Mdx.$$

$$\therefore \frac{\partial N}{\partial x} = \frac{\partial \mu}{\partial x}; \ \frac{\partial M}{\partial y} = (Py - Q)\frac{\partial \mu}{\partial y} + P\mu. \ \therefore \frac{\partial \mu}{\partial x} = (Py - Q)\frac{\partial \mu}{\partial y} + P\mu.$$

$$\therefore \frac{\partial \mu}{\partial x}dx = (Py - Q)\frac{\partial \mu}{\partial y}dx + P\mu dx = -\frac{\partial \mu}{\partial y}dy + P\mu dx.$$

$$\therefore \frac{\partial \mu}{\partial x}dx + \frac{\partial \mu}{\partial y}dy = d\mu = P\mu dx. \quad \therefore P = \frac{1}{\mu}\frac{d\mu}{dx}; \quad \therefore \int P dx = \log \mu;$$

and since $\log_e e = 1$, $(\int P dx)\log e = \log \mu$; consequently

$$\therefore \mu = e^{\int P dx}. \qquad . \qquad . \qquad . \qquad (9)$$

is the integrating factor of the given equation (7).

§ 124. Physical Meaning of Exact Differentials.

Fɪɢ. 144.

Let AP (Fig. 144) be the path of a particle under the influence of a force F making an angle θ with the tangent PT of the curve at the point $P(x, y)$. Let W denote the work done by the particle in passing from the fixed point $A(a, b)$ to its present position $P(x, y)$. Let the length AP be s. The work, dW, done by the particle in travelling a distance ds will now be

$$dW = F \cdot \cos \theta \cdot ds. \qquad . \qquad . \qquad . \qquad (1)$$

Let PT and PF respectively make angles α and β with the x-axis. Hence, as on page 126, $dx/ds = \cos \alpha$; $dy/ds = \sin \alpha$; $\therefore \theta = \alpha - \beta$.

$\therefore F \cos \theta = F \cos (\alpha - \beta) = F \cos \alpha \cdot \cos \beta + F \sin \alpha \cdot \sin \beta$, by a well-known trigonometrical transformation (24) page 612.

$$\therefore F \cos \theta = F \cos \beta \frac{dx}{ds} + F \sin \beta \frac{dy}{ds} = X \frac{dx}{ds} + Y \frac{dy}{ds}, \qquad (2)$$

where X is put for $F \cos \beta$, and Y for $F \sin \beta$; X and Y are obviously the two components of the force parallel with the coordinate axes. From (1),

$$dW = \left(X \frac{dx}{ds} + Y \frac{dy}{ds}\right) ds. \qquad . \qquad . \qquad (3)$$

I. Let $Xdx + Ydy$ be a complete differential.

Let us assume that $Xdx + Ydy$ is a complete differential of the function $u = f(x, y)$. Hence

$$dW = \left(\frac{\partial u}{\partial x} \cdot \frac{dx}{ds} + \frac{\partial u}{\partial y} \cdot \frac{dy}{ds}\right) ds = du, \qquad . \qquad . \qquad (4)$$

by partial differentiation. In order to fix our ideas, let $u = \tan^{-1}(y/x)$ Fig. 144. Hence, Ex. (5), page 49,

$$du = \frac{x}{r^2}dy - \frac{y}{r^2}dx,$$

where r^2 is put in place of $x^2 + y^2$. From (4),

$$\frac{dW}{ds} = \left(\frac{x}{r^2} \cdot \frac{dy}{ds} - \frac{y}{r^2}\frac{dx}{ds}\right) = \frac{du}{ds}.$$

The rate dW/ds at which the work is performed by the particle changes as it moves along the curve and is equal to the rate, du/ds, at which the function $f(x, y)$ changes. Any change in W is accompanied by a corresponding change in the value of u. Hence, as the particle passes from A to P, the work performed will be

$$dW = \frac{xdy - ydx}{r^2} = d \tan^{-1}\frac{y}{x} = du ;$$

and by integration,

$$W = u + \text{constant}.$$

This means that the work done by the particle in passing from a fixed point A to another point $P(x, y)$ depends only upon the value of u, and u is a function of the coordinates, x and y, of the point P.

It will be obvious that if the particle moves along a closed curve the work done will be zero. If the origin O lies within the closed curve, u will increase by 2π when P has travelled round the curve. In that case the work done is not zero. The function u is then a multi-valued function.

EXAMPLE.—If $X = y$, and $Y = x, dW = (xdx + ydy) = d(xy)$; or, by integration $W = xy + C$. We do not need to know the equation of the path. The work done is simply a function of the coordinates of the end state. The constant C serves to define the initial position of the point $A(a, b)$.

The first law of thermodynamics states that when a quantity of heat, dQ, is added to a substance, one part of the heat is spent in changing the internal energy, dU, of the substance and another part, dW, is spent in doing work against external forces. In symbols,

$$dQ = dU + dW.$$

In the special case, when that work is expansion against atmospheric pressure, $dW = p \cdot dv$. Now let the substance pass from any state A to another state B (Fig. 145). The internal energy of the substance in the state B is completely determined by the coordinates of that point, because U is quite independent of the nature of the transformation from the state A to the state B. It makes no difference to the magnitude of U whether that path has been *viâ* APB or AQB. In this case U is completely defined by the coordinates of the point corresponding

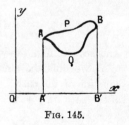

FIG. 145.

to any given state. In other words dU is a complete differential.

On the other hand, the external work done during the transformation from the one state to another, depends not only on the initial and final states of the substance, but also on the nature of the path described in passing from the state A to the state B. For example, the substance may perform the work represented by the area $AQBB'A'$ or by the area $APBB'A'$, in its passage from the state A to the state B. In fact the total work done in the passage from A to B and back again, is represented by the area $APBQ$. In order to know the work done during the passage from the state A to the state B, it is not only necessary to know the initial and final states of the substance as defined by the coordinates of the points A and B, but we must know the nature of the path from the one state to the other.

Similarly, the quantity of heat supplied to the body in passing from one state to the other, not only depends on the initial and final states of the substance, but also on the nature of the transformation. All this is implied when it is said that "dW and dQ are not perfect differentials". dW and dQ can be made into complete differentials by multiplying through with the integrating factor μ. The integrating factor is proved in thermodynamics to be equivalent to the so-called *Carnot's function*. To indicate that dW and dQ are not perfect differentials, some writers superscribe a comma to the top right-hand corner of the differential sign. The above equation would then be written,

$$d'Q = dU + d'W.$$

II. Let $Xdx + Ydy$ be an incomplete differential.

Now suppose that $Xdx + Ydy$ is not a complete differential. In that case, we cannot write $X = \partial u/\partial x$ and $Y = \partial u/\partial y$ as in (3) and (4). But from equation (3), by a rearrangement of the terms, we get

$$dW = \left(X + Y\frac{dy}{dx}\right)dx. \qquad . \qquad . \qquad . \qquad (5)$$

And now, to find the work done by the particle in passing from A to P, we must be able to express y in terms of x by using the equation of the path. Let $X = -y$, and $Y = x$; let the equation of the path be $y = ax^2$, $\therefore dy/dx = 2ax$. From (5)

$$dW = (-y + 2ax^2)dx = (-ax^2 + 2ax^2)dx = \tfrac{1}{3}ax^3 + C.$$

It is now quite clear that the value of $X + Ydy/dx$ will be different for different paths.   For example, if $y = ax^3$,

$$dW = (ax^3 + 3ax^3)dx = ax^4.$$

So that the work done depends upon the coordinates of the point P as well as upon the equation of the path.

EXAMPLE.—If $dU = dQ - pdv$, and dU is a complete differential, show that dQ is not a complete differential.   Hint. We know, page 80, that

$$dQ = \left(\frac{\partial Q}{\partial T}\right)_v dT + \left(\frac{\partial Q}{\partial v}\right)_T dv \; ; \; \therefore \; dU = \left(\frac{\partial Q}{\partial T}\right)_v dT + \left(\frac{\partial Q}{\partial v} - p\right)_T dv. \quad (6)$$

If U is a complete differential,

$$\frac{\partial}{\partial T}\left(\frac{\partial Q}{\partial v} - p\right) = \frac{\partial}{\partial v}\left(\frac{\partial Q}{\partial T}\right) \; ; \; \therefore \; \frac{\partial^2 Q}{\partial T \partial v} = \frac{\partial^2 Q}{\partial v \partial T} + \frac{\partial p}{\partial T} \qquad . \qquad (7)$$

From (6), if dQ is a complete differential,

$$\frac{\partial^2 Q}{\partial v \partial T} = \frac{\partial^2 Q}{\partial T \partial v}.$$

Hence (6) and (7) cannot both be true.

The question is discussed from another point of view in *Technics*, **1,** 615, 1904.

§ 125. Linear Differential Equations of the First Order.

A linear differential equation of the first order involves only the first power of the dependent variable y and of its first differential coefficients.   The general type, sometimes called **Leibnitz' equation,** is

$$\frac{dy}{dx} + Py = Q, \qquad . \qquad . \qquad . \qquad . \qquad (1)$$

where P and Q may be functions of x and explicitly independent of y, or constants.   We have just proved that $e^{\int Pdx}$ is an integrating factor of (1), therefore

$$e^{\int Pdx}(dy + Pydx) = e^{\int Pdx}Qdx,$$

is an exact differential equation.   Consequently, the general solution is,

$$ye^{\int Pdx} = \int e^{\int Pdx}Qdx + C; \; \text{or,} \; y = e^{-\int Pdx}\int e^{\int Pdx}Qdx + Ce^{-\int Pdx}. \quad (2)$$

The linear equation is one of the most important in applied mathematics.   In particular cases the integrating factor may assume a very simple form.

EXAMPLES.—(1) Solve $(1 + x^2)dy = (m + xy)dx$.   Reduce to the form (1) and we obtain

$$\frac{dy}{dx} - \frac{x}{1 + x^2}y = \frac{m}{1 + x^2}.$$

BB *

$$\therefore \int P dx = -\int \frac{x\,dx}{1 + x^2} = -\tfrac{1}{2}\log(1 + x^2) = -\log\sqrt{(1 + x^2)}.$$

Remembering $\log 1 = 0$, $\log e = 1$, the integrating factor is evidently,

$$\log e^{\int P dx} = \log 1 - \log\sqrt{1 + x^2}; \text{ or } e^{\int P dx} = \frac{1}{\sqrt{(1 + x^2)}}.$$

Multiply the original equation with this integrating factor, and solve the resulting exact equation as § 122, (4), or, better still, by (2) above. The solution: $y = mx + C\sqrt{(1 + x^2)}$ follows at once.

(2) Ohm's law for a variable current flowing in a circuit with a coefficient of self-induction L (henries), a resistance R (ohms), and a current of C (ampères) and an electromotive force E (volts), is given by the equation, $E = RC + LdC/dt$. This equation has the standard linear form (1). If E is constant, show that the solution is, $C = E/R + Be^{-Rt/L}$, where B is the arbitrary constant of integration (page 193). Show that C approximates to E/R after the current has been flowing some time, t. Hint for solution. Integrating factor is $e^{Rt/L}$.

(3) The equation of motion of a particle subject to a resistance varying directly as the velocity and as some force which is a given function of the time, is $dv/dt + kv = f(t)$. Show that $v = Ce^{-kt} + e^{-kt}\int e^{kt}f(t)dt$. If the force is gravitational, say g, $v = Ce^{-kt} + g/k$.

(4) Solve $xdy + ydx = x^3dx$. Integrating factor $= x$. Ansr. $y = \tfrac{1}{4}x^3 + C/x$.

(5) We shall want the integral of $dy/dt + k_2y = k_2a(1 - e^{-k_1t})$ very shortly. The solution follows thus:

$$y = Ce^{-\int k_2 dt} - e^{-\int k_2 dt}\int e^{\int k_2 dt}\{-k_2a(1 - e^{-k_1t})\}dt;$$
$$= Ce^{-k_2t} + e^{-k_2t}\{k_2a\int e^{k_2t} - \int e^{(k_2-k_1)t)}dt\};$$
$$= Ce^{-k_2t} + a - \frac{k_2a}{k_2 - k_1}e^{-k_1t}.$$

(6) We shall also want to solve

$$\frac{dy}{dx} + \frac{Ky}{a - x} = \frac{Kx}{a - x};$$

Here

$$e^{\int \frac{K dx}{a - x}} = e^{-K\log(a - x)} = e^{-\log(a - x)^K} = \frac{1}{(a - x)^K}.$$

$$\therefore \frac{y}{(a - x)^K} = C + K\int \frac{x\,dx}{(a - x)^{K+1}} = C + \frac{x}{(a - x)^K} - K\int \frac{dx}{(a - x)^K}$$

on integrating by parts. Finally, if $x = 0$, when $y = 0$,

$$y = C(a - x)^K + a - \frac{K(a - x)}{K - 1}; \quad C = \frac{1}{(K - 1)a^{K-1}}.$$

Many equations may be transformed into the linear type of equation, by a change in the variable. Thus, in the so-called **Bernoulli's equation,**

$$\frac{dy}{dx} + Py = Qy^n. \qquad . \qquad . \qquad . \qquad (3)$$

Divide by y^n, multiply by $(1 - n)$ and substitute $y^{1-n} = v$, in the result. Thus,

$$\frac{(1-n)}{y^n}\frac{dy}{dx} + (1-n)Py^{1-n} = (1-n)Q,$$

$$\therefore \frac{dv}{dx} + (1-n)Pv = Q(1-n),$$

which is linear in v. Hence, the solution follows at sight,

$$ve^{(1-n)\int Pdx} = (1-n)\int Qe^{(1-n)\int Pdx}dx + C.$$

$$\therefore y^{1-n}e^{(1-n)\int Pdx} = (1-n)\int Qe^{(1-n)\int Pdx}dx + C.$$

EXAMPLES.—(1) Solve $dy/dx + y/x = y^2$. Substitute $v = 1/y$. Integration factor is $e^{-\int dx/x} = e^{-\log x} = x^{-1}$. Ansr. $Cxy - xy\log x = 1$.

(2) Solve $dy/dx + x\sin 2y = x^3\cos^2 y$. Divide by $\cos^2 y$. Put $\tan y = v$. The integration factor is $e^{\int 2x dx}$, $i.e.$, e^{x^2}. Ansr. $e^{x^2}(\tan y - \frac{1}{2}x^2 + \frac{1}{2}) = C$. Hint. The steps are $\sec^2 y\, dy/dx + 2x\tan y = x^3$; $dv/dx + 2xu = x^3$; to solve $ve^{x^2} = \int x^3 e^{x^2}dx + C$. Put $x^2 = z$, $\therefore 2x dx = dz$, and this integral becomes $\frac{1}{2}\int ze^z dz$; or, $\frac{1}{2}e^z(z-1)$, (4) page 206, etc.

(3) Here is an instructive differential equation, which Harcourt and Esson encountered during their work on chemical dynamics in 1866.

$$\frac{1}{y^2}\cdot\frac{dy}{dx} + \frac{K}{y} - \frac{K}{x} = 0.$$

I shall give a method of solution in full, so as to revise some preceding work. The equation has the same form as Bernoulli's. Therefore, substitute

$$v = \frac{1}{y}; \; i.e., \frac{dv}{dx} = -\frac{1}{y^2}\cdot\frac{dy}{dx}. \; \therefore \frac{dv}{dx} - Kv + \frac{K}{x} = 0,$$

an equation linear in v. The integrating factor is $e^{\int Pdx}$; or, e^{-Kx}; Q, in (2), $= -K/x$; therefore, from (2),

$$ve^{-Kx} = -\int\frac{K}{x}e^{-Kx}dx + C.$$

From the method of § 111, page 341,

$$ve^{-Kx} = -K\int\frac{1}{x}\left\{1 - (Kx) + \frac{(Kx)^2}{1.2} - \frac{(Kx)^3}{1.2.3} + \dots\right\}dx + C.$$

$$\therefore ve^{-Kx} = -K\int\left\{\frac{dx}{x} - Kdx + \frac{K^2xdx}{1.2} - \frac{K^3x^2dx}{1.2.3} + \dots\right\} + C.$$

But $v = 1/y$. Multiply through with ye^{Kx}, and integrate.

$$1 = Ke^{Kx}\left\{C_1 - \log x + Kx - \frac{(Kx)^2}{1.2^2} + \frac{(Kx)^3}{1.2.3^2} - \dots\right\}y.$$

We shall require this result on page 437. Other substitutions may convert an equation into the linear form, for instance :

(4) I came across the equation $dx/dt = k(a-x)(x-y)$, where $y = a(1-e^{-mt})$, in studying some chemical reactions. Put $z = 1/k(a-x)$; $\therefore dx = -dz/kz^2$,

$$\therefore dz/dt - kze^{-mt} = 1.$$

This equation is linear. For the integrating factor note that $kedt = -ke/m$ $\vcenter{} = -u$, say. Consequently,

$$z = -\frac{1}{m}e^{-u}\int\left(\frac{e^u du}{u} + C\right) = -\frac{e^{-u}}{m}\left(\log u = u\frac{1}{2}\cdot\frac{u^2}{2!} + \frac{1}{3}\cdot\frac{u^3}{3!} + \dots + C\right).$$

$z = 0$ when $t = 0$; ∴ $u = k/m$ when $t = 0$. Let S denote the sum of the series when k/m is substituted in place of u, and s the sum as it stands above. When $z = 0$, $t = 0$, $C = -S$.

$$\therefore z = \frac{e^{-u}(S - s)}{m} = \frac{S - s}{me^u}; \ \therefore u = a - \frac{me^u}{k(S - s)},$$

if u is less than unity the series is convergent.

(5) J. W. Mellor and L. Bradshaw (*Zeit. phys. Chem.*, **48**, 353, 1904) have for the hydrolysis of cane sugar

$$du/dt + bu = Ab(1 - e^{-kt}); \ \therefore ue^{bt} = Ae^{bt} - be^{(b - kt)}/(b - k) + C.$$

(6) The law of cooling of the sun has been represented by the equation $dT/dt = aT^3 - bT$. To solve, divide by T^3; put $T^{-2} = z$, and hence $T^{-3}dT = -\frac{1}{2}dz$; hence $dz/dt - 2bz = -2a$. This is an ordinary linear equation with the solution $z = a/b + Ce^{2bt}$. Restore the value of z. The constant C can be evaluated in the usual manner.

§ 126. Differential Equations of the First Order and of the First or Higher Degree.—Solution by Differentiation.

Case i. *The equation can be split up into factors.* If the differential equation can be resolved into n factors of the first degree, equate each factor to zero and solve each of the n equations separately. The n solutions may be left either distinct, or combined into one.

EXAMPLES.—(1) Solve $x(dy/dx)^2 = y$. Resolve into factors of the first degree, $dy/dx = \pm \sqrt{y/x}$. Separate the variables and integrate, $\int x^{-\frac{1}{2}}dx \pm \int y^{-\frac{1}{2}}dy = \pm \sqrt{C}$, where $\sqrt{C}$ is the integration constant. Hence $\sqrt{x} \pm \sqrt{y} = \pm \sqrt{C}$, which, on rationalization, becomes $(x - y)^2 - 2C(x + y) + C^2 = 0$. Geometrically this equation represents a system of parabolic curves each of which touches the axis at a distance C from the origin. The separate equations of the above solution merely represent different branches of the same parabola.

(2) Solve $xy(dy/dx)^2 - (x^2 - y^2)dy/dx - xy = 0$. Ansr. $xy = C$, or $x^2 - y^2 = C$. Hint. Factors $(xp + y)(yp - x)$, where $p = dy/dx$. Either $xp + y = 0$, or $yp - x = 0$, etc.

(3) Solve $(dy/dx)^2 - 7dy/dx + 12 = 0$. Ansr. $y = 4x + C$, or $3x + C$.

Case ii. *The equation cannot be resolved into factors, but it can be solved for x, y, dy/dx, or y/x.* An equation which cannot be resolved into factors, can often be expressed in terms of x, y, dy/dx, or y/x, according to circumstances. The differential coefficient of the one variable with respect to the other may be then obtained by solving for dy/dx and using the result to eliminate dy/dx from the given equation.

EXAMPLES.—(1) Solve $dy/dx + 2xy = x^2 + y^2$. Since $(x - y)^2 = x^2 - 2xy + y^2$

$y = x + \sqrt{dy/dx}$. Put p in place of dy/dx. Differentiate, and we get

$$\frac{dy}{dx} = 1 + \frac{1}{2\sqrt{p}} \cdot \frac{dp}{dx}.$$

Separate the variables x and p, solve for dy/dx, and integrate by the method of partial fractions.

$$\therefore dx = \frac{dp}{2\sqrt{p}(p-1)}; \therefore x = \frac{1}{2}\log\frac{\sqrt{p}-1}{\sqrt{p}+1} + \log C; \sqrt{\frac{dy}{dx}} = \frac{C + e^{2x}}{C - e^{2x}}.$$

On eliminating p by means of the relation $y = x + \sqrt{p}$, we get the answer $y = x + (C + e^{2x})/(C - e^{2x})$.

(2) Solve $x(dy/dx)^2 - 2y(dy/dx) + ax = 0$. Ansr. $y = \frac{1}{2}(Cx^2 + a/c)$. Hint. Substitute for p. Solve for y and differentiate. Substitute pdx for dy, and clear of fractions. The variables p and x can be separated. Integrate $p = xC$. Substitute in the given equation for the answer.

(3) Solve $y(dy/dx)^2 + 2x(dy/dx) - y = 0$. Ansr. $y^2 = C(2x + C)$. Hint. Solve for x. Differentiate and substitute dy/p for dx, and proceed as in example (2). $yp = C$, etc.

Case iii. *The equation cannot be resolved into factors, x or y is absent.* If x is absent solve for dy/dx or y according to convenience; if y is absent, solve for dx/dy or x. Differentiate the result with respect to the absent letter if necessary and solve in the regular way.

EXAMPLES.—(1) Solve $(dy/dx)^2 + x(dy/dx) + 1 = 0$. For the sake of greater ease, substitute p for dy/dx. The given equation thus reduces to

$$- x = p + 1/p. \quad . \quad . \quad . \quad . \quad (1)$$

Differentiate with regard to the absent letter y, thus,

$$-\frac{1}{p} = \left(1 - \frac{1}{p^2}\right)\frac{dp}{dy}; \text{ or, } -\frac{dy}{dp} = p - \frac{1}{p}; \therefore y = \log p - \frac{1}{2}p^2 + e. \quad (2)$$

Combining (1) and (2), we get the required solution.

(2) Solve $dy/dx = y + 1/y$. Ansr. $y^2 = Ce^{2x} - 1$.

(3) Solve $dy/dx = x + 1/x$. Ansr. $y = \frac{1}{2}x^2 + \log x + C$.

§ 127. Clairaut's Equation.

The general type of this equation is

$$y = x\frac{dy}{dx} + f\left(\frac{dy}{dx}\right); \quad . \quad . \quad . \quad (1)$$

or, writing $dy/dx = p$, for the sake of convenience,

$$y = px + f(p). \quad . \quad . \quad (2)$$

Many equations of the first degree in x and y can be reduced to this form by a more or less obvious transformation of the variables, and solved in the following way: Differentiate (2) with respect to x, and equate the result to zero

$$p = p + x\frac{dp}{dx} + f'(p)\frac{dp}{dx}; \text{ or, } \{x + f'(p)\}\frac{dp}{dx} = 0.$$

Hence, either $dp/dx = 0$; or, $x + f'(p) = 0$. If the former,

$$\frac{dp}{dx} = 0 \; ; \; \therefore \; p = C,$$

where C is an arbitrary constant. Hence, $dy = Cdx$, and the solution of the given equation is

$$y = Cx + f(C).$$

Again, p in $x + f'(p)$ may be a solution of the given equation. To find p, eliminate p between

$$y = px + f(p), \text{ and } x + f'(p) = 0.$$

The resulting equation between x and y also satisfies the given equation. There are thus two classes of solutions to Clairaut's equation.

EXAMPLES.—(1) Find both solutions in $y = px + p^2$. Ansr. $Cx + C^2 = y$; and $x^2 + 4y = 0$.

(2) If $(y - px)(p - 1) = p$; show $(y - Cx)(C - 1) = C$; $\sqrt{y} + \sqrt{x} = 1$.

(3) In the velocity equation, Ex. (6), page 388, if $K = 2$, put $dy/dx = p$, solve for y, and differentiate the resulting equation,

$$y = x - \frac{a - x}{2}p; \; \frac{dy}{dx} = p = 1 + \frac{p}{2} - \frac{a - x}{2} \cdot \frac{dp}{dx}; \; \frac{dx}{a - x} = -\frac{dp}{p - 2}.$$

Integrate, and $-\log(a - x) = -\log(p - 2)$; $\therefore a - x = p - 2$, and we obtain $y = 2x - a - (a - x)^2$, which is the equation of a parabola $y_1 = x_1^2$, if we substitute $x = a + 1 + x_1$; $y = a + 1 - y_1$.

After working out the above examples, read over § 67, page 182.

§ 128. Singular Solutions.

Clairaut's equation introduces a new idea. Hitherto we have assumed that whenever a function of x and y satisfies an equation, that function, plus an arbitrary constant, represents the complete or general solution. We now find that a function of x and y can sometimes be found to satisfy the given equation, which, unlike the particular solution, is not included in the general solution. This function must be considered *a* solution, because it satisfies the given equation. But the existence of such a solution is quite an accidental property confined to special equations, hence their cognomen, **singular solutions.** Take the equation

$$y = \frac{dy}{dx}x + \frac{a}{\frac{dy}{dx}}; \text{ or, } y = px + \frac{a}{p}. \qquad . \qquad . \qquad (1)$$

Remembering that p has been written in place of dy/dx, differentiate with respect to x, we get, on rearranging terms,

$$\left(x - \frac{a}{p^2}\right)\frac{dp}{dx} = 0,$$

where either $x - a/p^2 = 0$; or, $dp/dx = 0$.   If the latter,

$$p = C ; \text{ or, } y = Cx + a/C ; \qquad . \qquad . \qquad (2)$$

and if the former, $p = \sqrt{a/x}$, which, when substituted in (1), gives the solution,

$$y^2 = 4ax. \qquad . \qquad . \qquad . \qquad . \qquad (3)$$

This is not included in the general solution, but yet it satisfies the given equation.   Hence, (3) is the singular solution of (1). Equation (2), the complete solution of (1), has been shown to represent a system of straight lines which differ only in the value of the arbitrary constant C; equation (3), containing no arbitrary constant, is an equation to the common parabola.   A point moving on this parabola has, at any instant, the same value of dy/dx as if it were moving on the tangent of the parabola, or on one of the straight lines of equation (2).   *The singular solution of a differential equation is geometrically equivalent to the envelope of the family of curves represented by the general solution.*   The singular solution is distinguished from the particular solution, in that the latter is contained in the general solution, the former is not.

Again referring to Fig. 96, it will be noticed that for any point on the envelope, there are two equal values of p or dy/dx, one for the parabola, one for the straight line.

In order that the quadratic

$$ax^2 + bx + c = 0,$$

may have equal roots, it is necessary (page 354) that

$$b^2 = 4ac ; \text{ or, } b^2 - 4ac = 0. . \qquad . \qquad . \qquad (4)$$

This relation is called the **discriminant**.   From (1), since

$$y = px + \frac{a}{p}; \therefore xp^2 - yp + a = 0. \qquad . \qquad . \qquad (5)$$

In order that equation (5) may have equal roots,

$$y^2 = 4ax,$$

as in (4).   This relation is the locus of all points for which two values of p become equal, hence it is called **the p-discriminant** of (1).

In the same way if C be regarded as variable in the general solution (2),

$$y = Cx + \frac{a}{C}; \text{ or, } xC^2 - yC + a = 0.$$

The condition for equal roots, is that

$$y^2 = 4ax,$$

which is the locus of all points for which the value of C is the same.   It is called the C-discriminant.

Before applying these ideas to special cases, we may note that the envelope locus may be a single curve (Fig. 96) or several (Fig. 97).   For an exhaustive discussion of the properties of these discriminant relations, I must refer the reader to the text-books on the subject, or to M. J. M. Hill, "On the Locus of Singular Points and Lines," *Phil. Trans.*, 1892.   To summarize:

1. **The envelope locus** satisfies the original equation but is not included in the general solution (see xx', Fig. 146).

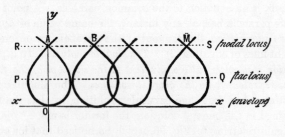

FIG. 146.—Nodal and Tac Loci.

2. **The tac locus** is the locus passing through the several points where two non-consecutive members of a family of curves touch.   Such a locus is represented by the lines AB (Fig. 97), PQ (Fig. 146).   The tac locus does not satisfy the original equation, it appears in the p-discriminant, but not in the C-discriminant.

3. **The node locus** is the locus passing through the different points where each curve of a given family crosses itself (the point of intersection—node—may be double, triple, etc.).   The node locus does not satisfy the original equation, it appears in the C-discriminant but not in the p-discriminant. RS (Fig. 146) is a nodal locus passing through the nodes $A, \ldots, B, \ldots, C, \ldots, M \ldots$

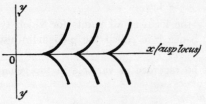

FIG. 147.—Cusp Locus.

4. **The cusp locus** passes through all the cusps (page 169) formed

by the members of a family of curves. The cusp locus does not
satisfy the original equation, it appears in the p- and in the C-
discriminants. It is the line Ox in Fig. 147. Sometimes the
nodal or cusp loci coincide with the envelope locus.

EXAMPLES.—(1) Find the singular solutions and the nature of the other
loci in the following equations: (1) $xp^2 - 2yp + ax = 0$. For equal roots
$y^2 = ax^2$. This satisfies the original equation and is not included in the general
solution: $x^2 - 2Cy + C^2 = 0$. $y^2 = ax^2$ is thus the singular solution.

(2) $4xp^2 = (3x - a)^2$. General solution: $(y + C)^2 = x(x - a)^2$. For equal
roots in p, $4x(3x - a)^2 = 0$, or $x(3x - a)^2 = 0$ (p-discriminant). For equal
roots in C, differentiate the general solution with respect to C. Therefore
$(x + C)dx/dC = 0$, or $C = - x$. ∴ $x(x - a)^2 = 0$ (C-discriminant) is the condition to be fulfilled when the C-discriminant has equal roots. $x = 0$ is
common to the two discriminants and satisfies the original equation (singular
solution); $x = a$ satisfies the C-discriminant but not the p-discriminant and,
since it is not a solution of the original equation, $x = a$ represents the node
locus; $x = \frac{1}{3}a$ satisfies the p- but not the C-discriminant nor the original
equation (tac locus).

(3) $p^2 + 2xp - y = 0$. General solution: $(2x^3 + 3xy + C)^2 = 4(x^2 + y)^3$;
p-discriminant: $x^2 + y = 0$; C-discriminant: $(x^2 + y)^3 = 0$. The original
equation is not satisfied by either of these equations and, therefore, there is
no singular solution. Since $(x^2 + y)$ appears in both discriminants, it represents a cusp locus.

(4) Show that the complete solution of the equation $y^2(p^2 + 1) = a^2$, is
$y^2 + (x - C)^2 = a^2$; that there are two singular solutions, $y = \pm a$; that
there is a tac locus on the x-axis for $y = 0$ (Fig. 97, page 183).

A trajectory is a curve which cuts another system of curves
at a constant angle. If this angle is 90° the curve is an orthogonal trajectory.

EXAMPLES.—(1) Let $xy = C$ be a system of rectangular hyperbolas, to
find the orthogonal trajectory, first eliminate C by differentiation with respect
to x, thus we obtain, $xdy/dx + y = 0$. If two curves are at right angles
($\frac{1}{2}\pi = 90°$), then from (17), § 32, $\frac{1}{2}\pi = (a' - a)$, where a, a' are the angles
made by tangents to the curves at the point of intersection with the x-axis.
But by the same formula, $\tan(\pm \frac{1}{2}\pi) = (\tan a' - \tan a)/(1 + \tan a . \tan a')$.
Now $\tan \pm \frac{1}{2}\pi = \infty$ and $1/\infty = 0$, ∴ $\tan a = - \cot a$; or, $dy/dx = - dx/dy$.
The differential equation of the one family is obtained from that of the other
by substituting dy/dx for $- dx/dy$. Hence the equation to the orthogonal
trajectory of the system of rectangular hyperbolas is, $xdx + ydy = 0$, or
$x^2 - y^2 = C$, a system of rectangular hyperbolas whose axes coincide with
the asymptotes of the given system. For polar coordinates it would have
been necessary to substitute $- (dr/r)d\theta$ for $rd\theta/dr$.

(2) Show that the orthogonal trajectories of the equipotential curves
$1/r - 1/r' = C$, are the magnetic curves $\cos \theta + \cos \theta' = C$.

§ 129. Symbols of Operation.

It has been found convenient, page 68, to represent the symbol of the operation "d/dx" by the letter "D". If we assume that the infinitesimal increments of the independent variable dx have the same magnitude, whatever be the value of x, we can suppose D to have a constant value. Thus,

$$Dy,\ D^2y,\ \ldots \text{ stand for } \frac{dy}{dx},\ \frac{d^2y}{dx^2},\ \frac{d^3y}{dx^3}\cdots,$$

respectively. The operations denoted by the symbols D, D^2, ..., satisfy the elementary rules of algebra except that they are not commutative[2] with regard to the variables. For example, we cannot write $D(xy) = xD(y)$, although we can write $D(ay) = aD(y)$. But the index law

$$D^m D^n u = D^{m+n}u$$

is true when m and n are positive integers. It also follows that if

$$Du = v;\ u = D^{-1}v;\ \text{ or, } u = \frac{1}{D}v;\ \therefore\ v = D\,.\,D^{-1}v;\ \text{ or, } D\,.\,D^{-1} = 1;$$

that is to say, by operating with D upon $D^{-1}v$ we annul the effect of the D^{-1} operator. In this notation, the equation

$$\frac{d^2y}{dx^2} - (a + \beta)\frac{dy}{dx} + a\beta y = 0,$$

can be written,

$$\{D^2 - (a + \beta)D + a\beta\}y = 0;\ \text{ or, } (D - a)(D - \beta)y = 0.$$

Now replace D with the original symbol, and operate on one factor with y, and we get

$$\left(\frac{d}{dx} - a\right)\left(\frac{d}{dx} - \beta\right)y = 0;\left(\frac{d}{dx} - a\right)\left(\frac{dy}{dx} - \beta y\right) = 0.$$

By operating on the second factor with the first, we get the original equation back again.

§ 130. Equations of Oscillatory Motion.

By Newton's second law, if a certain mass, m, of matter is subject to the action of an "elastic force," F_0, for a certain time, we have, in rational units,

$$F_0 = \text{Mass} \times \text{Acceleration of the particle.}$$

If the motion of the particle is subject to friction, we may regard the friction as a force tending to oppose the motion generated by

---

the elastic force.   Assume that this force is proportional to the velocity, V, of the motion of the particle, and equal to the product of the velocity and a constant called the *coefficient of friction,* written, say, μ.   Let F_1 denote the total force acting on the particle in the direction of its motion,

$$F_1 = F_0 - \mu V = m d^2 s / dt^2. \quad . \quad . \quad . \quad (1)$$

If there is no friction, we have, for unit mass,

$$F_0 = d^2 s / dt^2. \quad . \quad . \quad . \quad (2)$$

The motion of a pendulum in a medium which offers no resistance to its motion, is that of a material particle under the influence of a central force, F, attracting with an intensity which is proportional to the distance of the particle away from the centre of attraction.   We shall call F the effective force since this is the force which is effective in producing motion.   Consequently,

$$F = - q^2 s, \quad . \quad . \quad . \quad (3)$$

where q^2 is to be regarded as a positive constant which tends to restore the particle to a position of equilibrium—the so-called *coefficient of restitution.*   It is written in the form of a power to avoid a root sign later on.   The negative sign shows that the attracting force, F, tends to diminish the distance, s, of the particle away from the centre of attraction.   If $s = 1$, q^2 represents the magnitude of the attracting force unit distance away.   From (2), therefore,

$$\frac{d^2 s}{dt^2} = - q^2 s. \quad . \quad . \quad . \quad (4)$$

The integration of this equation will teach us how the particle moves under the influence of the force F.   We cannot solve the equation in a direct manner, but if we multiply by $2 ds/dt$ we can integrate term by term with regard to s ; thus,

$$2 \frac{ds}{dt} \cdot \frac{d^2 s}{dt^2} + 2 q^2 s \frac{ds}{dt} = 0 ; \text{ or, } \left(\frac{ds}{dt}\right)^2 = - q^2 s^2 + C.$$

Let us replace the constant C by the constant $q^2 r^2$; separate the variables, and integrate again ; we get from Table II., page 193,

$$\int \frac{ds}{\sqrt{r^2 - s^2}} = \pm q \int dt ; \text{ or, } \sin^{-1} \frac{s}{r} = \mp qt + \epsilon ; \text{ or, } s = \mp r \sin (qt + \epsilon),$$

where ϵ is a new integration constant.   Here we have s as an explicit function of t.   We have discussed this equation in an earlier chapter, pages 66 and 138.   It is, in fact, the typical equation of an oscillatory motion.   The particle moves to and fro on a straight line. The value of the sine function changes with time between the limits $+ 1$ and $- 1$, and consequently x changes between the limits $+ r$ and $- r$. Hence, r is the amplitude of the swing ; ϵ is the phase constant or epoch of page 138. The sine of an angle always repeats itself when the angle is increased by 2π, or some multiple of 2π. Let the time t be so chosen that after the elapse of an interval of time T_0 the particle is passing through the same position with the same velocity in the same direction, hence,

$$qT_0 = 2\pi \; ; \; \text{or,} \; T_0 = \frac{2\pi}{q} . \quad . \quad . \quad . \quad (5)$$

The two undetermined constants r and ϵ serve to adapt the relation

$$s = r \sin(qt + \epsilon)$$

to the initial conditions. This is easily seen if we expand the latter as indicated in (23) and (24), page 612 :

$$s = r \sin \epsilon . \cos qt \pm r \cos \epsilon . \sin qt.$$

Let C_1 and C_2 denote the undetermined constants $r \sin \epsilon$, and $r \cos \epsilon$ respectively, such that

$$r = \sqrt{C_1{}^2 + C_2{}^2} \; ; \; \epsilon = \tan^{-1}\frac{C_1}{C_2},$$

as indicated on page 138. Now differentiate

$$s = C_1 \cos qt + C_2 \sin qt \; ; \; \therefore \frac{ds}{dt} = - qC_1 \sin qt + qC_2 \cos qt.$$

Let s_0 denote the position of the particle at the time $t = 0$ when moving with a velocity V_0. The sine function vanishes, and the cosine function becomes unity. Hence, $C_1 = s_0$; $C_2 = V_0/q$, and the constants r and ϵ may be represented in terms of the initial conditions :

$$r = \sqrt{s_0{}^2 + \frac{V_0{}^2}{q^2}} \; ; \; \epsilon = \tan^{-1}\frac{qs_0}{V_0}.$$

In the sine galvanometer, the restitutional force tending to restore the needle to a position of equilibrium, is proportional to the sine of the angle of deflection of the needle. If J denotes the moment of inertia of the magnetic needle and G the directive force exerted by the current on the magnet, the equation of motion of the magnet, when there is no other retarding force, is

$$J\frac{d^2\phi}{dt^2} = - G \sin \phi. \quad . \quad . \quad . \quad (6)$$

For small angles of displacement, ϕ and $\sin \phi$ are approximately equal.   Hence,

$$\frac{d^2\phi}{dt^2} = -\frac{G}{J}\phi. \quad \bullet \quad \bullet \quad \bullet \quad \bullet \quad (7)$$

From (4), $q = \sqrt{G/J}$, and, therefore, from (5),

$$T_0 = 2\pi\sqrt{J/G}, \quad \bullet \quad \bullet \quad \bullet \quad (8)$$

a well-known relation showing that *the period of oscillation of a magnet in the magnetic field, when there is no damping action exerted on the magnet, is proportional to the square root of the moment of inertia of the magnetic needle, and inversely proportional to the square root of the directive force exerted by the current on the magnet.*

§ 131.   The Linear Equation of the Second Order.

As a general rule it is more difficult to solve differential equations of higher orders than the first.   Of these, the linear equation is the most important.   A **linear equation of the nth order** is one in which the dependent variable and its n derivatives are all of the first degree and are not multiplied together.   If a higher power appears the equation is not linear, and its solution is, in general, more difficult to find.   The typical form is

$$\frac{d^n y}{dx^n} + P\frac{d^{n-1}y}{dx^{n-1}} + \ldots + Qy = R.$$

Or, in our new symbolic notation,

$$D^n y + X_1 D^{n-1}y + \ldots + X_n y = X,$$

where $P, Q, \ldots, R$ are either constant magnitudes, or functions of the independent variable x.   If the coefficient of the highest derivative be other than unity, the other terms of the equation can be divided by this coefficient.   The equation will thus assume the typical form (1).

I. Linear equations with constant coefficients.

Let us first study the typical linear equation of the second order with constant coefficients P and Q,

$$\frac{d^2 y}{dx^2} + P\frac{dy}{dx} + Qy = 0. \quad \bullet \quad \bullet \quad \bullet \quad (1)$$

The linear equation has some special properties which considerably shorten the search for the general solution.   For example, let us substitute e^{mx} for y in (1).   By differentiation of e^{mx}, we obtain $dy/dx = my$; and $d^2y/dx^2 = m^2y$, therefore,

$$\frac{d^2 e^{mx}}{dx^2} + P\frac{d e^{mx}}{dx} + Q e^{mx} = (m^2 + Pm + Q)e^{mx} = 0 ;$$

provided

$$m^2 + Pm + Q = 0. \quad . \quad . \quad . \quad (2)$$

This is called the **auxiliary equation.** If m_1 be one value of m which satisfies (2), then $y = e^{m_1 x}$ is one integral of (1), and $y = e^{m_2 x}$ is another. But we must go further.

If we know two or more solutions of a linear equation, each can be multiplied by a constant, and their sum is an integral of the given equation. For example, if u and v are solutions of the equation

$$\frac{d^2 x}{dt^2} = - q^2 x, \quad . \quad . \quad . \quad . \quad (3)$$

each is called a **particular integral**, and we can substitute either u or v in place of x and so obtain

$$\frac{d^2 u}{dt^2} = - q^2 u ; \text{ or, } \frac{d^2 v}{dt^2} = - q^2 v. \quad . \quad . \quad (4)$$

Multiply each equation by arbitrary constants, say, C_1 and C_2 ; add the two results together, and $C_1 u + C_2 v$ satisfies equation (1),

$$\therefore \frac{d^2(C_1 u + C_2 v)}{dt^2} = - q^2(C_1 u + C_2 v). \quad . \quad . \quad (5)$$

This is a very valuable property of the linear equation. It means that if u and v are two solutions of (3), then the sum $C_1 u + C_2 v$ is also a solution of the given equation. Since the given equation is of the second order, and the solution contains two arbitrary constants, the equation is completely solved. The principle of the **superposition of particular integrals** here outlined is a mathematical expression of the well-known physical phenomena discussed on page 70, namely, the principle of the coexistence of different reactions ; the composition of velocities and forces ; the superposition of small impulses, etc. We shall employ this principle later on, meanwhile let us return to the auxiliary equation.

1. *When the auxiliary equation has two unequal roots,* say m_1 and m_2, the general solution of (1) may be written down without any further trouble.

$$y = C_1 e^{m_1 x} + C_2 e^{m_2 x}. \quad . \quad . \quad . \quad (6)$$

This result enables us to write down the solution of a linear equation at sight when the auxiliary has unequal roots.

EXAMPLES.—(1) Solve $(D^2 + 14D - 32)y = 0$. Assume $y = Ce^{mx}$ is a solution. The auxiliary becomes, $m^2 + 14m - 32 = 0$. The roots are $m = 2$ or -16. The required solution is, therefore, $y = C_1 e^{2x} + C_2 e^{-16x}$.

(2) Solve $d^2y/dx^2 + 4dy/dx + 3y = 0$. Ansr. $y = C_1 e^{-3x} + C_2 e^{-x}$.

(3) Fourier's equation for the propagation of heat in a cylindrical bar, is $d^2V/dx^2 - \beta^2 V = 0$. Hence show that $V = C_1 e^{\beta x} + Ce^{-\beta x}$.

2. *When the two roots of the auxiliary are equal.* If $m_1 = m_2$, in (6), it is no good putting $(C_1 + C_2)e^{m_1 x}$ as the solution, because $C_1 + C_2$ is really one constant. The solution would then contain one arbitrary constant less than is required for the general solution. We can find the other particular integral by substituting $m_2 = m_1 + h$, in (6), where h is some finite quantity which is to be ultimately made equal to zero. Substitute $m_2 = m_1 + h$ in (6); expand by Maclaurin's theorem, and, at the limit, when $h = 0$, we have

$$y = e^{m_1 x}(A + Bx). \qquad . \qquad . \qquad . \qquad (7)$$

This enables us to write down the required solution at a glance. For equations of a higher order than the second, the preceding result must be written,

$$y = e^{m_1 x}(C_1 + C_2 x + C_3 x^2 + \ldots + C_{r-2} x^{r-1}), \qquad (8)$$

where r denotes the number of equal roots.

EXAMPLES.—(1) Solve $d^3y/dx^3 - d^2y/dx^2 - dy/dx + y = 0$. Assume $y = Ce^{mx}$. The auxiliary equation is $m^3 - m^2 - m + 1 = 0$. The roots are $1, 1, -1$. Hence the general solution can be written down at sight :

$$y = C_1 e^{-x} + (C_2 + C_3 x)e^x.$$

(2) Solve $(D^3 + 3D^2 - 4)y = 0$. Ansr. $e^{-2x}(C_1 + C_2 x) + C_3 e^x$. Hint. The roots are obtained from $(x - 2)(x - 2)(x - 1) = x^3 + 3x^2 - 4$.

3. *When the auxiliary equation has imaginary roots, all unequal.* Remembering that imaginary roots are always found in pairs in equations with real coefficients, let the two imaginary roots be

$$m_1 = a + \iota\beta; \text{ and } m_2 = a - \iota\beta.$$

Instead of substituting $y = e^{mx}$ in (6), we substitute these values of m in (6) and get

$$y = C_1 e^{(a + \iota\beta)x} + C_2 e^{(a - \iota\beta)x} = e^{ax}(C_1 e^{\iota\beta x} + C_2 e^{-\iota\beta x});$$

where C_1 and C_2 are the integration constants. From (13) and (15), p. 286,

$$y = e^{ax}C_1(\cos \beta x + \iota \sin \beta x) + e^{ax}C_2(\cos \beta x - \iota \sin \beta x). \qquad (9)$$

Separate the real and imaginary parts, as in Ex. (3), p. 351,

$$\therefore y = e^{ax}\{(C_1 + C_2) \cos \beta x + \iota(C_1 - C_2) \sin \beta x\}.$$

If we put $C_1 + C_2 = A$, and $\iota(C_1 - C_2) = B$, we can write down the real form of the solution of a linear equation at sight when its auxiliary has unequal imaginary roots.

$$y = e^{\alpha x}(A \cos \beta x + B \sin \beta x). \qquad . \qquad . \qquad (10)$$

In order that the constants A and B in (10) may be real, the constants C_1 and C_2 must include the imaginary parts.

The undetermined constants A and B combined with the particular integrals u and v may be imaginary. Thus, u and v may be united with C_1 and ιC_1, and $Au + \iota Bv$ is then an integral of the same equation. It is often easier to find a complex solution of this character than a real expression. If we can find an integral $u + \iota v$, of the given equation, u and v can each be separately regarded as particular integrals of the given equation.

EXAMPLES.—(1) Show, from (9), and (2) and (3) of page 347, that we can write $y = (\cosh \alpha x + \sinh \alpha x)(A_1 \cos \beta x + B_1 \sin \beta x)$.

(2) Integrate $d^2y/dx^2 + dy/dx + y = 0$. The roots are $\alpha = -\frac{1}{2}$ and $\beta = \frac{1}{2}\sqrt{3}$
∴ $y = e^{-x/2}(A \cos \frac{1}{2}\sqrt{3} . x + B \sin \frac{1}{2}\sqrt{3} . x)$.

(3) The equation of a point vibrating under the influence of a periodic force, is, $d^2x/dt^2 + q^2x = 0$, the roots are given by $(D + \iota a)(D - \iota a) = 0$. From (10), $y = A \cos ax + B \sin ax$.

(4) In the theory of electrodynamics (*Encyc. Brit.*, **28**, 61, 1902) and in the theory of sound, as well as other branches of physics, we have to solve the equation

$$\frac{d^2\phi}{dr^2} + \frac{2}{r} \cdot \frac{d\phi}{dr} + k^2\phi = 0.$$

Multiply by r and notice that

$$\frac{d(r\phi)}{dr} = \phi\frac{dr}{dr} + r\frac{d\phi}{dr} = \phi + r\frac{d\phi}{dr}; \; \frac{d^2(\phi r)}{dr} = \frac{d\phi}{dr} + \frac{dr}{dr} \cdot \frac{d\phi}{dr} + r\frac{d^2\phi}{dr^2}.$$

$$\therefore r\frac{d^2\phi}{dr^2} + 2\frac{d\phi}{dr} = \frac{d^2(\phi r)}{dr^2}.$$

Hence we may write

$$\frac{d^2(\phi r)}{dr^2} = k^2(r\phi) = (D^2 + k^2)\phi r = (D + \iota k)(D - \iota k)\phi r = 0.$$

$$\therefore \phi r = Ae^{\iota kr} + Be^{-\iota kr}; \; \therefore \phi = \frac{1}{r}(A \cos kr + B \sin kr), \text{as in (9) and (10) above.}$$

4. *When some of the imaginary roots of the auxiliary equation are equal.* If a pair of the imaginary roots are repeated, we may proceed as in Case 2, since, when $m_1 = m_2$, $C_1e^{m_1x} + C_2e^{m_2x}$, is replaced by $(A + Bx)e^{m_1x}$; similarly, when $m_3 = m_4$, $C_3e^{m_3x} + C_4e^{m_4x}$ may be replaced by $(C + Dx)e^{m_3x}$. If, therefore,

$$m_1 = m_2 = \alpha + \iota\beta; \text{ and } m_3 = m_4 = \alpha - \iota\beta,$$

the solution

$$y = (C_1 + C_2x)e^{(\alpha + \iota\beta)x} + (C_3 + C_4x)e^{(\alpha - \iota\beta)x},$$

becomes

$$y = e^{ax}\{(A + Bx) \cos \beta x + (C + Dx) \sin \beta x\}. \quad . \quad (11)$$

EXAMPLES.—(1) Solve $(D^4 - 12D^3 + 62D^2 - 156D + 169)y = 0$. Given the roots of the auxiliary: $3 + 2\iota$, $3 + 2\iota$, $3 - 2\iota$, $3 - 2\iota$. Hence, the solution is $y = e^{3x}\{(C_1 + C_2x) \sin 2x + (C_3 + C_4x) \cos 2x\}$.

(2) If $(D^2+1)^2(D-1)^2y = 0$, $y = (A+Bx) \sin x + (C+Dx) \cos x + (E+Fx)e^x$.

II. Linear equations with variable coefficients.

Linear equations with variable coefficients can be converted into linear equations with constant coefficients by means of the substitution

$$x = e^z; \text{ or, } z = \log x, \quad . \quad . \quad . \quad (12)$$

as illustrated in the following example :—

EXAMPLE.—Solve the equation

$$x^2 \frac{d^2y}{dx^2} + 4x\frac{dy}{dx} + 2y = 0,$$

by means of the substitution (12). By differentiation of (12), we obtain

$$\frac{dx}{dz} = e^z; \therefore e^z\frac{dy}{dx} = \frac{dy}{dz}; \therefore \frac{dy}{dx} = \frac{1}{x} \cdot \frac{dy}{dz}.$$

Again,

$$\frac{d^2y}{dx} = \frac{1}{x}\frac{d^2y}{dz} - \frac{dx}{x^2} \cdot \frac{dy}{dz}; \therefore \frac{d^2y}{dx^2} = \frac{1}{x^2}\left(\frac{d^2y}{dz^2} - \frac{dy}{dz}\right),$$

since, from (12), $dx = xdz$. Introducing these values of dy/dx and d^2y/dx^2 in the given equation, we get the ordinary linear form

$$\frac{d^2y}{dz^2} + 3\frac{dy}{dz} + 2y = 0,$$

with constant coefficients. Hence, $y = C_1e^{2z} + C_2e^z = C_1x^2 + C_2x$.

If the equation has the form of the so-called **Legendre's equation**, say,

$$(a + x)^2\frac{d^2y}{dx^2} - 5(a + x)\frac{dy}{dx} + 6y = 0 ; \quad . \quad (13)$$

the substitution $z = a + x$ will convert it into form (12), and the substitution e^t for $a + x$ will convert it into the linear equation with constant coefficients. Hence, $dx = (a+x)dt$; $dx^2 = (a+x)^2dt^2$, and

$$\frac{d^2y}{dt^2} - 5\frac{dy}{dt} + 6y = 0 ; \therefore y = C_1e^{2t} + C_2e^{3t} = C_1(a + x)^2 + C_2(a + x)^3.$$

EXAMPLE.—In the theory of potential we meet with the equation

$$\frac{d^2V}{dr^2} + \frac{2}{r} \cdot \frac{dV}{dr} = 0 ; \therefore r^2\frac{d^2V}{dr^2} + 2r\frac{dV}{dr} = 0.$$

The roots of the auxiliary are $m = 0$, and $m = -1$. Hence, $V = C_1 + C_2r^{-1}$.

CC *

§ 132. Damped Oscillations.

The equation $\dfrac{d^2s}{dt^2} = - q^2s$ takes no account of the resistance to
which a particle is subjected as it moves through such resisting
media as air, water, etc. We know from experience that the
magnitude of the oscillations of all periodic motions gradually
diminishes asymptotically to a position of rest. This change is
called the damping of the oscillations.

When an electric current passes through a galvanometer, the needle is
deflected and begins to oscillate about a new position of equilibrium. In
order to make the needle come to rest quickly, so that the observations may
be made quickly, some resistance is opposed to the free oscillations of the
needle either by attaching mica or aluminium vanes to the needle so as to
increase the resistance of the air, or by bringing a mass of copper close to
the oscillating needle. The currents induced in the copper by the motion of
the magnetic needle, react on the moving needle, according to Lenz' law, so
as to retard its motion. Such a galvanometer is said to be damped. When
the damping is sufficiently great to prevent the needle oscillating at all, the
galvanometer is said to be "dead beat" and the motion of the needle is
aperiodic. In ballistic galvanometers, there is very much damping.

It is a matter of observation that the force which exerts the
damping action is directed against that of the motion; and it also
increases as the velocity of the motion increases. The most
plausible assumption we can make is that the damping force, at
any instant, is directly proportional to the prevailing velocity, and
has a negative value. To allow for this, equation (4) must have
an additional negative term. We thus get the typical equation of
the second order,

$$\frac{d^2s}{dt^2} = - \mu\frac{ds}{dt} - q^2s,$$

where μ is the coefficient of friction. For greater convenience, we
may write this $2f$, and we get

$$\frac{d^2s}{dt^2} + 2f\frac{ds}{dt} + q^2s = 0. \qquad . \qquad . \qquad . \qquad (1)$$

Before proceeding further, it will perhaps make things plainer
to put the meaning of this differential equation into words. The
manipulation of the equations so far introduced, involves little more
than an application of common algebraic principles. Dexterity in
solving comes by practice. Of even greater importance than quick
manipulation is the ability to form a clear concept of the physical
process symbolized by the differential equation. Some of the most

important laws of Nature appear in the guise of an "unassuming differential equation ".   The reader should spare no pains to acquire familiarity with the art of interpretation ; otherwise a mere system of differential equations may be mistaken for "laws of Nature". The late Professor Tait has said that "a mathematical formula, however brief and elegant, is merely a step towards knowledge, and an all but useless one until we can thoroughly read its meaning ".

Euler once confessed that he often could not get rid of the uncomfortable feeling that his science in the person of his pencil surpassed him in intelligence.   I dare say the beginner will have some such feeling as he works out the meaning of the above innocent-looking expression.   The term d^2s/dt^2, page 17, denotes the relative change of the velocity of the motion of the particle in unit time ; while $2f \cdot ds/dt$ shows that this motion is opposed by a force which tends to restore the body to a position of rest, the greater the velocity of the motion, the greater the retardation ; and q^2s represents another force tending to bring the moving body to rest, this force also increases directly as the distance of the body from the position of rest.   The whole equation represents the mutual action of these different effects.   To investigate this motion further, we must find a relation between s and t.   In other words, we must solve the equations.

We can write equation (1) in the symbolic form

$$(D^2 + 2fD + q^2)s = 0,$$

the roots of the auxiliary are, pages 353 and 354,

$$a = -f + \sqrt{f^2 - q^2} ; \ \beta = -f - \sqrt{f^2 - q^2}. \qquad . \qquad (2)$$

The solution of (1) thus depends on the relative magnitudes of f and q.   There are two important cases : the roots, a and β, may be real or imaginary.   Both have a physical meaning and represent two essentially different types of motion.   Suppose that we know enough about the moving system to be able to determine the integration constant.   When $t = 0$, let $V = V_0$ and $s = 0$.

I. *The roots of the auxiliary equation are imaginary, equal and of opposite sign.*   For equal roots of opposite sign, say $\pm iq$, we must have $f = 0$, as indicated upon page 401.   In this case, as in the typical equation for Case 3 of the preceding section,

$$s = C_1 \sin qt + C_2 \cos qt. \qquad . \qquad . \qquad (3)$$

To find what this means, let us suppose that $t = 0$, $s = 0$, $V_0 = 1$, $q = 2$, $f = 0$.   Differentiate (3),

$$ds/dt = qC_1 \cos qt - qC_2 \sin qt.$$

Hence $1 = 2C_1 \times 1 - 2 \times C_2 \times 0$, or $C_1 = \frac{1}{2}$; $\therefore C_2 = 0$. Hence the equation,

$$s = \tfrac{1}{2} \sin 2t. \quad . \quad . \quad . \quad . \quad (4)$$

Curve 1 (Fig. 148) was obtained, by plotting, from equation (4) by assigning arbitrary values to t in radians; converting the radians into degrees; and finding the sine of the corresponding angle from a Table of Natural Sines. Suppose we put $2t = 45°$, then sine $45° = 0\cdot79$; $t = 22\cdot5° = 0\cdot39$ radians from Table XIII.; if $2t = 630°$, $\sin 630° = \sin 45°$ in the fourth quadrant, it is therefore negative; $t = 320°$; $\therefore$ $t = (3\cdot1416 + \frac{1}{2}$ of $3\cdot1416 + 0\cdot39)$ radians. The numbers set out in the first three columns of the following table were calculated from equation (4) for the first complete vibration:—

$s = \frac{1}{2}\sin 2t.$			$s = \frac{1}{2}e^{-0\cdot1t}\sin 1\cdot997t$			
t radians.	sin 2t.	s.	t.	sin 1·7t.	$e^{-0\cdot1t}$.	s.
0	0	0	0	0	1·00	0
0·39	+ 0·79	+ 0·39	0·46	+ 0·79	0·96	+ 3·84
0·78	+ 1·00	+ 0·50	0·92	+ 1·00	0·91	+ 4·55
1·18	+ 0·79	+ 0·39	1·38	+ 0·79	0·87	+ 3·84
1·57	0	0	1·80	0	0·84	0
1·96	− 0·79	− 0·39	2·30	− 0·79	0·79	− 3·84
2·44	− 1·00	− 0·50	2·77	− 1·00	0·76	− 4·55
2·69	− 0·79	− 0·39	3·20	− 0·79	0·73	− 3·84
3·14	0	0	3·70	0	0·69	0

II. The roots of the auxiliary equation are imaginary. For imaginary roots, $-f \pm \sqrt{(f^2 - q^2)}$, or, say $-a \pm b\iota$, it is necessary that $f < q$ (page 354). In this case,

$$s = e^{-at}(C_1 \sin bt + C_2 \cos bt). \quad . \quad . \quad (5)$$

Let the coefficient of friction, $f = 0\cdot1$, $q = 2$, $t = 0$, $s = 0$, $V_0 = 1$. The roots of the auxiliary are $m = -0\cdot1 \pm \sqrt{0\cdot01 - 4} = 0\cdot1 \pm \sqrt{-3\cdot99} = -0\cdot1 \pm \iota 1\cdot997$, where $\iota = \sqrt{-1}$. Hence $a = 0\cdot1$, $b = 1\cdot997$. Differentiate (5),

$$ds/dt = -ae^{-at}(C_1 \sin bt + C_2 \cos bt) + be^{-at}(C_1 \cos bt - C_2 \sin bt)$$

From (5), $C_2 = 0$, and, therefore, $C_1 = 1/b = 0\cdot5$. Therefore,

$$s = 0\cdot5e^{-0\cdot1t} \sin 1\cdot997t, \quad . \quad . \quad . \quad (6)$$

a result which differs from that which holds for undamped oscillations by the introduction of the factor $e^{-0\cdot1t}$. The last four columns of the above table has the numbers computed for the first complete vibration from equation (6). The graph of the equation is curve 2 of Fig. 148.

The simple harmonic curve, 1, Fig. 148, represents the undamped oscillations of a particle. The effects of damping are brought out, by the diagram, curve 2, in an interesting manner. The net result is a **damped vibration**, which dies away at a rate depending on the resistance of the medium $(2fv)$ and on the magnitude of the oscillations $(q^2 s)$. Such is the motion of a

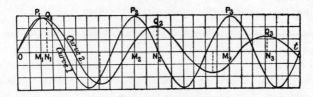

FIG. 148.

magnetic or galvanometer needle affected by the viscosity of the air and the electromagnetic action of currents induced in neighbouring masses of metal by virtue of its motion; it also represents the natural oscillations of a pendulum swinging in a medium whose resistance varies as the velocity. The effects of damping are twofold :

1. *The period of oscillation is augmented by damping,* from T_0 to T. From equation (5), we can show, page 138, that
$$s = e^{-at} A \sin bt. \qquad . \qquad . \qquad . \qquad (7)$$
The amplitude of this vibration corresponds to the value of t for which s has a maximum or a minimum value. These values are obtained in the usual way, by equating the first differential coefficient to zero, hence
$$e^{-at}(b \cos bt - a \sin bt) = 0. . \qquad . \qquad . \qquad (8)$$
If we now define the angle ϕ such that $bt = \phi$, or
$$\tan \phi = b/a, \qquad . \qquad . \qquad . \qquad . \qquad (9)$$
ϕ, lying between 0 and $\frac{1}{2}\pi$ (*i.e.*, 90°), becomes smaller as a increases in value. We have just seen that the imaginary roots of $-f \pm \sqrt{f^2 - q^2}$ are $-a \pm \iota b$, for values of f less than q. Consequently,
$$(-f + \sqrt{f^2 - q^2})(-f - \sqrt{f^2 - q^2}) = (a + \iota b)(a - \iota b); \text{ or, } a^2 + b^2 = q^2. \ (10)$$
The period of oscillation of an undamped oscillation is, by (5), page 398, $T_0 = 2\pi/q$, and similarly, for a damped oscillation $T = 2\pi/b$
$$\therefore \frac{T^2}{T^2_0} = \frac{q^2}{b^2} = \frac{a^2 + b^2}{b^2} = 1 + \frac{a^2}{b^2}; \therefore \frac{T}{T_0} = \frac{\sqrt{a^2 + b^2}}{b} \qquad (11)$$

which expresses the relation between the periods of oscillation of a damped and of an undamped oscillation. Consequently, $OT - OT_0 = 1·019$ (Fig. 148).

2 *The ratio of the amplitude of any vibration to the next, is constant.* The amplitudes of the undamped vibrations M_1P_1, M_2P_2, ... become, on damping N_1Q_1, N_2Q_2, ... It is easy to show, by plotting, that $\tan \phi$, of (9), is a periodic function such that

$$\tan \phi = \tan(\phi + \pi) = \tan(\phi + 2\pi) = \ldots$$

Hence ϕ; $\phi + \pi$; $\phi + 2\pi$; ... satisfy the above equation. It also follows that bt_1; $bt_2 + \pi$; $bt_3 + 2\pi$; ... also satisfy the equation, where t_1, t_2, t_3, ... are the successive values of the time. Hence

$$bt_2 = bt_1 + \pi; \; bt_3 = bt_1 + 2\pi; \; \ldots; \; \therefore t_2 = t_1 + \tfrac{1}{2}T; \; t_3 = t_1 + T; \; \ldots$$

Substitute these values in (7) and put s_1, s_2, s_3, ... for the corresponding displacements,

$$\therefore s_1 = Ae^{-at_1} \sin bt_1; \; - s_2 = Ae^{-at_2} \sin bt_2; \; \ldots$$

where the negative sign indicates that the displacement is on the negative side. Hence the amplitude of the oscillations diminishes according to the compound interest law,

$$\frac{s_1}{s_2} = e^{+a(t_1 - t_2)} = e^{\frac{1}{2}aT}; \; \frac{s_2}{s_3} = \frac{s_3}{s_4} = \ldots = e^{\frac{1}{2}aT}. \quad . \quad (12)$$

This ratio must always be a proper fraction. If a is small, the ratio of two consecutive amplitudes is nearly unity. The oscillations diminish as the terms of a geometrical series with a common ratio $e^{aT/2}$. By taking logarithms of the terms of a geometrical series the resulting arithmetical series has every succeeding term smaller than the term which precedes it by a constant difference. This difference can be found by taking logarithms of equations (12).

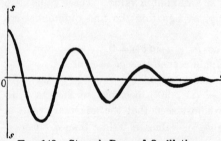

Fig. 149.—Strongly Damped Oscillations.

Plotting these successive values of s and t, in (12), we get the curve shown in Fig. 149. The ratio of the amplitude of one swing to the next is called the **damping ratio**, by Kohlrausch ("Dämpfungsverhaltnis"). It is written k. The natural logarithm of the damping ratio, is Gauss' **logarithmic decrement**, written λ (the ordinary logarithm of k, is written L).   Hence

$$\lambda = \log k = \tfrac{1}{2}aT \log e = \tfrac{1}{2}aT = a\pi/b, \qquad \text{.} \qquad (13)$$

and from (11),

$$\frac{T^2}{T^2_0} = 1 + \frac{\lambda^2}{\pi^2}; \ \text{ or, } \ T = T_0\Big(1 + \frac{1}{2}\cdot\frac{\lambda^2}{\pi^2} + \ldots\Big). \qquad (14)$$

Hence, if the damping is small, the period of oscillation is augmented by a small quantity of the second order.   The logarithmic
decrement allows the "damping constant" or "frictional coefficient" (μ of pages 397 and 404) to be determined when the
constant a and the period of oscillation are known.   It is therefore not necessary to wait until the needle has settled down to
rest before making an observation.   The following table contains
six observations of the amplitudes of a sequence of damped oscillations :

Observed Deflection.	k.	λ.	L.
69	1·438	0·3633	0·1578
48	1·434	0·3604	0·1565
33·5	1·426	0·3548	0·1541
23·5	1·425	0·3542	0·1538
16·5	1·435	0·3612	0·1569
11·5	1·438	0·3633	0·1578
8			

Observations of oscillating pendulums, vibrating needles, etc.,
play an important part in the measurement of the force charac-
terized by the constant q, whether that be the action of, say,
gravity on a pendulum, of a magnetic field on the motion of a
magnet.   The small oscillations of a pendulum in a viscous
medium furnish numerical values of the magnitude of fluid
friction or viscosity.

III. *The roots of the auxiliary equation are real and unequal.*
The condition for real roots $-\alpha$ and $-\beta$, in (2), is that f be greater
than q (page 354).   In this case,

$$s = C_1 e^{-\alpha t} + C_2 e^{-\beta t}, \qquad \text{.} \qquad \text{.} \qquad \text{.} \qquad (15)$$

solves equation (1).   To find what this means, let us suppose that
$f = 3, q = 2, t = 0, s = 0, V_0 = 1$.   From (2), therefore,

$$m = -3 \pm \sqrt{9 - 4} = -3 \pm 2\cdot24 = -\cdot76 \text{ and } -5\cdot24.$$

Substitute these values in (15) and differentiate for the velocity v

or ds/dt. Thus

$$s = C_1e^{-5\cdot2t} + C_2e^{-\cdot76t}; \quad ds/dt = -5\cdot24C_1e^{-5\cdot24t} - 0\cdot76C_2e^{-\cdot76t}.$$
$$\therefore -5\cdot24C_1 - \cdot76C_2 = 1.$$

From (15), when $t=0$, $s=0$; and $C_1+C_2=0$; or $-C_1 = +C_2 = 0\cdot225$,

$$\therefore s = 0\cdot225(e^{-\cdot76t} - e^{-5\cdot24t}). \quad . \quad . \quad (16)$$

Assign particular values to t, and plot the corresponding values
of s by means of Table IV., page 616. Curve 3 (Fig. 150) was

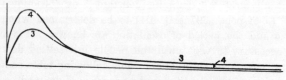

FIG. 150.

obtained by plotting corresponding values of s and t obtained in
this way. The curves have lost the sinuous character, Fig. 148.

IV. The roots of the auxiliary equation are real and equal.
The condition for real and equal roots is that $f = q$.

$$\therefore s = (C_1 + C_2t)e^{-ft}. \quad . \quad . \quad (17)$$

As before, let $f = 2$, $q = 2$, $t = 0$, $s = 0$, $V_0 = 1$. The roots of the
auxiliary are -2 and -2. Hence, to evaluate the constants,
$s=(C_1+C_2t)e^{-2t}$; $ds/dt = C_2e^{-2t} - 2(C_1+C_2t)e^{-2t}$; $C_2-2C_1=1$;
$C_1 = 0$ and $C_2 = 1$;

$$\therefore s = te^{-2t}. \quad . \quad . \quad . \quad (18)$$

Plot (18) in the usual manner. Curve 4 (Fig. 150) was so obtained.

Compare curves 3 and 4 (Fig. 148) with curves 1 and 2
(Fig. 150). Curves 3 and 4 (Fig. 150) represent the motion when
the retarding forces are so great that the vibration cannot take
place. The needle, when removed from its position of equilibrium,
returns to its position of rest asymptotically, *i.e.*, after the lapse of
an infinite time. What does this statement mean? E. du Bois
Raymond calls a movement of this character an **aperiodic motion.**

§ 133. Some Degenerates.

There are some equations derived from the general equation
by the omission of one or more terms. The dependent or the
independent variable may be absent. I have already shown,
pages 249 and 401, how to solve equations of this form:

$$\frac{d^2y}{dx^2} = g\;;\; \frac{d^2y}{dx^2} + q^2y = 0\;;\; \frac{d^2y}{dx^2} - q^2y = 0, \qquad (1)$$

where g and q are constants.

EXAMPLE.—The general equation for the deflection of a horizontal beam uniformly loaded and subjected to the pressure of its supports is

$$a\frac{d^4y}{dx^4} = w\;;\; \text{or},\; \frac{d^4y}{dx^4} = b,$$

where a and w are constants. If the beam has a length l and is supported at both ends, the integration constants are evaluated on the supposition that $y = 0$, and $d^2y/dx^2 = 0$ both when $x = 0$ and $x = l$. Hence show that the integration constants, taken in the same order as they appear in the integration, are $C_1 = -\frac{1}{2}bl$; $C_2 = 0$; $C_3 = \frac{1}{24}bl^3$; $C_4 = 0$. Hence the solution $y = \frac{1}{24}bx(x^3 - 2lx + l^3)$. If the beam is clamped at both ends, $y = 0$, and $dy/dx = 0$ for $x = 0$ and $x = l$. Show that the constants now become $C_1 = -\frac{1}{2}bl$; $C = \frac{1}{12}bl^2$; $C_3 = 0$; $C_4 = 0$. $\therefore y = \frac{1}{24}bx^2(x^2 - 2lx + l^2)$. If the beam is clamped at one end and free at the other, $y = 0$, $dy/dx = 0$ for $x = 0$; and $d^2y/dx^2 = 0$ and $d^3y/dx^3 = 0$ when $x = l$. Show that $C_1 = -bl$; $C = \frac{1}{2}bl$; $C_3 = 0$; $C_4 = 0$. $\therefore y = bx^2(x^2 - 4lx + 6l^2)$.

If kx denotes the "pull" of a spring balance when stretched a distance x, at the time t, the equation of motion is

$$\frac{d^2x}{dt^2} + \frac{k}{m}x = g, \qquad \qquad (2)$$

where m denotes the stretching weight; g is the familiar gravitation constant. For the sake of simplicity put $k/m = a^2$, and we can convert (2) into one of the above forms by substituting

$$x = u + \frac{g}{a^2}\;;\; \therefore \frac{d^2u}{dt^2} + a^2u = 0.$$

Solving this latter, as on page 401, we get

$u = C_1 \cos at + C_2 \sin at\;;\; \therefore x = C_2 \cos at + C_1 \sin at + g/a^2.$
Or, you can solve (2) by substituting

$$p = \frac{dy}{dx}\;;\; \therefore \frac{d^2y}{dx^2} = \frac{dp}{dx} = \frac{dy}{dx}\cdot\frac{dp}{dy} = p\frac{dp}{dy}, \qquad (3)$$

so as to convert the given equation into a linear equation of the first order. For the sake of ease, take the equation

$$\frac{d^2V}{dr^2} + \frac{1}{r}\cdot\frac{dV}{dr} = -\frac{P}{l\mu}, \qquad \qquad (4)$$

which represents the motion of a fluid in a cylindrical tube of radius r and length l. The motion is supposed to be parallel to the axis of the tube and the length of the tube very great in comparison with its radius r. P denotes the difference of the pressure at the two ends of the tube. If the liquid wets the walls of the tube, the velocity is a maximum at the axis of the tube and gradually diminishes to zero at the walls. This means that the velocity is a function of the distance, r_1, of the fluid from the axis of the tube. μ is a constant depending on the nature of the fluid. First substitute $p = dV/dr$, as in (3)

$$\therefore \frac{dp}{dr} + \frac{p}{r} = -\frac{P}{l\mu}; \ \therefore rdp + pdr = -\frac{P}{l\mu}rdr; \ \therefore pr = -\frac{P}{2l\mu}r^2 + C_1; (5)$$

$$\therefore \frac{dV}{dr} = -\frac{P}{2l\mu}r + \frac{C_1}{r}; \ V = -\frac{P}{4l\mu}r^2 + C_1 \log r + C_2.$$

To evaluate C_1 in (5), note that at the axis of the tube $r = 0$. This means that if C_1 is a finite or an infinite magnitude the velocity will be infinite. This is physically impossible, therefore, C_1 must be zero. To evaluate C_2, note that when $r = r_1$, V vanishes and, therefore, we get the final solution of the given equation in the form,

$$V = \frac{P(r_1{}^2 - r^2)}{4l\mu},$$

which represents the velocity of the fluid at a distance r_1 from the axis.

EXAMPLES.—(1) Show that if $d^2y/dx^2 = 32$, and a particle falls from rest, the velocity at the end of six seconds is 6×32 ft. per second; and the distance traversed is $\frac{1}{2} \times 32 \times 36$ ft.

(2) The equation of motion of a particle in a medium which resists directly as the square of the velocity is $d^2s/dt^2 = -a(ds/dt)^2$. Solve. Hint. Substitute as in (3); $\therefore dp/p^2 + adt = 0$; $\therefore p^{-1} = at + C_1$; $\therefore as = \log(at + C_1) + C_2$; etc.

(3) Solve $y \cdot d^2y/dx^2 + (dy/dx)^2 = 1$. Ansr. $y^2 = x^2 + C_1x + C_2$. Hint. Use (3), $pdp/dy + p^2/y = 1/y$; $\therefore py = x + C_1$, etc.

Exact equations may be solved by successive reduction. The equation of motion of a particle under the influence of a repulsive force which varies inversely as the distance is

$$\frac{d^2s}{dt^2} = \frac{a}{s}; \ \therefore \frac{ds}{dt} = a \log \frac{t}{C_1}; \ \therefore y = as(\log \frac{t}{C_1} - 1) + C_2,$$

on integration by parts. The equation of motion of a particle under the influence of an attractive force which varies inversely as the nth power of the distance is

$$\frac{d^2s}{dt^2} = -\frac{a}{s^n}; \ \therefore \left(\frac{ds}{dt}\right)^2 = \frac{2a}{n-1}\left(\frac{1}{s^{n-1}} - \frac{1}{a^{n-1}}\right). \quad . \quad (5)$$

Again integrating, we get

$$t = a^{\frac{1}{2}(n-1)}\sqrt{\frac{n-1}{2a}}\int_a^s \frac{s^{\frac{1}{2}(n-1)}ds}{\sqrt{a^{n-1} - s^{n-1}}}. \quad . \quad (6)$$

According to the tests of integrability, this may be integrated when
$n = \ldots \frac{5}{7}, \frac{3}{5}, \frac{1}{2}, -1, \frac{3}{1}, \frac{5}{3}, \ldots$; or when $n = \ldots \frac{3}{4}, \frac{2}{3}, \frac{1}{2}, 0, 2, \frac{3}{2}, \ldots$ (7)
as indicated on page 210.

EXAMPLES.—(1) If $n = \frac{1}{2}$, we get $(ds/dt)^2 = 4a(a^{\frac{1}{2}} - s^{\frac{1}{2}})$; consequently, $2\sqrt{a} \cdot dt = -(a^{\frac{1}{2}} - s^{\frac{1}{2}})^{-\frac{1}{2}} ds$. The negative sign is taken because s and t are inverse functions of one another.   Add and subtract $2\sqrt{a}/(3\sqrt{s}\sqrt{a^{\frac{1}{2}}} - s^{\frac{1}{2}})$. We get on rearranging terms,

$$2\sqrt{a} \cdot dt = \left(\frac{-3\sqrt{s} + 2\sqrt{a}}{3\sqrt{s}\sqrt{a^{\frac{1}{2}} - s^{\frac{1}{2}}}} - \frac{2\sqrt{a}}{3\sqrt{s}\sqrt{a^{\frac{1}{2}} - s^{\frac{1}{2}}}} \right) ds;$$

$$\therefore t = \frac{2}{3\sqrt{a}} \left\{ s^{\frac{1}{2}}(a^{\frac{1}{2}} - s^{\frac{1}{2}})^{\frac{1}{2}} + 2\sqrt{a}(a^{\frac{1}{2}} - s^{\frac{1}{2}})^{\frac{1}{2}} \right\} = \frac{2}{3\sqrt{a}}(s^{\frac{1}{2}} + 2a^{\frac{1}{2}})(a^{\frac{1}{2}} - s^{\frac{1}{2}})^{\frac{1}{2}}.$$

(2) If $d^2z/dt^2 - z \cdot dz/dt = 0$; show that $C_1 + z = (C_1 - z)e^{C_1(t + c_2)}$; Hint. We get on substituting $p = dz/dt$; $d^2z/dt^2 = dp/dt = dz/dt \times dp/dz$ $\therefore p = \frac{1}{2}(z - C_1^2)$.

(3) The equation of motion of a thin revolving disc is

$$r\frac{d^2u}{dr^2} + \frac{du}{dr} - \frac{u}{r} + ar^2 = 0; \ \therefore \frac{u}{r} = C_2 - \frac{C_1}{2r^2} - \frac{ar^2}{8}.$$

Hint. Add and subtract rdu/dr.
$$\left(r^2\frac{d^2u}{dr^2} + 2r\frac{du}{dr} \right) - \left(r\frac{du}{dr} + u \right) + ar^3 = 0; \ \therefore \frac{d}{dr}\left(r^2\frac{du}{dr} \right) - \frac{d}{dr}(ru) + \frac{d}{dr}\left(\frac{ar^4}{4} \right) = 0.$$

On integration we get an ordinary equation of the first order which can be solved (Ex. (16), p. 372) by substituting $vr = u$.

§ 134. Forced Oscillations.

We have just investigated the motion of a particle subject to an effective force, d^2s/dt^2, and to the impressed forces of restitution, q^2s, and resistance, $2fV$.   The particle may also be subjected to the action of a periodic force which prevents the oscillations dying away.   This is called an **external force**.   It is usually represented by the addition of a term $f(t)$ to the right-hand side of the regular equation of motion, so that

$$\frac{d^2s}{dt^2} + 2f\frac{ds}{dt} + q^2s = f(t). \quad . \quad . \quad . \quad (1)$$

The effective force and the three kinds of impressed force all produce their own effects, and each force is represented in the equation of motion by its own special term.   The term **complementary function,** proposed by Liouville (1832), is applied to the complete solution of the left member of (1), namely,

$$\frac{d^2s}{dt^2} + 2f\frac{ds}{dt} + q^2s = 0. \quad . \quad . \quad . \quad (2)$$

The complementary function gives the oscillations of the system when not influenced by disturbing forces. This integral, there-fore, is said to represent the **free or natural oscillations** of the system. The particular integral represents the effects of the external impressed force which produce the **forced oscillations.** The word "free" is only used in contrast with "forced". A free oscillation may mean either the principal oscillation or any motion represented by any number of terms from the complementary function.

Let equation (1) represent the motion of a pendulum when acted upon by a force which is a simple harmonic function of the time, such that

$$\frac{d^2s}{dt^2} + 2f\frac{ds}{dt} + q^2s = k\cos nt. \qquad . \qquad . \qquad (3)$$

We have already studied the complementary function of this equation in connection with damped oscillations. Any particular integral represents the forced vibration, but there is one particular integral which is more convenient than any other. Let

$$s = A\cos nt + B\sin nt, \qquad . \qquad . \qquad (4)$$

be this particular integral. The complementary function contains the two arbitrary constants which are necessary to define the initial conditions; consequently, *the particular integral needs no integration constant.* We must now determine the forced oscillation due to the given external force, and evaluate the constants A and B in (4).

First substitute (4) in (3), and two identical equations result. Pick out the terms in $\cos nt$, and in $\sin nt$. In this manner we find that

$$- An^2 + 2Bfn + q^2A = k \; ; \; \text{and}, \; - Bn^2 - 2Afn + q^2B = 0.$$

Solve these two equations for A and B, and we get

$$A = \frac{k(q^2 - n^2)}{(q^2 - n^2)^2 + 4f^2n^2} \; ; \; B = \frac{2kfn}{(q^2 - n^2)^2 + 4f^2n^2} \qquad (5)$$

It is here convenient to collect these terms under the symbols R, $\cos \epsilon$, and $\sin \epsilon$, so that

$$\left.\begin{array}{c} q^2 - n^2 = \cos \epsilon ; \; 2fn = \sin \epsilon ; \; \epsilon = \tan^{-1}\dfrac{2fn}{q^2 - n^2} ; \\[2mm] R = \dfrac{k}{\sqrt{(q^2 - n^2)^2 + 4f^2n^2}} ; \end{array}\right\} \qquad (6)$$

$$\therefore A = R\cos \epsilon ; \; B = R\sin \epsilon. \qquad . \qquad . \qquad (7)$$

From (4) we may now write the particular integral

$$s = R(\cos \epsilon . \cos nt + \sin \epsilon . \sin nt), \qquad . \qquad . \qquad (8)$$

or, making a well-known trigonometrical substitution,

$$s = R \cos(nt - \epsilon). \qquad . \qquad . \qquad . \qquad (9)$$

This expression represents the forced oscillations of the system which are due to the external periodic force. The forced oscillation is not in the same phase as the principal oscillation induced by the effective force, but lags behind a definite amount ϵ.

R in (6) always has the same sign whatever be the signs of n and q; $2f$ is positive, hence $\sin \epsilon$ is positive and the angle ϵ lying in the first two quadrants ranges from 0 to π. On the other hand, the sign of $\cos \epsilon$ does depend upon the relative magnitudes of n and q. If q be greater than n, ϵ is in the first quadrant; if q is less than n, ϵ is in the second quadrant (see Table XV., page 610); if $q = n$, $\epsilon = \frac{1}{2}\pi$. The amplitude, R, of the forced vibration is proportional to the intensity, k, of the external force. If f be small enough, we can neglect the term containing f under the root sign, and then

$$R = \frac{k}{q^2 - n^2}.$$

In that case the more nearly the numerical value of q approaches n, the greater will be the amplitude, R, of the forced vibration. Finally, when $q = n$, we should have an infinitely great amplitude. Consequently, when $q = n$, we cannot neglect the magnitude of f^2 and we must have

$$R_{max} = \frac{k}{2nf},$$

so that the magnitude of R is conditioned by the damping constant. If $f = 0$ as is generally assumed in the equation of motion of an unresisted pendulum,

$$\frac{d^2s}{dt^2} + q^2s = k \cos nt, \qquad . \qquad . \qquad . \qquad . \qquad (10)$$

the particular integral of which

$$s = \frac{k}{q^2 - n^2} \cos nt,$$

is indeterminate when $n = q$. The physical meaning of this is that when a particle is acted upon by a periodic force "in step" with the oscillations of the particle, the amplitude of the forced vibrations increase indefinitely, and equation (10) no longer represents the motion of the pendulum. See page 404. As a matter of fact, equation (10) is only a first approximation obtained by neglecting the second powers of small quantities (see E. J. Routh's *Advanced Rigid Dynamics*, London, 222, 1892). I assume that the reader knows the meaning of q and n, if not, see pages 137 and 397.

If the motion of the particle is strongly damped, the maximum excitation does not occur when $n = q$, but when the expression under the root sign is a minimum. If n be variable, the expression under the root sign is a minimum when $n^2 = q^2 - 2f^2$, as indicated in Ex. (5), page 166; and R is therefore a maximum under the same conditions. If n be gradually changed so that it gradually approaches q, and at the same time f be very small, R will remain small until the root sign approaches its vanishing point, and the forced oscillations attain a maximum value rather suddenly. For example, if a tuning fork be sounded about a metre away from another, the minute movements of air impinging upon the second fork will set it in motion.

If f be large, the expression under the root sign does not vanish and there is no sudden maximum. The amplitudes of the free vibration changes gradually with variations of n. The tympanum of the ear, and the receiver of a telephone or microphone are illustrations of this. Every ship has its own natural vibration together with the forced one due to the oscillation of the waves. If the two vibrations are synchronous, the rolling of the ship may be very great, even though the water appears relatively still. "The ship *Achilles*," says White in his *Manual of Naval Architecture*, "was remarkable for great steadiness in heavy weather, and yet it rolled very heavily off Portland in an almost dead calm." The natural period of the ship was no doubt in agreement with the period of the long swells. Iron bridges, too, have broken down when a number of soldiers have been marching over in step with the natural period of vibration of the bridge itself. And this when the bridge could have sustained a much greater load.

The complete solution of the linear equation is the sum of the particular integral and the complementary function. If the latter be given by *II.*, page 406, the solution of (3) must be written

$$s = R\cos(nt - \epsilon) + e^{-at}(C_1\cos qt + C_2\sin qt).$$

We can easily evaluate the two integration constants C_1 and C_2, when we know the initial conditions, as illustrated in the preceding section. If the particle be at rest when the external force begins to act,

$$C_1 = -R\cos\epsilon;\ C_2 = -R\left(\frac{n}{q}\sin\epsilon + \frac{2f}{q}\cos\epsilon\right).$$

At the beginning, therefore, the amplitude of the free vibrations is

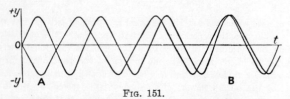

FIG. 151.

of the same order of magnitude as the forced oscillation. If the damping, $2f$, is small, and n is nearly equal to q, the damping factor, e^{-at}, will be very great nearly unity; $2f/q$ is nearly zero; n/q is nearly unity; and ϵ is nearly $\frac{1}{2}\pi$. In that case, $C_1 = 0$, and $C_2 = -R$. The motion is then approximately

$$s = R(\sin nt - \sin qt).$$

The two oscillations $\sin nt$ and $-\sin qt$ are superposed upon one another. If these two harmonic motions functions are plotted separately and conjointly, as in Fig. 151, we see at once that they almost annul one another at the beginning because the one is opposed by the other. This is shown at A. In a little while, the difference between q and n becomes more marked and the amplitude gradually increases up to a maximum, as shown at B. These phenomena recur at definite intervals, giving rise to the well-known phenomena of interference of light and sound waves, beats, etc.

EXAMPLES.—(1) Ohm's law for a constant current is $E = RC$; for a variable current of C ampères flowing in a circuit with a coefficient of self-induction of L henries, with a resistance of R ohms and an electromotive force of E volts, Ohm's law is represented by the equation,

$$E = RC + L \cdot d/Cdt, \quad . \quad . \quad . \quad (11)$$

where dC/dt evidently denotes the rate of increase of current per second, L is the equivalent of an electromotive force tending to retard the current.

(i) When E is constant, the solution of (11) has been obtained in a preceding set of examples, $C = E/R + Be^{-Rt/L}$, where B is the constant of integration. To find B, note that when $t = 0$, $C = 0$. Hence, $C = E(1 - e^{-Rt/L})/R$. The second term is the so-called "extra current at make," an evanescent factor due to the starting conditions. The current, therefore, tends to assume the steady condition: $C = E/R$, when t is very great.

(ii) When C is an harmonic function of the time, say, $C = C_0 \sin qt$; $\therefore dC/dt = C_0 q \cos qt$. Substitute these values in the original equation (11), and $E = RC_0 \sin qt + LC_0 q \cos qt$, or, $E = C_0 \sqrt{R^2 + L^2 q^2} \cdot \sin (qt + \epsilon)$, on compounding these harmonic motions, page 138, where $\epsilon = \tan^{-1}(Lq/R)$, the so-called lag[1] of the current behind the electromotive force, the expression $\sqrt{(R^2 + L^2 q^2)}$ is the so-called impedance.

(iii) When E is a function of the time, say, $f(t)$,

$$C = Be^{-\frac{R}{L}t} + \frac{e^{-\frac{R}{L}t}}{L} \int e^{\frac{R}{L}t} f(t) dt,$$

where B is the constant of integration to be evaluated as described above.

(iv) When E is a simple harmonic function of the time, say, $E = E_0 \sin qt$, then,

$$C = Be^{-\frac{R}{L}t} + \frac{E(R \sin qt - Lq \cos qt)}{R^2 + L^2 q^2}.$$

The evanescent term $e^{-Rt/L}$ may be omitted when the current has settled down into the steady state. (Why?)

---

[1] An alternating (periodic) current is not always in phase (or, "in step") with the impressed (electromotive) force driving the current along the circuit. If there is self-induction in the circuit, the current lags behind the electromotive force; if there is a condenser in the circuit, the current in the condenser is greatest when the electromotive force is changing most rapidly from a positive to a negative value, that is to say, the maximum current is in advance of the electromotive force, there is then said to be a lead in the phase of the current.

(v) When E is zero, $C = Be^{-Rt/L}$. Evaluate the integration constant B by putting $C = C_0$, when $t = 0$.

(2) The relation between the charge, q, and the electromotive force, E, of two plates of a condenser of capacity C connected by a wire of resistance R, is $E = R \cdot dq/dt + q/C$, provided the self-induction is zero. Solve for q. Show that when if E be 0; $q = Q_0 e^{-t/RC}$; (Q_0 is the charge when $t = 0$). If E be constant; $q = CE + Be^{-t/RC}$. If $E = f(t)$;

$$q = \frac{1}{R} e^{-\frac{t}{RC}} \int e^{\frac{t}{RC}} f(t) dt + Be^{-\frac{t}{RC}}.$$

(3) Show if $E = E_0 \sin qt$; $q = Be^{-\frac{t}{RC}} + \frac{CE(\sin qt + RCq \cos qt)}{1 + R^2 C^2 q^2}$.

§ 135. How to find Particular Integrals.

The particular integral of the linear equation,

$$(D^2 + PD + Q)y = f(x), \quad \cdot \quad \cdot \quad \cdot \quad (1)$$

it will be remembered, is any solution of this equation—the simpler the better. The particular integral contains no integration constant. The complete solution of the linear equation is the sum of the complementary function and the particular integral.

Complete solution = complementary function + particular integral.

We must now review the processes for finding particular integrals. Let R be written in place of $f(x)$, so that (1) may be written $f(D)y = R$. Consequently, we may write,

$$y = f(D)^{-1}R \; ; \; \text{or,} \; y = \frac{R}{f(D)}. \quad \cdot \quad \cdot \quad (2)$$

The right-hand side of either of equations (2), will furnish a particular integral of (1). The operation indicated in (2) depends on the form of $f(D)$. Let us study some particular cases.

I. When the operator $f(D)^{-1}$ can be resolved into factors.

Suppose that the linear equation

$$\frac{d^2 y}{dx^2} - 5 \frac{dy}{dx} + 6y = R,$$

can be factorized. The complementary function can be written down at sight by the method given on page 401,

$$(D^2 - 5D + 6)y = 0 \; ; \; \text{or,} \; (D - 3)(D - 2)y = 0.$$

According to (2), the particular integral, y_1, is

$$y_1 = \frac{1}{(D - 3)(D - 2)} R = \left(\frac{1}{D - 3} - \frac{1}{D - 2} \right) R \; ;$$

On page 396 we have defined $f(D)^{-1}R$ to be that function of x which gives R when operated upon by $f(D)$. Consequently,

$D^{-1}x^2 = \int x^2 dx$.   Hence, $D - 3$ acting upon $(D - 3)^{-1}R$ must, by definition, give R.   But $(D - 3)^{-1}R$ is the particular integral of the equation

$$\frac{dy}{dx} - 3y = R;$$

so that from (2), page 387, $y = e^{-\int - 3dx}\int e^{\int - 3dx}Rdx = e^{3x}\int e^{-3x}Rdx$.

$$\therefore y_1 = e^{3x}\int e^{-3x}Rdx - e^{2x}\int e^{-2x}Rdx.$$

from (2).   The general solution is

$$\therefore y = C_1e^{3x} + Ce^{2x} + e^{3x}\int e^{-3x}Rdx - e^{2x}\int e^{-2x}Rdx.$$

EXAMPLES.—(1) In the preceding illustration, put $R = e^{4x}$ and show that the general solution is, $C_1e^{3x} + C_2e^{2x} + \frac{1}{2}e^{4x}$.

(2) If $(D^2 - 4D + 3)y = 2e^{3x}$; $y = C_1e^x + C_2e^{3x} + xe^{3x}$.

(3) Solve $d^2y/dx^2 - 3dy/dx + 2y = e^{3x}$.   In symbolic notation this will appear in the form, $(D - 1)(D - 2)y = e^{3x}$.   The complementary function is $y = C_1e^x + C_2e^{2x}$.   The particular integral is obtained by putting

$$y_1 = \frac{1}{(D - 2)(D - 1)}e^{3x} = \left(\frac{1}{D - 2} - \frac{1}{D - 1}\right)e^{3x},$$

according to the method of resolution into partial fractions.   Operate with the first symbolic factor, as above, $y_1 = e^{2x}\int e^{-2x}e^{3x}dx - e^x\int e^{-x}e^{3x}dx = \frac{1}{2}e^{3x}$. The complete solution is, therefore, $y = C_1e^x + C_2e^{2x} + \frac{1}{2}e^{3x}$.

II. When R is a rational function of x, say x^n.

This case is comparatively rare.   The procedure is to expand $f(D)^{-1}$ in ascending powers of D as far as the highest power of x in R.   The expansion may be done by division or other convenient process.

EXAMPLES.—(1) Solve $d^2y/dx^2 - 4dy/dx + 4y = x^2$.   The complementary function is $y = e^{2x}(A + Bx)$; the particular integral is:

$$\frac{1}{(2 - D)^2}x^2 = \frac{1}{4}\left(1 + D + \frac{3}{4}D^2\right)x^2 = \frac{1}{8}(2x^2 + 4x + 3).$$

You will, of course, remember that the operation Dx^2 is $2x$; and D^2x^2 is 2.

(2) If $d^2y/dx^2 - y = 2 + 5x$; $y = C_1e^x + C_2e^{-x} - 5x - 2$.

(3) The particular integral of $(D^3 + 3D^2 + 2D)y = x^2$ is $\frac{1}{12}x(2x^2 - 9x + 21)$; the complementary function is $C_1 + C_2e^{-2x} + C_3e^{-x}$.   The steps are

$$\frac{1}{2D + 3D^2 + D^3}x^2 = \frac{1}{2D}\left(\frac{1}{1 + \frac{3}{2}D + \frac{1}{2}D^2}\right)x^2 = \frac{1}{2D}\left(1 - \frac{3}{2}D + \frac{7}{4}D^2\right)x^2.$$

Now proceed as in Ex. (1) for the operation Dx^2 and D^2x^2.   Then note that

$$\frac{1}{D}x = \int x dx; \quad \frac{1}{D}x^2 = \int x^2 dx; \text{ etc.}$$

III. When R contains an exponential factor, so that $R = e^{ax}X$.

Two cases arise according as X is or is not a function of x, a is constant.

(i) *When X is a function of x.* Since $D^n e^{ax} = a^n e^{ax}$, where n is any positive integer, we have

$$D(e^{ax}X) = e^{ax}DX + ae^{ax}X = e^{ax}(D + a)X,$$

and generally, as in Leibnitz' theorem, page 67,

$$D^n e^{ax}X = e^{ax}(D + a)^n X;$$

$$\therefore \frac{D^n e^{ax}}{(D + a)^n}X = e^{ax}X; \text{ and } \frac{1}{(D + a)^n}Xe^{ax} = e^{ax}\frac{1}{D^n}X. \quad (3)$$

Consequently, the operation $f(D)^{-1}e^{ax}X$ is performed by transplanting e^{ax} from the right- to the left-hand side of the operator $f(D)^{-1}$ and replacing D by $D + a$. This will, perhaps, be better understood from Exs. (1) and (2) below.

(ii) *When X is constant*, operation (3) reduces to

$$\frac{1}{f(D)}e^{ax} = \frac{1}{f(a)}e^{ax}. \quad \cdot \quad \cdot \quad \cdot \quad (4)$$

The operation $f(D)^{-1}e^{ax}$ is simply performed by replacing D by a.

EXAMPLES.—(1) Solve $d^2y/dx^2 - 2dy/dx + y = x^2e^{3x}$. The complete solution, by page 418, is $(C_1 + xC_2)e^x + (D + 2D + 1)^{-1}x^2e^{3x}$. The particular integral is

$$\frac{1}{D^2 - 2D + 1}x^2e^{3x} = \frac{1}{(D - 1)(D - 1)}x^2e^{3x}.$$

By rule: e^{3x} may be transferred from the right to the left side of the operator provided we replace D by $D + 3$.

$$\therefore y_1 = e^{3x}\frac{1}{(D + 2)^2} \cdot x^2.$$

We get from I above, $e^{3x}(\frac{1}{4}x^2 - \frac{1}{2}x + \frac{3}{8})$, as the value of the particular integral.

(2) Evaluate $(D - 1)^{-1}e^x\log x$. Ansr. $e^x(x \log x - x)$; or $xe^x\log(x/e)$. Integrate $\int \log x\,dx$ by parts.

(3) Find the particular integral in $(D^2 - 3D + 2)y = e^{3x}$,

$$\frac{1}{D^2 - 3D + 2}e^{3x} = \frac{1}{3^2 - 3.3 + 2}e^{3x} = \frac{1}{2}e^{3x}.$$

(4) Show that $\frac{1}{4}e^x$, is a particular integral in $d^2y/dx^2 + 2dy/dx + y = e^x$.

(5) Repeat Ex. 1, I, above, by this method.

An anomalous case arises when a is a root of $f(D) = 0$. By this method, we should get for the particular integral of $dy/dx - y = e^x$.

$$\frac{1}{D - 1}e^x = \frac{e^x}{1 - 1} = \infty e^x.$$

The difficulty is evaded by using the method (3) instead of (4). Thus,

$$\frac{1}{D - 1}e^x = e^x\frac{1}{D} \cdot 1 = xe^x.$$

The complete solution is, therefore, $y = Ce^x + xe^x$.

Another mode of treatment is the following: If a is a root of $f(D) = 0$, then as on page 354, $D - a$ must be a factor of $f(D)$.

Consequently,

$$f(D) = (D - a)f'(D) \, ;$$

and the particular integral is

$$\therefore \frac{1}{f(D)}e^{ax} = \frac{1}{(D - a)} \cdot \frac{1}{f'(D)}e^{ax} = \frac{1}{(D - a)} \cdot \frac{1}{f'(a)}e^{ax} = e^{ax}\frac{1}{f'(a)}\int dx. \quad (5)$$

If the factor $D - a$ occurs twice, then following the same rule

$$\frac{1}{f(D)}e^{ax} = \frac{1}{(D - a)^2 f'(D)}e^{ax} = \frac{1}{(D - a)} \cdot \frac{1}{f'(a)}e^{ax} = e^{ax}\frac{1}{f'(a)}\iint dxdx. \, ; (6)$$

and so on for any number of factors.

EXAMPLES.—(1) Find the particular integrals in, $(D + 1)^3 y = e^{-x}$. Ansr. $\frac{1}{6}x^3 e^{-x}$. Hint. Use (6) extended; or, since the root a is -1, we have to evaluate $e^{-x} \cdot D^{-3}$; that is, $e^{-x}\iiint dxdxdx$.

(2) $(D^3 - 1)y = xe^x$. Ansr. $e^x(\frac{1}{3}x^2 - \frac{1}{3}x)$. Hint. By the method of (3), and Ex. (3), II., above,

$$\frac{1}{D^3-1}xe^x = e^x \frac{1}{(D+1)^3-1}x = e^x \frac{1}{D^3+3D^2+3D}x = e^x \frac{1}{D}\left(\frac{1}{3} - \frac{1}{3}D\right)x = e^x \frac{1}{D}\left(\frac{x}{3} - \frac{1}{3}\right).$$

IV. When R contains sine or cosine factors.

By the successive differentiation of $\sin nx$, page 67, we find that

$$D\sin nx = \frac{d(\sin nx)}{dx} = n\cos nx \, ; \quad D^2\sin nx = \frac{d^2(\sin nx)}{dx^2} = -n^2\sin nx \, ; \ldots$$

$$\therefore (D^2)^n\sin(nx + a) = (-n^2)^n\sin(nx + a),$$

where n and a are constants. And evidently

$$f(D^2)\sin(nx + a) = f(-n^2)\sin(nx + a).$$

By definition of the symbol of operation, $f(D^2)^{-1}$, page 396, this gives us

$$\therefore \frac{1}{f(D^2)}\sin(nx + a) = \frac{1}{f(-n^2)}\sin(nx + a). \qquad (7)$$

It can be shown in the same way that,

$$\frac{1}{f(D^2)}\cos(nx + a) = \frac{1}{f(-n^2)}\cos(nx + a). \qquad (8)$$

EXAMPLES.—(1) $d^3y/dx^3 + d^2y/dx^2 + dy/dx + y = \sin 2x$. Find the particular integral.

$$\frac{R}{f(D)} = \frac{1}{D^3 + D^2 + D + 1}\sin 2x = \frac{1}{(D^2 + 1) + D(D^2 + 1)}\sin 2x.$$

Substitute -2^2 for D^2 as in (7). We thus get $-\frac{1}{3}(D + 1)^{-1}\sin 2x$. Multiply and divide by $D - 1$ and again substitute $D^2 = (-2^2)$ in the result. Thus we get $\frac{1}{15}(D - 1)\sin 2x$; or $\frac{1}{15}(2\cos 2x - \sin 2x)$.

(2) Solve $d^2y/dx^2 - k^2y = \cos mx$. Ansr. $C_1e^{kx} + C_2e^{-kx} - (\cos mx)/(m^2 + k^2)$.

(3) If a and β are the roots of the auxiliary equation derived from Helmholtz's equation, $d^2y/dt^2 + mdy/dt + n^2y = a\sin nt$, for the vibrations of a tuning-fork, show that $y = C_1e^{at} + C_2e^{\beta t} - (a\cos nt)/mn$ is the complete solution.

An anomalous case arises when D^2 in $D^2 + n^2$ is equal to $- n^2$. For instance, the particular integral of $d^2y/dx^2 + n^2y = {\cos \atop \sin} nx$, is $(D^2 + n^2)^{-1} {\cos \atop \sin} nx$. If the attempt is made to evaluate this, by substituting $D^2 = - n^2$, we get ${\cos \atop \sin} nx(- n^2 + n^2)^{-1} = \infty {\cos \atop \sin} nx$. We were confronted with a similar difficulty on page 420. The treatment is practically the same. We take the limit of $(D^2 + n^2)^{-1} {\cos \atop \sin} nx$, when n of ${\cos \atop \sin} nx$ and $- D^2$ become $n + h$ and h converges towards zero. In this manner we find that the particular integral assumes the form

$$+ \frac{x \sin nx}{2n} \text{ if } R = \cos nx; \text{ and } - \frac{x \cos nx}{2n} \text{ if } R = \sin nx. \quad (9)$$

EXAMPLES.—(1) Evaluate $(D^2 + 4)^{-1} \cos 2x$. Ansr. $\frac{1}{4}x \sin 2x$.

(2) Show that $- \frac{1}{2}x \cos x$, is the particular integral of $(D^2 + 1)y = \sin x$.

(3) Evaluate $(D^2 + 4)^{-1} \sin 2x$. Ansr. $- \frac{1}{4}x \cos 2x$.

V. When R contains any function of x, say X, such that R = xX.

The successive differentiation of a product of two variables, xX, gives, pages 40 and 67,

$$D^n xX = xD^n X + nD^{n-1}X.$$
$$\therefore f(D)xX = xf(D)X + f'(D)X. \qquad . \qquad (10)$$

Substitute $Y = f(D)X$, where Y is any function of x. Operate with $f(D)^{-1}$. We get the particular integral

$$\frac{1}{f(D)}xX = \left\{ x\frac{1}{f(D)} - \frac{f'(D)}{f(D)^2} \right\}X. \qquad . \qquad (11)$$

where $f'(D)/f(D)^2$ is the differential coefficient of $f(D)^{-1}$.

EXAMPLES.—(1) Find the particular integral in $d^3y/dx^3 - y = xe^{2x}$. Remember that $f(D)$ is the differential coefficient of $D^3 - 1$. From (11) the particular integral is

$$\left\{ x - \frac{1}{D^3 - 1} \cdot 3D^2 \right\} \frac{1}{D^3 - 1}e^{2x} = \left\{ x - \frac{1}{7} \cdot 3 \cdot 4 \right\} \frac{1}{7}e^{2x} = \left(\frac{x}{7} - \frac{12}{49} \right)e^{2x}.$$

(2) Show in this way, that the particular integral of $(D - 1)y = x \sin x$ is

$$x\frac{1}{D - 1}\sin x - \frac{1}{(D - 1)^2}\sin x = x\frac{D + 1}{D^2 - 1}\sin x - \frac{(D + 1)^2}{(D^2 - 1)^2}\sin x;$$
$$= \frac{1}{2}x(D + 1)\cos x - \frac{1}{4}(D^2 + 2D + 1)\cos x = \frac{1}{2}x(\cos x + \sin x) - \frac{1}{2}\cos x.$$

(3) If $d^2y/dx^2 - y = x^2\cos x$; $y = C_1 e^x + C_2 e^{-x} + x \sin x + \frac{1}{2}\cos x(1 - x^2)$. Hint. By substituting xX in place of X in (10), the particular integral may be transformed into

$$\frac{1}{f(D)}x^2X = \left\{ x^2\frac{1}{f(D)} + 2x\frac{f'(D)}{f(D)^2} + \frac{f''(D)}{f(D)^3} \right\}X, \qquad . \qquad (12)$$

where $f'(D)/f(D)^2$, and $f''(D)/f(D)^3$ respectively denote the first and second differential coefficient of $f(D)^{-1}$. Successive reduction of x^nX furnishes a similar formula. The numerical coefficients follow the binomial law. Returning to the original problem, the first and second differential coefficients of $(D^2 - 1)^{-1}$ are $- 2D(D^2 - 1)^{-2}$, and $(2D^1 - 2)(D^2 - 1)^{-3}$. Hence,

$$\frac{1}{f(D)}x^2\cos x = \left\{ x^2\frac{1}{D^2 - 1} + 2x\frac{- 2D}{(D^2 - 1)^2} + \frac{2(D^2 - 1)}{(D^2 - 1)} \right\}\cos x\,;$$
$$\therefore y_1 = - \tfrac{1}{2}x^2\cos x - \tfrac{1}{2}\sin x + \tfrac{1}{2}\cos x.$$

(4) Solve $d^3y/dx^3 - y = x \sin x$. The particular integral consists of two parts, $\tfrac{1}{2}\{(x - 3)\cos x - x\sin x\}$. Tho complementary function is

$$C_1e^x + e^{-\tfrac{1}{2}x}\{C_2\sin(\tfrac{1}{2}\sqrt{3}x) + C_3\cos(\tfrac{1}{2}\sqrt{3}x)\}.$$

§ 136.   The Gamma Function.

The equation of motion of a particle of unit mass moving under the influence of an attractive force whose intensity varies inversely as the distance of the particle away from the seat of attraction is obviously

$$\frac{d^2s}{dt^2} = - \frac{a}{s},$$

where a is a constant, and the minus sign denotes that the influence of the force upon the particle diminishes as time goes on. To find the time occupied by a particle in passing from a distance $s = s$ to $s = s_0$, we must integrate this equation. Here, on multiplying through by $2ds/dt$, we get

$$\int 2\frac{ds}{dt} \cdot \frac{d^2s}{dt^2} = - 2a\int\frac{1}{s} \cdot \frac{ds}{dt}\,; \; \therefore \frac{1}{2}\left(\frac{ds}{dt}\right)^2 = - a\log s + C.$$

If $v = 0$ when $s = s_0$,

$$\frac{ds}{dt} = \sqrt{2a\log\frac{s_0}{s}}\,; \; \text{or, } t = \sqrt{\frac{1}{2a}}\int_{s_0}^{s}\frac{ds}{\sqrt{\log\frac{s_0}{s}}}. \qquad (1)$$

For the sake of convenience, let us write y in place of $\log s_0/s$. From the well-known properties of logarithms discussed on page 24, it follows that if $s = s_0$, $y = 0$; and if $s = 0$, $y = \infty$. Hence, passing into exponentials,

$$\log\frac{s_0}{s} = y\,; \; \frac{s_0}{s} = e^y\,; \; s = s_0e^{-y}\,; \; ds = - s_0e^{-y}dy\,;$$

$$\therefore t = - \frac{s_0}{\sqrt{2a}}\int_0^{\infty}\frac{e^{-y}dy}{\sqrt{y}} = - \frac{s_0}{\sqrt{2a}}\int_0^{\infty}y^{-\frac{1}{2}}e^{-y}dy. \qquad (2)$$

It is sometimes found convenient, as here, to express the solution of a physical problem in terms of a definite integral whose numerical value is known, more or less accurately, for certain values of the variable. For example, there is Soldner's table of

$\int_0^a (\log x)^{-1} dx$; Gilbert's tables of Fresnel's integral $\int_0^v \cos \frac{1}{2} \pi v \,.\, dv$, or $\int_0^v \sin \frac{1}{2} \pi v \,.\, dv$; Legendre's tables of the elliptic integrals ; Kramp's table of the integral $\int_0^\infty e^{-t^2} .\, dt$; and Legendre's table of the integral $\int_0^\infty e^{-x} x^{n-1} .\, dx$, or the so-called "gamma function". We shall speak about the last three definite integrals in this work.

Following Legendre, the **gamma function**, or the "second Eulerian integral," is usually symbolised by $\Gamma(n)$. By definition, therefore,

$$\Gamma(n) = \int_0^\infty e^{-x} x^{n-1} .\, dx. \qquad . \qquad . \qquad (3)$$

Integrate by parts, and we get

$$\int_0^\infty e^{-x} x^n .\, dx = n \int_0^\infty e^{-x} x^{n-1} .\, dx - e^{-x} x^n. \qquad . \qquad (4)$$

The last term vanishes between the limits $x = 0$ and $x = \infty$. Hence

$$\int_0^\infty e^{-x} x^n .\, dx = n \int_0^\infty e^{-x} x^{n-1} .\, dx. \qquad . \qquad . \qquad (5)$$

In the above notation, this means that

$$\Gamma(n + 1) = n\Gamma(n). \qquad . \qquad . \qquad (6)$$

If n is a whole number, it follows from (6), that

$$\Gamma(n + 1) = 1 \,.\, 2 \,.\, 3 \ldots n = n! \,. \qquad . \qquad . \qquad (7)$$

This important relation is true for any function of n, though $n!$ has a real meaning only when n is integral.

The numerical value of the gamma function has been tabulated for all values of n between 1 and 2 to twelve decimal places. By the aid of such a table, the approximate value of all definite integrals reducible to gamma functions can be calculated as easily as ordinary trigonometrical functions, or logarithms. There are four cases:

1. n lies between 0 and 1. Use (16).

2. n lies between 1 and 2. Use Table V., below.

3. n is greater than 2. Use (6) so as to make the value of the given expression depend on one in which n lies between 1 and 2.

4. $\Gamma(1) = 1$; $\Gamma(2) = 1$; $\Gamma(0) = \infty$; $\Gamma(\frac{1}{2}) = \sqrt{\pi}$. . . (8)

I. The conversion of definite integrals into the gamma function.

The following are a few illustrations of the conversion of definite integrals into gamma functions. For a more extended discussion special text-books must be consulted. If a is independent of x,

$$\int_0^\infty e^{-ax}x^{m-1} . dx = \frac{1}{a^m}\Gamma(m); \qquad . \qquad . \qquad (9)$$

$$\int_0^1 x^{m-1}(1-x)^{n-1} . dx = \int_0^\infty \frac{x^{m-1}dx}{(1+x)^{m+n}} = \frac{\Gamma(m)\Gamma(n)}{\Gamma(m+n)}. \qquad (10)$$

The first member of (10) is sometimes called the *first Eulerian integral*, or *beta function*. It is written $B(m, n)$. The beta function is here expressed in terms of the gamma function. Substitute $x = ay/b$ in the second member of (10), and we get

$$\int_0^\infty \frac{y^{m-1}dy}{(ay+b)^{m+n}} = \frac{\Gamma(m)\Gamma(n)}{a^m b^n \Gamma(m+n)}. \qquad . \qquad (11$$

Other relations are :

$$\int_0^{\frac{1}{2}\pi} \sin^n x . dx = \int_0^{\frac{1}{2}\pi} \cos^n x . dx = \frac{\frac{1}{2}\sqrt{\pi}\Gamma\frac{1}{2}(n+1)}{\Gamma(\frac{1}{2}n+2)}. \qquad (12)$$

$$\int_0^{\frac{1}{2}\pi} \sin^p x . \cos^q x . dx = \frac{\Gamma[\frac{1}{2}(p+1)] . \Gamma[\frac{1}{2}(q+1)]}{2\Gamma[\frac{1}{2}(p+q)+1]}. \qquad (13)$$

$$\int_0^1 x^m \log\left(\frac{1}{x}\right)^n dx = \frac{\Gamma(n+1)}{(m+1)^{n+1}} \int_0^1 x^m \log x^n dx = \frac{(-1)^n\Gamma(n+1)}{(m+1)^{n+1}}. \qquad (14)$$

$$\int_0^\infty x^n e^{-ax}dx = a^{-(n+1)}\Gamma(n+1); \int_0^\infty e^{-a^2x^2}dx = \frac{\frac{1}{2}\Gamma(\frac{1}{2})}{a} = \frac{\frac{1}{2}\sqrt{\pi}}{a}. \qquad (15)$$

You can now evaluate (2). We get

$$t = \frac{s_0}{\sqrt{2a}}\Gamma(\tfrac{1}{2}) = \sqrt{\frac{\pi}{2a}}s_0.$$

Compare the result with that obtained by the process of integration described on pages 342 and 344.

EXAMPLES.—(1) Evaluate $\int_0^{\frac{1}{2}\pi} \sin^{10}x . dx$. Hint. From (12), $\frac{\frac{1}{2}\sqrt{\pi}\Gamma(\frac{11}{2})}{\Gamma(6)}$.

$$\therefore \frac{\sqrt{\pi}}{2} . \frac{\frac{9}{2}.\frac{7}{2}.\frac{5}{2}.\frac{3}{2}.\frac{1}{2}.\sqrt{\pi}}{5.4.3.2.1} = \frac{\pi}{2}.\frac{9}{10}.\frac{7}{8}.\frac{5}{6}.\frac{3}{4}.\frac{1}{2}.$$

(2) Evaluate $\int_0^\infty e^{-ax}x^5 . dx$. Use (9). Ansr. $\frac{\Gamma(6)}{a^6} = \frac{5.4.3.2.1}{a^6}$.

(3) If $\int_0^\infty \frac{x^{m-1}dx}{1+x} = \frac{\pi}{\sin m\pi}$, show that $\Gamma(m) . \Gamma(1-m) = \frac{\pi}{\sin m\pi}$; and

$\Gamma(1+m) . \Gamma(1-m) = \frac{m\pi}{\sin m\pi}$, by putting $m + n = 1$ in the beta function, etc.

These two results can be employed for evaluating the gamma function when n lies between 0 and 1. By division

$$\Gamma(m) = \frac{\Gamma(1+m)}{m}. \qquad . \qquad . \qquad . \qquad (16)$$

If $m = \frac{1}{4}$, $\Gamma(\frac{1}{4}) = 3\cdot6254$; log $\Gamma(\frac{1}{4}) = 0\cdot5594$; if $m = \frac{1}{2}$, $\Gamma(\frac{1}{2}) = 1\cdot7725$;

$\log_{10}\Gamma(\tfrac{1}{2}) = 0\cdot 248\bar{6}$; and if $m = \tfrac{3}{4}$, $\Gamma(\tfrac{3}{4}) = 1\cdot 2253$; $\log_{10}\Gamma(\tfrac{3}{4}) = 0\cdot 088\bar{3}$; where the bar shows that the figure has been strengthened.

II. Numerical computations.

Table V. gives the value of $\log_{10}\Gamma(n)$ to four decimal places for all values of n between 1 and 2. It has been adapted from Legendre's tables to twelve decimal places in his *Exercises de Calcul Intégral*, Paris, 2, 18, 1817. For all values of n between 1 and 2, $\log\Gamma(n)$ will be negative. Hence, as in the ordinary logarithmic tables of the trigonometrical functions, the tabular logarithm is often increased by the addition of 10 to the logarithm of $\Gamma(n)$. This must be allowed for when arranging the final result.

TABLE V.—COMMON LOGARITHMS OF $\Gamma(n)$ FROM $n = 1\cdot 00$ TO $n = 1\cdot 99$.

n.	0·00.	0·01.	0·02.	0·03.	0·04.	0·05.	0·06.	0·07.	0·08.	0·09.
1·0	0·0000	$\bar{1}$·9975	$\bar{1}$·9951	$\bar{1}$·9928	$\bar{1}$·9905	$\bar{1}$·9883	$\bar{1}$·9862	$\bar{1}$·9841	$\bar{1}$·9821	$\bar{1}$·9802
1·1	$\bar{1}$·9783	$\bar{1}$·9765	$\bar{1}$·9748	$\bar{1}$·9731	$\bar{1}$·9715	$\bar{1}$·9699	$\bar{1}$·9684	$\bar{1}$·9669	$\bar{1}$·9655	$\bar{1}$·9642
1·2	$\bar{1}$·9629	$\bar{1}$·9617	$\bar{1}$·9685	$\bar{1}$·9594	$\bar{1}$·9583	$\bar{1}$·9573	$\bar{1}$·9564	$\bar{1}$·9554	$\bar{1}$·9546	$\bar{1}$·9538
1·3	$\bar{1}$·9530	$\bar{1}$·9523	$\bar{1}$·9516	$\bar{1}$·9510	$\bar{1}$·9505	$\bar{1}$·9500	$\bar{1}$·9495	$\bar{1}$·9491	$\bar{1}$·9487	$\bar{1}$·9483
1·4	$\bar{1}$·9481	$\bar{1}$·9478	$\bar{1}$·9476	$\bar{1}$·9475	$\bar{1}$·9473	$\bar{1}$·9473	$\bar{1}$·9472	$\bar{1}$·9473	$\bar{1}$·9473	$\bar{1}$·9474
1·5	$\bar{1}$·9475	$\bar{1}$·9477	$\bar{1}$·9479	$\bar{1}$·9482	$\bar{1}$·9485	$\bar{1}$·9488	$\bar{1}$·9492	$\bar{1}$·9496	$\bar{1}$·9501	$\bar{1}$·9506
1·6	$\bar{1}$·9511	$\bar{1}$·9517	$\bar{1}$·9523	$\bar{1}$·9529	$\bar{1}$·9536	$\bar{1}$·9543	$\bar{1}$·9550	$\bar{1}$·9558	$\bar{1}$·9566	$\bar{1}$·9575
1·7	$\bar{1}$·9584	$\bar{1}$·9593	$\bar{1}$·9603	$\bar{1}$·9613	$\bar{1}$·9623	$\bar{1}$·9633	$\bar{1}$·9644	$\bar{1}$·9656	$\bar{1}$·9667	$\bar{1}$·9679
1·8	$\bar{1}$·9691	$\bar{1}$·9704	$\bar{1}$·9717	$\bar{1}$·9730	$\bar{1}$·9743	$\bar{1}$·9757	$\bar{1}$·9771	$\bar{1}$·9786	$\bar{1}$·9800	$\bar{1}$·9815
1·9	$\bar{1}$·9831	$\bar{1}$·9846	$\bar{1}$·9862	$\bar{1}$·9878	$\bar{1}$·9895	$\bar{1}$·9912	$\bar{1}$·9929	$\bar{1}$·9946	$\bar{1}$·9964	$\bar{1}$·9982

$$\log_{10}\sqrt{\pi} = 0\cdot 24857493635 = \log_{10}\Gamma(\tfrac{1}{2}).$$

EXAMPLE.—Evaluate $\int_{0}^{\frac{1}{2}\pi}\sqrt{\sin x}\, . \, dx$.   Ansr. $1\cdot 198$.   Hint. Use (13), $q = 0$, $p = \tfrac{1}{2}$. Hence,

$$\int_{0}^{\frac{1}{2}\pi}\sqrt{\sin x}\, . \, dx = \frac{\Gamma(\tfrac{3}{4})\Gamma(\tfrac{1}{2})}{2\Gamma(\tfrac{5}{4})} \cdot \log \frac{\Gamma(\tfrac{3}{4})\Gamma(\tfrac{1}{2})}{2\Gamma(\tfrac{5}{4})} = \log\Gamma(\tfrac{3}{4}) + \log\Gamma(\tfrac{1}{2}) - \log 2 - \log\Gamma(\tfrac{5}{4})$$

$$= 0\cdot 0883 + 0\cdot 2485 - 0\cdot 3010 - \bar{1}\cdot 9573 = 0\cdot 0823 = \log 1\cdot 198.$$

§ 137. Elliptic Integrals.

The equation of motion of a pendulum swinging through a finite angle is

FIG. 152

$$\frac{d^2\theta}{dt^2} = -\frac{g}{l}\sin\theta, \qquad (1)$$

where θ represents the angle, BOA (Fig. 152), described by the pendulum on one side of the vertical at the time t, reckoned from the instant the pendulum was vertical; g is the constant of gravitation ; l the length of the string AO. Hence, show that

$$\frac{1}{2}\Big(\frac{d\theta}{dt}\Big)^2 - \frac{g}{l}\cos\theta = C; \ \therefore \ C = -\frac{g}{l}\cos\alpha;$$

$$\therefore \frac{d\theta}{dt} = \pm\sqrt{\frac{2g}{l}(\cos\theta - \cos\alpha)} = \pm 2\sqrt{\frac{g}{l}\Big(\sin^2\frac{\alpha}{2} - \sin^2\frac{\theta}{2}\Big)}, \quad (2)$$

since $\cos\alpha = 1 - 2\sin^2\frac{1}{2}\alpha$; $\cos\theta = 1 - 2\sin^2\frac{1}{2}\theta$, and α is the value
of θ when $d\theta/dt = 0$, that is, α is the angle, less than 180°, through
which the pendulum oscillates on each side of the vertical. Since
θ is always less than α, we retain the negative sign.

The period of an oscillation, or double swing, T, can therefore
be obtained from (2). We have [1]

$$\frac{T}{4}\sqrt{\frac{g}{l}} = \int_0^\phi \frac{d\phi}{\sqrt{1 - \sin^2\frac{\alpha}{2} . \sin^2\phi}}, \quad . \quad . \quad (3)$$

since to pass from 0 to $\frac{1}{4}T$, θ increases from 0 to α, and ϕ from 0
to $\frac{1}{2}\pi$. Hence, we may write

$$\frac{T}{4}\sqrt{\frac{g}{l}} = \int_0^{\frac{1}{2}\pi} \frac{d\phi}{\sqrt{1 - k^2\sin^2\phi}}. \quad . \quad . \quad (4)$$

The expression on the right is called an **elliptic integral of the
first class,** and usually written $F(k, \phi)$. The constant $\sin\frac{1}{2}\alpha$ is
called the *modulus,* and it is usually represented by the symbol k.
The modulus is always a proper fraction, *i.e.,* less than unity. ϕ
is called the *amplitude* of $T\sqrt{g/l}$, and it is written $\phi = \text{am}\sqrt{g/l}\,T$.
We can always transform (2) by substituting $\sin\frac{1}{2}\theta = x\sin\frac{1}{2}\alpha$,
where x is a proper fraction. By differentiation,
$\frac{1}{2}\cos\frac{1}{2}\theta . d\theta = \sin\frac{1}{2}\alpha . dx$; $\therefore \ d\theta = 2(1 - \sin^2\frac{1}{2}\alpha . x^2)^{-1/2}\sin\frac{1}{2}\alpha . dx$.
This leads to the normal form of the elliptic integrals of the first
class, namely,

$$\frac{T}{4}\sqrt{\frac{g}{l}} = \int_0^x \frac{dx}{\sqrt{(1 - x^2)(1 - k^2x^2)}}, \quad . \quad . \quad (5)$$

commonly written $F(k, x)$. We can evaluate these integrals in

---

[1] The expression on the right of (2) can be put in a simpler form by writing
$\sin\frac{1}{2}\theta = \sin\frac{1}{2}\alpha . \sin\phi$; $\therefore \ \frac{1}{2}\cos\frac{1}{2}\theta . d\theta = \sin\frac{1}{2}\alpha . \cos\phi . d\phi$.

$$d\theta = \frac{2\sin\frac{1}{2}\alpha . \cos\phi . d\phi}{\cos\frac{1}{2}\theta} = \frac{2\sin\frac{1}{2}\alpha . \cos\phi d\phi}{\sqrt{1 - \sin^2\frac{1}{2}\theta}} = \frac{2\sin\frac{1}{2}\alpha\cos\phi d\phi}{\sqrt{1 - \sin^2\frac{1}{2}\alpha . \cos^2\phi}};$$

$$\frac{d\theta}{\sqrt{\sin^2\frac{1}{2}\alpha - \sin^2\frac{1}{2}\theta}} = \frac{\dfrac{2\sin\frac{1}{2}\alpha\cos\phi d\phi}{\sqrt{1 - \sin^2\frac{1}{2}\alpha\sin\phi}}}{\sin\frac{1}{2}\alpha\sqrt{1 - \sin^2\phi}} = \frac{\dfrac{2\cos\phi d\phi}{\sqrt{1 - \sin^2\frac{1}{2}\alpha . \sin^2\phi}}}{\cos\phi}.$$

Hence (3) above. These results follow directly from the statements on pages 611 and
612.

series as shown on Ex. (4), page 342. In this way we get, from (4), for the period of oscillation,

$$T = 2\pi \sqrt{\frac{l}{g}} \left\{ 1 + \left(\frac{1}{2}k\right)^2 + \left(\frac{1 \cdot 3}{2 \cdot 4}k^2\right)^2 + \ldots \right. \qquad . \qquad (6)$$

When the swing of the pendulum is small, the period of oscillation' $T = 2\pi \sqrt{l/g}$ seconds. If the angle of vibration is increased, in the first approximation, we see that the period must be increased by the fraction $\frac{1}{4}(\sin \frac{1}{2}a)^2$ of itself.

The integral (3) is obviously a function of its upper limit ϕ, and it therefore expresses $T\sqrt{g/l}$ as a function of ϕ. We can reverse this and represent ϕ as a function of $T\sqrt{g/l}$. This gives us the so-called **elliptic functions.**

$$\phi = \text{am}\,(T\sqrt{g/l}) : \text{mod } k = \sin \frac{1}{2}a.$$

The elliptic functions are thus related to the elliptic integrals the same as the trigonometrical functions are related to the inverse trigonometrical functions, for, as we have seen, if

$$y = \int_0^x \frac{dx}{\sqrt{1 - x^2}}\,; \quad \therefore \; y = \sin^{-1}x\,; \text{ and } x = \sin y.$$

We get, from (3) and (5),

$$\phi = \text{am}\,T\sqrt{g/l}\,; \quad x = \sin \phi\,; \quad \therefore \; x = \sin \text{am}\,T\sqrt{g/l},$$

according to Jacobi's notation, but which is now written, after Gudermann, $x = \text{sn}\,T\sqrt{g/l}$. Similarly the centrifugal force, F, of a pendulum bob of mass m oscillating like the above-described pendulum, is written $F = 4mg \sin \frac{1}{2}a \cdot \text{cn}\,T\sqrt{g/l}$, where $\text{cn}\,T\sqrt{g/l}$ is the cosine of the amplitude of $T\sqrt{g/l}$.

The elliptic functions bear important analogies with the ordinary trigonometrical functions. The latter may be regarded as special forms of the elliptic functions with a zero modulus, and there is a system of formulæ connecting the elliptic functions to each other. Many of these bear a formal resemblance to the ordinary trigonometrical relations. Thus,

$$\text{sn}^2u + \text{cn}^2u = 1\,; \quad x = \text{sn}\,u\,; \quad \text{cn}\,u = \sqrt{1 - x^2}\,; \text{ etc.}$$

The elliptic functions are periodic. The value of the period depends on the modulus k. We have seen that the period of oscillation of the pendulum is a function of the modulus. The substitution equation, $\sin \frac{1}{2}\theta = \sin \frac{1}{2}a \cdot \sin \phi$, shows how $\sin \frac{1}{2}\theta$ changes as ϕ increases uniformly from 0 to 2π.

As ϕ increases from   0 to $\tfrac{1}{2}\pi$, $\tfrac{1}{2}\theta$ increases to $+\tfrac{1}{2}a$.

As ϕ increases from $\tfrac{1}{2}\pi$ to π, $\tfrac{1}{2}\theta$ decreases to   0.

As ϕ increases from π to $\tfrac{3}{2}\pi$, $\tfrac{1}{2}\theta$ decreases to $-\tfrac{1}{2}a$

As ϕ increases from $\tfrac{3}{2}\pi$ to 2π, $\tfrac{1}{2}\theta$ increases to   0.

During the continuous increase of ϕ, therefore, $\tfrac{1}{2}\theta$ moves to and fro between the limits $\pm \tfrac{1}{2}a$.

The rectification of a great number of curves furnishes expressions which can only be integrated by approximation methods— say, in series. The lemniscate and the hyperbola furnish elliptic integrals of the first class which can only be evaluated in series. In the ellipse, the ratio oF_1/oP_2 (Fig. 22, page 100) is called the eccentricity of the ellipse, the " e " of Ex. (3), page 115.   Therefore,

$$c = ae \; ; \text{ but, } c^2 = a^2 - b^2, \therefore b^2/a^2 = 1 - e^2.$$

Substitute this in the equation of the ellipse (1), page 100.   Hence,

$$y^2 = (1 - e^2)(a^2 - x^2) \; ; \left(\frac{dy}{dx}\right)^2 = \frac{(1 - e^2)x^2}{a^2 - x^2}.$$

Therefore, the length, l, of the arc of the quadrant of the ellipse is

$$l = \int_0^a \sqrt{\frac{a^2 - e^2 x^2}{a^2 - x^2}} \cdot dx. \quad . \quad . \quad . \quad (7)$$

This expression cannot be reduced by the usual methods of integration.   Its value can only be determined by the usual methods of approximation.   Equation (7) can be put in a simpler form by writing $x = a \sin \phi$, where ϕ is the complement of the "eccentric" angle θ (Fig. 152).   Hence,

$$l = a \int_0^{\frac{1}{2}\pi} \sqrt{1 - e^2 \sin^2 \phi} \cdot d\phi.$$

The right member is an **elliptic integral of the second class,** which is usually written, for brevity's sake, $E(k, \phi)$, since k is usually put in place of our e.   The integral may also be written

$$E(k, x) = \int_0^x \sqrt{\frac{1 - k^2 x^2}{1 - x^2}} dx, \quad . \quad . \quad (8)$$

by a suitable substitution.   We are also acquainted with **elliptic integrals of the third class,**

$$\Pi(n, k, \phi) = \int_0^{\frac{1}{2}\pi} \frac{d\phi}{(1 + n\sin^2\phi)\sqrt{1 - k^2\sin^2\phi}} \; ; \text{ or, } \Pi(n, k, x), \text{ etc., } (9)$$

where n is any real number, called *Legendre's parameter*.   If the limits of the first and second classes of integrals are 1 and 0, instead of x and 0 in the first case and $\tfrac{1}{2}\pi$ and 0 in the second case, the integrals are said to be *complete*. Complete elliptic integrals of the first and second classes are denoted by the letters F and E respectively.

The integral of an irrational polynomial of the second degree, of the type,

$$\int \sqrt{a + bx + cx^2} \cdot X \cdot dx \; ; \; \text{or,} \; \int \frac{X dx}{\sqrt{a + bx + cx^2}}$$

(where X is a rational function of x), can be made to depend on algebraic, logarithmic, or on trigonometrical functions, which can be evaluated in the usual way. But if the irrational polynomial is of the third, or fourth degree, as, for example,

$$\int \sqrt{a + bx + cx^2 + dx^3 + ex^4} X dx \; ;$$

the integration cannot be performed in so simple a manner. Such integrals are also called **elliptic integrals**. If higher powers than x^4 appear under the radical sign, the resulting integrals are said to be **ultra-elliptic or hyper-elliptic integrals**. That part of an elliptic integral which cannot be expressed in terms of algebraic, logarithmic, or trigonometrical functions is always one of the three classes just mentioned.

Legendre has calculated short tables of the first and second class of elliptic integrals ; the third class can be connected with these by known formulæ. Given k and x, $F(k, \phi)$ or $E(k, \phi)$ can be read off directly from the tables. The following excerpt will give an idea of how the tables run :

NUMERICAL VALUES OF $F(k, \phi)$; $\sin \alpha = k$.

ϕ.	$\alpha = 0°$.	$\alpha = 5°$.	$\alpha = 10°$.	$\alpha = 15°$.	$\alpha = 20°$.	$\alpha = 25°$.
41°	0·7156	0·7160	0·7173	0·7193	0·7222	0·7258
42°	0·7330	0·7335	0·7348	0·7370	0·7401	0·7440
43°	0·7505	0·7510	0·7524	0·7548	0·7581	0·7622

EXAMPLE.—Show that $\int \dfrac{dx}{\sqrt{\sin x}} = \int \dfrac{dx}{\sqrt{\cos x}} = \sqrt{2} \int \dfrac{d\phi}{\sqrt{1 - \frac{1}{2}\sin^2\phi}}$, provided $\sqrt{2} \cdot \sin \frac{1}{2}x = \sin \phi$. Hint. The first step follows from (6), page 242. Next by differentiation, $\cos \frac{1}{2}x dx = \sqrt{2} \cdot \cos \phi d\phi$; $2 \sin^2\frac{1}{2}x = \sin^2\phi$. Hence,

$$\int \frac{dx}{\sqrt{\cos x}} = \int \frac{\sqrt{2} \cdot \cos \frac{1}{2}x \cdot dx}{\sqrt{2} \cdot \cos \frac{1}{2}x \sqrt{\cos x}} = \int \frac{\sqrt{2} \cdot \cos \phi \cdot d\phi}{\sqrt{1 - \sin^2\frac{1}{2}x}\sqrt{1 - 2\sin^2\frac{1}{2}x}}, \text{ etc.}$$

from (20) and (35), page 612.

We cannot spare space to go farther into this matter. Mascart and Joubert have tables of the coefficient of mutual induction of electric currents, in their *Electricity and Magnetism* (2, 126, 1888), calculated from E and F above. A. G. Greenhill's *The Applications of Elliptic Functions* (London, 1892), is the text-book on this subject.

§ 138. The Exact Linear Differential Equation.

A very simple relation exists between the coefficients of an exact differential equation which may be used to test whether the equation is exact or not. Take the equation,

$$X_0 \frac{d^3 y}{dx^3} + X_1 \frac{d^2 y}{dx^2} + X_2 \frac{dy}{dx} + X_3 y = R, \quad . \quad . \quad (1)$$

where X_0, X_1, ..., R are functions of x. Let their successive differential coefficients be indicated by dashes, thus X', X'', ...

Since $X_0 \cdot d^3y/dx^3$ has been obtained by the differentiation of $X_0 \cdot d^2y/dx^2$, this latter is necessarily the first term of the integral of (1). But,

$$\frac{d}{dx}\left(X_0 \frac{d^2 y}{dx^2}\right) = X_0 \frac{d^3 y}{dx^3} + X'_0 \frac{d^2 y}{dx^2}.$$

Subtract the right-hand side of this equation from (1).

$$(X_1 - X'_0)\frac{d^2 y}{dx^2} + X_2 \frac{dy}{dx} + X_3 y = R. \quad . \quad . \quad (2)$$

Again, the first term of this expression is a derivative of $(X_1 - X'_0)dy/dx$. This, therefore, is the second term of the integral of (1). Hence, by differentiation and subtraction, as before,

$$(X_2 - X'_1 + X''_0)\frac{dy}{dx} + X_3 y = R. \quad . \quad . \quad (3)$$

This equation may be deduced by the differentiation of $(X_2 - X'_1 + X''_0)y$, provided the first differential coefficient of $(X_2 - X'_1 + X''_0)$ with respect to x, is equal to X_3, that is to say,

$$X'_2 - X''_1 + X'''_0 = X_3 \,; \text{ or, } X_3 - X'_2 + X''_1 - X'''_0 = 0. \quad (4)$$

But if this is really the origin of (3), the original equation (1) has been reduced to a lower order, namely,

$$X_0 \frac{d^2 y}{dx^2} + (X_1 - X'_0)\frac{dy}{dx} + (X_2 - X'_1 + X''_0)y = \int R dx + C_1. \quad (5)$$

This equation is called the **first integral** of (1), because the order of the original equation has been lowered unity, by a process of integration. Condition (4) is *a test of the exactness of a differential equation.*

If the first integral is an exact equation, we can reduce it, in the same way, to another first integral of (1). The process of reduction may be repeated until an inexact equation appears, or until y itself is obtained. Hence, *an exact equation of the nth order has n independent first integrals.*

EXAMPLES.—(1) Is $x^5 . d^3y/dx^3 + 15x^4 . d^2y/dx^2 + 60x^3 . dy/dx + 60x^2y = e^x$ an exact equation? From (4), $X_3 = 60x^2$; $X'_2 = 180x^2$; $X''_1 = 180x^2$; $X'''_0 = 60x^2$. Therefore, $X_3 - X'_2 + X''_1 - X'''_0 = 0$ and the equation is exact. Solve the given equation. Ansr. $x^5y = e^x + C_1x^2 + C_2x + C_3$. Hints. From (5), the first integral is $(x^5D^2 + 10x^4D + 20x^3)y = e^x + C_1$. This is exact, because the new values of X for the first integral just obtained $X_2 - X'_1 + X''_0 = 0$, since, $20x^3 - 40x^3 + 20x^3 = 0$. For the next first integral, we have

$$X_2 \frac{dy}{dx} + (X_1 - X'_0)y = \int e^x dx + \int C_1 dx + C_2. \quad . \quad . \quad (6)$$

Hence $(x^5D + 5x^4)y = e^x + C_1x + C_2$. This is exact, because the new values of X, namely, $X_1 - X_0 = 0$. Hence, the third and last first integral is $x^5y = \int e^x dx + \int C_1x dx + \int C_2 dx + C_3$, etc.

(2) Solve $xd^3y/dx^3 + (x^2 - 3)d^2y/dx^2 + 4x . dy/dx + 2y = 0$, as far as possible, by successive reduction. The process can be employed twice, the residue is a linear equation of the first order, not exact. Complete solution : $x^{-5}e^{\frac{1}{2}x^2}y = C_1\int x^{-5}e^{\frac{1}{2}x^2}dx + C_2\int x^{-6}e^{\frac{1}{2}x^2}dx + C_3$.

There is another *quick practical test for exact differential equations* (Forsyth) which is not so general as the preceding. When the terms in X are either in the form of ax^m, or of the sum of expressions of this type, $x^m d^n y/dx^n$ is a perfect differential coefficient, if $m < n$. This coefficient can then be integrated whatever be the value of y. If $m = n$ or $m > n$, the integration cannot be performed by the method for exact equations. To apply the test, remove all the terms in which m is less than n, if the remainder is a perfect differential coefficient, the equation is exact and the integration may be performed.

EXAMPLES.—(1) Test $x^3 . d^4y/dx^4 + x^2 . d^3y/dx^3 + x . dy/dx + y = 0$. $x . dy/dx + y$ remains. This has evidently been formed by the operation $D(xy)$, hence the equation is a perfect differential.

(2) Apply the test to $(x^3D^4 + x^2D^3 + x^2D + 2x)y = \sin x$. $x^2 . dy/dx + 2xy$ remains. This is a perfect differential, formed from $D(x^2y)$. The equation is exact.

§ 139. The Velocity of Consecutive Chemical Reactions.

While investigating the rate of decomposition of phosphine, page 224, we had occasion to point out that the action may take place in two stages :—

STAGE I. $PH_3 = P + 3H$.   STAGE II. $4P = P_4$; $2H = H_2$.

The former change alone determines the velocity of the whole reaction. The physical meaning of this is that the speed of the reaction which occurs during the second stage, is immeasurably faster than the speed of the first. Experiment quite fails to reveal the complex nature of the complete reaction. J. Walker illustrates this by the following analogy (*Proc. Royal Soc. Edin.*, **22**, 22, 1898) : "The time occupied in the transmission of a telegraphic message depends both on the rate of transmission along the conducting wire and on the rate of the messenger who delivers the telegram ; but it is obviously this last, slower rate that is of really practical importance in determining the total time of transmission".

Suppose, for example, a substance A forms an intermediate compound M, and this, in turn, forms a final product B. If the speed of the reaction A = M, is one gram per $\frac{1}{100000}$ second, when the speed of the reaction M = B, is one gram per hour, the observed "order" of the complete reaction

$$A = B,$$

will be fixed by that of the slower reaction, M = B, because the methods used for measuring the rates of chemical reactions are not sensitive to changes so rapid as the assumed rate of transformation of A into M. Whatever the "order" of this latter reaction, M = B is alone accessible to measurement. If, therefore, A = B is of the first, second, or nth order, we must understand that one of the subsidiary reactions : A = M, or M = B, is (i) an immeasurably fast reaction, accompanied by (ii) a slower measurable change of the first, second or nth order, according to the particular system under investigation.

If, however, the velocities of the two reactions are of the same order of magnitude, the "order" of the complete reaction will not fall under any of the simple types discussed on page 218, and therefore some changes will have to be made in the differential equations representing the course of the reaction. Let us study some examples.

I. *Two consecutive unimolecular reactions.*

Let one gram molecule of the substance A be taken. At the end of a certain time t, the system contains x of A, y of M, z of B. The reactions are

$$A = M ; M = B.$$

The rate of diminution of x is evidently

$$-\frac{dx}{dt} = k_1 x, \quad . \quad . \quad . \quad . \quad (1)$$

where k_1 denotes the velocity constant of the transformation of A to M. The rate of formation of B is

$$\frac{dz}{dt} = k_2 y, \quad . \quad . \quad . \quad . \quad (2)$$

where k_2 is the velocity constant of the transformation of M to B. Again, the rate at which M accumulates in the system is evidently the difference in the rate of diminution of x and the rate of increase of z, or

$$\frac{dy}{dt} = k_1 x - k_2 y. \quad . \quad . \quad . \quad (3)$$

The speed of the chemical reactions,

$$A = M = B,$$

is fully determined by this set of differential equations. When the relations between a set of variables involves a set of equations of this nature, the result is said to be a system of **simultaneous differential equations.**

In a great number of physical problems, the interrelations of the variables are represented in the form of a system of such equations. The simplest class occurs when each of the dependent variables is a function of the independent variable.

The simultaneous equations are said to be solved when each variable is expressed in terms of the independent variable, or else when a number of equations between the different variables can be obtained free from differential coefficients. To solve the present set of differential equations, first differentiate (2),

$$\frac{d^2z}{dt^2} - k_2 \frac{dy}{dt} = 0 ;$$

Add and subtract $k_1 k_2 y$, substitute for dy/dt from (3) and for $k_2 y$ from (2), we thus obtain

$$\frac{d^2z}{dt^2} + (k_1 + k_2) \frac{dz}{dt} - k_1 k_2 (x + y) = 0.$$

But from the conditions of the experiment,
$$x + y + z = 1, \therefore z - 1 = -(x + y).$$
Hence, the last equation may be written,
$$\frac{d^2(z - 1)}{dt^2} + (k_1 + k_2)\frac{d(z - 1)}{dt} + k_1 k_2(z - 1) = 0. \qquad (4)$$

This linear equation of the second order with constant coefficients, is to be solved for $z - 1$ in the usual manner (§ 131). At sight, therefore,
$$z - 1 = C_1 e^{-k_1 t} + C_2 e^{-k_2 t}. \qquad \bullet \quad \bullet \quad (5)$$
But $z = 0$, when $t = 0$,
$$\therefore C_1 + C_2 = -1. \qquad \bullet \quad \bullet \quad \bullet \quad (6)$$
Differentiate (5). From (2) $dz/dt = 0$, when $t = 0$. Therefore making the necessary substitutions,
$$- C_1 k_1 - C_2 k_2 = 0. \qquad \bullet \quad \bullet \quad \bullet \quad (7)$$
From (6) and (7),
$$C_1 = k_2/(k_1 - k_2); \; C_2 = -k_1/(k_1 - k_2).$$
The final result may therefore be written,
$$z - 1 = \frac{k_2}{k_1 - k_2} e^{-k_1 t} \cdot - \frac{k_1}{k_1 - k_2} e^{-k_2 t} \qquad \bullet \quad (8)$$

Harcourt and Esson have studied the rate of reduction of potassium permanganate by oxalic acid.
$$2KMnO_4 + 3MnSO_4 + 2H_2O = K_2SO_4 + 2H_2SO_4 + 5MnO_2;$$
$$MnO_2 + H_2SO_4 + H_2C_2O_4 = MnSO_4 + 2H_2O + 2CO_2.$$

By a suitable arrangement of the experimental conditions this reaction may be used to test equations (5) or (8).

Let x, y, z, respectively denote the amounts of Mn_2O_7, MnO_2 and MnO (in combination) in the system. The above workers found that $C_1 = 28\cdot5$; $C_2 = 2\cdot7$; $e^{-k_1} = \cdot82$; $e^{-k_2} = \cdot98$. The following table places the above suppositions beyond doubt.

t Minutes.	$z-1$.		t Minutes	$z-1$.	
	Found.	Calculated.		Found.	Calculated.
0·5	25·85	25·9	3·0	10·45	10·4
1·0	21·55	21·4	3·5	8·95	9·0
1·5	17·9	17·8	4·0	7·7	7·8
2·0	14·9	14·9	4·5	6·65	6·6
2·5	12·55	12·5	5·0	5·7	5·8

EXAMPLE.—We could have deduced equation (8) by another line of reasoning. If x denotes the amount of A transformed into M in the time t, and z

the amount of M transformed into B at the time t, then, if a denotes the amount of A present at the beginning of the experiment,

$$\frac{dy}{dt} = k_1(a - y); \frac{dz}{dt} = k_2(y - z). \qquad . \qquad . \qquad . \quad (9)$$

From the first equation, $y = a(1 - e^{-k_1 t})$. Substitute this result in the second equation, and we get

$$\frac{dz}{dt} + k_2 z - k_2 a(1 - e^{-k_1 t}) = 0.$$

From Ex. (5), page 388, if $z = 0$, when $t = 0$, we get

$$z = Ce^{-k_2 t} + a - \frac{k_2 a}{k_2 - k_1} e^{-k_1 t}; \quad C = \frac{k_2 a}{k_2 - k_1} - a; \qquad . \quad (10)$$

and we get, finally, an expression resembling (8) above. Equation (8) has also been employed to represent the decay of the radioactivity excited in bodies exposed to radium and to thorium emanation.

II. Two bimolecular consecutive reactions.

During the saponification of ethyl succinate in the presence of sodium hydroxide.

$$C_2H_4(COOC_2H_5)_2 + NaOH = C_2H_5OH + C_2H_4 . COONa . COOC_2H_5;$$
$$C_2H_4 . COONa . COOH + NaOH = C_2H_5OH + C_2H_4(COONa)_2.$$

Or,

$$A + B = C + M; M + B = C + D.$$

Let x denote the amount of ethyl succinate, A, which has been transformed at the time t; $a - x$ will then denote the amount remaining in the solution at the same time. Similarly, if the system contains b of sodium hydroxide, B, at the beginning of the reaction, at the time t, x of this will have been consumed in the formation of sodium ethyl succinate, M, and y in the formation of sodium succinate, D, hence $b - x - y$ of sodium hydroxide, B, and $x - y$ of sodium ethyl succinate, M, will be present in the system at the time t. The rate of formation of sodium ethyl succinate, M, is therefore

$$\frac{dx}{dt} = k_1(a - x) (b - x - y); \qquad . \qquad . \quad (11)$$

and the rate of formation of sodium succinate, D, will be

$$\frac{dy}{dt} = k_2(x - y) (b - x - y). \qquad . \qquad . \quad (12)$$

By division, if $k_2/k_1 = K$,

$$\frac{dy}{dx} + \frac{K}{a - x}y = \frac{Kx}{a - x}.$$

This equation has been integrated in Ex. (6), p. 388.   Hence

$$y = \frac{1}{K-1}\left\{\frac{(a-x)^K}{a^k-1} - a + Kx\right\}. \qquad (13)$$

$$\therefore \frac{dx}{dt} = k_1(a-x)\left\{b - x - \frac{(a-x)^K}{(K-1)a^{K-1}} + \frac{a}{K-1} - \frac{Kx}{K-1}\right\}. \ (14)$$

This can only be integrated when we know the numerical value of K. As a rule, in dealing with laboratory measurements, it will be found most convenient to use the methods for approximate integration since the integration of (14) is usually impracticable, even when we know the value of K.

III. A unimolecular reaction followed by a bimolecular reaction.

Let x denote the amount of A which remains untransformed after the elapse of an interval of time t, y the amount of M, and z the amount of B present in the system after the elapse of the same interval of time t.   The reaction is

$$A = M; \ M + B = C.$$

Hence show that the rate of diminution of A, and the rate of diminution of M (or of B) are respectively

$$-\frac{dx}{dt} = k_1x; \ -\frac{dz}{dt} = k_2yz, \qquad . \qquad . \qquad (15)$$

the rate of formation of M^2 is the difference between the rate of formation of M by the reaction, and the velocity of transformation of M into C, by the second reaction and

$$\therefore \frac{dy}{dt} = k_1x - k_2yz. \qquad . \qquad . \qquad . \qquad (16)$$

If x, y, z, could be measured independently, it would be sufficient to solve these equations as in *I*, but if x and y are determined together, we must proceed a little differently.   If there are a equivalents of A, and of B originally present, then, at the time t we shall have $a - x = a - z + y$, or $y = z - x$.   Divide (16) by the first of equations (15) ; substitute $dy = dz - dx$ in the result; put $y = z - x$; divide by z^2, and we get

$$\frac{1}{z^2}\cdot\frac{dz}{dx} + \frac{K}{z} - \frac{K}{x} = 0, \qquad . \qquad . \qquad . \qquad (17)$$

where K has been written in place of k_2/k_1.   The solution of this equation has been previously determined, Ex. (3), page 389, in the form

$$Ke^{-Kx}\left\{C_1 - \log x + Kx - \frac{1}{1\cdot 2^2}(Kx)^2 + \ldots\right\}z = 1. \quad (18)$$

In some of Harcourt and Esson's experiments, $C_1 = 4\cdot 68$; $k_1 = \cdot 69$;

$k_2 = \cdot006364$. From the first of equation (9), it is easy to show that $x = ae^{-k_1t}$. Where does a come from? What does it mean? Obviously, the value of x when $t = 0$. Hence verify the third column in the following table :—

t Minutes.	z.	
	Found.	Calculated.
2	51·9	51·6
3	42·4	42·9
4	35·4	35·4
5	29·8	29·7

After the lapse of six minutes, the value of x was found to be negligibly small. The terms succeeding log x in (18) may, there-fore, be omitted without committing any sensible error. Substi-tute $x = ae^{-k_1t}$ in the remainder,

$$\frac{k_2}{k_1}(C_1 - \log a + k_1t)z = 1 \; ; \; \text{or} \; (C'_1 + t)z = \frac{1}{k_2},$$

where $C'_1 = C_1/k_1 - (\log a)/k_1$. Harcourt and Esson found that $C'_1 = 0\cdot1$, and $1/k_2 = 157$. Hence, in continuation of the preceding table, these investigators obtained the results shown in the follow-ing table. The agreement between the theoretical and experimental numbers is remarkable.

t Minutes.	z.		t Minutes.	z.	
	Found.	Calculated.		Found.	Calculated.
6	25·7	25·7	10	15·5	15·5
7	22·1	22·1	15	10·4	10·4
8	19·4	19·4	20	7·8	7·8
9	17·3	17·3	30	5·5	5·2

The theoretical numbers are based on the assumption that the chemical change consists in the gradual formation of a substance which at the same time slowly disappears by reason of its reaction with a proportional quantity of another substance.

This really means that the so-called "initial disturbances" in chemical reactions, are due to the fact that the speed during one stage of the reaction, is faster than during the other. The magni-tude of the initial disturbances depends on the relative magnitudes of k_1 and k_2. The observed velocity in the steady state depends on the difference between the steady diminution $- dx/dt$ and the steady rise dz/dt. If k_2 is infinitely great in comparison with k_1, (8) reduces to

$$z = a(1 - e^{-k_1 t}),$$

which will be immediately recognised as another way of writing the familiar equation

$$k_1 = \frac{1}{t} \log \frac{a}{a - z}.$$

So far as practical work is concerned, it is necessary that the solutions of the differential equations shall not be so complex as to preclude the possibility of experimental verification.

IV. Three consecutive bimolecular reactions.

In the hydrolysis of triacetin,

$$C_3H_5 . \overline{A}_3 + H . OH = 3A . H + C_3H_5(OH)_3,$$

where $\overline{A}$ has been written for $CH_3 . COO$, there is every reason to believe that the reaction takes place in three stages :

$C_3H_5 . \overline{A}_3 + H . OH = \overline{A} . H + C_3H_5 . \overline{A}_2 . OH$ (Diacetin) ;

$C_3H_5 . \overline{A}_2 . OH + H . OH = \overline{A} . H + C_3H_5 . \overline{A}(OH)_2$ (Monoacetin) ;

$C_3H_5 \overline{A} . (OH)_2 + H . OH = \overline{A} . H + C_3H_5(OH)_3$ (Glycerol).

These reactions are interdependent. The rate of formation of glycerol is conditioned by the rate of formation of monoacetin ; the rate of monoacetin depends, in turn, upon the rate of formation of diacetin. There are, therefore, three simultaneous reactions of the second order taking place in the system.

Let a denote the initial concentration (gram molecules per unit volume) of triacetin, b the concentration of the water ; let x, y, z, denote the number of molecules of mono,- di- and triacetin hydrolyzed at the end of t minutes. The system then contains $a - z$ molecules of triacetin, $z - y$, of diacetin, $y - x$, of monoacetin, and $b - (x + y + z)$ molecules of water. The rate of hydrolysis is therefore completely determined by the equations :

$$dx/dt = k_1(y - x) (b - x - y - z); \quad . \quad . \quad (19)$$
$$dy/dt = k_2(z - y) (b - x - y - z); \quad . \quad . \quad (20)$$
$$dz/dt = k_3(a - z) (b - x - y - z); \quad . \quad . \quad (21)$$

where k_1, k_2, k_3, represent the velocity coefficients (page 63) of the respective reactions.

Geitel tested the assumption: $k_1 = k_2 = k_3$. Hence dividing (21) by (19) and by (20), he obtained

$$dz/dy = (a - z)/(z - y);\ dz/dx = (a - z)/(y - x). \qquad (22)$$

From the first of these equations,

$$\frac{dy}{dz} + y\frac{1}{a - z} = \frac{z}{a - z},$$

which can be integrated as a linear equation of the first order. The constant is equated by noting that if $a = 1$, $z = 0$, $y = 0$. The reader might do this as an exercise on § 125. The answer is

$$y = z + (a - z)\log(a - z). \qquad . \qquad . \qquad (23)$$

Now substitute (23) in the second of equations (22), rearrange terms and integrate as a further exercise on linear equations of the first order. The final result is,

$$x = z + (a - z)\log(a - z) - \frac{a - z}{z}\{\log(a - z)\}^2. \qquad (24)$$

Geitel then assigned arbitrary numerical values to z (say from $0{\cdot}1$ to $1{\cdot}0$), calculated the corresponding amounts of x and y from (23) and (24) and compared the results with his experimental numbers. For experimental and other details the original memoir must be consulted.

A study of the differential equations representing the mutual conversion of red into yellow, and yellow into red phosphorus, will be found in a paper by G. Lemoine in the *Ann. Chim. Phys.* [4], **27**, 289, 1872. There is a series of papers by R. Wegscheider bearing on this subject in *Monats. Chemie*, **22**, 749, 1901; *Zeit. phys. Chem.*, **30**, 593, 1899; **34**, 290, 1900; **35**, 513, 1900; J. Wogrinz, *ib.*, **44**, 569, 1903; H. Kühl, *ib.*, **44**, 385, 1903. See also papers by A. V. Harcourt and W. Esson, *Phil. Trans.*, **156**, 193, 1866; A. C. Geitel, *Journ. prakt. Chem.* [2], **55**, 429, 1897; **57**, 113, 1898; J. Walker, *Proc. Roy. Soc. Edin.*, **22**, 22, 1898. It is somewhat surprising that Harcourt and Esson's investigations had not received more attention from the point of view of simultaneous and dependent reactions. The indispensable differential equations, simple as they are, might perhaps account for this. But chemists, in reality, have more to do with this type of reaction than any other. The day is surely past when the study of a particular reaction is abandoned simply because it " won't go " according to the stereotyped velocity equations of § 77.

§ 140. Simultaneous Equations with Constant Coefficients.

By way of practice it will be convenient to study a few more examples of simultaneous equations, since they are so common in many branches of physics.   The motion of a particle in space is determined by a set of three differential equations which determine the position of the moving particle at any instant of time.   Thus, if X, Y, Z, represent the three components of a force, F, acting on a particle of mass m, Newton's law, page 396, tells us that

$$X = m\frac{d^2x}{dt^2}\;;\;\; Y = m\frac{d^2y}{dt^2}\;;\;\; Z = m\frac{d^2z}{dt^2},$$

and it is necessary to integrate these equations in order to represent x, y, z as functions of the time t.   The solution of this set of equations contains six arbitrary constants which define the position and velocity of the moving body with respect to the x-, y-, and the z-axis when we began to take its motion into consideration.

In order to solve a set of simultaneous equations, there must be the same number of equations as there are independent variables. Quite an analogous thing occurs with the simultaneous equations in ordinary algebra.   The methods used for the solution of these equations are analogous to those employed for similar equations in algebra.   The operations here involved are chiefly processes of elimination and substitution, supplemented by differentiation or integration at various stages of the computation.   The use of the symbol of operation D often shortens the work.

Examples.—(1) Solve $dx/dt + ay = 0$, $dy/dt + bx = 0$.   Differentiate the first, multiply the second by a.   Subtract and y disappears.   Hence writing $ab = m^2$, $x = C_1 e^{mt} + C_2 e^{-mt}$; or, $y = C_2\sqrt{b/a}\,.\,e^{-mt} - C_1\sqrt{b/a}\,.\,e^{mt}$.   We might have obtained an equation in y, and substituted it in the second. Thus four constants appear in the result.   But one pair of these constants can be expressed in terms of the other two.   Thus: two of the constants, therefore, are not arbitrary and independent, while the integration constant is arbitrary and independent.   It is always best to avoid an unnecessary multiplication of constants by deducing the other variables from the first without integration.   The number of arbitrary constants is always equal to the sum of the highest orders of the set of differential equations under consideration.

(2) Solve $dx/dt + y = 3x$; $dy/dt - y = x$.   Differentiate the first.   Subtract each of the given equations from the result. $(D^2 - 4D + 4)x = 0$ remains. Solve as usual. $x = (C_1 + C_2 t)e^{2t}$.   Substitute this value of x in the first of the given equations and $y = (C_1 - C_2 + C_2 t)e^{2t}$.

(3) The rotation of a particle in a rigid plane, is represented by the equa-

tions $dx/dt = \mu y$; $dy/dt = \mu x$. To solve these, differentiate the first, multiply the second by μ, etc. Finally $x = C_1 \cos \mu t + C_2 \sin \mu t$; $y = C'_1 \cos \mu t + C'_2 \sin \mu t$. To find the relation between these constants, substitute these values in the first equation and $- \mu C_1 \sin \mu t + \mu C_2 \cos \mu t = \mu C'_1 \cos \mu t + \mu C'_2 \sin \mu t$, or $C_1 = - C'_2$ and $C_2 = C'_1$.

(4) Solve $d^2x/dt^2 = -n^2x$ $d^2y/dt^2 = -n^2y$. Each equation is treated separately as on page 400, thus $x = C_1 \cos nt + C_2 \sin nt$; $y = C'_1 \cos nt + C'_2 \sin nt$. Eliminate t so that

$$(C'_1 x - C_1 y)^2 + (C'_2 x - C_2 y)^2 = (C_1 C'_2 - C_2 C'_1)^2, \text{ etc.}$$

The result represents the motion of a particle in an elliptic path, subject to a central gravitational force.

(5) Solve $dy/dx + 3y - 4z = 5e^{5x}$; $dz/dx + y - 2x = - 3e^{5x}$. Differentiate the first and solve for dz/dx; substitute this value of dz/dx in the second equation. We thus get a linear equation of the second order:

$$\frac{d^2y}{dx^2} + \frac{dy}{dx} - 2y = 3e^{5x}; \therefore y = C_1 e^x + C_2 e^{-2x} + \tfrac{3}{18}e^{-5x},$$

when solved by the usual method. Now differentiate the last equation, and substitute the value of dy/dx so found in the first of the given equations. Also substitute the value of y just determined in the same equation. We thus get $z = C_1 e^x + \tfrac{1}{4}C_2 e^{-2x} - \tfrac{2}{7}\tfrac{9}{8}e^{5x}$.

(6) R. Wegscheider (*Zeit. phys. Chem.*, **41**, 52, 1902) has proposed the equations $dx/dt = k_1(a - x - y)$; $dy/dt = k_2(a - x - y)(b - y)$, to represent the speed of hydrolysis of sulphonic esters by water. Hence show that

$$\int \frac{dx}{a - (1 + bk)x + \tfrac{1}{2}bK^2 x^2} = k_1 t + C.$$

Hint. Divide the one equation by the other; expand e^{-Kx}; reject all but the first three terms of the series.

(7) J. W. Mellor and L. Bradshaw (*Zeit. phys. Chem.*, **48**, 353, 1904) solved the set of equations

$$\frac{dX}{dt} = k_1(a - X); \frac{du}{dt} = k_2(x - u); \frac{dv}{dt} = k_3(y - v)$$

with the assumption that $X = x + y + u + v$; $v = k_4 u$; $u = v = x = y = 0$ when $t = 0$. Show that

$$u = \frac{a}{2(k_4 + 1)} \left(1 - \frac{b}{b - k_1} e^{-k_1 t} + \frac{k^2}{b - k_1} e^{-bt} \right),$$

if b is put in place of $2k_2 k_3 (k_4 + 1)/(k_2 + k_3 k_4)$. See Ex. (5), page 390.

(8) J. J. Thomson (*Conduction of Electricity through Gases*, Cambridge, 86, 1903) has shown that the motion of a charged particle of mass m, and charge e, between two parallel plates with a potential gradient E between them when a magnetic field of induction H is applied normal to the plates, is given by the equations

$$m\frac{d^2x}{dt^2} = Ee - He\frac{dy}{dt}; \; m\frac{d^2y}{dt^2} = He\frac{dx}{dt}, \quad \cdot \quad \cdot \quad \cdot \quad (1)$$

provided that there is no resisting medium (say air) between the plates. To solve these equations with the initial conditions that $x, y, \dot{x}, \dot{y}$, are all zero, put

$$p = \frac{dx}{dt}; \; \therefore \frac{dp}{dt} = a - b\frac{dy}{dt}; \frac{d^2y}{dt^2} = bp; \; \therefore \frac{d^2p}{dt^2} = - b^2 p.$$

Hence, from page 405, and remembering that $\dot{x} = 0$, when $t = 0$,

$$p = C_1\sin bt + C_2\cos bt;\ C_2 = 0;\ \frac{dx}{dt} = C_1\sin bt;\ \therefore x = \frac{C_1}{b}(1 - \cos bt),\quad (2)$$

since, when $t = 0$, $x = 0$, and the integration constant is equal to C_1/b. From the third of equations (2), and the second of equations (1),

$$\frac{d^2y}{dt^2} = bC_1\sin bt;\ \therefore \frac{dy}{dt} = -C_1\cos bt + C_1,$$

the integration constant is equal to C_1 when $dy/dt = 0$, and $t = 0$; again integrating, and we get $y = C_1(bt - \sin bt)/b$, since $y = 0$, when $t = 0$. To evaluate the constant C_1, substitute for $\ddot{x}$ and $\dot{y}$, from (2) and the above, in the first of equations (1). We find $C_1 = a/b$, and consequently, if $a = Em/H^2e$, and $b = He/m$.

$$x = a(1 - \cos bt);\ y = a(bt - \sin bt),\quad \ldots \quad \ldots \quad (3)$$

Let us follow the motion of a particle moving on the path represented by equations (3). Of course we can eliminate bt and get one equation connecting x and y, but it is better to retain bt as the calculation is then more simple. When

$bt =$	$0,$	$\pi,$	$2\pi,$	$3\pi,$	$4\pi,$	$5\pi, \ldots;$
$x =$	$0,$	$2a,$	$0,$	$2a,$	$0,$	$2a, \ldots;$
$y =$	$0,$	$a\pi,$	$2a\pi,$	$3a\pi,$	$4a\pi,$	$5a\pi, \ldots$

Hence, x oscillates to and fro between 0 and $2a$; y too is periodic, repeating itself in the time $2\pi/b$; passing through a distance $2a\pi$ from the origin every period. In other words, the path of an electron moving under the above conditions is that of a cycloid traced by the rim of a wheel of radius a rolling upon a plate Oy, Fig. 153.

(9) Two vessels, capacity v_1 and v_2, are filled with the same gas but at different pressures p_1 and p_2 respectively. Assume that the vessels are connected by a capillary tube and that the quantity of gas which flows from one vessel to the other is proportional to the difference in the squares of the pressures in the two vessels, and to the time. What are the pressures, x_1 and x_2, in each vessel at the end of t seconds? (Lorentz.) The quantity of gas, dQ, which flows through the capillary during the infinitely small interval of time dt is by hypothesis

Fig. 153.

$$dQ = a(x_1{}^2 - x_2{}^2)dt,\quad \ldots \quad \ldots \quad \ldots \quad (4)$$

where a is a constant. Let b denote the quantity of gas in unit volume, bv will therefore denote the amount of gas which occupies v volumes at atmospheric pressure. If the pressure changes by an amount dx, the quantity of gas, dQ, changes an amount bv_2dx, hence,

$$dQ = bv_2\frac{\partial x_2}{\partial t}dt;\ dQ = -bv_1\frac{\partial x_1}{\partial t}dt.\quad \ldots \quad \ldots \quad (5)$$

The difference in sign shows that the gas which leaves one vessel enters the other. The temperature is of course supposed to remain constant. From (4) and (5),

$$\frac{dx_1}{dt} = -\frac{a}{bv_1}(x_1{}^2 - x_2{}^2);\ \frac{dx_2}{dt} = \frac{a}{bv_2}(x_1{}^2 - x_2{}^2).\quad \ldots \quad \ldots \quad (6)$$

But the total mass of gas remains constantly equal to ac, say

$$\therefore v_1x_1 + v_2x_2 = c \,;\; \therefore c = p_1v_1 + p_2v_2, \quad \cdot \quad \cdot \quad \cdot \quad (7)$$

by Boyle's law. Multiply the first of equations (6) with $x_2v_1v_2$, and the second by $x_1v_1v_2$; subtract the latter from the former; divide by $x_2{}^2$; substitute $x = x_1/x_2$ and

$$v_1v_2\frac{dx}{dt} = -\frac{ac}{b}(x^2 - 1)$$

remains. Solve this equation in the usual way, and we get

$$\frac{v_1v_2}{2}\log\frac{x+1}{x-1} = \frac{act}{b} + C \,;\; \text{or,} \frac{1}{t}\log\frac{(x_1 + x_2)\,(p_1 - p_2)}{(x_1 - x_2)\,(p_1 + p_2)} = \frac{2ac}{bv_1v_2}.$$

From this equation and the first of equations (7), it is possible to calculate x_1 and x_2 at any time t.

(10) If two adjacent circuits have currents C_1 and C_2, then, according to the theory of electromagnetic induction,

$$M\frac{dC_1}{dt} + L_2\frac{dC_2}{dt} + R_2C_2 = E_2 \,;\; M\frac{dC_2}{dt} + L_1\frac{dC_1}{dt} + R_1C_1 = E_1,$$

where R_1, R_2, denote the resistances of the two circuits, L_1, L_2, the coefficients of self-induction, E_1, E_2, the electromotive forces of the respective circuits and M the coefficient of mutual induction. All the coefficients are supposed constant.

First, solve these equations on the assumption that $E_1 = E_2 = 0$. Assume that $C_1 = ae^{mt}$; and $C_2 = be^{mt}$, satisfy the given equations. Differentiate each of these variables with respect to t, and substitute in the original equation

$$aMm + b(L_2m + R_2) = 0 \,;\; bMm + a(L_1m + R_1) = 0.$$

Multiply these equations so that

$$(L_1L_2 + M_2)m^2 + (L_1R_2 + R_1L_2)m + R_1R_2 = 0.$$

For physical reasons, the induction L_1L_2 must always be greater than M. The roots of this quadratic must, therefore, be negative and real (page 354), and

$$C_1 = a_1e^{-m_1t}, \text{ or, } a_2e^{-m_2t}\,;\; C_2 = b_1e^{-m_1t}, \text{ or, } b_2e^{-m_2t}.$$

Hence, from the preceding equation,

$$a_1Mm_1 + b_1L_2m_1 + b_1R_2 = 0 \,;\; \text{or } a_1/b_1 = -\,(L_2m_1 + R_2)/Mm_1 \,;$$

similarly, $a_2/b_2 = -\,Mm_2/(L_1m_2 + R_1)$. Combining the particular solutions for C_1 and C_2, we get the required solutions.

$$C_1 = a_1e^{-m_1t} + a_2e^{-m_2t}\,;\; C_2 = b_1e^{-m_1t} + b_2e^{-m_2t}.$$

Second, if E_1 and E_2 have some constant value,

$$C_1 = E_1/R_1 + a_1e^{-m_1t} + a_2e^{-m_2t}\,;\; C_2 = E_2/R_2 + b_1e^{-m_1t} + b_2e^{-m_2t},$$

are the required solutions.

§ 141. Simultaneous Equations with Variable Coefficients.

The general type of simultaneous equations of the first order, is

$$\left.\begin{array}{l} P_1dx + Q_1dy + R_1dz = 0 \,; \\ P_2dx + Q_2dy + R_2dz = 0, \ldots \end{array}\right\} \quad \cdot \quad \cdot \quad (1)$$

where the coefficients are functions of x, y, z. These equations can often be expressed in the form [1]

$$\frac{dx}{P} = \frac{dy}{Q} = \frac{dz}{R}, \quad . \quad . \quad . \quad . \quad (2)$$

which is to be looked upon as a typical set of simultaneous equations of the first order. If one pair of these equations involves only two differentials, the equations can be solved in the usual way, and the result used to deduce values for the other variables, as in the second of the subjoined examples.

When the members of a set of equations are symmetrical, the solution can often be simplified by taking advantage of a well-known theorem [2] in algebra—ratio. According to this,

$$\frac{dx}{P} = \frac{dy}{Q} = \frac{dz}{R} = \frac{ldx + mdy + ndz}{lP + mQ + nR} = \frac{l'dx + m'dy + n'dz}{l'P + m'Q + n'R} = \ldots, (3)$$

where l, m, n, l', m', n', ... may be constants or functions of x, y, z. Since l, m, n, ... are arbitrary, it is possible to choose l, m, n, ... so that

$$lP + mQ + nR = 0 \; ; \; l'P + m'Q + n'R = 0 \; ; \ldots \quad (4)$$
$$ldx + mdy + ndz = 0, \text{ etc.} \quad . \quad . \quad . \quad (5)$$

The same relations between x, y, z, that satisfy (5), satisfy (2); and if (4) be an exact differential equation, equal to say du, direct integration gives the integral of the given system, *viz.*,

$$u = C_1 \quad . \quad . \quad . \quad . \quad . \quad (6)$$

where C_1 denotes the constant of integration.

In the same way, if

$$l'dx + m'dy + n'dz = 0,$$

is an exact differential equation, equal to say dv, then, since dv is also equal to zero,

$$v = C_2 \quad . \quad . \quad . \quad . \quad . \quad (7)$$

is a second solution. These two solutions must be independent.

EXAMPLES.—(1) By way of illustration let us solve the equations

$$\frac{dx}{y - z} = \frac{dy}{z - x} = \frac{dz}{x - y}.$$

---

[1] The proof will come later, page 584.

[2] The proof is interesting. Let $dx\,P = dy/Q = dz/R = k$, say; then, $dx = Pk$; $dy = Qk$; $dz = Rk$; or, $ldx = lPk$; $mdy = mQk$; $ndz = nRk$. Add these results, $ldx + mdy + ndz = k(lP + mQ + nR)$,

$$\therefore \frac{ldx + mdy + ndz}{lP + mQ + nR} = k = \frac{dx}{P} = \frac{dy}{Q} = \frac{dz}{R}.$$

Here $P = y - z$; $Q = z - x$; $R = x - y$. Since, as in (4),
$$y - z + z - x + x - y = 0;\ l = m = n = 1;$$
and as in (6),
$$x(y - z) + y(z - x) + z(x - y) = 0;\ l' = x;\ m' = y;\ n' = z.$$
For the first combination, therefore
$$dx + dy + dz = 0;\ \text{or},\ x + y + z = C_1; \quad \cdot \quad \cdot \quad \cdot \quad (8)$$
and for the second combination
$$x\,dx + y\,dy + z\,dz = 0;\ \therefore x^2 + y^2 + z^2 = C_2 \quad \cdot \quad \cdot \quad (9)$$
The last of equations (8) and (9) define x and y as functions of z, and also contain two arbitrary constants, the conditions necessary and sufficient in order that these equations may be a complete solution of the given set of equations. Equations (8) and (9) represent a family of circles.

(2) Solve $dx/y = dy/x = dz/z$. The relation between dx and dy contains x and y only, the integral, $y^2 - x^2 = C_1$, follows at once. Use this result to eliminate x from the relation between dy and dz. The result is, p. 349,
$$dz/z = dy/\sqrt{(y^2 - C_1)};\ \text{or},\ y + \sqrt{(y^2 - C_1)} = C_2 z.$$
These two equations, involving two constants of integration, constitute a complete solution.

(3) Solve $dx/(mz - ny) = dy(nx - lz) = dz/(ly - mx)$. Here $P = mz - ny$; $Q = nx - lz$; $R = ly - mx$. l, m, n and x, y, z form a set of multipliers satisfying the above condition. Hence, each of the given equal fractions is equal to
$$\frac{l\,dx + m\,dy + n\,dz}{l(mz - ny) + m(nx - lz) + n(ly - mx)};$$
and to
$$\frac{x\,dx + y\,dy + z\,dz}{x(mz - ny) + y(nx - lz) + z(ly - mx)}.$$
Accordingly,
$$l\,dx + m\,dy + n\,dz = 0;\ x\,dx + y\,dy + z\,dz = 0.$$
The integrals of these equations are
$$u = lx + my + nz = C_1;\ v = x^2 + y^2 + z^2 = C_2,$$
which constitute a complete solution.

(4) Solve $\dfrac{dx}{x^2 - y^2 - z^2} = \dfrac{dy}{2xy} = \dfrac{dz}{2xz};\ \therefore = \dfrac{x\,dx + y\,dy + z\,dz}{x(x^2 - y^2 - z^2) + 2xy^2 + 2xz^2}.$

$\therefore \dfrac{dz}{z} = \dfrac{2x\,dx + 2y\,dy + 2z\,dz}{x^2 + y^2 + z^2};\ \therefore \log(x^2 + y^2 + z^2) = \log z + \log C_2;$

consequently, $x^2 + y^2 + z^2 = C_2 z$ is the second solution required.

It is thus evident that equation (5) must be integrable before the given set of simultaneous equations can be solved. The **criterion of integrability,** or the test of the exactness of an equation containing three or more variables is easily deduced. For instance, let
$$P\,dx + Q\,dy + R\,dz = 0;\ \therefore du = \frac{\partial u}{\partial x}dx + \frac{\partial u}{\partial y}dy + \frac{\partial u}{\partial z}dz. \quad (10)$$
The second of equations (10) is obviously exact, and equivalent to the first of equations (10), since both are derived from $u = C_1$. Hence certain conditions must hold in order that the first of

equations (10) may be reduced to the exact form of the second. As indicated above, there must exist a function of x, y, and z, say, μ, such that

$$\frac{\partial u}{\partial x} = \mu P; \quad \frac{\partial u}{\partial y} = \mu Q; \quad \frac{\partial u}{\partial z} = \mu R. \quad . \quad . \quad (11)$$

Let the student now differentiate each of equations (11), first with respect to y and z; second with respect to z and x; and third with respect to x and y, the result will be

$$\left. \begin{array}{l} P\dfrac{\partial u}{\partial y} + \mu\dfrac{\partial P}{\partial y} = Q\dfrac{\partial u}{\partial x} + \mu\dfrac{\partial Q}{\partial x}; \; \therefore \mu\!\left(\dfrac{\partial P}{\partial y} - \dfrac{\partial Q}{\partial x}\right) = Q\dfrac{\partial u}{\partial x} - P\dfrac{\partial u}{\partial y}; \\[2mm] Q\dfrac{\partial u}{\partial z} + \mu\dfrac{\partial Q}{\partial z} = R\dfrac{\partial u}{\partial y} + \mu\dfrac{\partial R}{\partial y}; \; \therefore \mu\!\left(\dfrac{\partial Q}{\partial z} - \dfrac{\partial R}{\partial y}\right) = R\dfrac{\partial u}{\partial y} - Q\dfrac{\partial u}{\partial z}; \\[2mm] R\dfrac{\partial u}{\partial x} + \mu\dfrac{\partial R}{\partial x} = P\dfrac{\partial u}{\partial z} + \mu\dfrac{\partial P}{\partial z}; \; \therefore \mu\!\left(\dfrac{\partial R}{\partial x} - \dfrac{\partial P}{\partial z}\right) = P\dfrac{\partial u}{\partial z} - R\dfrac{\partial u}{\partial x}. \end{array} \right\} (12)$$

Multiply the three equations on the right, in turn, by R, P, and Q respectively, and add the results together. The result gives us the relation which must hold between the coefficients P, Q, and R of the first of equations (10) in order that it may have an integral of the form $u = C$. We must have, in fact,

$$P\left(\frac{\partial Q}{\partial z} - \frac{\partial R}{\partial y}\right) + Q\left(\frac{\partial R}{\partial x} - \frac{\partial P}{\partial z}\right) + R\left(\frac{\partial P}{\partial y} - \frac{\partial Q}{\partial x}\right) = 0.$$

If equation (10) be not exact it can be made exact by means of an integrating factor.

EXAMPLES.—(1) Given $(y + z)dx + (z + x)dy + (x + y)dz = 0$, show that the condition of integrability is satisfied. To integrate an exact equation of this kind, first suppose that z is temporarily constant, and integrate. Thus, we get

$$(y + z)dx + (z + x)dy = 0; \; (y + z)(z + x) = C'. \quad . \quad . \quad (13)$$

The integration constant obviously includes the variable z; let $C' = f(z)$. To determine the form of this function, differentiate $(y + z)(z + x) = f(z)$ with respect to x, y, and z, and compare the result with the given equation. We get

$$(y + z)dx + (z + x)dy + (x + y)dz + 2zdz = \frac{\partial f(z)}{\partial z}dz;$$

$$\therefore 2zdz - df(z) = 0; \; \text{or, } f(z) = z^2 + C_2;$$

$$\therefore (y + z)(z + x) = z^2 + C_2; \; \text{or, } xy + yz + zx = C_2,$$

is the required solution. The same result could have been obtained more quickly, in this particular case, by expanding the given equation and so getting

$$(xdy + ydx) + (ydz + zdy) + (zdx + xdz) = 0; \; \therefore xy + yz + zx = C_2.$$

(2) Integrate $yzdx + xzdy + xydz = 0$. Divide by xyz, and

$$\frac{dx}{x} = \frac{dy}{y} = \frac{dz}{z} = 0; \; \therefore \log x + \log y + \log z = \log C; \; \therefore xyz = C.$$

(3) Integrate $xydx - zxdx - y^2dz = 0$.   Ansr. $x/y - \log z = C$.   Hint. Divide by $1/xy^2$ and the equation becomes exact.

(4) If $(ydx + xdy)(a - z) + xydz = 0$, show that $xy = C(z - a)$.   Hint. Proceed as in Ex. (1), making $z = $ constant, and afterwards showing that $xy = f(z)$, and then that $f(z) = C(z - a)$.

§ 142. Partial Differential Equations.

Equations obtained by the differentiation of functions of three or more variables are of two kinds :

1. Those in which there is only one independent variable, such as

$$Pdx + Qdy + Rdz = Sdt,$$

which involves four variables — three dependent and one independent.   These are called **total differential equations**.

2. Those in which there is only one dependent and two or more independent variables, such as,

$$P\frac{\partial z}{\partial x} + Q\frac{\partial z}{\partial y} + R\frac{\partial z}{\partial t} = 0,$$

where z is the dependent variable, x, y, t the independent variables. These equations are classed under the name **partial differential equations.**   The former class of equations are rare, the latter very common.   Physically, the differential equation represents the relation between the dependent and the independent variables when an infinitely small change is made in each of the independent variables.[1]

In the study of ordinary differential equations, we have always assumed that the given equation has been obtained by the elimination of constants from the original equation.   In solving, we have sought to find this primitive equation.   Partial differential equations, however, may be obtained by the elimination of arbitrary

---

[1] The reader will, perhaps, have noticed that the term " **independent variable** " is an equivocal phrase.   (1) If $u = f(z)$, u is a quantity whose magnitude changes when the value of z changes.   The two magnitudes u and z are mutually dependent.   For convenience, we fix our attention on the effect which a variation in the value of z has upon the magnitude of u.   If need be we can reverse this and write $z = f(u)$, so that u now becomes the " independent variable ".   (2) If $v = f(x, y)$, x and y are " independent variables " in that x and y are mutually independent of each other.   Any variation in the magnitude of the one has no effect on the magnitude of the other. x and y are also " independent variables " with respect to v in the same sense that z has just been supposed the " independent variable " with respect to u.

functions of the variables as well as of constants.   For example, if
$$u = f(ax + by),$$
be an arbitrary function of x and y, we get, as in Euler's theorem page 75,
$$\frac{\partial u}{\partial x} = 3af'(ax^3 + by^3) ; \quad \frac{\partial u}{\partial y} = 3bf'(ax^3 + by^3) ; \quad \therefore \; b\frac{\partial u}{\partial x} - a\frac{\partial u}{\partial y} = 0,$$
where the arbitrary function has disappeared.

EXAMPLES.—(1) If $u = f(at + x)$, show that
$$\frac{\partial u}{\partial t} = a\frac{\partial u}{\partial x} \quad \frac{\partial^2 u}{\partial t^2} = a^2\frac{\partial^2 u}{\partial x^2}.$$
Here $\partial u/\partial t = af'(at + x)$; $\partial u/\partial x = f'(at + x)$, etc.   Establish the result by giving $f(at + x)$ some specific form, say, $f(at + x) = at + x$; and $\sin(at + x)$

(2) Eliminate the arbitrary function from the thermodynamic equation
$$Q = f\!\left(\frac{p}{\rho}\right) - \frac{p}{a\rho}\log p.\ \ \therefore \frac{\partial Q}{\partial \rho} = -\frac{p}{\rho^2}f'\!\left(\frac{p}{\rho}\right) + \frac{p}{a\rho^2}\log p ; \ \frac{\partial Q}{\partial p} = \frac{1}{\rho}f'\!\left(\frac{p}{\rho}\right) - \frac{1}{a\rho}\log p - \frac{1}{a\rho}$$
$$\therefore p\frac{\partial Q}{\partial p} + \rho\frac{\partial Q}{\partial \rho} = -\frac{p}{a\rho},$$

(3) Remembering that the object of solving any given differential is to find the primitive from which the differential equation has been derived by the elimination of constants or arbitrary functions.   Show that $z = f_1(x) + f_2(y)$ is a solution of $\partial^2 z/\partial x\partial y = 0$.   Hint.   Eliminate the arbitrary function.

(4) Show that $z = f_1(x + at) + f_2(x - at)$ is a solution of $\partial^2 z/\partial t^2 = a^2\partial^2 z/\partial x^2$.

An arbitrary function of the variables must now be added to the integral of a partial differential equation instead of the constant hitherto employed for ordinary differential equations.   If the number of arbitrary constants to be eliminated is equal to the number of independent variables, the resulting differential equation is of the first order.   The higher orders occur when the number of constants to be eliminated, exceeds that of the independent variables.

If $u = f(x, y)$, there will be two differential coefficients of the first order ; three of the second ; ... Thus,
$$\frac{\partial u}{\partial x}, \frac{\partial u}{\partial y} ; \frac{\partial^2 u}{\partial x^2}, \frac{\partial^2 u}{\partial y^2}, \frac{\partial^2 u}{\partial x\partial y} ; \ldots$$

§ 143.   What is the Solution of a Partial Differential Equation?

Ordinary differential equations have two classes of solutions —the complete integral and the singular solution.   Particular solutions are only varieties of the complete integral.   Three classes of solutions can be obtained from some partial differential equations, still regarding the particular solution as a special case of the complete integral. These are indicated in the following example.

The equation of a sphere in three dimensions is,

$$x^2 + y^2 + z^2 = r^2, \qquad . \quad . \quad . \quad (1)$$

where the centre of the sphere coincides with the origin of the coordinate planes and r denotes the radius of the sphere. If the centre of the sphere lies somewhere on the xy-plane at a point (a, b), the above equation becomes

$$(x - a)^2 + (y - b)^2 + z^2 = r^2. \qquad . \quad . \quad (2)$$

When a and b are arbitrary constants, each or both of which may have any assigned magnitude, equation (2) may represent two infinite systems of spheres of radius r. The centre of any member of either of these two infinite systems—called a *double infinite system*—must lie somewhere on the xy-plane.

Differentiate (2) with respect to x and y.

$$x - a + z\frac{\partial z}{\partial x} = 0 \, ; \; y - b + z\frac{\partial z}{\partial y} = 0. \qquad . \quad (3)$$

Substitute for $x - a$ and $y - b$ in (2). We obtain

$$z^2 \left\{ \left(\frac{\partial z}{\partial x} \right)^2 + \left(\frac{\partial z}{\partial y} \right)^2 + 1 \right\} = r^2. \qquad . \quad . \quad (4)$$

Equation (2), therefore, is the **complete integral** of (4). By assigning any particular numerical value to a or b, a **particular solution** of (4) will be obtained, such is

$$(x - 1)^2 + (y - 79)^2 + z^2 = r^2. \qquad . \quad . \quad (5)$$

If (2) be differentiated with respect to a and b,

$$\frac{\partial}{\partial a}\{(x - a)^2 + (y + b)^2 + z^2 = r^2\} \, ; \; \frac{\partial}{\partial b}\{(x - a)^2 + (y - b)^2 + z^2 = r^2\},$$

or, $\qquad\qquad\qquad x - a = 0, \text{ and } y - b = 0.$

Eliminate a and b from (2),

$$z = \pm \, r. \qquad . \quad . \quad . \quad . \quad (6)$$

This result satisfies equation (4), but, unlike the particular solution, is not included in the complete integral (2). Such a solution of the differential equation is said to be a **singular solution.**

Geometrically, the singular solution represents two plane surfaces touched by all the spheres represented by equation (2). The singular solution is thus the envelope of all the spheres represented by the complete integral. If AB (Fig. 97) represents a cross section of the xy-plane containing spheres of radius r, CD and EF are cross sections of the plane surfaces represented by the singular solution.

If the one constant is some function of the other, say,

$$a = b,$$

(2) may be written

$$(x - a)^2 + (y + a)^2 + z^2 = r^2. \qquad . \qquad . \qquad (7)$$

Differentiate with respect to a. We find

$$a = \tfrac{1}{2}(x + y).$$

Eliminate a from (7). The resulting equation

$$x^2 + y^2 + 2z^2 - 2xy = 2r^2,$$

is called a **general integral** of the equation.

Geometrically, the general integral is the equation to the tubular envelope of a family of spheres of radius r and whose centres are along the line $x = y$. This line corresponds with the axis of the tube envelope. The general integral satisfies (4) and is also contained in the complete integral.

Instead of taking $a = b$ as the particular form of the function connecting a and b, we could have taken any other relation, say $a = \tfrac{1}{2}b$. The envelope of the general integral would then be like a tube surrounding all the spheres of radius r whose centres were along the line $x = \tfrac{1}{2}y$. Had we put $a^2 - b^2 = 1$, the envelope would have been a tube whose axis was an hyperbola $x^2 - y^2 = 1$.

A *particular solution* is one particular surface selected from the double infinite series represented by the complete solution. A *general integral* is the envelope of one particular family of surfaces selected from those comprised in the complete integral. A *singular solution* s an envelope of every surface included in the complete integral.[1]

Theoretically an equation is not supposed to be solved completely until the complete integral, the general integral and the singular solution have been indicated. In the ideal case, the complete integral is first determined ; the singular solution obtained by the elimination of arbitrary constants as indicated above ; the general integral then determined by eliminating a and $f(a)$.

Practically, the complete integral is not always the direct ob-

---

[1] G. B. Airy's little book, *An Elementary Treatise on Partial Differential Equations*, London, 1873, will repay careful study in connection with the geometrical interpretation of the solutions of partial differential equations.

ject of attack. It is usually sufficient to deduce a number of particular solutions to satisfy the conditions of the problem and afterwards to so combine these solutions that the result will not only satisfy the given conditions but also the differential equation.

Of course, the complete integral of a differential equation applies to any physical process represented by the differential equation. This solution, however, may be so general as to be of little practical use. To represent any particular process, certain limitations called **limiting conditions** have to be introduced. These exclude certain forms of the general solution as impossible.[1] We met this idea in connection with the solution of algebraic equations, page 363.

§ 144. The Linear Partial Equation of the First Order.

Let
$$u = C_1, \qquad \cdot \qquad \cdot \qquad \cdot \qquad \cdot \qquad (1)$$
be a solution of the linear partial equation of the first order and degree, namely of
$$P\frac{\partial z}{\partial x} + Q\frac{\partial z}{\partial y} = R, \qquad \cdot \qquad \cdot \qquad \cdot \qquad (2)$$
where P, Q, and R are functions of x, y, and z; and C_1 is a constant. Now differentiate (1) with respect to x, and y respectively, as on page 44, or Ex. (5), page 74.
$$\frac{\partial u}{\partial x} + \frac{\partial u}{\partial z}\cdot\frac{\partial z}{\partial x} = 0 ; \; \frac{\partial u}{\partial y} + \frac{\partial u}{\partial z}\cdot\frac{\partial z}{\partial y} = 0. \qquad \cdot \qquad (3)$$
Now solve the one equation for $\partial z/\partial x$, and the other for $\partial z/\partial y$, and substitute the results in (2). We thus obtain
$$P\frac{\partial u}{\partial x} + Q\frac{\partial u}{\partial y} + R\frac{\partial u}{\partial z} = 0. \qquad \cdot \qquad \cdot \qquad (4)$$
Again, let (1) be an integral of the equation
$$\frac{\partial x}{P} = \frac{\partial y}{Q} = \frac{\partial z}{R}. \qquad \cdot \qquad \cdot \qquad \cdot \qquad (5)$$
The total differential of u with respect to x, y, and z, is
$$\frac{\partial u}{\partial x}dx + \frac{\partial u}{\partial y}dy + \frac{\partial u}{\partial z}dz = 0 ; \qquad \cdot \qquad \cdot \qquad (6)$$
and since, by equations, $dx = kP$; $dy = kQ$; $dz = kR$, page 445 (footnote), we have
$$\frac{\partial u}{\partial x}P + \frac{\partial u}{\partial y}Q + \frac{\partial u}{\partial z}R = 0, \qquad \cdot \qquad \cdot \qquad (7)$$

---

[1] For examples, see the end of Chapter VIII. ; also page 460, and elsewhere.

which is identical with (4). This means that every integral of (2) satisfies (5), and conversely. The general integral of (2) will therefore be the general integral of (5).

What has just been proved in connection with $u = C_1$ also applies to the integral $v = C_2$ of (7), page 445. If therefore we can establish a relation between u and v such that

$$u = f(v) ; \text{ or, } \phi(u, v) = 0, \qquad . \qquad . \qquad (8)$$

this arbitrary function will be a solution of the given equation. This is known as **Lagrange's solution** of the linear differential equation ; equations (5) are called **Lagrange's auxiliary equations.**

We may now show that any equations of form (8) will furnish a definite partial equation of the linear form (2). Differentiate equations (8), say the first, with respect to each of the independent variables x and y. We get

$$\frac{\partial u}{\partial x} + \frac{\partial u}{\partial z} \cdot \frac{\partial z}{\partial x} = f'(v) \left(\frac{\partial v}{\partial x} + \frac{\partial v}{\partial z} \cdot \frac{\partial z}{\partial x} \right); \frac{\partial u}{\partial y} + \frac{\partial u}{\partial z} \cdot \frac{\partial z}{\partial y} = f'(v) \left(\frac{\partial v}{\partial y} + \frac{\partial v}{\partial z} \cdot \frac{\partial z}{\partial y} \right).$$

By division and rearrangement of terms, $f'(v)$ and the terms containing the product of $\partial z/\partial x$ with $\partial z/\partial y$ disappear,[1] and we get

$$\frac{dx}{\dfrac{\partial u}{\partial y} \cdot \dfrac{\partial v}{\partial z} - \dfrac{\partial u}{\partial z} \cdot \dfrac{\partial v}{\partial y}} + \frac{dy}{\dfrac{\partial u}{\partial z} \cdot \dfrac{\partial v}{\partial x} - \dfrac{\partial u}{\partial x} \cdot \dfrac{\partial v}{\partial z}} = \frac{dz}{\dfrac{\partial u}{\partial x} \cdot \dfrac{\partial v}{\partial y} - \dfrac{\partial u}{\partial y} \cdot \dfrac{\partial v}{\partial x}}. \quad (9)$$

This equation has the same form as Lagrange's equation

$$\frac{dx}{P} = \frac{dy}{Q} = \frac{dz}{R} ; \text{ and } P\frac{\partial z}{\partial x} + Q\frac{\partial z}{\partial y} = R,$$

hence, if $u = f(v)$ is a solution of (2), it is also a solution of (5).

EXAMPLES.—(1) Solve E. Clapeyron's equation (*Journ. de l'Ecole Roy. Polyt.*, **14**, 153, 1834),

$$p\frac{\partial Q}{\partial p} + \rho\frac{\partial Q}{\partial \rho} = -\frac{p}{a\rho}, \qquad . \qquad . \qquad . \qquad (10)$$

well known in thermodynamics. Here, $P = p$, $Q = \rho$, $R = -p/a\rho$, and Lagrange's auxiliary equations assume the form,

$$\frac{\partial p}{p} = \frac{\partial \rho}{\rho} = \frac{\dfrac{\partial Q}{p}}{a\rho}. . \qquad . \qquad . \qquad . \qquad . \qquad (11)$$

From the first pair of these equations we get $\log p - \log \rho = \log C_1$; consequently $p/\rho = C_1$. From the first and last of equations (11), we have

$$dQ = -\frac{p}{a\rho} \cdot \frac{dp}{p} ; \therefore Q = -\frac{p}{a\rho} \log p + C_2,$$

---

[1] When the reader has read Chapter XI. he will write the denominator in the form of a "Jacobian".

is the second solution of (10).   The complete solution is therefore

$$Q = -\frac{p}{a\rho}\log p + f\!\left(\frac{p}{\rho}\right).$$

(2) Solve $y \cdot \partial z/\partial x - x \cdot \partial z/\partial y = 0$; here, $P = y$, $Q = -x$, $R = 0$,

$$\therefore \frac{dx}{y} = \frac{dy}{-x} = \frac{dz}{0}; \therefore dz = 0, \text{ and } xdx + ydy = 0.$$

$$\therefore x^2 + y^2 = C_1; \text{ and } z = C_2; \text{ or, } z = f(x^2 + y^2).$$

(3) Solve $xz \cdot \partial z/\partial x + yz \cdot \partial z/\partial y = xy$.   Here, $P = 1/y$, $Q = 1/x$, $R = 1/z$. The auxiliary equations are therefore $ydx = xdy = zdz$.   From the first two terms we get $y/x = C_1$; and from the multipliers $l = y$; $m = x$; $n = -2z$, as on page 445 (4), we get

$$ldx + mdy + ndz = 0; \therefore ydx + xdy = 2zdz; \text{ or, } z^2 - xy = C_2,$$

from (5), page 445.   This is the second solution required.   Hence, the complete solution is $z^2 = xy + f(x/y)$; or, $\phi(z^2 - xy, x/y) = 0$.

(4) Moseley (*Phil. Mag.* [4], **37**, 370, 1869) represents the motion of imperfect fluids under certain conditions by the equation

$$\frac{\partial z}{\partial x} + \frac{\partial z}{\partial y} = mz; \therefore z = e^{my}f(x - y).$$

§ 145. Some Special Forms.

For the ingenious general methods of Charpit and G. Monge, the reader will have to consult the special text-books, say, A. R. Forsyth's *A Treatise on Differential Equations*, London, 1903. There are some special variations from the general equation which can be solved by " short cuts ".

I. The variables do not appear directly.   The general form is

$$f\!\left(\frac{\partial z}{\partial x}, \frac{\partial z}{\partial y}\right) = 0. \quad \bullet \quad \bullet \quad \bullet \quad \bullet \quad \textbf{I.}$$

The solution is

$$z = ax + by + C,$$

provided a and b satisfy the relation

$$f(a, b) = 0; \text{ or } b = f(a).$$

The complete integral is, therefore,

$$z = ax + yf(a) + C. \quad \quad \bullet \quad \bullet \quad \textbf{(1)}$$

EXAMPLES.—(1) If $\left(\dfrac{\partial z}{\partial x}\right)^2 + \left(\dfrac{\partial z}{\partial y}\right)^2 = m^2$, show $z = ax + by + C'$, provided $a^2 + b^2 = m^2$.   The solution is, therefore, $z = ax + y\sqrt{(m^2 - a^2)} + C$.   For the general integral, put $C = f(a)$.   Eliminate a between the two equations, $z = ax + \sqrt{(m^2 - a^2)}y + f(a)$; and $x - a(m^2 - a^2)^{-\frac{1}{2}}y + f'(a) = 0$, in the usual way.   The latter expression has been obtained from the former by differentiation with respect to a.

(2) Solve $z_x z_y = 1$. Ansr. $z = ax + y/a + C$. Hint. $ab = 1$, etc. NOTE.—
We shall sometimes write for the sake of brevity, $p = \partial z/\partial x = z_x$; $q = \partial z/\partial y = z_y$.

(3) Solve $a(z_x + z_y) = z$. Sometimes, as here, when the variables do appear in the equation, the function of x, which occurs in the equation, may be associated with $\partial z/\partial x$, or a function of y with $\partial z/\partial y$, by a change in the variables. We may write the given equation $ap/z + aq/z = 1$. Put $dz/z = dZ$; $dy/a = dY$, $dx/a = dX$, hence, $\partial Z/\partial Y + \partial Z/\partial X = 1$, the form required. Ansr. $Z = aX + Y(1 - a) + C$; where, $Z = \log z$; $Y = y/a$: $X = x/a$, etc.

(4) Solve $x^2 u_x{}^2 + y^2 u_y{}^2 = z^2$. Put $X = \log x$, $Y = \log y$, $Z = \log z$. Proceed as before. Ansr. $z = Cx^a y^{\sqrt{(1 - a^2)}}$.

If it is not possible to remove the dependent variable z in this way, the equation will possibly belong to the following class:—

II. The independent variables x and y are absent. The general form is,

$$f\left(z, \frac{\partial z}{\partial x}, \frac{\partial z}{\partial y}\right) = 0. \qquad . \qquad . \qquad \textbf{II.}$$

Assume as a trial solution, that

$$\frac{\partial z}{\partial y} = a\frac{\partial z}{\partial x}.$$

Let $\partial z/\partial x$ be some function of z obtained from II., say $u_x = \phi(z)$. Substitute these values in

$$dz = z_x dx + z_y dy.$$

We thus get an ordinary differential equation which can be readily integrated.

$$dz = \phi(z)dx + a\phi(z)dy. \quad \therefore x + ay = \int \frac{dz}{\phi(z)} + C. \qquad (2)$$

EXAMPLES.—(1) Solve $z_x{}^2 z + z_y{}^2 = 4$. Here put $\partial z/\partial y = a\partial z/\partial x$,
$$\therefore (a^2 + z)(dz/dx)^2 = 4. \quad \sqrt{a^2 + z} \cdot dz/dx = 2,$$
$$\therefore x + ay + C = \int \tfrac{1}{2}(a^2 + z)^{\frac{1}{2}}dz = \tfrac{1}{3}(a^2 + z)^{3/2}. \quad \text{Ansr. } 2(a^2 + z)^3 = 3(x + ay + C)^2.$$

(2) Solve $p(1 + q^2) = q(z - a)$. Ansr. $\frac{4}{b}(z - a) = (bx + y + C)^2 + 4$. Hint.

Put $q = bp$, etc. The integration and other constants are collected under C.

(3) Moseley (*Phil. Mag.*, [4], **37**, 370, 1869) has the equation of the motion of an imperfect fluid

$$\frac{\partial z}{\partial x} + \frac{\partial z}{\partial y} = mz.$$

Let $\dfrac{\partial z}{\partial y} = a\dfrac{\partial z}{\partial x}$; $\therefore \dfrac{\partial z}{\partial x} + a\dfrac{\partial z}{\partial x} = mz$; $\therefore \dfrac{\partial z}{\partial x} = \dfrac{mz}{1 + a}$; $\therefore \dfrac{\partial z}{\partial y} = \dfrac{amz}{1 + a}$, by substitution in the original equation. From (3),

$$dz = \frac{mz}{1 + a}dx + \frac{amz}{1 + a}dy; \frac{dz}{z} = \frac{m}{1 + a}(dx + ady); \therefore \log z = \frac{m}{1 + a}(x + ay) + C.$$

If z does not appear directly in the equation, we may be able to refer the equation to the next type.

III. z does not appear directly in the equation, but x and $\partial z/\partial x$ can be separated from y and $\partial z/\partial y$. The leading type is

$$f_1\left(x, \frac{\partial z}{\partial x}\right) = f_2\left(y, \frac{\partial z}{\partial y}\right). \qquad . \qquad . \qquad \textbf{III.}$$

Assume as a trial solution, that each member is equal to an arbitrary constant a, so that z_x, and z_y can be obtained in the form,

$$z_x = f_1(x, a)\,;\ \ z_y = f_2(y, a)\,;\ \ dz = z_x dx + z_y dy,$$

then assumes the form

$$z = \int f_1(x, a)dx + \int f_2(y, a)dy + C. \qquad . \qquad . \qquad (3)$$

EXAMPLES.—(1) Solve $z_y - z_x + x - y = 0$. Put $\partial z/\partial x - x = \partial z/\partial y - y = a$. Write $z_x = x + a\,;\ z_y = y + a\,;$

$$\therefore\ dz = (x + a)dx + (y + a)dy,\ z = \tfrac{1}{2}(x + a)^2 + \tfrac{1}{2}(y + a)^2 + C.$$

(2) Assume with S. D. Poisson (*Ann. de Chim.*, **23**, 337, 1823) that the quantity of heat, Q, contained in a mass of gas depends upon the pressure, p, and its density ρ, so that $Q = f(p, \rho)$. According to the well-known gas equation, $p = R\rho(1 + a\theta)$; if p is constant,

$$\frac{d\rho}{d\theta} = -\frac{R\rho}{1 + a\theta};\ \text{and},\ \frac{dp}{d\theta} = \frac{Rp}{1 + a\theta},$$

if ρ is constant. From (10) and (7), page 80, the specific heats at constant pressure, and constant volume (*i.e.*, $\rho = $ constant) may be written

$$C_p = \left(\frac{\partial Q}{\partial \rho}\right)_p\left(\frac{\partial \rho}{\partial \theta}\right)_p = -\left(\frac{\partial Q}{\partial \rho}\right)_p\frac{R\rho}{1 + a\theta};\ \text{and}\ C_v = \left(\frac{\partial Q}{\partial p}\right)_v\left(\frac{\partial p}{\partial \theta}\right)_v = \left(\frac{\partial Q}{\partial p}\right)_v\frac{Rp}{1 + a\theta}.$$

Assuming, with Laplace and Poisson, that $\gamma = C_p/C_v$ is constant, we get, by division.

$$\gamma p\left(\frac{\partial Q}{\partial p}\right)_a + \rho\left(\frac{\partial Q}{\partial \rho}\right)_p = 0.$$

This differential equation comes under (3). Put

$$\frac{\partial Q}{\partial p} = \frac{a}{\gamma p};\ \frac{dQ}{d\rho} = -\frac{a}{\rho};$$

$$\therefore\ dQ = a\left(\frac{1}{\gamma}\cdot\frac{dp}{p} - \frac{d\rho}{\rho}\right);\ \text{or},\ Q = \frac{a}{\gamma}\log p - a\log \rho + C.$$

If ϕ is an independent function,

$$Q = \phi\left(\frac{p^{\frac{1}{\gamma}}}{p}\right);\ \text{or},\ \frac{p^{\frac{1}{\gamma}}}{\rho} = \psi(Q),$$

where ψ is the inverse function of ϕ. If it be assumed that the quantity of heat contained in any gas during any change is constant, $\psi(Q)$ will remain constant. Otherwise expressed,

$$\frac{p^{\frac{1}{\gamma}}}{\rho} = \text{constant}\,;\ \text{or},\ pv^\gamma = \text{constant}.$$

since volume, v, varies inversely as the density, ρ. This relation was deduced another way on page 258.

(4) E. Clapeyron's equation, previously discussed on page 453, may be solved by the method of the separation of the variables.

$$p\frac{\partial Q}{\partial p} + \rho\frac{\partial Q}{\partial \rho} = -\frac{p}{\rho a} \; ; \; \therefore \frac{\partial Q}{\partial p} + \frac{1}{c}\cdot\frac{\partial Q}{\partial \rho} = -\frac{c}{ap} :$$

since $p = c\rho$ by Boyle's law.

$$\therefore \frac{\partial Q}{\partial p} + \frac{c}{ap} = A \; ; \; \frac{\partial Q}{\partial \rho} = Ac.$$

Hence, by integration and substitution in (3), we get

$$Q = Ap + Ac\rho + C - \frac{c}{a}\log p \; ; \text{ or, } Q = f\left(\frac{p}{\rho}\right) - \frac{p}{a\rho}\log p,$$

by collecting all the integration functions under the symbol $f(\ldots)$, and substituting for c from Boyle's law. Of course $f(p/\rho)$ can only be evaluated when the relation between p and ρ is known. C. Holtzmann assumed that this function could be written $= A + BT$, where A and B were constants, T the absolute temperature.

IV. Analogous to Clairaut's equation. The general type is

$$z = \frac{\partial z}{\partial x}\cdot x + \frac{\partial z}{\partial y}\cdot y + f\left(\frac{\partial z}{\partial x}\cdot\frac{\partial z}{\partial y}\right). \qquad \textbf{IV.}$$

The complete integral is

$$z = ax + by + f(a, b). \qquad (4)$$

EXAMPLES.—Solve the following equations:

(1) $z = z_x x + z_y y + z_x z_y$. Ansr. $z = ax + by + ab$. Singular solution $z = -xy$.

(2) $z = z_x x + z_y y + r\sqrt{(1 + z_x^2 + z_y^2)}$. Ansr. $z = ax + by + r\sqrt{1 + a^2 + b^2}$. Singular solution, $x^2 + y^2 + z^2 = r^2$. The singular solution is, therefore, a sphere; r, of course, is a constant.

(3) $z = z_x x + z_y y - n\sqrt[n]{z_x z_y}$. Ansr. $z = ax + by - n\sqrt[n]{ab}$. Singular solution, $z = (2 - n)(xy)^{1/(2-n)}$.

There are no general methods for the solution of partial differential equations, and it is only possible to perform the integration in special cases. The greatest advances in this direction have been made with the linear equation. Linear equations are often encountered in physical mathematics.

§ 146. The Linear Partial Equation of the Second Order.

Suppose an elastic medium (gas) to be confined in a tube of unit sectional area; let E denote the coefficient of compressional elasticity of the gaseous medium ; and p a force which will produce a compression du in a layer of the gas dx thick, then, since

Stress = elasticity × strain,

as in Hooke's well-known law—*ut tensio sic vis*—we get

$$p = E\frac{du}{dx}. \qquad \cdot \quad \cdot \quad \cdot \quad \cdot \quad (1)$$

Again, the layer dx will be moved forwards or backwards by the differences of pressure on the two sides of this layer. Let this difference be dp. Hence, by differentiation of p and du, we get

$$dp = E\frac{d^2u}{dx}. \qquad \cdot \quad \cdot \quad \cdot \quad \cdot \quad (2)$$

Let ρ denote the density of the gas in the layer dx, then, the mass m,

$$m = \rho dx.$$

Now the pressure which moves a body is measured, in dynamics, as the product of the mass into the acceleration, or

$$dp/m = \frac{d^2u}{dt^2} = \rho\frac{d^2u}{dt^2}dx.$$

The equation of motion of the lamina is

$$\therefore \frac{d^2u}{dt^2} = \frac{E}{\rho}\frac{d^2u}{dx^2}. \qquad \cdot \quad \cdot \quad \cdot \quad (3)$$

This linear homogeneous partial differential equation represents the motion of stretched strings, the small oscillations of air in narrow (organ) pipes, and the motion of waves on the sea if the water is neither too deep nor too shallow. Let us now proceed to the integration of this equation.

There are many points of analogy between the partial and the ordinary linear differential equations. Indeed, it may almost be said that every ordinary differential equation between two variables is analogous to a partial differential of the same form. The solution is in each case similar, but there are these differences:

First, the arbitrary constant of integration in the solution of an ordinary differential equation is replaced by a function of a variable or variables.

Second, the exponential form, Ce^{mx}, of the solution of the ordinary linear differential equation assumes the form $e^{mx\frac{\delta}{\delta y}}\phi(y)$.

The expression, $e^{mx\frac{\delta}{\delta y}}\phi(y)$, is known as the **symbolic form of Taylor's theorem.** Having had considerable practice in the use of the symbol of operation D for $\frac{\partial}{\partial x}$, we may now use D' to represent the operation $\frac{\partial}{\partial y}$. By

Taylor's theorem,

$$\phi(y + mx) = \phi(y) + mx \frac{\partial \phi(y)}{\partial y} + \frac{m^2 x^2}{2!} \cdot \frac{\partial^2 \phi(y)}{\partial y^2} + \dots,$$

where x is regarded as constant.

$$\therefore \; \phi(y + mx) = \left(1 + mx\frac{\partial}{\partial y} + \frac{m^2 x^2}{2!} \frac{\partial^2}{\partial y^2} + \dots \right)\phi(y).$$

The term in brackets is clearly an exponential series (page 285), equivalent to $e^{mx\frac{\delta}{\delta y}}$, or, writing D' for $\frac{\partial}{\partial y}$,

$$\phi(y + mx) = e^{mxD'}\phi(y). \quad \bullet \quad \bullet \quad \bullet \quad \bullet \quad (4)$$

Now convert equation (3) into

$$\frac{\partial^2 u}{\partial t^2} = a^2 \frac{\partial^2 u}{\partial x^2} \quad \bullet \quad \bullet \quad \bullet \quad \bullet \quad (5)$$

by writing $a^2 = E/\rho$. This expression is sometimes called **d'Alembert's equation.** Instead of assuming, as a trial solution, that $y = e^{mx}$, as was the case with the ordinary equation, suppose that

$$u = f(x + mt), \quad \bullet \quad \bullet \quad \bullet \quad \bullet \quad (6)$$

is a trial solution. Differentiate (6), with respect to t and x, we thus obtain,

$$\frac{\partial u}{\partial t} = mf'(x + mt)\,; \; \frac{\partial u}{\partial x} = f'(x + mt)\,; \; \frac{\partial^2 u}{\partial x \partial t} = mf''(x + mt)\,;$$

$$\frac{\partial^2 u}{\partial t^2} = m^2 f''(x + mt)\,; \; \frac{\partial^2 u}{\partial x^2} = f''(x + mt).$$

Substitute these values in equation (5) equated to zero, and divide out the factor $f''(x + mt)$. The auxiliary equation,

$$m^2 - a^2 = 0 \quad \bullet \quad \bullet \quad \bullet \quad \bullet \quad (7)$$

remains. If m is a root of this equation, $f''(x + mt) = 0$, is a part of the complementary function. Since $\pm a$ are the roots of (7), then

$$u = e^{-atD'}f_1(x) + e^{atD'}f_2(x). \quad \bullet \quad \bullet \quad (8)$$

From (4) and (6), therefore,

$$u = f_1(x - at) + f_2(x + at) \quad \bullet \quad \bullet \quad \bullet \quad (9)$$

Since $+ a$ and $- a$ are the roots of the auxiliary equation (7), we can write (5) in the form,

$$(D + aD')(D - aD')u = 0. . \quad \bullet \quad \bullet \quad (10)$$

EXAMPLES.—(1) If $\frac{\partial^2 z}{\partial^2 x} - \frac{\partial^2 z}{\partial y^2} = 0$, show $z = f_1(y + x) + f_2(y - x)$.

(2) If $\frac{\partial^2 z}{\partial x^2} - 4\frac{\partial^2 z}{\partial x \partial y} + 4\frac{\partial^2 z}{\partial y^2} = 0$, show $z = f_1(y + 2x) + f_2(y + 2x)$.

(3) If $2 \frac{\partial^2 z}{\partial x^2} - 3\frac{\partial^2 z}{\partial x \partial y} - 2\frac{\partial z^2}{\partial y^2} = 0$, show $z = f_1(2y - x) + f_2(y + 2x)$.

In the absence of data pertaining to some specific problem, we cannot say much about the undetermined functions $f_1(x + at)$

and $f_2(x-at)$ of (9). Consider a vibrating harp string, where no force is applied after the string has once been put in motion. Let

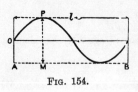

FIG. 154.

$x = l = AB$ (Fig. 154) denote the length of the string under a tension T; and m the mass of unit length of the vibrating string. In the equation of motion (5), in order to avoid a root sign later on, a^2 appears in place of T/m. Further, let $u\ PM$ represent the displacement of any part of the string we please, and let the ordinate of one end of the string be zero. Then, whatever value we assign to the time t, the ends of the string are fixed and have the limiting condition $u = 0$, when $x = 0$; and $u = 0$, when $x = l$.

$$\therefore f_1(at) + f_2(-at) = 0 ; f_1(l + at) + f_2(l - at) = 0, \qquad (11)$$

are solutions of d'Alembert's equation (5). From the former, it follows that

$$f_1(at) \text{ must always be equal to } - f_2(-at) \qquad . \qquad (12)$$

But at may have any value we please. In order to fix our ideas, suppose that we put $l + at$ for at in the second of equations (11) · then, from (12),

$$f_1(at + 2l) = f_1(at). \qquad . \qquad . \qquad (13)$$

The physical meaning of this solution is that when $f_1(\ldots)$ is increased or diminished by $2l$, the value of the function remains unaltered. Hence, when at is increased by $2l$, or, what is the same thing, when t is increased by $2l/a$, the corresponding portions of the string will have the same displacement. In other words, the string performs at least one complete vibration in the time $2l/a$. We can show the same thing applies for $4l$, $6l$. ... Hence, we conclude that d'Alembert's equation represents a finite periodic motion, with a period of oscillation.

$$at = 2l ; \text{ or, } t = \frac{2l}{a} ; \text{ or, } t = 2l\sqrt{\frac{m}{T}}. \qquad (14)$$

NUMERICAL EXAMPLE.—The middle C of a pianoforte vibrates 264 times per second, that is, once every $\frac{1}{264}$ second. If the length of the wire is $2\frac{1}{2}$ feet, and one foot of the wire weighs 0·002 lbs., find the tension T in lbs. Now mass equals the weight divided by g, that is by 32. Hence,

$$t = 2l\sqrt{\frac{w}{32T}}; \frac{1}{264} = 5\sqrt{\frac{0·002}{32 \times T}}; \therefore T = 108 \text{ lbs.}$$

Equation (5), or (9), represents a wave or pulse of air passing through a tube both from and towards the origin. If we consider

a pulse passing from the origin only,
$$u = f(x + at)$$
is the solution of the differential equation. By differentiation with regard to x, and with regard to t, we have already shown, Ex. (1), page 449, that
$$\frac{du}{dx} = \; ; f'(x + at). \; \frac{du}{dt} = af'(x + at).$$
The first of these equations represents the rate of expansion or contraction; the second, the velocity of a particle. The velocity of the wave is, by division,
$$\frac{dx}{dt} = a \; ; \text{ or, } V = \sqrt{\frac{E}{\rho}} \; ;$$
which is Newton's formula for the velocity of sound (Newton's *Principia*, ii., Prob. 43-50). Newton made E represent the isothermal elasticity, p; Laplace, the adiabatic elasticity γp of page 114.

When two of the roots in equation (7) are equal to, say, a. We know, page 401, that the solution of
$$(D - a)^2 z = 0, \text{ is } z = e^{mx}(C_1 x + C_2),$$
by analogy, the solution of
$$(D - aD')^2 z = 0, \text{ is } z = e^{mxD'}\{xf_1(y) + f_2(y)\},$$
or, $\qquad z = xf_1(y + ax) + f_2(y + ax).$.   .   (15)

EXAMPLES.—(1) Solve: $(D^3 - D^2 D' - DD'^2 + D'^3)z = 0.$
Ansr. $z = xf_1(y - x) + f_2(y - x) + f_3(y + x).$
(2) $\dfrac{\partial^2 z}{\partial x^2} + 2\dfrac{\partial^2 z}{\partial x \partial y} + \dfrac{\partial^2 z}{\partial y^2} = 0.$ Ansr. $z = xf_1(y + x) + f_2(y + x).$

If the equation be non-homogeneous, say,
$$A_0\frac{\partial^2 z}{\partial x^2} + A_1\frac{\partial^2 z}{\partial x \partial y} + A_2\frac{\partial^2 z}{\partial y^2} + A_3\frac{\partial z}{\partial x} + A_4\frac{\partial z}{\partial y} + A_5 z = 0, \quad (16)$$
and it can be separated into factors, the integral is the sum of the integrals corresponding to each symbolic factor, so that each factor of the form $D - mD'$, appears in the solution as a function of $y + mx$, and every factor of the form $D - mD' - a$, appears in the solution in the form $z = e^{ax}f(y + mx).$

EXAMPLES.—(1) Solve $\dfrac{\partial^2 z}{\partial x^2} - \dfrac{\partial^2 z}{\partial y^2} + \dfrac{\partial z}{\partial x} + \dfrac{\partial z}{\partial y} = 0.$
Factors, $(D + D')(D - D' + 1)z = 0.$ Ansr. $z = f_1(y - x) + e^{-x}f_2(y + x).$
(2) Solve $\dfrac{\partial^2 z}{\partial x^2} - \dfrac{\partial^2 z}{\partial x \partial y} + \dfrac{\partial z}{\partial x} - \dfrac{\partial z}{\partial y} = 0.$
Factors, $(D + 1)(D - D')z = 0.$ Ansr. $z = e^{-x}f_1(y) + f_2(x + y).$

It is, however, not often possible to represent the solutions of these equations in this manner, and in that case it is customary to take the trial solution,

$$z = e^{ax + \beta y}. \qquad . \qquad . \qquad . \qquad . \qquad (17)$$

Of course, if a is a function of β we can substitute $a = f(\beta)$ and so get rid of β. Now differentiate (17) so as to get

$$\frac{\partial z}{\partial x} = az \; ; \; \frac{\partial z}{\partial y} = \beta z \; ; \; \frac{\partial^2 z}{\partial x \partial y} = a\beta z \; ; \; \frac{\partial^2 z}{\partial x^2} = a^2 z \; ; \; \frac{\partial^2 z}{\partial y^2} = \beta^2 z.$$

Substitute these results in (16). We thus obtain the auxiliary equation

$$(A_0 a^2 + A_1 a\beta + A_2 \beta^2 + A_3 a + A_4 \beta + A_5)z = 0. \quad . \quad (18)$$

This may be looked upon as a bracketed quadratic in a and β. Given any value of β, we can find the corresponding value of a; or the value of β from any assigned value of a. There is thus an infinite number of particular solutions. Hence these important rules :

I. If u_1, u_2, u_3, . . . , are particular solutions of any partial differential equation, each solution can be multiplied by an arbitrary constant and each of the resulting products is also a solution of the equation.

II. The sum or difference of any number of particular solutions is a solution of the given equation.

It is usually not very difficult to find particular solutions, even when the general solution cannot be obtained. The chief difficulty lies in the combining of the particular solutions in such a way, that the conditions of the problem under investigation are satisfied. In order to fix these ideas let us study a couple of examples which will prepare the way for the next chapter.

EXAMPLES.—(1) Solve $(D^2 - D')z = 0$. Here $a^2 - \beta = 0$; $\therefore \beta = a^2$. Hence (17) becomes $z = Ce^{ax + a^2 y}$. Put $a = \frac{1}{2}, a = 1, a = 2, \ldots$ and we get the particular solutions $e^{\frac{1}{2}(2x + y)}, e^{x + y}, e^{2x + 4y}, \ldots$

$$\therefore z = C_1 e^{\frac{1}{2}(2x + y)} + C_2 e^{x + y} + C_3 e^{2x + 4y} + \ldots$$

Now the difference between any two terms of the form $e^{ax + \beta y}$, is included in the above solution, it follows, therefore, that the first differential coefficient of $e^{ax + \beta y}$, is also an integral, and, in the same way, the second, third and higher derivatives must be integrals. Since,

$$De^{ax + a^2 y} = (x + 2ay)e^{ax + a^2 y} \; ; \; D^2 e^{ax + a^2 y} = \{(x + 2ay) + 2y\}e^{ax + a^2 y} .$$

$$D^3 e^{ax + a^2 y} = \{(x + 2ay) + 6y(x + 2ay)\}e^{ax + a^2 y} \; ; \; \text{etc.},$$

we have the following solution :—

$$z = C_1(x + 2ay)e^{ax + a^2 y} + C_2\{(x + 2ay) + 2y\}e^{ax + a^2 y} + \ldots$$

If $a = 0$, we get the special case,

$$z = C_1 x + C_2(x^2 + 2y) + C_3(x^3 + 6xy) + \ldots$$

(2) Solve $\dfrac{\partial^2 z}{\partial x^2} - \dfrac{\partial^2 z}{\partial y^2} - 3\dfrac{\partial z}{\partial x} + 3\dfrac{\partial z}{\partial y} = 0.$ Put $z = Ce^{ax + \beta y}$; and we get

$(\alpha - \beta)(\alpha + \beta - 3) = 0.$ $\therefore \beta = \alpha,$ and $\beta = 3 - \alpha.$

$\therefore z = C_1 e^{a(x + y)} + e^{3y} C_2 e^{a(x - y)} = f_1(y + x) + e^{3y} f_2(x - y).$

The processes for finding the particular integrals are analogous to those employed for the particular integrals of ordinary differential equation, I shall not go further into the matter just now, but will return to the subject in the next chapter. Partial differential equations of a higher order than the second sometimes occur in investigations upon the action of magnetism on polarized light; vibrations of thick plates, or curved bars; the motion of a cylinder in a fluid; the damping of air waves by viscosity, etc.

§ 147. The Approximate Integration of Differential Equations.

There are two interesting and useful methods for obtaining the approximate solution of differential equations :

I. Integration in series. When a function can be developed in a series of converging terms, arranged in powers of the independent variable, an approximate value for the dependent variable can easily be obtained. The degree of approximation attained obviously depends on the number of terms of the series included in the calculation. The older mathematicians considered this an under-hand way of getting at the solution, but, for practical work, it is invaluable. As a matter of fact, solutions of the more advanced problems in physical mathematics are nearly always represented in the form of an abbreviated infinite series. Finite solutions are the exception rather than the rule.

EXAMPLES.—(1) It is required to find the solution $dy/dx = y$, in series. Assume that y has the form

$$y = a_0 + a_1 x + a_2 x^2 + a_3 x^3 + \ldots$$

Differentiate, and substitute for $\dot{y}$ and y in the given equation.

$$(a_1 - a_0) + (2a_2 - a_1)x + (3a_3 - a_2)x^2 + \ldots = 0.$$

If x is not zero, this equation is satisfied when the coefficients of x become zero. This requires that

$$a_1 = a_0 ; \ a_2 = \frac{1}{2} a_1 = \frac{1}{2} a_0 ; \ a_3 = \frac{1}{3} a_2 = \frac{1}{3!} a_0 ; \ \ldots$$

Hence, by substitution in (1), we obtain

$$y = a_0 \left(1 + x + \frac{1}{2!} x^2 + \frac{1}{3!} x^3 + \ldots \right) = a_0 e^x.$$

Put a for the arbitrary constant so that the final result is $y = ae^x$. That this is a complete solution, is proved by substitution in the original equation. We must proceed a little differently with equations of a higher order. Take as a second example

(2) Solve $dy/dx + ay + bx^2 = 0$ in series. By successive differentiation of this expression, and making $y = y_0$ when $x = 0$ in the results, we obtain

$$\left(\frac{dy}{dx}\right)_0 = -ay_0; \; \left(\frac{d^2y}{dx^2}\right)_0 = a^2y_0; \; \left(\frac{d^3y}{dx^3}\right)_0 = -a^3y_0 - 2b; \; \ldots$$

By Maclaurin's theorem,

$$y = y_0 + \left(\frac{dy}{dx}\right)_0 \frac{x}{1} + \left(\frac{d^2y}{dx^2}\right)_0 \frac{x^2}{2!} + \left(\frac{d^3y}{dx^3}\right)_0 \frac{x^3}{3!} + \ldots; \quad \bullet \quad \bullet \quad (1)$$

$$= y_0 - ay_0x + \tfrac{1}{2}a^2y_0x^2 - \tfrac{1}{6}(a^3y_0 + 2b)x^3 + \ldots;$$

$$= y_0(1 - ax + \tfrac{1}{2}a^2x^2 - \ldots) - 2ba^{-3}(\tfrac{1}{6}a^3x^3 - \tfrac{1}{24}a^4x^4 + \ldots);$$

$$= y_0 e^{-ax} + 2ba^{-3}(e^{-ax} - 1 + ax - \tfrac{1}{2}a^2x^2),$$

by making suitable transformations in the contents of the last pair of brackets. Hence finally $y = C_1 e^{-ax} - 2ba^{-3}(1 - ax + \tfrac{1}{2}a^2x^2)$. Verify this by the method of § 125, page 387.

(3) Solve $d^2y/dx^2 - a^2y = 0$ in series. By successive differentiation, and integration

$$\frac{d^3y}{dx^3} = a^2\frac{dy}{dx}; \; \frac{d^4y}{dx^4} = a^2\frac{d^2y}{dx^2}; \; \ldots \left(\frac{d^4y}{dx^4}\right)_0 = a^4y_0; \; \ldots,$$

when the integrations are performed between the limits $x = x$, and $x = 0$, so that y becomes y_0 when $x = 0$. From Maclaurin's theorem, (1) above, we get by substitution

$$y = y_0 + \left(\frac{dy}{dx}\right)_0 \frac{x}{1} + a^2y_0\frac{x^2}{2!} + a^2\left(\frac{dy}{dx}\right)_0\frac{x^3}{3!} + \ldots;$$

$$= y_0\left\{1 + \frac{a^2x^2}{2!} + \frac{a^4x^4}{4!} + \ldots\right\} + \frac{1}{a}\left(\frac{dy}{dx}\right)_0\left\{\frac{ax}{1} + \frac{a^3x^3}{3!} + \ldots\right\}.$$

By rearranging the terms in brackets and putting the constants $y_0 = A$, and $\dot{y}_0/a = B$, we get,

$$y = A\{(\tfrac{1}{2} + \tfrac{1}{2}ax + \tfrac{1}{4}a^2x^2 + \ldots) + (\tfrac{1}{2} - \tfrac{1}{2}ax + \tfrac{1}{4}a^2x^2 - \ldots) + B(\ldots)\};$$

$$= \tfrac{1}{2}A(e^{ax} + e^{-ax}) + B(e^{ax} - e^{-ax}) = C_1e^{ax} + C_2e^{-ax}.$$

Sometimes it is advisable to assume a series with undetermined indices and to evaluate this by means of the differential equation, as indicated in the next example.

(4) Solve

$$\frac{d^2y}{dx^2} - x\frac{dy}{dx} - cy = x^2. \quad \bullet \quad \bullet \quad \bullet \quad \bullet \quad (2)$$

(i) *The complementary function.* As a trial solution, put $y = a_0x^m$. The auxiliary equation is

$$m(m-1)a_0x^{m-2} - (m+c)a_0x^m = 0. \quad \bullet \quad \bullet \quad \bullet \quad (3)$$

This shows that the difference between the successive exponents of x in the assumed series, is 2. The required series is, therefore,

$$y = a_0x^m + a_1x^{m+2} + \ldots + a_{n-1}x^{m+2n-2} + a_nx^{m+2n} = 0, \; \bullet \quad (4)$$

which is more conveniently written

$$y = \sum_0^\infty a_nx^{m+2n} = 0. \quad \bullet \quad \bullet \quad \bullet \quad \bullet \quad (5)$$

In order to completely determine this series, we must know three things about it. Namely, the first term; the coefficients of x; and the different powers of x that make up the series. By differentiation of (4), we get

$$\dot{y} = \sum_0^\infty (m + 2n)a_n x^{m + 2n - 1}; \ \ddot{y} = \sum_0^\infty (m + 2n)(m + 2n - 1)a_n x^{m + 2n - 2}.$$

By substitution of this result and (4) in equation (2), we have

$$\sum_0^\infty \{(m + 2n)(m + 2n - 1)a_n x^{m + 2n - 2} - (m + 2n + c)a_n x^{m + 2n}\} = 0, \quad (6)$$

where n has all values from zero to infinity. If (5) is a solution of (2), equation (6) is identically zero, and the coefficient of each power of x must vanish. Hence, by equating the co-efficients of x^{m+2n}, and of $x^{m+2n - 2}$ to zero, we have

$$(m + 2n)(m + 2n - 1)a_n x^{m + 2n - 2} - (m + 2n + c)a_n x^{m + 2n} = 0;$$

and replacing n by $n - 1$ in the second term, we get

$$(m + 2n)(m + 2n - 1)a_n - (m + 2n - 2 + c)a_{n - 1} = 0; \quad (7)$$

since $(m + 2n)(m + 2n - 1) = 0$, when $n = 0$, $m(m - 1) = 0$; consequently, $m = 0$, or $m = 1$; for succeeding terms n is greater than zero, and the relation between any two consecutive terms is

$$a_n = \frac{m + 2n - 2 + c}{(m + 2n)(m + 2n - 1)}a_{n - 1}. \quad \cdot \quad \cdot \quad \cdot \quad (8)$$

This formula allows us to calculate the relation between the successive coefficients of x by giving n all integral values 1, 2, 3, . . . Let a_0 be the first term.

First, suppose $m = 0$, then we can easily calculate from (8),

$$a_1 = \frac{c}{1.2}a_0; \ a_2 = \frac{c + 2}{3.4}a_1 = \frac{c(c + 2)}{4!}a_0; \ \cdots$$

$$\therefore Y_1 = a_0\left\{1 + c\frac{x^2}{2!} + c(c + 2)\frac{x^4}{4!} + \cdots\right\}. \quad \cdot \quad \cdot \quad (9)$$

Next, put $m = 1$, and, to prevent confusion, write b, in (8), in place of a.

$$b_n = \frac{c + 2n - 1}{2n(1n + 1)}b_{n - 1};$$

proceed exactly as before to find successively b_1, b_2, b_3, . . .

$$\therefore Y_2 = b_0\left\{x + (c + 1)\frac{x^3}{3!} + (c + 1)(c + 3)\frac{x^5}{5!} + \cdots\right\}. \quad \cdot \quad (10)$$

The complete solution of the equation is the sum of these two series, (9) and (10); or, if we put $C_1 y_1 = Y_1$, $C_2 y_2 = Y_2$,

$$y = C_1 y_1 + C_2 y_2,$$

which contains the two arbitrary constants C_1 and C_2.

(ii.) *The particular integral.* By the above procedure we obtain the complementary function. For the particular integral, we must follow a somewhat similar method. *E.g.*, equate (7) to x^2 instead of to zero. The coefficient of x^{m-2}, in (3) becomes

$$m(m - 1)a_0 x^{m - 2} = x^2.$$

A comparison of the exponents shows that

$$m - 2 = 2; \text{ and } m(m - 1)a_0 = 1; \ \therefore m = 4; \ a_0 = \tfrac{1}{12}.$$

From (8), when $m = 4$,

$$a_n = \frac{2 + 2n + c}{2(n + 2)(2n + 3)}a_{n - 1},$$

Substitute successive values of $n = 1, 2, 3, . . .$ in the assumed expansion, and we obtain

Particular integral $= a_0 x^m + a_1 x^{m + 2} + a_2 x^{m + 4} + \cdots$,

where a_0, a_1, a_2, . . . and m have been determined.

GG

(5) The following velocity equations have been proposed for the catalytic action of an enzyme upon salicine (J. W. Mellor's *Chemical Statics and Dynamics*, London, 380, 1904) :—

$$\frac{dy}{dt} = k_1(a - x - y)(c - y) ; \quad \frac{dx}{dt} = k_2 y. \quad . \quad . \quad . \quad (11)$$

From Maclaurin's theorem,

$$x = x_0 + \left(\frac{dx}{dt}\right)_0 t + \left(\frac{d^2x}{dt^2}\right)_0 \frac{t^2}{2!} + \cdots \quad . \quad . \quad (12)$$

Hence, when $x = 0$, and $y = 0$, equations (11) furnish

$$\left(\frac{dx}{dt}\right)_0 = (k_2 y)_0 = 0 ; \therefore \left(\frac{dy}{dt}\right)_0 = k_1 ac ; \left(\frac{d^2x}{dt^2}\right)_0 = k_1 k_2 ac = A, \text{ say.} \quad (13)$$

By differentiation of the first of equations (11), we get

$$\left(\frac{d^2y}{dt^2}\right)_0 = -k_1(a - x - y)\frac{dy}{dt} - k_1(c - y)\left(\frac{dx}{dt} + \frac{dy}{dt}\right) ; \quad . \quad (14)$$

and from the second of equations (11), (13), and (14),

$$\left(\frac{d^3x}{dt^3}\right)_0 = -k_1{}^2 k_2 ac(a + c) = B, \text{ say.} \quad . \quad . \quad . \quad (15)$$

Again, differentiating (14),

$$\frac{d^3y}{dt^3} = k_1\left\{\left(\frac{dx}{dt} + \frac{dy}{dt}\right)\frac{dy}{dt} - (a - x - y)\frac{d^2y}{dt^2} + \frac{dy}{dt}\left(\frac{dx}{dt} + \frac{dy}{dt}\right) + (c - y)\left(\frac{d^2x}{dt^2} + \frac{d^2y}{dt^2}\right)\right\} ;$$

$$\left(\frac{d^3y}{dt^3}\right)_0 = 2k_1{}^3 a^2 c^2 + k_1{}^3 a^2 c(a + c) - k_1 c\{k_1 k_2 ac - k_1{}^2 ac(a + c)\} ;$$

$$= 2k_1{}^3 a^2 c^2 + k_1{}^3 a^2 c(a + c) - k_1{}^2 k_2 ac^2 + k_1{}^3 ac^2(a + c)$$

$$= k_1{}^3 ac(a + c)^2 + 2k_1{}^3 a^2 c^2 - k_1{}^2 k_2 ac^2.$$

$$\therefore \left(\frac{d^4x}{dt^4}\right)_0 = k_1{}^3 k_2 ac(a + c) + 2k_1{}^3 k_2 a^2 c^2 - k_1{}^2 k_2{}^2 ac^2 + C, \text{ say.} \quad . \quad (16)$$

Consequently, from (12), (13), (15), and (16), and collecting the constants together, under the symbols $A, B, C, \ldots$ we get

$$x = A\frac{t^2}{2!} + B\frac{t^3}{3!} + C\frac{t^4}{4!} + \cdots ; \therefore y = \frac{A}{k_2} \cdot \frac{t}{1} + \frac{B}{k_2} \cdot \frac{t^2}{2!} + \frac{C}{k_2} \cdot \frac{t^3}{3!} + \cdots \quad (17)$$

We have expressed x and y in terms of t and constants.

A great number of the velocity equations of consecutive chemical reactions are turned out by the integral calculus in the form of an infinite series. If the series be convergent all may appear to be well. But another point must here be emphasized. The constants in the series are evaluated from the numerical data and the agreement between the calculated and the observed results is quoted in support of a theory. As a matter of fact the series formula is quite empirical. Scores of hypotheses might be suggested which would all furnish a similar relation between the variables, and "best values" for the constants can be determined in the same way. Of course if it were possible to evaluate the constants by independent processes, and the resulting expression gave results in harmony with the experimental material, we might have a little more faith in the theory. These remarks in no way conflict with the discussion on page 324. There the constants were in questions, here we speak of the underlying theory.

But we are getting beyond the scope of this work. I hope enough has been said to familiarize the student with the notation and ideas employed in the treatment of differential equations so that when he consults more advanced books their pages will no longer appear as " unintelligible hieroglyphs ". For more extensive practical details, the reader will have to take up some special work such as A. R. Forsyth's *Differential Equations*, London, 1903; W. E. Byerly's *Fourier's Series and Spherical Harmonics*, Boston, 1895. H. F. Weber and B. Riemann's *Die Partiellen Differential-Gleichungen der Mathematischen Physik*, Braunschweig, 1900-1901, is *the* text-book for more advanced work. A. Gray and G. B. Mathews have *A Treatise on Bessel's Functions and their Application to Physics*, London, 1895.

II. Method of successive approximations. This method resembles, in principle, that used for the approximate solution of numerical equations, page 358. When some of the terms of the given equation are small, solve the equation as if these terms did not exist. Thus the equation of motion for the small oscillations of a pendulum in air,

$$\frac{d^2\theta}{dt^2} + q^2\theta = a\left(\frac{d\theta}{dt}\right)^2 ; \text{ becomes } \frac{d^2\theta}{dt^2} + q^2\theta = 0, \qquad (18)$$

provided the right member $a(d\theta/dt)^2$ is small. Solving the second of these equations by the method of page 401, we get $\theta = -r \cos qt$. If so then $a(d\theta/dt)^2$ must be $ar^2q^2\sin^2 qt$. Substituting this in the first of equations (18), and remembering that $1 - \cos 2x = 2 \sin^2 x$, page 612, we get

$$\frac{d^2\theta}{dt^2} + q^2\theta = \frac{ar^2q^2}{2}\left(1 - \cos 2qt\right); \text{ or, } \frac{d^2\theta}{dt^2} + q^2\left(\theta - \frac{ar^2}{2}\right) = -\frac{aq^2r^2}{2}\cos 2qt.$$

This gives $\theta = \frac{1}{2}ar^2 + (r - \frac{2}{3}ar^2) \cos qt + \frac{1}{6}ar^2 \cos 2qt$, when solved, as on page 421, with the conditions that when $t = 0$, $\theta = r$, and $d\theta/dt = 0$.

EXAMPLE.—A set of equations resembling those of Ex. (5), of the preceding set of examples is solved in *Technics*, 1, 514, 1904, by the method of successive approximation, and under the assumption that k_1 and a are small in comparison with k_2 and c. Hint. Differentiate the second of equations (11); multiply out the first ; and on making the proper substitution

$$\frac{1}{k_2}\frac{d^2x}{dt^2} = \frac{k_1}{k_2}\left(\frac{dx}{dt}\right)^2 + \frac{k_1}{k_2}\left(x - c - a\right)\frac{dx}{dt} + k_1 c(a - x).. \qquad (19)$$

Neglect terms in k_1/k_2, and $d^2(x - a)/dt^2 + q^2(x - a) = 0$ remains, if q^2 be put in place of $k_1 c k_2$. Hence, $x - a = - a \cos qt$, since x and y are both zero when $t = 0$. Differentiate and substitute the results in (19). We get

$$\frac{d^2x}{dt^2} + q^2(x - a) = - k_1(a \cos qt - c)aq \sin qt + \frac{k_1}{k_2}a^2q^2 \sin^2 qt;$$

$$\therefore \frac{d^2x}{dt^2} + \underline{q}^2(x - a) = q^3 \sin qt - \frac{a^2qk_1}{2}\sin 2qt + \frac{a^2q^2k_1}{2k_2}(1 - \cos 2\underline{q}t),$$

which can be solved by the method of page 421. The complete (approximate) solution—particular integral and complimentary function—is

$$x - a = + a \cos qt - \frac{q^2t \cos qt}{2} + \frac{a^2k_1 \sin 2 qt}{6q} + \frac{a^2k_1 \cos 2qt}{6k_2} + \frac{a^2k_1}{2k_2}.$$

This solution is not well fitted for practical work. It is too cumbrous.

CHAPTER VIII.

FOURIER'S THEOREM.

"Fourier's theorem is not only one of the most beautiful results of
modern analysis, but may be said to furnish an indispensable
instrument in the treatment of nearly every recondite question
in modern physics. To mention only sonorous vibrations, the
propagation of electric signals along a telegraph wire, and the
conduction of heat by the earth's crust, as subjects in their
generality intractable without it, is to give but a feeble idea of
its importance."—THOMSON AND TAIT.

§ 148. Fourier's Series.

SOUND, as we all know, is produced whenever the particles of air
are set into a certain state of vibratory motion. The to and fro
motion of a pendulum may be regarded as the simplest form of
vibration, and this is analogous to the vibration which produces a
simple sound such as the fundamental note of an organ pipe.
The periodic curve, Fig. 52, page 136, represented by the equations
$y = \sin x$; or $y = \cos x$, is a graphic representation of the motion
which produces a simple sound.

A musical note, however, is more complex, it consists of a
simple sound—called the fundamental note—compounded with a
series of auxiliary vibrations—called overtones. The periodic curve
of such a note departs greatly from the simplicity of that representing a simple sound. Fourier has shown that any periodic curve
can be reproduced by compounding a series of harmonic curves
along the same axis and having recurring periods $1, \frac{1}{2}, \frac{1}{3}, \frac{1}{4}, \ldots$ th
of the given curve. The only limitations are (i) the ordinates must
be finite (page 243); (ii) the curve must always progress in the same
direction. Fourier further showed that only one special combination of the elementary curves can be compounded to produce the
given curve. This corresponds with the fact observed by Helm-

holtz that the same composite sound is always resolved into the same elementary sounds. A composite sound can therefore be represented, in mathematical symbols, as a series of terms arranged, not in a series of ascending powers of the independent variable, as in Maclaurin's theorem, but in a series of sines and cosines of multiples of this variable.

Fourier's theorem *determines the law for the expansion of any arbitrary function in terms of sines or cosines of multiples of the independent variable, x.* If $f(x)$ is a periodic function with respect to time, space, temperature, or potential, Fourier's theorem states that

$$f(x) = A_0 + a_1 \sin x + a_2 \sin 2x + \ldots + b_1 \cos x + b_2 \cos 2x + \ldots \quad (1)$$

This is known as **Fourier's series.** It is easy to show, by plotting, as we shall do later on, that a trigonometrical series like that of Fourier passes through all its changes and returns to the same value when x is increased by 2π. This mode of dealing with motion is said to be more advantageous than any other form of mathematical reasoning, and it has been applied with great success to physical problems involving potential, conduction of heat, light, sound, electricity and other forms of propagation. Any physical property—density, pressure, velocity—which varies periodically with time and whose magnitude or intensity can be measured, may be represented by Fourier's series.

In view of the fact that the terms of Fourier's series are all periodic we may say that *Fourier's series is an artificial way of representing the propagation or progression of any physical quality by a series of waves or vibrations.* "It is only a mathematical fiction," says Helmholtz, "admirable because it renders calculation easy, but not necessarily corresponding with anything in reality."

§ 149. Evaluation of the Constants in Fourier's Series.

Assuming Fourier's series to be valid between the limits $x = +\pi$ and $x = -\pi$, we shall now proceed to find values for the coefficients A_0, a_1, a_2, ..., b_1, b_2, ..., which will make the series true.

I. *To find a value for the constant A_0.* Multiply equation (1) by dx and then integrate each term between the limits $x = +\pi$ and $x = -\pi$. Every term involving sine or cosine term vanishes, and

$$2\pi A_0 = \int_{-\pi}^{+\pi} f(x) \, . \, dx; \quad \text{or,} \quad A_0 = \frac{1}{2\pi}\int_{-\pi}^{+\pi} f(x) \, . \, dx, \qquad . \qquad (2)$$

remains. Therefore, when $f(x)$ is known, this integral can be integrated.[1]

I strongly recommend the student to master §§ 74, 75, 83 before taking up this chapter.

II. To find a value for the coefficients of the cosine terms, say b_n, where n may be any number from 1 to n. Equation (1) must not only be multiplied by dx, but also by some factor such that all the other terms will vanish when the series is integrated between the limits $\pm \pi$, $b_n \cos nx$ remains. Such a factor is $\cos nx \, . \, dx$. In this case,

$$\int_{-\pi}^{+\pi} \cos^2 nx \, . \, dx = b_n \pi,$$

(page 211), all the other terms involving sines or cosines, when integrated between the limits $\pm \pi$, will be found to vanish. Hence the desired value of b_n is

$$b_n = \frac{1}{\pi}\int_{-\pi}^{+\pi} f(x) \, . \, \cos nx \, . \, dx. \qquad . \qquad . \qquad (3)$$

This formula enables any coefficient, $b_1, b_2, \ldots, b_n$ to be obtained. If we put $n = 0$, the coefficient of the first term A_0 assumes the form,

$$A_0 = \tfrac{1}{2} b_0. \qquad . \qquad . \qquad . \qquad (4)$$

If this value is substituted in (1), we can dispense with (2), and write

$$f(x) = \tfrac{1}{2} b_0 + a_1 \sin x + b_1 \cos x + a_2 \sin 2x + b_2 \cos 2x + \ldots \quad (5)$$

III. To find a value for the coefficients of the sine terms, say a_n. As before, multiply through with $\sin nx\,dx$ and integrate between the limits $\pm \pi$. We thus obtain

$$a_n = \frac{1}{\pi}\int_{-\pi}^{+\pi} f(x) \sin nx \, . \, dx. \qquad . \qquad . \qquad (6)$$

EXAMPLES.—(1) Problems like these are sometimes set for practice. Put $\frac{2\pi t}{T} = x$, in (1), and develop the curve Fig. 155. Note T is a special value of t. The series to be developed is

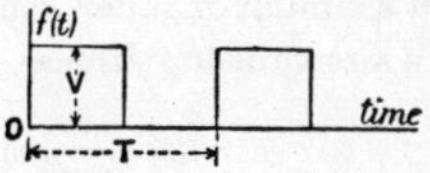

FIG. 155.

$$f(t) = A_0 + a_1 \sin \frac{2\pi t}{T} + \ldots + b_1 \cos \frac{2\pi t}{T} + \ldots$$

---

[1] I have omitted details because the reader should find no difficulty in working out the results for himself. It is no more than an exercise on preceding work—page 211.

To evaluate A_0, multiply by the periodic time, *i.e.*, by T, as in (2), and integrate between the limits 0 and T. From page 211.

$$A_0 = \frac{1}{T}\int_0^T f(t)dt = \text{Average height of } f(t) = \frac{V}{2}.$$

For the constants of the cosine and sine terms, multiply respectively by $\cos (2\pi t/T)dt$, and by $\sin (2\pi t/T)dt$ and integrate between the limits 0 and T. The answer is

$$f(t) = \frac{V}{2} + \frac{2V}{\pi}\Big(\sin \frac{2\pi t}{T} + \frac{1}{3}\sin \frac{6\pi t}{T} + \frac{1}{5}\sin \frac{10\pi t}{T} + \dots\Big).$$

Remember $\sin 2n\pi$ is zero if n is odd or even ; $\cos 2n\pi$ is $+1$ if n is even, and -1 if n is odd or even. The integration in this section can all be done by the methods of §§ 73 and 75. Note, however, $\int x \sin nx dx = n^{-2}(\sin nx - nx \cos nx)$, on integration by parts.

(2) In Fig. 156, the straight lines sloping downwards from right to left

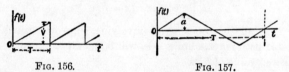

FIG. 156.   FIG. 157.

have the equation $f(t) = mt$, where m is a constant. When $t = T$, $f(t) = V$, so that $V = mT$, or $m = V/T$; $\therefore f(t) = Vt/T$. Hence show that

$$A_0 = \frac{V}{T}\int_0^T t \cdot dt = \frac{V}{2} ; \quad a_1 = \frac{2}{T}\int_0^T \frac{Vt}{T}\sin \frac{2\pi t}{T}dt = -\frac{V}{\pi},$$

and also

$$f(t) = \frac{V}{\pi}\Big(\frac{\pi}{2} - \sin \frac{2\pi t}{T} - \frac{1}{2}\sin \frac{4\pi t}{T} - \frac{1}{3}\sin \frac{6\pi t}{T} - \dots\Big).$$

(3) In Fig. 157, you can see that A_0 is zero because

$$A_0 = \frac{1}{T}\int_0^T f(t)dt = \text{Average height of } f(t) = 0; \quad a_1 = \frac{2}{T}\int_0^T f(t)\sin \frac{2\pi t}{T}dt.$$

Now notice that $f(t) = mt$ between the limits $-\frac{1}{4}T$ and $+\frac{1}{4}T$; and that when $t = \frac{1}{4}T$, $f(t) = a$ so that $a = \frac{1}{4}mT$; and $m = 4a/T$; while between the limits $t = \frac{1}{4}T$, and $t = \frac{3}{4}T$, $f(t) = 2a(1 - 2t/T)$; hence,

$$a_1 = \frac{2}{T}\int_{-\frac{1}{4}T}^{+\frac{1}{4}T}\frac{4at}{T}\sin \frac{2\pi t}{T}dt + \frac{2}{T}\int_{\frac{1}{4}T}^{\frac{3}{4}T}2a\Big(1 - \frac{2t}{T}\Big)\sin \frac{2\pi t}{T}dt = \frac{8a}{\pi^2}.$$

In a similar manner you can show that all the even a's vanish, and all the b's also vanish. Hence

$$f(t) = \frac{8a}{\pi}\Big(\sin \frac{2\pi t}{T} - \frac{1}{9}\sin \frac{6\pi t}{T} + \frac{1}{25}\sin \frac{10\pi t}{T} - \dots\Big).$$

There are several graphic methods for evaluating the coefficients of a Fourier's series. See J. Perry, *Electrician*, **28**, 362, 1892 ; W. B. Woodhouse, the same journal, **46**, 987, 1901 ; or, best of all, O. Henrici, *Phil. Mag.* [5], **38**, 110, 1894, when the series is used to express the electromotive force of an alternating current as a periodic function of the time.

EXAMPLE.—In any simultaneous drawing from each vessel, the probability that

Two white balls will occur is : $a_1 a_2/(a_1 + b_1) (a_2 + b_2)$; .   .   .   (5)

Two black balls will occur is : $b_1 b_2/(a_1 + b_1) (a_2 + b_2)$;   .   .   .   (6)

White ball drawn from the first, black ball from the next, is :

$$a_1 b_2/(a_1 + b_1) (a_2 + b_2) ; \quad . \quad . \quad . \quad . \quad (7)$$

Black ball drawn from the first, white ball from the next, is :

$$a_2 b_1/(a_1 + b_1) (a_2 + b_2) ; \quad \bullet \quad . \quad . \quad . \quad (8)$$

Black and white ball occur together, is : $(a_1 b_2 + b_1 a_2)/(a_1 + b_1) (a_2 + b_2)$.   (9)

The sum of (5), (6), (9) is unity. This condition is required by the above definition.

An event of this kind, produced by the composition of several events, is said to be a *compound event*. To throw three aces with three dice at one trial is a compound event dependent on the concurrence of three simple events. Errors of observation are compound events produced by the concurrence of several independent errors.

EXAMPLES.—(1) If the respective probabilities of the occurrence of each of n independent errors is $p, q, r \ldots$, the probability P of the occurrence of all together is $P = p \times q \times r \times \ldots$

(2) If, out of every 100 births, 49 are male and 51 female, what is the probability that the next two births shall be both boys ; both girls ; and a boy first, and a girl next ? Ansr. 0·2401 ; 0·2601 ; 0·2499. Hint. $\frac{49}{100} \times \frac{49}{100}$; $\frac{51}{100} \times \frac{51}{100}$; $\frac{49}{100} \times \frac{51}{100}$.

IV. The probability of the occurrence of several events which cannot occur together is the sum of the probabilities of their separate occurrences. If $p, q, \ldots$ denote the separate probabilities of different events, the probability, P, that one of the events will happen is,

$$P = p + q + \ldots \quad . \quad . \quad . \quad (10)$$

EXAMPLES.—(1) A bag contains 12 balls two of which are white, four black, six red, what is the probability that the first ball drawn will be a white, black, or a red one ? The probability that the ball will be a white is $\frac{1}{6}$, a black $\frac{1}{3}$, etc. The probability that the first ball drawn shall be a black or a white ball is $\frac{1}{2}$.

(2) In continuation of Ex. (2), preceding set, show that the probability that one shall be a boy and the other a girl is 0·4998 ; and that both shall be of the same sex, 0·5002. Hint. 0·2499 + 0·2499 ; 0·2401 + 0·2601.

V. If p denotes the probability that an event will happen on a single trial, the probability, P, that it will happen r times in n trials is

$$P = \frac{n(n - 1) \ldots (n - r + 1)}{r !} p^r (1 - p)^{n - r}. \quad . \quad (11)$$

The probability that the event will fail on any single trial is $1 - p$; the probability that it will fail every time is $(1 - p)^n$. The probability that it will happen on the first trial and fail on the succeeding $n-1$ trials is $p(1-p)^{n-1}$, from (4). But the event is just as likely to happen on the 2nd, 3rd... trials as on the first. Hence the probability that the event will happen just once in the n trials is, from (4), and (10),[1]

$$(p + p + \ldots + n \text{ times}) \times (1 - p)^{n-1} ; \text{ or, } np(1 - p)^{n-1}. \quad (12)$$

The probability that the event will occur on the first two trials and fail on the succeeding $n-2$ trials is $p^2(1-p)^{n-2}$. But the event is as likely to occur during the 1st and 3rd, 2nd and 4th,... trials. Hence the probability that it will occur just twice during the n trials is

$$\frac{1}{2!}n(n-1)p^2(1-p)^{n-2}. \quad . \quad . \quad . \quad (13)$$

The probability that it will occur r times in n trials is, therefore. represented by formula (11).

EXAMPLES.—(1) What is the probability of throwing an ace exactly three times in four trials with a single die? Ansr. $\frac{5}{324}$. Hint. $n = 4$; $r = 3$; there is one chance in six of throwing an ace on a single trial, hence $p = \frac{1}{6}$; $n - r = 1$; $p^r = (\frac{1}{6})^3$; $1 - p = \frac{5}{6}$. Hence, $\frac{4.3.2}{1.2.3} \times \frac{5}{6^4}$.

(2) What is the probability of throwing a deuce exactly three times in three trials? Ansr. $\frac{1}{216}$. $n = 3$; $r = 3$; $(1-p)^{n-r} = 5^0 = 1$; $p = \frac{1}{6}$, etc.

VI. If p denotes the very small probability that an event will happen on a single trial, the probability, P, that it will happen r times in a very great number, n, trials is

$$P = \frac{(np)^r}{r!}e^{-np}. \quad . \quad . \quad . \quad (14)$$

From formula (11), however small p may be, by increasing the number of trials, we can make the probability that the event will happen at least once in n trials as great as we please. The probability that the event will fail every time in n trials is $(1 - p)^n$, and if p be made small enough and n great enough, we can make $(1 - p)^n$ as small as we please.[2] If n is infinitely great and p infinitely small, we can write $n = n - 1 = n - 2 = \ldots$

$$\therefore (1-p)^n = 1 - np + \frac{n(n-1)}{2!}p^2 - \ldots = 1 - np + \frac{(np)^2}{2!} - \ldots \text{ (approx.)} ;$$

$$(1-p)^n = e^{-np} \text{ (approx.).} \quad . \quad . \quad . \quad (15)$$

---

[1] The student may here find it necessary to read over § 190, page 602.

[2] The reader should test this by substituting small numbers in place of p, and large ones for n. Use the binomial formula of § 97, page 282. See the remarks on page 14, § 11.

(14) follows immediately from (11) and (15). This result is very important.

EXAMPLE.—If n grains of wheat are scattered haphazard over a surface s units of area, show that the probability that a units of area will contain r grains of wheat is

$$\frac{\left(\dfrac{an}{s}\right)^r}{r!} e^{-\frac{an}{s}}.$$

Thus, $n \cdot ds/s$ represents the infinitely small probability that the small space ds contains a grain of wheat. If the selected space be a units of area, we may suppose each ds to be a trial, the number of trials will, therefore, be a/ds. Hence we must substitute an/s for np in (14) for the desired result.

VII. *The probability, P, that an event will occur* AT LEAST r *times in n trials is*

$$P = p^n + np^{n-1}(1-p) + \frac{n(n-1)}{2!}p^{n-2}(1-p)^2 + \dots \text{ to } (n-r) \text{ terms} \quad (16)$$

For if it occur every time, or fail only once, twice, ..., or $n - r$ times, it occurs r times. The whole probability of its occurring at least r times is therefore the sum of its occurring every time, of failing only once, twice, ..., $n - r$ times, etc.

EXAMPLE.—What is the probability of throwing a deuce three times at least in four trials? Ansr. $\frac{7}{432}$. Here $p^n = (\frac{1}{6})^4$; and the next term of (16) is $4 \times 5 \times (\frac{1}{6})^4$.

Sometimes a natural process proves far too complicated to admit of any simplification by means of "working hypotheses". The question naturally arises, can the observed sequence of events be reasonably attributed to the operation of a law of Nature or to chance? For example, it is observed that the average of a large number of readings of the barometer is greater at nine in the morning than at four in the afternoon; Laplace (*Théorie analytique des Probabilités*, Paris, 49, 1820) asked whether this was to be ascribed to the operation of an unknown law of Nature or to chance? Again, G. Kirchhoff (*Monatsberichte der Berliner Akademie*, Oct., 1859) inquired if the coincidence between 70 spectral lines in iron vapour and in sunlight could reasonably be attributed to chance. He found that the probability of a fortuitous coincidence was approximately as 1 : 1,000000,000000. Hence, he argued that there can be no reasonable doubt of the existence of iron in the sun. Mitchell (*Phil. Trans.*, **57**, 243, 1767; see also Kleiber, *Phil. Mag.*, [5], **24**, 439, 1887) has endeavoured to calculate if the number of star clusters is greater than what would be expected if the stars had been distributed haphazard over the heavens. A. Schuster (*Proc. Roy.*

Soc., **31**, 337, 1881) has tried to answer the question, Is the number of harmonic relations in the spectral lines of iron greater than what a chance distribution would give? Mallet (*Phil. Trans.*, **171**, 1003, 1880) and R. J. Strutt (*Phil. Mag.*, [6], **1**, 311, 1901) have asked, Do the atomic weights of the elements approximate as closely to whole numbers as can reasonably be accounted for by an accidental coincidence? In other words : Are there common-sense grounds for believing the truth of Prout's law, that " the atomic weights of the other elements are exact multiples of that of hydrogen " ?

The theory of probability does not pretend to furnish an infallible criterion for the discrimination of an accidental coincidence from the result of a determining cause. Certain conditions must be satisfied before any reliance can be placed upon its dictum. For example, a sufficiently large number of cases must be available. Moreover, the theory is applied irrespective of any knowledge to be derived from other sources which may or may not furnish corroborative evidence. Thus Kirchhoff's conclusion as to the probable existence of iron in the sun was considerably strengthened by the apparent relation between the brightness of the coincident lines in the two spectra.

For details of the calculations, the reader must consult the original memoirs. Most of the calculations are based upon the analysis in Laplace's old but standard *Théorie* (*l.c.*). An excellent *résumé* of this latter work will be found in the *Encyclopædia Metropolitana*. The more fruitful applications of the theory of probability to natural processes have been in connection with the kinetic theory of gases and the " law " relating to errors of observation.

§ 156. Application to the Kinetic Theory of Gases.

The purpose of the kinetic theory of gases is to explain the physical properties of gases from the hypothesis that a gas consists of a great number of molecules in rapid motion. The following illustrations are based, in the first instance, on a memoir by R. Clausius (*Phil. Mag.*, [4], **17**, 81, 1859). For further developments, O. E. Meyer's *The Kinetic Theory of Gases*, London, 1899, may be consulted.

I. To show that the probability that a single molecule, moving in a swarm of molecules at rest, will traverse a distance x without collision is

$$P = e^{-\frac{x}{i}}, \qquad . \qquad . \qquad . \qquad (17)$$

where l denotes the probable value of the free path the molecule
can travel without collision, and x/l denotes the ratio of the path
actually traversed to the mean length of the free path. " Free
path " is defined as the distance traversed by a molecule between
two successive collisions.   The " mean free path " is the average
of a great number of free paths of a molecule. Consider any
molecule moving under these conditions in a given direction. Let
a denote the probability that the molecule will travel a path one
unit long without collision, the probability that the molecule will
travel a path two units long is $a \cdot a$, or a^2, and the probability that
the molecule will travel a path x units long without collision is,
from (4),

$$P = a^x, \qquad . \qquad . \qquad . \qquad (18)$$

where a is a proper fraction. Its logarithm is therefore negative.
(Why ?) If the molecules of the gas are stationary, the value of
a is the same whatever the direction of motion of the single molecule. From (15), therefore,

$$P = e^{-\frac{x}{i}}$$

where $l = 1/\log a$. We can get a clear idea of the meaning of this
formula by comparing it with (15). Supposing the traversing of
unit path is reckoned a " trial," x in (17) then corresponds with n
in (15). $1/l$ in (17) replaces p in (15). $1/l$, therefore, represents
the probability that an event (collision) will happen during one
trial. If l trials are made, a collision is certain to occur. This is
virtually the definition of mean free path.

*II. To show that the length of the path which a molecule, moving
amid a swarm of molecules at rest can traverse without collision is
probably*

$$l = \frac{\lambda^3}{\rho^2 \pi}, \qquad . \qquad . \qquad . \qquad (19)$$

where λ denotes the mean distance between any two neighbouring
molecules, ρ the radius of the sphere of action corresponding to the
distance apart of the molecules during a collision, π is a constant
with its usual signification. Let unit volume of the gas contain N
molecules. Let this volume be divided into N small cubes, each of
which, on the average, contains only one molecule. Let λ denote
the length of the edge of one of these little cubes. Only one molecule is contained in a cube of capacity λ^3. The area of a cross

section through the centre of a sphere of radius ρ, is $\pi\rho^2$, (13), page 604.   If the moving molecule travels a distance λ, the hemispherical anterior surface of the molecule passes through a cylindrical space of volume $\pi\rho^2\lambda$ (26), page 605.   Therefore, the probability that there is a molecule in the cylinder $\pi\rho^2\lambda$ is to 1 as $\pi\rho^2\lambda$ is to λ^3, that is to say, the probability that the molecule under consideration will collide with another as it passes over a path of length λ, is $\pi\rho^2\lambda : \lambda^3$.   The probability that there will be no collision is $1 - \dfrac{\pi\rho^2}{\lambda^2}$.   From (17),

$$P = e^{-\frac{\lambda}{l}} = 1 - \frac{\rho^2\pi}{\lambda^2}. \quad . \quad . \quad . \quad (20)$$

According to the kinetic theory, one fundamental property of gases is that the intermolecular spaces are very great in comparison with the dimensions of the molecules, and, therefore, $\rho^2\pi/\lambda^2$ is very small in comparison with unity.   Hence also λ/l is a small magnitude in comparison with unity.   Expand $e^{-\lambda/l}$ according to the exponential theorem (page 285), neglect terms involving the higher powers of λ, and

$$e^{-\frac{\lambda}{l}} = 1 - \frac{\lambda}{l}. \, , \quad . \quad . \quad . \quad (21)$$

From (20) and (21),

$$l = \frac{\lambda^3}{\rho^2\pi} \,; \text{ or, } P = e^{-\frac{\rho^2\pi x}{\lambda^3}}. \quad . \quad . \quad . \quad (22)$$

EXAMPLE.—The behaviour of gases under pressure indicates that ρ is very much smaller than λ.   Hence show that " a molecule passes by many other molecules like itself before it collides with another".   Hint. From the first of equations (22), $l : \lambda = \lambda^2 : \rho^2\pi$.   Interpret the symbols.

III. To show that the mean value of the free path of n molecules moving under the same conditions as the solitary molecule just considered, is

$$l = \frac{\lambda^3}{\rho^2\pi}. \quad . \quad . \quad . \quad (23)$$

Out of n molecules which travel with the same velocity in the same direction as the given molecule, $ne^{-x/l}$ will travel the distance x without collision, and $ne^{-(x+dx)/l}$ will travel the distance $x + dx$ without collision.   Of the molecules which traverse the path x,

$$n\left(e^{-\frac{x}{l}} - e^{-\frac{x+dx}{l}}\right) = ne^{-\frac{x}{l}}\left(1 - e^{-\frac{dx}{l}}\right) = \frac{n}{l}e^{-\frac{x}{l}}dx,$$

of them will undergo collision in passing over the distance dx. The last transformation follows directly from (21).   The sum of all the paths traversed by the molecules passing x and $x + dx$ is

$$\frac{x}{l}ne^{-\frac{x}{i}}dx.$$

Since each molecule must collide somewhere in passing between the limits $x = 0$ and $x = \infty$, the sum of all the possible paths traversed by the n molecules before collision is

$$n\int_0^\infty \frac{x}{l}e^{-\frac{x}{i}}dx,$$

and the mean value of these n free paths is

$$\int_0^\infty \frac{x}{l}e^{-\frac{x}{i}}dx = l.$$

Integrate the indefinite integral as indicated on page 205. From (4) we get (23). This represents the mean free path of these molecules moving with a uniform velocity.

EXAMPLES.—(1) A molecule moving with a velocity V enters a space filled with n stationary molecules of a gas per unit volume, what is the probability that this molecule will collide with one of those at rest in unit time? Use the above notation. The molecule travels the space V in unit time. In doing this, it meets with $\pi n\rho^2 V$ molecules at rest. The probable number of collisions in unit time is, therefore, $\pi n\rho^2 V$, which represents the probability of a collision in unit time.

(2) Show that the probable number of collisions made in unit time by a molecule travelling with a uniform velocity V, in a swarm of N molecules at rest, is

$$\frac{V}{l} = \frac{V\rho^2\pi}{\lambda^3}. \qquad \cdots \cdots \quad (24)$$

What is the relation between this and the preceding result? Note the number of collisions $= V/l$; and $N\lambda^3 = 1$.

IV. The number of collisions made in unit time by a molecule moving with uniform velocity in a direction which makes an angle θ with the direction of motion of a swarm of molecules also moving with the same uniform velocity is probably

$$\frac{\rho^2\pi}{\lambda^3}2v \sin \tfrac{1}{2}\theta. \qquad \cdots \quad (25)$$

Let v be the resultant velocity of *one* molecule, and x_1, y_1, z_1 the three component velocities, then, from the parallelopiped of velocities, page 125,

$$v^2 = x_1^2 + y_1^2 + z_1^2$$
$$x_1 = v \cos \theta_1; \; y_1 = v \sin \theta_1 . \cos \phi_1; \; z_1 = v \sin \theta_1 . \sin \phi_1 \Big\}. \quad (26)$$

If one *set* of molecules moves with a uniform velocity, v, whose components are x, y, z, relative to the given molecule moving with the same uniform velocity, v, whose components are x_1, y_1, z_1, then,

$$v^2 = x^2 + y^2 + z^2 ; \qquad . \qquad . \qquad . \quad (27)$$

$$x = v \cos \theta ; \; y = v \sin \theta . \cos \theta ; \; z = \sin \theta . \cos \phi, \; . \quad (28)$$

and the relative resultant velocity, v, of one molecule with respect to the other considered at rest, is

$$V = \sqrt{(x_1 - x)^2 + (y_1 - y)^2 + (z_1 - z)^2}. \quad . \quad (29)$$

If we choose the three coordinate axes so that the x-axis coincides with the direction of motion of the given molecule, we may substitute these values in (26), remembering that $\cos 0° = 1$, $\sin 0° = 0$,

$$y_1 = 0 ; \; z_1 = 0 ; \; \therefore x_1 = v. \qquad . \qquad . \quad (30)$$

Substitute (30) and (26) in (29), we get

$$V = \sqrt{(v - v \cos \theta)^2 + v^2 \sin^2\theta . \cos^2\phi + v^2 \sin^2\theta . \sin^2\phi} ;$$

$$\therefore V = \sqrt{v^2 - 2v^2 \cos \theta + v^2 \cos^2\theta + v^2 \sin^2\theta},$$

since $\sin^2\phi + \cos^2\phi = 1$. Similarly, $\cos^2\theta + \sin^2\theta = 1$, and consequently

$$V = v \sqrt{2 - 2 \cos \theta} = v \sqrt{2(1 - \cos \theta)}.$$

But we know, page 612, that $1 - \cos x = 2(\sin \tfrac{1}{2}x)^2$, hence,

$$V = 2v \sin \tfrac{1}{2}\theta. \qquad . \qquad . \qquad . \quad (31)$$

Having found the relative velocity of the molecules, it follows directly from (24) and (31), that

$$\text{Number of collisions} = \frac{V\rho^2\pi}{\lambda^3} = \frac{\rho^2\pi}{\lambda^3} 2v \sin \tfrac{1}{2}\theta.$$

V. *The number of collisions encountered in unit time by a molecule moving in a swarm of molecules in all directions, is*

$$\frac{4}{3} . \frac{V\rho^2\pi}{\lambda^3}. \qquad . \qquad . \qquad . \qquad . \quad (32)$$

Let V denote the velocity of the molecules, then the different motions can be resolved into three groups of motions according to the parallelopiped of velocities. Proceed as in the last illustration. The number of molecules, n, moving in a direction between θ and $\theta + d\theta$ is to the total number of molecules, N, in unit volume as

$$n : N = 2\pi \sin \theta d\theta : 4\pi ; \text{ or, } n = \tfrac{1}{2}N \sin \theta d\theta. \quad (33)$$

Since the angle θ can increase from $0°$ to $180°$, the total number of collisions is

$$\frac{V\rho^2\pi}{\lambda^3} . \frac{n}{N} = \frac{V\rho^2\pi}{\lambda^3} \sin \frac{\theta}{2} . \frac{1}{2} \sin \theta d\theta.$$

To get the total number of collisions, it only remains to integrate for all directions of motion between $0°$ and $180°$. Thus if A denotes the number of collisions,

$$A = \frac{V\rho^2\pi}{\lambda^3}\int_0^\pi \sin\frac{\theta}{2}\cdot\sin\theta d\theta = \frac{2V\rho^2\pi}{\lambda^3}\int_0^\pi \sin^2\frac{\theta}{2}\cdot\cos\frac{\theta}{2}d\theta = \frac{4}{3}\cdot\frac{V\rho^2\pi}{\lambda^3},$$

by the method of integration on page 212.

EXAMPLE.—Find the length of the free path of a molecule moving in a swarm of molecules moving in all directions, with a velocity V. Ansr.

Length of free path $= V/A = \frac{3}{4}\lambda^3/\rho^2\pi$. . . . (34)

For the hypothesis of uniform velocity see § 164, page 534.

VI. *Assuming that two unlike molecules combine during a collision, the velocity of chemical reaction between two gases is*

$$\frac{dx}{dt} = kNN', ...   (35)$$

where N and N' are the number of molecules of each of the two gases respectively contained in unit volume of the mixed gases, dx denotes the number of molecules of one gas in unit volume which combines with the other in the time dt; k is a constant. Let the two gases be A and B.   Let λ and λ' respectively denote the distances between two neighbouring molecules of the same kind, then, as above,

$$N\lambda^3 = N'\lambda'^3 = 1.   .   .   .   (36)$$

Let ρ be the radius of the sphere of action, and suppose the molecules combine when the sphere of action of the two kinds of molecules approaches within 2ρ, it is required to find the rate of combination of the two gases.   The probability that a B molecule will come within the sphere of action of an A molecule in unit time is $V\pi\rho^2/\lambda^3$, by (24).   Among the N' molecules of B,

$$N'\frac{\pi\rho^2}{\lambda^3}Vdt; \text{ or, } NN'\pi\rho^2Vdt,   .   .   (37)$$

by (36), combine in the time dt.   But the number of molecules which combine in the time dt is $-dN = -dN'$, or, from (37),

$$dN = dN' = -NN'\pi\rho^2Vdt.$$

If dx represents the number of molecules in unit volume which combines in the time dt,

$$dx = dN = dN' = \pi\rho^2VNN'dt.   \therefore\frac{dx}{dt} = kNN',$$

by collecting together all the constants under the symbol k.   This will be at once recognized as the law of mass action applied to bimolecular reactions.   J. J. Thomson's memoir, "The Chemical Combination of Gases," *Phil. Mag.*, [5], **18**, 233, 1884, might now be read by the chemical student with profit.

§ 157. Errors of Observation.

If a number of experienced observers agreed to test, independently, the accuracy of the mark etched round the neck of a litre flask with the greatest precision possible, the inevitable result would be that every measurement would be different.   Thus, we might expect

$$1\cdot0003;\ 0\cdot9991;\ 1\cdot0007;\ 1\cdot0002;\ 1\cdot0001;\ 0\cdot9998;\ldots$$

Exactly the same thing would occur if one observer, taking every known precaution to eliminate error, repeats a measurement a great number of times.   The discrepancies doubtless arise from various unknown and therefore uncontrolled sources of error.

We are told that sodium chloride crystallizes in the form of cubes, and that the angle between two adjoining faces of a crystal is, in consequence, 90°.   As a matter of fact the angle, as measured, varies within 0·5° either way.   No one has yet exactly verified the Gay Lussac-Humboldt law of the combination of gases; nor has any one yet separated hydrogen and oxygen from water, by electrolysis, in the proportions required by the ratio, $2H_2 : O_2$.

The irregular deviations of the measurements from, say, the arithmetical mean of all are called **accidental errors.**   In the following discussion we shall call them "errors of observation" unless otherwise stated.   These deviations become more pronounced the nearer the approach to the limits of accurate measurement.   Or, as Lamb[1] puts it, "the more refined the methods employed the more vague and elusive does the supposed magnitude become; the judgment flickers and wavers, until at last in a sort of despair *some* result is put down, not in the belief that it is exact, but with the feeling that it is the best we can make of the matter".   It is the object of the remainder of this chapter to find what is the best we can make of a set of discordant measurements.

The simplest as well as the most complex measurements are invariably accompanied by these fortuitous errors.   Absolute agreement is itself an accidental coincidence.   Stanley Jevons says, "it is one of the most embarrassing things we can meet when experimental results agree too closely".   Such agreement should at once excite a feeling of distrust.

---

[1] H. Lamb, Presidential Address, B.A. meeting, 1904; *Nature*, 70, 372, 1904.

The observed relations between two variables, therefore, should not be represented by a point in space, rather by a circle around whose centre the different observations will be grouped (Fig. 165). Any particular observation will find a place somewhere within the circumference of the circle. The diagram (Fig. 165) suggests our old illustration, a rifleman aiming at the centre of a target. The rifleman may be likened to an observer; the place where the bullet hits, to an observation; the distance between the centre and the place where the bullet hits the target

Fig. 165.

resembles an error of observation. A shot at the centre of the target is thus an attempt to hit the centre, a scientific measurement is an attempt to hit the true value of the magnitude measured (Maxwell).

The greater the radius of the circle (Fig. 165), the cruder and less accurate the measurements; and, *vice versâ*, the less the measurements are affected by errors of observation, the smaller will be the radius of the circle. In other words, the less the skill of the shooter, the larger will be the target required to record his attempts to hit the centre.

§ 158. The "Law" of Errors.

These errors may be represented pictorially another way. Draw a vertical line through the centre of the target (Fig. 165) and let the hits to the right of this line represent positive errors and those to the left negative errors. Suppose that 500 shots are fired in a competition; of these, ten on the right side were between 0·4 and 0·5 feet from the centre of the target; twenty shots between 0·3 and 0·4 feet away; and so on, as indicated in the following table.

Positive Deviations from Mean between	Number of Errors.	Percentage Number of Errors.	Negative Deviations from Mean between	Number of Errors.	Percentage Number of Errors.
0·4 and 0·5	10	2	0·4 and 0·5	10	2
0·3 and 0·4	20	4	0·3 and 0·4	20	4
0·2 and 0·3	40	8	0·2 and 0·3	40	8
0·1 and 0·2	80	16	0·1 and 0·2	80	16
0·0 and 0·1	100	20	0·0 and 0·1	100	20

Plot, as ordinates, the numbers in the third column with the

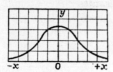

means of the two corresponding limits in the first column as abscissæ. The curve shown in Fig. 166 will be the result.

FIG. 166.—Probability
Curve.

By a study of the last two diagrams, we shall find that there is a regularity in the grouping of these irregular errors which, as a matter of fact, becomes more pronounced the greater the number of trials we take into consideration. Thus, it is found that—

1. Small errors are more frequent than large ones.

2. Positive errors are as frequent as negative errors.

3. Very large positive or negative errors do not occur.

Any mathematical relation between an error, x, and the frequency, or rather the probability, of its occurrence, y, must satisfy these characteristics. When such a function,

$$y = f(x),$$

is plotted, it must have a maximum ordinate corresponding with no error; it must be symmetrical with respect to the y-axis, in order to satisfy the second condition; and as x increases numerically, y must decrease until, when x becomes very large, y must become vanishingly small. Such is the curve represented by the equation,

$$y = ke^{-h^2x^2}, \qquad . \qquad . \qquad . \qquad . \qquad (1)$$

where h and k are constants.[1] The graph of this equation, called the **probability curve,** or curve of frequency, or curve of errors,

is obtained by assigning arbitrary constant values to h and k and plotting a set of corresponding values of x and y in the usual way.[2]

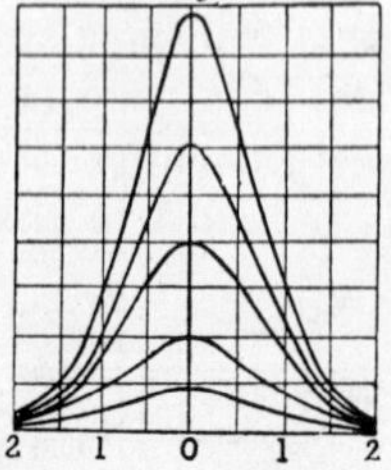

I. To find a meaning for the constant k. Put $x = 0$, then $y = k$, that is the maximum ordinate of the curve. Now put $h = 1$, and make k successively $\frac{1}{2}$, 1, 2, 3, 4. Plot corresponding values of x and y, as shown in Fig. 167. Another plan is "to bend a loop of wire into the form of one of the curves, and to place a lamp behind it so as to throw the shadow upon the screen. The loop and lamp might be easily made to move in such

FIG. 167.—Probability
Curves (h constant, k
variable).

---

[1] Use Table XVII., page 626.

[2] E. B. Sargant, "The Education of Examiners," *Nature,* **70,** 63, 1904.

a manner that the shadows in the successive positions gave the whole series of curves." If we agree to define an error as the deviation of each measurement from the arithmetical mean, k corresponds with those measurements which coincide with the mean itself, or are affected by no error at all. The height at which the curve cuts the y-axis represents the frequency of occurrence of the arithmetical mean ; k has nothing to do with the actual shape of the curve beyond increasing the length of the maximum ordinate as the accuracy of the observations increases.

II. To find a meaning for the constant h. Put $k = 1$, and plot corresponding values of x and y for $x = \pm\ 0\cdot3$, $\pm\ 0\cdot4$, $\pm\ 0\cdot5$, $\pm\ 0\cdot6$, ... when $h = \frac{1}{4}, \frac{1}{2}, 1, 2, 3, ...$, as shown in Fig. 168. In this way, it will be observed that although all the curves cut the y-axis at

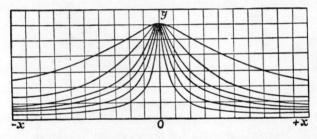

FIG. 168.—Probability Curves (k constant, h variable).

the same point, the greater the value of h, the steeper will be the curve in the neighbourhood of the central ordinate Oy. The physical signification of this is that the greater the magnitude of h, the more accurate the results and the less will be the magnitude of the deviation of individual measurements from the arithmetical mean of the whole set. Hence Gauss calls h the **absolute measure or modulus of precision.**

III. When h and k both vary, we get the set of curves shown on Fig. 169.

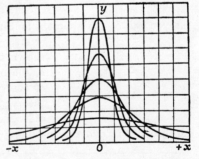

FIG. 169.—Probability Curves (h and k both variable).

A good shot will get a curve enclosing a very much smaller area than one whose shooting is wild.

We must now submit our empirical "law" to the test of experiment. Bessel has compared the errors of observation in 470 astronomical measurements made by Bradley with those which should occur according to the law of errors. The results of this comparison are shown in the following table :—[1]

Magnitude of Error in Parts of a Second of Arc, between:	Number of Errors of each Magnitude.	
	Observed.	Theory.
0 and 0·1	94	95
0·1 and 0·2	88	89
0·2 and 0·3	78	78
0·3 and 0·4	58	64
0·4 and 0·5	51	50
0·5 and 0·6	36	36
0·6 and 0·7	26	24
0·7 and 0·8	14	15
0·8 and 0·9	10	9
0·9 and 1·0	7	5
above 1·0	8	5

This is a remarkable verification of the above formula. The theory, be it observed, provides for errors of *any* magnitude, however large ; in practice, there is a limit above which no error will be found to occur. The dots in Fig. 170 represent the "observed errors" in some determinations of the velocity of light. The graph, plotted from the error curve

$$y = 8\cdot9e^{-0\cdot025x^2},$$

as you can see, is almost a faithful representation of the actual

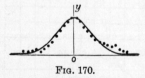
FIG. 170.

errors. Airy and Newcomb have also shown that the number and magnitude of the errors affecting extended series of observations are in fair accord with theory. But in every case, the number of large errors actually found is in *excess* of theory. To quote an instance. S. Newcomb examined 684 ob-

---

servations of the transit of Mercury. According to the "law" of errors, there should be 5 errors numerically greater than ± 27″. In reality 49 surpassed these limits. You can also notice how the "big" errors accumulate at the ends of the frequency curve in Fig. 170.

The theory assumes that the observations are all liable to the same errors, but differ in the accidental circumstances which give rise to the errors.[1] Equation (1) is by no means a perfect representation of *the* law of errors. The truth is more complex. The magnitude of the errors seems to depend, in some curious way, upon the number of observations. In an extended series of observations the errors may be arranged in groups. Each group has a different modulus of precision. This means that the modulus of precision is not constant throughout an extended series of observations. See *Encyc. Brit.*, F. Y. Edgeworth's art. "Law of Error," **28**, 280, 1902. But the probability curve represented by the formula

$$y = ke^{-h^2 x^2},$$

may be considered a very fair graphic representation of the law connecting the probability of the occurrence of an error with its magnitude. All our subsequent work is based upon this empirical law! J. Venn in his *Logic of Chance*, 1896, calls the "exponential law of errors," a *law*, because it expresses a physical fact relating to the frequency with which errors are found to present themselves in practice; while the "method of least squares" is a *rule* showing how the best representative value may be extracted from a set of experimental results. H. Poincaré, in the preface to his *Thermo-dynamique*, Paris, 1892, quotes the laconic remark, "everybody firmly believes in it (the law of errors), because mathematicians imagine that it is a fact of observation, and observers that it is a theorem of mathematics".

Adrian (1808) appears to have been the first to try to deduce the above formula on theoretical grounds. Several attempts have since been made, notably by Gauss, Hagen, Herschel, Laplace, etc., but I believe without success.

---

[1] Some observers' results seem more liable to these large errors than others, due, perhaps, to carelessness, or lapses of attention. Thomson and Tait, I presume, would call the abnormally large errors "avoidable mistakes".

§ 159. The Probability Integral.

Let x_0, x_1, x_2, ...x be a series of errors in ascending order of magnitude from x_0 to x. Let the differences between the successive values of x be equal. If x is an error, the probability of committing an error between x_0 and x is the sum of the separate probabilities $ke^{-h^2x_0{}^2}$, $ke^{-h^2x_1{}^2}$..., ,(10), page 501, or

$$P = k(e^{-h^2x_0{}^2} + e^{-h^2x_1{}^2} + \ldots) = k\Sigma_{x_0}^{x}e^{-h^2x^2}. \qquad (1)$$

If the summation sign is replaced by that of integration, we must let dx denote the successive intervals between any two limits x_0 and x, thu

$$P = \frac{k}{dx}\int_{x_0}^{x}e^{-h^2x^2}dx.$$

Now it is certain that all the errors are included between the limits $\pm \infty$, and, since certainty is represented by unity, we have

$$1 = \frac{k}{dx}\int_{-\infty}^{+\infty}e^{-h^2x^2}dx = \frac{k}{dx} \cdot \frac{\sqrt{\pi}}{h}, \qquad . \quad . \quad (2)$$

from page 345. Or,

$$k = \frac{h}{\sqrt{\pi}} \cdot dx. \qquad . \quad . \quad . \quad (3)$$

Substituting this value of k in the probability equation (1), preceding section, we get the same relation expressed in another form, namely,

$$\frac{h}{\sqrt{\pi}}e^{-h^2x^2}dx, \qquad . \quad . \quad . \quad (4)$$

a result which represents the probability of errors of observation between the magnitudes x and $x + dx$. By this is meant the ratio:

$$\frac{\text{Number of errors between } x \text{ and } x + dx}{\text{Total number of errors}}.$$

The symbols y and P are convenient abbreviations for this cumbrous phrase. For a large number of observations affected with accidental errors, the probability of an error of observation having a magnitude x, is,

$$y = \frac{h}{\sqrt{\pi}}e^{-h^2x^2}dx, \qquad . \quad . \quad . \quad (5)$$

which is known as **Gauss' law of errors.** This result has the same meaning as $y = ke^{-h^2x^2}$ of the preceding section. In (4) dx represents the interval, for any special case, between the successive values of x. For example, if a substance is weighed to the thousandth of a gram, $dx = 0\cdot001$; if in hundredths, $dx = 0\cdot01$, etc.   The probability that there will be no error is

$$\frac{h \cdot dx}{\sqrt{\pi}} ; \quad . \quad . \quad . \quad . \quad (6)$$

the probability that there will be no errors of the magnitude of a milligram is

$$\frac{0 \cdot 001 h}{\sqrt{\pi}} . . \quad . \quad . \quad . \quad . \quad (7)$$

The probability that an error will lie between any two limits x_0 and x is

$$P = \frac{h}{\sqrt{\pi}} \int_{x_0}^{x} e^{-h^2 x^2} dx. \quad . \quad . \quad . \quad (8)$$

The probability that an error will lie between the limits 0 and x is

$$P = \frac{2h}{\sqrt{\pi}} \int_{0}^{x} e^{-h^2 x^2} dx, \quad . \quad . \quad . \quad (9)$$

which expresses the probability that an error will be numerically less than x.   We may also put

$$P = \frac{2}{\sqrt{\pi}} \int_{0}^{hx} e^{-h^2 x^2} d(hx), \quad . \quad . \quad . \quad (10)$$

which is another way of writing the probability integral (8).   In (8), the limits x_0 and x; and in (9) and (10), $\pm x$.   By differentiation and the usual method for obtaining a minimum value of any function, we find, from (1), that y, in $y = ke^{-h^2 x^2}$, is a minimum when

$$x^2 = \frac{1}{2h^2} ; \therefore x_0^2 + x_1^2 + x_2^2 + \ldots + x_n^2 = \Sigma \frac{1}{2h^2}.$$

But we have seen that the more accurate the observations the greater the value of h.   The greater the value of h, the smaller the value of $\Sigma(x^2)$; $\Sigma(x^2)$ is a minimum when h is a maximum. This is nothing but **Legendre's principle of least squares**: *The most probable value for the observed quantities is that for which the sum of the squares of the individual errors is a minimum.* That is to say, when

$$x_0^2 + x_1^2 + x_2^2 + \ldots + x_n^2 = \text{A MINIMUM}, \quad (11)$$

where $x_1, x_2, \ldots, x_n$, represents the errors respectively affecting the first, second, and the nth observations.

To illustrate the reasonableness of the principle of least squares we may revert to an old regulation of the Belgian army in which the individual scores of the riflemen were formed by adding up the distances of each man's shots from the centre of the target.   The smallest sum won "le grand prix" of the regiment. It is not difficult to see that this rule is faulty. Suppose that one shooter scored a 1 and a 3 ; another shooter two 2's. It is obvious that the latter score shows better shooting than the former. The shots may deviate in any direction without affecting the score. Consequently, the magnitude of each deviation is proportional, not to the magnitude of the *straight line* drawn from the place where the bullet hits to the centre of the target, but to the *area* of the circle described about the centre of the target with that line as radius. This means that it would be better to give the grand prize to the score which had a minimum sum of the *squares* of the distances of the shots from the centre of the target.[1] This is nothing but a graphic representation of the principle of least squares, formula (11). In this way, the two shooters quoted above would respectively score a 10 and an 8.

§ 160. The Best Representative Value for a Set of Observations.

It is practically useless to define an error as the deviation of any measurement from the true result, because that definition would imply a knowledge which is the object of investigation. What then is an error ? Before we can answer this question, we must determine the most probable value of the quantity measured. The only available data, as we have just seen, are always associated with the inevitable errors of observation. The measurements, in consequence, all disagree among themselves within certain limits. In spite of this fact, the investigator is called upon to state *definitely* what he considers to be the most probable value of the magnitude under investigation. Indeed, *every chemical or physical constant in our text-books is the best representative value of a more or less extended series of discordant observations*. For instance, giant attempts have been made to find the exact length of a column of pure mercury of one square millimetre cross-sectional area which has a resistance of one ohm at 0° C. The following numbers have been obtained :

106·33 ;	106·31 ;	106·24 ;
106·32 ;	106·29 ;	106·21 ;
106·32 ;	106·27 ;	106·19,

---

[1] See properties of similar figures, page 603.

centimetres (J. D. Everett's *Illustrations of the C.G.S. System of Units*, London, 176, 1891). There is no doubt that the true value of the required constant lies somewhere between 106·19 and 106·33 ; but no reason is apparent why one particular value should be chosen in preference to another. The physicist, however, must select *one* number from the infinite number of possible values between the limits 106·19 and 106·33 cm.

I. *What is the best representative value of a set of discordant results ?* The arithmetical mean naturally suggests itself, and some mathematicians start from the axiom : " the arithmetical mean is the best representative value of a series of discrepant observations ". Various attempts, based upon the law of errors, have been made to show that the arithmetical mean is the best representative value of a number of observations made under the same conditions and all equally trustworthy. The proof rests upon the fact that the positive and negative deviations, being equally probable, will ultimately balance each other as shown in Ex. (1), below.[1]

EXAMPLES.—(1) If a_1, a_2, ... a_n are a series of observations, a their arithmetical mean, show that the algebraic sum of the residual errors is

$$(a_1 - a) + (a_2 - a) + \ldots + (a_n - a) = 0. \qquad . \qquad . \qquad (1)$$

Hint. By definition of arithmetical mean,

$$a = \frac{a_1 + a_2 + \ldots + a_n}{n}; \text{ or, } na = a_1 + a_2 + \ldots + a_n.$$

Distribute the n a's on the right-hand side so as to get (1), etc.

(2) Prove that the arithmetical mean makes the sum of the squares of the errors a minimum. Hint. See page 550.

En passant, notice that in calculating the mean of a number of observations which agree to a certain number of digits, it is not necessary to perform the whole of the addition. For example, the mean of the above nine measurements is written

$$106 + \tfrac{1}{9}(\cdot 33 + \cdot 32 + \cdot 32 + \cdot 31 + \cdot 29 + \cdot 27 + \cdot 24 + \cdot 21 + \cdot 19) = 106 \cdot 276.$$

II. *The best representative value of a constant interval.* When

---

[1] G. Hinrichs, in his *The Absolute Atomic Weights of the Chemical Elements*, criticizes the selection (and the selectors) of the arithmetical mean as the best representative value of a set of discordant observations. He asks : " If we cannot use the arithmetical mean of a large number of simple weighings of actual shillings as the true value of a (new) shilling, how dare we assume that the mean value of a few determinations of the atomic weight of a chemical element will give us its true value ? " But there seems to be a misunderstanding somewhere. F. Y. Edgeworth has " The Choice of Means," *Phil. Mag.*, [5], 24, 268, 1887, and several articles on related subjects in the same journal between 1883 and 1889.

the best representative value of a constant interval x in the expression $x_n = x_0 + nx$ (where n is a positive integer 1, 2 ...), is to be determined from a series of measurements x_0, x_1, x_2, ..., such that

$$x_1 = x_0 + x \; ; \; x_2 = x_0 + 2x \; ; \; \ldots x_n = x_0 + nx,$$

where x_0 denotes the first observation, x_1 the second reading when $n = 1$; x_2, the third reading when $n = 2$; ... The best value for the constant interval x has to be computed. Obviously,

$$x = x_1 - x_0 \; ; \; x = x_2 - x_1 \; ; \; \ldots x = x_n - x_{n-1}.$$

The arithmetical mean cannot be employed because it reduces to

$$x = \frac{x_n - x_0}{n}$$

the same as if the first and last term had alone been measured. In such cases it is usual to refer the results to the expression

$$x = 6\frac{(n-1)(x_n - x_1) + (n-3)(x_{n-1} - x_2) + \ldots}{n(n^2 - 1)}, \qquad (2)$$

which has been obtained from the last of equations (4), page 327, by putting

$$\Sigma(x) = \Sigma(n) = 1 + 2 + \ldots + n = \tfrac{1}{2}n(n+1);$$
$$\Sigma(x^2) = \Sigma(n^2) = 1^2 + 2^2 + \ldots + n^2 = \tfrac{1}{6}n(n+1)(2n+1);$$
$$\Sigma(y) = \Sigma(x_n) = x_1 + x_2 + \ldots x_n; \quad \Sigma(xy) = \Sigma(nx_n) = x_1 + 2x_2 + \ldots + nx_n.$$

If n is odd, the middle measurement does not come in at all. It is therefore advisable to make an even number of observations. Such measurements might occur in finding the length of a rod at different temperatures; the oscillations of a galvanometer needle; the interval between the dust figures in Kundt's method for the velocity of sound in gases; the influence of CH_2 on the physical and chemical properties of homologous series of organic chemistry, etc.

EXAMPLES.—(1) In a Kundt's experiment for the ratio of the specific heats of a gas, the dust figures were recorded in the laboratory notebook at 30·7, 43·1, 55·6, 67·9, 80·1, 92·3, 104·6, 116·9, 129·2, 141·7, 154·0, 166·1 centimetres. What is the best representative value for the distance between the nodes? Ansr. 12·3 cm.

(2) The following numbers were obtained for the time of vibration, in seconds, of the "magnet bar" in Gauss and Weber's magnetometer in some experiments on terrestrial magnetism: 3·25; 9·90; 16·65; 23·35; 30·00; 36·65; 43·30; 50·00; 56·70; 63·30; 69·80; 76·55; 83·30; 89·90; 96·65; 103·15; 109·80; 116·65; 123·25; 129·95; 136·70; 143·35. Show that the period of vibration is 6·707 seconds.

(3) An alternative method not dependent upon "least squares" is shown in the following example: a swinging galvanometer needle "reversed" at (a)

§ 161. PROBABILITY AND THE THEORY OF ERRORS. 521

10 min. 9·90 sec.; (b) 10 min. 23·20 sec.; (c) 10 min. 36·45 sec.; (d) 10 min.
49·80 sec.; (e) 11 min. 3·25 sec.; (f) 11 min. 16·60 sec., required the period of
oscillation. Subtract (a) from (d) and divide the result by 3. We get 13·300 ;
subtract (b) from (e). We get 13·350; similarly, from (c) and (f) we get 13·383.
Mean = 13·344 = period of oscillation.

§ 161. The Probable Error.

Some observations deviate so little from the mean that we may
consider that value to be a very close approximation to the truth, in
other cases the arithmetical mean is worth very little. The question,
therefore, to be settled is, What degree of confidence may we have in
selecting this mean as the best representative value of a series of observations? In other words, How good or how bad are the results?

We could employ Gauss' absolute measure of precision to answer
this question. It is easy to show that *the measure of precision of
two series of observations is inversely as their accuracy.* If the
probabilities of an error x_1, lying between 0 and l_1, and of an error
x_2, between 0 and l_2, are respectively

$$P_1 = \frac{1}{\sqrt{\pi}} \int_0^{l_1} e^{-h_1^2 x_1^2} d(h_1 x_1) \; ; \; P_2 = \frac{1}{\sqrt{\pi}} \int_0^{l_2} e^{-h_2^2 x_2^2} d(h_2 x_2),$$

it is evident that when the observations are worth an equal degree
of confidence, $P_1 = P_2$.

$$\therefore l_1 h_1 = l_2 h_2 \; ; \; \text{or,} \; l_1 : l_2 = h_2 : h_1,$$

or the measure of precision of two series of observations is inversely as their accuracy. An error l_1 will have the same degree
of probability as an error l_2 when the measure of precision of the
two series of observations is the same. For insta ce if $h_1 = 4h_2$,
$P_1 = P_2$ when $l_2 = 4l_1$, or four times the error will be committed in
the second series with the same degree of probability as the single
error in the first sct. In other words, the first series of observations will be four times as accurate as the second. On account
of certain difficulties in the application of this criterion, its use is
mainly confined to theoretical discussions.

One way of showing how nearly the arithmetical mean represents all the observations, is to suppose all the errors arranged
in their order of magnitude, irrespective of sign, and to select a
quantity which will occupy a place midway between the extreme
limits, so that the number of errors less than the assumed error is
the same as those which exceed it. This is called the **probable**

error, not "the most probable error," nor "the most probable value of the actual error".

The probable error determines the degree of confidence we may have in using the mean as the best representative value of a series of observations. For instance, the atomic weight of oxygen ($H = 1$) is said to be $15\cdot879$ with a probable error $\pm\ 0\cdot0003$. This means that the arithmetical mean of a series of observations is $15\cdot879$, and the probability is $\frac{1}{2}$—that is, the odds are even, or you may bet £1 against £1—that the true atomic weight of oxygen lies between $15\cdot8793$ and $15\cdot8787$.

Referring to Fig. 171, let MP and $M'P'$ be drawn at equal distances from Oy in such a way that the area bounded by these lines, the curve, and the x-axis (shaded part in the figure), is equal to half the whole area, bounded by the whole curve and the x-axis, then it will be obvious that half the total observations will have errors numerically less than OM', and half, numerically greater

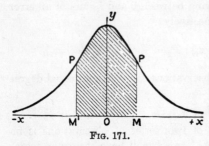

FIG. 171.

than OM, that is, OM represents the magnitude of the probable error, MP its probability.

The way some investigators refer to the smallness of the probable error affecting their results conveys the impression that this canon has been employed to emphasize the accuracy of the work. As a matter of fact, *the probable error does not refer to the accuracy of the work* nor to the magnitude of the errors, but only to the proportion in which the errors of different magnitudes occur. A series of measurements affected with a large probable error may be more accurate than another series with a small probable error, because the second set *may* be affected with a large constant error (*q.v.*).

The number of errors greater than the probable error is equal to the number of errors less than it. Any error selected at random is just as likely to be greater as less than the probable error. Hence, the probable error is the value of x in the integral

$$\frac{1}{2} = \frac{2}{\sqrt{\pi}} \int_0^{hx} e^{-h^2x^2} d(hx), \quad \cdot \quad \cdot \quad \cdot \quad (1)$$

page 517. From Table X., page 621, when $P = \frac{1}{2}$, $hx = 0\cdot4769$;

or, if r is the probable error,

$$hr = 0.4769. \qquad \cdot \qquad \cdot \qquad \cdot \qquad \cdot \qquad (2)$$

Now it has already been shown that

$$y = \frac{h\,dx}{\sqrt{\pi}}e^{-h^2x^2}, \qquad \cdot \qquad \cdot \qquad \cdot \qquad (3)$$

From page 500, therefore, the probability of the occurrence of the independent errors, $x_1, x_2, \ldots, x_n$ is the product of their separate probabilities, or

$$P = \frac{h^n(dx)^n}{\sqrt{\pi^n}}e^{-h^2\Sigma(x^2)}. \qquad \cdot \qquad \cdot \qquad \cdot \qquad (4)$$

For any set of observations in which the measurements have been as accurate as possible, h has a maximum value. Differentiating the last equation in the usual way, and equating dP/dh to zero,

$$h = \pm \sqrt{\frac{n}{2\Sigma(x^2)}}; \qquad \cdot \qquad \cdot \qquad \cdot \qquad (5)$$

Substitute this in (2)

$$r = \pm\,0.6745\sqrt{\frac{\Sigma(x^2)}{n}}. \qquad \cdot \qquad \cdot \qquad (6)$$

But $\Sigma(x^2)$ is the sum of the squares of the true errors. The true errors are unknown. By the principle of least squares, when measurements have an equal degree of confidence, the most probable value of the observed quantities are those which render the sum of the squares of the deviations of each observation from the mean, a minimum. Let $\Sigma(v^2)$ denote the sum of the squares of the deviations of each observation from the mean. If n is large, we may put $\Sigma(x^2) = \Sigma(v^2)$; but if n is a limited number,

$$\Sigma(v^2) < \Sigma(x^2); \quad \therefore \Sigma(x^2) = \Sigma(v^2) + u^2. \qquad \cdot \qquad (7)$$

All we know about u^2 is that its value decreases as n increases, and increases when $\Sigma(x^2)$ increases. It is generally supposed that the best approximation is obtained by writing

$$u^2 = \frac{\Sigma(x^2)}{n}; \quad \therefore \frac{\Sigma(x^2)}{n} = \frac{\Sigma(v^2)}{n-1}.$$

Hence, the probable error, r, of a single observation is

$$r = \pm\,0.6745\sqrt{\frac{\Sigma(v^2)}{n-1}}, \qquad \cdot \qquad \text{SINGLE OBSERVATION} \quad (8)$$

which is virtually **Bessel's formula**, for the probable error of a single observation. $\Sigma(v^2)$ denotes the sum of the squares of the numbers formed by subtracting each measurement from the arithmetical mean of the whole series, n denotes the number of measurements actually taken. The probable error, R, of the arithmetical mean of the whole series of observations is

$$R = \pm\ 0\text{·}6745 \sqrt{\frac{\Sigma(v^2)}{n(n - 1)}}. \qquad \text{ALL OBSERVATIONS} \quad (9)$$

The derivation of this formula is given as Ex. (2), page 531. The last two results show that the probable error is diminished by increasing the number of observations. (8) and (9) are only approximations. They have no signification when the number of observations is small. Hence we may write $\frac{2}{3}$ instead of $0\text{·}6745$. For numerical applications, see next section.

The great labour involved in the squaring of the residual errors of a large number of observations may be avoided by the use of **Peter's approximation formula.** According to this, the probable error, r, of a single observation is

$$r = \pm\ 0\text{·}8453\, \frac{\Sigma(+ v)}{\sqrt{n(n - 1)}}, \qquad \text{SINGLE OBSERVATION} \quad (10)$$

where $\Sigma(+ v)$ denotes the sum of the deviations of every observation from the mean, their sign being disregarded. The probable error, R, of the arithmetical mean of the whole series of observations is

$$R = \pm\ 0\text{·}8453\, \frac{\Sigma(+ v)}{n\sqrt{n - 1}}. \qquad \text{ALL OBSERVATIONS} \quad (11)$$

Tables VI. to IX., pages 619 to 623, will reduce the labour in numerical calculations with Bessel's and with Peter's formulæ.

§ 162. Mean and Average Errors.

The arbitrary choice of the probable error for comparing the errors which are committed with equal facility in different sets of observations, appears most natural because the probable error occupies the middle place in a series arranged according to order of magnitude so that the number of errors less than the fictitious probable error, is the same as those which exceed it. There are other standards of comparison. In Germany, the favourite method is to employ the **mean error,** which is defined as *the error whose square is the mean of the squares of all the errors,* or the "error which, if it alone were assumed in all the observations indifferently, would give the same sum of the squares of the errors as that which actually exists ". We have seen, on page 516, (5), that the ratio,

$$\frac{\text{Number of errors between } x \text{ and } x + dx}{\text{Total number of errors}} = \frac{h}{\sqrt{\pi}}e^{-h^2x^2}dx.$$

Multiply both sides by x^2 and we obtain

$$\frac{\text{Sum of squares of errors between } x \text{ and } x + dx}{\text{Total number of errors}} = \frac{h}{\sqrt{\pi}}x^2e^{h^2x^2}dx.$$

By integrating between the limits $+ \infty$ and $- \infty$ we get

$$\frac{\text{Sum of squares of } all \text{ the errors}}{\text{Total number of errors}} = \frac{\Sigma(x^2)}{n} = \frac{h}{\sqrt{\pi}}\int_{-\infty}^{+\infty} x^2e^{-h^2x^2}dx.$$

Let m denote the mean error, then, by integration as on page 343,

$$m^2 = \frac{h}{\sqrt{\pi}}\int_{-\infty}^{+\infty} x^2e^{-h^2x^2}dx = \frac{1}{2h^2}; \quad \cdot \quad \cdot \quad (1)$$

and from (2) of the preceding section, we get

$$r = 0{\cdot}6745m. \quad \cdot \quad \cdot \quad (2)$$

From (8) and (9), preceding section, the mean error, m, which affects each single observation is given by the expression

$$m = \pm \sqrt{\frac{\Sigma(v^2)}{n - 1}}; \quad \cdot \quad \cdot \quad \text{SINGLE OBSERVATION (3)}$$

and the mean error, M, which affects the whole series of results,

$$M = \pm \sqrt{\frac{\Sigma(v^2)}{n(n - 1)}}. \quad \cdot \quad \cdot \quad \text{ALL OBSERVATIONS (4)}$$

The mean error must not be confused with the "mean of the errors," or, as it is sometimes called, the **average error**,[1] another standard of comparison defined as the mean of all the errors regardless of sign. If a denotes the average error, we get from page 235,

$$a = \frac{\Sigma(+ v)}{n} = \frac{2h}{\sqrt{\pi}}\int_{0}^{\infty} xe^{-h^2x^2}dx = \frac{1}{h\sqrt{\pi}}; \ r = 0{\cdot}8454a. \quad (5)$$

The average error measures the average deviation of each observation from the mean of the whole series. It is a more useful standard of comparison than the probable error when the attention is directed to the relative accuracy of the individual observations in different series of observations. The average error depends not only upon the *proportion* in which the errors of differ-

---

[1] Some writers call our "average error" the "mean error," and our "mean error" the "error of mean square".

ent magnitudes occur, but also on the *magnitude* of the individual errors. The average error furnishes useful information even when the presence of (unknown) constant errors renders a further application of the "theory of errors" of questionable utility, because it will allow us to compare the magnitude of the constant errors affecting different series of observations, and so lead to their discovery and elimination.

The reader will be able to show presently that the average error, A, affecting the mean of n observations is given by the expression

$$A = \pm \frac{\Sigma(+ v)}{n \sqrt{n}}. \qquad . \qquad . \qquad . \qquad (6)$$

This determines the effect of the average error of the individual observations upon the mean, and serves as a standard for comparing the relative accuracy of the means of different series of experiments made under similar conditions.

EXAMPLES.—(1) The following galvanometer deflections were obtained in some observations on the resistance of a circuit: 37·0, 36·8, 36·8, 36·9, 37·1. Find the probable and mean errors. This small number of observations is employed simply to illustrate the method of using the above formulæ. In practical work, mean or probable errors deduced from so small a number of observations are of little value. Arrange the following table :—

Number of Observation.	Deflection Observed.	Departure from Mean.	v^2.
1	37·0	+ 0·08	0·0064
2	36·8	– 0·12	0·0144
3	36·8	– 0·12	0·0144
4	36·9	– 0·02	0·0004
5	37·1	+ 0·18	0·0324

Mean = 36·92; $\Sigma(v^2)$ = 0·0680.

The numbers in the last two columns have been calculated from those in the second. Since $n = 5$, and writing $\frac{2}{3}$ for 0·6745.

Mean error of a single result $= \pm \sqrt{\frac{0·068}{4}} = \pm 0·13.$

Mean error of the mean $= \pm \sqrt{\frac{0·068}{5.4}} = \pm 0·058.$

Probable error of a single result $= \pm \frac{2}{3} \sqrt{\frac{0·068}{4}} = \pm 0·087.$

Probable error of the mean $= \pm \frac{2}{3} \sqrt{\frac{0·068}{5.4}} = \pm 0·039.$

Average error of a single result $= \pm \frac{0·52}{5} = \pm 0·104.$

Average error of the mean $= \pm \frac{0·52}{5 \sqrt{5}} = \pm 0·0465.$

The mean error of the arithmetical mean of the whole set of observations is written, $36 \cdot 92 \pm 0 \cdot 058$; the probable error, $36 \cdot 92 \pm 0 \cdot 039$. It is unnecessary to include more than two significant figures. You will find the Tables on pages 619 and 620 convenient for the numerical work.

(2) F. Rudberg (*Pogg. Ann.*, **41**, 271, 1837), found the coefficient of expansion a of dry air by different methods to be $a \times 100 = 0 \cdot 3643$, $0 \cdot 3654$, $0 \cdot 3644$, $0 \cdot 3650$, $0 \cdot 3653$, $0 \cdot 3636$, $0 \cdot 3651$, $0 \cdot 3643$, $0 \cdot 3643$, $0 \cdot 3645$, $0 \cdot 3646$, $0 \cdot 3662$, $0 \cdot 3840$, $0 \cdot 3902$, $0 \cdot 3652$. Required the probable and mean errors on the assumption that the results are worth an equal degree of confidence.

(3) From Ex. (3), page 161, show that the mean error is the abscissa of the point of inflexion of the probability curve. For simplicity, put $h = 1$.

(4) Cavendish has published the result of 29 determinations of the mean density of the earth (*Phil. Trans.*, **88**, 469, 1798) in which the first significant figure of all but one is 5:—$4 \cdot 88$; $5 \cdot 50$; $5 \cdot 61$; $5 \cdot 07$; $5 \cdot 26$; $5 \cdot 55$; $5 \cdot 36$; $5 \cdot 29$; $5 \cdot 58$; $5 \cdot 65$; $5 \cdot 57$; $5 \cdot 53$; $5 \cdot 62$; $5 \cdot 29$; $5 \cdot 44$; $5 \cdot 34$; $5 \cdot 79$; $5 \cdot 10$; $5 \cdot 17$; $5 \cdot 39$; $5 \cdot 42$; $5 \cdot 47$; $5 \cdot 63$; $5 \cdot 34$; $5 \cdot 46$; $5 \cdot 30$; $5 \cdot 75$; $5 \cdot 68$; $5 \cdot 85$.   Verify the following results: Mean $= 5 \cdot 45$; $\Sigma(+v) = 5 \cdot 04$; $\Sigma(v^2) = 1 \cdot 367$; $M = \pm 0 \cdot 041$; $m = \pm 0 \cdot 221$; $R = \pm 0 \cdot 0277$; $r = \pm 0 \cdot 149$; $a = 0 \cdot 18$; $A = \pm 0 \cdot 033$.

The relation between the probable error, the mean error, the average error, and the absolute measure of an error can be obtained from (2), page 523; (2), page 516; and (5), page 516. We have, in fact, if modulus, $h = 1 \cdot 0000$; mean error, $m = 0 \cdot 7071$; average error, $a = 0 \cdot 5642$; probable error, $r = 0 \cdot 4769$.

The following results are convenient in combining measurements affected with different mean or probable errors:

I. The mean error of the SUM OR DIFFERENCE *of a number of observations is equal to the square root of the sum of the squares of the mean errors of each of the observations.* Let x_1, x_2, represent two independent measurements whose sum or difference combines to make a final result X, so that

$$X = x_1 + x_2.$$

Let the mean errors of x_1 and x_2, be m_1 and m_2 respectively. If M denotes the mean error in X,

$$X \pm M = (x_1 \pm m_1) + (x_2 \pm m_2).$$
$$\therefore \pm M = \pm m_1 \pm m_2.$$

However we arrange the signs of M, m_1, m_2, in the last equation, we can only obtain, by squaring, one or other of the following expressions:—

$$M^2 = m_1{}^2 + 2m_1 m_2 + m_2{}^2 ; \text{ or, } M^2 = m_1{}^2 - 2m_1 m_2 + m_2{}^2,$$

it makes no difference which.   Hence the mean error is to be found by taking the mean of both these results. That is to say,

$$M^2 = m_1{}^2 + m_2{}^2 ; \ \text{or,} \ M = \pm \ \sqrt{m_1{}^2 + m_2{}^2},$$

because the terms containing $+ \ m_1 m_2$ and $- \ m_1 m_2$ cancel each other. This means that the products of any pair of residual errors ($m_1 m_2$, $m_1 m_3$, ...) in an extended series of observations will have positive as often as negative signs. Consequently, the influence of these terms on the mean value will be negligibly small in comparison with the terms $m_1{}^2, m_2{}^2, m_3{}^2, \ldots$, which are always positive. Hence, for any number of observations,

$$M^2 = m_1{}^2 + m_2{}^2 + \ldots ; \ \text{or,} \ M = \pm \ \sqrt{(m_1{}^2 + m_2{}^2 + \ldots)}. \quad (7)$$

From equation (2), page 525, the mean error is proportional to the probable error R, m_1 to r_1, ..., hence,

$$R^2 = r_1{}^2 + r_2{}^2 + \ldots ; \ \text{or,} \ R = \pm \ \sqrt{(r_1{}^2 + r_2{}^2 + \ldots)}. \quad (8)$$

In other words, *the probable error of the* SUM *or* DIFFERENCE *of two quantities A and B respectively affected with probable errors* $\pm \ a$ *and* $\pm \ b$ *is*

$$R = \pm \ \sqrt{a^2 + b^2}. \quad \cdot \quad \cdot \quad \cdot \quad (9)$$

EXAMPLES.—(1) The molecular weight of titanium chloride ($TiCl_4$) is known to be 188·545 with a probable error $\pm$ 0·0092, and the atomic weight of chlorine 35·179 $\pm$ 0·0048, what is the atomic weight of titanium? Ansr. 47·829 $\pm$ 0·0213. Hints.

188·545 − 4 × 35·179 = 47·829 ; $R = \sqrt{(0·0092)^2 + (4 \times 0·0048)^2} = \pm$ ·0213.

It will be obvious that we shall ignore the advice given in § 94, pages 273 to 276, if we are not very careful in the interpretation of the probable error in these *illustrative* examples.

(2) The mean errors affecting θ_1 and θ_2 in the formula $R = k(\theta_2 - \theta_1)$ are respectively $\pm$ 0·0003 and $\pm$ 0·0004, what is the mean error affecting $\theta_2 - \theta_1$ and $3(\theta_2 - \theta_1)$? Ansr. $\pm$ 0·0005 and $\pm$ 0·0015.

II. *The probable error of the* PRODUCT *of two quantities A and B respectively affected with the probable errors* $\pm \ a$ *and* $\pm \ b$ *is*

$$R = \pm \ \sqrt{(Ab)^2 + (Ba)^2}. \quad \cdot \quad \cdot \quad (10)$$

If a third mean, C, with a probable error, $\pm \ c$, is included,

$$R = \pm \ \sqrt{(BCa)^2 + (ACb)^2 + (ABc)^2}. \quad \cdot \quad \cdot \quad (11)$$

EXAMPLES.—(1) Thorpe found that the molecular ratio

$$4Ag : TiCl_4 = 100 : 44·017 \pm 0·0031.$$

Hence determine the molecular weight of titanium tetrachloride, given the atomic weight of silver = 107·108 $\pm$ 0·0031. Ansr. 188·583 $\pm$ 0·0144. Hint.

$$R = \pm \ \sqrt{\{ (4 \times 107·108 \times 0·0031)^2 + (44·017 \times 4 \times 0·0031)^2 \}}.$$

(2) The specific heat of tin is 0·0537 with a mean error of $\pm$ 0·0014, and the atomic weight of the same metal is 118·150 $\pm$ 0·0089, show that the mean error of the product of these two quantities (Dulong and Petit's law) is 6·34 $\pm$ 0·1654.

III. The probable error of the QUOTIENT $(B \div A)$ *of two quantities A and B respectively affected with the probable errors $\pm a$ and $\pm b$ is*

$$R = \pm \frac{\sqrt{\left(\dfrac{Ba}{A}\right)^2 + b^2}}{A}. \qquad \qquad (12)$$

EXAMPLES.—(1) It is known that the atomic ratio

$$\text{Cu} : 2\text{Ag} = 100 : 339 \cdot 411 \pm 0 \cdot 0039,$$

what is the atomic weight of copper given $\text{Ag} = 107 \cdot 108 \pm 0 \cdot 0031$? Ansr. $63 \cdot 114 \pm 0 \cdot 0020$. Hint.

$$R = \pm \sqrt{\left(\frac{214 \cdot 216 \times 0 \cdot 0039}{339 \cdot 411}\right)^2 + (0 \cdot 0062)^2} \div 339 \cdot 411 = \pm 0 \cdot 0020.$$

$$\text{Cu} : 2 \times 107 \cdot 108 = 100 : 339 \cdot 411 ; \therefore \text{Cu} = 63 \cdot 114.$$

(2) Suppose that the maximum pressure of the aqueous vapour, f_1, in the atmosphere at 16° is found to be $8 \cdot 2000$, with a mean error $\pm 0 \cdot 0024$, and the maximum pressure of aqueous vapour, f_2, at the dewpoint, at 16°, is $13 \cdot 5000$, with a mean error of $\pm 0 \cdot 0012$. The relative humidity, h, of the air is given by the expression $h = f_1/f_2$. Show that the relative humidity at 16° is $0 \cdot 6074 \pm 0 \cdot 0002$.

IV. The probable error of the PROPORTION

$$A : B = C : x,$$

where A, B, C, are quantities respectively affected with the probable errors $\pm a$, $\pm b$, $\pm c$, is

$$R = \pm \frac{\sqrt{\left(\dfrac{BCa}{A}\right)^2 + (Cb)^2 + (Bc)^2}}{A}. \qquad \cdot \qquad (13)$$

EXAMPLE.—Stas found that AgClO_3 furnished $25 \cdot 080 \pm 0 \cdot 0019$ °/₀ of oxygen and $74 \cdot 920 \pm 0 \cdot 0003$ °/₀ of AgCl. If the atomic weight of oxygen is $15 \cdot 879 \pm 0 \cdot 0003$, what is the molecular weight of AgCl? Ansr. $142 \cdot 303 \pm 0 \cdot 0066$. Hints. $25 \cdot 080 : 74 \cdot 920 = 3 \times 15 \cdot 879 : x ; \therefore x = 142 \cdot 303.$

$$R = \pm \frac{\sqrt{\left\{\left(\dfrac{74 \cdot 92 \times 47 \cdot 637 \times 0 \cdot 001}{25 \cdot 08}\right) + (47 \cdot 637 \times 0 \cdot 001)^2 + (74 \cdot 92 \times 3 \times 0 \cdot 0009)^2\right\}}}{\sqrt{25 \cdot 08}}.$$

If the proportion be

$$A : B = C + x : D + x,$$

the probable error is given by

$$R = \pm \sqrt{\frac{(C - D)^2}{(A - B)^4}(B^2 a^2 + A^2 b^2) + \frac{B^2 c^2 + A^2 d^2}{(A - B)^2}}. \qquad (14)$$

EXAMPLE.—Stas found that $31 \cdot 488 \pm 0 \cdot 0006$ grams of NH_4Cl were equivalent to 100 grams of AgNO_3. Hence determine the atomic weight of nitrogen, given $\text{Ag} = 107 \cdot 108 \pm 0 \cdot 0031$; $\text{Cl} = 35 \cdot 179 \pm 0 \cdot 0048$; $\text{H} = 1$; $\text{O}_3 = 47 \cdot 637 \pm 0 \cdot 0009$. Ansr. $13 \cdot 911 \pm 0 \cdot 0048$.

V. *The probable error of the arithmetical mean of a series of observations is inversely as the square root of their number.* Let r_1, r_2, ..., r_n be the probable errors of a series of independent observations a_1, a_2, ..., a_n, which have to be combined so as to make up a final result u. Let the probable errors be respectively proportional to the actual errors da_1, da_2, ... da_n. The final result u is a function such that

$$u = f(a_1, a_2, ..., a_n).$$

The influence of each separate variable on the final result may be determined by partial differentiation so that

$$du = \frac{\partial u}{\partial a_1} da_1 + \frac{\partial u}{\partial a_2} da_2 + ... \qquad . \qquad . \qquad (15)$$

where da_1, da_2, ... represent the actual errors committed in measuring a_1, a_2, ...; the partial differential coefficients determine the effect of these variables upon the final result u; and du represents the actual error in u due to the joint occurrence of the errors da_1, da_2, ... Put R in place of du; r_1 in place of da_1, etc.; square (15) and

$$R^2 = \left(\frac{\partial u}{\partial a_1}\right)^2 r_1^2 + \left(\frac{\partial u}{\partial a_2}\right)^2 r_2^2 + ..., \qquad . \qquad . \qquad (16)$$

since cross products are negligibly small. The arithmetical mean of n observations is

$$u = \frac{a_1 + a_2 + ... + a_n}{n},$$

therefore,

$$\frac{\partial u}{\partial a_1} = \frac{\partial u}{\partial a_2} = ... = \frac{1}{n}; \therefore R^2 = \frac{r_1^2 + r_2^2 + ... + r_n^2}{n^2}.$$

But the observations have an equal degree of precision, and therefore, $r_1^2 = r_2^2 = ... = r_n^2 = r^2$.

$$\therefore R = \pm\sqrt{\frac{nr^2}{n^2}} = \pm\frac{r}{\sqrt{n}}. \qquad . \qquad . \qquad (17)$$

This result shows how easy it is to overrate the effect of multiplying observations. If R denotes the probable error of the mean of 8 observations, four times as many, or 32 observations must be made to give a probable error of $\frac{1}{2}R$; nine times as many, or 72 observations must be made to reduce R to $\frac{1}{3}R$, etc.

EXAMPLES.—(1) Two series of determinations of the atomic weight of oxygen by a certain process gave respectively $15·8726 \pm 0·00058$ and $15·8769 \pm 0·00058$. Hence show that the atomic weight is accordingly written $15·87475 \pm 0·00041$.

(2) In the preceding section, § 161, given formula (8) deduce (9). Hint. Use (17), present section.

(3) Deduce Peter's approximation formulæ (10) and (11), § 161. Hint. Since $\Sigma(x^2)/n = \Sigma(v^2)/(n - 1)$, page 524, we may suppose that on the average $\Sigma(x): \sqrt{n} = \Sigma(v) : \sqrt{n - 1}$, etc. $\Sigma x/n$ is the mean of the errors, and if $\Sigma x/n =$ probability integral, page 522, $= 1/h \sqrt{\pi}$, it follows from (2), page 523, $r = 0\cdot8453\ \Sigma x/n$, etc. See also (2) page 516.

(4) Show that when n is large, the result of dividing the mean of the squares of the errors by the square of the mean of the errors is constant. Hint. Show that

$$\frac{\Sigma(v^2)}{n} \div \left(\frac{\Sigma(v)}{n}\right)^2 = \frac{\pi}{2} = 1\cdot77. \qquad . \quad . \quad . \quad . \quad (18)$$

This has been proposed as a test of the fidelity of the observations, and of the accuracy of the arithmetical work. For instance, the numbers quoted in the example on page 554 give $\Sigma(v) = 55\cdot53$; $\Sigma(v^2) = 354\cdot35$; $n = 14$; constant $= 1\cdot60$. The canon does not usually work very well with a small number of observations.

(5) Show that the probable (or mean) error is inversely proportional to the absolute measure of precision. Hint. From (1) and (2)

$$r = \frac{1}{h} \times \text{constant}; \therefore r \propto \frac{1}{h}. \qquad (19)$$

§ 163. Numerical Values of the Probability Integrals.

We have discussed the two questions :

1. What is the best representative value of a series of measurements affected with errors of observations ?

2. How nearly does the arithmetical mean represent all of a given set of measurements affected with errors of observation ?

It now remains to inquire

3. *How closely does the arithmetical mean approximate to the absolute truth ?* To illustrate, we may use the results of Crookes' model research on the atomic weight of thallium (*Phil. Trans.*, **163**, 277, 1874). Crooke's determination of this constant gave

$$\left.\begin{array}{l} 203\cdot628;\ 203\cdot632;\ 203\cdot636;\ 203\cdot638;\ 203\cdot639 \\ 203\cdot642;\ 203\cdot644;\ 203\cdot649;\ 203\cdot650;\ 203\cdot666; \end{array}\right\} \text{Mean: } 203\cdot642.$$

The arithmetical mean is only one of an infinite number of possible values of the atomic weight of thallium between the extreme limits $203\cdot628$ and $203\cdot666$. It is very probable that $203\cdot642$ is *not* the true value, but it is also very probable that $203\cdot642$ is *very near* to the true value sought. The question "How near?" cannot be answered. Alter the question to "What is the probability that the truth is comprised between the limits $203\cdot642 \pm x$?" and the answer may be readily obtained however small we choose to make the number x.

First, suppose that the absolute measure of precision, h, of the arithmetical mean is known. Table X. gives the numerical values of the probability integral

$$P = \frac{2}{\sqrt{\pi}} \int_0^{hx} e^{-h^2 x^2} d(hx),$$

where P denotes the probability that an error of observation will have a positive or negative value equal to or less than x, h is the measure of the degree of precision of the results.

When h is unity, the value of P is read off from the table directly. To illustrate, we read that when $x = \pm 0.1$ $P = .112$; when $x = \pm 0.2$ $P = .223$; ..., meaning that if 1,000 errors are committed in a set of observations with a modulus of precision $h = 1$, 112 of the errors will lie between $+ 0.1$ and $- 0.1$, 223 between $+ 0.2$ and $- 0.2$, etc. Or, 888 of the errors will exceed the limits ± 0.1; 777 errors will exceed the limits ± 0.2; ... When h is not unity, we must use $\dfrac{0.1}{h}$ $\dfrac{0.2}{h}$, ..., in place of 0.1, 0.2.

EXAMPLES.—(1) If $hx = 0.64$, P, from the table, is 0.6346. Hence 0.6346 denotes the probability that the error x will be less than $0.64/h$, that is to say, $63.46\,\%$ of the errors will lie between the limits $\pm 0.64/h$. The remaining $36.54\,\%$ will lie outside these limits.

(2) Required a probability that an error will be comprised between the limits ± 0.3 ($h = 1$). Ansr. 0.329.

(3) Required the probability that an error will lie between $- 0.01$ and $+ 0.1$ of say a milligram. This is the sum of the probabilities of the limits from 0 to $- 0.01$ and from θ to $+ 0.1$ ($h - 1$).

(4) Required the probability that an error will lie between $+ 1.0$ and $+ 0.01$. This is the difference of the probabilities of errors between 1.0 and zero and between 0.01 and zero ($h = 1$). Ansr. $\frac{1}{2}(0.8427 - 0.0113) = 0.4157$.

This table, therefore, enables us to find the relation between the magnitude of an error and the frequency with which that error will be committed in making a large number of careful measurements. It is usually more convenient to work from the probable error R than from the modulus h. More practical illustrations have, in consequence, been included in the next set of examples.

Second, suppose that the probable error of the arithmetical mean is known. Table XI. gives the numerical values of the probability integral

$$P = \frac{2}{\sqrt{\pi}} \int_0^{\frac{ax}{r}} e^{-\left(\frac{x}{r}\right)^2} d\left(\frac{x}{r}\right),$$

where P denotes the probability that an error of observation of a positive or negative value, equal to or less than x, will be committed in the arithmetical mean of a series of measurements with probable error r (or R). This table makes no reference to h. To illustrate its use, of 1,000 errors, 54 will be less than $\frac{1}{10}R$; 500 less than R; 823 less than $2R$; 957 less than $3R$; 993 less than $4R$; and one will be greater than $5R$. r (or R) $= a/h$, where h is a measure of the precision and a is a constant of value 0·4769.

EXAMPLES.—(1) A series of results are represented by 6·9 with a probable error $\pm$ 0·25. The probability that the probable error is less than 0·25 is $\frac{1}{2}$. What is the probability that the actual error will be less than 0·75. Here $x/R = 0·75/0·25 = 3$. From the table, $p = 0·9570$ when $x/R = 3$. This means that 95·7 °/₀ of the errors will be less than 0·75 and 4·3 °/₀ greater.

(2) D. Gill finds the solar parallax to be 8·802″ $\pm$ 0·005. What is the probability that the solar parallax may lie between 8·802″ $\pm$ 0·025. Here $x/R = 0·025 \div 0·005 = 5$. When $R = 5$, Table XI., $P = 0·9993$. This means that £9993 might be bet in favour of the event, and £7, against the event.

(3) Dumas has recorded the following 19 determinations of the chemical equivalent of hydrogen (O = 100) using sulphuric acid (H_2SO_4) with some, and phosphorus pentoxide (P_2O_5) as the drying agent in other cases:

i. H_2SO_4 : 12·472, 12·480, 12·548, 12·489, 12·496, 12·522, 12·533, 12·546, 12·550, 12·562;

ii. P_2O_5 : 12·480, 12·491, 12·490, 12·490, 12·508, 12·547, 12·490, 12·551, 12·551. J. B. A. Dumas' "Recherches sur la Composition de l'Eau," *Ann. Chim. Phys.*, [3], **8**, 200, 1843. What is the probability that there will be an error between the limits $\pm$ 0·015 in the mean (12·515), assuming that the results are free from constant errors? The chemical student will perhaps see the relation of his answer to Prout's law. Hints. $x/R = t$; $R = 0·005685$; $x = 0·015$; $\therefore t = 2·63$. From Table XI., when $t = 2·63, P = 0·969$. Hence the odds are 969 to 31 that the mean 12·515 is affected by no greater error than is comprised within the limits $\pm$ 0·015. To exemplify Table X., $h = 0·4769/R = 102, \therefore hx = 102 \times 0·015 = 1·53$. From the Table, $P = 0·924$ when $hx = 1·53$, etc. That is to say, 96·9 °/₀ of the errors will be less and 3·1 °/₀ greater than the assigned limits.

(4) From W. Crookes' ten determinations of the atomic weight of thallium (above) calculate the probability that the atomic weight of thallium lies between 203·632 and 203·652. Here $x = \pm$ 0·01; $R \pm = 0·0023$; $\therefore t = x/R = 4·4$. From Table XI., $P = 0·997$. (Note how near this number is to unity indicating certainty.) The chances are 332 to 1 that the true value of the atomic weight of thallium lies between 203·632 and 203·652. We get the same result by means of Table X. Thus $h = 0·4769 \div 0·0023 = 207$; $\therefore hx = 207 \times 0·01 = 2·07$. When $hx = 2·07, P = 0·997$. If 1,000 observations were made under the same conditions as Crookes', we could reasonably expect 997 of them to be affected by errors numerically less than 0·01, and only 3 observations would be affected by errors exceeding these limits.

The rules and formulæ deduced up to the present are by no means inviolable. The reader must constantly bear in mind the fundamental assumptions upon which we are working. If these conditions are not fulfilled, the conclusions may not only be superfluous, but even erroneous. The necessary conditions are:

1. Every observation is as likely to be in error as every other one.

2. There is no perturbing influence to cause the results to have a bias or tendency to deviate more in some directions than in others.

3. A large number of observations has been made. In practice, the number of observations may be considerably reduced if the second condition is fulfilled. In the ordinary course of things from 10 to 25 is usually considered a sufficient number.

§ 164. Maxwell's Law of Distribution of Molecular Velocities.

In a preceding discussion, the velocities of the molecules of a gas were assumed to be the same. Can this simplifying assumption be justified?

According to the kinetic theory, a gas is supposed to consist of a number of perfectly elastic spheres moving about in space with a certain velocity. In case of impact on the walls of the bounding vessel, the molecules are supposed to rebound according to known dynamical laws. This accounts for the pressure of a gas. The velocities of all the molecules of a gas in a state of equilibrium are not the same. Some move with a greater velocity than others. At one time a molecule may be moving with a great velocity, at another time, with a relatively slow speed. The attempt has been made to find a law governing the distribution of the velocities of the motions of the different molecules, and with some success. Maxwell's law is based upon the assumption that the same relations hold for the velocities of the molecules as for errors of observation. This assumption has played a most important part in the development of the kinetic theory of gases. The probability y that a molecule will have a velocity equal to v is given by an expression of the type:

$$y = \frac{4}{\sqrt{\pi}} \left(\frac{v}{a}\right)^2 e^{-\left(\frac{v}{a}\right)^2} . \quad . \quad . \quad . \quad (1)$$

Very few molecules will have velocities outside a certain restricted range. It is possible for a molecule to have any velocity whatever, but the probability of the existence of velocities outside certain limits is vanishingly small. The reader will get a better idea of the distribution of the velocities of the molecules by plotting the graph of the above equation for himself. Remember that the ordinates are pro-

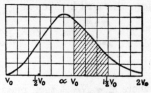

FIG. 172.

portional to the number of molecules, abscissæ to their speed. Areas bounded by the x-axis, the curve and certain ordinates will give an idea of the number of molecules possessing velocities between the abscissæ corresponding to the boundary ordinates. In Fig. 172 the shaded portion represents the number of molecules with velocities lying between V_0 and $1.5V_0$.

EXAMPLE.—By the ordinary methods for finding a maximum, show from (1), that y is a maximum when $v = a$.

Returning to the study of the kinetic theory of gases, p. 504, the number of molecules with velocities between v and $v + dv$ is assumed to be represented by an equation analogous to the expression employed to represent the errors of mean square of page 525, namely,

$$dN = \frac{4N}{\sqrt{\pi}}\left(\frac{v}{a}\right)^2 e^{-\left(\frac{v}{a}\right)^2} d\left(\frac{v}{a}\right), \quad . \quad . \quad . \quad (2)$$

where N represents the total number of molecules, a is a constant to be evaluated.

I. To find a value for the constant a in terms of the average velocity V_0 of the molecules. Since there are dN molecules with a velocity v, the sum of the velocities of all these dN molecules is vdN, and the sum of the velocities of *all* the molecules must be

$$\int_{v=0}^{v=\infty} vdN \; ; \; \therefore V_0 = \frac{4a}{\sqrt{\pi}}\int_0^\infty \left(\frac{v}{a}\right)^3 e^{-\frac{v^2}{a^2}} d\left(\frac{v}{a}\right) = \frac{4}{a^3\sqrt{\pi}}\cdot\frac{a^4}{2} = \frac{2a}{\sqrt{\pi}}$$

from (2). Where has N gone? The average velocity V_0 is one Nth of the sum of the velocities of the N given molecules. Hence,

$$a = \tfrac{1}{2}V_0\sqrt{\pi}. \quad . \quad . \quad . \quad . \quad (3)$$

II. To find the average velocity of the molecules of a gas. By a well-known theorem in elementary mechanics, the kinetic energy of a mass m moving with a velocity v is $\tfrac{1}{2}mv^2$. Hence, the sum of the kinetic energies of the dN molecules will be $\frac{1}{2}(mdN)v^2$, because there are dN molecules moving with a velocity v. From (2), therefore, the total kinetic energy (T) of *all* the molecules is

$$T = \int_{v=0}^{v=\infty} \tfrac{1}{2}mv^2 \, . \, dN = \frac{2Nm}{a^3\sqrt{\pi}} \int_0^\infty v^4 \, . \, e^{-\frac{v^2}{a^2}} dv = \frac{3}{4}Nma^2 = \frac{3}{4}Ma^2.$$

$$\therefore a = 2\sqrt{\frac{T}{3M}} \quad . \quad . \quad . \quad (4)$$

where $M = Nm =$ total mass of N molecules each of mass m. The total kinetic energy of N molecules of the same kind is

$$T = \tfrac{1}{2}mv_1^2 + \tfrac{1}{2}mv_2^2 + \ldots + \tfrac{1}{2}mv_N^2 = \tfrac{1}{2}m(v_1^2 + v_2^2 + \ldots + v_N^2). \quad (5)$$

The velocity of mean square, U, is defined as the velocity whose square is the average of the squares of the velocities of all the N molecules, or,

$$U^2 = \frac{v_1^2 + v_2^2 + \ldots v_N^2}{N}; \; \therefore \; T = \frac{1}{2}mNU^2 = \frac{1}{2}MU^2, \quad (6)$$

from (5). Again, from (4) and (6), we have

$$a = \frac{2U}{\sqrt{6}}; \; V_0 = \frac{4U}{\sqrt{6\pi}} = 0.9213U. \quad . \quad . \quad (7)$$

Most works on chemical theory give a simple method of proving that if p denotes the pressure and ρ the density of a gas,

$$p = \tfrac{1}{3}\rho \, U^2. \quad . \quad . \quad . \quad (8)$$

This in conjunction with (6) allows the average velocity of the molecules of a gas to be calculated from the known values of the pressure and density of the gas, as shown in any *Textbook on Physical Chemistry*.

The reader is no doubt familiar with the principle underlying Maxwell's law, and, indeed, the whole kinetic theory of gases. I may mention two examples. The number of passengers on say the 3.10 P.M. suburban daily train is fairly constant in spite of the fact that that train does not carry the same passenger two days running. Insurance companies can average the number of deaths per 1,000 of population with great exactness. Of course I say nothing of disturbing factors. A bank holiday may require provision for a supra-normal traffic, and an epidemic will run up the death rate of a community. The commercial success of these institutions is, however, sufficient testimony of the truth of the **method of averages**, otherwise called the **statistical method** of investigation. The same type of mathematical expression is required in each case.

It will thus be seen that calculations, based on the supposition that all the molecules possess equal velocities, are quite admissible in a first approximation. The net result of the "dance of the molecules" is a distribution of the different velocities among all the molecules, which is maintained with great exactness.

G. H. Darwin has deduced values for the mean free path, etc., from the hypothesis that the molecules of the same gas are not all the same size. He has examined the consequences of the assumption that the sizes of the molecules are ranged according to a law like that governing the frequency of errors of observation. For this, see his memoir "On the mechanical conditions of a swarm of meteorites" (*Phil. Trans.*, **180**, 1, 1889).

§ 165. Constant or Systematic Errors.

The irregular accidental errors hitherto discussed have this distinctive feature, they are just as likely to have a positive as a negative value. But there are errors which have not this character. If the barometer vacuum is imperfect, every reading will be too small; if the glass bulb of a thermometer has contracted after graduation, the zero point rises in such a way as to falsify all subsequent readings; if the points of suspension of the balance pans are at unequal distances from the centre of oscillation of the beam, the weighings will be inaccurate. A change of temperature of 5° or 6° may easily cause an error of 0·2 to 1·0 °/$_o$ in an analysis, owing to the change in the volume of the standard solution. Such defective measurements are said to be affected by **constant errors**.[1] By definition, constant errors are produced by well-defined causes which make the errors of observation preponderate more in one direction than in another. Thus, some of Dumas' determinations of the atomic weight of silver are affected by a constant error due to the occlusion of oxygen by metallic silver in the course of his work.

One of the greatest trials of an investigator is to detect and if

---

[1] **Personal error.** This is another type of constant error which depends on the personal qualities of the observer. Thus the differences in the judgments of the astronomers at the Greenwich Observatory as to the observed time of transit of a star and the assumed instant of its actual occurrence, are said to vary from $\frac{1}{100}$ to $\frac{1}{3}$ of a second, and to remain fairly constant for the same observer. Some persistently read the burette a little high, others a little low. Vernier readings, analyses based on colorimetric tests (such as Nessler's ammonia process), etc., may be affected by personal errors.

possible eliminate constant errors.   " The history of science teaches all too plainly the lesson that no single method is absolutely to be relied upon, and that sources of error lurk where they are least expected, and that they may escape the notice of the most experienced and conscientious worker." [1]   Two questions of the gravest moment are now presented.   How are constant errors to be detected ?   How may the effect of constant errors be eliminated from a set of measurements?   This is usually done by modifying the conditions under which the experiments are performed.   " It is only by the concurrence of evidence of various kinds and from various sources," continues Lord Rayleigh, " that practical certainty may at least be attained, and complete confidence restored."   Thus the magnitude is measured under different conditions, with different instruments, etc.   It is assumed that even though each method or apparatus has its own specific constant error, all these constant errors taken collectively will have the character of accidental errors. To take a concrete illustration, faulty " sights " on a rifle may cause a constant deviation of the bullets in one direction ; the " sights " on another rifle may cause a constant " error " in another direction, and so, as the number of rifles increases, the constant errors assume the character of accidental errors and thus, in the long run, tend to compensate each other.   This is why Stas generally employed several different methods to determine his atomic weights. To quote one practical case, Stas made two sets of determinations of the numerical value of the ratio Ag : KCl.   In one set, four series of determinations were made with KCl prepared from four different sources in conjunction with one specimen of silver, and in the other set different series of experiments were made with silver prepared from different sources in conjunction with one sample of KCl.   Unfortunately the latter set was never completed.

The calculation of an arithmetical mean is analogous to the process of guessing the centre of a target from the distribution of the " hits " (Fig. 165).   If all the shots are affected by the same constant error, the centre, so estimated, will deviate from the true centre by an amount depending on the magnitude of the (presumably unknown) constant error.   If this magnitude can be subsequently determined, a simple arithmetical operation (addition or subtraction) will give the correct value.   Thus Stas found that the amount of

---

potassium chloride equivalent to 100 parts of silver in one case was as

$$Ag : KCl = 100 : 69{\cdot}1209.$$

The KCl was subsequently found to contain $0{\cdot}00259$ per cent. of silica. The chemical student will see that $0{\cdot}00179$ has consequently to be subtracted from $69{\cdot}1209$. Hence,

$$Ag : KCl = 100 : 69{\cdot}11903.$$

After Lord Rayleigh (*Proc. Roy. Soc.*, **43**, 356, 1888) had proved that the capacity of an exhausted glass globe is less than when the globe is full of gas, all measurements of the densities of gases involving the use of exhausted globes had to be corrected for shrinkage. Thus Regnault's ratio, $1 : 15{\cdot}9611$, for the relative densities of hydrogen and oxygen was "corrected for shrinkage" to $1 : 15{\cdot}9105$. The proper numerical corrections for the constant errors of a thermometer are indicated on the well-known "Kew certificate," etc.

If the mean error of each set of results differs, by an amount to be expected, from the mean errors of the different sets measured with the same instrument under the same conditions, no constant error is likely to be present. The different series of atomic weight determinations of the same chemical element, published by the same, or by different observers, do not stand this test satisfactorily. Hence, Ostwald concludes that constant errors must have been present even though they have escaped the experimenter's ken.

EXAMPLE.—Discuss the following : "Merely increasing the *number* of experiments, without varying the conditions or method of observation, diminishes the influence of accidental errors. It is, however, useless to multiply the number of observations beyond a certain limit. On the other hand, the greater the *number and variety* of the observations, the more complete will be the elimination of the effects of both constant and accidental errors."

§ 166. Proportional Errors.

One of the greatest sources of error in scientific measurements occurs when the quantity cannot be measured directly. In such cases, two or more separate observations may have to be made on different magnitudes. Each observation contributes some little inaccuracy to the final result. Thus Faraday has determined the thickness of gold leaf from the weight of a certain number of sheets. Foucault measures time, Le Chatelier measures temperature in terms of an angular deviation. The determination of the rate of a chemical reaction often depends on a number of more or less troublesome analyses.[1]

For this reason, among others, many chemists prefer the standard $O = 16$ as the basis of their system of atomic weights. The atomic weights of most of the elements have been determined directly or indirectly with reference to oxygen. If $H = 1$ be the basis, the atomic weights of most of the elements depend on the nature of the relation between oxygen and hydrogen—a relation which has not yet been fixed in a satisfactory manner. The best determinations made since 1887 vary between $H : O = 1 : 15\cdot96$ and $H : O = 1 : 15\cdot87$. If the former ratio be adopted, the atomic weights of antimony and uranium would be respectively $119\cdot6$ and $239\cdot0$; while if the latter ratio be employed, these units become respectively $118\cdot9$ and $237\cdot7$, a difference of one and two units! It is, therefore, better to contrive that the atomic weights of the elements do not depend on the uncertainty of the ratio $H : O$, by adopting the basis: $O = 16$.

If the quantity to be determined is deduced by calculation from a measurement, Taylor's theorem furnishes a convenient means of criticizing the conditions under which any proposed experiment is to be performed, and at the same time furnishes a valuable insight into the effect of an error in the measurement on the whole result. It is of the greatest importance that every investigator should have a clear idea of the different sources of error to which his results are liable in order to be able to discriminate between important and unimportant sources of error, and to find just where the greatest attention must be paid in order to obtain the best results. The necessary accuracy is to be obtained with the least expenditure of labour.

I. Proportional errors of simple measurements. Let y be the desired quantity to be calculated from a magnitude x which can be measured directly and is connected with y by the relation

$$y = f(x).$$

$f(x)$ is always affected with some error dx which causes y to deviate from the truth by an amount dy. The error will then be

$$dy = (y + dy) - y = f(x + dx) - f(x).$$

---

[1] Indirect results are liable to another source of error. The formula employed may be so inexact that accurate measurements give but grossly approximate results. For instance, a first approximation formula may have been employed when the accuracy of the observations required one more precise; $\pi = \frac{2 \cdot 2}{7}$ may have been put in place of $\pi = 3\cdot14159$; or the coefficient of expansion of a perfect gas has been applied to an imperfect gas. Such errors are called **errors of method.**

dx is necessarily a small magnitude, therefore, by Taylor's theorem,

$$f(x + dx) = f(x) + f'(x) \cdot dx + \ldots,$$

or, neglecting the higher orders of magnitude,

$$dy = f'(x) \cdot dx.$$

The relation between the error and the total magnitude of y is

$$\frac{dy}{y} = \frac{f'(x) \cdot dx}{f(x)}. \qquad \qquad (1)$$

All this means is that the differential of a function represents the change in the value of the function when the variable suffers an infinitesimal change. The student learned this the first day he attacked the calculus. The ratio $dy : y$ is called the **proportional, relative, or fractional error,** that is to say, the ratio of the error involved in the whole process to the total quantity sought; while $100dy : y$ is called the **percentage error.** The degree of accuracy of a measurement is determined by the magnitude of the proportional error.

$$\text{Proportional Error} = \frac{\text{Magnitude of error}}{\text{Total magnitude of quantity measured}}.$$

Students often fail to understand why their results seem all wrong when the experiments have been carefully performed and the calculations correctly done. For instance, the molecular weight of a substance is known to be either 160, or some multiple of 160. To determine which, 0·380 (or w) grm. of the substance was added to 14·01 (or w_1) grms. of acetone boiling at $\theta_1°$ (or $3·50°$) on Beckmann's arbitrary scale, the temperature, in consequence, fell to $\theta_2°$ (or $3·36°$); the molecular weight of the substance, M, is then represented by the known formula

$$M = 1670\frac{w}{w_1(\theta_1 - \theta_2)}; \quad \text{or,} \quad M = 1670\frac{·380}{14·01 \times ·14} = 323,$$

or approximately 2×160. Now assume that the temperature readings may be $\pm 0·05°$ in error owing to convection currents, radiation and conduction of heat, etc. Let $\theta_1° = 3·55°$ and $\theta_2° = 3·31°$,

$$\therefore M = 1670\frac{0·380}{14·01 \times 0·24} = 188.$$

This means that an error of $\pm \frac{1}{20}°$ in the reading of the thermometer would give a result positively misleading. This example is by no means exaggerated. The simultaneous determination of the heat of fusion and of the specific heat of a solid by the solution of two simultaneous equations, and the determination of the latent heat of steam are specially liable to similar mistakes. A study of the reduction formula will show in every case that relatively small errors in the reading of the temperature are magnified into serious dimensions by the method used in the calculation of the final result.

EXAMPLES.—(1) Almost any text-book on optics will tell you that the radius of curvature, r, of a lens, is given by the formula

$$r = \frac{af}{f - a}.$$

Let the true values of f and a be respectively 20 and 15. Let f and a be liable to error to the extent of $\pm$ 0·5, say, f is read 20·5, and a 14·5. Then the true value of r is 60, the observed value 51·2. Fractional error $= \frac{8·8}{60}$. This means that an error of about 0·5 in 20, i.e., 2·5 %, in the determination of f and a may cause r to deviate 15 % from the truth.

(2) In applying the formula

$$V = 8 \cdot e^{5000 \frac{T_1 - T_0}{T_1 T_0}},$$

for the influence of temperature on the velocity, V, of a chemical reaction show that an error of 1° in the determination of T_1, at about 300° abs., will give a fractional error of 2·4 in the determination of V. Hint. Substitute $T_1 = 300$, $T_0 = 273$. Use Table IV. I make $V = 41·52$. Now put $T_1 = 301$. I get $V = 43·79$, etc. Hence an error of 1° will make V vary about 6 % from its true value.

If we knew that an astronomer had made an absolute error of 100,000 miles in estimating the distance between the earth and the sun, and also that a physicist had made an absolute error of the $\frac{1}{10000,000000}$th of a mile in measuring the wave length of a spectral line, we could form no idea of the relative accuracy of the two measurements in spite of the fact that the one error is the $\frac{1}{1000,000000,000000}$th part of the other. In the first measurement the error is about $\frac{1}{1,000}$ of the whole quantity measured, in the second case the error is about the same order of magnitude as the quantity measured. In the former case, therefore, the error is negligibly small; in the latter, the error renders the result nugatory.

It is therefore important to be able to recognise the weak and strong points of a given method of investigation; to grade the degree of accuracy of the different stages of the work so as to produce the required result; so as to have enough at all points, but no superfluity. I have already spoken of the need for "scientific perspective" in dealing with numerical computations.

EXAMPLES.—(1) It is required to determine the capacity of a sphere from the measurement of its diameter. Let y denote the volume, x the diameter, then, by a well-known mensuration formula, $y = \frac{1}{6}\pi x^3$. It is required to find the effect of a small error in the measurement of the diameter on the calculated volume. Suppose an error dx is committed in the measurement, then

$$y + dy = \frac{1}{6}\pi(x + dx)^3 = \frac{1}{6}\pi\{x^3 + 3x^2dx + 3x(dx)^2 + (dx)^3\}.$$

By hypothesis, dx is a very small fraction, therefore, by neglecting the higher powers of dx and dividing the result by the original expression

$$\frac{y + dy}{y} = \frac{1}{6}\pi\left(\frac{x^3 + 3x^2dx}{\frac{1}{6}\pi x^3}\right); \; \frac{dy}{y} = 3\frac{dx}{x}.$$

Or, the error in the calculated result is three times that made in the measurement. Hence the necessity for extreme precautions in measuring the diameter. Sometimes, we shall find, it is not always necessary to be so careful. The same result could have been more easily obtained by the use of Taylor's theorem as described above. Differentiate the original expression and divide the result by the original expression. We thus get the relative error without trouble.

(2) Criticize the method for the determination of the atomic weight of lead from the ratio Pb : O in lead monoxide. Let y denote the atomic weight of lead, a the atomic weight of oxygen (known). It is found experimentally that x parts of lead combine with one part of oxygen, the required atomic weight of lead is determined from the simple proportion

$$y : a = x : 1; \; \text{or,} \; y = ax; \; \text{or,} \; dy = adx; \; \therefore \; dy/y = dx/x. \qquad . \quad (2)$$

Thus an error of 1 % in the determination of x introduces an equal error in the calculated value of y. Other things being equal, this method of finding the atomic weight of lead is, therefore, very likely to give good results.

(3) Show that the result of determining the atomic weight of barium by precipitation of the chloride with silver nitrate is less influenced by experimental errors than the determination of the atomic weight of sodium in the same way. Assume that one part of silver as nitrate requires x parts of sodium (or barium) chloride for precipitation as silver chloride. Let a and b be the known atomic weights of silver and chlorine. Then, if y denotes the atomic weight of sodium, $y + b : a = x : 1$; or, $y = ax - b$; $\therefore a = (y + b)/x$. Differentiate, and substitute $y = 23$, $b = 35 \cdot 5$.

$$\frac{dy}{y} = \frac{a}{ax - b}dx = \frac{y + b}{y} \cdot \frac{dx}{x} = 2 \cdot 54 \frac{dx}{x},$$

or an error of 1 % in the determination of chlorine in sodium will introduce an error of $2 \cdot 5$ % in the atomic weight of sodium. Hence it is a disadvantage to have b greater than y. For barium, the error introduced is $1 \cdot 5$ % instead of $2 \cdot 5$ %.

(4) If the atomic weight of barium y is determined by the precipitation of barium sulphate from barium chloride solutions, and a denotes the known atomic weight of chlorine, b the known combining weight of SO_4, then when x parts of barium chloride are converted into one part of barium sulphate,

$$y + 2a : y + b = x : 1; \; \frac{dy}{y} = \frac{(b - 2a)dx}{(1 - x)(bx - 2a)}.$$

(5) An approximation formula used in the determination of the viscosity of liquids is

$$\eta = \frac{\pi p t r^4}{8vl},$$

where v denotes the volume of liquid flowing from a capillary tube of radius r and length l in the time t; p is the actual pressure exerted by the column of liquid. Show that the proportional error in the calculation of the viscosity η is four times the error made in measuring the radius of the tube.

(6) In a tangent galvanometer, the tangent of the angle of deflection of the needle is proportional to the current. Prove that the proportional error in the calculated value of the current due to a given error in the reading is least when the deflection is 45°. The strength of the current is proportional to the tangent of the displaced angle x, or

$$y = f(x) = C \tan x; \therefore dy = \frac{C \cdot dx}{\cos^2 x}; \text{ or, } \frac{dy}{y} = \frac{dx}{\sin x \cdot \cos x}.$$

To determine the minimum, put

$$\frac{d}{dx}\left(\frac{dy}{y}\right) = \frac{\sin^2 x - \cos^2 x}{\sin^2 x \cdot \cos^2 x} = 0; \therefore \sin^2 x = \cos^2 x, \text{ or, } \sin x = \cos x.$$

This is true only in the neighbourhood of 45° (Table XIV.), and, therefore, in this region an error of observation will have the least influence on the final result. In other words, the best results are obtained with a tangent galvonometer when the needle is deflected about 45°.

What will be the effect of an error of 0·25° in reading a deflection of 42°, on the calculated current? Note that x in the above formula is expressed in circular or radian measure (page 606). Hence,

$$0\text{·}25\text{(degrees)} = \frac{\pi \times 0\text{·}25}{180} = 0\text{·}00436\text{(radians)}.$$

$$\therefore \frac{dy}{y} = \frac{dx}{\sin x \cdot \cos x} = \frac{2dx}{\sin 2x} = \frac{0\text{·}00872}{\sin 84^v} = 0\text{·}009; \text{ i.e., } 0\text{·}9\,°/_\text{o},$$

since, from a Table of Natural Sines, sin 84°=0·9945.

(7) Show that the proportional error involved in the measurement of an electrical resistance on a Wheatstone's bridge is least near the middle of the bridge. Let R denote the resistance, l the length of the bridge, x the distance of the telephone from one end. $\therefore y = Rx/(l + x)$. Proceed as above and show that when $x = \frac{1}{2}l$ (the middle of the bridge), the proportional error is a minimum.

(8) By Newton's law of attraction, the force of gravitation, g, between two bodies varies directly as their respective masses—m_1, m_2—and inversely as the square of their distance apart, r. The mass of each body is supposed to be collected at its centroid (centre of gravity). The weight of one gram at Paris is equivalent to 980·868 dynes. The dyne is the unit of force. Hence Newton's law, $g = \mu m_1 m_2/r^2$ (dynes), may be written $w = a/r^2$ (grams), where a is a constant equivalent to $\mu \times m_1 \times m_2 \times 980\text{·}868$. Hence show that for small changes in altitude $dw/w = -2dr/r$. Marek was able to detect a difference of 1 in 500,000,000 when comparing the kilogram standards of the Bureau International des Poids et Mesures. Hence show that it is possible to detect a difference in the weight of a substance when one scale pan of the

balance is raised one centimetre higher than the other. Hint. Radius of earth
$= r = 637,130,000$ cm.; $w = 1$ kilogrm.; $dr = 1$ cm.;

$$\therefore -\frac{dw}{w} = \frac{2}{637,130,000} = \frac{1}{318,565,000}.$$ This is greater than $\frac{1}{500,000,000}$.

As a further exercise, show that a kilogram will lose 0·00003 grm., if it be
weighed 10 cm. above its original position.   Hint. Find $-dw$; r has its
former value; $w = 1000$ grm.; $dr = 10$ cm.

II. Proportional error of composite measurements. Whenever a
result has to be determined indirectly by combining several different
species of measurements—weight, temperature, volume, electromotive force, etc.—the effect of a percentage error of, say, 1 per
cent. in the reading of the thermometer will be quite different from
the effect of an error of 1 per cent. in the reading of a voltmeter.

It is obvious that some observations must be made with
greater care than others in order that the influence of each kind
of measurement on the final result may be the same.   If a large
error is compounded with a small error, the total error is not ap-
preciably affected by the smaller.   Hence Ostwald recommends
that "a variable error be neglected if it is less than one-tenth of
the larger, often, indeed, if it is but one-fifth".

EXAMPLES.—(1) Joule's relation between the strength of a current C
(ampères) and the quantity of heat Q (calories) generated in an electric conductor of resistance R (ohms) in the time t (seconds), is, $Q = 0.24 C^2 R t$. Show
that R and t must be measured with half the precision of C in order to have
the same influence on Q.

(2) What will be the fractional error in Q corresponding to a fractional
error of 0·1 °/₀ in R?   Ansr. 0·001, or 0·1 °/₀.

(3) What will be the percentage error in C corresponding to 0·02 °/₀ in Q?
Ansr. 0·01 °/₀.

(4) If the density s of a substance be determined from its weights (w, w_1)
in air and water, and remembering that $s = w_1/(w - w_1)$, show that

$$\frac{ds}{s} = \frac{w}{w - w_1}\left(\frac{dw_1}{w_1} - \frac{dw}{w}\right).$$

(5) The specific heat of a substance determined by the method of mixtures
is given by the formula

$$s = \frac{m_1 c(\theta_2 - \theta_1)}{m(\theta - \theta_2)},$$

where m is the weight of the substance before the experiment; m_1 the weight
of the water in the calorimeter; c the mean specific heat of water between
θ_2 and θ_1; θ is the temperature of the body before immersion; θ_1 the initial
temperature reached by the water in the calorimeter; θ_2 the temperature of
the system after equalization of the temperature has taken place. Supposing
the water equivalent of the apparatus is included in m_1, what will be the
effect of a small error in the determination of the different temperatures on
the result?

First, error in θ_1. Show that $ds/s = - d\theta_1/(\theta_2 - \theta_1)$. If an error of say $0.1°$ is made in a reading and $\theta_2 - \theta_1 = 10°$, the error in the resulting specific heat is about $1°/_o$. If a maximum error of $0.01°/_o$ is to be permitted, the temperature must be read to the $0.0001°$.

Second, error in θ. Show that $ds/s = - d\theta/(\theta - \theta_2)$. If a maximum error in the determination of s is to be $0.1°/_o$, when $\theta - \theta_2 = 50°$, θ must be read to the $0.05°$. If an error of $0.1°$ is made in reading the temperature and $\theta - \theta_2 = 50°$, show that the resulting error in the specific heat will be $0.2°/_o$.

Third, error in θ_2. Show that $ds/s = d\theta_2/(\theta_2 - \theta_1) + d\theta_2/(\theta - \theta_2)$. If the maximum error allowed is $0.1°/_o$ and $\theta_2 - \theta_1 = 10°$, $\theta - \theta_1 = 50°$, show that θ_2 must be read to the $\frac{1}{120}°$; while if an error of $0.1°$ is made in the reading of θ_2, show that the resulting error in the specific heat is $1.2°/_o$.

(6) In the preceding experiment, if $m_1 = 100$ grams, show that the weighing need not be taken to more than the 0.1 gram for the error in s to be within $0.1°/_o$; and for m, need not be closer than 0.5 gram when m is about 50 grams.

Since the actual errors are proportional to the probable errors, the most probable or mean value of the total error du, is obtained from the expression

$$(du)^2 = \left(\frac{\partial u}{\partial a_1} da_1\right)^2 + \left(\frac{\partial u}{\partial a_2} da_2\right)^2 + \ldots, \qquad . \qquad . \quad (3)$$

from (16), § 162, page 530. Note the squared terms are all positive. Since the errors are fortuitous, there will be as many positive as negative paired terms. These will, in the long run, approximately neutralize each other. Hence (3).

EXAMPLES.—(1) Divide equation (3) by u^2, it is then easy to show that

$$\left(\frac{dQ}{Q}\right)^2 = 4\left(\frac{dC}{C}\right)^2 + \left(\frac{dR}{R}\right)^2 + \left(\frac{dt}{t}\right)^2,$$

from the preceding set of examples. Hence show that the fractional error in Q, corresponding to the fractional errors of 0.03 in C, 0.02 in R and 0.03 in t, is 0.07.

(2) The regular formula for the determination of molecular weight of a substance by the freezing point method, is $M = Kw/\theta$, where K is a constant, M the required molecular weight, w the weight of the substance dissolved in 100 grams of the solvent, θ the lowering of the freezing point. In an actual determination, $w = 0.5139$, $\theta = 0.295$, $K = 19$ (Perkin and Kipping's *Organic Chemistry*), what would be the effect on M of an error of 0.01 in the determination of w, and of an error of 0.01 in the determination of θ? Also show that an error of 0.01 in the determination of θ affects M to an extent of $- 3.39$, while an error of $.01$ in the determination of w only affects M to the extent of 0.94. Hence show that it is not necessary to weigh to more than 0.01 of a gram.

From (16), § 162, page 530, when the effect of each observation on the final result is the same, the partial differential coefficients are all equal. If u denotes the sum of n observations, $a_1, a_2, \ldots, a_n$.

$$u = a_1 + a_2 + \ldots + a_n ; \quad \therefore \; \frac{\partial u}{\partial a_1} = \frac{\partial u}{\partial a_2} = \ldots = 1.$$

But, in order that the actual errors affecting each observation may be the same, we must have, from (17), page 530,

$$da_1 = da_2 = \ldots = da_n = \frac{du}{\sqrt{n}} ; \qquad . \qquad . \qquad (4)$$

with the fractional errors :

$$\therefore \; \frac{da_1}{u} = \frac{da_2}{u} = \ldots = \frac{da_n}{u} = \frac{du}{u} \cdot \frac{1}{\sqrt{n}}. \qquad . \qquad . \qquad (5)$$

EXAMPLES.—(1) Suppose the greatest allowable fractional error in Q (preceding examples) is $0.5\,^{\circ}/_{\circ}$, what is the greatest percentage error in each of the variables C, R, t, allowable under equal effects ? Here,

$$2\frac{dC}{C} = \frac{dR}{R} = \frac{dt}{t} = \frac{0.005}{\sqrt{3}}.$$

Ansr. 0.22 for R and t; and $0.11\,^{\circ}/_{\circ}$ for C.

(2) If a volume v of a given liquid flows from a long capillary tube of radius r and length l in t seconds, the viscosity of the liquid is $\eta = \pi p r^4 t / 8 v l$, where p denotes the excess of the pressure at the outlet of the tube over atmospheric pressure. What would be the errors dr, dv, dl, dt, dp, necessary under equal effects to give η with a precision of $0.1\,^{\circ}/_{\circ}$? Here,

$$\frac{dp}{p} = \frac{dt}{t} = 4\frac{dr}{r} = -\frac{dv}{v} = -\frac{dl}{l} = \frac{0.001}{\sqrt{5}} = 0.00045.$$

It is now necessary to know the numerical values of p, t, v, r, l, before dp, dt, $\ldots$ can be determined. Thus, if r is about 2 mm., the radius must be measured to the 0.00022 mm. for an error of $0.1\,^{\circ}/_{\circ}$ in η. It has been shown how the best working conditions may be determined by a study of the formula, to which the experimental results are to be referred. The following is a more complex example.

(3) The resistance X of a cell is to be measured. Let C_1, C_2 respectively denote the currents produced by the cell when working through two known external resistances r_1 and r_2, and let R_1, R_2 be the total resistances of the circuit, E the electromotive force of the cell is constant. Your text-book on practical physics will tell you that

$$X = \frac{C_2 r_2 - C_1 r_1}{C_1 - C_2}. \qquad . \qquad . \qquad . \qquad . \qquad (6)$$

What ratio $C_1 : C_2$ will furnish the best result? As usual, by partial differentiation, (4) above,

$$(dX)^2 = \left(\frac{\partial X}{\partial C_1} dC_1\right)^2 + \left(\frac{\partial X}{\partial C_2} dC_2\right)^2. \qquad . \qquad . \qquad (7)$$

Find values for $\partial X/\partial C_1$ and $\partial X/\partial C_2$ from (6); and put R_1 for r_1; R_2 for r_2. From Ohm's law, $E = CR$, E being constant, $C_1 : C_2 = R_2 : R_1$. Thus

$$\frac{\partial X}{\partial C_1} = -\frac{C_2(r_2 - r_1)}{(C_1 - C_2)^2} = -\frac{R_1^2 R_2}{E(R_2 - R_1)} ; \; \frac{\partial X}{\partial C_2} = \frac{C_1(r_2 - r_1)}{(C_1 - C_2)^2} = \frac{R_1 R_2^2}{E(R_2 - R_1)}. \; (8)$$

Substitute this result in (7).

(i) If a mirror galvanometer is used, $dC_1 = dC_2 = dC$ (say) = constant.

$$\therefore (dX)^2 = \frac{(R_1{}^4 R_2{}^2 + R_1{}^2 R_2{}^4)\,(dC)^2}{E^2(R_2 - R_1)^2} = \frac{R_1{}^4(x^2 + x^4)\,(dC)^2}{E^2(x-1)^2}, \qquad (9)$$

by substituting $x = R_2 : R_1$. For a minimum error, we have, by the usual method,

$$\frac{d}{dx}\left(\frac{x^4 - x^2}{x^2 - 2x + 1}\right) = 0 \; ; \; \therefore \; x^3 - 2x^2 - 1 = 0 \; ; \; \therefore \; x = 2 \cdot 2 \text{ approx.}$$

Or, $R_2 = 2 \cdot 2 R_1$; or, $C_1 - 2 \cdot 2 C_2$, from Ohm's law. Substitute this value of x in (9), and we get

$$dX = \frac{\sqrt{20} R_1{}^2 . dC'_1}{E}, \qquad \cdots \quad (10)$$

which shows that the external resistance, R_1, should be as small as is consistent with the polarization of the battery.

(ii) If a tangent galvanometer is used, dC/C is constant. The above method will not work. Hence substitute $C_1 = ER_1$ and $C_2 = ER_2$ in the first of equations (8), we get

$$(dX)^2 = 2\left(\frac{R_1 R_2}{R_2 - R_1}\right)^2 = \left(\frac{dC}{C}\right)^2 ; \; dX = \frac{\sqrt{2}}{\dfrac{1}{R_1} - \dfrac{1}{R_2}} \cdot \frac{dC}{C}. \qquad (11)$$

From this it can be shown there is no best ratio $R_2 : R_1$. From the last expression we can see that the error dX decreases as R_1 diminishes, and as R_2 increases. Hence R_2 should be made as large and R_1 as small as is consistent with the range of the galvanometer and the polarization of the battery.

You can easily get the fractional errors in each case. From (10) and (11) respectively

$$\frac{dC_1}{C_1} = \frac{1}{\sqrt{20}} \cdot \frac{X}{R_1} \cdot \frac{dX}{X} \; ; \; \frac{dC}{C} = \frac{1}{2} \cdot \frac{X}{R_1} \cdot \frac{dX}{X},$$

assuming in the latter case that $C_1 : C_2 = 3 : 1$; so that the intermediate step from (11) is $dX = \sqrt{2} \cdot 3 R_1{}^2 / (3 R_1 - R_1) \times dC/C$.

§ 167. Observations of Different Degrees of Accuracy.

Hitherto it has been assumed that the individual observations of any particular series, are equally reliable, or that there is no reason why one observation should be preferred more than another. As a general rule, measurements made by different methods, by different observers, or even by the same observer at different times,[1] are not liable to the same errors. Some results

---

[1] I am reminded that Dumas, discussing the errors in his great work on the gravimetric composition of water, alluded to a few pages back, adds the remarks : "The length of time required for these operations compelled me to prolong the work far into the night, generally finishing with the weighings about 2 or 3 o'clock in the morning. This may be the cause of a substantial error, for I dare not venture to assert that such weighings deserve as much confidence as if they had been performed under more favourable conditions and by an observer not so worn out with fatigue, the inevitable result of fifteen to twenty hours continued attention."

are more trustworthy than others. In order to fix this idea, suppose that twelve determinations of the capacity of a flask by the same method, gave the following results : six measurements each 1·6 litres ; four, 1·4 litres ; and two, 1·2 litres. The numbers 6, 4, 2, represent the relative values of the three results 1·6, 1·4. 1·2, because the measurement 1·6 has cost three times as much labour as 1·2. The former result, therefore, is worth three times as much confidence as the latter. In such cases, it is customary to say that the relative practical value, or the weight of these three sets of observations, is as 6 : 4 : 2, or, what is the same thing, as 3 : 2 : 1. In this sense, the **weight** of an observation, or set of observations, represents the *relative* degree of precision of that observation in comparison with other observations of the same quantity. It tells us nothing about the *absolute* precision, h, of the observations.

It is shown below that the weight of an observation is, in theory, inversely as its probable error; in practice, it is usual to assign arbitrary weights to the observations. For instance, if one observation is made under favourable conditions, another under adverse conditions, it would be absurd to place the two on the same footing. Accordingly, the observer pretends that the best observations have been made more frequently. That is to say, if the observations $a_1, a_2, \ldots, a_n$, have weights $p_1, p_2, \ldots, p_n$, respectively, the observer has assumed that the measurement a_1 has been repeated p_1 times with the result a_1, and that a_n has been repeated p_n times with the result a_n.

To take a concrete illustration, Morley [1] has made three accurate series of determinations of the density of oxygen gas with the following results :—

I. 1·42879 ± 0·000034 ; II. 1·42887 ± 0·000048 ;
III. 1·42917 ± 0·000048.

The probable errors of these three means would indicate that the first series were worth more than the second. For experimental reasons, Morley preferred the last series, and gave it double weight. In other words, Morley pretended that he had made four series of experiments, two of which gave 1·42917, one gave 1·42879, and one

---

[1] E. Morley, "On the densities of oxygen and hydrogen and on the ratio of their atomic weights," *Smithsonian Contributions to Knowledge*, No. 980, 55, 1895.

gave 1·42887. The result is that 1·42900, not 1·42894, is given as the best representative value of the density of oxygen gas.

The product of an observation or of an error with the weight of the observation, is called a **weighted observation** in the former case, and a **weighted error** in the other.

The practice of weighting observations is evidently open to some abuse. It is so very easy to be influenced rather by the differences of the results from one another, than by the intrinsic quality of the observation. This is a fatal mistake.

I. *The best value to represent a number of observations of equal weight, is their arithmetical mean.* If P denotes the most probable value of the observed magnitudes $a_1, a_2, \ldots a_n$, then $P - a_1, P - a_2, \ldots, P - a_n$, represent the several errors in the n observations. From the principle of least squares these errors will be a minimum when

$$(P - a_1)^2 + (P - a_2)^2 + \ldots + (P - a_n)^n = \text{a minimum.}$$

Hence, from the regular method for finding minimum values,

$$P = \frac{a_1 + a_2 + \ldots + a_n}{n}, \quad \ldots \quad (1)$$

or the best representative value of a given series of measurements of an unknown quantity, is an arithmetical mean of the n observations, provided that the measurements have the same degree of confidence.

II. *The best value to represent a number of observations of different weight, is obtained by multiplying each observation by its weight and dividing the sum of these products by the sum of their different weights.* With the same notation as before, let $p_1, p_2, \ldots, p_n$, be the respective weights of the observations $a_1, a_2, \ldots, a_n$. From the definition of weight, the quantity a_1 may be considered as the mean of p_1 observations of unit weight; a_2 the mean of p_2 observations of unit weight, etc. The observed quantities may, therefore, be resolved into a series of fictitious observations all of equal weight. Applying the preceding rule to each of the resolved observations, the total number of standard observations of unit weight will be $p_1 + p_2 + \ldots + p_n$; the sum of the p_1 standard observations of unit weight will be $p_1 a_1$; the sum of p_2 standard observations, $p_2 a_2$, etc. Hence, from (1), the most probable value of a series of observations of different weights is

$$P' = \frac{p_1 a_1 + p_2 a_2 + \ldots + p_n a_n}{p_1 + p_2 + \ldots + p_n}. \quad \ldots \quad (2)$$

Note the formal resemblance between this formula and that for finding the centre of gravity of a system of particles of different weights arranged in a straight line.

Weighted observations are, therefore, fictitious results treated as if they were real measurements of equal weight. With this convention, the value of P' in (2) is an arithmetical mean sometimes called the **general or probable mean**.

III. The weight of an observation is inversely as the square of its probable error. Let a be a set of observations whose probable error is R and whose weight is unity. Let $p_1, p_2, \ldots, p_n$ and $r_1, r_2, \ldots, r_n$, be the respective weights and probable errors of a series of observations $a_1, a_2, \ldots, a_n$, of the same quantity. By definition of weight, a_1 is equivalent to p_1 observations of equal weight. From (17), page 530,

$$r_1 = \frac{R}{\sqrt{p_1}}; \; p_1 = \frac{R^2}{r_1^2}; \; p_2 = \frac{R^2}{r_2^2}; \ldots \therefore p_1 : p_2 : p_3 \ldots = \frac{1}{r_1^2} : \frac{1}{r_2^2} : \frac{1}{r_3^2} \ldots \, (3)$$

EXAMPLES.—(1) If n observations have weights $p_1, p_2, \ldots, p_n$, show that

$$R = \pm \frac{r_1}{\sqrt{\Sigma(p)}}. \qquad \cdots \qquad (4)$$

Differentiate (2) successively with respect to $a_1, a_2, \ldots$ and substitute the results in (16), page 530.

(2) Show that the mean error of a series of observations of weights, $p_1, p_2, \ldots, p_n$, is

$$M = \pm \sqrt{\frac{\Sigma(px^2)}{(n-1)\Sigma(p)}}.$$

Hint. Proceed as in § 161 but use px^2 and pv^2 in place of x^2 and v^2 respectively. If the sum of the weights of a series of observations is $\Sigma(p) = 40$, and the sum of the products of the weights of each observation with the square of its deviation from the mean of nine observations is $\Sigma(px^2) = 0.3998$, show that $M = \pm 0.035$.

(3) The probable errors of four series of observations are respectively 1·2, 0·8, 0·9, 1·1, what are the relative weights of the corresponding observations? Ansr. 7 : 16 : 11 : 8. Use (3).

(4) Determinations of the percentage amount of copper in a sample of malachite were made by a number of chemical students, with the following results: (1) 39·1 ; (2) 38·8, 38·7, 38·6 ; (3) 39·9, 39·1, 39·3 ; (4) 37·7, 37·9. If these analyses had an equal degree of confidence, the mean, 38·8, would best represent the percentage amount of copper in the ore—formula (1). But the analyses are not of equal value. The first was made by the teacher. To this we may assign an arbitrary weight 10. Sets (2) and (3) were made by two different students using the electrolytic process. Student (2) was more experienced than student (3), in consequence, we are led to assign to the former an arbitrary weight 6, to the latter, 4. Set (4) was made by a student precipitating the copper as CuS, roasting and weighing as CuO. The danger

of loss of CuS by oxidation to $CuSO_4$ during washing, leads us to assign to this set of results an arbitrary weight 2. From these *assumptions*, show that 38·91 best represents the percentage amount of copper in the ore. For the sake of brevity use values above 37 in the calculation. From formula (2), $\frac{84·0}{44} = 1·91$. Add 37 for the general mean. It is unfortunate when so fantastic a method has to be used for calculating the most probable value of a " constant of Nature," because a redetermination is then urgently required.

(5) H. A. Rowland (*Proc. Amer. Acad.*, **15**, 75, 1879) has made an exhaustive study of Joule's determinations of the mechanical equivalent of heat, and he believes that Joule's several values have the weights here appended in brackets: 442·8 (0); 427·5 (2); 426·8 (10); 428·7 (2); 429·1 (1); 428·0 (1); 425·8 (2); 428·0 (3); 427·1 (3); 426·0 (5); 422·7 (1); 426·3 (1). Hence Rowland concludes that 426·9 best represents the result of Joule's work. Verify this. Notice that Rowland rejects the number 442·8 by giving it zero weight.

(6) Encke gives the 8·60816″ ± 0·037 as the value of the solar parallax; D. Gill gives 8·802″ ± 0·005. Hence the merit of Encke's work is to the merit of Gill's work, as $(0·005)^2 : (0·037)^2 = 25 : 1369 = 1 : 54·76$. Or £54·76 may be bet in favour of Gill's number against £1 in favour of Encke.

IV. To combine several arithmetical means each of which is affected with a known probable (or mean) error, into one general mean. One hundred parts of silver are equivalent to

$$49·5365 \pm 0·013 \text{ of } NH_4Cl, \text{ according to Pelouze ;}$$

49·523	± 0·0055	,,	,,	Marignac ;
49·5973	± 0·0005	,,	,,	Stas (1867) ;
49·5992	± 0·00039	,,	,,	Stas (1882),

where the first number represents the arithmetical mean of a series of experiments, the second number the corresponding probable error. How are we to find the best representative value of this series of observations? The first thing is to decide what weight shall be assigned to each result. Individual judgment on the " internal evidence " of the published details of the experiments is not always to be trusted. Nor is it fair to assign the greatest weight to the last two values simply because they are by Stas.

L. Meyer and K. Seubert, in a paper *Die Atomgewichte der Elemente, aus der Originalzahlen neu berechnet,* Leipzig, 1883, weighted each result according to the mass of material employed in the determination. They assumed that the magnitude of the errors of observation were inversely as the quantity of material treated. That is to say, an experiment made on 20 grams of material is supposed to be worth twice as much as one made on 10 grams. This seems to be a somewhat gratuitous assumption.

One way of treating this delicate question is to assign to each arithmetical mean a weight inversely as the square of its mean error. F. W. Clarke in his "Recalculation of the Atomic Weights," *Smithsonian Miscellaneous Collections*, 1075, 1897, employed the probable error. Although this method of weighting did not suit Morley in the special case mentioned on page 549, Clarke considers it a safe, though not infallible guide. Let A, B, C, ..., be the arithmetical mean of each series of experiments; a, b, c, ..., the respective probable (or mean) errors, then, from (2),

$$\text{General Mean} = \frac{\dfrac{A}{a^2} + \dfrac{B}{b^2} + \dfrac{C}{c^2} + \dots}{\dfrac{1}{a^2} + \dfrac{1}{b^2} + \dfrac{1}{c^2} + \dots}; \quad . \quad . \quad (5)$$

$$\text{Probable Error} = \pm \frac{1}{\sqrt{\dfrac{1}{a^2} + \dfrac{1}{b^2} + \dfrac{1}{c^2} + \dots}}. \quad . \quad . \quad (6)$$

EXAMPLES.—(1) From the experimental results just quoted, show that the best value for the ratio

$$\text{Ag} : \text{NH}_4\text{Cl is } 100 : 49\cdot5983 \pm 0\cdot00031.$$

Hint. Substitute $A = 49\cdot5365$, $a = 0\cdot013$; $B = 49\cdot523$, $b = 0\cdot0055$; $C = 49\cdot5973$, $c = 0\cdot0005$; $D = 49\cdot5992$, $d = 0\cdot00039$, in equations (5).

(2) The following numbers represent the most trustworthy results yet published for the atomic weight of gold ($H = 1$) : $195\cdot605 \pm 0\cdot0099$; $195\cdot711 \pm 0\cdot0224$; $195\cdot808 \pm 0\cdot0126$; $195\cdot624 \pm 0\cdot0224$; $195\cdot896 \pm 0\cdot0131$; $195\cdot770 \pm 0\cdot0082$. Hence show that the best representative value for this constant is $196\cdot743 \pm 0\cdot0049$.

(3) In three series of determinations of the vapour pressure of water vapour at 0° Regnault found the following numbers :

I. $4\cdot54$; $4\cdot54$; $4\cdot52$; $4\cdot54$; $4\cdot52$; $4\cdot54$; $4\cdot52$; $4\cdot50$; $4\cdot50$; $4\cdot54$.

II. $4\cdot66$; $4\cdot67$; $4\cdot64$; $4\cdot62$; $4\cdot64$; $4\cdot66$; $4\cdot67$; $4\cdot66$; $4\cdot66$.

III. $4\cdot54$; $4\cdot54$; $4\cdot54$; $4\cdot58$; $4\cdot58$; $4\cdot57$; $4\cdot58$.

Show that the best representative value of series I. is $4\cdot526$, with a probable error $\pm 0\cdot0105$; series II., $4\cdot653$, probable error $\pm 0\cdot0105$; series III., $4\cdot561$, probable error $\pm 0\cdot0127$. The most probable value of the vapour pressure of aqueous vapour at 0° is, therefore, $4\cdot582$, with an equal chance of its possessing an error greater or less than $0\cdot0064$.

As a matter of fact the theory of probability is of little or no importance, when the constant, or systematic errors are greater than the accidental errors. Still further, this use of the probable error cannot be justified, even when the different series of experiments are only affected with accidental errors, because *the probable error only shows how* UNIFORMLY *an experimenter has conducted a certain process, and not how suitable that process is for the required purpose.* In combining different sets of determinations it is still more unsatisfactory to calculate the probable error of the general mean by weighting the individual errors according to Clarke's criterion when the probable errors differ very considerably among themselves. For example, Clarke (*l.c.*, page 126) deduces the general mean 136·315 ± 0·0085 for the atomic weight of barium from the following results :

136·271 ± 0·0106 ; 136·390 ± 0·0141 ; 135·600 ± 0·2711 ;
136·563 ± 0·0946.

The individual series here deviate from the general mean more than the magnitude of its probable error would lead us to suppose. The constant errors, in consequence, must be greater than the probable errors. In such a case as this, the computed probable error ± 0·0085 has no real meaning, and we can only conclude that the atomic weight of barium is, at its best, not known more accurately than to five units in the second decimal place.[1]

V. Mean and probable errors of observations of different degrees of accuracy. In a series of observations of unequal weight the mean and probable errors of a single observation of unit weight are respectively

$$m = \pm \sqrt{\frac{\Sigma(pv^2)}{n-1}}; \text{ and } r = \pm \, 0.6745 \sqrt{\frac{\Sigma(pv^2)}{n-1}}; \qquad (7)$$

The mean of a series of observations of unequal weight has the respective mean and probable errors

$$M = \pm \sqrt{\frac{\Sigma(pv^2)}{(n-1)\,\Sigma(p)}}; \text{ and } R = \pm \, 0.6745 \sqrt{\frac{\Sigma(pv^2)}{(n-1)\,\Sigma(p)}}. \qquad (8)$$

EXAMPLE.—An angle was measured under different conditions fourteen times. The observations all agreed in giving 4° 15′, but for seconds of arc the following values were obtained (the weight of each observation is given in brackets) : 45″·00 (5); 31″·25 (4) : 42″·50 (5); 45″·00 (3) ; 37″·50 (3); 38″·33 (3); 27″·50 (3) : 43″·33 (3) : 40″·63 (4); 36″·25 (2) ; 42″·50 (3) ; 39″·17 (3); 45″·00 (2); 40″·83 (3). Show that the mean error of a single observation of unit weight s ± 9″·475, the mean error of the mean 39″·78 is 1″·397. Hint. $\Sigma(p) = 46$ $\Sigma(pv)^2 = 1167·03$; $n = 14$; $\Sigma(pa) = 1830·00$.

The mean and probable errors of a single observation of weight p are respectively

$$m = \pm \sqrt{\frac{\Sigma(pv^2)}{(n-1)p}}; \text{ and } r = \pm \, 0.6745 \sqrt{\frac{\Sigma(pv^2)}{(n-1)p}}. \cdot \qquad (9)$$

---

[1] W. Ostwald's *critique* on Clarke's work (*l.c.*) in the *Zeit. phys. Chem.*, **23**, 187,1897.

EXAMPLE.—In the preceding examples show that the mean error of an observation of weight (2) is $\pm 6'''{\cdot}70$; of weight (3) is $\pm 5'''{\cdot}47$; of weight (4) $\pm 4'''{\cdot}74$; and of weight (5) $\pm 4'''{\cdot}24$.

VI. *The principle of least squares for observations of different degrees of precision* states that "the most probable values of the observed quantities are those for which the sum of the weighted squares of the errors is a minimum," that is,

$$p_1^2 v_1^2 + p_2^2 v_2^2 + \ldots + p_n^2 v_n^2 = \text{a minimum.}$$

An error v is the deviation of an observation from the arithmetical mean of n observations; a "weighted square" is the product of the weight, p, and the square of an error, v.

§ 168. Observations Limited by Conditions.

On adding up the results of an analysis, the total weight of the constituents ought to be equal to the weight of the substance itself; the three angles of a plane triangle must add up to exactly $180°$; the sum of the three triangles of a spherical triangle always equal $180°$ + the spherical excess; the sum of the angles of the normals on the faces of a crystal in the same plane must equal $360°$. Measurements subject to restrictions of this nature, are said to be **conditioned observations**. The number of conditions to be satisfied is evidently less than the number of unknown quantities, *i.e.*, observations, otherwise the value of the unknown could be deduced from the conditions, without having recourse to measurement.

In practice, measurements do not come up to the required standard, the percentage constituents of a substance do not add up to 100; the angles of a triangle are either greater or less than $180°$. Only in the ideal case of perfect accuracy are the conditions fulfilled. It is sometimes desirable to find the best representative values of a number of imperfect conditioned observations. The method to be employed is illustrated in the following examples.

EXAMPLES.—(1) The analysis of a compound gave the following results: $37{\cdot}2\%$ of carbon, $44{\cdot}1\%$ of hydrogen, $19{\cdot}4\%$ of nitrogen. Assuming each determination is equally reliable, what is the best representative value of the percentage amount of each constituent? Let C, H, N, respectively denote the percentage amounts of carbon, hydrogen, and nitrogen required, then $C + H = 100 - N \equiv 100{\cdot}0 - 19{\cdot}4 = 80{\cdot}6$. $\therefore 2C + H = 117{\cdot}8$; $C + 2H = 124{\cdot}7$. Solve the last two simultaneous equations in the usual way. Ansr. $C = 36{\cdot}97\%$; $H = 43{\cdot}86\%$; $N = 19{\cdot}17\%$. Note that this result is quite independent of any hypothesis as to the structure of matter. The chemical student will know a better way of correcting the analysis. This example will remind us how the atomic hypothesis introduces order into apparent chaos. Some analytical chemists before publishing their results, multiply or divide their percentage results to get them to add up to 100. In some cases, one constituent is left undetermined and then calculated by difference. Both practices are objectionable in exact work.

(2) The three angles of a triangle A, B, C, were measured with the result that $A=51°$; $B=94° 20'$; $C=34° 56'$. Show that the most probable values of the unknown angles are $A=51° 56'$; $B=94° 15'$; $C=34° 49$.

(3) The angles between the normals on the faces of a cubic crystal were found to be respectively $α = 91° 13'$; $β = 89° 47'$; $γ = 91° 15'$; $δ = 89° 42'$. What numbers best represent the values of the four angles? Ansr. $α = 90° 43' 45''$; $β = 89° 17' 45''$; $γ = 90° 0' 45''$; $δ = 89° 57' 45''$.

(4) The three angles of a triangle furnish the respective observation equations: $A = 36° 25' 47''$; $B = 90° 36' 28''$; $C = 52° 57' 57''$; the equation of condition requires that $A + B + C - 180° = 0$. Let x_1, x_2, x_3, respectively denote the errors affecting A, B, C, then we must have

$$x_1+x_2+x_3=-12. \qquad \qquad (1)$$

I. *If the observations are equally trustworthy*, $x_1 = x_2 = x_3 = k$, say. Substitute this value of x_1, x_2 x_3, in (1), and we get $3k + 12 = 0$; or, $k = -4$;

$$\therefore A = 36° 25' 43''; \ B = 90° 36' 24''; \ C = 53° 57' 53''.$$

The formula for the mean error of each observation is

$$\pm \sqrt{\frac{\Sigma(v^2)}{n - w + q}},$$

where w denotes the number of unknown quantities involved in the n observation equations; q denotes the number of equations of condition to be satisfied. Consequently the w unknown quantities reduce to $w - q$ independent quantities. $\Sigma(v^2)$ denotes the sum of the squares of the differences between the observed and calculated values of A, B, C. Hence, the mean error $= \pm \sqrt{48} = \pm 6''.93$.

II. *If the observations have different weights.* Let the respective weights of A, B, C, be $p_1 = 4$; $p_2 = 2$; $p_3 = 3$. It is customary to assume that the magnitude of the error affecting each observation will be inversely as its weight. (Perhaps the reader can demonstrate this principle for himself.) Instead of $x_1 = x_2 = x_3 = k$, therefore, we write $x_1 = \frac{1}{4}k$; $x_2 = \frac{1}{2}k$; $x_3 = \frac{1}{3}k$. From (1), therefore, $13k + 144 = 0$; $k = -11.07$; $x_1 = -2''.77$; $x_2 = -5''.54$; $x_3 = -3''.69$.

$$m = \text{Mean error} = \pm \sqrt{\frac{\Sigma(pv^2)}{n - w + q}}.$$

or $m = \pm 11.52$. The mean errors m_1, m_2, m_3, respectively affecting a, b, c, are

$$m_1 = \pm \frac{m}{\sqrt{p}}; \ m_2 = \pm \frac{m}{\sqrt{p}}; \ m_3 = \pm \frac{m}{\sqrt{p}}.$$

Hence

$$A = 36° 25' 44''.23 \pm 5''.76; \ B=90° 36' 22''.46 \pm 8''.15; \ C=52° 57' 53''.31 \pm 6''.65.$$

It is, of course, only permissible to reduce experimental data in this manner when the measurements have to be used as the basis for subsequent calculations. In every case the actual measurements must be stated along with the "cooked" results.

§ 169. Gauss' Method of Solving a Set of Linear Observation Equations.

In continuation of § 108, page 328, let x, y, z, represent the unknowns to be evaluated, and let a_1, a_2, ..., b_1, b_2, ..., c_1, c_2, R_1, R^2, ..., represent actual numbers whose values have been determined by the series of observations set forth in the following **observation equations**:

$$\left.\begin{aligned}
a_1 x + b_1 y + c_1 z &= R_1; \\
a_2 x + b_2 y + c_2 z &= R_2; \\
a_3 x + b_3 y + c_3 z &= R_3; \\
a_4 x + b_4 y + c_4 z &= R_4.
\end{aligned}\right\} \qquad \cdot \quad \cdot \quad \cdot \quad (1)$$

If only three equations had been given, we could easily calculate the corresponding values of x, y, z, by the methods of algebra, but these values would not necessarily satisfy the fourth equation. The problem here presented is to find the best possible values of x, y, z, which will satisfy the four given observation equations. We have selected four equations and three unknowns for the sake of simplicity and convenience. Any number may be included in the calculation. But sets involving more than three unknowns are comparatively rare. We also assume that the observation equations have the same degree of accuracy. If not, multiply each equation by the square root of its weight, as in example (3) below. This converts the equations into a set having the same degree of accuracy.

I. *To convert the observation equations into a set of normal equations solvable by ordinary algebraic processes.* Multiply the first equation by a_1, the second by a_2, the third by a_3, and the fourth by a_4. Add the four results. Treat the four equations in the same way with b_1, b_2, b_3, b_4, and with c_1, c_2, c_3, c_4. Now write, for the sake of brevity,

$$[aa]_1 = a_1{}^2 + a_2{}^2 + a_3{}^2 + a_4{}^2; \qquad [bb]_1 = b_1{}^2 + b_2{}^2 + b_3{}^3 + b_4{}^2;$$
$$[ab]_1 = a_1 b_1 + a_2 b_2 + a_3 b_3 + a_4 b_4; \qquad [ac]_1 = c_1 c_1 + a_2 c_2 + a_3 c_3 + a_4 c_4;$$
$$[aR]_1 = a_1 R_1 + a_2 R_2 + a_3 R_3 + a_4 R_4; [bR]_1 = b_1 R_1 + b_2 R_2 + b_3 R_3 + b_4 R_4;$$

and likewise for $[cc]_1$, $[bc]_1$, $[cR]_1$. The resulting equations are

$$\left.\begin{array}{l} [aa]_1 x + [ab]_1 y + [ac]_1 z = [aR]_1 ; \\ [ab]_1 x + [bb]_1 y + [bc]_1 z = [bR]_1 ; \\ [ac]_1 x + [bc]_1 y + [cc]_1 z = [cR]_1. \end{array}\right\} \qquad (2)$$

These three equations are called **normal equations** (first set) in x, y, z.

II. To solve the normal equations. We can determine the values of x, y, z, from this set of simultaneous equations (2) by any method we please, determinants (§ 179), cross-multiplication, indeterminate multipliers, or by the method of substitution.[1] The last method is adopted here. Solve the first normal equation for x, thus

$$x = -\frac{[ab]_1}{[aa]_1} y - \frac{[ac]_1}{[aa]_1} z + \frac{[aR]_1}{[aa]_1}. \qquad (3)$$

Substitute this value of x in the other two equations for a second set of normal equations in which the term containing x has disappeared.

$$\left([bb]_1 - \frac{[ab]_1}{[aa]_1}[ab]_1\right) y + \left([bc]_1 - \frac{[ac]_1}{[aa]_1}[ab]_1\right) z = \left([bR]_1 - \frac{[ab]_1}{[aa]_1}[aR]_1\right);$$

$$\left([bc]_1 - \frac{[ac]_1}{[aa]_1}[ab]_1\right) y + \left([cc]_1 - \frac{[ac]_1}{[aa]_1}[ac]_1\right) z = \left([cR]_1 - \frac{[ac]_1}{[aa]_1}[aR]_1\right).$$

For the sake of simplicity, write

$$[bb]_2 = [bb]_1 - \frac{[ab]_1}{[aa]_1}[ab]_1 ; \quad [cc]_2 = [cc]_1 - \frac{[ac]_1}{[aa]_1}[ac]_1 ;$$

$$[bc]_2 = [bc]_1 - \frac{[ac]_1}{[aa]_1}[ab]_1 ;$$

$$[bR]_2 = [bR]_1 - \frac{[ab]_1}{[aa]_1}[aR]_1 ; \quad [cR]_2 = [cR]_1 - \frac{[ac]_1}{[aa]_1}[aR]_1 ;$$

The second set of normal equations may now be written :

$$\left.\begin{array}{l} [bb]_2 y + [bc]_2 z = [bR]_2 ; \\ [bc]_2 y + [cc]_2 z = [cR]_2. \end{array}\right\} \qquad (4)$$

Solve the first of these equations for y,

$$y = -\frac{[bc]_2}{[bb]_2} z + \frac{[bR]_2}{[bb]_2}. \qquad (5)$$

Substitute this in the second of equations (4), and we get a third set of normal equations,

$$\left([cc]_2 - \frac{[bc]_2}{[bb]_2}[bc]_2\right) z = \left([cR]_2 - \frac{[bc]_2}{[bb]_2}[bR]_2\right),$$

---

[1] The equations cannot be solved if any two are identical, or can be made identical by multiplying through with a constant.

which may be abbreviated into $[cc]_3 z_i = [cR]_3$.   Hence,

$$z = \frac{[cR]_3}{[cc]_3}. \qquad \cdot \quad \cdot \quad \cdot \quad \cdot \quad (6)$$

$[bb]_2$, $[bc]_2$, ..., $[cc]_3$, ... are called **auxiliaries**.   Equations (3) (5), (7), collectively constitute a set of **elimination equations** :

$$
\left.
\begin{aligned}
x &= -\frac{[ab]_1}{[aa]_1}y - \frac{[ac]_1}{[aa]_1}z + \frac{[aR]_1}{[aa]_1}; \\
y &= -\frac{[bc]_2}{[bb]_2}z + \frac{[bR]_2}{[bb]_2}; \\
z &= \frac{[cR]_3}{[cc]_3}.
\end{aligned}
\right\} \quad \cdot \quad \cdot \quad (7)
$$

The last equation gives the value of z directly; the second gives the value of y when z is known, and the first equation gives the value of x when the values of y and z are known.

Note the symmetry of the coefficients in the three sets of normal equations.   Hence it is only necessary to compute the coefficients of the first equation in full.   The coefficients of the first horizontal row and vertical column are identical.   So also the second row and second column, etc.   The formation and solution of the auxiliary equations is more tedious than difficult.   Several schemes have been devised to lessen the labour of calculation as well as for testing the accuracy of the work.   These we pass by.

IV. The weights of the values of x, y, z.   Without entering into any theoretical discussion, the respective weights of z, y, and x are given by the expressions :

$$p_s = [cc]_3; \; p = p_\nu\frac{[bb]_2}{[cc]_2}; \; p_x = p_z\frac{[ca]_1[bb]_2}{[cc]_1[bb]_1 - [bc]^1[bc]_1}. \quad (8)$$

III. The mean errors affecting the values of x, y, z.   Let

$$a_1 x + b_1 y + c_1 z - R_1 = v_1;$$
$$a_2 x + b_2 y + c_2 z - R_2 = v_2;$$
$$\cdots \quad \cdots \quad \cdots$$

Let M denote the mean error of any observed quantity of unit weight,

$$
\left.
\begin{aligned}
M &= \pm\sqrt{\frac{\Sigma(v^2)}{n-w}} \text{ for equal weights}; \\
M &= \pm\sqrt{\frac{\Sigma(pv^2)}{n-w}} \text{ for unequal weights}
\end{aligned}
\right\}, \quad \cdot \quad \cdot \quad (9)
$$

where n denotes the number of observation equations, w the number of quantities x, y, z, ... Here $w = 3$, $n = 4$. Let M_x, M_y, M_z, respectively denote the mean errors respectively affecting x, y, z.

$$\therefore\ M_x = \pm \frac{M}{\sqrt{p_x}};\quad M_y = \pm \frac{M}{\sqrt{p_y}};\quad M_z = \pm \frac{M}{\sqrt{p_z}}.\quad . \quad (10)$$

EXAMPLES.—(1) Find the values of the constants a and b in the formula

$$y = a + bx,\quad . \quad . \quad . \quad . \quad . \quad (11)$$

from the following determinations of corresponding values of x and y :—

$$y = 3\cdot5,\qquad 5\cdot7\qquad 8\cdot2\qquad 10\cdot3,\ldots;$$
$$x = 0,\qquad 88\qquad 182,\qquad 274,\ldots$$

We want to find the best numerical values of a and b in equation (11). Write x for a, and y for b, so as to keep the calculation in line with the preceding discussion. The first set of normal equations is obviously

$$[aa]_1 x + [ab]_1 y = [aR]_1;\text{ and } [ab]_1 x + [bb]_1 y = [bR]_1.$$
$$\therefore\ x = -\frac{[ab]_1}{[aa]_1}y + \frac{[aR]_1}{[aa]_1};\ \therefore\ y = \frac{[bR]_2}{[bb]_2}.$$

Again, $[aa]_1 = 4$; $[bb]_1 = 115{,}944$; $[ab]_1 = 544$; $[aR]_1 = 27\cdot7$; $[bR]_1 = 4{,}816\cdot2$; $[bb]_2 = 4{,}853\cdot67$; $[bR]_2 = 115{,}951\cdot4$. $x = 3\cdot52475$; $y = 0\cdot02500$; or, reconverting x into a, and y into b, (11) is to be written,

$$y = 3\cdot525 + 0\cdot025x.$$

a.	b.		Difference between Calculated and Observed.	Square of Difference between Calculated and Observed.
	Calculated.	Observed.		
0	3·525	3·5	+ 0·025	0·000625
88	5·725	5·7	+ 0·025	0·000625
182	8·075	8·2	− 0·125	0·015625
274	10·375	10·3	+ 0·075	0·005625
				0·0225

$$\therefore\ M = \pm\, 0\cdot106.$$

Weight of $b = p_y = [bb]_2 = 41{,}960$; $M_b = \pm\, 0\cdot106/\sqrt{41{,}960} = \pm\, 0\cdot0004$.

Weight of $a = p_x = \dfrac{[aa]_1}{[bb]_1} = 1\cdot5$; $M_a = \pm\, 0\cdot106/\sqrt{1\cdot5} = \pm\, 0\cdot087$.

(2) The following equations were proposed by C. F. Gauss in his *Theoria motus corporum coelestium* (Hamburg, 1809; Gauss' *Werke*, **7**, 240, 1871) to illustrate the above method :

$$\left.\begin{array}{l}x - y + 2z = 3;\quad 4x + y + 4z = 21;\\ 3x + 2y - 5z = 5;\ -x + 3y + 3z = 14.\end{array}\right\}\quad . \quad . \quad (12)$$

Hence show that $x = -+ 2\cdot470$; $y = + 3\cdot551$; $z = + 1\cdot916$; $\Sigma(v^2) = 0\cdot0804$; $M = \pm\, 284$; $p_x = 246$; $p_y = 136$; $p_z = 539$; $M_x = \pm\, 0\cdot057$; $M_y = \pm\, 0\cdot077$; $M_z = \pm\, 0\cdot039$. Hint. The first set of normal equations is

$$27x + 6y = 88;\ 6x + 15y + z = 70;\ y + 54z = 107.$$

(3) The following equations were also proposed by C. F. Gauss (*l.c.*) to illustrate his method of solution: $x - y + 2z = 3$, with weight 1; $3x + 2y - 5z = 5$,

with weight 1 ; $4x + y + 4z = 21$, with weight 1 ; $- 2x + 6y + 6z = 28$, with weight $\frac{1}{4}$. By the rule, multiply the last equation by $\sqrt{\frac{1}{4}} = \frac{1}{2}$ and we get set (12). Show that $x = + 2\cdot47$ with a weight $24\cdot6$; $y = + 3\cdot55$ with a weight $13\cdot6$; and $z = + 1\cdot9$ with a weight $53\cdot9$. It only remains to substitute these values of x, y, z, in (14) to find the residuals v. Hence show that $M = \pm 295$. Proceed as before for M_x, M_y, M_z.

(4) The length, l, of a seconds pendulum at any latitude L, may be represented by A. C. Clairaut's equation : $l = L_0 + A \sin^2 L$, where L_0 and A are constants to be evaluated from the following observations :

$$L = 0° \ 0', \qquad 18° \ 27', \qquad 48° \ 24', \qquad 58° \ 15', \qquad 67° \ 4' ;$$
$$l = 0\cdot990564, \ 0\cdot991150, \ 0\cdot993867, \ 0\cdot994589, \ 0\cdot995325.$$

Hence show that $l = 0\cdot990555 + 0\cdot005679 \sin^2 L$. Hint. The normal equations are,

$$x + 0\cdot44765 \, y = 0\cdot993099 ; \ x + 070306 \, y = 0\cdot994548.$$

(5) Hinds and Callum (*Journ. Amer. Chem. Soc.*, **24**, 848, 1902) represent their readings of the percentage strength, y, of a solution of iron with the photometric readings, x, of the intensity of transmitted light by the formula $y(x + b) = a$. The readings were

$$x \qquad = 3\cdot8, \quad 4\cdot3, \quad 4\cdot7, \quad 5\cdot3, \quad 6\cdot0, \quad 6\cdot7, \quad 7\cdot4, \quad 8\cdot1, \quad 8\cdot7, \quad 9\cdot7 ;$$
$$y \times 10^2 = 8\cdot64, \ 7\cdot57, \ 6\cdot92, \ 6\cdot06, \ 5\cdot28, \ 4\cdot70, \ 4\cdot22, \ 3\cdot79, \ 3\cdot52, \ 3\cdot13.$$

The authors state that $a = 0\cdot2955$; $b = 0\cdot375$. The probable error of one determination of y is given as $0\cdot000034$, or as 3 parts in 10,000,000. Use (9).

The above is based on the principle of least squares. A quicker method, not so exact, but accurate enough for most practical purposes, is due to Mayer. We can illustrate **Mayer's method** by equations (12).

First make all the coefficients of x positive, and add the results to form a new equation in x. Similarly for equations in y and z. We thus obtain,

$$9x - y - 2z = 15 ; \ 5x + 7y = 37 ; \ x + y + 14z = 33.$$

Solve this set of simultaneous equations by algebraic methods and we get $x = 2\cdot485$; $y = 3\cdot511$; $z = 1\cdot929$. Compare these values of x, y, z, with the best representative values for these magnitudes obtained in Ex. (2), above.

V. Errors affecting two or more dependent observations. There is a tendency in computing atomic weights and other constants for all the errors to accumulate upon the constant last determined. The atomic weight of fluorine is obtained from the ratio : $CaF_2 : CaSO_4$. The calculation not only includes the experimental errors in the measurement of this ratio, but also the errors in the atomic weight determinations of calcium and sulphur. It has been pointed out by J. D. van der Plaats (*Compt. Rend.*, **116**, 1362, 1893) that with sufficient experimental data the given ratio can be made to furnish

three atomic weights over which the errors of observation are
equally distributed, and not accumulated upon a single factor.
F. W. Clarke (*Amer. Chem. Journ.*, **27**, 32, 1902) illustrates the
method by calculating the seven atomic weights: silver, chlorine,
bromine, iodine, nitrogren, sodium and potassium—given $O = 16$;
$H = 1·0079$—from thirty ratios arranged in the form of thirty
linear equations, thus,

$$Ag : Br = 100 : 74·080; \quad \therefore 100 \, Br = 74·080 \, Ag;$$
$$KClO_3 : O_3 = 100 : 39·154; \quad \therefore 39·154 \, K + 39·154 \, Cl = 2920·608;$$

... ...

These thirty linear equations are reduced to seven normal equations as indicated above.   By solving these, the atomic weights of
the seven elements are obtained with the errors of observation
evenly distributed among them according to the method of least
squares.

When two observed quantities are afflicted with errors of observation and it is required to find the most probable relation
between the quantities concerned, we can proceed as indicated in
the following method.   The observed quantities are, say,

$$y = 0·5, \qquad 0·8, \qquad 1·0, \qquad 1·2;$$
$$x = 0·4, \qquad 0·6, \qquad 0·8, \qquad 0·9,$$

and we want to find the best representative values for a and b in
the equation

$$y = ax + b.$$

You can get approximate values for a and b by the graphic method
of page 355; or, take any two of the four observation equations
and solve for a and b.   Thus, taking the first and third,

$$0·5 = 0·4a + b; \quad 1·0 = 0·8a + b; \quad \therefore a = 1·25; \; b = 0.$$

Let a and β be the corrections required to make these values
satisfy the conditions of the problem in hand.   The required
equation is, therefore,

$$y = (1·25 + a)x + \beta.$$

Insert the observed values of x and y, so as to form the four
observation equations:

$$0·5 = (1·25 + a)0·4 + \beta; \quad 1·0 = (1·25 + a)0·8 + \beta;$$
$$0·8 = (1·25 + a)0·6 + \beta; \quad 1·2 = (1·25 + a)0·9 + \beta;$$

From these we get the two normal equations

$$0.1250 = 2.70a + 4.0\beta; \quad 0.0975 = 1.97a + 2.7\beta.$$
$$\therefore a = + 0.089; \quad \beta = - 0.029.$$

And finally

$$a = 1.25 + 0.089 = + 1.339; \quad b = 0.000 - 0.029 = - 0.029.$$

The best representative equation for the above observations is therefore,

$$y = 1.339x - 0.029.$$

See A. F. Ravenshear, *Nature*, **63**, 489, 1901. The above method is given by M. Merriman in *A Textbook on the Method of Least Squares*, New York, 127, 1891; W. H. Keesom has given a more general method in the *Communications from the Physical Laboratory at the University of Leiden*, Suppl. No. 4, 1902.

§ 170. When to Reject Suspected Observations.

There can be no question about the rejection of observations which include some mistake, such as a wrong reading of the eudiometer or burette, a mistake in adding up the weights, or a blunder in the arithmetical work, provided the mistake can be detected by check observations or calculations. Sometimes a most exhaustive search will fail to reveal any reason why some results diverge in an unusual and unexpected manner from the others. It has long been a vexed question how to deal with abnormal errors in a set of observations, for these can only be conscientiously rejected when the mistake is perfectly obvious. It would be a dangerous thing to permit an inexperienced or biassed worker to exclude some of his observations simply because they do not fit in with the majority. "Above all things," said S. W. Holman in his *Discussion on the Precision of Measurements*, New York, 1901, " the integrity of the observer must be beyond question if he would have his results carry any weight and it is in the matter of the rejection of doubtful or discordant observations that his integrity in scientific or technical work meets its first test. It is of hardly less importance that he should be as far as possible free from bias due either to preconceived opinions or to unconscious efforts to obtain concordant results."

Several criteria have been suggested to guide the investigator in deciding whether doubtful observations shall be included in the mean. Such criteria have been deduced by W. Chauvenet, Hagen, Stone, Pierce, etc. None of these tests however is altogether satisfactory. **Chauvenet's criterion** is perhaps the simplest to understand and most convenient to use. It is an attempt to show, from the theory of probability, that reliable observations will not deviate from the arithmetical mean beyond certain limits. We have learned from (2) and (6), page 523,

$$r = \frac{0.4769}{h} = 0.6745\sqrt{\frac{\Sigma(v^2)}{n-1}}.$$

If $x = rt$, where rt represents the number of errors less than x which may be expected to occur in an extended series of observations when the total number of observations is taken as unity, r represents the probable error of a single observation. Any measurement containing an error greater than x is to be rejected. If n denotes the number of observations and also the number of errors, then nP indicates the number of errors less than rt, and $n(1 - P)$ the number of errors greater than the limit rt. If this number is less than $\frac{1}{2}$, any error rt will have a greater probability against than for it, and, therefore, may be rejected.

The criterion for the rejection of a doubtful observation is, therefore,

$$\frac{x}{r} = t \; ; \; \frac{1}{2} = n(1 - P) \; ; \; \therefore P = \frac{2n - 1}{2n} = \frac{2}{\sqrt{\pi}}\int_0^t e^{-t^2}dt. \qquad (1)$$

By a successive application of these formulæ, two or more doubtful results may be tested. The value of t, or, what is the same thing, of P, and hence also of n, can be read off from the table of integrals, page 622 (Table XI.). Table XII. contains the numerical value of x/r corresponding to different values of n.

EXAMPLES.—(1) The result of 13 determinations of the atomic weight of oxygen made by the same observer is shown in the first column of the subjoined table. Should 19·81 be rejected? Calculate the other two columns of the table in the usual way.

Observation.	x.	x^2.	Observation.	x.	x^2.
15·96	− 0·26	0·0676	15·88	− 0·34	0·1156
19·81	+ 3·59	12·8881	15·86	− 0·36	0·1296
15·95	− 0·27	0·0729	16·01	− 0·21	0·0441
15·95	− 0·27	0·0729	15·96	− 0·26	0·0676
15·91	− 0·31	0·0961	15·88	− 0·34	0·1156
15·88	− 0·34	0·1156	15·93	− 0·29	0·0841
15·91	− 0·31	0·0961			

Mean of 13 observations = 16·22 ; $\Sigma(x^2) = 13.9659$.

The deviation of the suspected observation from the mean, is 3·59.   By Chauvenet's criterion, probable error $= r = 0·7281$, $n = 13$.   From Table XII., $x/r = 3·07$, $\therefore x = 3·07 \times 0·7281 = 22·7$.   Since the observation 19·81 deviates from the mean more than the limit 22·7 allowed by Chauvenet's criterion, that observation must be rejected.

(2) Should 16·01 be rejected from the preceding set of observations ? Treat the twelve remaining after the rejection of 19·81 exactly as above.

(3) Should the observations 0·3902 and 0·3840 in F. Rudberg's results, page 527, be retained ?

(4) Do you think 203·666 in W. Crookes' data, page 531, is affected by some " mistake " ?

(5) Would H. A. Rowland have rejected the " 442·8 " result in Joule's work, page 552, if he had been solely guided by W. Chauvenet's criterion ?

(6) Some think that " 4·88 " in Cavendish's data, page 527, is a mistake. Would you reject this number if guided by the above criterion ?

These examples are given to illustrate the method of applying the criterion.   Nothing more.   Any attempt to establish an arbitrary criterion applicable to all cases, by eliminating the knowledge of the investigator, must prove unsatisfactory.   It is very questionable if there can be a better guide than the unbiassed judgment and common sense of the investigator himself.   The theory you will remember is only " common sense reduced to arithmetic ".

Any observation set aside by reason of its failure to comply with any test should always be recorded.   As a matter of fact, the rare occurrence of abnormal results serves only to strengthen the theory of errors developed from the empirical formula, $y = ke^{-h^2 x^2}$. There can be no doubt that as many positive as negative chance deviations would appear if a sufficient number of measurements were available.[1]   " Every observation," says C. L. Gerling in his *Die Ausgleichungs-Rechnungen der praktischen Geometrie*, Hamburg, 68, 1843, " suspected by the observer is to me a witness of its truth.   He has no more right to suppress its evidence under the pretence that it vitiates the other observations than he has to shape it into conformity with the majority."   The whole theory of errors is founded on the supposition that a sufficiently large number of observations has been made to locate the errors to which the measurements are susceptible.   When this condition is not fulfilled, the abnormal measurement, if allowed to remain, would exercise a disproportionate influence on the mean.   The result

---

[1] F. Y. Edgeworth has an interesting paper " On Discordant Observations " in the *Phil. Mag.* [5], **23**, 364, 1887.

would then be less accurate than if the abnormal deviation had been rejected. *The employment of the above criterion is, therefore, permitted solely because of the narrow limit to the number of observations.* It is true that some good observations may be so lost, but that is the price paid to get rid of serious mistakes.

It is perhaps needless to point out that a suspected observation may ultimately prove to be a real exception requiring further research. To ignore such a result is to reject the clue to a new truth. The trouble Lord Rayleigh recently had with the density of nitrogen prepared from ammonia is now history. The "ammonia" nitrogen was found to be $\frac{1}{1,000}$th part lighter than that obtained from atmospheric air. Instead of putting this minute "error" on one side as a "suspect," Lord Rayleigh persistently emphasized the discrepancy, and thus opened the way for the brilliant work of W. Ramsay and M. W. Travers on "Argon and Its Companions".

CHAPTER X.

THE CALCULUS OF VARIATIONS.

"Natura operatur per modos faciliores et expeditiones."—P. DE FERMAT.[1]

§ 171. Differentials and Variations.

Nearly two hundred years ago Maupertius tried to show that the principle of least action was one which best exhibited the wisdom of the Creator, and ever since that time the fact that a great many natural processes exhibit maximum or minimum qualities has attracted the attention of natural philosophers. In dealing with the available energy of chemical and physical phenomena, for example, the chemist seeks to find those conditions which make the entropy a maximum, or the free energy a minimum, while if the problems are treated by the methods of energetics, Hamilton's principle :

"If a system of bodies is at A at the time t_1, and at B at the time t_2, it will pass from A to B by such a path that the mean value of the difference between the kinetic and potential energy of the system in the interval $t_2 - t_1$ is a minimum"

is used. Problems of this nature often require a more powerful mathematical tool than the differential calculus. The so-called **calculus of variations** is used.

If it be required to draw a curve of a certain fixed length from O to A (Fig. 173) so that the area bounded by OB, BA, and the curve may be a maximum. The inquiry is directed to the nature of the curve itself. In other words, we want the equation of the curve. This is a very different kind of problem from those

---

[1] "Nature works by the easiest and readiest means."—P. de Fermat in a letter to M. de la Chambre, 1662.

hitherto considered where we have sought what special values must be assigned to certain variables in a given expression in order that this function may attain a maximum or minimum value.

Whatever be the equation of the curve, we know that the area must be furnished by the integral $\int y\,dx$; or $\int f(x)\,dx$. The problem now before us is to find what must be the form of $f(x)$ in order that this integral may be a maximum. It is easy to see that if the form of the function $y = f(x)$ is variable, the value of y can change infinitesimally in two ways, either

(i) By an increment in the value of the independent variable x; or

(ii) By a change in the form of the function as it passes from the shape $f(x)$ to, say, the shape $\phi(x)$; or, to be more explicit, say from $y = \sin x$ to, say, $y = \tan x$.

The first change is represented by the ordinary differential dy; the second change is called a **variation,** and is symbolized, in Lagrange's notation, by δy. Consequently, the differential

$$dy = f(x + dx) - f(x);$$

while the variation

$$\delta y = \phi(x) - f(x). \qquad . \qquad . \qquad . \qquad (1)$$

Care must be taken that the symbol "δ" is only applied to those

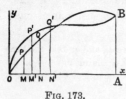

FIG. 173.

measurements which are produced by a change in the *form* of the function. The change, dy, is represented in Fig. 173 by $dy = NQ - MP$; the change δy by $\delta y = M'P' - MP$; $dx = MN$; $\delta x = MM'$. It is not difficult to show from the above diagram that the symbols of differentiation and variation are interchangeable, so that

$$d\delta y = \delta dy. \qquad . \qquad . \qquad . \qquad . \qquad (2)$$

§ 172. The Variation of a Function.

To find the variation—not the differential—of a function. Let y be the given function. Write $y + \delta y$ in place of y, and subtract the new function from the old, and there you have it. We at once recognize the formal analogy of the operation with the process of differentiation. Thus, if

$$u = y^n,$$

the variation of u is

$$\delta u = (y + \delta y)^n - y^n = \frac{du}{dy}\delta y, \qquad . \qquad . \qquad (3)$$

by Taylor's theorem, neglecting the higher order of infinitesimals. Let us adopt Newton's notation, and write $\dot{y}$ for dy/dx; $\ddot{y}$ for d^2y/dx^2; ..., then, if

$$u = f(y, \dot{y}),$$

when y changes to $y + \delta y$, $\dot{y}$ becomes $\dot{y} + \delta\dot{y}$. Accordingly

$$\delta u = \frac{du}{dy}\delta y + \frac{du}{d\dot{y}}\delta\dot{y}; \ \text{or,} \ \delta u = \frac{du}{dy}\delta y + \frac{du}{d\left(\frac{dy}{dx}\right)}\delta\left(\frac{dy}{dx}\right), \qquad (4)$$

by the extension of Taylor's theorem, neglecting the higher powers of small magnitudes.   You will remember that "δ," on page 19, was used to represent a small finite change in the value of the independent variable, while here "δ" denotes an infinitesimal change in the form of the function.

To evaluate $\delta\dot{y}$, $\delta\ddot{y}$, $\delta\dddot{y}$ you follow exactly the same methods.

$$\delta\dot{y} = \delta\left(\frac{dy}{dx}\right) = \frac{d(y + \delta y)}{dx} - \frac{dy}{dx} = \frac{d\delta y}{dx}; \ \delta\frac{d^2y}{dx^2} = \frac{d^2\delta y}{dx^2}; \ \dots \ (5)$$

So far as I know the verb " to variate " or " to vary," meaning to find the variation of a function in the same way that " to differentiate" means to find the differential of a function, is not used.

§ 173. The Variation of an Integral with Fixed Limits.

Let it be required to find the variation of the integral

$$U = \int_{x_0}^{x_1} V.dx \qquad . \qquad . \qquad . \qquad . \qquad (6)$$

where

$$V = f\left(x, y, \frac{dy}{dx}, \frac{d^2y}{dx^2}, \ \dots\right); \ \text{or,} \ V = f(x, y, \dot{y}, \ddot{y}, \dots). \qquad (7)$$

The value of U may be altered either by

(i) A change in the limits x_1 and x_0; or,
(ii) A change in the form of the function.

We have already seen that if the end values of the integral are fixed, any change in the independent variable x does not affect the value of U.   Let us assume that the limits are fixed or constant. The only way that the value of U can now change is to change the form of $V = f(\dots)$.   But the variation of V is δV, and, by the above-mentioned rule,

$$\delta V = \frac{dV}{dy}\delta y + \frac{dV}{d\dot{y}}\delta \dot{y} + \frac{dV}{d\ddot{y}}\delta \ddot{y} + \dots \quad . \quad . \quad (8)$$

For the sake of brevity, let us put

$$P = \frac{dV}{dy}\,; \quad Q = \frac{dV}{d\dot{y}}\,; \quad R = \frac{dV}{d\ddot{y}}\,; \dots \quad . \quad . \quad (9)$$

and we get

$$\delta U = \Big|_{x_0}^{x_1}\delta V \,.\, dx = \Big|_{x_0}^{x_1}\Big(P\delta y + Q\frac{d\delta y}{dx} + R\frac{d^2\delta y}{dx^2} + \dots\Big)dx. \quad (10)$$

Let us now integrate term by term. We know of old (**A**), page 205, that

$$\Big|u\frac{dv}{dx}dx = uv - \Big|v\frac{du}{dx}dx,$$

so that if we put $Q = u\,; \; dQ = du\,; \; d\delta y = dv\,; \; v = y$, then

$$\int Q\frac{d\delta y}{dx}dx = Q\delta y - \int\frac{dQ}{dx}\delta y dx\,;$$

similarly, by a double application of the method of integration by parts, we find that

$$\int R\frac{d^2\delta y}{dx^2}dx = R\frac{d\delta y}{dx} - \int\frac{dR}{dx}\cdot\frac{d\delta y}{dx}dx = R\frac{d\delta y}{dx} - \frac{dR}{dx}\delta y + \int\frac{d^2R}{dx^2}\delta y dx,$$

and consequently, after substituting the last two results in (10), we get

$$\delta U = \int_{x_0}^{x_1}\Big(P - \frac{dQ}{dx} + \frac{d^2R}{dx^2}\Big)\delta y dx + \Big|_{x_0}^{x_1}\Big(Q - \frac{dR}{dx}\Big)\delta y + \Big|_{x_0}^{x_1}R\frac{d\delta y}{dx}. \quad (11)$$

The last two terms do not involve any integrations, and depend upon the form of the function only. Let I_0 represent the aggregate of terms formed when x_0 is put for x; and I_1 the aggregate of terms when x_1 is put for x; then (11) assumes the form

$$\delta U = I_1 - I_0 + \int_{x_0}^{x_1}K\delta y dx, \quad . \quad . \quad . \quad (12)$$

where K has been put in place of the series

$$K = P - \frac{dQ}{dx} + \frac{d^2R}{dx^2}. \quad . \quad . \quad . \quad (13)$$

The variation when the function V includes higher derivatives than $\ddot{y}$, is found in a similar manner.

§ 174. Maximum or Minimum Values of a Definite Integral.

Perhaps the most important application of the calculus of variations is the determination of the form of the function involved in a definite integral in such a manner that the integral, say,

$$U = \int_{x_0}^{x_1} V.dx, \qquad . \qquad . \qquad . \quad (14)$$

shall have a maximum or a minimum value. In order to find a maximum or a minimum value of a function, we must find such a value of x that a small change in the value of x will produce a change in the value of the function which is indefinitely small in comparison with the value of x itself. We must have

$$\delta U = 0 \; ; \; \text{and} \; I_1 - I_0 + \int_{x_0}^{x_1} K\delta y dx = 0. \qquad . \quad (15)$$

This requires that

$$I_1 - I_0 = 0 \; ; \; \text{and} \int_{x_0}^{x_1} K\delta y dx = 0, \qquad . \qquad . \quad (16)$$

for if each member did not vanish, each would be determined by the value of the other. Since δy is arbitrary, the second condition can only be satisfied by making

$$K = 0 \; ; \; \text{or,} \; P - \frac{dQ}{dx} + \frac{d^2R}{dx^2} - \ldots = 0. \qquad . \quad (17)$$

Most of your troubles in connection with this branch of the calculus of variations will arise from this equation. It is often very refractory ; sometimes it proves too much for us. The equation then remains unsolved. The nature of the problem will often show directly, without any further trouble, whether it be a maximum or a minimum value of the function we are dealing with ; if not, the sign of the second differential coefficients must be examined. The second derivative is positive, if the function is a minimum ; and negative, if the function is a maximum. But you will have to look up some text-book for particulars, say B. Williamson's *Integral Calculus*, London, 463, 1896.

EXAMPLES.—(1) What is the shortest line between two points ? A straight line of course. But let us see what the calculus of variations has to say about this. The length of a curve between two points whose abscissæ are x_1 and x_0, is, page 246,

$$\int_{x_0}^{x_1} \sqrt{1 + \left(\frac{dy}{dx}\right)^2} dx. \qquad . \qquad . \qquad . \qquad . \quad (18)$$

This must be a minimum. Here V is a function of $\hat{y}$. Hence all the terms except dQ/dx vanish from (17), and we get

$$\frac{dQ}{dx} = 0 \; ; \; \text{or,} \; Q = C, \; . \qquad . \qquad . \qquad . \quad (19)$$

where C is constant. But, by definition (9),

$$Q = \frac{dV}{d\hat{y}} = \frac{\dot{y}}{\sqrt{1 + \hat{y}^2}} = C, \qquad . \qquad . \qquad . \quad (20)$$

since $V = \sqrt{1 + \dot{y}^2}$; $\therefore dV = (1 + \dot{y}^2)^{-\frac{1}{2}} \dot{y} . d\dot{y}$. Accordingly,

$$y = (1 + \dot{y}^2)C^{\frac{1}{2}}; \therefore \dot{y}^2(1 - C^2) = 1; \therefore \dot{y} = a, \quad \cdot \quad \cdot \quad (21)$$

where a must be constant, since C is constant. Hence, by integrating $\dot{y} = a$, we get

$$y = ax + b, \quad \cdot \quad \cdot \quad \cdot \quad \cdot \quad (22)$$

where b is the constant of integration. The required curve is therefore a straight line (8), page 90. Again, from (16) and (20),

$$I_1 - I_0 = \frac{y_1}{\sqrt{1 + \dot{y}_1{}^2}} \delta y_1 - \frac{y_0}{\sqrt{1 + \dot{y}_0{}^2}} \delta y_0. \quad \cdot \quad \cdot \quad \cdot \quad (23)$$

If the two given points are fixed, $\delta y_1 = 0$, and $\delta y_0 = 0$, hence $I_1 - I_0$ vanishes. Let x_0, y_0, and x_1, y_1, be the two fixed points. Then,

$$y_0 = ax_0 + b; \ y_1 = ax_1 + b. \quad \cdot \quad \cdot \quad \cdot \quad (24)$$

If only x_0, and x_1 are given, so that y_0 and y_1 are undetermined, we have, by the differentiation of (24), $\dot{y}_1 = a$. Hence, by substitution in (23),

$$\frac{dy}{dx} = a; \therefore \frac{a}{\sqrt{1 - a^2}} (\delta y_1 - \delta y_0) = 0, \quad \cdot \quad \cdot \quad (25)$$

Since δy and δy are arbitrary, (25) can only be satisfied when $a = 0$. The straight line is then $y = b$. This expresses the obvious fact that when two straight lines are parallel, the shortest distance between them is obtained by drawing a straight line perpendicular to both.

(2) To find the "curve of quickest descent" from one given point to another. Or, as Todhunter puts it, "suppose an indefinitely thin smooth tube connects the two points, and a heavy particle to slide down this tube; we require to know the form of the tube in order that the time of descent may be a minimum". This problem, called the *brachistochrone* (*brachistos* = shortest ; *chronos* = time), was first proposed by John Bernoulli in June, 1696, and the discussion which it invoked has given rise to the calculus of variations. Any book on mechanics will tell you that the velocity of a body which starts from rest is, page 376, Ex. (4),

$$\frac{ds}{dt} = \sqrt{2gy}, \quad \cdot \quad \cdot \quad \cdot \quad \cdot \quad (26)$$

where the axis y is measured vertically downwards, and the x-axis starts from the upper given part. The time of descent is therefore

$$t = \int \frac{ds}{\sqrt{2gy}} = \frac{1}{\sqrt{2g}} \int \sqrt{\frac{1 + \dot{y}^2}{y}} dx = \frac{1}{\sqrt{2g}} \int V . dx, \quad \cdot \quad (27)$$

as you will see by glancing at page 569, (6). Accordingly, we take

$$V = \sqrt{\frac{1 + \dot{y}^2)}{y}}, \quad \cdot \quad \cdot \quad \cdot \quad (28)$$

so that V only involves y and $\dot{y}$. Hence, for a minimum, we have

$$P - \frac{dQ}{dx} = 0; \text{ or, } \frac{dV}{dy} - \frac{d}{dx}\left(\frac{dV}{d\dot{y}}\right) = 0. \quad \cdot \quad \cdot \quad (29)$$

When V does not contain x explicitly, the complete differential of the function

$$V = f(y, \dot{y}, \ddot{y}, \ldots), \quad \cdot \quad \cdot \quad \cdot \quad \cdot \quad (30)$$

is evidently

$$\frac{dV}{dx} = \frac{\partial V}{\partial y} . \frac{dy}{dx} + \frac{\partial V}{\partial \dot{y}} . \frac{d\dot{y}}{dx} + \ldots = P\frac{dy}{dx} + Q\frac{d\dot{y}}{dx} + R\frac{d\ddot{y}}{dx} + \ldots, \quad (31)$$

as indicated on page 72.   Multiply (17) through with dy/dx, and subtract the result from (31).   The P terms vanish, and

$$\frac{dV}{dx} = \left(\frac{dQ}{dx}\cdot\frac{dy}{dx} + Q\frac{d\dot{y}}{dx}\right) - \left(\frac{d^2R}{dx^2}\cdot\frac{dy}{dx}\right) - Rdy/dx + \ldots,$$

remains.   This may be written more concisely,

$$\frac{dV}{dx} = \frac{d}{dx}\left(Q\frac{dy}{dx}\right) - \frac{d}{dx}\left(\frac{dR}{dx}\cdot\frac{dy}{dx} - R\ddot{y}\right) +$$

which becomes, on integration,

$$V = Q\frac{dy}{dx} - \frac{dR}{dx}\cdot\frac{dy}{dx} - R\frac{d^2y}{dx^2} + \ldots + C, \qquad . \qquad . \qquad (32)$$

where C is the constant of integration.   Particular cases occur when P, Q, or R vanish.   The most useful case occurs, as here, when V involves only y and $\dot{y}$.   In that case, (29) reduces to

$$V = Q\frac{dy}{dx} + C. \qquad . \qquad . \qquad . \qquad . \qquad . \qquad . \qquad (33)$$

From (28) we get

$$V = \sqrt{\frac{1 + \dot{y}^2}{y}} = \frac{\dot{y}^2}{\sqrt{y(1 + \dot{y}^2)}} + C; \therefore \frac{1}{\sqrt{y(1 + \dot{y}^2)}} = C; \qquad (34)$$

Consequently,

$$y(1 + \dot{y}^2) = \text{constant, say} = 2a. \qquad . \qquad . \qquad . \qquad (35)$$

$$\therefore \left(\frac{dy}{dx}\right)^2 = \frac{2a - y}{y}; \therefore \frac{dx}{dy} = \left(\frac{y}{2a - y}\right)^{\frac{1}{2}} = \frac{y}{\sqrt{2ay - y^2}}. \qquad (36)$$

On integration, using (17), page 193,

$$x = a \text{ vers}^{-}\frac{y}{a} - \sqrt{2y - y^2} + b, \qquad (37)$$

where b is an integration constant.   This is the well-known equation called the *cycloid* (Fig. 174). The base of the cycloid is the x-axis, and the curve meets the base at a distance b, or, Ox,

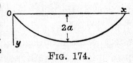

FIG. 174.

Fig. 174, from the origin.   When $b = 0$, the origin is at the upper point so that $x = 0$, when $b = 0$.   Now

$$I_1 - I_0 = \frac{\dot{y}_1\,\delta y_1}{\sqrt{y_1(1 - \dot{y}_1^2)}} - \frac{\dot{y}_0\,\delta y_0}{\sqrt{y_0(1 - \dot{y}_0^2)}} = \frac{1}{\sqrt{2a}}(\dot{y}_1\,\delta y_1 - y_0\,\delta y_0). \qquad (38)$$

But the extreme points are fixed so that δy_0 and δy_1 vanish, hence, $I_1 - I_0$ also vanishes.   If only the abscissa of the lower point is given, not the ordinates, I_0 vanishes, as before, and therefore,

$$I_1 = \frac{\dot{y}_1\,\delta y}{\sqrt{2a}}. \qquad . \qquad . \qquad . \qquad . \qquad (39)$$

But δy_1 is arbitrary, hence, if I_1 is to vanish, $\dot{y}_1$ must be zero.   This means that the tangent to the cycloid at the lower limiting point must be horizontal with the x-axis.

§ 175. The Variation of an Integral with Variable Limits.

The preceding problem becomes a little more complex if we assume that we have two given curves, and it is required to find "the curve of quickest descent" from the one given curve to the other. Here we have not only to find the path of descent, but also the point at which the particle is to leave one curve and arrive at the other. The former part of the question is evidently work for the calculus of variations, and the latter is readily solved by the differential calculus : given the curve, to find its position to make t a minimum. The value of the integral

$$U = \int_{x_0}^{x_1} V dx, \quad . \quad . \quad . \quad (40)$$

not only changes when y is changed to $y + \delta y$, but also when the limits x_1 and x_0 become $x_1 + dx_1$, and $x_0 + dx_0$ respectively. The change of the limits augments U by the amount

$$dU = \int_{x_1}^{x_1 + ax_1} V_1 . dx - \int_{x_0}^{x_0 + dx_0} V_0 . dx; \quad . \quad (41)$$

or, neglecting the higher powers of dx_1 and dx_0, U receives the increment

$$dU = V_1 dx_1 - V_0 dx_0. \quad . \quad . \quad (42)$$

The total increment of U is therefore

Total incr. $U = dU + \delta U = V_1 dx_1 - V_0 dx_0 + \delta \int_{x_0}^{x_1} V . dx.$ (43)

In words, the total increment which a quantity receives from the operation of several effects is the sum of the increments which each effect would produce if it acted separately. This is nothing but the principle of the superposition of small motions, pages 70 and 400, under another guise.

The maximum-minimum condition is that the total increment be zero. This can only obtain when $V_1 = 0$, and $V_0 = 0$. We thus have two new conditions to take into consideration besides those indicated in the preceding section.

EXAMPLE.—Find the " curve of quickest descent" from one given curve to another. Ex. (2), page 572, has taught us that the "curve of quickest descent" is a cycloid. The problem now before us is to find the relation between the cycloid and the two given curves. We see from (15) and (43) that the maximum-minimum condition is

$$V_1 dx_1 - V_0 dx_0 + I_1 - I_0 + \int_{x_0}^{x_1} K \delta y dx = 0. . \quad . \quad (44)$$

But we can use the results of Ex. (2), page 573, equations (33) and (38), therefore the maximum-minimum condition becomes

$$V_1 dx_1 - V_0 dx_0 + \frac{y_1 \delta y_1}{\sqrt{y_1(1 + \dot{y}_1^2)}} - \frac{y_0 \delta y_0}{\sqrt{y_0(1 + \dot{y}_3^2)}} + \int_{x_0}^{x_1} \left(P - \frac{dQ}{dx}\right) \delta y dx. \quad (45)$$

As before, (29) holds good, consequently,

$$\sqrt{y_1(1 + \dot{y}^2)} = \sqrt{2a}. \quad \cdots \quad (46)$$

$$\therefore V_1 dx_1 - V_0 dx_0 + \frac{1}{\sqrt{2a}}\left(\frac{dy_1}{dx_1}\delta y_1 - \frac{dy_0}{dx_0}\delta y_0\right) = 0. \quad \cdots \quad (47)$$

Remembering that the end values of the curve are x_0, y_0, and x_1, y_1, let y suffer a variation δy so that

$$Y = y + \delta y. \quad \cdots \quad \cdots \quad (48)$$

with fixed limits, and, at the same time, x_0, y_0, and x_1, y_1, respectively become x_0, Y_0, and x_1, Y_1. Let us find how δy_0 and δy_1 are affected when the values of x change respectively to $x_0 + dx_0$, and $x_1 + dx_1$. By Taylor's theorem, instead of y_1 becoming Y_1, we have Y_1 changed to

$$Y_1 + \frac{dY_1}{dx_1}dx_1 + \frac{1}{2!}\cdot\frac{d^2Y_1}{dx_1{}^2}(dx_1)^2 + \cdots \quad \cdots \quad \cdots \quad (49)$$

or, from (4) and (48),

$$(y_1 + \delta y_1) + \left(\frac{dy_1}{dx_1}dx_1 + \frac{dY_1}{d\dot{y}_1}\delta\dot{y}_1 . dx_1\right) + \cdots \quad \cdots \quad (50)$$

Neglecting the higher powers of dx_1 and the product $\delta\dot{y}_1$, dx_1,

$$Y_1 \text{ becomes } y_1 + \delta y_1 + \dot{y}_1 dx_1, \quad \cdots \quad \cdots \quad (51)$$

as a result of the variation and of the change of x_1 into $x_1 + dx_1$.

Let the equation of one of the curves be

$$y = f(x_1), \quad \cdots \quad \cdots \quad \cdots \quad (52)$$

then the abscissa of the end value of Y_1 is changed into $f(x_1 + dx_1)$ after the variation. Consequently, after variation,

$$y_1 + \delta y_1 + \dot{y}_1 dx_1 = f(x_1 + dx_1) = f(x_1) + f'(x_1)dx_1,$$

by Taylor's theorem. From (50) we can cancel out the y's and

$$\delta y_1 = \{f'(x_1) - \dot{y}_1\}dx, \quad \cdots \quad \cdots \quad \cdots \quad (53)$$

remains. A similar relation holds good between δy_0 and dx_0.

Let us return after this digression to (47), and, in order to fix our ideas, let the two given curves be

$$y_1 = mx_1 + a \; ; \; y_0 = mx_0 + b \; ; \; \therefore \; \dot{y}_1 = m \; ; \; \dot{y}_0 = n. \quad \cdots \quad (54)$$

From (53) we have

$$\delta y_1 = (m - \dot{y}_1)dx_1 \; ; \; \delta y_0 = (n - \dot{y}_0)dx_0. \quad \cdots \quad \cdots \quad (55)$$

Substitute these values in (47), and

$$\left\{V_1 + \frac{\dot{y}_1}{\sqrt{2a}}(m - \dot{y}_1)\right\}dx_1 - \left\{V_0 + \frac{\dot{y}_0}{\sqrt{2a}}(n - \dot{y}_0)\right\}dx_0 = 0. \quad \cdots \quad (56)$$

Since dx_1 and dx_0 are arbitrary, the coefficients of dx_1 and dx_0 must be separately zero in order that (56) may vanish.

$$\therefore 1 + \dot{y}_1 m = 0 \; ; \; 1 + \dot{y}_0 n = 0 \; ; \; \text{ or, } \; \frac{dy_1}{dx_1} = -\frac{1}{m} \; ; \; \frac{dy_0}{dx_0} = -\frac{1}{n}. \quad \cdots \quad (57)$$

Now compare this result with (18), page 96, and you will see that the two given curves are at right angles with the "curve of quickest descent".

§ 176. Relative Maxima and Minima.

After the problem of the brachistochrone had been solved, James Bernoulli, brother of John, proposed another variety of problem—the so-called *isoperimetrical problem*—of which the following is a type : Find the maximum or minimum values of a certain integral, U_1, when another integral, U_2, involving the same variables has a constant value. The problem proposed at the beginning of this chapter is a more concrete illustration. Here, δU_1 must not only vanish, but it must vanish for those values of the variables which make U_2 constant. It will be obvious that if U_1 be a maximum or a minimum, so will $U_1 + aU_2$ also be a maximum or a minimum; a is an arbitrary constant. The problem therefore reduces to the determination of the maximum or minimum values of $U_1 + aU_2$. If

$$U_1 = \int_{x_0}^{x_1} V_1 dx \; ; \quad U_2 = \int_{x_0}^{x_1} V_2 dx \; ; \qquad (58)$$

$U_1 + aU_2$ will be a maximum or a minimum when

$$\int_{x_0}^{x_1} (V_1 + V_2 a) dx = 0, \qquad (59)$$

is a maximum or a minimum. When U_2 is known, a can be evaluated.

EXAMPLE.—Find the curve of given length joining two fixed points so that the area bounded by the curve, the x-axis, and the ordinates at the fixed points may be a maximum. Here we have

$$U_1 = \int_{x_0}^{x_1} y dx \; ; \quad U_2 = \int_{x_0}^{x_1} \sqrt{1 + \left(\frac{dy}{dx}\right)^2} dx, \cdot \quad (60)$$

as indicated on page 246. Here then

$$V_1 + aV_2 = y + a\sqrt{1 + \dot{y}^2}. \qquad (61)$$

We require the maximum value of the integral

$$U = \int_{x_0}^{x_1} V \cdot dx = \int_{x_2}^{x_1} \left\{ y + a\sqrt{1 + \left(\frac{dy}{dx}\right)^2} dx \right\}. \qquad (62)$$

V is a function of y and $\dot{y}$, hence from (19) we must have

$$V = P\dot{y} + C \; ; \qquad (63)$$

$$\therefore y + a\sqrt{1 + \dot{y}^2} = \frac{a\dot{y}^2}{\sqrt{1 + \dot{y}^2}} + C_1 \; ; \; \therefore y + \frac{a}{\sqrt{1 + \dot{y}^2}} = C_1, \cdot \quad (64)$$

By a transposition of terms,

$$1 + \left(\frac{dy}{dx}\right)^2 = \frac{a}{(y - C_1)^2} \; ; \; \therefore \left(\frac{dy}{dx}\right)^2 = \frac{(y - C_1)^2}{a^2 - (y - C_1)^2} \; ; \qquad (65)$$

which becomes, on integration,

$$x - C_2 = \sqrt{a^2 - (y - C_1)^2} \; ; \; \text{or,} \; (x - C_2)^2 + (y - C_1)^2 = a^2. \qquad (66)$$

This is obviously the equation of a circular line. The limits are fixed, and therefore $I_1 - I_0 = 0$. The constants a, C_1, and C_2 can be evaluated when the fixed points and the length of the curve are known.

§ 177. The Differentiation of Definite Integrals.

I must now make a digression. I want to show how to find the differential coefficient, du/da, of the definite integral $u = \int f'(x, a)dx$ between the limits y_1 and y_0, when y_1 and y_0 are functions of a. Let $f'(x, a)dx$ become $f(x, a)$ after integration, we have therefore

$$u = \int_{y_0}^{y_1} f'(x, a)dx = f(y_1, a) - f(y_0, a). \quad \cdot \quad (67)$$

Hence, on partial differentiation with respect to y_1, when y_0 is constant; and then with respect to y_0, when y_1 is constant, we get

$$\frac{\partial u}{\partial y_1} = \frac{d}{dy_1} f(y_1, a) = f'(y_1, a); \; -\frac{\partial u}{\partial y_0} = \frac{d}{dy_0} f(y_0, a) = f'(y_0, a). \quad (68)$$

Now suppose that a suffers a small increment so that when a becomes $a + h$, u becomes $u + k$, then, keeping the limits constant,

$$\text{Incr. } v = \int \{ f'(x, a+h) - f'(x, a) \}dx. \quad \cdot \quad \cdot \quad (69)$$

Dividing by δa, and passing to the limit, we have

$$\frac{\text{Incr. } u}{\text{Incr. } a} = \int_{y_0}^{y_1} \frac{f'(x, a+h) - f'(x, a)}{h}dx; \; \therefore \frac{du}{da} = \int_{y}^{y_1} \frac{df'(x, a)}{da}dx. \quad (70)$$

If both y_1 and y_0 are functions of a, then du/da must be the sum of three separate terms, (i) the change due to a; (ii) the change due to y_1; and (iii) the change due to y_0. These separate effects have been evaluated in equations (68) and (70), consequently,

$$\frac{du}{da} = \frac{d}{da}\int_{y_0}^{y_1} f'(x, a)dx = \int_{y_0}^{y_1} \frac{df'(x, a)}{da}dx + \frac{\partial u}{\partial y_1}\frac{dy_1}{da} - \frac{\partial u}{\partial y_0}\cdot\frac{dy_0}{da}. \quad (71)$$

$$\therefore \frac{du}{da} = \int_{y_0}^{y_1} \frac{df'(x, a)}{da}dx + f'(y_1, a)\frac{dy_1}{da} - f'(y_0, a)\frac{dy_0}{da}. \quad \cdot \quad (72)$$

The higher derivatives can be obtained by an application of the same methods.

§ 178. Double and Triple Integrals.

We now pass to double integrals, say,

$$U = \iint Vdxdy, \quad \cdot \quad \cdot \quad \cdot \quad (73)$$

where V is a function of $x, y, z, p,$ and q, and

$$p = \frac{dz}{dx}; \; q = \frac{dz}{dy}. \quad \cdot \quad \cdot \quad (74)$$

We apply the same general methods as those employed for single integrals, but there are some difficulties in connection with the limits of integration of multiple integrals. Let δz denote the variation of z which occurs when the form of the function connecting z with x, and y is known, x and y remaining constant during the variation. Further, let δV denote the variation of V, and δU the variation of U, when z becomes δz; then by the preceding methods,

$$\delta V = \frac{dV}{dx}\delta_2 + \frac{dV}{dp}\delta p + \frac{dV}{dq}\delta q = P\delta z + Q\delta p + R\delta q, \qquad (75)$$

where we have put for the sake of convenience,

$$P = \frac{dV}{dz}; \quad Q = \frac{dV}{dp}; \quad R = \frac{dV}{dq}. \qquad (76)$$

We therefore write, from (75),

$$\delta U = \iint \delta V dx dy = \iint \left(P\delta z + Q\frac{d\delta z}{dx} + R\frac{d\delta z}{dy} \right) dx dy. \qquad (77)$$

Still keeping on the old track,

$$\left.\begin{array}{l} U = \displaystyle\int_{x_0}^{x_1}\int_{y_0}^{y_0} \left(P - \frac{dQ}{dx} + \frac{dR}{dy} \right)\delta z\, dx\, dy\, + \\[3mm] \displaystyle\int_{x_0}^{x_1}\int_{y_0}^{y_1} \left\{ \frac{d}{dx}(Q\delta z) + \frac{d}{dy}(R\delta z) \right\} dx\, dy \end{array}\right\} \qquad (78)$$

The differential coefficients with respect to x and y are complete. We get, on integration with respect to y,

$$\int_{x_0}^{x_1}\int_{y_0}^{y_1}\frac{d}{dx}(R\delta z)dx dy = \int_{x_0}^{x_1}\left[R\delta z \right]_{y_0}^{y_1}dx, \qquad (79)$$

where $\left[R\delta z \right]_{y_0}^{y_1}$, as on page 232, represents the value of $R\delta z$ when y_1 and y_0 are each substituted in place of y, and the latter then subtracted from the former. Again, from (70) followed by a transposition of terms, we get

$$\int_{y_0}^{y_1}\frac{d(Q\delta x)}{dx}dy = \frac{d}{dx}\int_{y_0}^{y_1} Q\delta z dy - \left[(Q\delta x)\frac{dy}{dx} \right]_{y_0}^{y_1}, \qquad (80)$$

where $\left[(Q\delta z)y \right]_{y_0}^{y_1}$ denotes the value of $(Q\delta z)\dot{y}$ when y_1 and y_0 are each substituted in place of y, in Qdx, and the latter subtracted from the former. Hence, we may write

$$\int_{x_0}^{x_1}\int_{y_0}^{y_1}\frac{d(Q\delta z)}{dx}dx dy = \left[\int_{y_0}^{y_1} Q\delta z dy \right]_{x_0}^{x_1} - \int_{x_0}^{x_1}\left[(Q\delta z)\frac{dy}{dx} \right]_{y_0}^{y_1}. \qquad (81)$$

By substituting (79) and (81) in place of (78), we get

$$\left.\begin{array}{l} \delta U = \displaystyle\int_{x_0}^{x_1}\int_{y_0}^{y_1} \left(P - \frac{dQ}{dx} - \frac{dR}{dy} \right)\delta z\, dx\, dy + \displaystyle\int_{x_0}^{x_1}\left[R\delta z \right]_{y_0}^{y_1}dx\, + \\[3mm] \left[\displaystyle\int_{y_0}^{y_1} Q\delta z dy \right]_{x_0}^{x_1} - \displaystyle\int_{x_0}^{x_1}\left[(Q\delta z)\frac{dy}{dx} \right]_{y_0}^{y_1}dx \end{array}\right\} \qquad (82)$$

If the limits y_1 and y_0 are constant, $\dot{y}_1$ and $\dot{y}_0$ vanish, and we can therefore neglect the last term. If the limits also change, we must add on a new term in accordance with the principles laid down in § 175.

For the maximum-minimum condition, δU of (82) can only vanish when the coefficient of δz, namely,

$$P - \frac{dQ}{dx} - \frac{dR}{dy} = 0. \qquad \cdots \qquad (83)$$

The solution of this partial differential equation furnishes z in terms of x, y, and arbitrary functions; the latter must be so determined that the remaining terms of (82) vanish.

For the triple integral

$$U = \iiint V dx dy dz, \qquad \cdots \qquad (84)$$

where V is a given function of u, x, y, z, p, q, r; and u is a function such that

$$p = \frac{du}{dx}; \quad q = \frac{du}{dy}; \quad r = \frac{du}{dz}. \qquad \cdots \qquad (85)$$

We have also

$$\delta U = \iiint \delta V dx dy dz. \qquad \cdots \qquad (86)$$

As before,

$$\delta V = N\delta u + P\frac{d\delta u}{dx} + Q\frac{d\delta u}{dy} + R\frac{d\delta u}{dz}, \qquad \cdots \qquad (87)$$

where

$$N = \frac{dV}{du}; \quad P = \frac{dV}{dp}; \quad Q = \frac{dV}{dq}; \quad R = \frac{dV}{dr}, \qquad \cdots \qquad (88)$$

and the variation works out to

$$\left.\begin{array}{l} \delta U = \iiint \left(N - \frac{dP}{dx} - \frac{dQ}{dy} - \frac{dR}{dz} \right)\delta u\, dx dy dz + \\[2mm] \iiint \left\{ \frac{d}{dx}(P\delta u) + \frac{d}{dy}(Q\delta u) + \frac{d}{dz}(R\delta u) \right\} dx dy dz \end{array}\right\}. \qquad (89)$$

For the maximum-minimum condition, we must solve the partial differential equation

$$N - \frac{dP}{dx} - \frac{dQ}{dy} + \frac{dR}{dz} - 0, \qquad \cdots \qquad (90)$$

and fit the arbitrary constants so that the remaining terms of δU vanish. A complete exposition of the subject would be quite outside the limits of this volume. J. H. Jellet's *An Elementary Treatise on the Calculus of Variations*, Dublin, 1850, is a good text-book; O. Bolza, in his *Lectures on the Calculus of Variations*, Chicago, 1904, has a review of modern theory.

J. H. van der Waals seeks the maximum value of a triple integral in his *Binäre Gemische*, Leipzig, 34, 1900, but the physical conditions of the problem enable the solution of (90) to be obtained in a simple manner.

CHAPTER XI.

DETERMINANTS.

"Operations involving intense mental effort may frequently be replaced by the aid of other operations of a routine character, with a great saving of both time and energy. By means of the theory of determinants, for example, certain algebraic operations can be solved by writing down the coefficients according to a prescribed scheme and operating with them mechanically."— E. MACH.

§ 179. Simultaneous Equations.

THIS chapter is for the purpose of explaining and illustrating a system of notation which is in common use in the different branches of pure and applied mathematics.

I. *Homogeneous simultaneous equations in two unknowns.*

The homogeneous equations,

$$a_1x + b_1y = 0 ; \ a_2x + b_2y = 0, \qquad . \quad . \quad (1)$$

represent two straight lines passing through the origin. In this case (§ 29), $x = 0$ and $y = 0$, a deduction verified by solving for x and y. Multiply the first of equations (1) by b_2, and the second by b_1. Subtract. Or, multiply the second of equations (1) by a_1, and the first by a_2. Subtract. In each case, we obtain,

$$x(a_1b_2 - a_2b_1) = 0 ; \ y(a_2b_1 - a_1b_2) = 0. \quad . \qquad . \quad (2)$$

Hence, $x = 0$; and $y = 0$; or,

$$a_1b_2 - a_2b_1 = 0 ; \ \text{and} \ a_2b_1 - a_1b_2 = 0. \quad . \qquad . \quad (3)$$

The relations in equations (3) may be written,

$$\begin{vmatrix} a_1, & b_1 \\ a_2, & b_2 \end{vmatrix} = 0 ; \ \text{and} \begin{vmatrix} a_2, & b_2 \\ a_1, & b_1 \end{vmatrix} = 0, \qquad . \quad . \quad (4)$$

where the left-hand side of each expression is called a **determinant**. This is nothing more than another way of writing down the difference of the diagonal products. The letters should always be taken

580

in cyclic order so that b follows a, c follows b, a follows c. In the same way 2 follows 1, 3 follows 2, and 1 follows 3.

The products a_1b_2, a_2b_1, are called the **elements** of the determinant; a_1, b_1, a_2, b_2, are the **constituents** of the determinants. Commas may or may not be inserted between the constituents of the horizontal rows. When only two elements are involved, the determinant is said to be of the **second order**.

From the above equations, it follows that *only when the determinant of the coefficients of two homogeneous equations in x and y is equal to zero can x and y possess values differing from zero.*

II. *Linear and homogeneous equations in three unknowns.*

Solving the linear equations

$$a_1x + b_1y + c_1 = 0 \; ; \; a_2x + b_2y + c_2 = 0, \qquad . \qquad . \quad (5)$$

for x and y, we get

$$x = \frac{b_1c_2 - b_2c_1}{a_1b_2 - b_1a_2} \; ; \; y = \frac{c_1a_2 - c_2a_1}{a_1b_2 - b_1a_2}. \qquad . \qquad . \quad (6)$$

If $a_1b_2 - b_1a_2 = 0$, x and y become infinite. In this case, the two lines represented by equations (5) are either parallel or coincident. When

$$x = \frac{b_1c_1 - b_2c_1}{0} = \infty \; ; \; y = \frac{c_1a_2 - c_2a_1}{0} = \infty,$$

the lines intersect at an infinite distance away. Reduce equations (5) to the tangent form, page 90,

$$y = -\frac{a_1}{b_1}x - \frac{c_1}{b_1} \; ; \; y = -\frac{a_2}{b_2}x - \frac{c_2}{b_2} \; ; \qquad . \qquad . \quad (7)$$

but since $a_1b_2 - b_1a_2 = 0$, $a_1/b_1 = a_2/b_2 =$ the tangent of the angle of inclination of the lines; in other words, two lines having the same slope towards the x-axis are parallel to each other.[1]

When the two lines cross each other, the values of x and y in (6) satisfy equations (5). Make the substitution required.

$$a_1(b_1c_2 - b_2c_1) + b_1(c_1a_2 - c_2a_1) + c_1(a_1b_2 - a_2b_1) = 0,$$
$$a_2(b_1c_2 - b_2c_1) + b_2(c_1a_2 - c_2a_1) + c_2(a_1b_2 - a_2b_1) = 0,$$

or, writing

$$x = \frac{X}{Z} \; ; \; \text{and} \; y = \frac{Y}{Z}, \qquad . \qquad . \qquad . \quad (8)$$

we get a pair of homogeneous equations in X, Y, Z, namely,

$$a_1X + b_1Y + c_1Z = 0 \; ; \; a_2X + b_2Y + c_2Z = 0. \qquad (9)$$

---

[1] Thus the definition, "parallel lines meet at infinity," means that as the point of intersection of two lines goes further and further away, the lines become more and more nearly parallel.

Equate coefficients of like powers of the variables in these identical equations.

$$\therefore a_1 : b_1 : c_1 = a_2 : b_2 : c_2,$$

or, from (8) and (6),

$$X : Y : Z = b_1 c_2 - b_2 c_1 : c_1 a_2 - c_2 a_1 : a_1 b_2 - a_2 b_1,$$

$$= \begin{vmatrix} b_1 & c_1 \\ b_2 & c_2 \end{vmatrix} : \begin{vmatrix} c_1 & a_1 \\ c_2 & a_2 \end{vmatrix} : \begin{vmatrix} a_1 & b_1 \\ a_2 & b_2 \end{vmatrix} . \qquad . \qquad . \quad (10)$$

The three determinants on the right, are symbolized by

$$\begin{Vmatrix} a_1 & b_1 & c_1 \\ a_2 & b_2 & c_2 \end{Vmatrix} \qquad . \qquad . \qquad . \qquad (11)$$

where the number of columns is greater than the number of rows.[1] The determinant (11), is called a **matrix**. It is evaluated, by taking the difference of the diagonal products of any two columns.

The results obtained in (10) are employed in solving linear equations.

EXAMPLES.—(1) Solve $4x + 5y = 7$; $3x - 10y = 19$.

$$X : Y : Z = \begin{vmatrix} 5, & -7 \\ -10, & -19 \end{vmatrix} : \begin{vmatrix} -7, & 4 \\ -19, & 3 \end{vmatrix} : \begin{vmatrix} 4, & 5 \\ 3, -10 \end{vmatrix} ;$$

$$= -165 : 55 : -55; \text{ or } x = +3 \text{ and } y = -1.$$

(2) Solve $20x - 19y = 23$; $19x - 20y = 16$. Ansr. $x = 4$, $y = 3$.

(3) Solve the observation equations:

$\cdot 5x - \cdot 2y = \cdot 4$; $\cdot 14x + \cdot 3y = 1 \cdot 18$. Ansr. $x = 2$, $y = 3$.

(4) Solve $\frac{1}{2}x - \frac{1}{3}y = 6$; $\frac{1}{4}x - \frac{1}{2}y = -1$. Ansr. $x = 24$, $y = 18$.

The condition that three straight lines represented by the equations

$$a_1 x + b_1 y + c_1 = 0; \ a_2 x + b_2 y + c_2 = 0; \ a_3 x + b_3 y + c_3 = 0, \quad (12)$$

may meet in a point, is that the roots of any two of the three lines may satisfy the third (§ 32). In this case we get a set of simultaneous equations in X, Y, Z.

$$a_1 X + b_1 Y + c_1 Z = a_2 X + b_2 Y + c_2 Z = a_3 X + b_3 Y + c_3 Z = 0, \quad (13)$$

by writing $x = X/Z$ and $y = Y/Z$ in equations (12). From the last pair,

$$X : Y : Z = \begin{vmatrix} b_2, & c_2 \\ b_3, & c_3 \end{vmatrix} : \begin{vmatrix} c_2, & a_2 \\ c_3, & a_3 \end{vmatrix} : \begin{vmatrix} a_2, & b_2 \\ a_3, & b_3 \end{vmatrix} . \qquad . \quad (14)$$

But these values of x and y, also satisfy the first of equations (3), hence, by substitution,

$$a_1 \begin{vmatrix} b_2, & c_2 \\ b_3, & c_3 \end{vmatrix} + b_1 \begin{vmatrix} c_2, & a_2 \\ c_3, & a_3 \end{vmatrix} + c_1 \begin{vmatrix} a_2, & b_2 \\ a_3, & b_3 \end{vmatrix} = 0, \qquad . \quad (15)$$

---

[1] It is customary to call the vertical columns, simply " columns " ; the horizontal rows, " rows ".

which is more conveniently written

$$\begin{vmatrix} a_1 & b_1 & c_1 \\ a_2 & b_2 & c_2 \\ a_3 & b_3 & c_3 \end{vmatrix} = 0, \quad . \quad . \quad . \quad . \quad (16)$$

a determinant of the third order.

It follows directly from equations (13), (14), (16), *only when the determinant of the coefficients of three homogeneous equations in x, y, z, is equal to zero, can x, y, z, possess values differing from zero.* This determinant is called the **eliminant** of the equations. Each determinant in (14) is called a **subdeterminant, or minor** of (16).

§ 180. The Expansion of Determinants.

It follows from (15) and (16), that

$$\begin{vmatrix} a_1 & b_1 & c_1 \\ a_2 & b_2 & c_2 \\ a_3 & b_3 & c_3 \end{vmatrix} = a_1 b_2 c_3 + a_2 b_3 c_1 + a_3 b_1 c_2 - a_1 b_3 c_2 - a_2 b_1 c_3 - a_3 b_2 c_1. \quad (17)$$

A determinant is expanded, by taking the product of one letter in each horizontal row with one letter from each of the other rows. The first element, called the **leading element,** is the product of the diagonal constituents from the top left-hand corner, *i.e.*, $a_1 b_2 c_3$; its sign is taken as positive. The signs of the other five terms [1] are obtained by arranging alphabetically, and observing whether they can be obtained from the leading element by an odd or an even number of changes in the subscripts; if the former, the element is negative, if the latter, positive. For example, $a_2 b_1 c_3$, is obtained by one interchange of the subscripts 2 and 1 in the leading element; $a_2 b_1 c_3$ is, therefore, a negative element; $a_2 b_3 c_1$ requires two such transformations, 2 and 1, and 2 and 3, hence its sign is positive.

EXAMPLES.—(1) Show $\begin{vmatrix} 2 & 2 & 2 \\ 3 & 1 & 1 \\ 4 & 2 & 1 \end{vmatrix} = 2 + 12 + 8 - 4 - 6 - 8 = 4.$

(2) Show $\begin{vmatrix} 0 & b & c \\ b & 0 & a \\ c & a & 0 \end{vmatrix} = 2abc.$

---

[1] The number of elements in a determinant of the second order is 2 × 1, or 2 ! of the third order 3 × 2 × 1, or 3 !, of the fourth order, 4 !, etc.

§ 181. The Solution of Simultaneous Equations.

Continuing the discussion in § 179, let the equations

$$a_1x + b_1y + c_1z = d_1 \; ; \; a_2x + b_2y + c_2z = d_2 \; ; \; a_3x + b_3y + c_3z = d_3, \quad (18)$$

be multiplied by suitable quantities, so that y and z may be eliminated. Thus multiply the first equation by A_1, the second by A_2, the third by A_3, where A_1, A_2, A_3, are so chosen that

$$b_1A_1 + b_2A_2 + b_3A_2 = 0 \; ; \; c_1A_1 + c_2A_2 + c_3A_3 = 0. \quad (19)$$

Hence, by substitution,

$$x(a_1A_1 + a_2A_2 + a_3A_3) = d_1A_1 + d_2A_2 + d_3A_3. \quad (20)$$

Equations (19) being homogeneous in A_1, A_2, A_3, we get, from (10),

$$A_1 : A_2 : A_3 = \begin{vmatrix} b_2 & b_3 \\ c_2 & c_3 \end{vmatrix} : \begin{vmatrix} b_3 & b_1 \\ c_3 & c_1 \end{vmatrix} : \begin{vmatrix} b_1 & b_2 \\ c_1 & c_2 \end{vmatrix}.$$

Substituting these values of A_1, A_2, A_3, in equations (20), we get, as in equations (14), (15), (16),

$$x \begin{vmatrix} a_1 & b_1 & c_1 \\ a_2 & b_2 & c_2 \\ a_3 & b_3 & c_3 \end{vmatrix} = \begin{vmatrix} d_1 & b_1 & c_1 \\ d_2 & b_2 & c_2 \\ d_3 & b_3 & c_3 \end{vmatrix} . \quad . \quad . \quad . \quad (21)$$

In the same way, on multiplying by B_1, B_2, B_3, and by C_1, C_2, C_3.

$$y \begin{vmatrix} a_1 & b_1 & c_1 \\ a_2 & b_2 & c_2 \\ a_3 & b_3 & c_3 \end{vmatrix} = \begin{vmatrix} a_1 & d_1 & c_1 \\ a_2 & d_2 & c_2 \\ a_3 & d_3 & c_3 \end{vmatrix} ; \; z \begin{vmatrix} a_1 & b_1 & c_1 \\ a_2 & b_2 & c_2 \\ a_3 & b_3 & c_3 \end{vmatrix} = \begin{vmatrix} a_1 & b_1 & d_1 \\ a_2 & b_2 & d_2 \\ a_3 & b_3 & d_3 \end{vmatrix} . \quad (22)$$

EXAMPLES.—Solve the following set of equations:

(1) $5x + 3y + 3z = 48$; $2x + 6y - 3z = 18$; $8x - 3y + 2z = 21$. From (21)

$$x = \begin{vmatrix} 48 & 3 & 3 \\ 18 & 6 & -3 \\ 21 & -3 & 2 \end{vmatrix} \div \begin{vmatrix} 5 & 3 & 3 \\ 2 & 6 & -3 \\ 8 & -3 & 2 \end{vmatrix} = 3 \; ;$$

similarly $y = 5$; $z = 6$.

(2) H. E. Roscoe and C. Schorlemmer (*Treatise on Chemistry*, **1**, 704, London, 1878) use the following set of equations in the analysis of a mixture of gases containing C_2H_4, C_3H_6, and C_6H_6 gases:

$$x + y + z = a; \; 2x + 3y + 6z = b; \; 2x + \tfrac{3}{2}y + \tfrac{3}{2}z = c,$$

where a, b, c, are numbers obtained from the gas burette. Solve for x, y, z.

(3) Field's process (*Jour. Chem. Soc.*, **10**, 234, 1858) for the determination of chlorine, bromine, and iodine when mixed in solution involves the equations

$$x + y + z = a; \; 1 \cdot 31x + y + z = b; \; 1 \cdot 637x + 1 \cdot 25y + z = c,$$

where a, b, and c are numbers determined by analysis. Similar equations arise in the indirect process of analysis of a mixture of sodium and potassium salts. Find x, y, z.

(4) Solve the observation equations:

$\cdot 3x + \cdot 2y + \cdot 5z = 3 \cdot 2$; $\cdot 2x + \cdot 3y + \cdot 4z = 2 \cdot 9$; $\cdot 4x + \cdot 3y + \cdot 5z = 3 \cdot 7$.

Ansr. $x = 2$, $y = 3$, $z = 4$.

(5) To illustrate the solution of simultaneous equations " by the writing down of the coefficients according to a fixed scheme and operating upon them according to a prescribed scheme," take the proof of (2), from (1), page 444, as an exercise. In equation (1) take z as an independent variable and solve the two simultaneous equations for dx/dz and dy/dz. Hence,

$$\frac{dx}{dz} = \frac{\begin{vmatrix} Q_1 & R_1 \\ Q_2 & R_2 \end{vmatrix}}{\begin{vmatrix} P_1 & Q_1 \\ P_2 & Q_2 \end{vmatrix}}; \; \frac{dy}{dz} = \frac{\begin{vmatrix} R_1 & P_1 \\ R_2 & P_2 \end{vmatrix}}{\begin{vmatrix} P_1 & Q_1 \\ P_2 & Q_2 \end{vmatrix}}; \; \therefore \frac{dx}{\begin{vmatrix} Q_1 & R_1 \\ Q_2 & R_2 \end{vmatrix}} = \frac{dy}{\begin{vmatrix} R_1 & P_1 \\ R_2 & P_2 \end{vmatrix}} = \frac{dz}{\begin{vmatrix} P_1 & Q_1 \\ P_2 & Q_2 \end{vmatrix}}$$

which has the same form as (2), page 445.

§ 182. Test for Consistent Equations.

It is easy to find values of x and y in the two equations

$$a_1x + b_1y + c_1 = 0; \; a_2x + b_2y + c_2 = 0,$$

as shown in § 179, (6); similarly, values for x, y, and z in the equations

$$a_1x + b_1y + c_1z + d_1 = 0; \; a_2x + b_2y + c_2z + d_2 = 0;$$
$$a_3x + b_3y + c_3z + d_3 = 0,$$

can be readily obtained, and generally, in order to find the value of 1, 2, 3, ... unknowns, it is necessary and sufficient to have 1, 2, 3, ... independent relations (equations) respectively between the unknowns.

If there are, say, three equations and only two unknowns, it is possible that the values of the unknowns found from any two of these equations will not satisfy the third. For example, take the set

$$3x - 2y = 4; \; 2x + 4y = 24; \; x + y = 2.$$

On solving the first two equations, we get $x = 4$, $y = 4$. But these values of x and y do not satisfy the third equation. On solving the last two, $x = -8$, $y = 10$, and these values of x and y do not satisfy the remaining equation. In other words, the three equations are inconsistent. Consequently, it is a useful thing to be able to find if a number of equations are consistent with each other; in other words, to find if values of x and y can be determined to satisfy all of a given set of equations. For instance, is the set

$$a_1x + b_1y + c_1 = 0; \; a_2x + b_2y + c_2 = 0; \; a_3x + b_3y + c_3 = 0, \quad (23)$$

consistent? From the first two equations, page 581, we get

$$x = \frac{b_1c_2 - b_2c_1}{a_1b_2 - b_1a_2}; \; y = \frac{c_1a_2 - c_2a_1}{a_1b_2 - b_1a_2}. \quad . \quad . \quad (24)$$

Substitute these values of x and y in the last of equations (23), the two unknowns disappear, and, if the equations are consistent,

$$a_3(b_1c_2 - b_2c_1) + b_3(c_1a_2 - c_2a_1) + c_3(a_1b_2 - a_2b_1) = 0,$$

remains. But this result is obviously the expansion of the determinant

$$\begin{vmatrix} a_1 & b_1 & c_1 \\ a_2 & b_2 & c_2 \\ a_3 & b_3 & c_3 \end{vmatrix} = 0, \quad \cdot \quad \cdot \quad \cdot \quad (25)$$

and this in consequence called the **eliminant** of the three given equations. Hence we conclude that *three equations are consistent with each other only when the determinant of the coefficients and absolute term of the three linear equations in x, y, z, is equal to zero.*

EXAMPLES.—(1) Show that the following equations are consistent with one another,

$$x + y - z = 0; \; x - y + z = 2; \; y + z - x = 4; \; x + y + z = 6.$$

Hint. The eliminant is $\begin{vmatrix} 1 & 1 & -1 & 0 \\ 1 & -1 & 1 & 2 \\ -1 & 1 & 1 & 4 \\ 1 & 1 & 1 & 6 \end{vmatrix} = 0.$

(2) A point oscillates freely in space under the action of a force directed from the origin of the coordinates. The equations of motion are

$$\frac{d^2x}{dt^2} = -q^2x; \; \frac{d^2y}{dt^2} = -q^2y; \; \frac{d^2z}{dt^2} = -q^2z.$$

Find the path of the point. First solve the equations as in Ex. (4), page 442. $x = C_1 \cos qt + C_4 \sin qt \, ; \; y = C_2 \cos qt + C_5 \sin qt \, ; \; z = C_3 \cos qt + C_6 \sin qt.$ Now eliminate t, because time does not determine the form or position of the path. Now $\cos qt$, and $\sin qt$, may be regarded as independent variables to be treated as " unknowns ". Of course two equations would be sufficient for the elimination, but three are given and all must be satisfied. For consistency we must have

$$\begin{vmatrix} x & C_1 & C_4 \\ y & C_2 & C_5 \\ z & C_3 & C_6 \end{vmatrix} = 0.$$

When the determinant is expanded, the result is a linear homogeneous equation in x, y, and z which is the equation of a plane passing through the origin, and whose position is determined by the constants C. Suppose the plane to be rotated so that it coincides with the xy-plane, then $z = 0$. Solve for $\cos qt$, and $\sin qt$, and substitute the results in the well-known equation (19), page 611, $\sin^2 qt + \cos^2 qt = 1$. The equation is of the second degree. Expand and put $C_2^2 + C_5^2 = a \, ; \; 2C_1C_2 - C_4C_5 = b; \; C_1^2 + C_4^2 = c, \; (C_1C_5 - C_2C_4)^2 = h.$

$$\therefore \; ax - bxy + cy = h.$$

In the discriminant $b^2 - 4ac$, a and c are necessarily positive, consequently the curve is either an ellipse or a circle.

§ 183. Fundamental Properties of Determinants.

The student will get an idea of the peculiarities of determinants by reading over the following :—

I. *The value of a determinant is not altered by changing the columns into rows, or the rows into columns.*

It follows directly, by simple expansion, that

$$\begin{vmatrix} a_1 & b_1 \\ a_2 & b_2 \end{vmatrix} = \begin{vmatrix} a_1 & a_2 \\ b_1 & b_2 \end{vmatrix}; \text{ and } \begin{vmatrix} a_1 & b_1 & c_1 \\ a_2 & b_2 & c_2 \\ a_3 & b_3 & c_3 \end{vmatrix} = \begin{vmatrix} a_1 & a_2 & a_3 \\ b_1 & b_2 & b_3 \\ c_1 & c_2 & c_3 \end{vmatrix}. \qquad (26)$$

It follows, as a corollary, that whatever law is true for the rows of a determinant is also true for the columns, and conversely.

II. *The sign, not the numerical value, of a determinant is altered by interchanging any two rows, or any two columns.*

By direct calculation,

$$\begin{vmatrix} a_1 & b_1 \\ a_2 & b_2 \end{vmatrix} = - \begin{vmatrix} b_1 & a_1 \\ b_2 & a_2 \end{vmatrix}; \begin{vmatrix} a_1 & b_1 & c_1 \\ a_2 & b_2 & c_2 \\ a_3 & b_3 & c_3 \end{vmatrix} = - \begin{vmatrix} b_1 & a_1 & c_1 \\ b_2 & a_2 & c_2 \\ b_3 & a_3 & c_3 \end{vmatrix}. \qquad (27)$$

III. *If two rows or two columns of a determinant are identical, the determinant is equal to zero.*

If two identical rows or columns are interchanged, the sign, not the value, of the determinant, is altered. This is only possible if the determinant is equal to zero. The same thing can be proved by the expansion of, say,

$$\begin{vmatrix} a_1 & a_1 & c_1 \\ a_2 & a_2 & c_2 \\ a_3 & a_3 & c_3 \end{vmatrix} = 0.$$

IV. *When the constituents of two rows or two columns differ by a constant factor, the determinant is equal to zero.*

Thus by expansion show that

$$\begin{vmatrix} 4 & 1 & 5 \\ 8 & 2 & 6 \\ 12 & 3 & 7 \end{vmatrix} = 4 \begin{vmatrix} 1 & 1 & 5 \\ 2 & 2 & 6 \\ 3 & 3 & 7 \end{vmatrix} = 4 \times 0 = 0. \qquad (28)$$

V. *If a determinant has a row or column of cyphers it is equal to zero.*

This is illustrated by expansion,

$$\begin{vmatrix} 0 & b_1 & c_1 \\ 0 & b_2 & c_2 \\ 0 & b_3 & c_3 \end{vmatrix} = 0. \qquad (29)$$

VI. *In order to multiply a determinant by any factor, multiply each constituent in one row or in one column by this factor*

This is illustrated by the expansion of the following :

$$m \begin{vmatrix} a_1 & b_1 & c_1 \\ a_2 & b_2 & c_2 \\ a_3 & b_3 & c_3 \end{vmatrix} = \begin{vmatrix} ma_1 & b_1 & c_1 \\ ma_2 & b_2 & c_2 \\ ma_3 & b_3 & c_3 \end{vmatrix}. \quad \bullet \quad \bullet \quad \bullet \quad (30)$$

VII. In order to divide a determinant by any factor, divide each constituent in one row or in one column by that factor.

This follows directly from the preceding proposition. It is conveniently used in the reduction of determinants to simpler forms. Thus,

$$\begin{vmatrix} 6 & 9 & 8 \\ 12 & 18 & 4 \\ 24 & 27 & 2 \end{vmatrix} = 9.6.2 \begin{vmatrix} 1 & 1 & 4 \\ 2 & 2 & 2 \\ 4 & 3 & 1 \end{vmatrix} = 9.6.2.2 \begin{vmatrix} 1 & 1 & 2 \\ 1 & 1 & 1 \\ 4 & 3 & 1 \end{vmatrix}. \quad \bullet \quad (31)$$

VIII. If the sign of every constituent in a row or column is changed, the sign of the determinant is changed.

$$\begin{vmatrix} a_1 & b_1 & c_1 \\ a_2 & b_2 & c_2 \\ a_3 & b_3 & c_3 \end{vmatrix} = - \begin{vmatrix} -a_1 & b_1 & c_1 \\ -a_2 & b_2 & c_2 \\ -a_3 & b_3 & c_3 \end{vmatrix} = \begin{vmatrix} -a_1 & -b_1 & c_1 \\ -a_2 & -b_2 & c_2 \\ -a_3 & -b_3 & c_3 \end{vmatrix}. \quad \bullet \quad (32)$$

IX. One row or column of any determinant can be reduced to unity (Dostor's theorem).

This will need no more explanation than the following illustration :

$$\begin{vmatrix} 3 & 4 & 6 \\ 2 & 8 & 8 \\ 6 & 7 & 9 \end{vmatrix} = 12 \begin{vmatrix} 1 & 1 & 1 \\ 1 & 3 & 2 \\ 8 & 7 & 6 \end{vmatrix}. \quad \bullet \quad \bullet \quad \bullet \quad (33)$$

X. If each constituent of a row or column can be expressed as the sum or difference of two or more terms, the determinant can be expressed as the sum or difference of two other determinants.

This can be proved by expanding each of the following determinants, and rearranging the letters.

$$\begin{vmatrix} a_1 \pm p, & b_1, & c_1 \\ a_2 \pm q, & b_2, & c_2 \\ a_3 \pm r, & b_3, & c_3 \end{vmatrix} = \begin{vmatrix} a_1 & b_1 & c_1 \\ a_2 & b_2 & c_2 \\ a_3 & b_3 & c_3 \end{vmatrix} \pm \begin{vmatrix} p & b_1 & c_1 \\ q & b_2 & c_2 \\ r & b_3 & c_3 \end{vmatrix}. \quad \bullet \quad (34)$$

In general, if each constituent of a row or column consists of n terms, the determinant can be expressed as the sum of n determinants.

EXAMPLE.—Show by this theorem, that

$$\begin{vmatrix} b+c, & a-b, & a \\ c+a, & b-c, & b \\ a+b, & c-a, & c \end{vmatrix} = 3abc - a^3 - b^3 - c^3.$$

XI. The value of a determinant is not changed by adding to or subtracting the constituents of any row from the corresponding constituents of one or more of the other rows or columns.

Thus from X. and III.,

$$\begin{vmatrix} a_1 \pm b_1, & b_1, & c_1 \\ a_2 \pm b_2, & b_2, & c_2 \\ a_3 \pm b_3, & b_3, & c_3 \end{vmatrix} = \begin{vmatrix} a_1 & b_1 & c_1 \\ a_2 & b_2 & c_2 \\ a_3 & b_3 & c_3 \end{vmatrix} \pm \begin{vmatrix} b_1 & b_1 & c_1 \\ b_2 & b_2 & c_2 \\ b_3 & b_3 & c_3 \end{vmatrix}, \qquad . \quad . \quad (35)$$

which proves the rule, because the determinant on the right vanishes. This result is employed in simplifying determinants.

EXAMPLES.—(1) Show $\begin{vmatrix} 1, & x, & y + z \\ 1, & y, & z + x \\ 1, & z, & x + y \end{vmatrix} = 0.$

Add the second column to the last and divide the result by $x + y + z$. The determinant vanishes (3).

(2) Show $\begin{vmatrix} x & y & z \\ z & x & y \\ y & z & x \end{vmatrix} = (x + y + z) \begin{vmatrix} 1 & 1 & 1 \\ z & x & y \\ y & z & x \end{vmatrix}$

Add the second and third rows to the first and divide by $x + y + z$.

(3) Why is $\begin{vmatrix} a_1 & b_1 & c_1 \\ a_2 & b_2 & c_2 \\ a_3 & b_3 & c_3 \end{vmatrix}$ not equal to $\begin{vmatrix} a_1 + b_1, & b_1 + a_1, & c_1 \\ a_2 + b_2, & b_2 + a_2, & c_2 \\ a_3 + b_3, & b_3 + a_3, & c_3 \end{vmatrix}$?

(4) Show $\begin{vmatrix} 4 & 1 & 7 \\ 3 & 6 & -2 \\ 5 & 1 & 8 \end{vmatrix} = -23.$

XII. *If all but one of the constituents of a row or column are cyphers, the determinant can be reduced to the product of the one constituent, not zero, into a determinant whose order is one less than the original determinant.*

For example,

$$\begin{vmatrix} 1 & a & b \\ 0 & a_1 & b_1 \\ 0 & a_2 & b_2 \end{vmatrix} = 1 \begin{vmatrix} a_1 & b_1 \\ a_2 & b_2 \end{vmatrix}; \quad \begin{vmatrix} 0 & 0 & -7 \\ 5 & 6 & -2 \\ -3 & 1 & 8 \end{vmatrix} = -7 \begin{vmatrix} 5 & 6 \\ -3 & 1 \end{vmatrix} \qquad (36)$$

The converse proposition holds. The order of a determinant can be raised by similar and obvious transformations.

XIII. *If all the constituents of a determinant on one side of the diagonal from the top left-hand corner are cyphers, the determinant reduces to the leading term.*

Thus, $\begin{vmatrix} a_1 & b_1 & c_1 \\ 0 & b_2 & c_2 \\ 0 & 0 & c_3 \end{vmatrix} = a_1 \begin{vmatrix} b_2 & c_2 \\ 0 & c_3 \end{vmatrix} = a_1 b_2 c_3.$ $\qquad . \quad . \quad . \quad (37)$

The determinant $\begin{vmatrix} b_2 & c_2 \\ 0 & c_3 \end{vmatrix}$ is called the **co-factor or complement** of the constituent a_1.

§ 184.　The Multiplication of Determinants.

This is done in the following manner :

$$\begin{vmatrix} a_1 & b_1 \\ a_2 & b_2 \end{vmatrix} \times \begin{vmatrix} d_1 & e_1 \\ d_2 & e_2 \end{vmatrix} = \begin{vmatrix} a_1 d_1 + b_1 e_1, & a_1 d_2 + b_1 e_2 \\ a_2 d_1 + b_2 e_1, & a_2 d_2 + b_2 e_2 \end{vmatrix} \qquad (38)$$

The proof follows directly on expanding the right side of the equation. We thus obtain,

$$= \begin{vmatrix} a_1d_1, & b_1e_2 \\ a_2d_1, & b_2e_2 \end{vmatrix} + \begin{vmatrix} b_1e_1, & a_1d_2 \\ b_2e_1, & a_2d_2 \end{vmatrix};$$

$$= d_1e_2 \begin{vmatrix} a_1 & b_1 \\ a_2 & b_2 \end{vmatrix} + d_2e_1 \begin{vmatrix} b_1 & a_1 \\ b_2 & a_2 \end{vmatrix};$$

$$= (d_1e_2 - d_2e_1) \begin{vmatrix} a_1 & b_1 \\ a_2 & b_2 \end{vmatrix} = \begin{vmatrix} a_1 & b_1 \\ a_2 & b_2 \end{vmatrix} \times \begin{vmatrix} d_1 & e_1 \\ d_2 & e_2 \end{vmatrix}.$$

Since the value of a determinant is not altered by writing the columns in rows and the rows in columns, the product of two determinants may be written in several equivalent forms which all give the same result on expansion. Thus, instead of the right side of (38), we may have

$$\begin{vmatrix} a_1d_1 + b_1d_2, & a_1e_1 + b_1e_2 \\ a_2d_1 + b_2d_2, & a_2e_1 + b_2e_2 \end{vmatrix}; \quad \begin{vmatrix} a_1d_1 + a_2d_2, & a_1e_1 + a_2e_2 \\ b_1d_1 + b_2d_2, & b_1e_1 + b_2e_2 \end{vmatrix}, \text{ etc.}$$

EXAMPLES.—(1) $\begin{vmatrix} a_1 & b_1 \\ a_2 & b_2 \end{vmatrix}^2 = \begin{vmatrix} a^2_1 + b^2_1, & a_1a_2 + b_1b_2 \\ a_1a_2 + b_1b_2, & a^2_2 + b^2_2 \end{vmatrix}.$

(2) Multiply $\begin{vmatrix} a_1 & b_1 & c_1 \\ a_2 & b_2 & c_2 \\ a_3 & b_3 & c_3 \end{vmatrix}$ and $\begin{vmatrix} d_1 & e_1 & f_1 \\ d_2 & e_2 & f_2 \\ d_3 & e_3 & f_3 \end{vmatrix}$

The answer may be written in several different forms; one form is

$$\begin{vmatrix} a_1d_1 + b_1e_1 + c_1f_1, & a_1d_2 + b_1e_2 + c_1f_2, & a_1d_3 + b_1e_3 + c_1f_3 \\ a_2d_1 + b_2e_1 + c_2f_1, & a_2d_2 + b_2e_2 + c_2f_2, & a_2d_3 + b_2e_3 + c_2f_3 \\ a_3d_1 + b_3e_1 + c_3f_1, & a_3d_2 + b_3e_2 + c_3f_2, & a_3d_3 + b_3e_3 + c_3f_3 \end{vmatrix}.$$

This can be verified by the laborious operation of expansion. There are twenty-seven determinants all but six of which vanish.

When two constituents of a determinant hold the same relative position with respect to the leading constituents, they are said to be **conjugate.** Thus in the last of the determinants in (34) b_1 and q are conjugate, so are b_3 and c_2, r and c_1. If the conjugate elements are equal, the determinant is **symmetrical**, if equal but opposite in sign, we have a **skew determinant**. *The square of a determinant is a symmetrical determinant.*

§ 185. The Differentiation of Determinants.

Suppose that the constituents of a determinant are independent and that

$$D = \begin{vmatrix} x_1 & y_1 \\ x_2 & y_2 \end{vmatrix} = x_1y_2 - x_2y_1,$$

then, $\qquad d(D) = x_1 dy_2 + y_2 dx_1 - x_2 dy_1 - y_1 dx_2\,;$

$$= (y_2 dx_1 - y_1 dx_2) + (x_1 dy_2 - x_2 dy_1)\,;$$

$$= \begin{vmatrix} dx_1 & y_1 \\ dx_2 & y_2 \end{vmatrix} + \begin{vmatrix} x_1 & dy_1 \\ x_2 & dy_2 \end{vmatrix}. \qquad . \qquad . \qquad . \qquad (39)$$

If the constituents of the determinant are functions of an independent variable, say t, then, writing $\dot{x}_1$ for dx/dt, $\dot{y}_2$ for dy_2/dt and so on, it can be proved, in the same way,

$$D = \begin{vmatrix} x_1 & y_1 \\ x_2 & y_2 \end{vmatrix}; \quad d(D)/dt = \begin{vmatrix} \dot{x}_1 & y_1 \\ \dot{x}_2 & y_2 \end{vmatrix} + \begin{vmatrix} x_1 & \dot{y}_1 \\ x_2 & \dot{y}_2 \end{vmatrix}. \qquad (40)$$

EXAMPLES.—(1) Show that if $D = \begin{vmatrix} x_1 & y_1 & z_1 \\ x_2 & y_2 & z_2 \\ x_3 & y_3 & z_3 \end{vmatrix}$;

$$d(D) = \begin{vmatrix} dx_1 & y_1 & z_1 \\ dx_2 & y_2 & z_2 \\ dx_3 & y_3 & z_3 \end{vmatrix} + \begin{vmatrix} x_1 & dy_1 & z_1 \\ x_2 & dy_2 & z_2 \\ x_3 & dy_3 & z_3 \end{vmatrix} + \begin{vmatrix} x_1 & y_1 & dz_1 \\ x_2 & y_2 & dz_2 \\ x_3 & y_3 & dz_3 \end{vmatrix};$$

$$d(D)/dt = \begin{vmatrix} \dot{x}_1 & y_1 & z_1 \\ \dot{x}_2 & y_2 & z_2 \\ \dot{x}_3 & y_3 & z_3 \end{vmatrix} + \begin{vmatrix} x_1 & \dot{y}_1 & z_1 \\ x_2 & \dot{y}_2 & z_2 \\ x_3 & \dot{y}_3 & z_3 \end{vmatrix} + \begin{vmatrix} x_1 & y_1 & \dot{z}_1 \\ x_2 & y_2 & \dot{z}_2 \\ x_3 & y_3 & \dot{z}_3 \end{vmatrix}.$$

(2) If $a_1, b_2, c_1, a_2, b_2, \ldots$, are constants, show that

$$d \begin{vmatrix} a_1 x & b_1 y & c_1 z \\ a_2 x & b_2 y & c_2 z \\ a_3 & b_3 y & c_3 z \end{vmatrix} = \begin{vmatrix} a_1 dx & b_1 y & c_1 z \\ a_2 dx & b_2 y & c_2 z \\ & b_3 y & c_3 z \end{vmatrix} + \text{, etc.,} = dx \begin{vmatrix} b_1 y & c_1 z \\ b_2 y & c_2 z \end{vmatrix}, \text{ etc.}$$

§ 186. Jacobians and Hessians.

I. Definitions. If u, v, w, be functions of the independent variables, x, y, z, the determinant

$$\begin{vmatrix} \dfrac{\partial u}{\partial x} & \dfrac{\partial u}{\partial y} & \dfrac{\partial u}{\partial z} \\[2ex] \dfrac{\partial v}{\partial x} & \dfrac{\partial v}{\partial y} & \dfrac{\partial v}{\partial z} \\[2ex] \dfrac{\partial w}{\partial x} & \dfrac{\partial w}{\partial y} & \dfrac{\partial w}{\partial z} \end{vmatrix}, \qquad . \qquad . \qquad . \qquad (41)$$

is called a **Jacobian** and is variously written,

$$\frac{\partial(u,\, v,\, w)}{\partial(x,\, y,\, z)}\,; \text{ or } J(u,\, v,\, w)\,; \text{ or simply } J, \qquad . \qquad . \qquad (42)$$

when there can be no doubt as to the variables under consideration.

In the special case, where the functions u, v, w are themselves differential coefficients of the one function, say u, with respect to x, y and z, the determinant

$$\begin{vmatrix} \dfrac{\partial^2 u}{\partial x^2} & \dfrac{\partial^2 u}{\partial x \partial y} & \dfrac{\partial^2 u}{\partial x \partial z} \\ \dfrac{\partial^2 u}{\partial y \partial x} & \dfrac{\partial^2 u}{\partial y^2} & \dfrac{\partial^2 u}{\partial y \partial z} \\ \dfrac{\partial^2 u}{\partial z \partial x} & \dfrac{\partial^2 u}{\partial y \partial z} & \dfrac{\partial^2 u}{\partial z^2} \end{vmatrix}, \quad \cdot \quad \cdot \quad \cdot \quad (43)$$

is called a **Hessian** of u and written $H(u)$, or simply H. The Hessian, be it observed, is a symmetrical determinant whose constituents are the second differential coefficients of u with respect to x, y, z. In other words, the Hessian of the primitive function u, is the Jacobian of the first differential coefficients of u, or in the notation of (42),

$$H(u) = \frac{\partial\left(\dfrac{\partial u}{\partial x}, \dfrac{\partial u}{\partial y}, \dfrac{\partial u}{\partial z}\right)}{\partial(x,\, y,\, z)}. \quad \cdot \quad \cdot \quad \cdot \quad (44)$$

II. Jacobians and Hessians of interdependent functions. If

$$u = f(v),$$

$$\frac{\partial u}{\partial x} = f'(v)\frac{\partial v}{\partial x}; \text{ and } \frac{\partial u}{\partial y} = f'(v)\frac{\partial v}{\partial y}.$$

Eliminate the function $f'(v)$ as described on page 449.

$$\frac{\partial u}{\partial x}\cdot\frac{\partial v}{\partial y} - \frac{\partial u}{\partial y}\cdot\frac{\partial v}{\partial x} = 0,$$

or,

$$\begin{vmatrix} \dfrac{\partial u}{\partial x} & \dfrac{\partial u}{\partial y} \\ \dfrac{\partial v}{\partial x} & \dfrac{\partial v}{\partial y} \end{vmatrix} = 0. \quad \cdot \quad \cdot \quad \cdot \quad \cdot \quad (45)$$

That is to say, *if u is a function of v, the Jacobian of the functions of u and v with respect to x and y will be zero.*

The converse of this proposition is also true. If the relation (45) holds good, u will be a function of v.

In the same way, it can be shown that *only when the Hessian of u is not equal to zero are the first derivatives of u with respect to x and y independent of each other.*

EXAMPLES.—(1) If the denominators of (9), *et seq.*, page 453, that is, if P, Q, and R vanish, show that u can be expressed as a function of v, or, u and v are not independent. Ansr. The expression is a Jacobian. If u is a function of v, the Jacobian vanishes. R vanishes if either u or v is a function of z only ; P, Q, and R all vanish if u is a function of v; and $f(u, v) = 0$ can be represented by $v = c$ which contains no arbitrary function.

(2) Show that $\dfrac{\partial(\phi,\,u,\,v)}{\partial(x,\,y,\,z)} = 0$ is a condition that $\phi = 0$ shall be an integral of $P\partial z/\partial x + Q\partial z/\partial y = R$. *Hint.* ϕ is a function of x, y, z, and can be expressed as a function of u and v.

(3) If P, Q, and R are given, the Jacobian of u and v must be proportional to P, Q and R. This follows from the equations on page 453.

III. The Jacobian of a function of a function. If u_1, u_2, are functions of x_1 and x_2, and x_1 and x_2 are functions of y_1 and y_2,

$$\frac{\partial u_1}{\partial y_1} = \frac{\partial u_1}{\partial x_1}\cdot\frac{\partial x_1}{\partial y_1} + \frac{\partial u_1}{\partial x_2}\cdot\frac{\partial x_2}{\partial y_1}\,;\;\; \frac{\partial u_1}{\partial y_2} = \frac{\partial u_1}{\partial x_1}\cdot\frac{\partial x_1}{\partial y_2} + \frac{\partial u_1}{\partial x_2}\cdot\frac{\partial x_2}{\partial y_2}.$$

By the rule for the multiplication of determinants,

$$\begin{vmatrix} \dfrac{\partial u_1}{\partial y_1} & \dfrac{\partial u_1}{\partial y_2} \\[2ex] \dfrac{\partial u_2}{\partial y_1} & \dfrac{\partial u_2}{\partial y_2} \end{vmatrix} = \begin{vmatrix} \dfrac{\partial u_1}{\partial x_1} & \dfrac{\partial u_1}{\partial y_1} \\[2ex] \dfrac{\partial u_2}{\partial x_2} & \dfrac{\partial u_2}{\partial y_2} \end{vmatrix} \cdot \begin{vmatrix} \dfrac{\partial x_1}{\partial y_1} & \dfrac{\partial x_1}{\partial y_2} \\[2ex] \dfrac{\partial x_2}{\partial y_1} & \dfrac{\partial x_2}{\partial y_2} \end{vmatrix}, \qquad (46)$$

or,
$$\frac{\partial(u_1,\,u_2)}{\partial(y_1,\,y_2)} = \frac{\partial(u_1,\,u_2)}{\partial(x_1,\,x_2)}\cdot\frac{\partial(x_1,\,x_2)}{\partial(y_1,\,y_2)}.$$

This bears a close formal analogy with the well-known

$$\frac{\partial u}{\partial x} = \frac{\partial u}{\partial y}\cdot\frac{\partial y}{\partial x}.$$

IV. The Jacobian of implicit [1] *functions.* If u and v, instead of being explicitly connected with the independent variables x and y, are so related that

$$p = f_1(x,\,y,\,u,\,v) = 0\,;\;\; q = f_2(x,\,y,\,u,\,v) = 0,$$

u and v may be regarded as implicit functions of x and y. By differentiation

$$\frac{\partial x}{\partial p} + \frac{\partial u}{\partial p}\cdot\frac{\partial u}{\partial x} + \frac{\partial p}{\partial v}\cdot\frac{\partial v}{\partial x} = 0\,;\;\; \frac{\partial p}{\partial y} + \frac{\partial p}{\partial u}\cdot\frac{\partial u}{\partial y} + \frac{\partial p}{\partial v}\cdot\frac{\partial v}{\partial y} = 0\,;$$

$$\frac{\partial q}{\partial x} + \frac{\partial q}{\partial u}\cdot\frac{\partial u}{\partial x} + \frac{\partial q}{\partial v}\cdot\frac{\partial v}{\partial x} = 0\,;\;\; \frac{\partial q}{\partial y} + \frac{\partial q}{\partial u}\cdot\frac{\partial u}{\partial y} + \frac{\partial q}{\partial v}\cdot\frac{\partial v}{\partial x} = 0\,;$$

and by the rule for the multiplication of determinants,

$$\begin{vmatrix} \dfrac{\partial p}{\partial u} & \dfrac{\partial p}{\partial v} \\[2ex] \dfrac{q}{\partial u} & \dfrac{\partial q}{\partial v} \end{vmatrix} \times \begin{vmatrix} \dfrac{\partial u}{\partial x} & \dfrac{\partial v}{\partial x} \\[2ex] \dfrac{\partial u}{\partial y} & \dfrac{\partial v}{\partial y} \end{vmatrix} = - \begin{vmatrix} \dfrac{\partial p}{\partial x} & \dfrac{\partial p}{\partial y} \\[2ex] \dfrac{\partial q}{\partial x} & \dfrac{q}{\partial y} \end{vmatrix}. \qquad (47)$$

---

[1] A function is said to be **explicit** when it can be expressed directly in terms of the variable or variables, *e.g.*, z is an explicit function of x in the expression : $z = x^2$; $z + a = bx^4$. A function is **implicit** when it cannot be so expressed in terms of the independent variable. Thus $x^2 + xy = y^2$; $x + y = z^x$, are implicit functions.

Or,
$$\frac{\delta(p,\,q)}{\delta(u,\,v)} \cdot \frac{\delta(u,\,v)}{\delta(x,\,y)} = -\frac{\delta(p,\,q)}{\delta(x,\,y)}.$$

A result which may be extended to include any number of independent relations.

§ 187. Illustrations from Thermodynamics.

Determinants, Jacobians and Hessians are continually appearing in different branches of applied mathematics. The following results will serve as a simple exercise on the mathematical methods of some of the earlier sections of this work. The reader should find no difficulty in assigning a meaning to most of the coefficients considered. See J. E. Trevor, *Journ. Phys. Chem.*, **3**, 523, 573, 1899; **10**, 99, 1906; also R. E. Baynes' *Thermodynamics*, Oxford, 95, 1878.

If U denotes the internal energy, ϕ the entropy, p the pressure, v the volume, T the absolute temperature, Q the quantity of heat in a system of constant mass and composition, the two laws of thermodynamics state that

$$dQ = dU + p\,.\,dv\,;\quad dQ = Td\phi,\quad . \quad . \quad . \quad (1)$$

pages 80 and 81. To find a value for each of the partial derivatives

$$\left(\frac{\delta\phi}{\delta p}\right)_v,\;\left(\frac{\delta\phi}{\delta p}\right)_T,\;\left(\frac{\delta\phi}{\delta T}\right)_p,\;\left(\frac{\delta\phi}{\delta T}\right)_v,\;\left(\frac{\delta\phi}{\delta v}\right)_p,\;\left(\frac{\delta\phi}{\delta v}\right)_T;$$

$$\left(\frac{\delta v}{\delta p}\right)_T,\;\left(\frac{\delta v}{\delta p}\right)_\phi,\;\left(\frac{\delta v}{\delta T}\right)_p,\;\left(\frac{\delta v}{\delta T}\right)_\phi,\;\left(\frac{\delta v}{\delta\phi}\right)_p,\;\left(\frac{\delta v}{\delta\phi}\right)_T,$$

in terms of the derivatives of U.

I. When v or ϕ is constant. From (1),

$$-p = \delta U/\delta v\,;\;\text{and }T = \delta U/\delta\phi.\quad . \quad . \quad (2)$$

First, differentiate each of the expressions (2), with respect to ϕ at constant volume.

$$-\left(\frac{\delta p}{\delta\phi}\right)_v = \frac{\delta^2 U}{\delta v\delta\phi}\,;\;\text{and }\left(\frac{\delta T}{\delta\phi}\right)_v = \frac{\delta^2 U}{\delta\phi^2}.\quad . \quad . \quad (3)$$

By division,
$$-\left(\frac{\delta p}{\delta T}\right) = \frac{\dfrac{\delta^2 U}{\delta v\delta\phi}}{\dfrac{\delta^2 U}{\delta\phi^2}}.\quad . \quad . \quad . \quad (4)$$

Next, differentiate each of equations (2) with respect to v at constant entropy.

$$-\left(\frac{\delta p}{\delta v}\right)_\phi = \frac{\delta^2 U}{\delta v^2}\,;\;\left(\frac{\delta T}{\delta v}\right)_\phi = \frac{\delta^2 U}{\delta\phi\delta v}.\quad . \quad . \quad (5)$$

By division, $-\left(\dfrac{\partial p}{\partial T}\right)_\phi = \dfrac{\dfrac{\partial^2 U}{\partial v^2}}{\dfrac{\partial^2 U}{\partial\phi\partial v}}.$.   .   .   (6)

II. When either p or T is constant. We know that

$$dp = \frac{\partial p}{\partial v}dv + \frac{\partial p}{\partial\phi}dp; \quad \text{and } dT = \frac{\partial\theta}{\partial v}dv + \frac{\partial T}{\partial\phi}d\phi. \quad (7)$$

First, when p is constant, eliminate dv or $d\phi$ between equations (7). Hence show that

$$\frac{dv}{-\dfrac{\partial p}{\partial\phi}} = \frac{d\phi}{\dfrac{\partial p}{\partial v}} = \frac{d\theta}{J},$$

where J denotes the Jacobian $\partial(p,\ T)/\partial(v,\ \phi)$. If H denotes the Hessian of U, show that

$$-\left(\frac{\partial v}{\partial\phi}\right)_p = \frac{\dfrac{\partial^2 U}{\partial v\partial\phi}}{\dfrac{\partial^2 U}{\partial v^2}}\ ; \quad -\left(\frac{\partial v}{\partial T}\right)_p = \frac{\dfrac{\partial^2 U}{\partial v\partial\phi}}{H}; \quad \left(\frac{\partial\phi}{\partial T}\right)_p = \frac{\dfrac{\partial^2 U}{\partial v^2}}{H}. \quad (8)$$

Finally, if T is constant, show that

$$\left(\frac{\partial\phi}{\partial v}\right)\frac{\dfrac{\partial^2 U}{\partial v\partial\phi}}{\dfrac{\partial^2 U}{\partial\phi^2}}\ ; \quad \left(\frac{\partial\phi}{\partial p}\right)_T = \frac{\dfrac{\partial^2 U}{\partial v\partial\phi}}{H}; \quad -\left(\frac{\partial v}{\partial p}\right)_T = \frac{\dfrac{\partial^2 U}{\partial\phi^2}}{H}. \quad (9)$$

§ 188. Study of Surfaces.

Just as an equation of the first degree between two variables represents a straight line of the first order, so does an equation of the first degree between three variables represent a **surface of the first order.** Such an equation in its most general form is

$$Ax + By + Cz + D = 0,$$

the equation to a plane.

An equation of the second degree between three variables represents a **surface of the second order.** The most general equation of the second degree between three variables is

$$Ax^2 + By^2 + Cz^2 + Dxy + Eyz + Fz\dot{x} + \ldots + N = 0.$$

All plane sections of surfaces of the second order are either circular, parabolic, hyperbolic, or elliptical, and are comprised under the generic word *conicoids*, of which *spheroids, paraboloids, hyperboloids* and *ellipsoids* are special cases.

J. Thomson (*Phil. Mag.*, **43**, 227, 1871) developed a surface of the second degree by plotting from the gas equation

$$f(p, v, T) = 0 \; ; \; \text{or} \; pv = RT,$$

by causing p, v and T to vary simultaneously. The surface $pabv$ (Fig. 175) was developed in this way.

Since any section cut perpendicular to the T- or θ-axis is a rectangular hyperbola, the surface is a hyperboloid. The iso-thermals T, T_2, T_3, ... (Fig. 29, page 111) may be looked upon as plane sections cut perpendicular to the θ-axis at points correspond-ing to T_1, T_2, ..., and then projected upon the pv-plane. In Fig. 176, the curves corresponding to pv and ab have been so projected.

As a general rule, the surface generated by three variables is not so simple as the one represented by a gas obeying the simple laws of Boyle and Charles.

Van der Waals' "ψ" surfaces are developed by using the variables ψ, x, v, where ψ denotes the thermodynamic potential at

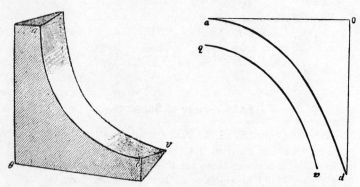

FIG. 175.—$pv\theta$-surface.   FIG. 176.—Two Isothermals.

constant volume ($U - T\phi$) ; x the composition of the substance ; v the volume of the system under investigation. The "ψ" surface is analogous to, but not identical with, $pabv$ in the above figure.

The so-called **thermodynamic surfaces of Gibbs** are obtained in the same way from the variables v, U, ϕ (where v denotes the volume, U the internal energy, and ϕ the entropy) of the given system.

The solubility of a double salt may be studied with respect to three variables—temperature, θ, and the concentrations s_1 and s_2 of each component in the presence of its own solid. Thus a mixed solution of magnesium sulphate, $MgSO_4$, and potassium sulphate, K_2SO_4, will deposit the double salt, $MgSO_4.K_2SO_4.6H_2O$, under certain conditions. The surface so obtained is called a **surface of solubility.** The solution can also deposit other solids under certain conditions. For example, we may also have crystals of $MgSO_4.7H_2O$ deposited in such a manner as to form another surface of solubility. This is not all. The above system may deposit crystals of the hydrate $MgSO_4.6H_2O$, the double salt $MgSO_4.K_2SO_4.4H_2O$, or the separate components. The final result is the set of surfaces shown in Fig. 177.

The surface which is represented by the equation,

$$f(x, y, z) = 0 \; ; \; \text{or,} \; z = \phi(x, y),$$

will exhibit the characteristic properties of any substance with respect to the three variables x, y, and z. The surface, in fact,

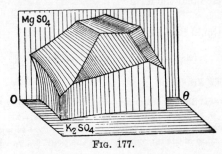

FIG. 177.

will possess certain geometrical peculiarities which depend upon the nature of the substance. It is therefore necessary to be able to study the nature of the surface at any point when we know the equation of the surface.

I. The tangent line, and tangent plane. Let the point $P(x_1, y_1, z_1)$ be upon the surface

$$u = f(x, y, z). \qquad . \qquad . \qquad . \qquad . \qquad (1)$$

The equations of a line through the point P are, page 131,

$$\frac{x - x_1}{l} = \frac{y - y_1}{m} = \frac{z - z_1}{n} = r, \qquad . \qquad . \qquad . \qquad (2)$$

and where the line meets the surface

$$u = f(x_1 + lr, y_1 + mr, z_1 + nr) = 0. \qquad . \qquad . \qquad (3)$$

By Taylor's theorem,

$$r\left[l\frac{du}{dx_1} + m\frac{du}{dy_1} + n\frac{du}{dz_1} \right] + \frac{r^2}{\lfloor 2} \left[\frac{d^2u}{dx_1^2} + m\frac{d^2u}{dy_1^2} + n\frac{d^2u}{dz_1^2} \right] + \ldots = 0. \; (4)$$

One value of r must be zero since P is on the surface ; and if we choose the line so that

$$l\frac{du}{dx_1} + m\frac{du}{dy_1} + n\frac{du}{dz_1} = 0, \quad \cdot \quad \cdot \quad \cdot \quad (5)$$

another value of r will vanish ; so that for this direction another point, Q, will coincide with P and the line will be a tangent line. Equation (6) gives the relation between the direction cosines of a tangent line to the surface at the point $P(x_1, y_1, z_1)$. Eliminating l, m, and n, between (2) and (5), we get

$$(x - x_1)\frac{\partial u}{\partial x_1} + (y - y_1)\frac{\partial u}{\partial y_1} + (z - z_1)\frac{\partial u}{\partial z_1} = 0. \quad \cdot \quad (6)$$

This equation being of the first degree in x, y, and z represents a plane surface. All the tangent lines lie in one plane. Equation (6) is the **equation of a tangent plane** at the point (x_1, y_1, z_1).

If the surface had the form

$$z = f(x, y) \quad \cdot \quad \cdot \quad \cdot \quad \cdot \quad (7)$$

equation (6) would have been

$$(x - x_1)\frac{\partial z_1}{\partial x_1} + (y - y_1)\frac{\partial z_1}{\partial y_1} = z - z_1, \quad \cdot \quad (8)$$

at the point (x_1, y_1, z_1).

EXAMPLES.—(1) Show that the tangent plane of the sphere $x_1^2 + y_1^2 + z_1^2 = r^2$ at the point (x, y, z) is $xx_1 + yy_1 + zz_1 = r^2$. Hint. $\partial u/\partial x_1 = 2x_1$; $\partial u/\partial y_1 = 2y_1$; $\partial u/\partial z_1 = 2z_1$. Substitute in (6) and it follows that $xx_1 + yy_1 + zz_1 = x^2 + y^2 + z^2 = r^2$.

(2) The equation of the tangent plane at the point (x_1, y_1, z_1) on the paraboloid

$$\frac{x^2}{a^2} + \frac{y^2}{b^2} = 4px ; \text{ is } \frac{xx_1}{a^2} + \frac{yy_1}{b^2} = 2p(z + z_1).$$

(3) Show that the tangent plane to the surface (1) or (6) above is horizontal, that is, parallel to the xy-plane. $z - z_1 = 0$. Hint. When a line is parallel to the x-axis, the angle it makes with the axis is zero, and $\tan 0° = 0$, hence we must have $\partial u/\partial x$ and $\partial u/\partial y$ both zero ; and $\partial u/\partial z$ not zero.

II. *The normal.* By analogy with (1), page 106, or by more workmanlike proofs which the student can discover for himself, we can write the condition that a plane normal to, or perpendicular to, the tangent of the surface $f(x, y, z)$ 0 at the point (x_1, y_1, z_1) is

$$\frac{x - x_1}{\dfrac{\partial u}{\partial x}} = \frac{y - y_1}{\dfrac{\partial u}{\partial y}} = \frac{z - z_1}{\dfrac{\partial u}{\partial z}} \ 0 ; \quad \text{or,} \quad \frac{x - x_1}{\dfrac{\partial u}{\partial x}} = \frac{y - y_1}{\dfrac{\partial u}{\partial y}} \ z - z_1. \quad (9)$$

EXAMPLES.—(1) Show that the normal to the sphere $x^2 + y^2 + z^2 = r^2$, is $x/x_1 = y/y_1 = z/z_1$. Use the results of Ex. (1) above, and substitute in (10).

(2) The normal to the surface $xyz = a^3$ at the point (x_1, y_1, z_1) is $xx_1 - x_1{}^2 = xy_1 - y_1{}^2 = zz_1 - z_1{}^2$.

(3) Show that the equations of the normal and of the tangent to the curve $y^2 = 2x - x^2$; $z^2 = 4^2 - 2x$, at the point $(2, 3, -1)$ are respectively $z - 2 = \frac{1}{2}(y - 3) = z + 1$; and $z - 2 = -3(y - 3) = z + 1$.

(4) We do not know the characteristic equation connecting p, v, and T. If the substance is an ideal gas, we have $pv = RT$. From equations (13) and (15), pages 81 and 82, we get the fundamental equation

$$dU = Td\phi - pdv, \quad \cdot \quad \cdot \quad \cdot \quad \cdot \quad (10)$$

connecting v, U, and ϕ. This expression is the differential equation of some surface of the form

$$U = f(v, \phi) ; \therefore dU = \left(\frac{\partial U}{\partial \phi}\right)_v d\phi + \left(\frac{\partial U}{\partial v}\right)_\phi dv. \quad \cdot \quad \cdot \quad (11)$$

Where -1, and the two partial derivatives are proportional to the direction cosines of the normal to the surface at any point. Again, it follows from (10) and (11) that

$$\left(\frac{\partial v}{\partial \phi}\right)_v = T ; \text{ and } \left(\frac{\partial U}{\partial v}\right)_\phi = -p. \quad \cdot \quad \cdot \quad \cdot \quad (12)$$

In other words the direction cosines of the normal at any point on the surface are proportional to T, $-p$, and -1 respectively. Hence, v, U, and ϕ are the coordinates of the point on the surface, and the remaining pair of variables p and T are given by the direction cosines of the normal at the same point. The whole five quantities p, v, T, U, and ϕ can thus be represented in a very simple manner.

III. Inflexional tangents. We can discuss the equations of a surface by the aid of the extension of Taylor's theorem, on page 292, and the methods described in § 101. There are an infinite number of lines

$$\frac{x - x_1}{l} = \frac{y - y_1}{m} = \frac{z - z_1}{n}, \quad \cdot \quad \cdot \quad \cdot \quad (13)$$

which satisfy the relations

$$l^2 + m^2 + n^2 = 1 ; \quad l\frac{\partial z}{\partial x} + m\frac{\partial z}{\partial y} - n = 0. \quad \cdot \quad (14)$$

These lines cut the surface at two coincident points; two of these lines also satisfy the relation

$$l\frac{\partial^2 z}{\partial x^2} + 2lm\frac{\partial^2 z}{\partial x \partial y} + m\frac{\partial^2 z}{\partial y^2} = 0. \quad \cdot \quad \cdot \quad (15)$$

These two lines cut the surface at three coincident points. These lines are called **inflexional tangents.** They are real and distinct, coincident, or imaginary, according as the quadratic in l, and m,

$$z_{xx}l^2 + 2z_{xy}lm + z_{yy}m^2 \quad \cdot \quad \cdot \quad \cdot \quad (16)$$

has real and different, double, or imaginary roots. This depends upon whether

$$\frac{\partial^2 z}{\partial x^2} \cdot \frac{\partial^2 z}{\partial y^2} - \left(\frac{\partial^2 z}{\partial x \partial y}\right)^2 = \begin{cases} + & = \text{cusp}; \\ 0 & = \text{conjugate point}; \\ - & = \text{node}. \end{cases} \quad . \quad (17)$$

Each inflexional tangent to the surface will cut the curve in three coincident points at the point of contact. The inflexional tangents have a closer contact with the surface than any of the other tangent lines. At the point of contact of the curve with the tangent plane there will be a cusp, conjugate point, or a node, according as the above expression is positive, zero, or negative.

The equations of the inflexional tangents at the point (x_1, y_1, z_1) are obtained by the elimination of l, m, and n between (13); the second of equations (14); and (15). If we treat the equation of the surface

$$u = f(x, y, z) = 0, \quad . \quad . \quad . \quad (18)$$

in a similar manner, we find that we must know the value of

$$l^2 + m^2 + n^2 = 1; \; l\frac{\partial u}{\partial x} + m\frac{\partial u}{\partial y} + n\frac{\partial u}{\partial z} = 0, \quad . \quad (19)$$

as well as of

$$\left(l\frac{\partial}{\partial x} + m\frac{\partial}{\partial y} + n\frac{\partial}{\partial z}\right)^2 u = 0, \quad . \quad . \quad (20)$$

in order to determine the inflexional tangents. These tangents will be real and different, coincident, or imaginary according as the determinant

$$\begin{vmatrix} u_{xx} & u_{xy} & u_{xz} & u_x \\ u_{xy} & u_{yy} & u_{yz} & u_y \\ u_{xz} & u_{yz} & u_{zz} & u_z \\ u_x & u_y & u_z & u_0 \end{vmatrix} \quad . \quad . \quad . \quad (21)$$

is negative, positive, or zero. When the inflexional tangents are imaginary, the surface is either convex or concave at the point, and conversely. Furthermore, if

$$\begin{vmatrix} u_{xx} & u_{xy} \\ u_{xy} & u_{yy} \end{vmatrix}; \text{ and, } u \begin{vmatrix} u_{xx} & u_{xy} & u_{xz} \\ u_{xy} & u_{yy} & u_{yz} \\ u_{xz} & u_{yz} & u_{zz} \end{vmatrix} \quad . \quad . \quad (22)$$

are positive at the point $P(x, y, z)$ the surface is concave provided $\partial^2 u/\partial x^2$ and $\partial u/\partial z$ have the same sign; and convex when $\partial^2 u/\partial x^2$ and $\partial u/\partial z$ have different signs.

APPENDIX I.

COLLECTION OF FORMULÆ AND TABLES FOR REFERENCE.

"When for the first time I have occasion to add five objects to seven others, I count the whole lot through; but when I afterwards discover that by starting to count from five I can save myself part of the trouble, and still later, by remembering that five and seven always add up to twelve, I can dispense with the counting altogether."—E. MACH.

§ 189. Calculations with Small Quantities.

THE discussion on approximate calculations in Chapter V. renders any further remarks on the deduction of the following formulæ superfluous.

For the sign of equality read "is approximately equal to," or "is very nearly equal to". Let $a, \beta, \gamma, \ldots$ be small fractions in comparison with unity or x:

$$(1 \pm a)(1 \pm \beta) = 1 \pm a \pm \beta. \qquad \qquad \text{(1)}$$

$$(1 \pm a)(1 \pm \beta)(1 \pm \gamma) \ldots = 1 \pm a \pm \beta \pm \gamma \pm \ldots \qquad \text{(2)}$$

$$(1 \pm a)^2 = 1 \pm 2a; \quad (1 \pm a)^n = 1 \pm na. \qquad \text{(3)}$$

$$\sqrt{(1 + a)} = 1 + \tfrac{1}{2}a. \quad \sqrt{a\beta} = \tfrac{1}{2}(a + \beta). \qquad \text{(4)}$$

$$\frac{1}{(1 \pm a)} = 1 \mp a; \quad \frac{1}{(1 \pm a)^n} = 1 \mp na; \quad \frac{1}{\sqrt{(1 + a)}} = 1 - \tfrac{1}{2}a. \qquad \text{(5)}$$

$$\frac{(1 \pm a)(1 \pm \beta)}{(1 \pm \gamma)(1 \pm \delta)} = 1 \pm a \pm \beta \mp \gamma \mp \delta. \qquad \text{(6)}$$

The third member of some of the following results is to be regarded as a second approximation, to be employed only when an exceptional degree of accuracy is required.

$$e^a = 1 + a; \quad a^a = 1 + a \log a. \qquad \text{(7)}$$

$$\log(1 + a) = a = a - \tfrac{1}{2}a^2. \qquad \text{(8)}$$

$$\log(x + a) = \log x + a/x - \tfrac{1}{2}a^2/x^2. \qquad \text{(9)}$$

$$\log\frac{x + a}{x - a} = \frac{2a}{x} + \frac{2}{3} \cdot \frac{a^3}{x^2} \qquad \text{(10)}$$

By Taylor's theorem, § 98,

$$\sin(x + \beta) = \sin x + \beta \cos x - \tfrac{1}{2}\beta^2 \sin x - \tfrac{1}{6}\beta^3 \cos x + \ldots$$

If the angle β is not greater than $2\tfrac{1}{2}°$, $\beta < \cdot 044 : \tfrac{1}{2}\beta^2 < \cdot 001; \tfrac{1}{6}\beta^3 < \cdot 00001$. But $\sin x$ does not exceed unity, therefore, we may look upon

$$\sin(x + \beta) = \sin x + \beta \cos x,$$

correct up to three decimal places. The addition of another term " $- \frac{1}{2}\beta^2$ " will make the result correct to the fifth decimal place.

$$\sin \alpha = \alpha = \alpha(1 - \frac{1}{6}\alpha^2);\ \cos\alpha = 1 = 1 - \frac{1}{2}\alpha^2. \quad . \quad . \quad . \quad (11)$$
$$\sin(x \pm \beta) = \sin x \pm \beta \cos x;\ \cos(x \pm \beta) = \cos x \pm \beta \sin x. \quad . \quad (12)$$
$$\tan\alpha = \alpha = \alpha(1 + \frac{1}{3}\alpha^2);\ \tan(x \pm \beta) = \tan x \pm \beta \sec^2 x. \quad . \quad (13)$$

EXAMPLE.—Show that the square root of the product of two small fractions is very nearly equal to half their sum. See (4). Hence, at sight, $\sqrt{24\cdot00092 \times 24\cdot00098} = 24\cdot00095.$

§ 190. Permutations and Combinations.

Each arrangement that can be made by varying the order of some or all of a number of things is called a permutation. For instance, there are two permutations of two things a and b, namely ab and ba; a third thing can be added to each of these two permutations in three ways so that abc, acb, cab, bac, bca, cba results. The permutations of three things taken all together is, therefore, $1 \times 2 \times 3$; a fourth thing can occupy four different places in each of these six permutations, or, there are $1 \times 2 \times 3 \times 4$ permutations when four different things are taken all together. More generally, the permutations of n things taken all together is

$$n(n - 1)\ (n - 2) \ldots 3.2.1 = n!$$

$n!$ is called "factoral n".[1] It is generally written $\lfloor n$.

Using the customary notation $_nP_n$ to denote the number of permutations of n things taken n at a time,

number of things P number of things taken $= {}_nP_n = n!$

If some of these n things are alike, say p of one kind, q of another, r of another,

$${}_nP_n = \frac{n!}{p!\ q!\ r!}. \quad . \quad . \quad . \quad (2)$$

If only r of the n things are taken in each set,

$${}_nP_r = n(n - 1)\ (n - 2) \ldots (n - r + 1) = \frac{n!}{(n - r)!}. \quad . \quad (3)$$

Each set of arrangements which can be made by taking some or all of a number of things, without reference to the internal arrangement of the things in each group, is called a combination. In permutations, the variations, or the order of the arrangement of the different things, is considered; in combinations, attention is only paid to the presence or absence of a certain thing. The number of combinations of two things taken two at a time is one, because the set ab contains the same thing as ba. The number of combinations of three things taken two at a time is three, namely, ab, ca, bc; of four things, ab, ac, ad, bc, bd, cd. But when each set consists of r things, each set can be arranged in $r!$ different ways.

---

[1] It is worth remembering that $n! = \Gamma(n + 1)$, the gamma function of § 136. When n is very great

$$n! = n^n e^{-n}\sqrt{2\pi n},$$

known as Stirling's formula. This allows $n!$ to be evaluated by a table of logarithms. The error is of the order $\frac{1}{12}n$ of the value of $n!$

Let $_nC_r$ denote the number of combinations of n things taken r at a time. We observe that the $_nC_r$ combinations will produce $_nC_r \times r!$ permutations. This is the same thing as the number of permutations of n things in sets of r things.   Hence, by (3),

$$_nC_r = \frac{_nP_r}{r!} = \frac{n(n-1)(n-2)\ldots(n-r+1)}{r!}. \quad \text{.   .   (4)}$$

$$_nC_r = \frac{n!}{r!\,(n-r)!}. \quad \text{.   .   .   .   (5)}$$

Nearly all questions on arrangement and variety can be referred to the standard formulæ (3) and (5). Special cases are treated in any text-book on algebra. In spite of the great number of organic compounds continually pouring into the journals, chemists have, in reality, made no impression on the great number which might exist. To illustrate, Hatchett's (*Phil. Trans.*, **93**, 193, 1803) has suggested that a systematic examination of all possible alloys of all the metals be made, proceeding from the binary to the more complicated ternary and quaternary. Did he realize the magnitude of the undertaking?

EXAMPLES.—(1) Show that if one proportion of each of thirty metals be taken, 435 binary, 4,060 ternary and 27,405 quaternary alloys would have to be considered.

(2) If four proportions of each of thirty metals be employed, show that 6,655 binary, 247,660 ternary and 1,013,985 quaternary alloys would have to be investigated.

The number of possible isomers in the hydrocarbon series involving side chains, etc., are discussed in the following memoirs: Cayley (*Phil. Mag.* [4], **13**, 172, 1857; **47**, 444, 1874; or, *B. A. Reports*, 257, 1875) first opened up this question of side chains. See also O. J. Lodge (*Phil. Mag.*, [4], **50**, 367, 1875), Losanitsch (*Ber.*, **30**, 1,917, 1897), Hermann (*ib.*, 3,423), H. Rey (*ib.*, **33**, 1,910, 1900), H. Kauffmann (*ib.*, 2,231).

§ 191. Mensuration Formulæ.

Reference has frequently been made to Euclid, i., 47—**Pythagoras' theorem.** In any right-angled triangle, say, Fig. 184,

Square on hypotenuse = Sum of squares on the other two sides.   (1)
Also to Euclid, vi., 4. If two triangles ABC and DEF are equiangular so that the angles at A, B, and C of the one are respectively equal to the angles D, E, and F of the other, the sides about the equal angles are proportional— **Rule of similar triangles**—so that

$$AB:BC = DE:EF; \quad BC:CA = EF:FD; \quad AB:AC = DE:DF.$$

$\pi = 3.1416$, or, $\frac{22}{7}$, or, $180°$; $\theta =$ degrees of arc; r denotes the radius of a circle.

I. Lengths (arcs and perimeters).

CHORD OF CIRCLE (angle subtended at centre θ) $= 2r \sin \frac{1}{2}\theta$.   .   (2)

ARC OF CIRCLE (angle subtended θ) $= \frac{\theta}{180}\pi r$.   .   .   .   (3)

PERIMETER OF CIRCLE $= 2\pi r = \pi \times$ diameter.   .   .   .   (4)

PERIMETER OF ELLIPSE (semiaxes, a, b) $= 2\pi \sqrt{\frac{1}{2}(a^2 + b^2)}$.   .   (5)

TRIANGLE. $a^2 = b^2 + c^2 - 2bc \cos A$.   .   .   .   .   (5a)

II. Areas.

RECTANGLE (sides a, b) = $a : b$. . . . . . . (6)

PARALLELOGRAM (sides a, b; included angle θ) = $ab \sin \theta$. . . (7)

RHOMBUS = $\frac{1}{2}$ product of the two diagonals. . . . . (8)

TRIANGLE (altitude h; base b)

$$= \tfrac{1}{2}h . b = \tfrac{1}{2}ab \sin C = \sqrt{s(s-a)(s-b)(s-c)}, \qquad \Big\} \quad (9)$$

where a, b, c, are the sides opposite the respective angles A, B, C, of Fig. 178, and $s = \frac{1}{2}(a + b + c)$.

SPHERICAL TRIANGLE = $(A + B + C - \pi)r^2$, ... (10)

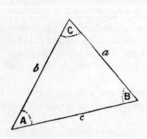
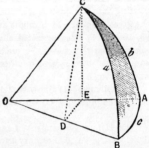

FIG. 178.   FIG. 179.—Spherical Triangle.

where r is the radius of the sphere, A, B, C, are the angles of the triangle (Fig. 179).

TRAPEZIUM (altitude h; parallel sides a, b) = $\frac{1}{2}h(a + b)$. . . (11)

POLYGON OF n EQUAL SIDES (length of side a) = $\frac{1}{4}na^2 \cot \frac{180}{n}$. . (12)

CIRCLE = $\pi r^2 = \frac{1}{4}\pi \times$ diameter squared. . . . . . (13)

CIRCULAR SECTOR (included angle θ) = $\frac{1}{2}$ arc × radius = $\frac{\theta}{360}\pi r^2$. (14)

CIRCULAR SEGMENT = area of sector − area of triangle $\frac{\theta}{360}\pi r^2 - \frac{1}{2}r^2 \sin \theta$ (15)

The triangle is made by joining the two ends of the arc to each other and to the centre of the circle. θ is angle at centre of circle.

PARABOLA CUT OFF BY DOUBLE ORDINATE ($2y$) = $\frac{4}{3}xy$;
= $\frac{2}{3}$ Area of parallelogram of same base and height. $\quad \Big\} \quad (16)$

ELLIPSE = $\pi a . b$. . . . . (17)

CURVILINEAR AND IRREGULAR FIGURES. See Simpson's rule.

SIMILAR FIGURES. The areas of similar figures are as the squares of the corresponding sides. The area of any plane figure is proportional to the square of any linear dimension. *E.g.*, the area of a circle is proportional to the square of its radius.

III. Surfaces (*omit top and base*).

SPHERE = $4\pi r^2$. . . . . (18)

CYLINDER (height h) = $2\pi rh$. . . . . (19)

PRISM (perimeter of the base p) = ph. . . . . . (20)

CONE OR PYRAMID = $\frac{1}{2}p \times$ slant height. . . . . . (21)

SPHERICAL SEGMENT (height h) = $2\pi rh$. . . . . . (22)

IV. Volumes.

RECTANGULAR PARALLELOPIPED (sides a, b, c) = $a \cdot b \cdot c$. (23)

SPHERE = $\frac{2}{3}$ circumscribing cylinder;
$= \frac{4}{3}\pi r^3 = 4 \cdot 189 r^3 = \frac{1}{6}\pi$ diameter^3. } (24)

SPHERICAL SEGMENT (height h) = $\frac{1}{3}\pi(3r - h) h^2$. . . . . (25)

CYLINDER OR PRISM = area of base × height = $\pi r^2 h$. . . . (26)

CONE OR PYRAMID = $\frac{1}{3}$ circumscribing cylinder or prism;
$= $ area of base × $\frac{1}{3}$ height $= \frac{1}{3}\pi r^2 h = 1 \cdot 047 r^2 h$. } (27)

FRUSTUM OF RIGHT CIRCULAR CONE = $\frac{1}{3}\pi h(a^2 + ab + b^2)$.
a and b are radii of circular ends. } (28)

SIMILAR FIGURES. The volumes of similar solids are as the cubes of corresponding sides. The volume of any solid figure is proportional to the cube of any linear dimension. *E.g.*, the volume of a sphere is proportional to the cube of its radius.

V. Centres of Gravity.

PLANE TRIANGULAR LAMINA. Two-thirds the distance from the apex of the triangle to a point bisecting the base.

CONE OR PYRAMID. Three-fourths the distance from the apex to the centre of gravity of base.

Bayer's "strain theory" of carbon ring compounds has attracted some attention amongst organic chemists. It is based upon the assumption that the four valencies of a carbon atom act only in the directions of the lines joining the centre of gravity of the atom with the apices of a regular tetrahedron. In other words, the chemical attraction between any two such atoms is exerted only along these four directions. When several carbon atoms unite to form ring compounds, the "direction of the attraction" is deflected. This is attended by a proportional strain. The greater the strain, the less stable the compound. Apart from all questions as to the validity of the assumptions, we may find the angle of deflection of the "directions of attraction" for two to six ring compounds as an exercise in mensuration.

I. To find the angle between these "directions of attraction" at the centre of a carbon atom assumed to have the form of a regular tetrahedron. Let s be the slant height,

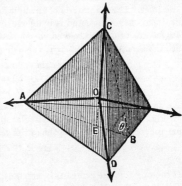

FIG. 180.

AB, or BC, of a regular tetrahedron (Fig. 180); $h = EC$, the vertical height; l, the length of any edge, DC or AC; ϕ, the angle DOC, or AOC, made by the lines joining any two apices with the centre of the tetrahedron.
∴ $s^2 + (\frac{1}{2}l)^2 = l^2$; $s^2 = \frac{3}{4}l^2$. But h divides s in the ratio 2:1, hence (§ 191),

$h^2 = l^2 - (\frac{2}{3}s)^2 = \frac{2}{3}l^2$.   But $CD = 2BD = l$; $BC = AB = s$; $CE = h$. Hence, $h = \sqrt{\frac{2}{3}l^2}$. From a result in V, above, the middle of the tetrahedron cuts CE at O in the ratio $3 : 1$.

$$\therefore \sin \tfrac{1}{2}\phi = \tfrac{1}{2}AC \div OC = \tfrac{1}{2}l/\tfrac{3}{4}h \text{; or, } \phi = 109° \ 28'. \quad . \quad . \quad (29)$$

II. To find the angle of deflection of the " direction of attraction" when 2 to 6 carbon atoms form a closed ring. From (29), for *acetelyne* $H_2C : CH_2$, the angle is deflected from $109° \ 28'$ to $\tfrac{1}{2}(109° \ 28')$, or $55° \ 44'$. For *trimethylene*, assuming the ring is an equilateral triangle, the angle is deflected $\tfrac{1}{2}(109° \ 28' - 60°) = 24° \ 44'$. For *tetramethylene*, assuming the ring is a square, the angle of deflection is $\tfrac{1}{2}(109° \ 28' - 90°) = 9° \ 34'$. For *pentamethylene*, assuming the ring to be a regular pentagon, the angle of deflection is $\tfrac{1}{2}(109° \ 28' - 108°)$, or $0° \ 44'$. For *hexamethylene*, assuming the ring is a regular hexagon, the angle of deflection is $\tfrac{1}{2}(109° \ 28' - 120°)$. or $-5° \ 76'$.

The value of the angle θ, in Fig. 180, is $70° \ 32'$. See H. Sachse "On the Configuration of the Polymethylene Ring," *Zeit. phys. Chem.*, **10**, 203, 1892.

§ 192. Plane Trigonometry.

Beginners in the calculus often trip over the trigonometrical work. The following outline will perhaps be of some assistance. Trigonometry deals with the relations between the sides and angles of triangles. If the triangle is drawn on a plane surface, we have plane trigonometry; if the triangle is drawn on the surface of a sphere, spherical trigonometry. The trigonometry employed in physics and chemistry is a mode of reasoning about lines and angles, or rather, about quantities represented by lines and angles (whether parts of a triangle or not), which is carried on by means of certain ratios or functions of an angle.

1. The measurement of angles. An angle is formed by the intersection of two lines. The magnitude of an angle depends only on the relative directions, or slopes of the lines, and is independent of their lengths. In practical work, angles are usually measured in degrees, minutes and seconds. These units are the subdivisions of a right-angle defined as

1 right angle = 90 degrees, written 90°;
1 degree   = 60 minutes, written 60';
1 minute   = 60 seconds, written 60".

In theoretical calculations, however, this system is replaced by another. In Fig. 181, the length of the circular arcs $P'A'$, PA, drawn from the centre O, are proportional to the lengths of the radii OA' and OA, or

$$\frac{\text{arc } P'A'}{\text{radius } OA'} = \frac{\text{arc } PA}{\text{radius } OA}.$$

If the angle at the centre O is constant, the ratio, arc/radius, is also constant. This ratio, therefore, furnishes a method for measuring the magnitude of an angle. The ratio

$$\frac{\text{arc}}{\text{radius}} = 1, \text{ is called a radian.}$$

Two right angles = $180° = \pi$ radians, where $\pi = 180° = 3\cdot14159$.   (1)

The ratio, arc/radius, is called the **circular or radian measure of an angle.** (Radian = unit angle.)

2. Relation between degrees and radians. The circumference of a circle of radius r, is $2\pi r$, or, if the radius is unity, 2π. The angles $360°$, $180°$, $90°$, ... correspond to the arcs whose lengths are respectively, 2π, π, $\frac{1}{2}\pi$, ... If the angle AOP (Fig. 181) measures D degrees, or α radians,

$$D° : 360° = \alpha : 2\pi. \quad \therefore D° = \frac{\alpha}{2\pi}360; \text{ or, } \alpha = \frac{D}{360}2\pi. \quad . \quad . \quad (2)$$

EXAMPLES.—(1) How many degrees are contained in an arc of unit length? Here $\alpha = 1$,

$$\therefore D = \frac{360}{2\pi} = 57\cdot295° = 57° \ 17' \ 44\cdot8''. \quad . \quad . \quad . \quad (3)$$

(2) How many radians are there in $1°$? Ansr. $\pi/180$; or, $0\cdot0175$.

(3) How many radians in $2\frac{1}{2}°$? Ansr. $0\cdot044$.

A table of the numerical relations between angles expressed in degrees and radians is given on pages 624 and 625.

3. Trigonometrical ratios of an angle as functions of the sides of a triangle. There are certain functions of the angles, or rather of the arc PA (Fig. 181)

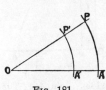

FIG. 181.   FIG. 182.

called trigonometrical ratios. From P drop the perpendicular PM on to OM (Fig. 182). In the triangle OPM,

(i.) The ratio $\dfrac{MP}{OM}$, or, $\dfrac{\text{perpendicular}}{\text{base}}$, is called **the tangent** of the angle POM, and written, **tan POM.**

It is necessary to show that *the magnitude of this ratio depends only on the magnitude of the angle POM*, and is quite independent of the size of the triangle. Drop perpendiculars PM and $P'M'$ from P and P' on to OA (Fig. 181). The two triangles POM and $P'OM'$, are equiangular and similar, therefore, as on page 603, $M'P'/OM' = MP/OM$.

(ii.) The ratio $\dfrac{OM}{MP}$, or, $\dfrac{\text{base}}{\text{perpendicular}}$, is called the **cotangent** of the angle POM, and written, **cot POM.** Note that the cotangent of an angle is the reciprocal of its tangent.

(iii.) The ratio $\dfrac{MP}{OP} = \dfrac{\text{perpendicular}}{\text{hypotenuse}}$, is called the **sine** of the angle POM, and written, **sin POM.**

(iv.) The ratio $\dfrac{OP}{MP} = \dfrac{\text{hypotenuse}}{\text{perpendicular}}$, is called the **cosecant** of the angle POM, and written, **cosec POM.** The cosecant of an angle is the reciprocal of its sine.

(v.) The ratio $\dfrac{OM}{OP} = \dfrac{\text{base}}{\text{hypotenuse}}$, is called the cosine of the angle POM, and written, **cos POM**.

(vi.) The ratio $\dfrac{OP}{OM} = \dfrac{\text{hypotenuse}}{\text{base}}$, is called the **secant** of the angle POM, and written, **sec POM**. The secant of an angle is the reciprocal of its cosine.

EXAMPLE.—If x be used in place of POM, show that

$$\sin x = \frac{1}{\operatorname{cosec} x}; \quad \cot x = \frac{1}{\tan x}; \quad \cos x = \frac{1}{\sec x}.$$

The squares of any of these ratios, $(\sin x)^2$, $(\cot x)^2, \ldots$, are generally written $\sin^2 x$, $\cot^2 x \ldots$; $(\sin x)^{-1}$, $(\cot x)^{-1}, \ldots$, meaning $\dfrac{1}{\sin x}$, $\dfrac{1}{\cot x}, \ldots$, cannot be written in the forms $\sin^{-1} x$, $\cot^{-1} x, \ldots$ because this latter symbol has a different meaning.

4. To find a numerical value for the trigonometrical ratios.

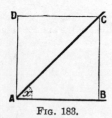

FIG. 183.   FIG. 184.

(i.) **45° or $\tfrac{1}{4}\pi$.** Draw a square $ABCD$ (Fig. 183). Join AC. The angle $BAC =$ half a right angle $= 45°$. In the right-angled triangle BAC (Euclid, i., 47),

$$AC^2 = AB^2 + BC^2.$$

Since AB and BC are the sides of a square, $\therefore AB = BC$, hence,

$$AC^2 = 2AB^2 = 2BC^2; \text{ or, } AC = \sqrt{2}.\, AB = \sqrt{2}.\, BC.$$

$$\therefore \sin 45° = \frac{BC}{AC} = \frac{1}{\sqrt{2}}; \quad \cos 45° = \frac{AB}{AC} = \frac{1}{\sqrt{2}}; \quad \tan 45° = \frac{BC}{AB} = 1. \qquad (4)$$

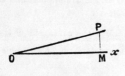

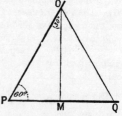

FIG. 185.   FIG. 186.

(ii.) **90° or $\tfrac{1}{2}\pi$.** In Fig. 184, if POM is a right-angled triangle, as M approaches O, the angle MOP approaches 90°. When MP coincides with OB, $OP = MP$, and $OM =$ zero.

$$\therefore \sin 90° = \frac{MP}{OP} = 1 \ ; \quad \cos 90° = \frac{OM}{OP} = 0 \ ; \quad \tan 90° = \frac{MP}{OM} = \infty \ . \qquad (5)$$

(iii.) 0°. In Fig. 185 as the angle MOP becomes smaller, OP approaches OM, and at the limit coincides with it. Hence, $PM = 0$; $OM = OP$.

$$\therefore \sin 0° = \frac{MP}{OP} = 0 \ ; \quad \cos 0° = \frac{CM}{OP} = 1 \ ; \quad \tan 0° = \frac{MP}{OM} = 0. \qquad (6)$$

(iv.) 60° or $\frac{1}{2}\pi$. In the equilateral triangle (Fig. 186), each of the three angles is equal to 60°. Drop the perpendicular OM on to PQ. Then

$$2PM = PQ = PO.$$

By Euclid, i., 47,

$$PO^2 = MP^2 + MO^2. \quad \therefore \ 4PM^2 = MO^2 + PM^2 \ ; \ \text{or} \ MO^2 = 3PM^2.$$

$$\therefore \ MO = \sqrt{3} \ . \ PM \ ; \ \text{angle} \ MPO = 60°.$$

$$\therefore \sin 60° = \frac{MO}{PO} = \frac{\sqrt{3}}{2} \ ; \quad \cos 60° = \frac{PM}{PO} = \frac{1}{2} \ ; \quad \tan 60° = \frac{MO}{PM} = \sqrt{3}. \qquad (7)$$

(v.) 30° or $\frac{1}{3}\pi$. Using the preceding results,

$$\therefore \sin 30° = \frac{MP}{OP} = \frac{1}{2} \ ; \quad \cos 30° = \frac{MO}{OP} = \frac{\sqrt{3}}{2} \ ; \quad \tan 30° = \frac{MP}{OM} = \frac{1}{\sqrt{3}}. \qquad (8)$$

The following table summarizes these results :

TABLE XIV.—NUMERICAL VALUES OF THE TRIGONOMETRICAL RATIOS.

Angle.	0° to 360°.	30°.	45°.	60°.	90°.	180°.	270°.
sine	0	$\frac{1}{2}$	$\frac{1}{\sqrt{2}}$	$\frac{\sqrt{3}}{2}$	1	0	-1
cosine	1	$\frac{\sqrt{3}}{2}$	$\frac{1}{\sqrt{2}}$	$\frac{1}{2}$	0	-1	0
tangent	0	$\frac{1}{\sqrt{3}}$	1	$\sqrt{3}$	∞	0	∞

To these might be added $\sin 15° = (\sqrt{3} - 1)/2\sqrt{2}$; $\sin 18° = \frac{1}{4}(\sqrt{5} - 1)$. See also page 608.

It must be clearly understood that although an angle is always measured in the degree-minute-second system, the numerical equivalent in radian or circular measure is employed in the calculations, unless special provision has been made for the direct introduction of degrees. This was done in example (6), page 544 (q.v.). Suppose that we have occasion to employ the approximation formula

$$\sin (x + \theta) = \sin x + \theta \cos x,$$

of § 189, and that $x = 35°$ and $\theta = 50''$. The Tables of Natural Sines, Cosines, Tangents, and their reciprocals, will furnish the numerical values of $\sin 35°$ and $\cos 35°$, but θ must be converted into radian measure. Hence show that

$$\sin (x + \theta) = \sin 35° + \frac{0 \cdot 00926 \times \pi}{180} \cos 35°.$$

Hint. $50'' = (\frac{5 0}{6 0})' = (\frac{5 0}{6 0} \times \frac{1}{6 0})° = 0 \cdot 00926°.$ The numerical values of $\sin 35°$ and

QQ

of cos 35° to four decimal places are respectively 0·5736 and 0·8192. The value of sin $(x+\theta)$ is, therefore, ·5737.

5. Conventions as to the sign of the trigonometrical ratios. This subject has been treated on page 123. In the following table, these results are summarized. The change in the value of the ratio as it passes through the four quadrants is also given.

TABLE XV.—SIGNS OF THE TRIGONOMETRICAL RATIOS.

If the Angle is in Quadrant.		sin x.	cos x.	tan x.	cot x.	sec x.	cosec x.
I.	sign	+	+	+	+	+	+
	value	0 to 1	1 to 0	0 to ∞	∞ to 0	1 to ∞	∞ to 1
II.	sign	+	—	—	—	—	+
	value	1 to 0	0 to 1	∞ to 0	0 to ∞	∞ to 1	1 to ∞
III.	sign	—	—	+	+	—	—
	value	0 to 1	1 to 0	0 to ∞	∞ to 0	1 to ∞	∞ to 1
IV.	sign	—	+	—	—	+	—
	value	1 to 0	0 to 1	∞ to 0	0 to ∞	∞ to 1	1 to ∞

6. Trigonometrical ratios of the supplement of an angle. The angle is $180° - x$, or $\pi - x$, is called the **supplement** of the angle x. In Fig. 187, let $MOP = x$, produce OM to M'. Then the angle MOP' is the supplement of x. Make the angle $P'OM' = MOP$. Let $OP' = OP$. Drop perpendiculars $P'M'$ and PM on to BA. The triangles OPM and $OP'M'$ are equal in all respects. If OM is positive, OM' is negative

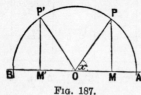

FIG. 187.

∴ $M'P' = MP$; and $OM' = -OM$.

sin $(180 - x) = \sin(\pi - x) = \sin POM' = \sin M'OP = \sin x.$

cos $(180° - x) = -\cos x$; tan $(180° - x) = -\tan x.$

EXAMPLES.—(1) Find the value of sin 120°.

sin 120° = sin (180° − 60°) = sin 60 = $\sqrt{3}/2$.

(2) Evaluate tan 120°. Ansr. − $\sqrt{3}$.

7. Trigonometrical ratios of the complement of an angle. The angle $90° - x$, or $\frac{1}{2}\pi - x$, is called the **complement** of x. In Fig. 188, PN and PM are perpendiculars on OB and on OA respectively. Then $OM = NP$, $ON = MP$.

sin $(90° - x) = \sin (\frac{1}{2}\pi - x) = \sin NOP = \dfrac{NP}{OP} = \dfrac{OM}{OP} = \cos x.$

cos $(90° - x) = \sin x$; tan $(90° - x) = \cot x$; cot $(90° - x) = \tan x.$

8. To prove that sin x/cos x = tan x.

$$\frac{\sin x}{\cos x} = \frac{MP}{OP} \bigg/ \frac{OM}{OP} = \frac{MP}{OP} \times \frac{OP}{OM} = \frac{MP}{OM} = \tan x.$$

9. To prove that $\sin^2 x + \cos^2 x = 1$. In Fig. 189, by Euclid, i., **47,** $OP^2 = MP^2 + OM^2$. Divide through by OP^2, and

$$1 = \frac{OP^2}{OP^2} = \frac{MP^2}{OP^2} + \frac{OM^2}{OP^2} = \left(\frac{MP}{OP}\right)^2 + \left(\frac{OM}{OP}\right)^2. \quad \therefore \sin^2 x + \cos^2 x = 1.$$

10. To show that sin $(x + y) = $ sin x . cos y + cos x . sin y. In Fig. 189, PQ is perpendicular to OQ, the angle HPQ = angle NOQ (Euclid, i., 15 and 32)

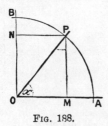

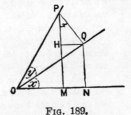

FIG. 188.   FIG. 189.

$$\therefore \sin (x+y) = \frac{MP}{OP} = \frac{PH}{OP} + \frac{QN}{OP} = \frac{PH}{PQ} \cdot \frac{PQ}{OP} + \frac{NQ}{OQ} \cdot \frac{OQ}{OP};$$
$$= \sin x . \cos y + \cos x . \sin y.$$

11. Summary of trigonometrical formulæ (*for reference*). The above definitions lead to the following relations, which form routine exercises in elementary trigonometry. Most of them may be established geometrically as in the preceding illustrations :

Note : π = 180° ; or, 3·14159 radians ; one radian = 57·2958°.

$$\left.\begin{array}{l} \sin (\tfrac{1}{2}\pi + x) = \cos x ; \; \cos (\tfrac{1}{2}\pi - x) = \sin x ; \\ \operatorname{cosec} (\tfrac{1}{2}\pi - x) = \sec x ; \; \sec (\tfrac{1}{2}\pi - x) = \operatorname{cosec} x ; \\ \tan (\tfrac{1}{2}\pi - x) = \cot x ; \; \cot (\tfrac{1}{2}\pi - x) = \tan x. \end{array}\right\} \quad \cdot \quad \cdot \quad \cdot \quad (9)$$

$$\left.\begin{array}{l} \sin(\pi - x) = \sin x ; \; \cos (\pi - x) = -\cos x ; \\ \tan (\pi - x) = -\tan x ; \; \cot (\pi - x) = -\cot x. \end{array}\right\} \quad \cdot \quad \cdot \quad \cdot \quad (10)$$

$$\left.\begin{array}{l} \sin (\tfrac{1}{2}\pi + x) = \cos x ; \; \cos (\tfrac{1}{2}\pi + x) = -\sin x ; \\ \tan (\tfrac{1}{2}\pi + x) = -\cot x, \; \cot (\tfrac{1}{2}\pi + x) = -\tan x. \end{array}\right\} \quad \cdot \quad \cdot \quad \cdot \quad (11)$$

$$\left.\begin{array}{l} \sin (\pi + x) = -\sin x ; \; \cos (\pi + x) = -\cos x ; \\ \tan (\pi + x) = \tan x ; \; \cot (\pi + x) = \cot x. \end{array}\right\} \quad \cdot \quad \cdot \quad \cdot \quad (12)$$

$$\sin (-x) = -\sin x ; \; \cos (-x) = \cos x ; \; \tan (-x) = -\tan x. \quad , \quad \cdot \quad (13)$$

$$Lt_{x=0} \frac{\sin x}{x} = \frac{\tan x}{x} = \cos x = 1 ; \quad \frac{\sin^{-1} x}{x} = \frac{\tan^{-1} x}{x} = 1. \quad \cdot \quad \cdot \quad (14)$$

When n is any negative or positive integer or zero.

$$\sin x = \sin \{n\pi + (-1)^n x\}. \quad \cdot \quad \cdot \quad \cdot \quad \cdot \quad \cdot \quad (15)$$

$$\cos x = \cos (2n\pi \pm x). \quad \cdot \quad \cdot \quad \cdot \quad \cdot \quad \cdot \quad (16)$$

$$\tan x = \tan (n\pi + x). \quad \cdot \quad \cdot \quad \cdot \quad \cdot \quad \cdot \quad (17)$$

$$\tan x = \sin x/\cos x ; \; \cot x = \cos x/\sin x. \quad \cdot \quad \cdot \quad \cdot \quad (18)$$

$$\sin^2 x + \cos^2 x = 1. \quad \cdot \quad \cdot \quad \cdot \quad \cdot \quad (19)$$

$$\sin x = \sqrt{1 - \cos^2 x}; \quad \cos x = \sqrt{1 - \sin^2 x}. \qquad (20)$$

$$\operatorname{cosec} x = \sqrt{1 + \cot^2 x}; \quad \sec x = \sqrt{1 + \tan^2 x}. \qquad (21)$$

$$\sin x = \frac{\tan x}{\sqrt{1 + \tan^2 x}}; \quad \cos x = \frac{1}{\sqrt{1 + \tan^2 x}}. \qquad (22)$$

$$\sin (x \pm y) = \sin x . \cos y \pm \cos x . \sin y. \qquad (23)$$

$$\cos (x \pm y) = \cos x . \cos y \mp \sin x . \sin y. \qquad (24)$$

$$\sin (x + y) + \sin (x - y) = 2 \sin x . \cos y. \qquad (25)$$

$$\sin (x + y) - \sin (x - y) = 2 \cos x . \sin y. \qquad (26)$$

$$\cos (x + y) + \cos (x - y) = 2 \cos x . \cos y. \qquad (27)$$

$$\cos (x + y) - \cos (x - y) = - 2 \sin x . \sin y. \qquad (28)$$

If $x = y$, from (23) and (24),

$$\sin 2x = 2 \sin x . \cos x. \qquad (29)$$

$$\cos 2x = \cos^2 x - \sin^2 x. \qquad (30)$$

$$= 2 \cos^2 x - 1. \qquad (31)$$

$$= 1 - 2 \sin^2 x. \qquad (32)$$

$$\sin x = 2 \sin \tfrac{1}{2}x . \cos \tfrac{1}{2}x. \qquad (33)$$

$$\cos x = 2 \cos^2 \tfrac{1}{2}x - 1; \text{ or, } 1 + \cos x = 2 \cos^2 \tfrac{1}{2}x. \qquad (34)$$

$$= 1 - 2 \sin^2 \tfrac{1}{2}x; \text{ or, } 1 - \cos x = 2 \sin^2 \tfrac{1}{2}x. \qquad (35)$$

$$\sin 3x = 3 \sin x - 4 \sin^3 x. \qquad (36)$$

$$\cos 3x = 4 \cos^3 x - 3 \cos x. \qquad (37)$$

If in (25) to (28), we suppose $x + y = \alpha$; $x - y = \beta$; $x = \tfrac{1}{2}(\alpha + \beta)$; $y = \tfrac{1}{2}(\alpha - \beta)$. Now put x for α, and y for β, for the sake of uniformity. Thus,

$$\sin x + \sin y = 2 \sin \tfrac{1}{2}(x + y) . \cos \tfrac{1}{2}(x - y). \qquad (38)$$

$$\sin x - \sin y = 2 \cos \tfrac{1}{2}(x + y) . \sin \tfrac{1}{2}(x - y). \qquad (39)$$

$$\cos x + \cos y = 2 \cos \tfrac{1}{2}(x + y) . \cos \tfrac{1}{2}(x - y). \qquad (40)$$

$$\cos x - \cos y = - 2 \sin \tfrac{1}{2}(x + y) . \sin \tfrac{1}{2}(x - y). \qquad (41)$$

By division of the proper formulæ above,

$$\tan (x + y) = \frac{\tan x + \tan y}{1 - \tan x . \tan y}. \qquad (42)$$

$$\tan (x - y) = \frac{\tan x - \tan y}{1 + \tan x . \tan y}. \qquad (43)$$

$$\tan 2x = \frac{2 \tan x}{1 - \tan^2 x}. \qquad (44)$$

$$\tan x \pm \tan y = \frac{\sin (x \pm y)}{\cos x . \cos y}. \qquad (45)$$

$$\cot x \pm \cot y = \frac{\sin (x \pm y)}{\sin x . \sin y}. \qquad (46)$$

$$\cos \tfrac{1}{2}x = \sqrt{\frac{1 + \cos x}{2}}; \quad \sin \tfrac{1}{2}x = \sqrt{\frac{1 - \cos x}{2}}; \quad \tan \tfrac{1}{2}x = \sqrt{\frac{1 - \cos x}{1 + \cos x}}. \qquad (47)$$

§ 193. Relations among the Hyperbolic Functions.

$$\cos x = \cosh \iota x = \tfrac{1}{2}(\epsilon^{\iota x} + \epsilon^{- \iota x}). \qquad (1)$$

$$\sin x = \frac{1}{\iota}\sinh \iota x = \frac{1}{2\iota}(\epsilon^{\iota x} - \epsilon^{- \iota x}). \qquad (2)$$

$$\cos x + \iota \sin x = \cosh \iota x + \sinh \iota x = \epsilon^{\iota x}. \qquad (3)$$

$$\cos x - \iota \sin x = \cosh \iota x - \sinh \iota x = \epsilon^{- \iota x}. \qquad (4)$$

$$\cosh x = \cos \iota x; \quad \iota \sinh x = \sin \iota x. \qquad (5)$$

$$\left.\begin{array}{l} \tanh x = \sinh x/\cosh x\,;\ \coth x = \cosh x/\sinh x, \\ \operatorname{cosech} x = 1/\sinh x\,;\ \operatorname{sech} x = 1/\cosh x. \end{array}\right\} \quad \cdot \quad \cdot \quad \cdot \quad \textbf{(6)}$$

$$\cosh 0 = 1\,;\ \sinh 0 = 0\,;\ \tanh 0 = 0. \quad \cdot \quad \cdot \quad \cdot \quad \textbf{(7)}$$

$$\cosh (\pm \infty) = +\infty\,;\ \sinh (\pm \infty) = \pm\infty\,;\ \tanh (\pm \infty) = \pm 1. \quad \cdot \quad \cdot \quad \textbf{(8)}$$

$$Lt_{x=0}\frac{\sinh x}{x} = 1\,;\ Lt_{x=0}\frac{\tanh x}{x} = 1\,;\ Lt_{x=0}\frac{\cosh x}{x} = 1. \quad \cdot \quad \cdot \quad \textbf{(9)}$$

$$\sinh (-x) = -\sinh x\,;\ \cosh (-x) = \cosh x\,;\ \tanh (-x) = -\tanh x. \quad \cdot \quad \textbf{(10)}$$

$$\sinh (x \pm y) = \sinh x\,.\,\cosh y \pm \cosh x\,.\,\sinh y. \quad \cdot \quad \cdot \quad \cdot \quad \textbf{(11)}$$

$$\cosh (x \pm y) = \cosh x\,.\,\cosh y \pm \sinh x\,.\,\sinh y. \quad \cdot \quad \cdot \quad \cdot \quad \textbf{(12)}$$

$$\tanh (x \pm y) = \frac{\tanh x \pm \tanh y}{1 \pm \tanh x\,.\,\tanh y}. \quad \cdot \quad \cdot \quad \cdot \quad \cdot \quad \textbf{(13)}$$

$$\left.\begin{array}{l} \cosh (x+\iota y) = \cosh x\,.\,\cosh \iota y + \sinh x\,.\,\sinh \iota y\,; \\ \quad = \cosh x\,.\,\cos y + \iota \sinh x\,.\,\sin y. \end{array}\right\} \quad \cdot \quad \cdot \quad \textbf{(14)}$$

$$\left.\begin{array}{l} \sinh (x+\iota y) = \sinh x\,.\,\cosh \iota y + \cosh x\,.\,\sinh \iota y\,; \\ \quad = \sinh x\,.\,\cos y + \iota \cosh x\,.\,\sin y. \end{array}\right\} \quad \cdot \quad \cdot \quad \textbf{(15)}$$

$$\sinh x + \sinh y = 2 \sinh \tfrac{1}{2}(x+y)\,.\,\cosh \tfrac{1}{2}(x-y). \quad \cdot \quad \cdot \quad \cdot \quad \textbf{(16)}$$

$$\sinh x - \sinh y = 2 \cosh \tfrac{1}{2}(x+y)\,.\,\sinh \tfrac{1}{2}(x-y). \quad \cdot \quad \cdot \quad \cdot \quad \textbf{(17)}$$

$$\cosh x + \cosh y = 2 \cosh \tfrac{1}{2}(x+y)\,.\,\cosh \tfrac{1}{2}(x-y). \quad \cdot \quad \cdot \quad \cdot \quad \textbf{(18)}$$

$$\cosh x - \cosh y = 2 \sinh \tfrac{1}{2}(x+y)\,.\,\sinh \tfrac{1}{2}(x-y). \quad \cdot \quad \cdot \quad \cdot \quad \textbf{(19)}$$

$$\sinh 2x = 2 \sinh x\,.\,\cosh x = 2 \tanh x/(1 - \tanh^2 x). \quad \cdot \quad \cdot \quad \cdot \quad \textbf{(20)}$$

$$\cosh 2x = \cosh^2 x + \sinh^2 x\,; \quad \cdot \quad \cdot \quad \cdot \quad \cdot \quad \cdot \quad \textbf{(21)}$$

$$= 1 + 2 \sinh^2 x = 2 \cosh^2 x - 1\,; \quad \cdot \quad \cdot \quad \cdot \quad \cdot \quad \textbf{(22)}$$

$$= (1 + \tanh^2 x)/(1 - \tanh^2 x). \quad \cdot \quad \cdot \quad \cdot \quad \cdot \quad \textbf{(23)}$$

$$\cosh x + 1 = 2 \cosh^2 \tfrac{1}{2}x\,;\ \cosh x - 1 = 2 \sinh^2 \tfrac{1}{2}x. \quad \cdot \quad \cdot \quad \cdot \quad \textbf{(24)}$$

$$\left.\begin{array}{l} \tanh \tfrac{1}{2}x = \sinh x/(1 + \cosh x)\,; \\ \quad = (\cosh x - 1)/\sinh x. \end{array}\right\} \quad \cdot \quad \cdot \quad \cdot \quad \textbf{(25)}$$

$$\sinh^2 x - \cosh^2 x = 1. \quad \cdot \quad \cdot \quad \cdot \quad \cdot \quad \cdot \quad \textbf{(26)}$$

$$1 - \tanh^2 x = \operatorname{sech}^2 x\,;\ \coth^2 x - 1 = \operatorname{cosech}^2 x. \quad \cdot \quad \cdot \quad \textbf{(27)}$$

$$\cosh x = 1/\sqrt{(1 - \tanh^2 x)}\,;\ \sinh x = \tanh x/\sqrt{(1 - \tanh^2 x)}. \quad \cdot \quad \textbf{(28)}$$

$$\sinh 3x = 3 \sinh x + 4 \sinh^3 x. \quad \cdot \quad \cdot \quad \cdot \quad \cdot \quad \cdot \quad \textbf{(29)}$$

$$\cosh 3x = 4 \cosh^3 x - 3 \cosh x. \quad \cdot \quad \cdot \quad \cdot \quad \cdot \quad \cdot \quad \textbf{(30)}$$

Inverse hyperbolic functions.   If $\sinh^{-1}y = x$, then $y = \sinh x$. Since

$$y = \sinh x = \tfrac{1}{2}(e^x - e^{-x})\,;\ \therefore\ e^{2x} - 2ye^x - 1 = 0\,;\ \therefore\ e^x = y \pm \sqrt{y^2 + 1}.$$

For real values of x the negative sign is excluded from $\sinh^{-1}x$.

$$\therefore\ \sinh^{-1}x = \log\{y + \sqrt{y^2 + 1}\}\,;\ \cosh^{-1}y = \log\{y \pm \sqrt{y^2 - 1}\}. \quad \textbf{(31)}$$

$$\tanh^{-1}y = \tfrac{1}{2}\log\{(1 + y)/(1 - y)\}\,;\ \coth^{-1}y = \tfrac{1}{2}\log\{(y + 1)/(y - 1)\}. \quad \textbf{(32)}$$

$$\operatorname{sech}^{-1}y = \log\{(1 + \sqrt{1 - y^2})/y\}\,;\ \operatorname{cosech}^{-1}y = \log\{(1 - \sqrt{1 + y^2})/y\}. \quad \textbf{(33)}$$

Gudermannians.   In Fig. 138, page 347,

$$\theta = \cos^{-1}\operatorname{sech} x\,;\ \cos\theta = \operatorname{sech} x\,;\ \sec\theta = \cosh x. \quad \cdot \quad \cdot \quad \textbf{(34)}$$

$$e^\theta = \cos\theta + \sinh x = \sec\theta + \tan\theta. \quad \cdot \quad \cdot \quad \cdot \quad \textbf{(35)}$$

$$\theta = \log (\sec\theta \tan\theta) = \log\tan (\tfrac{1}{4}\pi + \tfrac{1}{2}\theta). \quad \cdot \quad \cdot \quad \textbf{(36)}$$

$$\tanh \tfrac{1}{2}x = \tan \tfrac{1}{2}\theta. \quad \cdot \quad \cdot \quad \cdot \quad \cdot \quad \textbf{(37)}$$

when θ is connected with x by any of these relations θ is said to be the gudermannian of x and is written gd x.

Analogous to Demoivre's theorem

$$(\cosh x \pm \sinh x)^n = \cosh nx \pm \sinh nx. \quad \cdot \quad \cdot \quad \textbf{(38)}$$

It is instructive to compare the above formulæ with the corresponding trigonometrical functions in § 192. The analogy is also brought out by tabulating corresponding indefinite integrals in Tables I. and III., side by side. A few additional integrals are here given to be verified and then added to the table of indefinite integrals which the student has been advised to compile for his own use.

TABLE XVI.—HYPERBOLIC AND TRIGONOMETRICAL FUNCTIONS.

Hyperbolic.	Trigonometrical.	
$\int \frac{dx}{\sqrt{x^2 + a^2}} = \sinh^{-1}\frac{x}{a}.$	$\int \frac{dx}{\sqrt{a^2 - x^2}} = \sin^{-1}\frac{x}{a}.$	(39)
$\int \frac{dx}{\sqrt{x^2 - a^2}} = \cosh^{-1}\frac{x}{a}.$	$\int \frac{-dx}{\sqrt{a^2 - x^2}} = \cos^{-1}\frac{x}{a}.$	(40)
$\int \frac{dx}{a^2 - x^2} = \frac{1}{a}\tanh^{-1}\frac{x}{a},$ when $x < a$. When $x > a,$	$\int \frac{dx}{a^2 + x^2} = \frac{1}{a}\tan^{-1}\frac{x}{a}.$	(41)
$\int \frac{-dx}{x^2 - a^2} = \frac{1}{a}\coth^{-1}\frac{x}{a}.$	$\int \frac{-dx}{a^2 + x^2} = \frac{1}{a}\cot^{-1}\frac{x}{a}.$	(42)
$\int \frac{-dx}{x\sqrt{a^2 - x^2}} = \frac{1}{a}\text{sech}^{-1}\frac{x}{a}.$	$\int \frac{dx}{x\sqrt{x^2 - a^2}} = \frac{1}{a}\sec^{-1}\frac{x}{a}.$	(43)
$\int \frac{-dx}{x\sqrt{a^2 + x^2}} = \frac{1}{a}\text{cosech}^{-1}\frac{x}{a}.$	$\int \frac{-dx}{x\sqrt{x^2 - a^2}} = \frac{1}{a}\text{cosec}^{-1}\frac{x}{a}.$	(44)
$\int \text{sech}\,x\,.\,dx = \text{gd}\,x.$	$\int \sec x\,.\,dx = \text{gd}^{-1}x.$	(45)

Numerical values of the hyperbolic functions may be computed by means of the series formulæ.

APPENDIX II.

REFERENCE TABLES.

"The human mind is seldom satisfied, and is certainly never exercising its highest functions, when it is doing the work of a calculating machine."—J. C. MAXWELL.

THE results of old arithmetical operations most frequently required are registered in the form of mathematical tables. The use of such tables not only prevents the wasting of time and energy on a repetition of old operations but also conduces to more accurate work, since there is less liability to error once accurate tables have been compiled. Most of the following tables have been referred to in different parts of this work, and are reproduced here because they are not usually found in the smaller current sets of "Mathematical Tables". Besides those here you ought to have "Tables of Reciprocals, Squares, Cubes and Roots," "Tables of Logarithms of Numbers to base 10," "Tables of Trigonometrical Sines, Cosines and Tangents" for natural angles and logarithms of the same. See page xix. of the Introduction.

Table I.—Singular Values of Functions.
(Page 168.)

Table II.—Standard Integrals.
(Page 193.)

Table III.—Standard Integrals (*Hyperbolic functions.*)
(Pages 349 and 614.)

Table IV.—Numerical Values of the Hyperbolic Sines, Cosines, e^x, and e^{-x}.

x.	e^x.	e^{-x}.	cosh x.	sinh x.	x.	e^x.	e^{-x}.	cosh x.	sinh x.
0·00	1·00000	1·00000	1·00000	·00000	0·40	1·49182	0·67032	1·08107	0·41075
·01	1·01005	·99005	1·00005	·01000	·41	1·50682	·66365	1·08523	·42158
·02	1·02021	·98020	1·00020	·02000	·42	1·52196	·65705	1·08950	·43246
·03	1·03045	·97045	1·00045	·03000	·43	1·53726	·65051	1·09388	·44337
·04	1·04081	·96080	1·00080	·04001	·44	1·55271	·64404	1·09837	·45434
·05	1·05127	·95123	1·00125	·05002	·45	1·56831	.63763	1·10297	·46534
·06	1·06184	·94177	1·00180	·06004	·46	1·58407	·63128	1·10768	·47640
·07	1·07251	·93239	1·00245	·07006	·47	1·59999	·62500	1·11250	·48750
·08	1·08329	·92312	1·00320	·08009	·48	1·61607	·61878	1·11743	·49865
·09	1·09417	·91393	1·00405	·09012	·49	1·63232	·61263	1·12247	·50985
·10	1·10517	·90484	1·00500	·10017	·50	1·64872	·60653	1·12763	·52110
·11	1·11628	·89583	1·00606	·11022	·51	1·66529	·60050	1·13289	·53240
·12	1·12750	·88692	1·00721	·12029	·52	1·68203	·59452	1·13827	·54375
·13	1·13883	·87810	1·00846	·13037	·53	1·69893	·58860	1·14377	·55516
·14	1·15027	·86936	1·00982	·14046	·54	1·71601	·58275	1·14938	·56663
·15	1·16183	·86071	1·01127	·15056	·55	1·73325	·57695	1·15510	·57815
·16	1·17351	·85214	1·01283	·16068	·56	1·75067	·57121	1·16094	·58973
·17	1·18530	·84366	1·01448	·17082	·57	1·76827	·56553	1·16690	·60137
·18	1·19722	·83527	1·01624	·18097	·58	1·78604	·55990	1·17297	·61307
·19	1·20925	·82696	1·01810	·19115	·59	1·80399	·55433	1·17916	·62483
·20	1·22140	·81873	1·02007	·20134	·60	1·82212	.54881	1·18547	·63665
·21	1·23368	·81058	1·02213	·21155	·61	1·84043	·54335	1·19189	·64854
·22	1·24608	·80252	1·02430	·22178	·62	1·85893	·53794	1·19844	·66049
·23	1·25860	·79453	1·02657	·23203	·63	1·87761	·53259	1·20510	·67251
·24	1·27125	·78663	1·02894	·24231	·64	1·89648	·52729	1·21189	·68459
·25	1·28403	·77880	1·03141	·25261	·65	1·91554	·52205	1·21879	·69675
·26	1·29693	·77105	1·03399	·26294	·66	1·93479	·51685	1·22582	·70897
·27	1·30996	·76338	1·03667	·27329	·67	1·95424	·51171	1·23297	·72126
·28	1·32313	·75578	1·03946	·28367	·68	1·97388	·50662	1·24025	·73363
·29	1·33643	·74826	1·04235	·29408	·69	1·99372	·50158	1·24765	·74607
·30	1·34986	·74082	1·04534	·30452	·70	2·01375	·49659	1·25517	·75858
·31	1·36343	·73345	1·04844	·31499	·71	2·03399	·49164	1·26282	·77117
·32	1·37713	·72615	1·05164	·32549	·72	2·05443	·48675	1·27059	·78384
·33	1·39097	·71892	1·05495	·33602	·73	2·07508	·48191	1·27850	·79659
·34	1·40495	·71177	1·05836	·34659	·74	2·09594	·47711	1·28652	·80941
·35	1·41907	·70469	1·06188	·35719	·75	2·11700	·47237	1·29468	·82232
·36	1·43333	·69768	1·06550	·36783	·76	2·13828	·46767	1·30297	·83530
·37	1·44773	·69073	1·06923	·37850	·77	2·15977	·46301	1·31139	·84838
·38	1·46228	·68386	1·07307	·38921	·78	2·18147	·45841	1·31994	·86153
·39	1·47698	·67706	1·07702	·39996	·79	2·20340	·45384	1·32862	·87478

Table IV.—*Continued.*

x.	eˣ.	e⁻ˣ.	cosh x.	sinh x.	x.	eˣ.	e⁻ˣ.	cosh x.	sinh x.
·80	2·22554	·44933	1·33743	·88811	1·20	3·32012	·30119	1·81066	1.50946
·81	2·24791	·44486	1·34638	·90152	1·21	3·35348	·29820	1·82584	1·52764
·82	2·27050	·44043	1·35547	·91503	1·22	3·38719	·29523	1·84121	1·54598
·83	2·29332	·43605	1·36468	·92863	1·23	3·42123	·29229	1·85676	1·56447
·84	2·31637	·43171	1·37404	·94233	1·24	3·45561	·28938	1·87250	1·58311
·85	2·33965	·42741	1·38353	·95612	1·25	3·49034	·28650	1·88842	1·60192
·86	2·36316	·42316	1·39316	·97000	1·26	3·52542	·28365	1·90454	1·62088
·87	2·38691	·41895	1·40293	·98398	1·27	3·56085	·28083	1·92084	1·64001
·88	2·41090	·41478	1·41284	·99806	1·28	3·59664	·27804	1·93734	1·65930
·89	2·43513	·41066	1·42289	1·01224	1·29	3·63279	·27527	1·95403	1·67876
·90	2·45960	·40657	1·43309	1·02652	1·30	3·66930	·27253	1·97091	1·69838
·91	2·48432	·40252	1·44342	1·04090	1·31	3·70617	·26982	1·98800	1·71818
·92	2·50929	·39852	1·45390	1·05539	1·32	3·74342	·26714	2·00528	1·73814
·93	2·53451	·39455	1·46453	1·06998	1·33	3·78104	·26448	2·02276	1·75828
·94	2·55998	·39063	1·47530	1·08468	1·34	3·81904	·26185	2·04044	1·77860
·95	2·58571	·38674	1·48623	1·09948	1·35	3·85743	·25924	2·05893	1·79909
·96	2·61170	·38289	1·49729	1·11440	1·36	3·89619	·25666	2·07643	1·81977
·97	2·63794	·37908	1·50851	1·12943	1·37	3·93535	·25411	2·09473	1·84062
·98	2·66446	·37531	1·51988	1·14457	1·38	3·97490	·25158	2·11324	1·86166
·99	2·69123	·37158	1·53141	1·15983	1·39	4·01485	·24908	2·13196	1·88289
1·00	2·71828	·36788	1·54308	1·17520	1·40	4·05520	·24660	2·15090	1·90430
1·01	2·74560	·36422	1·55491	1·19069	1·41	4·09596	·24414	2·17005	1·92591
1·02	2·77319	·36059	1·56689	1·20630	1·42	4·13712	·24171	2·18942	1·94770
1·03	2·80107	·35701	1·57904	1·22203	1·43	4·17870	·23931	2·20900	1·96970
1·04	2·82922	·35345	1·59134	1·23788	1·44	4·22070	·23693	2·22881	1·99188
1·05	2·85765	·34994	1·60379	1·25386	1·45	4·26311	·23457	2·24884	2·01428
1·06	2·88637	·34646	1·61641	1·26996	1·46	4·30596	·23224	2·26910	2·03686
1·07	2·91538	·34301	1·62919	1·28619	1·47	4·34924	·22993	2·28958	2·05965
1·08	2·94468	·33960	1·64214	1·30254	1·48	4·39295	·22764	2·31029	2·08265
1·09	2·97427	·33622	1·65525	1·31903	1·49	4·43710	·22537	2·33123	2·10586
1·10	3·00417	·33287	1·66852	1·33565	1·50	4·48169	·22313	2·35241	2·12928
1·11	3·03436	·32956	1·68196	1·35240	1·51	4·52673	·22091	2·37382	2·15291
1·12	3·06485	·32628	1·69557	1·36929	1·52	4·57223	·21871	2·39547	2·17676
1·13	3·09566	·32303	1·70934	1·38631	1·53	4·61818	·21654	2·41736	2·20082
1·14	3·12677	·31981	1·72329	1·40347	1·54	4·66459	·21438	2·43949	2·22510
1·15	3·15819	·31664	1·73741	1·42078	1·55	4·71147	·21225	2·46186	2·24961
1·16	3·18993	·31349	1·75171	1·43822	1·56	4·75882	·21014	2·48448	2·27434
1·17	3·22199	·31037	1·76618	1·45581	1·57	4·80665	·20805	2·50735	2·29930
1·18	3·25437	·30728	1·78083	1·47355	1·58	4·85496	·20598	2·53047	2·32449
1·19	3·28708	·30422	1·79565	1·49143	1·59	4·90375	·20393	2·55384	2·34991

Table IV.—*Continued*.

$x.$	$e^x.$	$e^{-x}.$	cosh $x.$	sinh $x.$	$x.$	$e^x.$	e^{-x}	cosh $x.$	sinh $x.$
1·60	4·95303	·20190	2·57746	2·37557	2·0	7·38906	·13534	3·76220	3·62686
1·61	5·00281	·19989	2·60135	2·40146	2·1	8·16617	·12246	4·14431	4·02186
1·62	5·05309	·19790	2·62549	2·42760	2·2	9·02501	·11080	4·56791	4·45711
1·63	5·10387	19593	3·64990	2·45397	2·3	9·97418	·10026	5·03722	4·93696
1·64	5·15517	·19398	2·67457	2·48059	2·4	11·0232	·09072	5·55695	5·46623
1·65	5·20698	·19205	2·69951	2·50746	2·5	12·1825	·08208	6·13229	6·05020
1·66	5·25931	·19014	2·72472	2·53459	2·6	13·4637	·07427	6·76900	6·69473
1·67	5·31217	·18825	2·75021	2·56196	2·7	14·8797	·06721	7·47347	7·40626
1·68	5·36556	·18637	2·77596	2·58959	2·8	16·4446	·06081	8·25273	8·19192
1·69	5·41948	·18452	2·80200	2·61748	2·9	18·1741	·05502	9·11458	9·05956
1·70	5·47395	·18268	2·82832	2·64563	3·0	20·0855	·04979	10·0677	10·0179
1·71	5·52896	·18087	2·85491	2·67405	3·1	22·1980	·04505	11·1215	11·0765
1·72	5·58453	·17907	2·88180	2·70273	3·2	24·5325	·04076	12·2866	12·2459
1·73	5·64065	·17728	2·90897	2·73168	3·3	27·1126	·03688	13·5747	13·5379
1·74	5·69743	·17552	2·93643	2·76091	3·4	29·9641	·03337	14·9987	14·9654
1·75	5·75460	·17377	2·96419	2·79041	3·5	33·1155	·03020	16·5728	16·5426
1·76	5·81244	·17204	2·99224	2·82020	3·6	36·5982	·02732	18·3128	18·2855
1·77	5·87085	·17033	3·02059	2·85026	3·7	40·4473	·02472	20·2360	20·2113
1·78	5·92986	·16864	3·04925	2·88061	3·8	44·7012	·02237	22·3618	22·3394
1·79	5·98945	·16696	3·07821	2·91125	3·9	49·4024	·02024	24·7113	24·6911
1·80	6·04965	·16530	3·10747	2·94217	4·0	54·5982	·01832	27·3082	27·2899
1·81	6·11045	·16365	3·13705	2·97340	4·1	60·3408	·01657	30·1784	30·1619
1·82	6·17186	·16203	3·16694	3·00492	4·2	66·6863	·01500	33·3507	33·3357
1·83	6·23389	·16041	3·19715	3·03674	4·3	73·6998	·01357	36·8567	36·8431
1·84	6·29654	·15882	3·22768	3·06886	4·4	81·4509	·01228	40·7316	40·7193
1·85	6·35982	·15724	3·25853	3·10129	4·5	90·0171	·01111	45·0141	45·0030
1·86	6·42374	·15567	3·28970	3·13403	4·6	99·4843	·01005	49·7472	49·7371
1·87	6·48830	·15412	3·32121	3·16709	4·7	109·947	·00910	54·9781	54·9690
1·88	6·55350	·15259	3·35305	3·20046	4·8	121·510	·00823	60·7593	60·7511
1·89	6·61937	·15107	3·38522	3·23415	4·9	134·290	·00745	67·1486	67·1412
1·90	6·68589	·14957	3·41773	3·26816	5·0	148·413	·00674	74·2099	74·2032
1·91	6·75309	·14808	3·45058	3·30250	5·1	164·022	·00610	82·0140	82·0079
1·92	6·82096	·14661	3·48378	3·33718	5·2	181·272	·00552	90·6388	90·6333
1·93	6·88951	·14515	3·51733	3·37218	5·3	200·337	·00499	100·171	100·167
1·94	6·95875	·14370	3·55123	3·40752	5·4	221·406	·00452	110·705	110·701
1·95	7·02869	·14227	3·58548	3·44321	5·5	244·692	·00409	122·348	122·344
1·96	7·09933	·14086	3·62009	3·47923	5·6	270·426	·00370	135·215	135·211
1·97	7·17068	·13946	3·65507	3·51561	5·7	298·867	·00335	149·435	149·432
1·98	7·24274	·13807	3·69041	3·55234	5·8	330·300	·00303	165·151	165·148
1·99	7·31553	·13670	3·72611	3·58942	5·9	365·037	·00274	182·520	182·517
					6·0	403·429	·00248	201·716	201·714

Table V.—Common Logarithms of the Gamma Function.
(Page 426.)

Table VI.—Numerical Values of the Factor

$$0\cdot6745\sqrt{\frac{1}{n-1}}.\quad\text{(Page 523.)}$$

n.	$\dfrac{0\cdot6745}{\sqrt{n-1}}$									
	0.	1.	2.	3.	4.	5.	6.	7.	8.	9.
0			0·6745	0·4769	0·3894	0·3372	0·3016	0·2754	0·2549	0·2385
10	0·2248	0·2133	·2029	·1947	·1871	·1803	·1742	·1686	·1636	·1590
20	·1547	·1508	·1472	·1438	·1406	·1377	·1349	·1323	·1298	·1275
30	·1252	·1231	·1211	·1192	·1174	·1157	·1140	·1124	·1109	·1094
40	·1080	·1066	·1053	·1041	·1029	·1017	·1005	·0994	·0984	·0974
50	0·0964	0·0954	0·0944	0·0935	0·0926	0·0918	0·0909	0·0901	0·0893	0·0886
60	·0878	·0871	·0864	·0857	·0850	·0843	·0837	·0830	·0824	·0818
70	·0812	·0806	·0800	·0795	·0789	·0784	·0778	·0773	·0768	·0763
80	·0759	·0754	·0749	·0745	·0740	·0736	·0731	·0727	·0723	·0719
90	·0715	·0711	·0707	·0703	·0699	·0696	·0692	·0688	·0685	·0681

Table VII.—Numerical Values of the Factor

$$\frac{0\cdot6745}{\sqrt{n(n-1)}}.\quad\text{(Page 524.)}$$

n.	$\dfrac{0\cdot6745}{\sqrt{n(n-1)}}$									
	0.	1.	2.	3.	4.	5.	6	7.	8.	9.
0			0·4769	0·2754	0·1947	0·1508	0·1231	0·1041	0·0901	0·0795
10	0·0711	0·0643	·0587	·0540	·0500	·0465	·0435	·0409	·0386	·0365
20	·0346	·0329	·0314	·0300	·0287	·0275	·0265	·0255	·0245	·0237
30	·0229	·0221	·0214	·0208	·0201	·0196	·0190	·0185	·0180	0175
40	·0171	·0167	·0163	·0159	·0155	·0152	·0148	·0145	·0142	·0139
50	0·0136	0·0134	0·0131	0·0128	0·0126	0·0124	0·0122	0·0119	0·0117	0·0115
60	·0113	·0111	·0110	·0108	·0106	·0105	·0103	·0101	·0100	·0098
70	·0097	·0096	·0094	·0093	·0092	·0091	·0089	·0088	·0087	·0086
80	·0085	·0084	·0083	·0082	·0081	·0080	·0080	·0079	·0077	·0076
90	·0075	·0074	·0073	·0073	·0072	·0071	·0070	·0069	·0069	·0068

Table VIII.—Numerical Values of the Factor

$$0.8453 \sqrt{\frac{1}{n(n-1)}}. \quad \text{(Page 524.)}$$

$n.$	0.	1.	2.	3.	4.	5.	6.	7.	8.	9.
0			0·5978	0·3451	0·2440	0·1890	0·1543	0·1304	0·1130	0·0996
10	0·0891	0·0806	·0736	·0677	·0627	·0583	·0546	·0513	·0483	·0457
20	·0434	·0412	·0393	·0376	·0360	·0345	·0331	·0319	·0307	·0297
30	·0287	·0277	·0268	·0260	·0252	·0245	·0238	·0232	·0225	·0220
40	·0214	·0209	·0204	·0199	·0194	·0190	·0186	·0182	·0178	·0174
50	0·0171	0·0167	0·0164	0·0161	0·0158	0·0155	0·0152	0·0150	0·0147	0·0145
60	·0142	·0140	·0137	·0135	·0133	·0132	·0129	·0127	·0125	·0123
70	·0122	·0120	·0118	·0117	·0115	·0113	·0112	·0110	·0109	·0108
80	·0106	·0105	·0104	·0102	·0101	·0100	·0099	·0098	·0097	·0096
90	·0095	·0093	·0092	·0091	·0090	·0089	·0089	·0088	·0087	·0086

Table IX.—Numerical Values of the Factor

$$0.8453 \frac{1}{n\sqrt{n-1}}. \quad \text{(Page 524.)}$$

$n.$	0.	1.	2.	3.	4.	5	6.	7.	8.	9.
0			0·4227	0·1993	0·1220	0·0845	0·0630	0·0493	0·0399	0·0332
10	0·0282	0·0243	·0212	·0188	·0167	·0151	·0136	·0124	·0114	·0105
20	·0097	·0090	·0084	·0078	·0073	·0069	·0065	·0061	·0058	·0055
30	·0052	·0050	·0047	·0045	·0043	·0041	·0040	·0038	·0037	·0035
40	·0034	·0033	·0031	·0030	·0029	·0028	·0027	·0027	·0026	·0025
50	0·0024	0·0023	0·0023	0·0022	0·0022	0·0021	0·0020	0·0020	0·0019	0·0019
60	·0018	·0018	·0017	·0017	·0017	·0016	·0016	·0016	·0015	·0015
70	·0015	·0014	·0014	·0014	·0013	·0013	·0013	·0012	·0012	·0012
80	·0012	·0012	·0011	·0011	·0011	·0011	·0011	·0010	·0010	·0010
90	·0010	·0010	·0010	·0009	·0009	·0009	·0009	·0009	·0009	·0009

Table X.—Numerical Values of the Probability Integral

$$P = \frac{2}{\sqrt{\pi}} \int_0^{hx} e^{-h^2x^2} d(hx), \text{ (Page 532)},$$

where P represents the probability that an error of observation will have a positive or negative value equal to or less than x, h is the measure of precision.

$hx.$	P.									
	0.	1.	2.	3.	4.	5.	6.	7.	8.	9.
0·0	0·0000	0·0113	0·0226	0·0338	0·0451	0·0564	0·0676	0·0789	0·0901	0·1013
0·1	·1125	·1236	·1348	·1459	·1569	·1680	·1790	·1900	·2009	·2118
0·2	·2227	·2335	·2443	·2550	·2657	·2763	·2869	·2974	·3079	·3183
0·3	·3286	·3389	·3491	·3593	·3694	·3794	·3893	·3992	·4090	·4187
0·4	·4284	·4380	·4475	·4569	·4662	·4755	·4847	·4937	·5027	·5117
0·5	0·5205	0·5292	0·5379	0·5465	0·5549	0·5633	0·5716	0·5798	0·5879	0·5959
0·6	·6039	·6117	·6194	·6270	·6346	·6420	·6494	·6566	·6638	·6708
0·7	·6778	·6847	·6914	·6981	·7047	·7112	·7175	·7238	·7300	·7361
0·8	·7421	·7480	·7538	·7595	·7651	·7707	·7761	·7814	·7867	·7918
0·9	·7969	·8019	·8068	·8116	·8163	·8209	·8254	·8299	·8342	·8385
1·0	0·8427	0·8468	0·8508	0·8548	0·8586	0·8624	0·8661	0·8698	0·8733	0·8768
1·1	·8802	·8835	·8868	·8900	·8931	·8961	·8991	·9020	·9048	·9076
1·2	·9103	·9130	·9155	·9181	·9205	·9229	·9252	·9275	·9297	·9319
1·3	·9340	·9361	·9381	·9400	·9419	·9438	·9456	·9473	·9490	·9507
1·4	·9523	·9539	·9554	·9569	·9583	·9597	·9611	·9624	·9637	·9649
1·5	0·9661	0·9673	0·9684	0·9695	0·9706	0·9716	0·9726	0·9736	0·9745	0·9755
1·6	·9763	·9772	·9780	·9788	·9796	·9804	·9811	·9818	·9825	·9832
1·7	·9838	·9844	·9850	·9856	·9861	·9867	·9872	·9877	·9882	·9886
1·8	·9891	·9895	·9899	·9903	·9907	·9911	·9915	·9918	·9922	·9925
1·9	·9928	·9931	·9934	·9937	·9939	·9942	·9944	·9947	·9949	·9951
2·0	0·9953	0·9955	0·9957	0·9959	0·9961	0·9963	0·9964	0·9966	0·9967	0·9969
2·1	·9970	·9972	·9973	·9974	·9975	·9976	·9977	·9979	·9980	·9980
2·2	·9981	·9982	·9983	·9984	·9985	·9985	·9986	·9987	·9987	·9988
2·3	·9989	·9989	·9990	·9990	·9991	·9991	·9992	·9992	·9992	·9993
2·4	·9993	·9993	·9994	·9994	·9994	·9995	·9995	·9995	·9995	·9996
2·5	0·9996	0·9996	0·9996	0·9997	0·9997	0·9997	0·9997	0·9997	0·9998	0·9998
2·6	·9998	·9998	·9998	·9998	·9998	·9998	·9998	·9998	·9998	·9999
∞	1·0000									

Table XI.—Numerical Values of the Probability Integral

$$P = \frac{2}{\sqrt{\pi}} \int_0^{x/r} e^{\left(\frac{x}{r}\right)^2} d\left(\frac{x}{r}\right), \text{ (Page 532),}$$

where P represents the probability that an error of observation will have a positive or negative value equal to or less than x, r denotes the probable error, and equals a/h where h is a measure of the precision, and a is a constant of value $0·4769$.

$\frac{x}{r}$	P.									
	0.	1.	2.	3.	4.	5.	6.	7.	8.	9.
0·0	0·	0·0054	0·0108	0·0161	0·0215	0·0269	0·0323	0·0377	0·0430	0·0484
0·1	·0538	·0591	·0645	·0699	·0752	·0806	·0859	·0913	·0966	·1020
0·2	·1073	·1126	·1180	·1233	·1286	·1339	·1392	·1445	·1498	·1551
0·3	·1603	·1656	·1709	·1761	·1814	·1866	·1918	·1971	·2023	·2075
0·4	·2127	·2179	·2230	·2282	·2334	·2385	·2436	·2488	·2539	·2590
0·5	0·2641	0·2691	0·2742	0·2793	0·2843	0·2893	0·2944	0·2994	0·3043	0·3093
0·6	·3143	·3192	·3242	·3291	·3340	·3389	·3438	·3487	·3535	·3583
0·7	·3632	·3680	·3728	·3775	·3823	·3870	·3918	·3965	·4012	·4059
0·8	·4105	·4152	·4198	·4244	·4290	·4336	·4381	·4427	·4472	·4517
0·9	·4562	·4606	·4651	·4695	·4739	·4783	·4827	·4860	·4914	·4957
1·0	0·5000	0·5043	0·5085	0·5128	0·5170	0·5212	0·5254	0·5295	0·5337	0·5378
1·1	·5419	·5460	·5500	·5540	·5581	·5620	·5660	·5700	·5739	·5778
1·2	·5817	·5856	·5894	·5932	·5970	·6008	·6046	·6083	·6120	·6157
1·3	·6194	·6231	·6267	·6303	·6339	·6375	·6410	·6445	·6480	·6515
1·4	·6550	·6584	·6618	·6652	·6686	·6719	·6753	·6786	·6818	·6851
1·5	0·6883	0·6915	0·6947	0·6979	0·7011	0·7042	0·7073	0·7104	0·7134	0·7165
1·6	·7195	·7225	·7255	·7284	·7313	·7342	·7371	·7400	·7428	·7457
1·7	·7485	·7512	·7540	·7567	·7594	·7621	·7648	·7675	·7701	·7727
1·8	·7753	·7778	·7804	·7829	·7854	·7879	·7904	·7928	·7952	·7976
1·9	·8000	·8023	·8047	·8070	·8093	·8116	·8138	·8161	·8183	·8205
2·0	0·8227	0·8248	0·8270	0·8291	0·8312	0·8332	0·8353	0·8373	0·8394	0·8414
2·1	·8433	·8453	·8473	·8492	·8511	·8530	·8549	·8567	·8585	·8604
2·2	·8622	·8639	·8657	·8674	·8692	·8709	·8726	·8742	·8759	·8775
2·3	·8792	·8808	·8824	·8840	·8855	·8870	·8886	·8901	·8916	·8930
2·4	·8945	·8960	·8974	·8988	·9002	·9016	·9029	·9043	·9056	·9069
2·5	0·9082	0·9095	0·9108	0·9121	0·9133	0·9146	0·9158	0·9170	0·9182	0·9193
2·6	·9205	·9217	·9228	·9239	·9250	·9261	·9272	·9283	·9293	·9304
2·7	·9314	·9324	·9334	·9344	·9354	·9364	·9373	·9383	·9392	·9401
2·8	·9410	·9419	·9428	·9437	·9446	·9454	·9463	·9471	·9479	·9487
2·9	·9495	·9503	·9511	·9519	·9526	·9534	·9541	·9548	·9556	·9563
3·0	0·9570	0·9577	0·9583	0·9590	0·9597	0·9603	0·9610	0·9616	0·9622	0·9629
3·1	·9635	·9641	·9647	·9652	·9658	·9664	·9669	·9675	·9680	·9686
3·2	·9691	·9696	·9701	·9706	·9711	·9716	·9721	·9726	·9731	·9735
3·3	·9740	·9744	·9749	·9753	·9757	·9761	·9766	·9770	·9774	·9778
3·4	·9782	·9786	·9789	·9793	·9797	·9800	·9804	·9807	·9811	·9814
3·	0·9570	0·9635	0·9691	0·9740	0·9782	0·9818	0·9848	0·9874	0·9896	0·9915
4·	·9930	·9943	·9954	·9963	·9970	·9976	·9981	·9985	·9988	·9990
5·	·9993	·9994	·9996	·9997	·9997	·9998	·9998	·9999	·9999	·9999
∞	1·0000									

Table XII.—Numerical Values of $\frac{x}{r}$ Corresponding to Different Values of n, in the Application of Chauvenet's Criterion.

(Page 564.)

n.	0.	1.	2.	3.	4.	5.	6.	7.	8.	9.
0				2·05	2·27	2·44	2·57	2·67	2·76	2·84
10	2·91	2·96	3·02	3·07	3·12	3·16	3·19	3·22	3·26	3·29
20	3·32	3·35	3·38	3·41	3·43	3·45	3·47	3·49	3·51	3·53
30	3·55	8·57	3·58	3·60	3·62	3·64	3·65	3·67	3·68	3·69
40	3·71	8·72	3·73	3·74	3·75	3·77	3·78	3·79	3·80	3·81
50	3·82	3·83	3·84	3·85	3·86	3·87	3·88	3·88	3·89	3·90
60	3·91	3·92	3·93	3·94	3·95	3·95	3·96	3·97	3·97	3·98
70	3·99	3·99	4·00	4·01	4·02	4·02	4·03	4·04	4·05	4·05
80	4·06	4·06	4·06	4·07	4·07	4·08	4·09	4·09	4·10	4·11
90	4·11	4·12	4·13	4·14	4·14	4·15	4·15	4·15	4·16	4·16

If $n = 100$, $t = 4·16$; $n = 200$, $t = 4·48$; $n = 500$, $t = 4·90$.

Table XIII.—Circular or Radian Measure of Angles.

(Page 606.)

Degrees.	0'.	6'.	12'.	18'.	24'.	30'.	36'.	42'.	48'.	54'.
0	·00000	·00175	·00349	·00524	·00698	·00873	·01047	·01222	·01396	·01571
1	·01745	·01920	·02094	·02269	·02443	·02618	·02793	·02967	·03142	·03316
2	·03491	·03665	·03840	·04014	·04189	·04363	·04538	·04712	·04887	·05061
3	.05236	·05411	·05585	·05760	·05934	·06109	·06283	·06458	·06632	·06807
4	·06981	·07156	·07330	·07505	·07679	·07854	·08029	·08203	·08378	·08552
5	·08727	·08901	·09076	·09250	·09425	·09599	·09774	·09948	·10123	·10297
6	·10472	·10647	·10821	·10996	·11170	·11345	·11519	·11694	·11868	·12043
7	·12217	·12392	·12566	·12741	·12915	·13090	·13265	·13439	·13614	·13788
8	·13963	·14137	·14312	·14486	·14661	·14835	·15010	·15184	·15359	·15533
9	·15708	·15882	·16057	·16232	·16406	·16581	·16755	·16930	·17104	·17279
10	·17453	·17628	·17802	·17977	·18151	·18326	·18500	·18675	·18850	·19024
11	·19199	·19373	·19548	·19722	·19897	·20071	·20246	·20420	·20595	·20769
12	·20944	·21118	·21293	·21468	·21642	·21817	·21991	·22166	·22340	·22515
13	·22689	·22864	·23038	·23213	·23387	·23562	·23736	·23911	·24086	·24260
14	·24435	·24609	·24784	·24958	·25133	·25307	·25482	·25656	·25831	·26005
15	·26180	·26354	·26529	·26704	·26878	·27053	·27227	·27402	·27576	·27751
16	·27925	·28100	·28274	·28449	·28623	·28798	·28972	·29147	·29322	·29496
17	·29671	·29845	·30020	·30194	·30369	·30543	·30718	·30892	·31067	·31241
18	·31416	·31590	·31765	·31940	·32114	·32289	·32463	·32638	·32812	·32987
19	·33161	·33336	·33510	·33685	·33859	·34034	·34208	·34383	·34558	·34732
20	·34907	·35081	·35256	·35430	·35605	·35779	·35954	·36128	·36303	·36477
21	·36652	·36826	·37001	·37176	·37525	·37525	·37699	·37874	·38048	·38223
22	·38397	·38572	·38746	·38921	·39095	·39270	·39444	·39619	·39794	·39968
23	·40143	·40317	·40492	·40666	·40841	·41015	·41190	·41364	·41539	·41713
24	·41888	·42062	·42237	·42412	·42586	·42761	·42935	·43110	·43284	·43459
25	·43633	·43808	·43982	·44157	·44331	·44506	·44680	·44855	·45029	·45204
26	·45379	·45553	·45728	·45902	·46077	·46251	·46426	·46600	·46775	·46949
27	·47124	·47298	·47473	·47647	·47822	·47997	·48171	·48346	·48520	·48695
28	·48869	·49044	·49218	·49393	·49567	·49742	·49916	·50091	·50265	·50440
29	·50615	·50789	·50964	·51138	·51313	·51487	·51662	·51836	·52011	·52185
30	·52360	·52534	·52709	·52883	·53058	·53233	·53407	·53582	·53756	·53931
31	·54105	·54280	·54454	·54629	·54803	·54978	·55152	·55327	·55501	·55676
32	·55851	·56025	·56200	·56374	·56549	·56723	·56898	·57072	·57247	·57421
33	·57596	·57770	·57945	·58119	·58294	·58469	·58643	·58818	·58992	·59167
34	·59341	·59516	·59690	·59865	·60039	·60214	·60388	·60563	·60737	·60912
35	·61087	·61261	·61436	·61610	·61785	·61959	·62134	·62308	·62483	·62657
36	·62832	·63006	·63181	·63355	·63530	·63705	·63879	·64054	·64228	·64403
37	·64577	·64752	·64926	·65101	·65275	·65450	·65624	·65799	·65973	·66148
38	·66323	·66497	·66672	·66846	·67021	·67195	·67370	·67544	·67719	·67893
39	·68068	·68242	·68417	·68591	·68766	·68941	·69115	·69290	·69464	·69639
40	·69813	·69988	·70162	·70337	·70511	·70686	·70860	·71035	·71209	·71384
41	·71558	·71733	·71908	·72082	·72257	·72431	·72606	·72780	·72955	·73129
42	·73304	·73478	·73653	·73827	·74002	·74176	·74351	·74526	·74700	·74875
43	·75049	·75224	·75398	·75573	·75747	·75922	·76096	·76271	·76445	·76620
44	·76794	·76969	·77144	·77318	·77493	·77667	·77842	·78016	·78191	·78365

Table XIII.—*Continued.*

Degrees.	0'.	6'.	12'.	18'.	24'.	30'.	36'.	42'.	48'.	54'.
45	·78540	·78714	·78889	·79063	·79238	·79412	·79587	·79762	·79936	·80114
46	·80285	·80460	·80634	·80809	·80983	·81158	·81332	·81507	·81681	·81856
47	·82030	·82205	·82380	·82554	·82729	·82903	·83078	·83252	·83427	·83601
48	·83776	·83950	·84125	·84299	·84474	·84648	·84823	·84998	·85172	·85347
49	·85521	·85696	·85870	·86045	·86219	·86394	·86568	·86743	·86917	·87092
50	·87266	·87441	·87616	·87790	·87965	·88139	·88314	·88488	·88663	·88837
51	·89012	·89186	·89361	·89535	·89710	·89884	·90059	·90234	·90408	·90583
52	·90757	·90932	·91106	·91281	·91455	·91630	·91804	·91979	·92153	·92328
53	·92502	·92677	·92852	·93026	·93201	·93375	·93550	·93724	·93899	·94073
54	·94284	·94422	·94597	·94771	·94946	·95120	·95295	·95470	·95644	·95819
55	·95993	·96168	·96342	·96517	·96691	·96866	·97040	·97215	·97389	·97564
56	·97738	·97913	·98088	·98262	·98437	·98611	·98786	·98960	·99135	·99309
57	·99484	·99658	·99833	1·00007	1·00182	1·00356	1·00531	1·00706	1·00880	1·01055
58	1·01229	1·01404	1·01578	1·01753	1·01927	1·02102	1·02276	1·02451	1·02625	1·02800
59	1·02974	1·03149	1·03323	1·03498	1·03673	1·03847	1·04022	1·04196	1·04371	1·04545
60	1·04720	1·04894	1·05069	1·05243	1·05418	1·05592	1·05767	1·05941	1·06116	1·06291
61	1·06465	1·06640	1·06814	1·06989	1·07163	1·03387	1·07512	1·07687	1·07861	1·08036
62	1·08210	1·08385	1·08559	1·08734	1·08909	1·09083	1·09258	1·09432	1·09607	1·09781
63	1·09956	1·10130	1·10305	1·10479	1·10654	1·10828	1·11003	1·11177	1·11352	1·11527
64	1·11701	1·11876	1·12050	1·12225	1·12399	1·12574	1·12748	1·12923	1·13097	1·13272
65	1·13446	1·13621	1·13795	1·13970	1·14145	1·14319	1·14494	1·14668	1·14843	1·15017
66	1·15192	1·15366	1·15541	1·15715	1·15890	1·16064	1·16239	1·16413	1·16588	1·16763
67	1·16937	1·17112	1·17286	1·17461	1·17635	1·17810	1·17984	1·18152	1·18333	1·18508
68	1·18682	1·18857	1·19031	1·19206	1·19381	1·19555	1·19730	1·19904	1·20079	1·20253
69	1·20428	1·20602	1·20777	1·20951	1·21126	1·21300	1·21475	1·21649	1·21824	1·21999
70	1·22175	1·22348	1·22522	1·22697	1·22871	1·23046	1·23220	1·23395	1·23569	1·23744
71	1·23918	1·24093	1·24267	1·24442	1·24617	1·24791	1·24966	1·25140	1·25315	1·25489
72	1·25664	1·25838	1·26013	1·26187	1·26362	1·26536	1·26711	1·26885	1·27060	1·27235
73	1·27409	1·27584	1·27758	1·27933	1·28107	1·28282	1·28456	1·28631	1·28805	1·28980
74	1·29154	1·29329	1·29503	1·29678	1·29852	1·30027	1·30202	1·30376	1·30551	1·30725
75	1·30900	1·31074	1·31249	1·31423	1·31598	1·31772	1·31947	1·32121	1·32296	1·32470
76	1·32645	1·32820	1·32994	1·33169	1·33343	1·33518	1·33692	1·33867	1·34041	1·34216
77	1·34390	1·34565	1·34739	1·34914	1·35088	1·35263	1·35438	1·35612	1·35787	1·35961
78	1·36136	1·36310	1·36485	1·36659	1·36834	1·37008	1·37183	1·37357	1·37532	1·37706
79	1·37881	1·38056	1·38230	1·38405	1·38579	1·38754	1·38928	1·39103	1·39277	1·39452
80	1·39626	1·39801	1·39975	1·40150	1·40324	1·40499	1·40674	1·40848	1·41023	1·41197
81	1·41372	1·41546	1·41721	1·41895	1·42070	1·42244	1·42419	1·42593	1·42768	1·42942
82	1·43117	1·43292	1·43466	1·43641	1·43815	1·43990	1·44164	1·44339	1·44513	1·44688
83	1·44862	1·45037	1·45211	1·45386	1·45560	1·45735	1·45910	1·46084	1·46259	1·46433
84	1·46608	1·46782	1·46957	1·47131	1·47306	1·47480	1·47655	1·47829	1·48004	1·48178
85	1·48353	1·48528	1·48702	1·48877	1·49051	1·49226	1·49400	1·49575	1·49749	1·49924
86	1·50098	1·50273	1·50447	1·50622	1·50796	1·50971	1·51146	1·51320	1·51495	1·51669
87	1·51844	1·52018	1·52193	1·52367	1·52542	1·52716	1·52891	1·53065	1·53240	1·53414
88	1·53589	1·53764	1·53938	1·54113	1·54287	1·54462	1·54636	1·54811	1·54985	1·55160
89	1·55334	1·55509	1·55683	1·55858	1·56032	1·56207	1·56382	1·56556	1·56731	1·56905

Table XIV.—Numerical Values of some Trigonometrical Ratios.
(Page 609.)

Table XV.—Signs of the Trigonometrical Ratios.
(Page 610.)

Table XVI.—Comparison of Hyperbolic and Trigonometrical Functions.
(Page 614.)

Table XVII.—Numerical Values of e^{x^2} and e^{-x^2} from $x = 0\cdot1$ to $x = 5\cdot0$.

x.	e^{x^2}.	e^{-x^2}.	x.	e^{x^2}.	e^{-x^2}.
0·1	1·0101	0·99005	2·6	$8\cdot6264 \times 10^2$	$1\cdot1592 \times 10^{-3}$
0·2	1·0408	·96079	2·7	$1\cdot4656 \times 10^3$	$6\cdot8233 \times 10^{-4}$
0·3	1·0904	·91393	2·8	2·5402 „	3·9367 „
0·4	1·1735	·85214	2·9	4·4918 „	2·2263 „
0·5	1·2840	·77880	3·0	8·1031 „	1·2341 „
0·6	1·4333	0·69768	3·1	$1\cdot4913 \times 10^4$	$6\cdot7055 \times 10^{-5}$
0·7	1·6323	·61263	3·2	2·8001 „	3·5713 „
0·8	1·8965	·52729	3·3	5·2960 „	1·8644 „
0·9	2·2479	·44486	3·4	$1\cdot0482 \times 10^5$	$9\cdot5402 \times 10^{-6}$
1·0	2·7183	·36788	3·5	2·0898 „	4·7851 „
1·1	3·3535	0·29820	3·6	$4\cdot2507 \times 10^5$	$2\cdot3526 \times 10^{-6}$
1·2	4·2207	·23693	3·7	8·8205 „	1·1337 „
1·3	5·4195	·18452	3·8	$1\cdot8673 \times 10^6$	$5\cdot3554 \times 10^{-7}$
1·4	7·0993	·14086	3·9	4·0329 „	2·4796 „
1·5	9·4877	·10540	4·0	8·8861 „	1·1254 „
1·6	12·936	0·077306	4·1	$1\cdot9976 \times 10^7$	$5\cdot0062 \times 10^{-8}$
1·7	17·993	·055576	4·2	4·5809 „	2·1829 „
1·8	25·534	·039164	4·3	$1\cdot0718 \times 10^8$	$9\cdot3303 \times 10^{-9}$
1·9	36·996	·027052	4·4	2·5583 „	3·9088 „
2·0	54·598	·018316	4·5	6·2297 „	1·6052 „
2·1	82·269	0·012155	4·6	$1\cdot5476 \times 10^9$	$6\cdot4614 \times 10^{-10}$
2·2	126·47	·0²79070 [1]	4·7	3·9228 „	2·5494 „
2·3	198·34	·0²50418	4·8	$1\cdot0143 \times 10^{10}$	$9\cdot8595 \times 10^{-11}$
2·4	317·35	·0²31511	4·9	2·6755 „	3·7376 „
2·5	518·02	·0²19304	5·0	7·2005 „	1·3888 „

[1] 0·0²555 means 0·00555 ; 0·0⁴55 means 0·000055.

Table XVIII.—Natural Logarithms of Numbers.

Many formulæ require natural logarithms, and it is convenient to have at hand a table of these logarithms to avoid the necessity of having recourse to the conversion formulæ, page 28. Table XVIII. is used as follows :

I. For numbers greater than 10, follow the method of Ex. (2) and (3) below.

II. For numbers between 1 *and* 10 *not in the table*, use interpolation formulæ, say proportional parts.

III. For numbers less than 1, use the method of Ex. (5) below.

If there is going to be much trouble finding the natural log it may be better to use standard tables of logarithms to base 10 and multiply by 2·3026 in the ordinary way.

$$\log_e 10 = 2\text{·}3026.$$

EXAMPLES.—(1) Show that $\log_e \pi = \log_e(3\text{·}1416) = 1\text{·}1447$.

(2) Required the logarithm of 5,540 to the base e. Here

$$\log_e 5{,}540 = \log_e(5\text{·}540 \times 1{,}000) = \log_e(5\text{·}54 \times 10^3) ;$$

hence, $\log_e 5{,}540 = \log_e 5\text{·}54 + 3 \log_e 10 = 8\text{·}6198$.

(3) Show that $\log_e 100 = 4\text{·}6052$; $\log_e 1{,}000 = 6\text{·}9078$; $\log_e 10{,}000 = 9\text{·}2103$ $\log_e 100{,}000 = 11\text{·}5129$. Hint. $\log 1{,}000 = \log 10^3 = 3 \log 10$.

(4) If 100 c.c. of a gas at a pressure of 5,000 grams per square centimetre expands until the gas occupies a volume of 557 c.c., what work is done during the process? From page 254,

$$W = p_1 v_1 \log_e \frac{v_2}{v_1} = 5{,}000 \times 100 \times \log_e 5\text{·}57 = 850{,}700 \text{ grm. cm.}$$

If a table of ordinary logarithms had been employed we should have written $2\text{·}3026 \times \log_{10} 5\text{·}57$ in place of $\log_e 5\text{·}57$.

(5) Find $\log_e 0\text{·}00051$; $\log 0\text{·}0031$; and $\log 0\text{·}51$. Here we have $\log 0\text{·}00051 = \log 5\text{·}1 - \log 10{,}000 = \log 5\text{·}1 - \log 10^4 = \log 5\text{·}1 - 4 \log 10 = 1\text{·}6292 - 4 \times 2\text{·}3026 = 1\text{·}6292 - 9\text{·}2104 = \overline{9}\text{·}4188$, or $-8\text{·}5812$; $\log_e 0\text{·}0031 = 1\text{·}1314 - 6\text{·}9077 = \overline{6}\text{·}2237$, or $-5\text{·}7763$; $\log 0\text{·}51 = 0\text{·}6292 - 2\text{·}3026 = \overline{2}\text{·}3166$ or $-1\text{·}6734$.

The bar over the first figure has a similar meaning to the " bar " of ordinary logs.

n.	·00.	·01.	·02.	·03.	·04.	·05.	·06.	·07.	·08.	·09.
1·0	0·0000	0·0100	0·0198	0·0296	0·0392	0·0488	0·0583	0·0677	0·0770	0·0862
1·1	·0953	·1044	·1133	·1222	·1310	·1398	·1484	·1570	·1655	·1740
1·2	·1823	·1906	·1989	·2070	·2151	·2231	·2311	·2390	·2469	·2546
1·3	·2624	·2700	·2776	·2852	·2927	·3001	·3075	·3148	·3221	·3293
1·4	·3365	·3436	·3507	·3577	·3646	·3716	·3784	·3853	·3920	·3988
1·5	0·4055	0·4121	0·4187	0·4253	0·4318	0·4383	0·4447	0·4511	0·4574	0·4637
1·6	·4700	·4762	·4824	·4886	·4947	·5008	·5068	·5128	·5188	·5247
1·7	·5306	·5365	·5423	·5481	·5539	·5596	·5653	·5710	·5766	·5822
1·8	·5878	·5933	·5988	·6043	·6098	·6152	·6206	·6259	·6313	·6366
1·9	·6419	·6471	·6523	·6575	·6627	·6678	·6729	·6780	·6831	·6881
2·0	0·6932	0·6981	0·7031	0·7080	0·7130	0·7178	0·7227	0·7276	0·7324	0·7372
2·1	·7419	·7467	·7514	·7561	·7608	·7655	·7701	·7747	·7793	·7839
2·2	·7885	·7930	·7975	·8020	·8065	·8109	·8154	·8198	·8242	·8286
2·3	·8329	·8372	·8416	·8459	·8502	·8544	·8587	·8629	·8671	·8713
2·4	·8755	·8796	·8838	·8879	·8920	·8961	·9002	·9042	·9083	·9123
2·5	0·9163	0·9203	0·9243	0·9282	0·9322	0·9361	0·9400	0·9439	0·9478	0·9517
2·6	·9555	·9594	·9632	·9670	·9708	·9746	·9783	·9821	·9858	·9895
2·7	·9933	·9970	1·0006	1·0043	1·0080	1·0116	1·0152	1·0189	1·0225	1·0260
2·8	1·0296	1·0332	·0367	·0403	·0438	·0472	·0508	·0543	·0578	·0613
2·9	·0647	·0682	·0716	·0750	·0784	·0818	·0852	·0886	·0919	·0953
3·0	1·0986	1·1019	1·1053	1·1086	1·1119	1·1151	1·1184	1·1217	1·1249	1·1282
3·1	·1314	·1346	·1378	·1410	·1442	·1474	·1506	·1537	·1569	·1600
3·2	·1632	·1663	·1694	·1725	·1756	·1787	·1817	·1848	·1878	·1909
3·3	·1939	·1970	·2000	·2030	·2060	·2090	·2119	·2149	·2179	·2208
3·4	·2238	·2267	·2296	·2326	·2355	·2384	·2413	·2442	·2470	·2499
3·5	1·2528	1·2556	1·2585	1·2613	1·2641	1·2670	1·2698	1·2726	1·2754	1·2782
3·6	·2809	·2837	·2865	·2892	·2920	·2947	·2975	·3002	·3029	·3056
3·7	·3083	·3110	·3137	·3164	·3191	·3218	·3244	·3271	·3297	·3324
3·8	·3350	·3376	·3403	·3429	·3455	·3481	·3507	·3533	·3558	·3584
3·9	·3610	·3635	·3661	·3686	·3712	·3737	·3762	·3788	·3813	·3838
4·0	1·3863	1·3888	1·3913	1·3938	1·3963	1·3987	1·4012	1·4036	1·4061	1·4086
4·1	·4110	·4134	·4159	·4183	·4207	·4231	·4255	·4279	·4303	·4327
4·2	·4351	·4375	·4398	·4422	·4446	·4469	·4493	·4516	·4540	·4563
4·3	·4586	·4609	·4633	·4656	·4679	·4702	·4725	·4748	·4771	·4793
4·4	·4816	·4839	·4861	·4884	·4907	·4929	·4954	·4974	·4996	·5019
4·5	1·5041	1·5063	1·5085	1·5107	1·5129	1·5151	1·5173	1·5195	1·5217	1·5239
4·6	·5261	·5282	·5304	·5326	·5347	·5369	·5390	·5412	·5433	·5454
4·7	·5476	·5497	·5518	·5539	·5560	·5581	·5602	·5623	·5644	·5665
4·8	·5686	·5707	·5728	·5748	·5769	·5790	·5810	·5831	·5851	·5872
4·9	·5892	·5913	·5933	·5953	·5974	·5994	·6014	·6034	·6054	·6074
5·0	1·6094	1·6114	1·6134	1·6154	1·6174	1·6194	1·6214	1·6233	1·6253	1·6273
5·1	·6292	·6312	·6332	·6351	·6371	·6390	·6409	·6429	·6448	·6467
5·2	·6487	·6506	·6525	·6544	·6563	·6582	·6601	·6620	·6639	·6658
5·3	·6677	·6696	·6715	·6734	·6752	·6771	·6790	·6808	·6827	·6845
5·4	·6864	·6882	·6901	·6919	·6938	·6956	·6975	·6993	·7011	·7029

ι.	·00.	·01.	·02.	·03.	·04.	·05.	·06.	·07.	·08.	·09.
5·5	1·7048	1·7066	1·7083	1·7102	1·7120	1·7138	1·7156	1·7174	1·7192	1·7210
5·6	·7228	·7246	·7263	·7281	·7299	·7317	·7334	·7352	·7370	·7387
5·7	·7405	·7422	·7440	·7457	·7475	·7492	·7509	·7527	·7544	·7561
5·8	·7579	·7596	·7613	·7630	·7647	·7664	·7682	·7699	·7716	·7733
5·9	·7750	·7766	·7783	·7800	·7817	·7834	·7851	·7868	·7884	·7901
6·0	1·7917	1·7934	1·7951	1·7967	1·7984	1·8001	1·8017	1·8034	1·8050	1·8067
6·1	·8083	·8099	·8116	·8132	·8148	·8165	·8181	·8197	·8213	·8229
6·2	·8246	·8262	·8278	·8294	·8310	·8326	·8342	·8358	·8374	·8390
6·3	·8406	·8421	·8437	·8453	·8469	·8485	·8500	·8516	·8532	·8547
6·4	·8563	·8579	·8594	·8610	·8625	·8641	·8656	·8672	·8687	·8703
6·5	1·8718	1·8733	1·8749	1·8764	1·8779	1·8795	1·8810	1·8825	1·8840	1·8856
6·6	·8871	·8886	·8901	·8916	·8931	·8946	·8961	·8976	·8991	·9006
6·7	·9021	·9036	·9051	·9066	·9081	·9095	·9110	·9125	·9140	·9155
6·8	·9169	·9184	·9199	·9213	·9228	·9243	·9257	·9272	·9286	·9301
6·9	·9315	·9330	·9344	·9359	·9373	·9387	·9402	·9416	·9431	·9445
7·0	1·9459	1·9473	1·9488	1·9502	1·9516	1·9530	1·9544	1·9559	1·9573	1·9587
7·1	·9601	·9615	·9629	·9643	·9657	·9671	·9685	·9699	·9713	·9727
7·2	·9741	·9755	·9769	·9782	·9796	·9810	·9824	·9838	·9851	·9865
7·3	·9879	·9892	·9906	·9920	·9933	·9947	·9961	·9974	·9988	2·0001
7·4	2·0015	2·0028	2·0042	2·0055	2·0069	2·0082	2·0096	2·0109	2·0122	·0136
7·6	2·0149	2·0162	2·0176	2·0189	2·0202	2·0216	2·0229	2·0242	2·0255	2·0268
7·6	·0282	·0295	·0308	·0321	·0334	·0347	·0360	·0373	·0386	·0399
7·7	·0412	·0425	·0438	·0451	·0464	·0477	·0490	·0503	·0516	·0528
7·8	·0541	·0554	·0567	·0580	·0592	·0605	·0618	·0631	·0643	·0656
7·9	·0669	·0681	·0694	·0707	·0719	·0732	·0744	·0757	·0769	·0728
8·0	2·0794	2·0807	2·0819	2·0832	2·0844	2·0857	2·0869	2·0882	2·0894	2·0906
8·1	·0919	·0931	·0943	·0956	·0968	·0980	·0992	·1005	·1017	·1029
8·2	·1041	·1054	·1066	·1078	·1090	·1102	·1114	·1126	·1138	·1151
8·3	·1163	·1175	·1187	·1199	·1211	·1223	·1235	·1247	·1259	·1270
8·4	·1282	·1294	·1306	·1318	·1330	·1342	·1354	·1365	·1377	·1389
8·5	2·1401	2·1412	2·1424	2·1436	2·1448	2·1459	2·1471	2·1483	2·1494	2·1506
8·6	·1518	·1529	·1541	·1552	·1564	·1576	·1587	·1599	·1610	·1622
8·7	·1633	·1645	·1656	·1668	·1679	·1691	·1702	·1713	·1725	·1736
8·8	·1748	·1759	·1770	·1782	·1793	·1804	·1816	·1827	·1838	·1849
8·9	·1861	·1872	·1883	·1894	·1905	·1917	·1928	·1939	·1950	·1961
9·0	2·1972	2·1983	2·1994	2·2006	2·2017	2·2028	2·2039	2·2050	2·2061	2·2072
9·1	·2083	·2094	·2105	·2116	·2127	·2138	·2149	·2159	·2170	·2181
9·2	·2192	·2203	·2214	·2225	·2235	·2246	·2257	·2268	·2279	·2289
9·3	·2300	·2311	·2322	·2332	·2343	·2354	·2364	·2375	·2386	·2396
9·4	·2407	·2418	·2428	·2439	·2450	·2460	·2471	·2481	·2492	·2502
9·5	2·2512	2·2523	2·2534	2·2544	2·2555	2·2565	2·2576	2·2586	2·2597	2·2607
9·6	·2618	·2628	·2638	·2649	·2659	·2670	·2680	·2690	·2701	·2711
9·7	·2721	·2732	·2742	·2752	·2762	·2773	·2783	.2792	·2803	·2814
9·8	·2824	·2834	·2844	·2854	·2865	·2875	·28 85	·2895	·2905	·2915
9·9	·2925	·2935	·2946	·2956	·2966	·2976	·29 86	·2996	·3006	·3016

INDEX.

FOUNDATIONS OF PHYSICS
by Robert Bruce Lindsay and Henry Margenau

A bridge between semipopular works for the general reader and technical treatises written for specialists, this excellent work discusses the foundation ideas and background of modern physics. It is not a text on theoretical physics, but a discussion of the methods of physical description and construction of theory. It is especially valuable for the physicist with a background in elementary calculus who is interested in the ideas which give meaning to the data and tools of modern physics.

Contents include a thorough discussion of theory, data, symbolism, mathematical equations; space and time in physics, foundations of mechanics; probability and its application; the statistical point of view; the physics and continua; the electron theory and special relativity; the general theory of relativity; quantum mechanics; the problem of causality.

"Thorough and yet not overdetailed. Unreservedly recommended," **NATURE (London)**.

Unabridged, newly corrected edition. New listing of recommended readings. 35 illustrations. xi + 537pp. 5⅜ x 8.

Paperbound **$2.45**

INTRODUCTION TO SYMBOLIC LOGIC
by Susanne Langer

This is probably the clearest book ever written on symbolic logic for the philosopher, general scientist and layman. It will be particularly appreciated by those who have been rebuffed by other introductory works because of insufficient mathematical training. No special knowledge of mathematics is required. Even if you have forgotten most of your high school algebra, you can learn to use mathematical logic by following the directions in this book. You start with the simplest symbols and conventions and end up with a remarkable grasp of the Boole-Schroeder and Russell-Whitehead systems.

"One of the clearest and simplest introductions to a subject which is very much alive. The style is easy, symbolism is introduced gradually, and the intelligent non-mathematician should have no difficulty in following the argument," MATHEMATICS GAZETTE.

Partial contents. Study of forms. Essentials of logical structure. Generalization. Classes. Principal relations among classes. Universe of classes. The deductive system of classes. The algebra of logic. Abstraction of interpretation. Calculus of propositions. The assumptions of PRINCIPIA MATHEMATICA by Whitehead and Russell. Logistics. Symbolic logic and the logic of the syllogism. Proofs of theorems.

Second edition, with many additions and revisions. New appendix on truth-value tables. 368pp. 5⅜ x 8.

S164 Paperbound **$1.75**

INTRODUCTION TO THE THEORY OF FOURIER'S SERIES AND INTEGRALS

by H. S. Carslaw

As an introductory explanation of the theory of Fourier's series, this clear, detailed text has long been recognized as outstanding. This third revised edition contains tests for uniform convergence of series; a thorough treatment of term by term integration and the Second Theorem of Mean Value; enlarged sets of examples on Infinite Series and Integrals; and a section dealing with the Riemann-Lebesgue Theorem and its consequences. An appendix compares the Lebesgue Definite Integral with the classical Riemann Integral.

CONTENTS: Historical Introduction. Rational and irrational numbers. Infinite sequences and series. Functions of single variable. Limits and continuity. Definite integral. Theory of infinite series, whose terms are functions of a single variable. Definite integrals containing an arbitrary parameter. Fourier's series. Nature of convergence of Fourier's series and some properties of Fourier's constants. Approximation curves and Gibbs phenomenon in Fourier's series. Fourier's integrals. Appendices: Practical harmonic analysis and periodogram analysis; Lebesgue's theory of the definite integral.

"For the serious student of mathematical physics, anxious to have a firm grasp of Fourier theory as far as the Riemann integral will serve, Carslaw is still unsurpassed," MATHEMATICAL GAZETTE.

Bibliography. Index. 39 figures. 96 examples for students. xiii + 368pp. 5⅜ x 8.

S48 Paperbound **$1.95**

TABLES OF FUNCTIONS WITH FORMULAE AND CURVES

by Eugene Jahnke and Fritz Emde

This new edition of Jahnke and Emde's TABLES OF FUNCTIONS contains corrections of 396 tabular errors detected in the preceding edition, and a supplementary bibliography of 43 titles. Also added is an exhaustive 76-page appendix of tables and formulae of elementary functions. This appendix does not appear in other American editions of Jahnke and Emde. Hundreds of reliefs of functions give a helpful picture of functional relations.

PARTIAL CONTENTS. 1. Sine, cosine, and logarithmic integral. 2. Factorial function. 3. Error integral and related functions. 4. Theta-functions. 5. Elliptic integrals. 6. Elliptic functions. 7. Legendre functions. 8. Bessel functions. 9. The Riemann-Zeta function. 10. Confluent hypergeometric functions. 11. Mathieu functions. 12. Some often used constants. 13. Table of powers. 14. Auxiliary tables for computation with complex numbers. 15. Cubic equations. 16. Elementary transcendental equations. 17. Exponential function. 18. Planck's radiation function. 19. Source functions of heat conduction. 20. The hyperbolic functions. 21. Circular and hyperbolic functions of a complex variable. Bibliography and supplementary bibliography. Indexed.

Fourth revised edition. 212 figures. 400pp. (Text in both English and German.) 5⅜ x 8.

"There is hardly any single volume which could be more useful to the general applied mathematician and the mathematical physicist than this remarkable work of Jahnke and Emde," BULLETIN, NATIONAL RESEARCH COUNCIL.

"Most physicists probably know the tables of Jahnke and Emde, in which many of us look for those out-of-the-way functions for which we know no other source," SCIENTIFIC COMPUTING SERVICE LTD.

S133 Paperbound **$2.00**

HOW TO CALCULATE QUICKLY
by Henry Sticker
Do you want to double or triple the speed with which you calculate?

Can you run a rapid mental check over the results of your calculating machines? Can you check bills worked out for you by grocery store cash registers, on waiters' checks, department store charge accounts? Or do you simply take **their** word for the disposal of **your** money?

Don't envy friends who can perform these calculations with lighting speed and complete accuracy. Theirs is not wholly an inborn ability. You can acquire these skills by the methods described in this book.

HOW TO CALCULATE QUICKLY is a tried and true method for helping you in the mathematics of daily life — addition, subtraction, multiplication, division, and fractions.

The author can awaken for you a faculty which is surprisingly dormant in persons who deal with figures: accountants, engineers, scientists, businessmen. This is "Number Sense" — or the ability to recognize relations between numbers considered as whole quantities. Lack of this Number Sense makes it entirely possible for a scientist to be proficient in higher mathematics, but to bog down in the arithmetic of everday life.

This book teaches those necessary mathematical techniques which schools neglect to teach. Horizontal addition. Left to right multiplication and division. You will learn a method of multiplication so rapid that you'll be able to do products in not much more time than it would take to write the problem down on paper.

This is not a collection of tricks which work on only a very few special numbers, but a serious capably planned course of basic mathematics for self-instruction. It contains over 9,000 short problems and their solutions for work on streetcars, in taxis, at lunch, during spare moments. Five or ten minutes spent daily on this book will, within ten weeks, give you a Number Sense that will doubde or triple your calculation speed.

256pp.

T295 Paperbound $1.00

TRIGONOMETRY REFRESHER FOR TECHNICAL MEN

by A. Albert Klaf

This modern question and answer text covers most important aspects of plane and spherical trigonometry. 913 specially selected questions and detailed answers will help you to brush up your trigonometry or clear up difficulties on special areas.

The first portion of this book discusses plane trigonometry, covering angles, quadrants, trigonometrical functions, graphical representation, interpolation, equations, logarithms, solution of triangles, and the use of the slide rule, and similar topics. 188 pages then discuss the application of plane trigonometry to special problems in navigation, surveying, elasticity, architecture, and various fields of engineering. Small angles, periodic functions, vectors, polar coordinates, De Moivre's theorem are fully examined. The third section of the book then discusses spherical trigonometry and the solution of spherical triangles, with their application in terrestrial and astronomical problems.

Methods of saving time in numerical calculations, a simplification of the principal functions of an angle by use of a "shadow and perpendicular" concept, and much practical information on calculation aids make this an especially valuable book.

913 questions answered for you. 1738 problems to test your progress; answers to odd numbers. 494 figures. 24 pages of useful formulaes, functions. Index. x + 629pp. 5⅜ x 8. Paperbound **$1.95**

Catalogue of Dover
SCIENCE BOOKS

BOOKS THAT EXPLAIN SCIENCE

THE NATURE OF LIGHT AND COLOUR IN THE OPEN AIR, M. Minnaert. Why is falling snow sometimes black? What causes mirages, the fata morgana, multiple suns and moons in the sky; how are shadows formed? Prof. Minnaert of U. of Utrecht answers these and similar questions in optics, light, colour, for non-specialists. Particularly valuable to nature, science students, painters, photographers. "Can best be described in one word—fascinating!" Physics Today. Translated by H. M. Kremer-Priest, K. Jay. 202 illustrations, including 42 photos. xvi + 362pp. 5⅜ x 8.   T196 Paperbound **$1.95**

THE RESTLESS UNIVERSE, Max Born. New enlarged version of this remarkably readable account by a Nobel laureate. Moving from sub-atomic particles to universe, the author explains in very simple terms the latest theories of wave mechanics. Partial contents: air and its relatives, electrons and ions, waves and particles, electronic structure of the atom, nuclear physics. Nearly 1000 illustrations, including 7 animated sequences. 325pp. 6 x 9.   T412 Paperbound **$2.00**

MATTER AND LIGHT, THE NEW PHYSICS, L. de Broglie. Non-technical papers by a Nobel laureate explain electromagnetic theory, relativity, matter, light, radiation, wave mechanics, quantum physics, philosophy of science. Einstein, Planck, Bohr, others explained so easily that no mathematical training is needed for all but 2 of the 21 chapters. "Easy simplicity and lucidity . . . should make this source-book of modern physcis available to a wide public," Saturday Review. Unabridged. 300pp. 5⅜ x 8.   T35 Paperbound **$1.60**

THE COMMON SENSE OF THE EXACT SCIENCES, W. K. Clifford. Introduction by James Newman, edited by Karl Pearson. For 70 years this has been a guide to classical scientific, mathematical thought. Explains with unusual clarity basic concepts such as extension of meaning of symbols, characteristics of surface boundaries, properties of plane figures, vectors, Cartesian method of determining position, etc. Long preface by Bertrand Russell. Bibliography of Clifford. Corrected. 130 diagrams redrawn. 249pp. 5⅜ x 8.   T61 Paperbound **$1.60**

THE EVOLUTION OF SCIENTIFIC THOUGHT FROM NEWTON TO EINSTEIN, A. d'Abro. Einstein's special, general theories of relativity, with historical implications, analyzed in non-technical terms. Excellent accounts of contributions of Newton, Riemann, Weyl, Planck, Eddington, Maxwell, Lorentz, etc., are treated in terms of space, time, equations of electromagnetics, finiteness of universe, methodology of science. "Has become a standard work," Nature. 21 diagrams. 482pp. 5⅜ x 8.   T2 Paperbound **$2.00**

BRIDGES AND THEIR BUILDERS, D. Steinman, S. R. Watson. Engineers, historians, everyone ever fascinated by great spans will find this an endless source of information and interest. Dr. Steinman, recent recipient of Louis Levy Medal, is one of the great bridge architects, engineers of all time. His analysis of great bridges of history is both authoritative and easily followed. Greek, Roman, medieval, oriental bridges; modern works such as Brooklyn Bridge, Golden Gate Bridge, etc. described in terms of history, constructional principles, artistry, function. Most comprehensive, accurate semi-popular history of bridges in print in English. New, greatly revised, enlarged edition. 23 photographs, 26 line drawings. xvii + 401pp. 5⅜ x 8.   T431 Paperbound **$1.95**

CONCERNING THE NATURE OF THINGS, Sir William Bragg. Christmas lectures at Royal Society by Nobel laureate, dealing with atoms, gases, liquids, and various types of crystals. No scientific background is needed to understand this remarkably clear introduction to basic processes and aspects of modern science. "More interesting than any bestseller," London Morning Post. 32pp. of photos. 57 figures. xii + 232pp. 5⅜ x 8.   T31 Paperbound **$1.35**

THE RISE OF THE NEW PHYSICS, A. d'Abro. Half million word exposition, formerly titled "The Decline of Mechanism," for readers not versed in higher mathematics. Only thorough explanation in everyday language of core of modern mathematical physical theory, treating both classical, modern views. Scientifically impeccable coverage of thought from Newtonian system through theories of Dirac, Heisenberg, Fermi's statistics. Combines history, exposition; broad but unified, detailed view, with constant comparison of classical, modern views. "A must for anyone doing serious study in the physical sciences," J. of the Franklin Inst. "Extraordinary faculty . . . to explain ideas and theories . . . in language of everyday life," Isis. Part I of set: philosophy of science, from practice of Newton, Maxwell, Poincaré, Einstein, etc. Modes of thought, experiment, causality, etc. Part II: 100 pp. on grammar, vocabulary of mathematics, discussions of functions, groups, series, Fourier series, etc. Remainder treats concrete, detailed coverage of both classical, quantum physics: analytic mechanics, Hamilton's principle, electromagnetic waves, thermodynamics, Brownian movement, special relativity, Bohr's atom, de Broglie's wave mechanics, Heisenberg's uncertainty, scores of other important topics. Covers discoveries, theories of d'Alembert, Born, Cantor, Debye, Euler, Foucault, Galois, Gauss, Hadamard, Kelvin, Kepler Laplace, Maxwell, Pauli, Rayleigh Volterra, Weyl, more than 180 others. 97 illustrations. ix + 982pp. 5⅜ x 8.
T3 Vol. 1 Paperbound **$2.00**
T4 Vol. II Paperbound **$2.00**

SPINNING TOPS AND GYROSCOPIC MOTION, John Perry. Well-known classic of science still unsurpassed for lucid, accurate, delightful exposition. How quasi-rigidity is induced in flexible, fluid bodies by rapid motions; why gyrostat falls, top rises; nature, effect of internal fluidity on rotating bodies; etc. Appendixes describe practical use of gyroscopes in ships, compasses, monorail transportation. 62 figures. 128pp. 5⅜ x 8.
T416 Paperbound **$1.00**

FOUNDATIONS OF PHYSICS, R. B. Lindsay, H. Margenau. Excellent bridge between semi-popular and technical writings. Discussion of methods of physical description, construction of theory; valuable to physicist with elementary calculus. Gives meaning to data, tools of modern physics. Contents: symbolism, mathematical equations; space and time; foundations of mechanics; probability; physics, continua; electron theory; relativity; quantum mechanics; causality; etc. "Thorough and yet not overdetailed. Unreservedly recommended," Nature. Unabridged corrected edition. 35 illustrations. xi + 537pp. 5⅜ x 8.   S377 Paperbound **$2.45**

FADS AND FALLACIES IN THE NAME OF SCIENCE, Martin Gardner. Formerly entitled "In the Name of Science," the standard account of various cults, quack systems, delusions which have masqueraded as science: hollow earth fanatics, orgone sex energy, dianetics, Atlantis, Forteanism, flying saucers, medical fallacies like zone therapy, etc. New chapter on Bridey Murphy, psionics, other recent manifestations. A fair reasoned appraisal of eccentric theory which provides excellent innoculation. "Should be read by everyone, scientist or non-scientist alike," R. T. Birge, Prof. Emeritus of Physics, Univ. of Calif; Former Pres., Amer. Physical Soc. x + 365pp. 5⅜ x 8.   T394 Paperbound **$1.50**

ON MATHEMATICS AND MATHEMATICIANS, R. E. Moritz. A 10 year labor of love by discerning, discriminating Prof. Moritz, this collection conveys the full sense of mathematics and personalities of great mathematicians. Anecdotes, aphorisms, reminiscences, philosophies, definitions, speculations, biographical insights, etc. by great mathematicians, writers: Descartes, Mill, Locke, Kant, Coleridge, Whitehead, etc. Glimpses into lives of great mathematicians, from Archimedes to Euler, Gauss, Weierstrass. To mathematicians, a superb browsing-book. To laymen, exciting revelation of fullness of mathematics. Extensive cross index. 410pp. 5⅜ x 8.   T489 Paperbound **$1.95**

GUIDE TO THE LITERATURE OF MATHEMATICS AND PHYSICS, N. G. Parke III. Over 5000 entries under approximately 120 major subject headings, of selected most important books, monographs, periodicals, articles in English, plus important works in German, French, Italian, Spanish, Russian (many recently available works). Covers every branch of physics, math, related engineering. Includes author, title, edition, publisher, place, date, number of volumes, number of pages. 40 page introduction on basic problems of research, study provides useful information on organization, use of libraries, psychology of learning, etc. Will save you hours of time. 2nd revised edition. Indices of authors, subjects. 464pp. 5⅜ x 8.   S447 Paperbound **$2.49**

THE STRANGE STORY OF THE QUANTUM, An Account for the General Reader of the Growth of Ideas Underlying Our Present Atomic Knowledge, B. Hoffmann. Presents lucidly, expertly, with barest amount of mathematics, problems and theories which led to modern quantum physics. Begins with late 1800's when discrepancies were noticed; with illuminating analogies, examples, goes through concepts of Planck, Einstein, Pauli, Schroedinger, Dirac, Sommerfield, Feynman, etc. New postscript through 1958. "Of the books attempting an account of the history and contents of modern atomic physics which have come to my attention, this is the best," H. Margenau, Yale U., in Amer. J. of Physics. 2nd edition. 32 tables, illustrations. 275pp. 5⅜ x 8.   T518 Paperbound **$1.45**

HISTORY OF SCIENCE
AND PHILOSOPHY OF SCIENCE

THE VALUE OF SCIENCE, Henri Poincaré. Many of most mature ideas of "last scientific universalist" for both beginning, advanced workers. Nature of scientific truth, whether order is innate in universe or imposed by man, logical thought vs. intuition (relating to Weierstrass, Lie, Riemann, etc), time and space (relativity, psychological time, simultaneity), Herz's concept of force, values within disciplines of Maxwell, Carnot, Mayer, Newton, Lorentz, etc. iii + 147pp. 5⅜ x 8. S469 Paperbound **$1.35**

PHILOSOPHY AND THE PHYSICISTS, L. S. Stebbing. Philosophical aspects of modern science examined in terms of lively critical attack on ideas of Jeans, Eddington. Tasks of science, causality, determinism, probability, relation of world physics to that of everyday experience, philosophical significance of Planck-Bohr concept of discontinuous energy levels, inferences to be drawn from Uncertainty Principle, implications of "becoming" involved in 2nd law of thermodynamics, other problems posed by discarding of Laplacean determinism. 285pp. 5⅜ x 8. T480 Paperbound **$1.65**

THE PRINCIPLES OF SCIENCE, A TREATISE ON LOGIC AND THE SCIENTIFIC METHOD, W. S. Jevons. Milestone in development of symbolic logic remains stimulating contribution to investigation of inferential validity in sciences. Treats inductive, deductive logic, theory of number, probability, limits of scientific method; significantly advances Boole's logic, contains detailed introduction to nature and methods of probability in physics, astronomy, everyday affairs, etc. In introduction, Ernest Nagel of Columbia U. says, "[Jevons] continues to be of interest as an attempt to articulate the logic of scientific inquiry." liii + 786pp. 5⅜ x 8. S446 Paperbound **$2.98**

A HISTORY OF ASTRONOMY FROM THALES TO KEPLER, J. L. E. Dreyer. Only work in English to give complete history of cosmological views from prehistoric times to Kepler. Partial contents: Near Eastern astronomical systems, Early Greeks, Homocentric spheres of Euxodus, Epicycles, Ptolemaic system, Medieval cosmology, Copernicus, Kepler, much more. "Especially useful to teachers and students of the history of science . . . unsurpassed in its field," Isis. Formerly "A History of Planetary Systems from Thales to Kepler." Revised foreword by W. H. Stahl. xvii + 430pp. 5⅜ x 8. S79 Paperbound **$1.98**

A CONCISE HISTORY OF MATHEMATICS, D. Struik. Lucid study of development of ideas, techniques, from Ancient Near East, Greece, Islamic science, Middle Ages, Renaissance, modern times. Important mathematicians described in detail. Treatment not anecdotal, but analytical development of ideas. Non-technical—no math training needed. "Rich in content, thoughtful in interpretations," U.S. Quarterly Booklist. 60 illustrations including Greek, Egyptian manuscripts, portraits of 31 mathematicians. 2nd edition. xix + 299pp. 5⅜ x 8. S255 Paperbound **$1.75**

THE PHILOSOPHICAL WRITINGS OF PEIRCE, edited by Justus Buchler. A carefully balanced expositon of Peirce's complete system, written by Peirce himself. It covers such matters as scientific method, pure chance vs. law, symbolic logic, theory of signs, pragmatism, experiment, and other topics. "Excellent selection . . . gives more than adequate evidence of the range and greatness," Personalist. Formerly entitled "The Philosophy of Peirce." xvi + 368pp. T217 Paperbound **$1.95**

SCIENCE AND METHOD, Henri Poincaré. Procedure of scientific discovery, methodology, experiment, idea-germination—processes by which discoveries come into being. Most significant and interesting aspects of development, application of ideas. Chapters cover selection of facts, chance, mathematical reasoning, mathematics and logic; Whitehead, Russell, Cantor, the new mechanics, etc. 288pp. 5⅜ x 8. S222 Paperbound **$1.35**

SCIENCE AND HYPOTHESIS, Henri Poincaré. Creative psychology in science. How such concepts as number, magnitude, space, force, classical mechanics developed, how modern scientist uses them in his thought. Hypothesis in physics, theories of modern physics. Introduction by Sir James Larmor. "Few mathematicians have had the breadth of vision of Poincaré, and none is his superior in the gift of clear exposition," E. T. Bell. 272pp. 5⅜ x 8. S221 Paperbound **$1.35**

ESSAYS IN EXPERIMENTAL LOGIC, John Dewey. Stimulating series of essays by one of most influential minds in American philosophy presents some of his most mature thoughts on wide range of subjects. Partial contents: Relationship between inquiry and experience; dependence of knowledge upon thought; character logic; judgments of practice, data, and meanings; stimuli of thought, etc. viii + 444pp. 5⅜ x 8. T73 Paperbound **$1.95**

WHAT IS SCIENCE, Norman Campbell. Excellent introduction explains scientific method, role of mathematics, types of scientific laws. Contents: 2 aspects of science, science and nature, laws of chance, discovery of laws, explanation of laws, measurement and numerical laws, applications of science. 192pp. 5⅜ x 8. S43 Paperbound **$1.25**

FROM EUCLID TO EDDINGTON: A STUDY OF THE CONCEPTIONS OF THE EXTERNAL WORLD, Sir **Edmund Whittaker.** Foremost British scientist traces development of theories of natural philosophy from western rediscovery of Euclid to Eddington, Einstein, Dirac, etc. 5 major divisions: Space, Time and Movement; Concepts of Classical Physics; Concepts of Quantum Mechanics; Eddington Universe. Contrasts inadequacy of classical physics to understand physical world with present day attempts of relativity, non-Euclidean geometry, space curvature, etc. 212pp. 5⅜ x 8. T491 Paperbound **$1.35**

THE ANALYSIS OF MATTER, Bertrand Russell. How do our senses accord with the new physics? This volume covers such topics as logical analysis of physics, prerelativity physics, causality, scientific inference, physics and perception, special and general relativity, Weyl's theory, tensors, invariants and their physical interpretation, periodicity and qualitative series. "The most thorough treatment of the subject that has yet been published," The Nation. Introduction by L. E. Denonn. 422pp. 5⅜ x 8. T231 Paperbound **$1.95**

LANGUAGE, TRUTH, AND LOGIC, A. Ayer. A clear introduction to the Vienna and Cambridge schools of Logical Positivism. Specific tests to evaluate validity of ideas, etc. Contents: function of philosophy, elimination of metaphysics, nature of analysis, a priori, truth and probability, etc. 10th printing. "I should like to have written it myself," Bertrand Russell. 160pp. 5⅜ x 8. T10 Paperbound **$1.25**

THE PSYCHOLOGY OF INVENTION IN THE MATHEMATICAL FIELD, J. Hadamard. Where do ideas come from? What role does the unconscious play? Are ideas best developed by mathematical reasoning, word reasoning, visualization? What are the methods used by Einstein, Poincaré, Galton, Riemann? How can these techniques be applied by others? One of the world's leading mathematicians discusses these and other questions. xiii + 145pp. 5⅜ x 8. T107 Paperbound **$1.25**

GUIDE TO PHILOSOPHY, C. E. M. Joad. By one of the ablest expositors of all time, this is not simply a history or a typological survey, but an examination of central problems in terms of answers afforded by the greatest thinkers: Plato, Aristotle, Scholastics, Leibniz, Kant, Whitehead, Russell, and many others. Especially valuable to persons in the physical sciences; over 100 pages devoted to Jeans, Eddington, and others, the philosophy of modern physics, scientific materialism, pragmatism, etc. Classified bibliography. 592pp. 5⅜ x 8. T50 Paperbound **$2.00**

SUBSTANCE AND FUNCTION, and **EINSTEIN'S THEORY OF RELATIVITY, Ernst Cassirer.** Two books bound as one. Cassirer establishes a philosophy of the exact sciences that takes into consideration new developments in mathematics, shows historical connections. Partial contents: Aristotelian logic, Mill's analysis, Helmholtz and Kronecker, Russell and cardinal numbers, Euclidean vs. non-Euclidean geometry, Einstein's relativity. Bibliography. Index. xxi + 464pp. 5⅜ x 8. T50 Paperbound **$2.00**

FOUNDATIONS OF GEOMETRY, Bertrand Russell. Nobel laureate analyzes basic problems in the overlap area between mathematics and philosophy: the nature of geometrical knowledge, the nature of geometry, and the applications of geometry to space. Covers history of non-Euclidean geometry, philosophic interpretations of geometry, especially Kant, projective and metrical geometry. Most interesting as the solution offered in 1897 by a great mind to a problem still current. New introduction by Prof. Morris Kline, N.Y. University. "Admirably clear, precise, and elegantly reasoned analysis," International Math. News. xii + 201pp. 5⅜ x 8. S233 Paperbound **$1.60**

THE NATURE OF PHYSICAL THEORY, P. W. Bridgman. How modern physics looks to a highly unorthodox physicist—a Nobel laureate. Pointing out many absurdities of science, demonstrating inadequacies of various physical theories, weighs and analyzes contributions of Einstein, Bohr, Heisenberg, many others. A non-technical consideration of correlation of science and reality. xi + 138pp. 5⅜ x 8. S33 Paperbound **$1.25**

EXPERIMENT AND THEORY IN PHYSICS, Max Born. A Nobel laureate examines the nature and value of the counterclaims of experiment and theory in physics. Synthetic versus analytical scientific advances are analyzed in works of Einstein, Bohr, Heisenberg, Planck, Eddington, Milne, others, by a fellow scientist. 44pp. 5⅜ x 8. S308 Paperbound **60¢**

A SHORT HISTORY OF ANATOMY AND PHYSIOLOGY FROM THE GREEKS TO HARVEY, Charles Singer. Corrected edition of "The Evolution of Anatomy." Classic traces anatomy, physiology from prescientific times through Greek, Roman periods, dark ages, Renaissance, to beginning of modern concepts. Centers on individuals, movements, that definitely advanced anatomical knowledge. Plato, Diocles, Erasistratus, Galen, da Vinci, etc. Special section on Vesalius. 20 plates. 270 extremely interesting illustrations of ancient, Medieval, Renaissance, Oriental origin. xii + 209pp. 5⅜ x 8. T389 Paperbound **$1.75**

SPACE-TIME-MATTER, Hermann Weyl. "The standard treatise on the general theory of relativity," (Nature), by world renowned scientist. Deep, clear discussion of logical coherence of general theory, introducing all needed tools: Maxwell, analytical geometry, non-Euclidean geometry, tensor calculus, etc. Basis is classical space-time, before absorption of relativity. Contents: Euclidean space, mathematical form, metrical continuum, general theory, etc. 15 diagrams. xviii + 330pp. 5⅜ x 8. S267 Paperbound **$1.75**

4

DOVER SCIENCE BOOKS

MATTER AND MOTION, James Clerk Maxwell. Excellent exposition begins with simple particles, proceeds gradually to physical systems beyond complete analysis; motion, force, properties of centre of mass of material system; work, energy, gravitation, etc. Written with all Maxwell's original insights and clarity. Notes by E. Larmor. 17 diagrams. 178pp. 5⅜ x 8.
S188 Paperbound **$1.25**

PRINCIPLES OF MECHANICS, Heinrich Hertz. Last work by the great 19th century physicist is not only a classic, but of great interest in the logic of science. Creating a new system of mechanics based upon space, time, and mass, it returns to axiomatic analysis, understanding of the formal or structural aspects of science, taking into account logic, observation, a priori elements. Of great historical importance to Poincaré, Carnap, Einstein, Milne. A 20 page introduction by R. S. Cohen, Wesleyan University, analyzes the implications of Hertz's thought and the logic of science. 13 page introduction by Helmholtz. xlii + 274pp. 5⅜ x 8.
S316 Clothbound **$3.50**
S317 Paperbound **$1.75**

FROM MAGIC TO SCIENCE, Charles Singer. A great historian examines aspects of science from Roman Empire through Renaissance. Includes perhaps best discussion of early herbals, penetrating physiological interpretation of "The Visions of Hildegarde of Bingen." Also examines Arabian, Galenic influences; Pythagoras' sphere, Paracelsus; reawakening of science under Leonardo da Vinci, Vesalius; Lorica of Gildas the Briton; etc. Frequent quotations with translations from contemporary manuscripts. Unabridged, corrected edition. 158 unusual illustrations from Classical, Medieval sources. xxvii + 365pp. 5⅜ x 8.
T390 Paperbound **$2.00**

A HISTORY OF THE CALCULUS, AND ITS CONCEPTUAL DEVELOPMENT, Carl B. Boyer. Provides laymen, mathematicians a detailed history of the development of the calculus, from beginnings in antiquity to final elaboration as mathematical abstraction. Gives a sense of mathematics not as technique, but as habit of mind, in progression of ideas of Zeno, Plato, Pythagoras, Eudoxus, Arabic and Scholastic mathematicians, Newton, Leibniz, Taylor, Descartes, Euler, Lagrange, Cantor, Weierstrass, and others. This first comprehensive, critical history of the calculus was originally entitled "The Concepts of the Calculus." Foreword by R. Courant. 22 figures. 25 page bibliography. v + 364pp. 5⅜ x 8.
S509 Paperbound **$2.00**

A DIDEROT PICTORIAL ENCYCLOPEDIA OF TRADES AND INDUSTRY, Manufacturing and the Technical Arts in Plates Selected from "L'Encyclopédie ou Dictionnaire Raisonné des Sciences, des Arts, et des Métiers" of Denis Diderot. Edited with text by C. Gillispie. First modern selection of plates from high-point of 18th century French engraving. Storehouse of technological information to historian of arts and science. Over 2,000 illustrations on 485 full page plates, most of them original size, show trades, industries of fascinating era in such great detail that modern reconstructions might be made of them. Plates teem with men, women, children performing thousands of operations; show sequence, general operations, closeups, details of machinery. Illustrates such important, interesting trades, industries as sowing, harvesting, beekeeping, tobacco processing, fishing, arts of war, mining, smelting, casting iron, extracting mercury, making gunpowder, cannons, bells, shoeing horses, tanning, papermaking, printing, dying, over 45 more categories. Professor Gillispie of Princeton supplies full commentary on all plates, identifies operations, tools, processes, etc. Material is presented in lively, lucid fashion. Of great interest to all studying history of science, technology. Heavy library cloth. 920pp. 9 x 12.
T421 2 volume set **$18.50**

DE MAGNETE, William Gilbert. Classic work on magnetism, founded new science. Gilbert was first to use word "electricity," to recognize mass as distinct from weight, to discover effect of heat on magnetic bodies; invented an electroscope, differentiated between static electricity and magnetism, conceived of earth as magnet. This lively work, by first great experimental scientist, is not only a valuable historical landmark, but a delightfully easy to follow record of a searching, ingenious mind. Translated by P. F. Mottelay. 25 page biographical memoir. 90 figures. lix + 368pp. 5⅜ x 8.
S470 Paperbound **$2.00**

HISTORY OF MATHEMATICS, D. E. Smith. Most comprehensive, non-technical history of math in English. Discusses lives and works of over a thousand major, minor figures, with footnotes giving technical information outside book's scheme, and indicating disputed matters. Vol. I: A chronological examination, from primitive concepts through Egypt, Babylonia, Greece, the Orient, Rome, the Middle Ages, The Renaissance, and to 1900. Vol. II: The development of ideas in specific fields and problems, up through elementary calculus. "Marks an epoch . . . will modify the entire teaching of the history of science," George Sarton. 2 volumes, total of 510 illustrations, 1355pp. 5⅜ x 8. Set boxed in attractive container.
T429, 430 Paperbound, the set **$5.00**

THE PHILOSOPHY OF SPACE AND TIME, H. Reichenbach. An important landmark in development of empiricist conception of geometry, covering foundations of geometry, time theory, consequences of Einstein's relativity, including: relations between theory and observations; coordinate definitions; relations between topological and metrical properties of space; psychological problem of visual intuition of non-Euclidean structures; many more topics important to modern science and philosophy. Majority of ideas require only knowledge of intermediate math. "Still the best book in the field," Rudolf Carnap. Introduction by R. Carnap. 49 figures. xviii + 296pp. 5⅜ x 8.
S443 Paperbound **$2.00**

5

FOUNDATIONS OF SCIENCE: THE PHILOSOPHY OF THEORY AND EXPERIMENT, N. Campbell. A critique of the most fundamental concepts of science, particularly physics. Examines why certain propositions are accepted without question, demarcates science from philosophy, etc. Part I analyzes presuppositions of scientific thought: existence of material world, nature of laws, probability, etc; part 2 covers nature of experiment and applications of mathematics: conditions for measurement, relations between numerical laws and theories, error, etc. An appendix covers problems arising from relativity, force, motion, space, time. A classic in its field. "A real grasp of what science is," Higher Educational Journal. xiii + 565pp. 5⅝ x 8⅜. S372 Paperbound **$2.95**

THE STUDY OF THE HISTORY OF MATHEMATICS and **THE STUDY OF THE HISTORY OF SCIENCE, G. Sarton.** Excellent introductions, orientation, for beginning or mature worker. Describes duty of mathematical historian, incessant efforts and genius of previous generations. Explains how today's discipline differs from previous methods. 200 item bibliography with critical evaluations, best available biographies of modern mathematicians, best treatises on historical methods is especially valuable. 10 illustrations. 2 volumes bound as one. 113pp. + 75pp. 5⅜ x 8. T240 Paperbound **$1.25**

MATHEMATICAL PUZZLES

MATHEMATICAL PUZZLES OF SAM LOYD, selected and edited by **Martin Gardner.** 117 choice puzzles by greatest American puzzle creator and innovator, from his famous "Cyclopedia of Puzzles." All unique style, historical flavor of originals. Based on arithmetic, algebra, probability, game theory, route tracing, topology, sliding block, operations research, geometrical dissection. Includes famous "14-15" puzzle which was national craze, "Horse of a Different Color" which sold millions of copies. 120 line drawings, diagrams. Solutions. xx + 167pp. 5⅜ x 8. T498 Paperbound **$1.00**

SYMBOLIC LOGIC and THE GAME OF LOGIC, Lewis Carroll. "Symbolic Logic" is not concerned with modern symbolic logic, but is instead a collection of over 380 problems posed with charm and imagination, using the syllogism, and a fascinating diagrammatic method of drawing conclusions. In "The Game of Logic" Carroll's whimsical imagination devises a logical game played with 2 diagrams and counters (included) to manipulate hundreds of tricky syllogisms. The final section, "Hit or Miss" is a lagniappe of 101 additional puzzles in the delightful Carroll manner. Until this reprint edition, both of these books were rarities costing up to $15 each. Symbolic Logic: Index. xxxi + 199pp. The Game of Logic: 96pp. 2 vols. bound as one. 5⅜ x 8. T492 Paperbound **$1.50**

PILLOW PROBLEMS and A TANGLED TALE, Lewis Carroll. One of the rarest of all Carroll's works, "Pillow Problems" contains 72 original math puzzles, all typically ingenious. Particularly fascinating are Carroll's answers which remain exactly as he thought them out, reflecting his actual mental process. The problems in "A Tangled Tale" are in story form, originally appearing as a monthly magazine serial. Carroll not only gives the solutions, but uses answers sent in by readers to discuss wrong approaches and misleading paths, and grades them for insight. Both of these books were rarities until this edition, "Pillow Problems" costing up to $25, and "A Tangled Tale" $15. Pillow Problems: Preface and Introduction by Lewis Carroll. xx + 109pp. A Tangled Tale: 6 illustrations. 152pp. Two vols. bound as one. 5⅜ x 8. T493 Paperbound **$1.50**

NEW WORD PUZZLES, G. L. Kaufman. 100 brand new challenging puzzles on words, combinations, never before published. Most are new types invented by author, for beginners and experts both. Squares of letters follow chess moves to build words; symmetrical designs made of synonyms; rhymed crostics; double word squares; syllable puzzles where you fill in missing syllables instead of missing letter; many other types, all new. Solutions. "Excellent," Recreation. 100 puzzles. 196 figures. vi + 122pp. 5⅜ x 8. T344 Paperbound **$1.00**

MATHEMATICAL EXCURSIONS, H. A. Merrill. Fun, recreation, insights into elementary problem solving. Math expert guides you on by-paths not generally travelled in elementary math courses—divide by inspection, Russian peasant multiplication; memory systems for pi; odd, even magic squares; dyadic systems; square roots by geometry; Tchebichev's machine; dozens more. Solutions to more difficult ones. "Brain stirring stuff . . . a classic," Genie. 50 illustrations. 145pp. 5⅜ x 8. T350 Paperbound **$1.00**

THE BOOK OF MODERN PUZZLES, G. L. Kaufman. Over 150 puzzles, absolutely all new material based on same appeal as crosswords, deduction puzzles, but with different principles, techniques. 2-minute teasers, word labyrinths, design, pattern, logic, observation puzzles, puzzles testing ability to apply general knowledge to peculiar situations, many others. Solutions. 116 illustrations. 192pp. 5⅜ x 8. T143 Paperbound **$1.00**

MATHEMAGIC, MAGIC PUZZLES, AND GAMES WITH NUMBERS, R. V. Heath. Over 60 puzzles, stunts, on properties of numbers. Easy techniques for multiplying large numbers mentally, identifying unknown numbers, finding date of any day in any year. Includes The Lost Digit, 3 Acrobats, Psychic Bridge, magic squares, triangles, cubes, others not easily found elsewhere. Edited by J. S. Meyer. 76 illustrations. 128pp. 5⅜ x 8. T110 Paperbound **$1.00**

PUZZLE QUIZ AND STUNT FUN, J. Meyer. 238 high-priority puzzles, stunts, tricks—math puzzles like The Clever Carpenter, Atom Bomb, Please Help Alice; mysteries, deductions like The Bridge of Sighs, Secret Code; observation puzzlers like The American Flag, Playing Cards, Telephone Dial; over 200 others with magic squares, tongue twisters, puns, anagrams. Solutions. Revised, enlarged edition of "Fun-To-Do." Over 100 illustrations. 238 puzzles, stunts, tricks. 256pp. 5⅜ x 8. **T337 Paperbound $1.00**

101 PUZZLES IN THOUGHT AND LOGIC, C. R. Wylie, Jr. For readers who enjoy challenge, stimulation of logical puzzles without specialized math or scientific knowledge. Problems entirely new, range from relatively easy to brainteasers for hours of subtle entertainment. Detective puzzles, find the lying fisherman, how a blind man identifies color by logic, many more. Easy-to-understand introduction to logic of puzzle solving and general scientific method. 128pp. 5⅜ x 8. **T367 Paperbound $1.00**

CRYPTANALYSIS, H. F. Gaines. Standard elementary, intermediate text for serious students. Not just old material, but much not generally known, except to experts. Concealment, Transposition, Substitution ciphers; Vigenere, Kasiski, Playfair, multafid, dozens of other techniques. Formerly "Elementary Cryptanalysis." Appendix with sequence charts, letter frequencies in English, 5 other languages, English word frequencies. Bibliography. 167 codes. New to this edition: solutions to codes. vi + 230pp. 5⅜ x 8⅜. **T97 Paperbound $1.95**

CRYPTOGRAPY, L. D. Smith. Excellent elementary introduction to enciphering, deciphering secret writing. Explains transposition, substitution ciphers; codes; solutions; geometrical patterns, route transcription, columnar transposition, other methods. Mixed cipher systems; single, polyalphabetical substitutions; mechanical devices; Vigenere; etc. Enciphering Japanese; explanation of Baconian biliteral cipher; frequency tables. Over 150 problems. Bibliography. Index. 164pp. 5⅜ x 8. **T247 Paperbound $1.00**

MATHEMATICS, MAGIC AND MYSTERY, M. Gardner. Card tricks, metal mathematics, stage mind-reading, other "magic" explained as applications of probability, sets, number theory, etc. Creative examination of laws, applications. Scores of new tricks, insights. 115 sections on cards, dice, coins; vanishing tricks, many others. No sleight of hand—math guarantees success. "Could hardly get more entertainment . . . easy to follow," Mathematics Teacher. 115 illustrations. xii + 174pp. 5⅜ x 8. **T335 Paperbound $1.00**

AMUSEMENTS IN MATHEMATICS, H. E. Dudeney. Foremost British originator of math puzzles, always witty, intriguing, paradoxical in this classic. One of largest collections. More than 430 puzzles, problems, paradoxes. Mazes, games, problems on number manipulations, unicursal, other route problems, puzzles on measuring, weighing, packing, age, kinship, chessboards, joiners', crossing river, plane figure dissection, many others. Solutions. More than 450 illustrations. viii + 258pp. 5⅜ x 8. **T473 Paperbound $1.25**

THE CANTERBURY PUZZLES H. E. Dudeney. Chaucer's pilgrims set one another problems in story form. Also Adventures of the Puzzle Club, the Strange Escape of the King's Jester, the Monks of Riddlewell, the Squire's Christmas Puzzle Party, others. All puzzles are original, based on dissecting plane figures, arithmetic, algebra, elementary calculus, other branches of mathematics, and purely logical ingenuity. "The limit of ingenuity and intricacy," The Observer. Over 110 puzzles, full solutions. 150 illustrations. viii + 225 pp. 5⅜ x 8. **T474 Paperbound $1.25**

MATHEMATICAL PUZZLES FOR BEGINNERS AND ENTHUSIASTS, G. Mott-Smith. 188 puzzles to test mental agility. Inference, interpretation, algebra, dissection of plane figures, geometry, properties of numbers, decimation, permutations, probability, all are in these delightful problems. Includes the Odic Force, How to Draw an Ellipse, Spider's Cousin, more than 180 others. Detailed solutions. Appendix with square roots, triangular numbers, primes, etc. 135 illustrations. 2nd revised edition. 248pp. 5⅜ x 8. **T198 Paperbound $1.00**

MATHEMATICAL RECREATIONS, M. Kraitchik. Some 250 puzzles, problems, demonstrations of recreation mathematics on relatively advanced level. Unusual historical problems from Greek, Medieval, Arabic, Hindu sources; modern problems on "mathematics without numbers," geometry, topology, arithmetic, etc. Pastimes derived from figurative, Mersenne, Fermat numbers: fairy chess; latruncles: reversi; etc. Full solutions. Excellent insights into special fields of math. "Strongly recommended to all who are interested in the lighter side of mathematics," Mathematical Gaz. 181 illustrations. 330pp. 5⅜ x 8. **T163 Paperbound $1.75**

FICTION

FLATLAND, E. A. Abbott. A perennially popular science-fiction classic about life in a 2-dimensional world, and the impingement of higher dimensions. Political, satiric, humorous, moral overtones. This land where women are straight lines and the lowest and most dangerous classes are isosceles triangles with 3° vertices conveys brilliantly a feeling for many concepts of modern science. 7th edition. New introduction by Banesh Hoffmann. 128pp. 5⅜ x 8. **T1 Paperbound $1.00**

SEVEN SCIENCE FICTION NOVELS OF H. G. WELLS. Complete texts, unabridged, of seven of Wells' greatest novels: The War of the Worlds, The Invisible Man, The Island of Dr. Moreau, The Food of the Gods, First Men in the Moon, In the Days of the Comet, The Time Machine. Still considered by many experts to be the best science-fiction ever written, they will offer amusements and instruction to the scientific minded reader. "The great master," Sky and Telescope. 1051pp. 5⅜ x 8. **T264 Clothbound $3.95**

28 SCIENCE FICTION STORIES OF H. G. WELLS. Unabridged! This enormous omnibus contains 2 full length novels—Men Like Gods, Star Begotten—plus 26 short stories of space, time, invention, biology, etc. The Crystal Egg, The Country of the Blind, Empire of the Ants, The Man Who Could Work Miracles, Aepyornis Island, A Story of the Days to Come, and 20 others "A master . . . not surpassed by . . . writers of today," The English Journal. 915pp. 5⅜ x 8. **T265 Clothbound $3.95**

FIVE ADVENTURE NOVELS OF H. RIDER HAGGARD. All the mystery and adventure of darkest Africa captured accurately by a man who lived among Zulus for years, who knew African ethnology, folkways as did few of his contemporaries. They have been regarded as examples of the very best high adventure by such critics as Orwell, Andrew Lang, Kipling. Contents: She, King Solomon's Mines, Allan Quatermain, Allan's Wife, Maiwa's Revenge. "Could spin a yarn so full of suspense and color that you couldn't put the story down," Sat. Review. 821pp. 5⅜ x 8. **T108 Clothbound $3.95**

CHESS AND CHECKERS

LEARN CHESS FROM THE MASTERS, Fred Reinfeld. Easiest, most instructive way to improve your game—play 10 games against such masters as Marshall, Znosko-Borovsky, Bronstein, Najdorf, etc., with each move graded by easy system. Includes ratings for alternate moves possible. Games selected for interest, clarity, easily isolated principles. Covers Ruy Lopez, Dutch Defense, Vienna Game openings; subtle, intricate middle game variations; all-important end game. Full annotations. Formerly "Chess by Yourself." 91 diagrams. + 144pp. 5⅜ x 8. **T362 Paperbound $1.00**

REINFELD ON THE END GAME IN CHESS, Fred Reinfeld. Analyzes 62 end games by Alekhine, Flohr, Tarrasch, Morphy, Capablanca, Rubinstein, Lasker, Reshevsky, other masters. Only 1st rate book with extensive coverage of error—tell exactly what is wrong with each move you might have made. Centers around transitions from middle play to end play. King and pawn, minor pieces, queen endings; blockage, weak, passed pawns, etc. "Excellent . . . a boon," Chess Life. Formerly "Practical End Play." 62 figures. vi + 177pp. 5⅜ x 8. **T417 Paperbound $1.25**

HYPERMODERN CHESS as developed in the games of its greatest exponent, ARON NIMZOVICH, edited by Fred Reinfeld. An intensely original player, analyst, Nimzovich's approaches startled, often angered the chess world. This volume, designed for the average player, shows how his iconoclastic methods won him victories over Alekhine, Lasker, Marshall, Rubinstein, Spielmann, others, and infused new life into the game. Use his methods to startle opponents, invigorate play. "Annotations and introductions to each game . . . are excellent," Times (London). 180 diagrams. viii + 220pp. 5⅜ x 8. **T448 Paperbound $1.35**

THE ADVENTURE OF CHESS, Edward Lasker. Lively reader, by one of America's finest chess masters, including: history of chess, from ancient Indian 4-handed game of Chaturanga to great players of today; such delights and oddities as Maelzel's chess-playing automaton that beat Napoleon 3 times; etc. One of most valuable features is author's personal recollections of men he has played against—Nimzovich, Emanuel Lasker, Capablanca, Alekhine, etc. Discussion of chess-playing machines (newly revised). 5 page chess primer. 11 illustrations. 53 diagrams. 296pp. 5⅜ x 8. **S510 Paperbound $1.45**

THE ART OF CHESS, James Mason. Unabridged reprinting of latest revised edition of most famous general study ever written. Mason, early 20th century master, teaches beginning, intermediate player over 90 openings; middle game, end game, to see more moves ahead, to plan purposefully, attack, sacrifice, defend, exchange, govern general strategy. "Classic . . . one of the clearest and best developed studies," Publishers Weekly. Also included, a complete supplement by F. Reinfeld, "How Do You Play Chess?", invaluable to beginners for its lively question-and-answer method. 448 diagrams. 1947 Reinfeld-Bernstein text. Bibliography. xvi + 340pp. 5⅜ x 8. **T463 Paperbound $1.85**

MORPHY'S GAMES OF CHESS, edited by P. W. Sergeant. Put boldness into your game by flowing brilliant, forceful moves of the greatest chess player of all time. 300 of Morphy's best games, carefully annotated to reveal principles. 54 classics against masters like Anderssen, Harrwitz, Bird, Paulsen, and others. 52 games at odds; 54 blindfold games; plus over 100 others. Follow his interpretation of Dutch Defense, Evans Gambit, Giuoco Piano, Ruy Lopez, many more. Unabridged reissue of latest revised edition. New introduction by F. Reinfeld. Annotations, introduction by Sergeant. 235 diagrams. x + 352pp. 5⅜ x 8. **T386 Paperbound $1.75**

8

DOVER SCIENCE BOOKS

WIN AT CHECKERS, M. Hopper. (Formerly "Checkers.") Former World's Unrestricted Checker Champion discusses principles of game, expert's shots, traps, problems for beginner, standard openings, locating best move, end game, opening "blitzkrieg" moves to draw when behind, etc. Over 100 detailed questions, answers anticipate problems. Appendix. 75 problems with solutions, diagrams. 79 figures. xi + 107pp. 5⅜ x 8.   T363 Paperbound **$1.00**

HOW TO FORCE CHECKMATE, Fred Reinfeld. If you have trouble finishing off your opponent, here is a collection of lightning strokes and combinations from actual tournament play. Starts with 1-move checkmates, works up to 3-move mates. Develops ability to lock ahead, gain new insights into combinations, complex or deceptive positions; ways to estimate weaknesses, strengths of you and your opponent. "A good deal of amusement and instruction," Times, (London). 300 diagrams. Solutions to all positions. Formerly "Challenge to Chess Players." 111pp. 5⅜ x 8.   T417 Paperbound **$1.25**

A TREASURY OF CHESS LORE, edited by Fred Reinfeld. Delightful collection of anecdotes, short stories, aphorisms by, about masters; poems, accounts of games, tournaments, photographs; hundreds of humorous, pithy, satirical, wise, historical episodes, comments, word portraits. Fascinating "must" for chess players; revealing and perhaps seductive to those who wonder what their friends see in game. 49 photographs (14 full page plates). 12 diagrams. xi + 306pp. 5⅜ x 8.   T458 Paperbound **$1.75**

WIN AT CHESS, Fred Reinfeld. 300 practical chess situations, to sharpen your eye, test skill against masters. Start with simple examples, progress at own pace to complexities. This selected series of crucial moments in chess will stimulate imagination, develop stronger, more versatile game. Simple grading system enables you to judge progress. "Extensive use of diagrams is a great attraction," Chess. 300 diagrams. Notes, solutions to every situation. Formerly "Chess Quiz." vi + 120pp. 5⅜ x 8.   T433 Paperbound **$1.00**

MATHEMATICS:
ELEMENTARY TO INTERMEDIATE

HOW TO CALCULATE QUICKLY, H. Sticker. Tried and true method to help mathematics of everyday life. Awakens "number sense"—ability to see relationships between numbers as whole quantities. A serious course of over 9000 problems and their solutions through techniques not taught in schools: left-to-right multiplications, new fast division, etc. 10 minutes a day will double or triple calculation speed. Excellent for scientist at home in higher math, but dissatisfied with speed and accuracy in lower math. 256pp. 5 x 7¼.
Paperbound **$1.00**

FAMOUS PROBLEMS OF ELEMENTARY GEOMETRY, Felix Klein. Expanded version of 1894 Easter lectures at Göttingen. 3 problems of classical geometry: squaring the circle, trisecting angle, doubling cube, considered with full modern implications: transcendental numbers, pi, etc. "A modern classic . . . no knowledge of higher mathematics is required," Scientia. Notes by R. Archibald. 16 figures. xi + 92pp. 5⅜ x 8.   T298 Paperbound **$1.00**

HIGHER MATHEMATICS FOR STUDENTS OF CHEMISTRY AND PHYSICS, J. W. Mellor. Practical, not abstract, building problems out of familiar laboratory material. Covers differential calculus, coordinate, analytical geometry, functions, integral calculus, infinite series, numerical equations, differential equations, Fourier's theorem probability, theory of errors, calculus of variations, determinants. "If the reader is not familiar with this book, it will repay him to examine it," Chem. and Engineering News. 800 problems. 189 figures. xxi + 641pp. 5⅜ x 8.   S193 Paperbound **$2.25**

TRIGONOMETRY REFRESHER FOR TECHNICAL MEN, A. A. Klaf. 913 detailed questions, answers cover most important aspects of plane, spherical trigonometry—particularly useful in clearing up difficulties in special areas. Part I: plane trig, angles, quadrants, functions, graphical representation, interpolation, equations, logs, solution of triangle, use of slide rule, etc. Next 188 pages discuss applications to navigation, surveying, elasticity, architecture, other special fields. Part 3: spherical trig, applications to terrestrial, astronomical problems. Methods of time-saving, simplification of principal angles, make book most useful. 913 questions answered. 1738 problems, answers to odd numbers. 494 figures. 24 pages of formulas, functions. x + 629pp. 5⅜ x 8.   T371 Paperbound **$2.00**

CALCULUS REFRESHER FOR TECHNICAL MEN, A. A. Klaf. 756 questions examine most important aspects of integral, differential calculus. Part I: simple differential calculus, constants, variables, functions, increments, logs, curves, etc. Part 2: fundamental ideas of integrations, inspection, substitution, areas, volumes, mean value, double, triple integration, etc. Practical aspects stressed. 50 pages illustrate applications to specific problems of civil, nautical engineering, electricity, stress, strain, elasticity, similar fields. 756 questions answered. 566 problems, mostly answered. 36pp. of useful constants, formulas. v + 431pp. 5⅜ x 8.   T370 Paperbound **$2.00**

MONOGRAPHS ON TOPICS OF MODERN MATHEMATICS, edited by J. W. A. Young. Advanced mathematics for persons who have forgotten, or not gone beyond, high school algebra. 9 monographs on foundation of geometry, modern pure geometry, non-Euclidean geometry, fundamental propositions of algebra, algebraic equations, functions, calculus, theory of numbers, etc. Each monograph gives proofs of important results, and descriptions of leading methods, to provide wide coverage. "Of high merit," Scientific American. New introduction by Prof. M. Kline, N.Y. Univ. 100 diagrams. xvi + 416pp. 6⅛ x 9¼.
$289 Paperbound **$2.00**

MATHEMATICS IN ACTION, O. G. Sutton. Excellent middle level application of mathematics to study of universe, demonstrates how math is applied to ballistics, theory of computing machines, waves, wave-like phenomena, theory of fluid flow, meteorological problems, statistics, flight, similar phenomena. No knowledge of advanced math required. Differential equations, Fourier series, group concepts, Eigenfunctions, Planck's constant, airfoil theory, and similar topics explained so clearly in everyday language that almost anyone can derive benefit from reading this even if much of high-school math is forgotten. 2nd edition. 88 figures. viii + 236pp. 5⅜ x 8.
T450 Clothbound **$3.50**

ELEMENTARY MATHEMATICS FROM AN ADVANCED STANDPOINT, Felix Klein. Classic text, an outgrowth of Klein's famous integration and survey course at Göttingen. Using one field to interpret, adjust another, it covers basic topics in each area, with extensive analysis. Especially valuable in areas of modern mathematics. "A great mathematician, inspiring teacher, . . . deep insight," Bul., Amer. Math Soc.

Vol. I. ARITHMETIC, ALGEBRA, ANALYSIS. Introduces concept of function immediately, enlivens discussion with graphical, geometric methods. Partial contents: natural numbers, special properties, complex numbers. Real equations with real unknowns, complex quantities. Logarithmic, exponential functions, infinitesimal calculus. Transcendence of e and pi, theory of assemblages. Index. 125 figures. ix + 274pp. 5⅜ x 8. S151 Paperbound **$1.75**

Vol. II. GEOMETRY. Comprehensive view, accompanies space perception inherent in geometry with analytic formulas which facilitate precise formulation. Partial contents: Simplest geometric manifold; line segments, Grassman determinant principles, classication of configurations of space. Geometric transformations: affine, projective, higher point transformations, theory of the imaginary. Systematic discussion of geometry and its foundations. 141 illustrations. ix + 214pp. 5⅜ x 8. S151 Paperbound **$1.75**

A TREATISE ON PLANE AND ADVANCED TRIGONOMETRY, E. W. Hobson. Extraordinarily wide coverage, going beyond usual college level, one of few works covering advanced trig in full detail. By a great expositor with unerring anticipation of potentially difficult points. Includes circular functions; expansion of functions of multiple angle; trig tables; relations between sides, angles of triangles; complex numbers; etc. Many problems fully solved. "The best work on the subject," Nature. Formerly entitled "A Treatise on Plane Trigonometry." 689 examples. 66 figures. xvi + 383pp. 5⅜ x 8. S353 Paperbound **$1.95**

NON-EUCLIDEAN GEOMETRY, Roberto Bonola. The standard coverage of non-Euclidean geometry. Examines from both a historical and mathematical point of view geometries which have arisen from a study of Euclid's 5th postulate on parallel lines. Also included are complete texts, translated, of Bolyai's "Theory of Absolute Space," Lobachevsky's "Theory of Parallels." 180 diagrams. 431pp. 5⅜ x 8. S27 Paperbound **$1.95**

GEOMETRY OF FOUR DIMENSIONS, H. P. Manning. Unique in English as a clear, concise introduction. Treatment is synthetic, mostly Euclidean, though in hyperplanes and hyperspheres at infinity, non-Euclidean geometry is used. Historical introduction. Foundations of 4-dimensional geometry. Perpendicularity, simple angles. Angles of planes, higher order. Symmetry, order, motion; hyperpyramids, hypercones, hyperspheres; figures with parallel elements; volume, hypervolume in space; regular polyhedroids. Glossary. 78 figures. ix + 348pp. 5⅜ x 8. S182 Paperbound **$1.95**

MATHEMATICS: INTERMEDIATE TO ADVANCED

GEOMETRY (EUCLIDEAN AND NON-EUCLIDEAN)

THE GEOMETRY OF RENÉ DESCARTES. With this book, Descartes founded analytical geometry. Original French text, with Descartes's own diagrams, and excellent Smith-Latham translation. Contains: Problems the Construction of Which Requires only Straight Lines and Circles; On the Nature of Curved Lines; On the Construction of Solid or Supersolid Problems. Diagrams. 258pp. 5⅜ x 8. S68 Paperbound **$1.50**

DOVER SCIENCE BOOKS

THE WORKS OF ARCHIMEDES, edited by T. L. Heath. All the known works of the great Greek mathematician, including the recently discovered Method of Archimedes. Contains: On Sphere and Cylinder, Measurement of a Circle, Spirals, Conoids, Spheroids, etc. Definitive edition of greatest mathematical intellect of ancient world. 186 page study by Heath discusses Archimedes and history of Greek mathematics. 563pp. 5⅜ x 8.   S9 Paperbound **$2.00**

COLLECTED WORKS OF BERNARD RIEMANN. Important sourcebook, first to contain complete text of 1892 "Werke" and the 1902 supplement, unabridged. 31 monographs, 3 complete lecture courses, 15 miscellaneous papers which have been of enormous importance in relativity, topology, theory of complex variables, other areas of mathematics. Edited by R. Dedekind, H. Weber, M. Noether, W. Wirtinger. German text; English introduction by Hans Lewy. 690pp. 5⅜ x 8.   S226 Paperbound **$2.85**

THE THIRTEEN BOOKS OF EUCLID'S ELEMENTS, edited by Sir Thomas Heath. Definitive edition of one of very greatest classics of Western world. Complete translation of Heiberg text, plus spurious Book XIV. 150 page introduction on Greek, Medieval mathematics, Euclid, texts, commentators, etc. Elaborate critical apparatus parallels text, analyzing each definition, postulate, proposition, covering textual matters, refutations, supports, extrapolations, etc. This is the full Euclid. Unabridged reproduction of Cambridge U. 2nd edition. 3 volumes. 995 figures. 1426pp. 5⅜ x 8.   S88, 89, 90, 3 volume set, paperbound **$6.00**

AN INTRODUCTION TO GEOMETRY OF N DIMENSIONS, D. M. Y. Sommerville. Presupposes no previous knowledge of field. Only book in English devoted exclusively to higher dimensional geometry. Discusses fundamental ideas of incidence, parallelism, perpendicularity, angles between linear space, enumerative geometry, analytical geometry from projective and metric views, polytopes, elementary ideas in analysis situs, content of hyperspacial figures. 60 diagrams. 196pp. 5⅜ x 8.   S494 Paperbound **$1.50**

ELEMENTS OF NON-EUCLIDEAN GEOMETRY, D. M. Y. Sommerville. Unique in proceeding step-by-step. Requires only good knowledge of high-school geometry and algebra, to grasp elementary hyperbolic, elliptic, analytic non-Euclidean Geometries; space curvature and its implications; radical axes; homophetic centres and systems of circles; parataxy and parallelism; Gauss' proof of defect area theorem; much more, with exceptional clarity. 126 problems at chapter ends. 133 figures. xvi + 274pp. 5⅜ x 8.   S460 Paperbound **$1.50**

THE FOUNDATIONS OF EUCLIDEAN GEOMETRY, H. G. Forder. First connected, rigorous account in light of modern analysis, establishing propositions without recourse to empiricism, without multiplying hypotheses. Based on tools of 19th and 20th century mathematicians, who made it possible to remedy gaps and complexities, recognize problems not earlier discerned. Begins with important relationship of number systems in geometrical figures. Considers classes, relations, linear order, natural numbers, axioms for magnitudes, groups, quasi-fields, fields, non-Archimedian systems, the axiom system (at length), particular axioms (two chapters on the Parallel Axioms), constructions, congruence, similarity, etc. Lists: axioms employed, constructions, symbols in frequent use. 295pp. 5⅜ x 8.
S481 Paperbound **$2.00**

CALCULUS, FUNCTION THEORY (REAL AND COMPLEX), FOURIER THEORY

FIVE VOLUME "THEORY OF FUNCTIONS" SET BY KONRAD KNOPP. Provides complete, readily followed account of theory of functions. Proofs given concisely, yet without sacrifice of completeness or rigor. These volumes used as texts by such universities as M.I.T., Chicago, N.Y. City College, many others. "Excellent introduction . . . remarkably readable, concise, clear, rigorous," J. of the American Statistical Association.

ELEMENTS OF THE THEORY OF FUNCTIONS, Konrad Knopp. Provides background for further volumes in this set, or texts on similar level. Partial contents: Foundations, system of complex numbers and Gaussian plane of numbers, Riemann sphere of numbers, mapping by linear functions, normal forms, the logarithm, cyclometric functions, binomial series. "Not only for the young student, but also for the student who knows all about what is in it," Mathematical Journal. 140pp. 5⅜ x 8.   S154 Paperbound **$1.35**

THEORY OF FUNCTIONS, PART I, Konrad Knopp. With volume II, provides coverage of basic concepts and theorems. Partial contents: numbers and points, functions of a complex variable, integral of a continuous function, Cauchy's intergral theorem, Cauchy's integral formulae, series with variable terms, expansion and analytic function in a power series, analytic continuation and complete definition of analytic functions, Laurent expansion, types of singularities. vii + 146pp. 5⅜ x 8.   S156 Paperbound **$1.35**

THEORY OF FUNCTIONS, PART II, Konrad Knopp. Application and further development of general theory, special topics. Single valued functions, entire, Weierstrass. Meromorphic functions: Mittag-Leffler. Periodic functions. Multiple valued functions. Riemann surfaces. Algebraic functions. Analytical configurations, Riemann surface. x + 150pp. 5⅜ x 8.
S157 Paperbound **$1.35**

11

PROBLEM BOOK IN THE THEORY OF FUNCTIONS, VOLUME I, Konrad Knopp. Problems in elementary theory, for use with Knopp's "Theory of Functions," or any other text. Arranged according to increasing difficulty. Fundamental concepts, sequences of numbers and infinite series, complex variable, integral theorems, development in series, conformal mapping. Answers. viii + 126pp. 5⅜ x 8. **S 158 Paperbound $1.35**

PROBLEM BOOK IN THE THEORY OF FUNCTIONS, VOLUME II, Konrad Knopp. Advanced theory of functions, to be used with Knopp's "Theory of Functions," or comparable text. Singularities, entire and meromorphic functions, periodic, analytic, continuation, multiple-valued functions, Riemann surfaces, conformal mapping. Includes section of elementary problems. "The difficult task of selecting . . . problems just within the reach of the beginner is here masterfully accomplished," AM. MATH. SOC. Answers. 138pp. 5⅜ x 8.
S159 Paperbound $1.35

ADVANCED CALCULUS, E. B. Wilson. Still recognized as one of most comprehensive, useful texts. Immense amount of well-represented, fundamental material, including chapters on vector functions, ordinary differential equations, special functions, calculus of variations, etc., which are excellent introductions to these areas. Requires only one year of calculus. Over 1300 exercises cover both pure math and applications to engineering and physical problems. Ideal reference, refresher. 54 page introductory review. ix + 566pp. 5⅜ x 8.
S504 Paperbound $2.45

LECTURES ON THE THEORY OF ELLIPTIC FUNCTIONS, H. Hancock. Reissue of only book in English with so extensive a coverage, especially of Abel, Jacobi, Legendre, Weierstrass, Hermite, Liouville, and Riemann. Unusual fullness of treatment, plus applications as well as theory in discussing universe of elliptic integrals, originating in works of Abel and Jacobi. Use is made of Riemann to provide most general theory. 40-page table of formulas. 76 figures. xxiii + 498pp. 5⅜ x 8. **S483 Paperbound $2.55**

THEORY OF FUNCTIONALS AND OF INTEGRAL AND INTEGRO-DIFFERENTIAL EQUATIONS, Vito Volterra. Unabridged republication of only English translation. General theory of functions depending on continuous set of values of another function. Based on author's concept of transition from finite number of variables to a continually infinite number. Includes much material on calculus of variations. Begins with fundamentals, examines generalization of analytic functions, functional derivative equations, applications, other directions of theory, etc. New introduction by G. C. Evans. Biography, criticism of Volterra's work by E. Whittaker. xxxx + 226pp. 5⅜ x 8. **S502 Paperbound $1.75**

AN INTRODUCTION TO FOURIER METHODS AND THE LAPLACE TRANSFORMATION, Philip Franklin. Concentrates on essentials, gives broad view, suitable for most applications. Requires only knowledge of calculus. Covers complex qualities with methods of computing elementary functions for complex values of argument and finding approximations by charts; Fourier series; harmonic anaylsis; much more. Methods are related to physical problems of heat flow, vibrations, electrical transmission, electromagnetic radiation, etc. 828 problems, answers. Formerly entitled "Fourier Methods." x + 289pp. 5⅜ x 8.
S452 Paperbound $1.75

THE ANALYTICAL THEORY OF HEAT, Joseph Fourier. This book, which revolutionized mathematical physics, has been used by generations of mathematicians and physicists interested in heat or application of Fourier integral. Covers cause and reflection of rays of heat, radiant heating, heating of closed spaces, use of trigonometric series in theory of heat, Fourier integral, etc. Translated by Alexander Freeman. 20 figures. xxii + 466pp. 5⅜ x 8.
S93 Paperbound $2.00

ELLIPTIC INTEGRALS, H. Hancock. Invaluable in work involving differential equations with cubics, quatrics under root sign, where elementary calculus methods are inadequate. Practical solutions to problems in mathematics, engineering, physics; differential equations requiring integration of Lamé's, Briot's, or Bouquet's equations; determination of arc of ellipse, hyperbola, lemsicate; solutions of problems in elastics; motion of a projectile under resistance varying as the cube of the velocity; pendulums; more. Exposition in accordance with Legendre-Jacobi theory. Rigorous discussion of Legendre transformations. 20 figures. 5 place table. 104pp. 5⅜ x 8. **S484 Paperbound $1.25**

THE TAYLOR SERIES, AN INTRODUCTION TO THE THEORY OF FUNCTIONS OF A COMPLEX VARIABLE, P. Dienes. Uses Taylor series to approach theory of functions, using ordinary calculus only, except in last 2 chapters. Starts with introduction to real variable and complex algebra, derives properties of infinite series, complex differentiation, integration, etc. Covers biuniform mapping, overconvergence and gap theorems, Taylor series on its circle of convergence, etc. Unabridged corrected reissue of first edition. 186 examples, many fully worked out. 67 figures. xii + 555pp. 5⅜ x 8. **S391 Paperbound $2.75**

LINEAR INTEGRAL EQUATIONS, W. V. Lovitt. Systematic survey of general theory, with some application to differential equations, calculus of variations, problems of math, physics. Includes: integral equation of 2nd kind by successive substitutions; Fredholm's equation as ratio of 2 integral series in lambda, applications of the Fredholm theory, Hilbert-Schmidt theory of symmetric kernels, application, etc. Neumann, Dirichlet, vibratory problems. ix + 253pp. 5⅜ x 8.
S175 Clothbound $3.50
S176 Paperbound $1.60

DOVER SCIENCE BOOKS

DICTIONARY OF CONFORMAL REPRESENTATIONS, H. Kober. Developed by British Admiralty to solve Laplace's equation in 2 dimensions. Scores of geometrical forms and transformations for electrical engineers, Joukowski aerofoil for aerodynamics, Schwartz-Christoffel transformations for hydro-dynamics, transcendental functions. Contents classified according to analytical functions describing transformations with corresponding regions. Glossary. Topological index. 447 diagrams. 6⅛ x 9¼. .S160 Paperbound **$2.00**

ELEMENTS OF THE THEORY OF REAL FUNCTIONS, J. E. Littlewood. Based on lectures at Trinity College, Cambridge, this book has proved extremely successful in introducing graduate students to modern theory of functions. Offers full and concise coverage of classes and cardinal numbers, well ordered series, other types of series, and elements of the theory of sets of points. 3rd revised edition. vii + 71pp. 5⅜ x 8. S171 Clothbound **$2.85**
S172 Paperbound **$1.25**

INFINITE SEQUENCES AND SERIES, Konrad Knopp. 1st publication in any language. Excellent introduction to 2 topics of modern mathematics, designed to give student background to penetrate further alone. Sequences and sets, real and complex numbers, etc. Functions of a real and complex variable. Sequences and series. Infinite series. Convergent power series. Expansion of elementary functions. Numerical evaluation of series. v + 186pp. 5⅜ x 8. S152 Clothbound **$3.50**
S153 Paperbound **$1.75**

THE THEORY AND FUNCTIONS OF A REAL VARIABLE AND THE THEORY OF FOURIER'S SERIES, E. W .Hobson. One of the best introductions to set theory and various aspects of functions and Fourier's series. Requires only a good background in calculus. Exhaustive coverage of: metric and descriptive properties of sets of points; transfinite numbers and order types; functions of a real variable; the Riemann and Lebesgue integrals; sequences and series of numbers; power-series; functions representable by series sequences of continuous functions; trigonometrical series; representation of functions by Fourier's series; and much more. "The best possible guide," Nature. Vol. I: 88 detailed examples, 10 figures. Index. xv + 736pp. Vol. II: 117 detailed examples, 13 figures. x + 780pp. 6⅛ x 9¼.
Vol. I: S387 Paperbound **$3.00**
Vol. II: S388 Paperbound **$3.00**

ALMOST PERIODIC FUNCTIONS, A. S. Besicovitch. Unique and important summary by a well known mathematician covers in detail the two stages of development in Bohr's theory of almost periodic functions: (1) as a generalization of pure periodicity, with results and proofs; (2) the work done by Stepanof, Wiener, Weyl, and Bohr in generalizing the theory. xi + 180pp. 5⅜ x 8. S18 Paperbound **$1.75**

INTRODUCTION TO THE THEORY OF FOURIER'S SERIES AND INTEGRALS, H. S. Carslaw. 3rd revised edition, an outgrowth of author's courses at Cambridge. Historical introduction, rational, irrational numbers, infinite sequences and series, functions of a single variable, definite integral, Fourier series, and similar topics. Appendices discuss practical harmonic analysis, periodogram analysis, Lebesgue's theory. 84 examples. xiii + 368pp. 5⅜ x 8. S48 Paperbound **$2.00**

SYMBOLIC LOGIC

THE ELEMENTS OF MATHEMATICAL LOGIC, Paul Rosenbloom. First publication in any language. For mathematically mature readers with no training in symbolic logic. Development of lectures given at Lund Univ., Sweden, 1948. Partial contents: Logic of classes, fundamental theorems, Boolean algebra, logic of propositions, of propositional functions, expressive languages, combinatory logics, development of math within an object language, paradoxes, theorems of Post, Goedel, Church, and similar topics. iv + 214pp. 5⅜ x 8. S227 Paperbound **$1.45**

INTRODUCTION TO SYMBOLIC LOGIC AND ITS APPLICATION, R. Carnap. Clear, comprehensive, rigorous, by perhaps greatest living master. Symbolic languages analyzed, one constructed. Applications to math (axiom systems for set theory, real, natural numbers), topology (Dedekind, Cantor continuity explanations), physics (general analysis of determination, causality, space-time topology), biology (axiom system for basic concepts). "A masterpiece," Zentralblatt für Mathematik und Ihre Grenzgebiete. Over 300 exercises. 5 figures. xvi + 241pp. 5⅜ x 8. S453 Paperbound **$1.85**

AN INTRODUCTION TO SYMBOLIC LOGIC, Susanne K. Langer. Probably clearest book for the philosopher, scientist, layman—no special knowledge of math required. Starts with simplest symbols, goes on to give remarkable grasp of Boole-Schroeder, Russell-Whitehead systems, clearly, quickly. Partial Contents: Forms, Generalization, Classes, Deductive System of Classes, Algebra of Logic, Assumptions of Principia Mathematica, Logistics, Proofs of Theorems, etc. "Clearest . . . simplest introduction . . . the intelligent non-mathematician should have no difficulty," MATHEMATICS GAZETTE. Revised, expanded 2nd edition. Truth-value tables. 368pp. 5⅜ 8. S164 Paperbound **$1.75**

TRIGONOMETRICAL SERIES, Antoni Zygmund. On modern advanced level. Contains carefully organized analyses of trigonometric, orthogonal, Fourier systems of functions, with clear adequate descriptions of summability of Fourier series, proximation theory, conjugate series, convergence, divergence of Fourier series. Especially valuable for Russian, Eastern European coverage. 329pp. 5⅜ x 8.   S290 Paperbound **$1.50**

THE LAWS OF THOUGHT, George Boole. This book founded symbolic logic some 100 years ago. It is the 1st significant attempt to apply logic to all aspects of human endeavour. Partial contents: derivation of laws, signs and laws, interpretations, eliminations, conditions of a perfect method, analysis, Aristotelian logic, probability, and similar topics. xvii + 424pp. 5⅜ x 8.   S28 Paperbound **$2.00**

SYMBOLIC LOGIC, C. I. Lewis, C. H. Langford. 2nd revised edition of probably most cited book in symbolic logic. Wide coverage of entire field; one of fullest treatments of paradoxes; plus much material not available elsewhere. Basic to volume is distinction between logic of extensions and intensions. Considerable emphasis on converse substitution, while matrix system presents supposition of variety of non-Aristotelian logics. Especially valuable sections on strict limitations, existence theorems. Partial contents: Boole-Schroeder algebra; truth value systems, the matrix method; implication and deductibility; general theory of propositions; etc. "Most valuable," Times, London. 506pp. 5⅜ x 8.   S170 Paperbound **$2.00**

GROUP THEORY AND LINEAR ALGEBRA, SETS, ETC.

LECTURES ON THE ICOSAHEDRON AND THE SOLUTION OF EQUATIONS OF THE FIFTH DEGREE, Felix Klein. Solution of quintics in terms of rotations of regular icosahedron around its axes of symmetry. A classic, indispensable source for those interested in higher algebra, geometry, crystallography. Considerable explanatory material included. 230 footnotes, mostly bibliography. "Classical monograph . . . detailed, readable book," Math. Gazette. 2nd edition. xvi + 289pp. 5⅜ x 8.   S314 Paperbound **$1.85**

INTRODUCTION TO THE THEORY OF GROUPS OF FINITE ORDER, R. Carmichael. Examines fundamental theorems and their applications. Beginning with sets, systems, permutations, etc., progresses in easy stages through important types of groups: Abelian, prime power, permutation, etc. Except 1 chapter where matrices are desirable, no higher math is needed. 783 exercises, problems. xvi + 447pp. 5⅜ x 8.   S299 Clothbound **$3.95**
S300 Paperbound **$3.00**

THEORY OF GROUPS OF FINITE ORDER, W. Burnside. First published some 40 years ago, still one of clearest introductions. Partial contents: permutations, groups independent of representation, composition series of a group, isomorphism of a group with itself, Abelian groups, prime power groups, permutation groups, invariants of groups of linear substitution, graphical representation, etc. "Clear and detailed discussion . . . numerous problems which are instructive," Design News. xxiv + 512pp. 5⅜ x 8.   S38 Paperbound **$2.45**

COMPUTATIONAL METHODS OF LINEAR ALGEBRA, V. N. Faddeeva, translated by C. D. Benster. 1st English translation of unique, valuable work, only one in English presenting systematic exposition of most important methods of linear algebra—classical, contemporary. Details of deriving numerical solutions of problems in mathematical physics. Theory and practice. Includes survey of necessary background, most important methods of solution, for exact, iterative groups. One of most valuable features is 23 tables, triple checked for accuracy, unavailable elsewhere. Translator's note. x + 252pp. 5⅜ x 8.   S424 Paperbound **$1.95**

THE CONTINUUM AND OTHER TYPES OF SERIAL ORDER, E. V. Huntington. This famous book gives a systematic elementary account of the modern theory of the continuum as a type of serial order. Based on the Cantor-Dedekind ordinal theory, which requires no technical knowledge of higher mathematics, it offers an easily followed analysis of ordered classes, discrete and dense series, continuous series, Cantor's transfinite numbers. "Admirable introduction to the rigorous theory of the continuum . . . reading easy," Science Progress. 2nd edition. viii + 82pp. 5⅜ x 8.   S129 Clothbound **$2.75**
S130 Paperbound **$1.00**

THEORY OF SETS, E. Kamke. Clearest, amplest introduction in English, well suited for independent study. Subdivisions of main theory, such as theory of sets of points, are discussed, but emphasis is on general theory. Partial contents: rudiments of set theory, arbitrary sets, their cardinal numbers, ordered sets, their order types, well-ordered sets, their cardinal numbers. vii + 144pp. 5⅜ x 8.   S141 Paperbound **$1.35**

CONTRIBUTIONS TO THE FOUNDING OF THE THEORY OF TRANSFINITE NUMBERS, Georg Cantor. These papers founded a new branch of mathematics. The famous articles of 1895-7 are translated, with an 82-page introduction by P. E. B. Jourdain dealing with Cantor, the background of his discoveries, their results, future possibilities. ix + 211pp. 5⅜ x 8.
S45 Paperbound **$1.25**

DOVER SCIENCE BOOKS

NUMERICAL AND GRAPHICAL METHODS, TABLES

JACOBIAN ELLIPTIC FUNCTION TABLES, L. M. Milne-Thomson. Easy-to-follow, practical, not only useful numerical tables, but complete elementary sketch of application of elliptic functions. Covers description of principle properties; complete elliptic integrals; Fourier series, expansions; periods, zeros, poles, residues, formulas for special values of argument; cubic, quartic polynomials; pendulum problem; etc. Tables, graphs form body of book: Graph, 5 figure table of elliptic function sn (u m); cn (u m); dn (u m). 8 figure table of complete elliptic integrals K, K', E, E', nome q. 7 figure table of Jacobian zeta-function Z(u). 3 figures. xi + 123pp. 5⅜ x 8. **S194 Paperbound $1.35**

TABLES OF FUNCTIONS WITH FORMULAE AND CURVES, E. Jahnke, F. Emde. Most comprehensive 1-volume English text collection of tables, formulae, curves of transcendent functions. 4th corrected edition, new 76-page section giving tables, formulae for elementary functions not in other English editions. Partial contents: sine, cosine, logarithmic integral; error integral; elliptic integrals; theta functions; Legendre, Bessel, Riemann, Mathieu, hypergeometric functions; etc. "Out-of-the-way functions for which we know no other source." Scientific Computing Service, Ltd. 212 figures. 400pp. 5⅝ x 8⅜. **S133 Paperbound $2.00**

MATHEMATICAL TABLES, H. B. Dwight. Covers in one volume almost every function of importance in applied mathematics, engineering, physical sciences. Three extremely fine tables of the three trig functions, inverses, to 1000th of radian; natural, common logs; squares, cubes; hyperbolic functions, inverses; $(a^2 + b^2)$ exp. ½a; complete elliptical integrals of 1st, 2nd kind; sine, cosine integrals; exponential integrals; Ei(x) and Ei($-$x); binomial coefficients; factorials to 250; surface zonal harmonics, first derivatives; Bernoulli, Euler numbers, their logs to base of 10; Gamma function; normal probability integral; over 60pp. Bessel functions; Riemann zeta function. Each table with formulae generally used, sources of more extensive tables, interpolation data, etc. Over half have columns of differences, to facilitate interpolation. viii + 231pp. 5⅜ x 8. **S445 Paperbound $1.75**

PRACTICAL ANALYSIS, GRAPHICAL AND NUMERICAL METHODS, F. A. Willers. Immensely practical hand-book for engineers. How to interpolate, use various methods of numerical differentiation and integration, determine roots of a single algebraic equation, system of lineaι equations, use empirical formulas, integrate differential equations, etc. Hundreds of short-cuts for arriving at numerical solutions. Special section on American calculating machines, by T. W. Simpson. Translation by R. T. Beyer. 132 illustrations. 422pp. 5⅜ x 8. **S273 Paperbound $2.00**

NUMERICAL SOLUTIONS OF DIFFERENTIAL EQUATIONS, H. Levy, E. A. Baggott. Comprehensive collection of methods for solving ordinary differential equations of first and higher order. 2 requirements: practical, easy to grasp; more rapid than school methods. Partial contents: graphical integration of differential equations, graphical methods for detailed solution. Numerical solution. Simultaneous equations and equations of 2nd and higher orders. "Should be in the hands of all in research and applied mathematics, teaching," Nature. 21 figures. viii + 238pp. 5⅜ x 8. **S168 Paperbound $1.75**

NUMERICAL INTEGRATION OF DIFFERENTIAL EQUATIONS, Bennet, Milne, Bateman. Unabridged republication of original prepared for National Research Council. New methods of integration by 3 leading mathematicians: "The Interpolational Polynomial," "Successive Approximation," A. A. Bennett, "Step-by-step Methods of Integration," W. W. Milne. "Methods for Partial Differential Equations," H. Bateman. Methods for partial differential equations, solution of differential equations to non-integral values of a parameter will interest mathematicians, physicists. 288 footnotes, mostly bibliographical. 235 item classified bibliography. 108pp. 5⅜ x 8. **S305 Paperbound $1.35**

Write for free catalogs!

Indicate your field of interest. Dover publishes books on physics, earth sciences, mathematics, engineering, chemistry, astronomy, anthropology, biology, psychology, philosophy, religion, history, literature, mathematical recreations, languages, crafts, art, graphic arts, etc.

Write to Dept. catr
Dover Publications, Inc.
180 Varick St., N. Y. 14, N. Y.

Science A

15